MICROBIOLOGY: CONCEPTS AND APPL

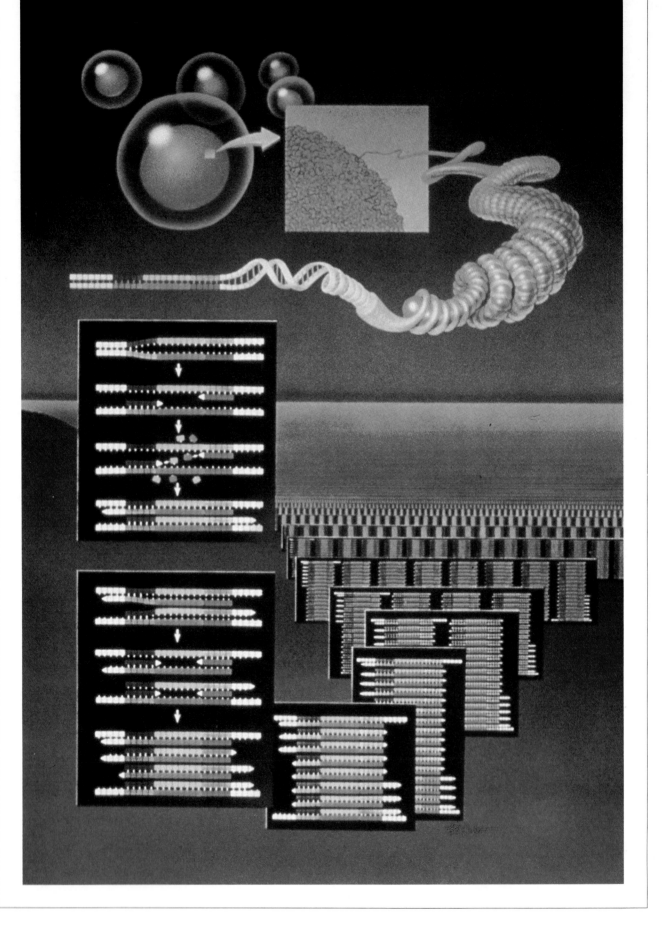

MICROBIOLOGY
CONCEPTS AND APPLICATIONS

Michael J. Pelczar, Jr.
Emeritus Vice President, Graduate Studies and Research
Emeritus Professor of Microbiology
University of Maryland

E. C. S. Chan
Professor of Microbiology, Faculty of Medicine, Faculty of Dentistry
McGill University

Noel R. Krieg
Professor of Microbiology and Immunology
Virginia Polytechnic Institute and State University

Diane D. Edwards
Science Writer

Merna F. Pelczar
Contributor

McGRAW-HILL, INC.

New York St. Louis San Francisco Auckland Bogotá Caracas Lisbon London Madrid
Mexico Milan Montreal New Delhi Paris San Juan Singapore Sydney Tokyo Toronto

This book is dedicated to the late Walter A. Konetzka, Emeritus Professor of Microbiology, Indiana University, for his numerous contributions to the science of microbiology and especially for his innovative efforts to improve education in microbiology.

1 2 3 4 5 6 7 8 9 0   VNH   VNH   9 0 9 8 7 6 5 4 3 2

ISBN 0-07-049258-1

This book was set in Caledonia by York Graphic Services, Inc.
The editors were Kathi M. Prancan and Holly Gordon;
the text and cover designer was Gayle Jaeger;
the production supervisor was Janelle S. Travers.
The photo editor was Safra Nimrod;
the photo researcher was Mira Schachne.
Drawings were done by Precision Graphics.
Von Hoffmann Press, Inc., was printer and binder.

Library of Congress Cataloging-in-Publication Data

Pelczar, Michael J. (Michael Joseph), (date).
    Microbiology—concepts and applications / Michael J. Pelczar, Jr.,
E. C. S. Chan, Noel R. Krieg; Diane D. Edwards, science writer;
Merna F. Pelczar, contributor.—1st ed.
        p.   cm.
    Includes bibliographical references and index.
    ISBN 0-07-049258-1
    1. Microbiology.   I. Chan, E. C. S. (Eddie Chin Sun)
II. Krieg, Noel R.   III. Title.
QR41.2.P42   1993
576—dc20   92-8267

About the Cover

The cover illustration represents various stages of biotechnological processes associated with the development of a product derived from a genetically engineered microorganism. In this case, the product is human insulin.

Top left: Bacterial cells can be genetically altered by inserting a modified plasmid into them. This plasmid contains additional genetic information that codes for a specific product. (*Huntington Potter/David Dressler, Life Magazine © Time Warner, Inc.*)

Top right: The DNA of plasmids can be separated and purified by agarose gel electrophoresis. A dye, ethidium bromide, which fluoresces under UV light, is used to stain the DNA. (*Dan McCoy/Rainbow*)

Bottom left: Once the modified plasmid is in the bacterial cells, the microorganisms can begin synthesis of the desired product. Laboratory fermentors having sophisticated controls are used for growing the bacteria that produce the insulin. (*Dan McCoy/Rainbow*)

Bottom right: Crystals of human insulin. (*Visuals Unlimited*)

About the Title Page

This illustrates the polymerase chain reaction (PCR)—the most important technological development in molecular biology in the last ten years. The PCR can produce millions of copies of a gene from a trace amount of DNA; thus it has become a powerful tool for detecting cells infected by the AIDS virus, for diagnosing various genetic diseases in a fetus in utero, and for a host of other useful applications. See page 357 for further details. (*Cetus Corporation*)

About the Part-Opening Images

The images that were used for the part and chapter openings were computer generated by Gayle Jaeger. They were scanned from micrographs of the following:

Prologue Human fibroblasts in a culture infected with cytomegalovirus, which appears as round particles. **I** *Giardia lamblia*, a parasitic, flagellated protozoan that can inhabit the intestines of people and certain wild and domesticated animals. **II** *Streptococcus pneumoniae*, a bacterium; one of the causes of pneumonia. **III** *Pseudomonas fluorescens*, a common saprophytic bacterium that occurs widely in soil and water. **IV** *Eurotium amotelodami*, a fungus; the conidial (spore) stage corresponds to that of *Aspergillus* spp. **V** *Anabaena azollae*, a cyanobacterium that grows symbiotically (fixing nitrogen) with the water fern *Azolla*; widely used in rice farming. **VI** A bacterial plasmid (appearing as a molecule of looped DNA) identified as carrying resistance to the antibiotic ampicillin. **VII** Herpesvirus; large, enveloped double-stranded DNA virus occurring widely in both humans and other animals. **VIII** Bacteria (spirochetes) stained with a fluorescent dye-antibody complex; the antibody is specific for this microorganism. **IX** *Neisseria meningitidis*, a bacterium that is one of the causative agents of bacterial meningitis. **X** *Escherichia coli*, a bacterium that commonly occurs in the human intestines; frequently used in laboratory tests as an indicator of pollution. **XI** Cells of the bacterium *Achromobacter* sp. immobilized on an inorganic matrix; these bacteria degrade a pollutant as it is passed over the matrix.

Credits for photographs and illustrations begin on page C.1.

About the Authors

Michael J. Pelczar, Jr.

Michael J. Pelczar, Jr., is Emeritus Vice President for Graduate Studies and Research and Emeritus Professor of Microbiology at the University of Maryland, College Park, Maryland. Dr. Pelczar received his B.S. in Bacteriology and his M.S. in Bacteriology and Biochemistry from the University of Maryland. His teaching experience spans 30 years, most of which was accomplished at the University of Maryland. His Ph.D. was earned at the University of Iowa in the area of Bacteriology and Biochemistry.

Subsequent to his many years teaching introductory microbiology, Dr. Pelczar was appointed to a number of administrative positions that ultimately led to his position as President of the Council of Graduate Schools in Washington, D.C.

A staunch advocate for improving the balance of scholarship between undergraduate instruction and research in higher educational institutions, Dr. Pelczar continues to keep his finger on the pulse of this important issue. For example, he delivered the Second Annual Lecture on Microbiology Education at the 1990 Annual Meeting of the American Society for Microbiology. A testament to his dedication toward teaching is the fact that *three* of his former students have received the ASM National Carski Award for excellence in teaching.

Dr. Pelczar is an active member of a number of scholarly societies and continues to serve on scientific advisory committees at the state and national levels.

E. C. S. Chan

Eddie C. S. Chan is a professor of microbiology in the Faculty of Medicine and the Faculty of Dentistry of McGill University, Montreal, Canada. He has been a faculty member of this institution for the past 26 years and has taught courses in Introductory Microbiology, Microbial Physiology, Pathogenic Microbiology, and Oral Microbiology. He received his B.A. in Biological Sciences from the University of Texas at El Paso. His M.A. in Bacteriology was from the University of Texas at Austin; and his Ph.D. in Microbiology was from the University of Maryland at College Park. Upon graduation, he became a National Research Council of Canada postdoctoral fellow for two years in Ottawa, Canada. Dr. Chan began his teaching career in the Department of Biology at the University of New Brunswick in eastern Canada, where he stayed for three years. He has published more than 100 abstracts and papers in soil microbiology and oral microbiology. His current research interest is in microbiology of the oral cavity with particular focus on anaerobic spirochetes and other bacteria associated with periodontal disease. He is an active member of many scholarly societies and regularly presents his research findings at meetings of the American Society for Microbiology and the International Association for Dental Research.

Noel R. Krieg

Noel R. Krieg joined the faculty of Virginia Polytechnic Institute and State University in 1960 and is presently in the Microbiology and Immunology Section of the Department of Biology. In 1983 he was promoted to the rank of Distinguished Professor—the university's highest academic rank. Dr. Krieg's academic background includes a B.A. with high honors and with distinction from the University of Connecticut in 1955; an M.S. in Bacteriology from the University of Connecticut in 1957; and a Ph.D. from the University of Maryland in 1960. Among his teaching honors are the Carski Distinguished Teaching Award from the American Society for Microbiology; Virginia Polytechnic's William E. Wine Award for outstanding teaching; and membership in the university's Academy of Teaching Excellence. Dr. Krieg served on the board of directors of the Bergey's Manual Trust from 1976 to 1991 and was editor of Volume 1 of *Bergey's Manual of Systematic Bacteriology*. He has authored numerous research articles on the taxonomy and physiology of *Azospirillum, Aquaspirillum, Oceanospirillum, Spirillum*, and *Campylobacter*. He is presently studying the physiology of microaerophiles—organisms for which he says "oxygen is both a blessing and a curse."

Merna Foss Pelczar

Merna Foss Pelczar has been an active participant in the preparation of Pelczar et al. microbiology textbooks since the first edition in the 1950s. She is a graduate of the University of Northern Iowa and the College of Nursing of the State University of Iowa. One of her special contributions to this new book is the chapter on nosocomial infections.

Diane D. Edwards

Diane Edwards, who has masters' degrees in Microbiology and Mass Communications, is a former industrial research microbiologist, university lecturer, magazine and newspaper journalist, and medical technologist. She currently is a wheat farmer in northern Montana and a doctoral student in the History of Science program at the University of Wisconsin, Madison.

Contents in Brief

Contents

PART VIII
MICROORGANISMS AND DISEASE: RESISTANCE TO INFECTION 453

PART IX
MICROORGANISMS AND DISEASE: MICROBIAL DISEASES 589

22 NOSOCOMIAL INFECTIONS 590

23 SEXUALLY TRANSMITTED DISEASES 614

PART X
MICROBIAL ECOLOGY 771

29	**MICROBIOLOGY OF NATURAL WATERS, DRINKING WATER, AND WASTEWATER 806**

**PART XI
INDUSTRIAL
MICROBIOLOGY 841**

30	**MICROBIOLOGY OF FOOD 842**

Preface

Dear God, what marvels there are in so small a creature!

> —Leeuwenhoek's draftsman, as related by Leeuwenhoek in his letter of October 15, 1693, to the Royal Society of London

Organisms that must be magnified hundreds or thousands of times to be seen have fascinated people since the days of Leeuwenhoek. How such tiny entities can exhibit all the properties of life has been the subject of intensive research by many biologists. The fundamental knowledge of microorganisms has, over the course of the last decade, accumulated at a pace that can be characterized as an explosion of new knowledge. Knowledge of the ultrastructure, metabolism, and hereditary properties of microorganisms has contributed much of what we know today about the fundamental nature of *all* living organisms.

Although microbes are interesting in and for themselves, they are doubly interesting because they impinge on nearly every aspect of human existence, with beneficial or detrimental effects. For this reason, even people who are not scientists should have some familiarity with the properties and activities of microorganisms.

It is important that students realize that all life on this planet ultimately depends on the activities of microorganisms. Moreover, microbes are contributing solutions to many human problems of immediate concern, such as improvements in food production, the mining of ores, and the cleaning-up of oil spills. Through the techniques of genetic engineering and molecular biology, microbes are being "tailor-made" to produce valuable industrial and pharmaceutical chemicals, disease-resistant crops, vaccines, and other products. These developments of recent years have given us the incentive to write an up-to-date textbook in microbiology: *Microbiology: Concepts and Applications*. In this new book we have attempted to capture some of the excitement of microbiology—past, present, and future, but more particularly the present and the future—which has been greatly enhanced by the studies and use of microbes at the molecular level.

The importance of microbiology as a blend of both basic and applied science appeals not only to biology students but also to students of other disciplines: human resources, forestry, agriculture, food and animal science, human nutrition, allied health sciences, nursing, liberal arts, law, political science, and business. It is especially important that nonbiology students gain some familiarity with microbiology, because many of these students will become the business, political, and financial leaders of the future. In these positions of leadership they will profoundly influence the progress of science. Most introductory textbooks of microbiology, however, are not written for this important and diverse group of people. Instead, introductory microbiology texts have become formidable, overstuffed compendiums of information difficult even for biology students to digest in an introductory course. Many of the details should be saved for advanced microbiology courses.

Microbiology: Concepts and Applications is written for undergraduate students taking their introductory course in microbiology. We anticipate that this audience will have limited prior knowledge of chemistry and biology. Accordingly, special attention has been given to selection of fundamental concepts, straightforward explanations of various phenomena, highlighting of unique features of the biology of microorganisms, and explanations of technical terms as they are introduced in each chapter.

To ensure "student-friendly" readability, clarity, and a consistent writing style we were fortunate to have the services of a professional science writer, Diane D. Edwards, who monitored all manuscripts for the clarity and quality of our writing, providing a final version that enabled the three of us to speak with one voice.

CONTENTS AND ORGANIZATIONAL FEATURES

The main themes of this book—what microorganisms are and what they do—reflect the fundamentals and applications of the science. On the basis of our own teaching experiences we have presented the material in a logical sequence of eleven parts, each part containing two or more chapters. Historical perspective is presented in the Prologue. In Part I, the initial chapter provides the basic chemical and biochemical information that students need in order to understand nearly everything else that follows in the book, because microorganisms are, in a sense, chemical machines. The scope of microbiology and the characteristics of both procaryotic and eucaryotic microorganisms are covered in the rest of the chapters of Part I.

Part II discusses the nutritional needs and unique growth habits of microbes. Part III deals with the control of microorganisms by physical and chemical agents. A comprehensive survey of the major groups of procaryotic and eucaryotic microbes is found in Part IV. Microbial metabolism is a difficult subject for many microbiology students. Understanding of this subject is facilitated by many unifying diagrams as are found in Part V.

The essential and current topics of microbial genetics and molecular biology are found in Chapters 13 and 14 of Part VI. Part VII characterizes the nature of viruses. Part VIII deals with host resistance to infection. The normal flora of the human body is revealed in Chapter 17. Chapters 18, 19, and 20 present the science of immunology, together with all its distinct vocabulary, to the student. Chemotherapeutic agents are discussed in Chapter 21.

Part IX describes medical microbiology with the mode of transmission as the unifying theme for each chapter. Up-to-date information includes coverage of Lyme disease and AIDS. Part X deals with the role microorganisms play in the ecosystem as well as in public health. Part XI highlights the numerous applications of microorganisms in industry.

We recognize that in some local situations the instructor may choose to rearrange the emphasis and the order of "parts." This can be achieved successfully; for example Part IX, "Microorganisms and Disease: Microbial Diseases," could be exchanged with Parts X and XI, "Microbial Ecology" and "Industrial Microbiology." The material can be presented with equal effectiveness when it is rearranged to fit individual preferences.

We have taken particular care to provide a proper balance among the various aspects of microbiology, so that no single aspect dominates the book. For instance, the principles of medical microbiology are covered without neglecting other important topics, such as environmental microbiology and microbial genetics. We have omitted much of the detailed material that may be present in other texts, choosing instead to concentrate on basic information, major concepts, and important principles. For instance, we did not include comprehensive metabolic pathways in the chapter on microbial energy production, preferring instead to spend more time on the generation and functioning of the protonmotive force. We have given great attention to current develop-

ments in microbiology. For instance, Chapter 14 is devoted to genetic engineering, a major portion of Chapter 23 deals with the current AIDS pandemic, Chapter 19 describes recent developments in cellular immunology, and Chapter 31 provides several examples of modern biotechnology.

Generally speaking, our new book contains more material than can be covered in one term. However, this provides the instructor with flexibility and the choice to make selective assignments that take into consideration any special circumstances relating to the students in the class. It is our hope that the student, after successful completion of this course, will have acquired an understanding of the biology of microorganisms, their tremendous biochemical diversity, and their role in our environment, our health, and our economy.

PEDAGOGY

Our author team has consistently argued for a strong commitment to high-quality undergraduate instruction. This commitment is coupled with decades of experience in instruction of undergraduate students. Thus, in writing this book we have given special attention to all aspects of its production that would enhance its pedagogic value.

We have also included more teaching aids in our book than are usually found in introductory microbiology textbooks. We designed these aids to reinforce the student's understanding and retention of the text material. Each chapter begins with a list of objectives and an overview intended to provide an advance organizer of the information to come. At the end of each major section in each chapter, we have introduced a few "ask yourself" questions so that students can immediately assess their comprehension of what they have just read. The end-of-chapter summary ties together the major concepts presented in the material that precedes. Essay questions for review and discussion are provided at the end of the chapter. Most important of all is the Review Guide at the end of each chapter—a series of programmed "exam-style" review questions (multiple-choice, matching, and fill-in-the-blank questions) that closely follow the order of presentation of material in the text. If the student does not know the answer to a question in the Review Guide, he or she can quickly refer to the appropriate text material in the chapter. Moreover, each chapter contains one or more Discover boxes that highlight topics of special interest, such as bacteria that always swim north, bacteria that grow at temperatures above the boiling point of water, and microorganisms that replace chemical insecticides.

ILLUSTRATIONS

We have paid great attention to the book's illustrations and have personally devised hundreds of new, original drawings which are printed in full color throughout the book. For instance, the metabolic pathways depicted in Chapters 11 and 12 become more interesting—and therefore more readily comprehended by the student—because of the different shapes and colors used for the various metabolites. Similarly, in Chapter 26, the use of different-colored backgrounds in depicting the life cycle of malaria protozoa makes it easy to differentiate the stages occurring in the patient from those in the mosquito. We also make an attempt to provide a context within which structures occur. See, for example, FIGURE 4.8 on page 114 in Chapter 4.

ACKNOWLEDGMENTS

We are extremely grateful to the many individuals and corporations who provided us with materials for this textbook. We are particularly grateful to the following individuals: Joseph O. Falkinham III, Virginia Polytechnic Institute and State University, for special help with the chapters on microbial genetics and genetic engineering; and Malcolm G. Baines, McGill University, for special help with the chapters on immunology.

Several of our colleagues were helpful in providing speciality reviews on specific chapters. We wish to thank these reviewers: John R. Chipley, Senior Microbiologist, United States Tobacco Company; Frank B. Dazzo, Michigan State University; Klaus D. Elgert, Virginia Polytechnic Institute and State University; Dennis D. Focht, Professor of Soil Microbiology, University of California, Riverside; L. E. Hallas, Monsanto Agricultural Co.; Thomas R. Jewell, University of Wisconsin; Ted R. Johnson, St. Olaf College; Daniel E. Morse, University of California, Santa Barbara; Michael E. Pelczar, St. Agnes Hospital; and H. Jean Shadomy, Virginia Commonwealth University.

We also wish to thank the many manuscript reviewers: Robert K. Alico, Indiana University of Pennsylvania; Glenn W. Allman, Brigham Young University; Paul V. Benko, Sonoma State University; Frank X. Biondo, Long Island University, C. W. Post Campus; Jonathan W. Brosin, Sacramento City College; Albert G. Canaris, University of Texas at El Paso; Sally S. DeGroot, St. Petersburg Junior College; Monica A. Devanas, Rutgers University; James G. Garner, Long Island University, C. W. Post Campus; Joseph J. Gauthier, University of Alabama at Birmingham; Robert Gessner, Western Illinois University; Caryl E. Heintz, Texas Tech University; Alice C. Helm, University of Illinois, Urbana; Diane S. Herson, University of Delaware; Gary R. Jacobson, Boston University; Thomas R. Jewell, University of Wisconsin, Eau Claire; Pat Hilliard Johnson, Palm Beach Community College; H. Bruce Johnston, Fresno City College; Joseph S. Layne, Memphis State University; Glendon R. Miller, Wichita State University; Vladimir Munk, SUNY Plattsburgh; Richard L. Myers, Southwest Missouri State University; William B. Nelson, SUNY College of Technology, Delhi; Robert Pacha, Central Washington University; Dorothy Read, University of Massachusetts, Dartmouth; Virginia Schurman, Essex Community College; H. Jean Shadomy, Virginia Commonwealth University; Michael P. Shiaris, University of Massachusetts, Boston; Carl E. Sillman, Pennsylvania State University; Deborah Simon-Eaton, Santa Fe Community College; Samuel Singer, Western Illinois University; Robert E. Sjogren, University of Vermont; Jay F. Sperry, University of Rhode Island; Richard St. John, Widener University; Frank van Steenbergen, San Diego State University; Rosalie H. Stillwell, Hofstra University; William L. Tidwell, Professor Emeritus, San Jose State University; Thomas Weber, University of Nebraska at Omaha; and Gary Wilson, McMurry University. The valuable suggestions and modifications from each of these individuals have contributed immeasurably to the quality of this new book.

We are grateful to our colleagues at McGraw-Hill for their excellent professional and constructive cooperation and assistance in the task of preparing and publishing this book. We particularly wish to thank our McGraw-Hill biology editor, Kathi Prancan, for her editorial wisdom, organizational ability, talent, and encouragement. The overall guidance and support from our publisher, Denise Schanck, is gratefully acknowledged. We are also grateful to our editing supervisor, Holly Gordon, for her devoted work and sound judgment; to Safra Nimrod, for overseeing the photo research; and to Gayle Jaeger, for her vision in developing and implementing the outstanding illustration program. Special thanks are also due to Arthur Ciccone, for his excellent advice and help with our illustrations.

Michael J. Pelczar, Jr.
E. C. S. Chan
Noel R. Krieg

Supplements Overview

FOR THE STUDENT

A *Student's Study Guide*, prepared by Clinton L. Benjamin, Lower Columbia College, Longview, Washington, and Gregory R. Garman, Centralia College, Washington, presents factual and conceptual information to reinforce what is learned in the microbiology text. Each chapter includes learning objectives and an annotated outline coordinated with the text, an interactive outline that gives students the opportunity to distill and translate text information while following the same organization of the text, a listing of key terms, and mastery test questions with answers. Extensive cross-referencing by page number allows the student to locate discussions and descriptions within the text.

The *Laboratory Manual* was prepared by the textbook authors, E. C. S. Chan, Michael J. Pelczar, and Noel R. Krieg. This lab manual contains student-tested laboratory exercises organized to correspond to the text. Each section offers exercises of various lengths and levels to accommodate specific laboratory sessions. Individual lab exercise units feature an overview providing relevant background information with highlighted key terms; learning objectives; references to the text and to other useful sources; a list of materials; procedures; and a report section with labeling exercises, table completion, and review questions.

FOR THE INSTRUCTOR

A *Test Bank Manual/Instructor's Manual* was prepared by Valerie M. Nelson, Senior Testing Specialist for American College Testing Corporation. This manual contains suggested course schedules and answers to the textbook Discussion Questions in addition to approximately 50 questions for each chapter. Each question has been checked for level, clarity, and validity. Answers are given at the end of the manual. The test questions are also available on diskette for IBM PC and compatibles and for Macintosh computers.

Overhead Transparencies for 100 important illustrations, photographs, and electron micrographs from the text are available free to adopters. Lettered callouts are consistently large and bold so that they can be viewed easily, even from the back of a large lecture room.

Case Study Software was prepared by Fred J. Stutzenberger of Clemson University. This program includes five case studies, each with a different application: immunology, food and beverage production, water quality control, medical, and pharmaceutical. Each real-life case includes a scenario wherein students are asked to resolve a problem. Critical reasoning will be required as students are led toward the resolution. This problem-solving program is available on diskette for Macintosh computers and is free to adopters.

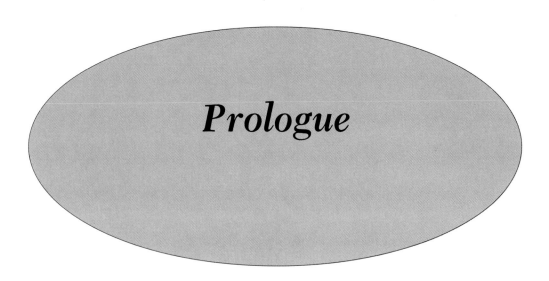

Prologue

Discovering the Microbial World

In all human affairs . . . there is a single dominant factor—time. To make sense of the present state of science, we need to know how it got like that: we cannot avoid an historical account. . . . To extrapolate into the future we must look backwards a little into the past.

—J. M. Ziman*

Microbiology, the study of microscopic organisms, derived its name from three Greek words: *mikros* ("small"), *bios* ("life"), and *logos* ("science"). Taken together they mean the study of microscopic life.

Scientists conclude that microorganisms originated an estimated 4 billion years ago from complex organic materials in ocean waters, or possibly in vast cloud banks surrounding our primitive earth. As the first life on earth, microorganisms are thought to be the ancestors of all other life forms.

Although microorganisms are ancient by any standards, microbiology itself is a comparatively young science. It seems incredible that explorers first observed microorganisms only a little more than 300 years ago and that microorganisms were poorly understood for many years after their discovery. There was a lapse of almost

*J. M. Ziman, *The Force of Knowledge*, Cambridge University Press, Cambridge, England, 1976.

200 years from the time microbes were first seen to the widespread recognition of their importance.

From among the many scientific breakthroughs of new knowledge about microorganisms, a few can be singled out as having had a major influence in establishing the science of microbiology. The initial breakthrough came during the latter half of the nineteenth century when scientists proved that these microscopic organisms originate from parents like themselves, not from supernatural causes or from putrefactive decay of plant and animal material. Scientists later proved that microbes are not the result but the cause of the fermentative changes in grape juice that produce wine. They also discovered that a specific kind of microbe causes a specific disease. This knowledge was the beginning of the recognition and understanding of the critical influence these "new" forms of life have on human health and welfare. During the early part of the twentieth century, microbiologists learned that microbes are capable of bringing about a great variety of chemical changes both by breaking down substances and by synthesizing (building up) new compounds. The term *biochemical diversity* was coined to characterize microorganisms. But equally important was the observation that the mechanism by which these chemical changes are produced by microorganisms is very much like that which occurs in higher forms of life.

MICROBIOLOGY, SCIENCE, AND SOCIETY

Microorganisms during the last few decades have emerged as part of the mainstream of the biological sciences. Among the reasons for this are the concept of "unity in biochemistry," which means that many of the biochemical processes of microorganisms are essentially the same in all forms of life including humans, and the more recent discovery that all of the genetic information of all organisms, from microbes to human beings, is encoded in DNA. Because of the relative simplicity of performing experiments with microorganisms, coupled with their rapid rate of growth and their wide range of biochemical activities, microorganisms became the experimental model of choice for the study of genetics. They now are used extensively in the investigation of fundamental biological phenomena.

Microorganisms have also emerged as a new source of products and processes for the benefit of society. For example, alcohol produced by fermentation of grain may become a new source of fuel (gasohol). New varieties of microorganisms, produced by genetic engineering, can produce important medicinal substances such as human insulin. For years, only bovine insulin, extracted from the pancreas of calves, was available for treatment of diabetes, and some patients could not use it. Today, human insulin can be produced in unlimited quantities by a genetically engineered bacterium. Microorganisms have great potential for assisting in the cleanup of the environment—from the decomposition of petroleum compounds in oil spills to the decomposition of herbicides and insecticides used in agriculture. In fact, specific varieties of microorganisms are in use, and others are being developed, to replace chemicals presently used to control insects. The ability to genetically engineer microorganisms for specific purposes has created a new field of industrial microbiology, namely, *biotechnology*.

The development and use of genetically engineered microorganisms in the open environment has created a major problem—a problem of global dimensions. The question raised is, might the newly introduced microbe have an adverse effect upon the environment? Many international and national conferences have addressed the question. Heated debates, frequently emotionally

FIGURE P.1
Leeuwenhoek demonstrating his microscopes to Queen Catherine of England.

charged, argue the pros and cons of this issue. National and international guidelines and regulations are being established to regulate this practice.

As you read about microorganisms, you will learn to appreciate the often invisible worlds of bacteria, algae, fungi, protozoa, and viruses. Some are harmful in that they may cause diseases of humans, other animals, and plants. Some bring about deterioration of fabrics, wood, and metals. But many more are very important in bringing about changes in the environment which are essential for the maintenance of life, as we know it, on planet Earth. Still others are exploited to manufacture a variety of useful substances ranging from medicinal products and food to chemicals used in industry.

To understand the present state of the science of microbiology, we need to know how we arrived to where we are at present. The discovery of the world of microorganisms includes stories about pride, nationalism, public clamor for cures, and questions about ethics. Those early scientists who chose to study microbiology were pushed—along with their discoveries—by competition, inspiration, and just plain luck. There were misconceptions that led to truth, and truths that first went unrecognized. It started with those fascinated by what others could not see.

LEEUWENHOEK AND HIS MICROSCOPES

Some momentous discoveries in science are made by amateurs, rather than by professional scientists. One of the major figures in the history of microbiology owned his own dry goods store, was the city hall janitor, and served as the official wine taster for the city of Delft in Holland. Antony van Leeuwenhoek (1632–1723; FIGURE P.1) was familiar with the use of magnifying glasses for inspecting fibers and weaving in cloth. As a hobby he ground glass lenses and mounted them between thin sheets of silver or brass to form simple microscopes [FIGURE P.2]. He was not the first person to use microscopes to study disease organisms or other extremely small living organisms. But Leeuwenhoek had an insatiable curiosity about the natural world, and it is his detailed descriptions of what he saw that make him one of the founders of microbiology.

Leeuwenhoek used his primitive microscope to observe river water, pepper infusions, saliva, feces, and more. He became excited by large numbers of minute, moving objects not visible to the naked eye. He called these microscopic bodies *animalcules*, because he thought they were tiny living animals. This finding fired his enthusiasm to make more observations, and to grind and mount more lenses. He eventually made more than

FIGURE P.2

The Leeuwenhoek microscope. [A] Replica of a microscope made in 1673 by Leeuwenhoek. [B] Construction of the Leeuwenhoek microscope: (1) lens; (2) pin for placement of specimen; (3, 4) focusing screws.

[A]

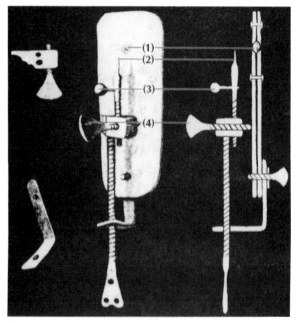

[B]

250 microscopes, with the most powerful able to magnify an object 200 to 300 times.

Leeuwenhoek carefully recorded his observations in a series of letters to the British Royal Society. In one of the first letters, dated September 7, 1674, he described the "very little animalcules" now recognized as free-living protozoa. On October 9, 1676, he wrote:

In the year 1675, I discovered living creatures in rain water which had stood but a few days in a new earthen pot, glazed blue within. This invited me to view this water with great attention, especially those little animals appearing to me ten thousand times less than those . . . which may be perceived in the water with the naked eye.

He described his little "animals" in great detail, leaving little doubt to the modern reader that he saw bacteria, fungi, and many forms of protozoa. For example, on June 16, 1675, while examining well water into which he had put a whole pepper the day before, he recorded the following:

I discovered, in a tiny drop of water, incredibly many very little animalcules, and these of diverse sorts and sizes. They moved with bendings, as an eel always swims with its head in front, and never tail first, yet these animalcules swam as well backwards as forwards, though their motion was very slow.

In one letter, this amateur microscopist provided the first recorded drawings of microorganisms now known as bacteria [FIGURE P.3]. He saw them in material scraped from his teeth. Between 1673 and 1723, Leeuwenhoek described his meticulously recorded observations and sketches in more than 300 letters. These letters alerted the world to the existence of microscopic forms of life and gave birth to microbiology.

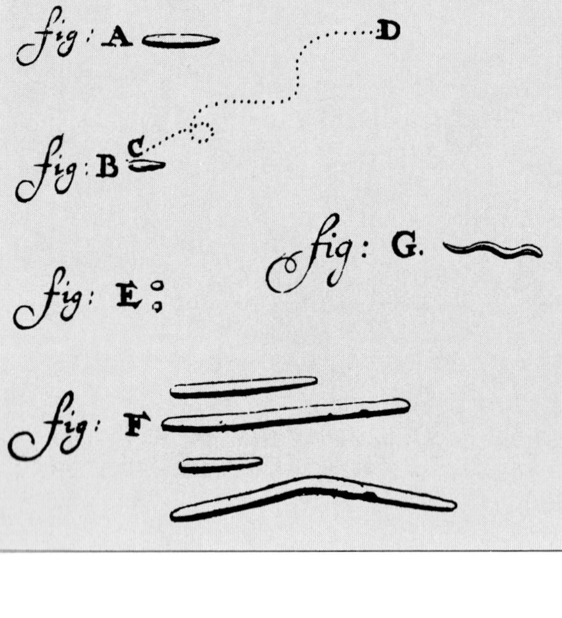

ORIGIN OF LEEUWENHOEK'S ANIMALCULES

Leeuwenhoek's discovery of microorganisms, a menagerie of living forms invisible to the unaided eye, spurred heated arguments over the origin of these animalcules. Two schools of thought on the origin of microorganisms emerged. One was willing to admit the existence of these structures, but argued that they came into being as a result of the decomposition of plant or animal tissue (i.e., through fermentation or putrefaction). In other words, microorganisms were the result of, rather than the cause of, changes in these tissues. Those supporting this view believed that life arose from the nonliving, a process called *abiogenesis.* This basically was the concept of *spontaneous generation.*

Those on the other side of the debate argued that Leeuwenhoek's animalcules came from parents, as do higher forms of life. This idea that the already existing animalcules produced offspring was given the name *biogenesis.*

Microbiology as a science could not advance until the false concept of spontaneous generation was disproved. It took many clever experiments, which appear simple today, and more than a hundred years to resolve the controversy.

Biogenesis versus Abiogenesis

The idea of spontaneous generation dates back at least to the ancient Greeks, who believed that frogs and worms arose spontaneously from the mud of ponds and streams. Others were convinced that maggots and flies were produced in the same manner from decaying meat. There were even recipes for producing mice, such as stuffing rags into a container and placing it in a remote area for several weeks. But by the seventeenth century, critical thinkers were disagreeing with these ideas. One opponent was an Italian physician named Francesco Redi (1626–1697), who showed in 1668 that worms found on putrefying meat were the larvae from eggs of flies, and not the product of spontaneous generation. But it was one thing to study fly larvae and quite another to understand the source of organisms that could be seen only through a microscope.

FIGURE P.3
Leeuwenhoek's sketches of bacteria from the human mouth. These drawings show that he observed rods, cocci, and spiral-shaped bacteria. In addition, he recorded motility of some microbes, i.e., the path from C to D.

Disproof of Abiogenesis

There were both champions and challengers of the concept of spontaneous generation, each with a new and sometimes fantastic explanation or bit of experimental evidence. In 1745, John Needham (1713–1781) cooked pieces of meat to destroy preexisting organisms, and placed them in open flasks. Eventually he saw colonies of microorganisms on the surface and concluded that they arose spontaneously from the meat. In 1769, Lazzaro Spallanzani (1729–1799) boiled beef broth in flasks for an hour and then sealed the flasks. No microorganisms appeared in the broth, thus arguing against abiogenesis. But Needham simply insisted that air was essential to all life and to the spontaneous generation of microbes, and that it had been excluded from Spallanzani's flasks.

Nearly 100 years after Needham's first experiments, two other investigators tried to resolve the "air is essential" controversy. In 1836, Franz Schulze (1815–1873) passed air through strong acid solutions and into boiled meat broth in a sealed flask [FIGURE P.4A]. The next year, Theodor Schwann (1810–1882) forced air through heated tubes and then into a flask of broth [FIGURE P.4B]. Microbes did not appear in the broth in either case, because microbes present in the air had been killed by acid or heat. But the advocates of spontaneous generation were not convinced. They said acid and heat altered air so that it could not support microbial growth. Not until 1854 did scientists solve this debate by passing air through cotton-filled tubes into flasks containing boiled broth [FIGURE P.4C]. Microbes were filtered out, and air was allowed to enter. Yet nothing grew in these flasks, providing evidence that supported biogenesis.

Proof of Biogenesis

During the same period when these experiments were done, a new figure was emerging in science, a Frenchman named Louis Pasteur (1822–1895), who was educated as a chemist [FIGURE P.5]. Pasteur later threw his considerable talents into the study of microorganisms. As a result, he became interested in the French wine industry and the role of microbes in making alcohol. This interest thrust him into the continuing debate over the origin of microorganisms.

One of the staunch supporters of spontaneous generation during Pasteur's time was a French naturalist, Félix Archimède Pouchet (1800–1872). He published an extensive report in 1859 that supported abiogenesis. But he failed to reckon with the stubborn, ingenious Pasteur. Irritated by Pouchet's logic and data, Pasteur did a series of definitive experiments. He used flasks with long, curved stems resembling swan necks [FIGURE P.6], which were filled with broth and heated. Air could pass

FIGURE P.4
Design of experiments performed in the mid-nineteenth century to gain evidence to disprove spontaneous generation (abiogenesis). Each of the experiments was based upon the assumption that microbes were carried on dust particles in air. If the air was treated to kill or remove microbes (or to remove dust particles), materials previously sterilized would not show growth after such "treated" air was introduced. **[A]** Schulze passed air through strong solutions of acid before it entered flasks of previously boiled meat. **[B]** Schwann passed air through a red-hot tube before the air entered a flask of sterile broth. **[C]** Schröder and von Dusch passed air through a tube containing cotton prior to its entry into a flask containing sterile broth.

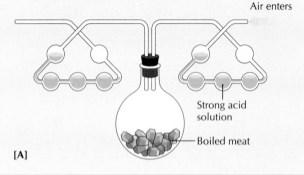

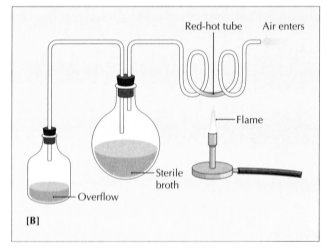

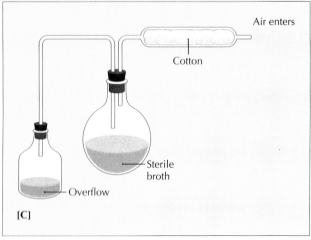

FIGURE P.5
Louis Pasteur in his laboratory.

FIGURE P.6
Pasteur's gooseneck flask, which he designed for experiments to disprove spontaneous generation. Dust particles settled in the lower curved region of the neck of the flask, so that microorganisms were prevented from contaminating the broth in the flask. This flask is preserved in the Pasteur Museum.

For I have kept from them, and am still keeping from them, that one thing that is above the power of man to make; I have kept from them the germs that float in the air, I have kept them from life.

He could not resist flinging a few darts that day at the abiogenesis group:

There is no condition known today in which you can affirm that microscopic beings come into the world without germs, without parents like themselves. They who allege it have been the sport of illusions, of ill-made experiments, vitiated by errors which they have not been able to perceive and have not known how to avoid.

One of the traditional arguments against biogenesis was the claim that heat used to sterilize the air or specimens during experiments was also destroying an essential "vital force." Those supporting abiogenesis said that, without this force, microorganisms could not spontaneously appear. In response to this argument, the physicist John Tyndall (1820–1883) showed that air could be freed of microorganisms by simply allowing dust particles to settle to the bottom of a closed box [FIGURE P.7]. He then inserted test tubes containing sterile liquid into the box. The liquid remained sterile, proving that a "vital force" had nothing to do with the appearance of microorganisms.

Pasteur's and Tyndall's experiments promoted the general acceptance of biogenesis. Pasteur then moved on to his studies on the role of microorganisms in wine production and on microorganisms as the cause of disease.

FIGURE P.7
Tyndall's dust-free box. So long as this box was dust-free (one could tell by looking at the beam of light passing through the middle), sterile broth in the tubes would remain sterile even though the air in the box was in direct contact with the outside air through the openings in the convoluted tubes.

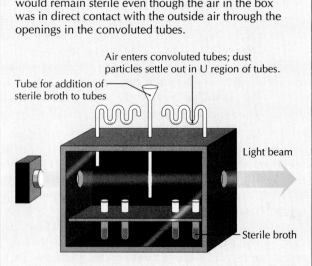

freely through the open necks, but no microbes appeared in the solution. Dust particles and microbes had settled in the U-shaped section of the curved tube but did not reach the broth.

Pasteur also carried flasks of broth high into the Pyrenees and Alps, where the flasks were opened and then resealed. The chemist-turned-microbiologist knew that dust particles carried microorganisms through the air, and his mountain experiments showed that the purer the air allowed to enter flasks, the less likely that contamination would occur.

Pasteur reported his conclusive results with a flourish at the Sorbonne in Paris. On April 7, 1864, he said:

GERM THEORY OF FERMENTATION

When grape juice is allowed to stand, *fermentation* occurs, and through a series of biochemical changes alcohol and other substances are produced from grape sugar. One reason Pasteur was eager to disprove spontaneous generation was his conviction that fermentation products from grape juice were a result of microorganisms present, not that fermentation produced microorganisms, as some believed.

Many ancient cultures developed beverages and foods that we now know are products of microbial fermentations. Wine making has occurred for so long that the early Greeks believed wine was invented by Dionysus, mythical god of fertility, wine, and drama. A Chinese rice beer, called *kiu*, has been traced back to 2300 B.C. *Sake* is a Japanese wine produced by the microbial fermentation of a rice mash [FIGURE P.8]. Derived from fermented beans, the soy sauces of China and Japan have been made for centuries. For hundreds of years, peoples of the Balkan countries have consumed fermented milk products. Central Asiatic tribes have long enjoyed *koumiss*, an alcoholic beverage made from fermented mare's or camel's milk. Anthropologists and historians know of no society that did not use fermentation to make food or drink.

In the 1850s Pasteur answered a call for help from the French wine industry. By examining both good and bad batches of wine, he found microorganisms of different kinds. Certain types of microbes predominated in the good-tasting wines, while others were more numerous in lower-quality wine. Pasteur concluded that proper selection of microbes could ensure a consistently good product. To achieve this, he destroyed microbes

FIGURE P.8
The brewing of sake in Japan as illustrated in a historic woodcut scene.

already in grape juice by first heating the juice and, after cooling, inoculated the juice with some high-quality wine which contained the desired kind of microbe. He also observed that the finished product (wine) could be preserved, without any damage to flavor, if it was heated to 50 to 60°C for several minutes.

Today this latter process, called *pasteurization,* is widely used in the food industry. But to the general public, treatment of milk and milk products remains the most familiar use of pasteurization.

During ancient times, people improved upon their fermented products by trial and error, unaware that the product quality depends on providing special kinds of microorganisms.

GERM THEORY OF DISEASE

While Pasteur and his assistants were revolutionizing the wine industry, they also were affirming a new theory of what causes disease. In doing so, they discovered the *causative agents* of some of the most serious diseases affecting humans and animals. But long before Pasteur proved that microbes cause some diseases, several careful observers had made strong arguments for the **germ theory of disease.** Prior to their observations, it was believed at various times in human history that disease was caused by such vague factors as bad air or bad blood.

In 1546, Girolamo Fracastoro of Verona (1483–1553) had suggested that diseases might be due to organisms, too small to be seen, that were transmitted from one person to another. Much of his information came from conversations with sailors returning from expeditions abroad, where they had witnessed the spread of many diseases. More than 200 years later, Anton von Plenciz (1705–1786) stated in Vienna that not only were living agents the cause of disease, but different agents were responsible for different diseases. At the same time, the concept of one organism living in or on another from which it derives nutrients was becoming accepted. This phenomenon of *parasitism* is reflected in a verse written in the eighteenth century by the English satirist Jonathan Swift (1667–1745):

So, naturalists observe, a flea
Hath smaller fleas that on him prey;
And these have smaller still to bite 'em;
And so proceed ad infinitum.

After his success with fermentation, Pasteur was asked to investigate a silkworm disease that threatened to ruin the French silk industry. He spent 6 years proving that a type of microorganism called a *protozoan* caused the disease. He also showed silkworm farmers how to eliminate the disease by selecting only healthy, disease-free silkworms to breed new crops of the insects.

In Germany, Robert Koch (1843–1910) had started his professional career as a physician. After his wife gave him a microscope for his twenty-eighth birthday, he began exploring the microbial world already seen by Pasteur. Both Pasteur and Koch, who became lifelong professional rivals, were eager to discover the cause of anthrax, a disease decimating the herds of cattle and sheep in Europe. Koch eventually found the disease-causing rod-shaped bacteria in the blood of sheep that had died of anthrax.

Often neglecting his medical practice, Koch proved these bacteria were the cause of anthrax by separating them from any other bacteria present and then injecting them into healthy mice. The mice developed anthrax; bacteria taken from them were identical to those isolated earlier from sick sheep. In 1876, about 6 years after he first stared into his new microscope, Koch announced to the world he had found the anthrax bacterium. He also suggested that sick animals be killed and burned or buried deep, after he realized that spores made by the bacteria could survive for months in contaminated fields.

With his anthrax discoveries, Koch was the first to prove that one kind of microbe causes one definite kind of disease. Later he and his colleagues discovered the bacteria that cause tuberculosis and cholera.

DEVELOPMENT OF LABORATORY TECHNIQUES TO STUDY MICROORGANISMS

At this point in the history of microbiology, information came from observations of specimens in drops of fluid, which often contained mixtures of microorganisms. Study of these specimens was difficult, given the minute size, transparency, and motility of what Pasteur once called "organized corpuscles." There obviously was a need for laboratory techniques to isolate and study individual types of microbes.

Koch and his staff supplied many of those techniques. Among them were procedures for staining bacteria for light-microscopic observation [FIGURE P.9]. One of Koch's protégés, Paul Ehrlich (1854–1915), who did research on dyes, used them to stain bacteria, including the bacterium that causes tuberculosis.

Pure Culture Techniques

By accident, the German scientists saw colonies growing on boiled potatoes and subsequently found ways to separate individual microbes. To do this, they developed

FIGURE P.9

Robert Koch (1843-1910) at the microscope viewing a specimen. Koch and his associates contributed several bacteriological laboratory procedures of such fundamental significance that they are still in use today.

specific *media* (singular, *medium*) to grow microorganisms. Media are substances that satisfy the nutritional needs of microorganisms. Koch and his colleagues also showed how an algal substance called *agar* could solidify media. They learned to cultivate specific microbes in *pure cultures*, using methods described later in this book. Richard J. Petri (1852–1921) invented a special glass-covered dish to hold the agar media. This dish, called a Petri dish, is still in use today, the only difference being that today most are plastic instead of glass. By 1892, using these techniques, Koch and his pupils had found the causative agents for typhoid, diphtheria, tetanus, glanders, acute lobar pneumonia, and more.

Koch advocated the use of animals as models of human disease, injecting bacteria into healthy mice, rabbits, guinea pigs, or sheep. He even attached a camera to his microscope and took pictures, using them to convince the dubious [FIGURE P.10].

FIGURE P.10
Robert Koch's laboratory. Note the homemade photographic equipment on the left, which he used to take pictures of the anthrax and tuberculosis bacteria.

Koch's Postulates

About 1880, Koch took advantage of the newly developed laboratory methods and set forth the criteria needed to prove a specific microbe causes a particular disease. These criteria are known as ***Koch's postulates:***

1 A specific microorganism can always be found associated with a given disease.
2 The microorganism can be isolated and grown in pure culture in the laboratory.
3 The pure culture of the microorganism will produce the disease when injected into a susceptible animal.
4 It is possible to recover the injected microorganism from the experimentally infected animal.

Subsequent discovery of viruses, agents that do not grow in the laboratory on artificial media as do bacteria, has required some modifications of Koch's postulates. Also, we now know that there are some diseases caused by more than one microorganism, while other microbes can cause several different diseases. Regardless of these modifications, within a short period of time after the germ theory was established (less than 30 years), the criteria led to the discovery of most bacteria that cause disease in humans [TABLE P.1].

It was through the study of the causes of diseases in plants that other scientists discovered ***viruses*** (from Latin *virus*, meaning a slimy liquid or a poison). In 1892, Dmitri Ivanovski (1864–1920) discovered that the causative agent of tobacco mosaic disease could be transmitted by the filtered juice from a diseased plant. The filter, invented by a collaborator of Pasteur, was known to prevent the passage of bacteria. Further experimentation showed that the material that passed through the filter contained a new class of disease-causing agent which was much smaller than bacteria.

An American botanist, Thomas J. Burrill (1839–1916; FIGURE P.11), at the University of Illinois found

FIGURE P.11
T. J. Burrill (1839-1916) was among the first generation of American microbiologists. In 1878 he discovered that fire blight of pears was caused by a bacterium.

FIGURE P.12

E. F. Smith (1854–1929) did much of the pioneer research which established the role of microorganisms as the causative agents for many plant and animal diseases.

that a disease of pear trees known as *fire blight* was caused by a bacterium. His research helped to establish that plants, like animals, are susceptible to bacterial diseases. Working for the U.S. Department of Agriculture, Erwin F. Smith (1854–1929; FIGURE P.12) transmitted the plant disease called *peach yellows* from diseased to healthy plants, but he could not find the causative agent. Several decades later, other researchers showed that this was a viral disease.

Another American, Theobald Smith (1859–1934), was a physician who had taught himself microbiology. Employed at the U.S. Bureau of Animal Industry, he set out to conquer Texas fever in cattle. He proved that a protozoan was to blame and that it lived inside ticks that fed on cattle. It was the first description of a microbe carried by an arthropod. The importance of this observation is difficult to exaggerate, for it led to research on arthropod-borne microbial diseases. Among the diseases successfully prevented as a result of Smith's discovery are malaria, yellow fever, and sleeping sickness.

Yellow fever was the first human disease attributed to viruses. In 1900 an army surgeon named Walter Reed (1851–1902; FIGURE P.13), using human volunteers, proved that the virus was carried by certain mosquitoes. The previous year, two scientists in India and Italy had shown that other mosquitoes carried malaria protozoa. One of the most important measures taken to prevent these diseases was the removal of pools of stagnant water used by mosquitoes as breeding grounds.

FIGURE P.13

Major Walter Reed and members of his Yellow Fever Commission observe a patient. Their research, performed in Havana, Cuba, demonstrated that the disease was caused by a virus transmitted by mosquitoes. Subsequent mosquito control programs virtually eliminated epidemic yellow fever from Cuba and areas of Central and South America and made it possible to complete the Panama Canal.

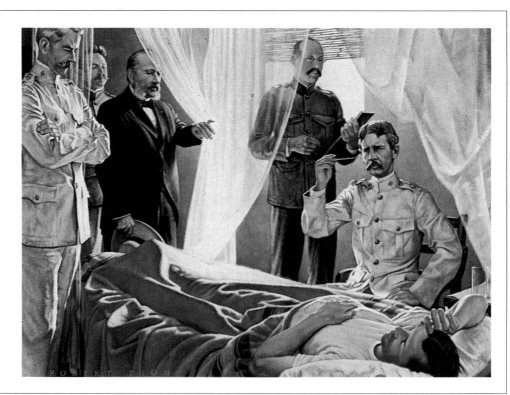

TABLE P.1
The Rapid, Early Discovery of Bacteria Causing Human and Animal Diseases

Date	Disease or infection	Causative agent*	Discoverer†
1876	Anthrax	*Bacillus anthracis*	Koch
1879	Gonorrhea	*Neisseria gonorrhoeae*	Neisser
1880	Typhoid fever	*Salmonella typhi*	Eberth
1880	Malaria	*Plasmodium* spp.	Laveran
1881	Wound infections	*Staphylococcus aureus*	Ogston
1882	Tuberculosis	*Mycobacterium tuberculosis*	Koch
1882	Glanders	*Pseudomonas mallei*	Loeffler and Schütz
1883	Cholera	*Vibrio cholerae*	Koch
1883–1884	Diphtheria	*Corynebacterium diphtheriae*	Klebs and Loeffler
1885	Swine erysipelas	*Erysipelothrix rhusiopathiae*	Loeffler
1885	Tetanus	*Clostridium tetani*	Nicolaier
1886	Bacterial pneumonia	*Streptococcus pneumoniae*	Fraenkel
1887	Meningitis	*Neisseria meningitidis*	Weichselbaum
1887	Malta fever	*Brucella* spp.	Bruce
1888	Equine strangles	*Streptococcus* spp.	Schütz
1889	Chancroid	*Haemophilus ducreyi*	Ducrey
1892	Gas gangrene	*Clostridium perfringens*	Welch and Nuttall
1894	Plague	*Yersinia pestis*	Kitasato and Yersin
1895	Fowl typhoid	*Salmonella gallinarum*	Moore
1896	Botulism (food poisoning)	*Clostridium botulinum*	Van Ermengem
1897	Bang's disease (bovine abortion)	*Brucella abortus*	Bang
1898	Dysentery	*Shigella dysenteriae*	Shiga
1898	Pleuropneumonia of cattle	*Mycoplasma mycoides*	Nocard and Roux
1905	Syphilis	*Treponema pallidum*	Schaudinn and Hoffman
1906	Whooping cough	*Bordetella pertussis*	Bordet and Gengou
1909	Rocky Mountain spotted fever	*Rickettsia rickettsii*	Ricketts
1912	Tularemia	*Francisella tularensis*	McCoy and Chapin

*Present name of causative agent; original name, in many instances, was different.
†In some instances the individual simply observed the causative agent; in other instances the investigator isolated the agent in pure culture.

DEVELOPMENTS IN DISEASE PREVENTION

It is difficult to comprehend the magnitude of human misery and devastation caused by microbial and viral diseases prior to the latter half of the twentieth century. Plague, typhus, diphtheria, smallpox, cholera, and influenza devastated vast regions of the world. An epidemic (a disease that strikes many in a particular locality) of bubonic plague, known as the "black death" and caused by a bacterium, occurred in Europe during the period 1347–1350. One-third to one-half of the French population died from the disease, and an estimated 25 million people in Europe were dead from the plague by the time its spread subsided. Rodents, especially rats, serve as a reservoir for the plague bacillus, and it is transmitted from rats to humans by fleas.

Another disease caused by a virus, influenza, was both epidemic and pandemic (occurring worldwide) in 1173, and there were at least 37 outbreaks between 1510 and 1973. Deaths caused by influenza and its complications during the 1917–1919 epidemic killed about half a million Americans and 21 million people worldwide— almost 3 times the number killed in World War I. Microbes proved more deadly than bullets.

With the knowledge that microorganisms cause disease, scientists focused their attention on prevention and treatment. Hospital staffs adopted *antisepsis*, which prevents the spread of infectious diseases by inhibiting or destroying the causative agents. *Immunization*, a process that stimulates body defenses against infection, was discovered. *Chemotherapy*, treating disease with a chemical substance, expanded as researchers found better drugs. Less dramatic but even more effective, improved public health measures like better sanitation, particularly as related to water and food, reduced the spread of microorganisms and the incidence of disease.

Antisepsis

In general, the word *sepsis* refers to the toxic effects of disease-causing microorganisms on the body during infection, while *antisepsis* refers to measures that stop those effects by preventing infection. Antisepsis was practiced even before the germ theory of disease was proved.

Oliver Wendell Holmes (1809–1894), a successful American physician as well as a man of letters, insisted in 1843 that childbed fever was contagious, and therefore carried from one woman to another on the hands of physicians and midwives. Now called *puerperal fever*, it was a serious and often fatal infection of the mother after childbirth. In 1846, Hungarian physician Ignaz Philipp Semmelweis (1818–1865) worked to convince his colleagues that the use of chlorine solutions would disinfect the hands of obstetricians.

In the 1860s, an English surgeon named Joseph Lister (1827–1912) was searching for a way to keep microbes out of incisions made by surgeons. At that time, deaths from infection following surgery were frequent. In 1864, for example, Lister's records showed that 45 percent of his own patients died in this way.

Carbolic acid, also called *phenol*, was known to kill bacteria. Lister used a dilute solution of this chemical to soak surgical dressings and to spray the operating room [FIGURE P.14]. So remarkable was his success that the technique was quickly accepted by other surgeons astute enough to recognize the significance of Lister's findings. His experiments were the origin of present-day *aseptic techniques* that prevent infections. Today a variety of chemical substances and physical devices can reduce the number of microorganisms in operating rooms, nurseries for premature infants, and rooms where drugs are dispensed into sterile containers.

Immunization

In 1880, Pasteur used Koch's techniques to isolate and culture the bacterium that causes chicken cholera. To prove his discovery, he arranged a public demonstration of an experiment that had been successful many times in the laboratory. He injected healthy chickens with pure cultures of cholera bacteria and waited for them to develop symptoms and die. But to his dismay, the chickens remained alive and well [FIGURE P.15]!

Pasteur, on reviewing each step of his failed experiment, found he had accidentally used cultures that were several weeks old, instead of the fresh culture prepared especially for the demonstration. Some weeks later, he repeated the experiment using two groups of chickens: one inoculated, or injected, during the earlier experiment with old cultures, the other never inoculated. Both groups received bacteria from young, fresh cultures. This time the chickens in the second group died, but those in the first group stayed healthy.

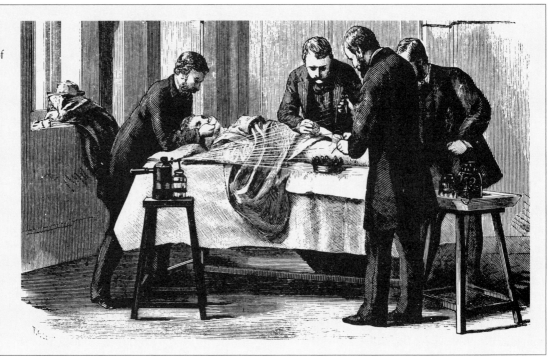

FIGURE P.14
Joseph Lister producing a fog of carbolic acid (phenol) spray during an operation, to reduce the incidence of infection.

FIGURE P.15

The principle of immunization as demonstrated by Pasteur. Pasteur first inoculated chickens with a culture of chicken cholera bacteria which was several weeks old; these chickens remained healthy. Several weeks later he inoculated these same chickens with a fresh culture of chicken cholera bacteria. This fresh virulent culture did not make them sick, but it did kill chickens that had not been inoculated previously with the "old" culture. This experiment demonstrated that the "old" culture of chicken cholera bacteria, even though unable to produce disease, was capable of causing the chickens to produce protective substances called *antibodies* in their blood.

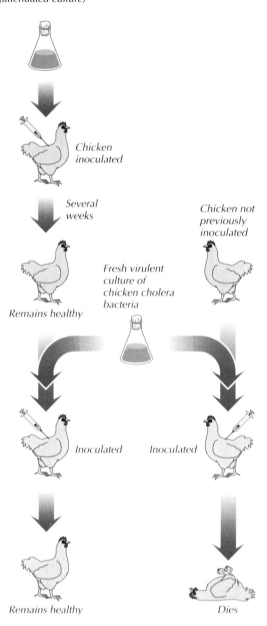

Pure culture of chicken cholera bacteria 8 weeks old (attenuated culture)

Chicken inoculated

Several weeks

Remains healthy

Chicken not previously inoculated

Fresh virulent culture of chicken cholera bacteria

Inoculated   *Inoculated*

Remains healthy   *Dies*

Puzzled at first, Pasteur soon found an explanation. He had discovered that bacteria, if allowed to grow old, could become **avirulent** (that is, lose their **virulence,** or ability to cause disease). But these avirulent bacteria could still stimulate something in the host—in this case, chickens—to resist subsequent infection and thus be **immune** to that disease.

Pasteur next applied this principle of immunization to the prevention of anthrax, and again it worked. He called the avirulent cultures **vaccines** (from the Latin *vacca,* "cow") and immunization with such cultures **vaccination.** By using these terms, Pasteur recognized the earlier work of Edward Jenner (1749–1823), who had successfully vaccinated a boy against smallpox in 1798 [FIGURE P.16]. Jenner had heard that milkmaids who got cowpox from their cows never developed the more serious smallpox. He hypothesized that exposure to cowpox somehow protected against smallpox. To test his hypothesis, he inoculated James Phipps, first with cowpox-causing material taken from sores, and later with smallpox-causing material. The boy did not get smallpox.

Now famous throughout France and beyond, Pasteur was considered by many to be a miracle worker with microorganisms. It was not surprising that he was asked to make a vaccine against hydrophobia, or rabies—a disease transmitted to people by a bite from infected dogs, cats, and other animals. A chemist and not a physician, Pasteur was not accustomed to treating humans. But he

FIGURE P.16

Edward Jenner vaccinating (inoculating) James Phipps with cowpox material, which resulted in the development of resistance to smallpox infection.

finally agreed to turn his usual determination and skill toward rabies, which was almost invariably fatal.

Despite the fact that the causative agent of rabies was unknown, Pasteur felt strongly that it was a microorganism. He could produce the disease in rabbits by inoculating them with saliva from rabid dogs. After an inoculated rabbit died, Pasteur and his assistants removed its brain and spinal cord, dried them for several days, pulverized them, and then mixed the powder into a liquid. Inoculating dogs with a series of shots using this mixture protected them from rabies.

But vaccinating dogs was quite different from treating a sick human. Then, in July 1885, a boy named Joseph Meister was bitten by a rabid wolf, and his family persuaded Pasteur to inoculate the child. The worried Pasteur was as relieved as anyone when, after the weeks needed to complete the inoculations, the boy did not die [FIGURE P.17].

FIGURE P.18

Elie Metchnikoff, a Russian microbiologist working in Pasteur's laboratory, was the first person to recognize the role of certain white blood cells in combating a bacterial infection.

FIGURE P.17

This monument, on the grounds of the Pasteur Institute, Paris, commemorates Pasteur's contribution to the control of rabies.

When Pasteur later saved most of a group of Russian peasants bitten by a rabid wolf, the czar sent him 100,000 francs. This money, along with other donations from around the world, was the beginning of the world-famous Pasteur Institute in Paris.

Another fundamental concept of immunology was discovered by Elie Metchnikoff (1845–1916), a Russian [FIGURE P.18]. While studying starfish larvae, he observed that certain cells engulfed splinters that he had introduced into the larvae. Calling these cells *phagocytes*, from Greek words meaning "devouring cells," Metchnikoff, while at the Pasteur Institute in Paris, went on to establish that certain leucocytes (white blood cells) "eat" disease-producing bacteria in most animals, including humans. He formulated the theory that the phagocytes were the body's first and most important line of defense against infection. For this discovery, he (along with Paul Ehrlich) received the Nobel Prize in 1908.

Chemotherapy

Chemotherapy has been practiced for hundreds of years. Mercury was used to treat syphilis as early as 1495, and cinchona bark (which contains quinine) was used in South America in the seventeenth century for the treatment of malaria. Before the time of Columbus's voyage to America, natives of Brazil used the ipecac root to treat dysentery. Plants thus served as the original source of chemotherapeutic agents. But it was not until the brilliant research of Paul Ehrlich that modern chemotherapy began.

Ehrlich's ambition was to find a "magic bullet"—a chemical that would be so precise in its aim that it would kill a specific disease-causing microbe while at the same time leaving the patient's cells unharmed. He particularly wished to find a magic bullet which could be used to treat patients suffering from syphilis. To that end, he systematically synthesized hundreds of chemical compounds, with limited success. In 1909, a year after he won a Nobel Prize for earlier work on how antibodies are formed, Ehrlich made his 606th compound. It was a synthetic arsenic compound called *Salvarsan* that proved effective against the syphilis bacterium.

Another major advance in chemotherapy occurred in 1932, in time to save soldiers during World War II. Gerhard Domagk (1895–1964), a German physician, discovered that the group of chemicals called *sulfonamides,* or sulfa drugs, was very effective against several bacterial infections. As an example of their effectiveness, the fatality rate from meningococcal infections among American soldiers in World War II was only 3.9 percent, compared with 39 percent in World War I. Domagk won a Nobel Prize for his efforts and helped launch a second wave of research on chemotherapeutic agents. These agents joined the older, plant-derived chemicals as weapons against disease.

The discovery of *penicillin* opened another dramatic era for chemotherapy, one that relied on substances produced by microorganisms. In 1928, years before the advent of sulfonamide treatment, the Scottish microbiologist Alexander Fleming (1881–1955) reported that a substance made by the common mold *Penicillium notatum* prevented the growth of certain bacteria. It was a momentous discovery.

The discovery of the substance, which he called penicillin, took a circuitous route. One day Fleming noticed that a mold had contaminated some culture plates of bacteria he was studying, and he nearly threw out what he thought were worthless plates. But when he looked more closely, he noticed that the bacteria were not growing near the mold, which proved to be *Penicillium notatum.* Fleming guessed correctly that the mold was producing some substance that inhibited the growth of bacteria. His original report went virtually unnoticed until 10 years later, when a group from Oxford University set out to find antibacterial substances of microbial origin. Part of the impetus for this search was the threat of a second world war and the battlefield diseases it would entail. The group, led by Howard W. Florey (1898–1968) and Ernst Chain (1906–1979), conducted clinical trials with penicillin that produced results so dramatic that penicillin was quickly referred to as the "miracle drug." Florey, Chain, and Fleming later shared the 1945 Nobel Prize for their work.

DEVELOPMENTS IN NONMEDICAL MICROBIOLOGY

It is natural that the first developments in microbiology to attract wide notice were those in medical microbiology. However, the discoveries of Pasteur and Koch on the role of microorganisms in diseases were very soon matched by results of research on the role of microorganisms in agriculture and industry. The field of soil microbiology was opened in the late nineteenth century by the Russian microbiologist Sergei Winogradsky (1856–1953; FIGURE P.19A). He discovered that certain soil bacteria could take nitrogen from the air and convert this nitrogen into a form that can be used as a nutrient for plants. He also found that other species of bacteria could convert ammonia, which was released from decaying plant and animal materials, to nitrate nitrogen—a primary source of nitrogen for plants. Winogradsky made fundamental observations on the role of microorganisms in performing chemical changes involving sulfur, iron, and their compounds. In the course of his studies he discovered that certain microbes would grow only on a mixture of inorganic compounds—an example of one of the particular nutritional categories of microorganisms that will be described in this text. They would not grow on the nutrient agar media used by Koch and his associates for the cultivation of microbes that caused diseases.

A contemporary of Winogradsky, the Dutch microbiologist Martinus W. Beijerinck (1851–1931; FIGURE P.19B), is credited along with Winogradsky with having introduced the enrichment culture technique—a procedure that greatly improves the possibility of isolating special kinds of microorganisms from sources such as soil and water. For example, suppose you want to isolate from soil a microbe that has the ability to decompose cellulose, which is the major carbon-containing substance in plants. First you would prepare a liquid medium with cellulose added as the only carbon source and dispense it into flasks or test tubes. Then you would inoculate the medium with soil, incubate it for several days, and make a transfer to fresh medium. This process is repeated several times. The microbes which have the ability to use cellulose will increase in numbers (the medium is *enriched* with this population). In a way this procedure is analogous to the process of natural selection—the composition of the medium favors the growth of a particular kind of microbe. Using this technique, Beijerinck discovered that the foul odor of the Delft canals in the summer was due to a bacterium that could change sulfates to hydrogen sulfide, which has the odor of rotten eggs.

Beijerinck also discovered the bacteria that grow in the root tissue of leguminous plants, such as alfalfa, clo-

FIGURE P.19

Two major contributors to our knowledge of the important role of microorganisms in soil: **[A]** Sergei Winogradsky (1856–1953) and **[B]** Martinus Beijerinck (1851–1931) discovered many of the basic chemical changes performed by microorganisms in the soil.

[A]

[B]

ver, and soybeans. They cause an enlargement of the root tissue, forming a nodule. These bacteria capture nitrogen from the atmosphere and feed it to the plants. Today farmers inoculate seeds of legumes prior to planting with special cultures of these bacteria to enhance crop yield.

The introduction of microbiology to industry was suggested earlier by the research of Pasteur on the fermentation of grapes in wine making. However, a more calculated approach was launched by Emil Christian Hansen (1842–1909) in Copenhagen, Denmark. Hansen promoted the use of *starter cultures*, cultures of the desired types of microorganisms to produce a particular product. This took the "guesswork" out of using microorganisms for an industrial process. Today, wineries, breweries, and manufacturers of cheeses, butter, and fermented products such as yogurt all rely upon starter cultures of microorganisms for the quality of their product.

MICROBIOLOGY AND BIOCHEMISTRY

During the early part of the twentieth century there was a growing awareness of the tremendous capacity of microorganisms to produce chemical changes. The research of Winogradsky, Beijerinck, and others revealed the chemical activities of microorganisms in soil. It was increasingly understood that the use of microorganisms for the manufacture of industrial products was dependent upon their ability to produce chemical changes. Furthermore, the need for more descriptive information to characterize and differentiate microorganisms was recognized. Soon research on the chemical activities of microorganisms—their biochemistry—began to yield volumes of information. There seemed to be no limit to the kinds of substances microbes could decompose or to the kinds of new chemical compounds they could produce. The studies were refined to determine step by step the pathway for these chemical reactions.

This seemingly perplexing biochemical diversity among microorganisms was brought into an orderly interpretation by the brilliance of the Dutch microbiologist A. J. Kluyver (1888–1956). Kluyver succeeded Beijerinck as the leader of the Delft school of microbiologists. He observed that many of the microbial chemical reactions also occurred in other organisms including humans. He concluded that despite this apparent diversity there is a significant degree of similarity among living systems, or *unity of biochemistry*. One of Kluyver's students, C. B. van Niel (1897–1985), became the director of the Pacific Grove Marine Laboratory, where he pursued the theme of unity of biochemistry

FIGURE P.20

A. J. Kluyver (1888–1956) and C. B. van Niel (1897–1985). Kluyver succeeded Beijerinck as the director of the Microbiological Laboratory of the Technical University, Delft, Holland, in 1922. He—first alone and later with his student C. B. van Niel—made significant contributions to our understanding of the chemical activities of microorganisms.

among microorganisms. Many contemporary microbiologists were educated and trained under his supervision.

Further evidence for the concept of unity in the biochemistry of living systems came from experimental evidence on the nutritional requirements of bacteria. It had been known for a long time that the growth of many species of bacteria is dependent upon, or enhanced by, very small amounts of extracts from liver, yeast, or other materials. These extracts, referred to as *growth factors*, were later discovered to be vitamins, including thiamine (vitamin B_1), pyridoxine (vitamin B_6), cobalamin (vitamin B_{12}), and others. Some bacteria require the same vitamins that are required by animals and humans; the function of individual vitamins is the same in all biological systems.

The achievements during this era of the development of microbiology were highlighted by Kluyver and van Niel in 1954, at Harvard University, in a lecture series entitled *The Microbes' Contribution to Biology* [FIGURE P.20].

MICROBIOLOGY AND GENETICS (MOLECULAR BIOLOGY)

Prior to the 1940s there was speculation, with little factual support, about genetics of microorganisms. Knowl-

edge of genetic phenomena came from research on plants and animals. It was an open question how much, if any, of the results of this research was applicable to microorganisms. But a radical turnaround occurred in the 1940s—a series of discoveries thrust microbes into the front line of genetics research. George Beadle and Edward Tatum in 1941, working with the fungus *Neurospora*, isolated mutants which had different, but specific, deficiencies in their ability to synthesize a particular compound. The parent strain of *Neurospora* did not have any of these deficiencies. With this kind of information, that is, mutants with deficiencies at different steps in the synthesis of a compound, it was possible to establish the pathway by which the compound is synthesized. Beadle [FIGURE P.21A] and Tatum [FIGURE P.21B] were awarded the Nobel Prize in 1958 for their discovery of genetic phenomena in *Neurospora*. They were joined in this award by Joshua Lederberg [FIGURE P.21C], who discovered that genetic material could be transferred from one bacterium to another.

The role of DNA in bacterial genetics was observed in 1944 by Oswald Avery, Colin MacLeod, and Maclyn McCarty, in their research at the Rockefeller Institute with a bacterium that causes pneumonia, namely, the pneumococcus. They found that DNA material from one type of pneumococcus could "transfer" a hereditary characteristic (genetic information) to another type of pneumococcus. Later came the epoch-making discovery

[A]

[B]

TABLE P.2
Some Major Events in the Development of Microbiology

Event	Researcher	Era
Discovery of the world of microorganisms	Antony van Leeuwenhoek	Seventeenth century
First classification system for living organisms	Carl Linnaeus	Eighteenth century
Discovery that vaccination with cowpox prevented smallpox	Edward Jenner	
Disproof of the concept of spontaneous generation	Louis Pasteur	Nineteenth century
Establishment that childbed fever is carried from patient to patient on physicians' hands	Ignaz Semmelweis	
Development of the concept of aseptic technique	Joseph Lister	
Proof of the germ theory of fermentation	Pasteur	
Establishment of the germ theory of disease	Pasteur and Robert Koch	
Development of microbiological laboratory techniques	Koch	
Koch's postulates: criteria to establish causative agent of a disease	Koch	
Discovery that avirulent cultures produced immunity	Pasteur	
Description of the role of white blood cells and the cellular theory of immunity (phagocytosis)	Elie Metchnikoff	
Discovery of chemical activities of microorganisms in soil	Sergei Winogradsky and Martinius Beijerinck	
Development of a differential stain for bacteria (Gram stain)	Hans Christian Gram	
Discovery of plant diseases caused by bacteria	Thomas J. Burrill and Erwin S. Smith	
Discovery of viruses	Dmitri Ivanovski	Twentieth century, First decade
Discovery of the relationship of viruses to cancer	Beijerinck and Peyton Rous	
Discovery of a specific chemotherapeutic agent to cure a bacterial disease—concept of chemotherapy	Paul Ehrlich	
Discovery of bacterial viruses (bacteriophage)	Felix d' Herelle and Frederick Twort	
Recognition of the diversity of chemical activities of microorganisms and development of the concept of unity in the biochemistry of living systems	A. J. Kluyver and C. B. van Niel	Second decade

[C]

FIGURE P.21

In 1958 the Nobel Prize in physiology or medicine was awarded to [A] George W. Beadle, [B] Edward L. Tatum, and [C] Joshua Lederberg for their discoveries of genetic phenomena in microorganisms.

Event	Researcher	Era
Cultivation of viruses in animal cells (tissue culture)	F. Parker and R. N. Nye	
First edition of *Bergey's Manual*	D. Bergey and R. Buchanan	
Discovery of antibacterial effects of sulfonamide-prontosil	Gerhard Domagk	Third decade
Discovery of antibiotics (penicillin)	Alexander Fleming, E. B. Chain, and H. W. Florey	
Introduction of electron microscopy	Max Knoll and Ernst Ruska	
Crystallization of a virus	Wendell Stanley	
Isolation of biochemical mutants and discovery that exposure to x-rays increased rate of mutations	George W. Beadle and Edward L. Tatum	Fourth decade
Definition of DNA as the chemical substance responsible for heredity	Oswald Avery, Colin MacLeod, and Maclyn McCarty	
Discovery of genetic processes in microorganisms that regulate specific chemical processes	Beadle, Joshua Lederberg, and Tatum	Fifth decade
Discovery of citric acid cycle	Hans A. Krebs	
Discovery of the double-stranded helical structure of DNA and opened field of molecular genetics	James Watson and Francis Crick	
Development of polio vaccines	Jonas Salk and Albert Sabin	Sixth decade
DNA demonstrated to control viral replication	Alfred D. Hershey and Martha C. Chase	
Discovery of interferon, an inhibitor of viral replication	Alick Isaacs	
Discovery of the nature of control regions of the DNA molecule regulating enzyme production (operon theory)	Francis Jacob, Jacques Monod, and André Lwoff	
Deciphering of the genetic code	Robert W. Holley, H. Gobind Khorama, and Marshall Nirenberg	Seventh decade
Development of techniques to study genetic organization (genetic mapping)	Werner Arber, Daniel Nathans, and Hamilton O. Smith	
Discoveries of interaction between tumor viruses and the genetic material of cells	David Baltimore, Howard M. Temin, and Renato Dulbecco	
Development of genetic engineering using recombinant DNA technology	Paul Berg, Walter Gilbert, and Frederick Sanger	
Unifying theory of cancer development—showed oncogenes in cells	J. Michael Bishop and Harold E. Varnus	Eighth decade

of the molecular structure of DNA by James Watson, Francis Crick, and Maurice Wilkins (Nobel Prize winners in 1962). These discoveries, together with others, established that the genetic information of all organisms was coded in DNA. This made microorganisms extremely attractive models for genetic research. Many major fundamental discoveries of genetic processes at the molecular level have been made in recent years through research using microorganisms. Scientists also have analyzed and differentiated DNA isolated from many organisms. In addition, technical skills and the use of novel enzymes have been developed whereby the DNA molecule can be "cut and spliced" to incorporate a new DNA fragment; this new DNA fragment conveys to the recipient microbe a new biochemical capability. This technique of transferring a fragment of DNA from one organism to another is called *recombinant DNA technology*, or *genetic engineering*. The results of genetic research with microorganisms have been of such significance that many investigators beyond those already mentioned have been honored with the Nobel Prize for their discoveries.

Thus, in a period of approximately 150 years (as summarized in TABLE P.2), we have seen microbiology emerge from debates about the existence and origin of microbes to a major scientific discipline within the biological sciences. In addition, microbes have become a powerful experimental "tool" for the exploration of biological phenomena in all forms of life.

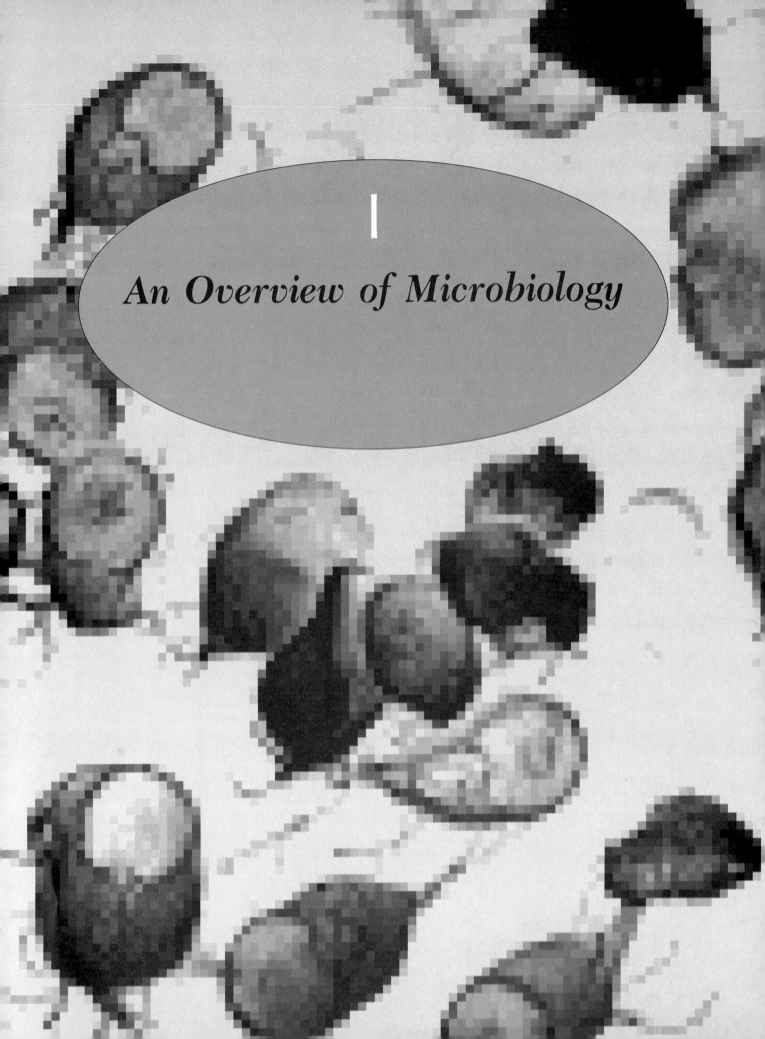

An Overview of Microbiology

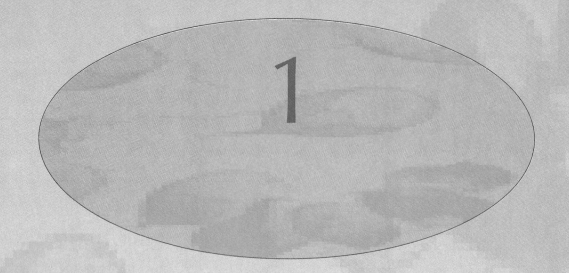

1

Essential Biochemistry for Microbiology

OBJECTIVES

After reading this chapter you should be able to

1 Differentiate among atoms, ions, elements, and molecules.

2 Understand the basic principles of the three types of chemical bonding.

3 Account for the difference in solubility properties of various chemical compounds.

4 Differentiate between percent and molarity of dissolved substances, between acids and bases, and between pH and hydrogen ion concentration.

5 Describe the four major classes of biologically important compounds.

6 List the building blocks for polysaccharides, fats, phospholipids, proteins, DNA, and RNA.

7 Identify those features that make one protein different from another.

8 Understand the nature of enzymes and the vital role they perform in living organisms.

OVERVIEW

Living organisms are often thought of as "chemical machines," because they are made of chemical compounds and live by means of chemical reactions. Thus an understanding of *chemistry* is essential to an understanding of living organisms. Chemistry is the science that deals with the composition, structure, and properties of substances and the transformations they undergo. The process of gasoline combustion which propels an automobile down the road is a chemical reaction. A branch of chemistry called *biochemistry* deals specifically with chemistry in relation to life processes, such as the chemical reactions involved in respiration and photosynthesis.

Like all matter, living organisms contain atoms and molecules as their most basic structural units. How these atoms and molecules interact determines the fundamental qualities of compounds such as solubility and acidity. Such aspects of chemistry are also of great importance to microorganisms, which depend on soluble nutrients and are affected by their environment. The important chemical substances in living organisms are based on the element carbon and include carbohydrates, lipids, proteins, and nucleic acids. Biochemical processes depend on special substances called *enzymes,* which can greatly increase the speed at which a specific reaction occurs.

By balancing the production and utilization of thousands of chemicals, each microorganism can adjust, and even contribute, to its surroundings.

ATOMS AND MOLECULES

Matter is the substance of which any physical object is composed. It may be the silicon particles and other minerals that form a rock. But scientists are able to look at much smaller components of matter. Experimental evidence indicates that all matter consists ultimately of elementary particles of comparatively few kinds. Three kinds of these elementary particles are especially important in understanding chemical compounds and their role in the microbial world: *electrons, protons,* and *neutrons.* An electron has one unit of negative electric charge (-1) and is a relatively light particle. In contrast, a proton has one unit of positive electric charge $(+1)$ and is about 1840 times heavier than an electron. A neutron is roughly the same weight as a proton, but it carries no electric charge and is considered "neutral."

Atoms

Electrons, protons, and neutrons occur in various combinations to form *atoms,* the smallest units of matter that have unique chemical characteristics. First described in 1808, atoms have a dense central region called the *nucleus,* composed of protons and neutrons. Electrons revolve at high speed around the nucleus, and their number *equals the number of protons* in the atom. The result is an atom without a net charge, because the total positive electric charge of the protons in the nucleus is exactly balanced by the total negative charge of the electrons orbiting the nucleus.

Electrons orbit the nucleus in a complex manner, making it impossible to pinpoint the position of an electron at any given instant. Because these electrons are so elusive, scientists study the regions of space where there is a high probability that an electron will be present. Such a region is called the *orbital* of an electron [FIGURE 1.1]. But to understand the basic chemical properties of atoms, you can use even simpler models of the atom, in which electrons are located in a series of concentric rings called *energy levels* and designated K, L, M, N, and so on [FIGURE 1.2A].

These rings do not represent the actual orbitals, but rather the energy possessed by the electrons due to the high speed at which they are traveling around the nucleus. The electrons in the outermost ring travel at the highest speed and have the greatest energy, while those in the innermost ring, or K ring, have the lowest energy. The maximum numbers of electrons allowable in the K and L rings are 2 and 8, respectively. For higher energy levels, if a ring is the outermost ring it is allowed a maximum of eight electrons. Otherwise it can accommodate

FIGURE 1.1

Examples of orbitals, regions around an atomic nucleus where electrons are most likely to be found. The arrows represent three-dimensional space, and the atomic nucleus is shown as a central black dot. **[A]** Electrons at the lowest electron energy level, called the K level, occupy a single spherical orbital that can contain up to two electrons. **[B]** Electrons at the next higher energy level, called the L level, occupy four orbitals, one that is spherical and three that are dumbbell-shaped. Each orbital can contain up to two electrons; thus the L energy level can contain a maximum of eight electrons. Additional higher energy levels may occur, depending on the particular atom.

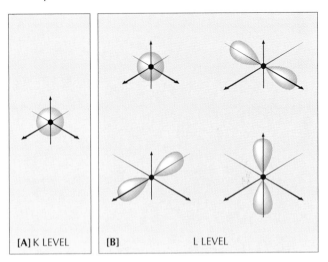

[A] K LEVEL [B] L LEVEL

more (for example, up to 18 electrons in the M ring). If an energy level holds all the electrons allowed, it contains a "full complement" of electrons.

Elements. There are 92 naturally occurring kinds of atoms, each called an *element* [TABLE 1.1]. Examples are oxygen, copper, nitrogen, calcium, sulfur, and tin. An element is defined by its *atomic number,* the number of protons in the atomic nucleus. Because the number of protons does not vary for a given element, all atoms of that particular element have the same atomic number. Except for those of hydrogen, the nuclei of all atoms also contain neutrons. The number of neutrons, however, may vary in the atoms of a given element. Atoms that have the same number of protons in their nuclei but differ in the number of neutrons are called *isotopes.*

For practical purposes, the *atomic weight* of an atom is equal to the sum of the neutrons and protons in the nucleus. The simplest atom is the hydrogen atom, which has only one proton and one electron [FIGURE 1.2B]. The single proton means that the atomic number of hydrogen is 1, and the absence of neutrons means that the atomic weight of hydrogen is the same as its atomic number. On the other hand, a carbon atom contains six protons, six neutrons, and six electrons. Thus the atomic number of carbon is 6 and the atomic weight is $6 + 6 = 12$.

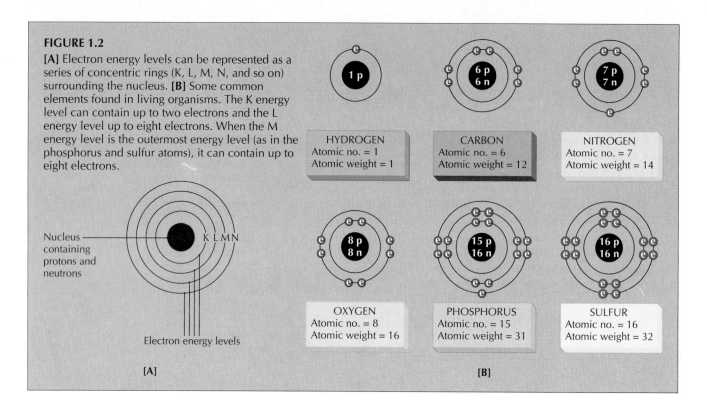

FIGURE 1.2
[A] Electron energy levels can be represented as a series of concentric rings (K, L, M, N, and so on) surrounding the nucleus. [B] Some common elements found in living organisms. The K energy level can contain up to two electrons and the L energy level up to eight electrons. When the M energy level is the outermost energy level (as in the phosphorus and sulfur atoms), it can contain up to eight electrons.

Nucleus containing protons and neutrons

K L M N

Electron energy levels

[A]

HYDROGEN
Atomic no. = 1
Atomic weight = 1

CARBON
Atomic no. = 6
Atomic weight = 12

NITROGEN
Atomic no. = 7
Atomic weight = 14

OXYGEN
Atomic no. = 8
Atomic weight = 16

PHOSPHORUS
Atomic no. = 15
Atomic weight = 31

SULFUR
Atomic no. = 16
Atomic weight = 32

[B]

TABLE 1.1
Some Essential Elements in Microorganisms

Element	Symbol
MAJOR ELEMENTS (ABUNDANT IN MICROORGANISMS)	
Hydrogen	H
Carbon	C
Nitrogen	N
Oxygen	O
MINOR ELEMENTS (SMALL AMOUNTS IN MICROORGANISMS)	
Phosphorus	P
Sulfur	S
Sodium (Latin *natrium*)	Na
Magnesium	Mg
Chlorine	Cl
Potassium (Latin *kalium*)	K
Iron (Latin *ferrum*)	Fe
Calcium	Ca
TRACE ELEMENTS (MINUTE AMOUNTS IN MICROORGANISMS)	
Copper (Latin *cuprum*)	Cu
Zinc	Zn
Manganese	Mn
Cobalt	Co
Molybdenum	Mo
Nickel	Ni
Boron	B
Vanadium	V

Ions. Atoms are electrically neutral because the number of electrons, with their negative charge, equals the number of positively charged protons. However, an atom may gain or lose electrons, in which case it acquires a net electric charge and becomes an *ion* [FIGURE 1.3]. If the overall charge is positive, the ion is a *cation;* if it is negative, the ion is an *anion.* For example, if a sodium atom (Na) loses an electron, it will then have one extra positive electric charge and become a sodium cation (Na^+). A chlorine atom (Cl) may gain the electron lost by the sodium atom and thus have one unit of negative charge, making it an anion (Cl^-). The two new ions, in combination, are the basis for the formation of ordinary table salt (NaCl).

Some kinds of atoms may gain or lose more than one electron. The resulting ions will then have more than one unit of electric charge, such as a magnesium ion (Mg^{2+}) with a net positive charge of two units.

Molecules

By the time the French chemist Antoine Lavoisier was beheaded by revolutionaries in 1794 for collecting taxes from the common folk, he had distinguished between chemical elements and chemical compounds. In 1811 the Italian scientist Amedeo Avogadro described the differences between atoms and *molecules.* Molecules are formed by linking atoms together. Substances composed of a single kind of molecule are called *compounds.* One example is ferric oxide, a compound made of iron and oxygen that is the primary component of rust.

Any compound can be abbreviated in a *formula* that denotes its atomic composition. NaCl is the formula for the compound known as sodium chloride (table salt). This formula indicates that every molecule of this compound consists of one sodium atom and one chlorine atom. CH_4 is the formula for methane gas, a by-product of plant decomposition in the digestive tracts of ruminants. Every molecule of this compound contains one carbon atom and four hydrogen atoms. The carbohydrate glucose has the more complex formula of $C_6H_{12}O_6$. *Inorganic compounds,* such as NaCl and H_2O (water), contain no carbon, whereas compounds with carbon are called *organic compounds.*

Three main types of bonds link together the atoms of a molecule, or link an atom on one molecule with an atom on another molecule. Depending on the type of interaction between the atoms involved, these are called *ionic bonds, covalent bonds,* and *hydrogen bonds.* Chemical bonding is based on the tendency of an atom to seek a full complement of electrons in the outermost energy level, this being the most stable arrangement.

Ionic Bonds. In some instances two atoms can each achieve a full complement of outer electrons if one atom *donates* electrons to the other atom. This is the case with table salt. A chlorine atom has only seven electrons in its M ring [FIGURE 1.3]. If it could gain one electron, it would have a full complement of eight electrons. On the other hand, a sodium atom has only a single electron in its M ring. If it could lose that electron, it would be left with its next lower energy level (the L ring) and thus a complete complement of eight electrons in its new outermost ring. If a sodium atom donates its excess electron to the chlorine atom, the positively charged sodium ion becomes bound by a strong electrical attraction to the negatively charged chloride ion. The result is a molecule of sodium chloride. This is an example of an *ionic bond,* where there is an electrical attraction between an atom that has gained electrons and one that has lost electrons.

Covalent Bonds. Atoms may also achieve a full complement of outer electrons by *sharing* electrons with other atoms. The most common example is a molecule of water. A hydrogen atom has only a single electron in its outermost energy level (K level), whereas a full comple-

FIGURE 1.3

An atom, which is normally electrically neutral, may gain or lose electrons from its outermost electron energy level and become an ion, which has a net electric charge.

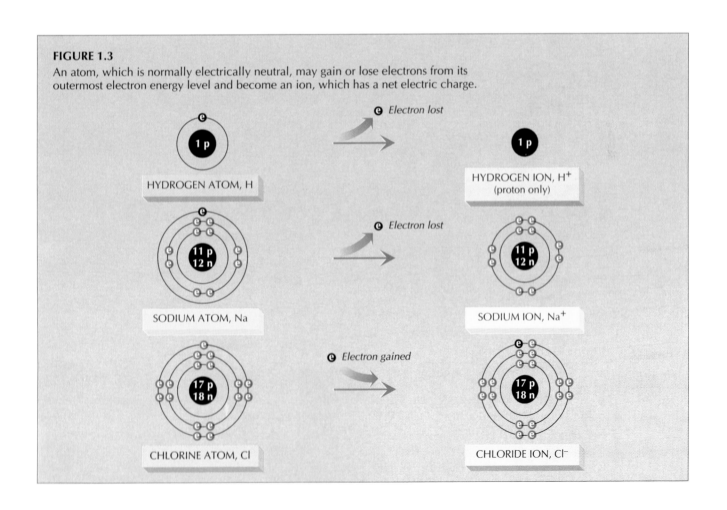

FIGURE 1.4
Covalent bonds are formed when electrons are shared between atoms.

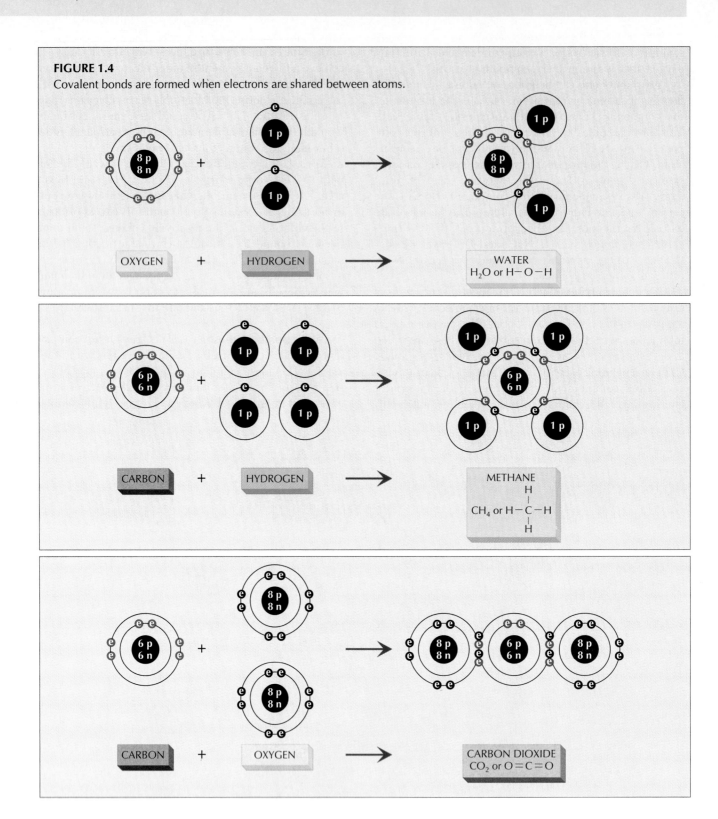

OXYGEN + HYDROGEN → WATER
H_2O or H—O—H

CARBON + HYDROGEN → METHANE
CH_4 or
$$H—C—H$$
with H above and below C

CARBON + OXYGEN → CARBON DIOXIDE
CO_2 or O=C=O

ment would be two electrons. But an oxygen atom has six electrons in its outermost energy level (L level), whereas a full complement would be eight electrons. To stabilize both, two hydrogen atoms can share their electrons with one oxygen atom, thus forming a molecule of H_2O [FIGURE 1.4]. This type of bond based on sharing a pair of electrons is a ***covalent bond,*** which can be represented in writing by a dash connecting two symbols for elements in a formula:

H—O—H
Water

Similarly, four hydrogen atoms can share their electrons with a carbon atom to form a molecule of methane (CH_4), as shown in FIGURE 1.4. The abbreviated form is:

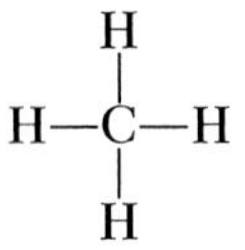

$$
\begin{array}{c}
\text{H} \\
| \\
\text{H}-\text{C}-\text{H} \\
| \\
\text{H}
\end{array}
$$

Methane

In some instances, two pairs of electrons are shared between two atoms, thus forming a *double covalent bond* like those seen in a molecule of carbon dioxide (CO_2):

$$O=C=O$$

Carbon dioxide

Two atoms may even share three pairs of electrons, forming a *triple covalent bond,* as in a molecule of nitrogen gas (N_2):

$$N\equiv N$$

Nitrogen gas

Although the abbreviations for molecules used thus far make them look flat, molecules actually have three-dimensional shapes [FIGURE 1.5]. These shapes depend upon the compound, how many atoms are involved, and what type of bonding takes place.

FIGURE 1.6

Water molecules can be linked by hydrogen bonds. The small spheres are hydrogen atoms; the large spheres are oxygen atoms.

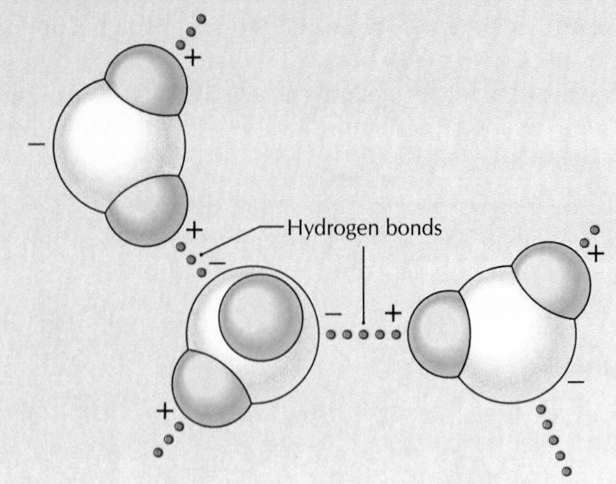

Hydrogen bonds

In some covalent bonds the electrons are not shared equally between the two atoms. They may be drawn closer to the nucleus of one atom than to the other. Such bonds are called *polar covalent bonds.* To again use the example of water, the oxygen atom draws the shared electrons closer to its own nucleus and farther away from the hydrogen nuclei. The result is a molecule with electrical polarity: the oxygen atom acquires a slight negative charge because it has partially gained electrons, whereas the hydrogen atoms acquire a slight positive charge because they have partially lost electrons. Molecules with positively and negatively charged areas are called *polar molecules.*

Hydrogen Bonds. Polar molecules tend to be attracted to other polar molecules; for instance, water molecules are attracted to each other, giving water some of its physical properties like the tendency to form raindrops. This is because the positively charged hydrogen atoms of one water molecule are attracted to the negatively charged oxygen atom of another water molecule [FIGURE 1.6]. This type of linkage between a polar hydrogen atom and another polar atom is called a **hydrogen bond.** Hydrogen bonds can form not only between water molecules, but between other polar molecules and even between polar regions within the same molecule. They are much weaker than ionic or covalent bonds, but if there are many hydrogen bonds in a substance the total effect can be significant.

A good illustration of this principle is the amount of energy it takes to heat different substances. Heating causes molecules to move more freely in a compound, which raises the temperature. Boiling water is a common

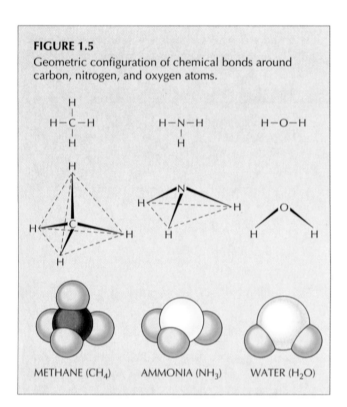

FIGURE 1.5

Geometric configuration of chemical bonds around carbon, nitrogen, and oxygen atoms.

METHANE (CH_4)   AMMONIA (NH_3)   WATER (H_2O)

event in most households, but it takes much more energy to heat water than to heat most other substances. This is because the extensive hydrogen-bonded network in water must be disrupted before an increase in temperature occurs. Once heated, water cools more slowly because, as the hydrogen bonds re-form, the heat originally needed to break them is liberated. Thus water retains heat longer, providing the scientific basis for some solar heating systems that use water tanks or water-filled pipes for heat collection.

ASK YOURSELF

1 What is an atom? An ion? An element? A molecule?

2 If an atom has eight protons, eight neutrons, and eight electrons, what is its atomic number? What is its atomic weight?

3 What is the difference between an ionic bond, a covalent bond, and a hydrogen bond?

4 How does an inorganic compound differ from an organic compound?

SOLUBILITY OF COMPOUNDS

About 80 to 90 percent of the weight of cells is actually water, with the rest a combination of other chemical compounds. If you removed the water from animals or microorganisms, only a small amount of residue would remain. Cells of all types need water in order to grow and multiply. This essential liquid serves several important functions for living organisms:

1 Water tends to resist heating or cooling because of its extensive hydrogen bonding. Thus it acts as an insulator and protects cells from sudden drastic changes in temperature.
2 Water serves as the fluid medium in which most of the biochemical reactions of a cell occur.
3 Water directly participates in many of the biochemical activities of a cell, especially those activities involving **hydrolysis** (splitting by water), where water is used to break the chemical bonds within molecules.
4 Water is unequaled in its ability to dissolve a great variety of substances (called **solutes**), and so it is an excellent **solvent.**

This last feature is very important because most microorganisms can live only on nutrients dissolved in water, although certain microorganisms such as protozoa can ingest insoluble food particles. Thus it is essential to understand how water acts as a solvent and what kinds of chemical compounds can be dissolved in water.

Solubility of Ionizable Compounds

Molecules of table salt do not exist individually. Instead they join together to form a *crystal*, which can be large enough to be visible to the eye without a magnifying glass or microscope. Crystals are solid material with a regularly repeating arrangement of atoms or molecules.

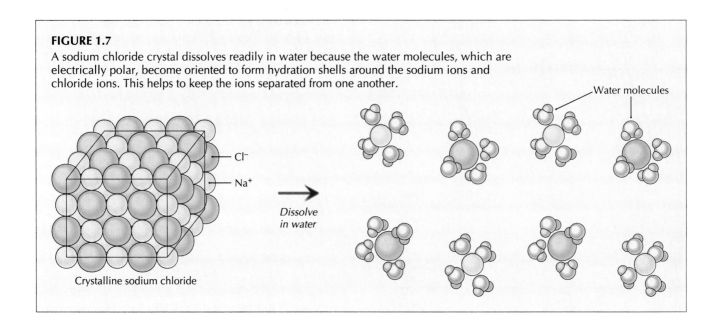

FIGURE 1.7
A sodium chloride crystal dissolves readily in water because the water molecules, which are electrically polar, become oriented to form hydration shells around the sodium ions and chloride ions. This helps to keep the ions separated from one another.

Water molecules

Cl^-

Na^+

Dissolve in water

Crystalline sodium chloride

TABLE 1.2
Some Chemical Groups That Affect the Water Solubility of Molecules

Chemical group*	Abbreviated form	Name	Properties
$R-\overset{\displaystyle O}{\underset{\displaystyle OH}{C}}$	R—COOH	Carboxyl group (acidic)	Ionizes to R—COO$^-$
$R-\overset{\displaystyle H}{\underset{\displaystyle H}{N}}$	R—NH$_2$	Amino group (basic)	Ionizes to R—NH$_3^+$
$R-\overset{\displaystyle OH}{\underset{\displaystyle OH}{P}}=O$	R—PO$_3$H$_2$	Phosphate group (acidic)	Ionizes to R—PO$_3^{2-}$
R—OH	. . . .	Hydroxyl group	Polar
$\overset{\displaystyle R}{\underset{\displaystyle R}{C}}=O$	R—CO—R	Carbonyl group (keto group)	Polar
$R-\overset{\displaystyle H}{\underset{\displaystyle H}{C}}-H$	R—CH$_3$	Methyl group	Nonpolar
$R-\overset{H}{\underset{H}{C}}-\overset{H}{\underset{H}{C}}-H$	R—CH$_2$—CH$_3$	Ethyl group	Nonpolar
$R-\overset{H}{\underset{H}{C}}-\overset{H}{\underset{H}{C}}-\overset{H}{\underset{H}{C}}-H$	R—CH$_2$—CH$_2$—CH$_3$	Propyl group	Nonpolar
R—(phenyl ring)	R—⬡	Phenyl group	Nonpolar

*R = rest of molecule.

Ionic bonding between the positively charged sodium ions and the negatively charged chloride ions forms the salt crystals. However, when you add NaCl crystals to water, each sodium ion and chloride ion is surrounded by a shell of water molecules [FIGURE 1.7]. These "hydration shells" keep the sodium and chloride ions separated, or dissociated, and allow the salt to dissolve readily in water. The ability of ions to attract water molecules indicates that ions are *hydrophilic* ("water-loving"). Compounds that dissociate into ions are considered ionizable, and the presence of ionic groups confers water solubility on molecules [TABLE 1.2].

An atom that has gained or lost electrons is called an ion, but the term *ion* is also applied to molecules that contain atoms that have lost or gained electrons. For instance, the following dissociation occurs if crystals of the microbial nutrient called sodium acetate are dissolved in water:

$$
\underset{\text{Sodium acetate}}{
\begin{array}{c}
\text{H} \quad \text{O} \\
| \quad \quad \| \\
\text{H—C—C—O—Na} \\
| \\
\text{H}
\end{array}}
\rightarrow
\underset{\text{Acetate ion}}{
\begin{array}{c}
\text{H} \quad \text{O} \\
| \quad \quad \| \\
\text{H—C—C—O}^- \\
| \\
\text{H}
\end{array}}
+ \underset{\text{Sodium ion}}{\text{Na}^+}
$$

The acetate ion is an example of an anion; the sodium ion is a cation. Both the acetate and sodium ions become surrounded by water molecules, which means that sodium acetate is readily dissolved in the water inside or outside a cell.

If the water in such a solution evaporates or is otherwise removed, crystals can re-form. Minerals dissolving in water and then re-forming into crystals lead to the intriguing rock formations in some underground caverns. They also cause the troublesome soil condition called *saline seep*, in which soil becomes too alkaline for agriculture because of chemicals deposited by water.

Solubility of Polar Compounds

Other cell nutrients, such as the sugar glucose, contain no ionic bonds, yet they too can dissolve readily in water. This is because these nutrients are made up of polar molecules, containing chemical groups that have electric charge, or polarity. Glucose, which is a nutrient for many living organisms, contains several —OH (hydroxyl) groups that give the molecule a slight electric charge. When a crystal of glucose mixes with water, each glucose molecule is surrounded by water molecules attracted to the —OH groups. TABLE 1.2 lists several common polar groups that help make molecules soluble in water and render them hydrophilic.

Solubility of Nonpolar Compounds

Compounds that do not ionize and do not have polar groups are **nonpolar compounds.** They show little solubility in water and are seldom used as nutrients by microorganisms, unless first broken down by microbial enzymes to smaller molecules that are water-soluble; such compounds contain nonpolar chemical groups [TABLE 1.2] that make them insoluble. Examples of nonpolar compounds are oils and fats. When placed in water, nonpolar molecules tend to stick together and are not dispersed. Separation of oil and vinegar in a salad dressing, and layers of oil floating on top of the ocean after a spill, are examples of this phenomenon. This tendency to aggregate in water has been termed *hydrophobic* ("water-hating") *bonding*. However, this is not a true bonding between molecules but merely a shared aversion to polar solvents such as water. Nonpolar compounds are soluble in nonpolar solvents such as chloroform and ether.

Amphipathic Compounds

Some compounds contain polar or ionized groups at one end of the molecule and a nonpolar region at the opposite end. Such compounds are called **amphipathic** compounds. Examples are soaps, such as sodium oleate. When placed in water, the oleate ions form spherical clusters called *micelles*, in which the hydrophilic regions are facing outward toward the water and the hydrophobic regions are on the inside away from the water [FIGURE 1.8]. Soaps owe their cleaning abilities to the fact that they trap dirt within the hydrophobic center of micelles so that it is removed when the item being washed is rinsed free of soap. Later in this chapter you will see that certain amphipathic molecules called *phospholipids* play an important role in the structure of cell membranes.

ASK YOURSELF

1 What accounts for the difference in the solubility properties of various chemical compounds?

2 How does a crystal of NaCl dissolve in water?

3 How do polar chemical groups differ from nonpolar groups? How do hydrophilic compounds differ from hydrophobic compounds?

4 What property of soap molecules results in the formation of micelles in water?

CONCENTRATION OF COMPOUNDS IN SOLUTION

Different solutions contain different amounts, or concentrations, of dissolved compounds. This concentration is important in microbiology, because some microorganisms are very particular about how much of a certain compound they require or can tolerate. For example, a mold that thrives on a piece of bread may not be able to grow on a much saltier slice of ham.

FIGURE 1.8

Sodium oleate, a soap, ionizes in water to form oleate ions, which have a negatively charged carboxyl group at one end and a nonpolar hydrocarbon group at the other. Thus the oleate ion is amphipathic. In water, oleate ions form aggregates called micelles in which the nonpolar groups face inward and the ionized groups face outward.

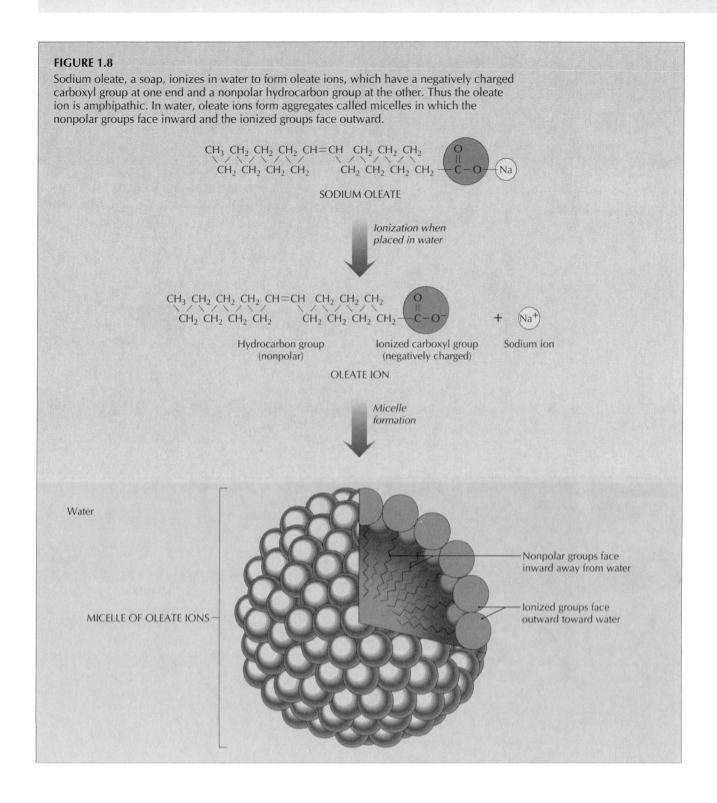

One common way to express the concentration of a chemical compound in solution is in terms of *percent*, or units per 100 units of solution. Percent can be expressed on a weight per weight (w/w) basis: if there is 10 grams (g) of NaCl in every 100 grams of solution, the NaCl concentration is 10% (w/w). Or percent can be expressed as weight per volume (w/v): dissolving 10 grams of NaCl in solvent so that the final volume is 100 milliliters results in a 10% solution (w/v). [One liter equals 1.05671 quart, and one milliliter (ml) is 1/1000 of a liter.]

Biochemists generally use a different system for expressing concentration, based on the *molecular weight* of a compound. *A molecular weight is the sum of the atomic weights of all the atoms in a molecule of a compound.*

For example, the molecular weight of NaCl equals the atomic weight of sodium (23) plus the atomic weight of chlorine (35), or 23 + 35 = 58. However, scientists cannot work with individual molecules in the laboratory, because they are too small.

This problem is solved by using a larger, easy-to-measure quantity called the *gram-molecular weight*, or *mole*, of a compound. *This is the weight of a compound in grams equal to the numerical value of its molecular weight.* Avogadro determined that a mole of any compound contains the same number of molecules (Avogadro's constant, 6.023×10^{23}). Thus one mole (1 mol) of NaCl weighs 58 grams, a quantity easily weighed on a laboratory balance, and this quantity contains 6.023×10^{23} molecules of NaCl. You can calculate the number of moles in any weight of a compound as follows:

$$\text{Number of moles} = \frac{\text{weight in grams}}{\text{molecular weight}}$$

In expressing concentration, a *one molar* (1 *M*) solution of a compound contains one mole of the compound dissolved in solvent so that the final volume is 1 liter. Thus a 1 *M* solution of NaCl is one that contains 58 grams of NaCl per liter of final solution. The advantage of expressing concentration in terms of molarity is that, *if different compounds in solution each have a 1 M concentration, then each liter of solution contains the same number of molecules (Avogadro's constant) no matter which compound it contains.*

ACIDS, BASES, AND pH

Whether a substance is acidic or alkaline (basic) depends on its concentration of hydrogen ions. This quality is critical to many microorganisms, as well as to other cells. Living organisms generally tolerate only a certain range of acidity or alkalinity in their environment. In turn, they can produce substances that are acidic or basic. Microorganisms, for example, are used to manufacture sauerkraut, vinegar, and yogurt commercially because of their acid-producing ability. Some microorganisms that make acid are unwelcome, such as those that sour milk and contaminate wine.

The phenomenon of acids and bases relies on ionization of substances. For example, pure water can ionize into hydrogen ions and hydroxyl ions in the following manner:

$$\text{H—O—H} \rightarrow \text{H}^+ + \text{OH}^-$$
$$\text{Water} \qquad \text{Hydrogen ion} \quad \text{Hydroxyl ion}$$

However, only a relatively few hydrogen and hydroxyl

ions actually occur alone in water, because they have a strong tendency to recombine with each other. One liter of water contains 55.55 mol of water, but only 10^{-7} mol (0.0000001 mol) is in the ionized form. Only one water molecule out of every 555,500,000 is separated into ions. Since each molecule that does ionize gives rise to one H^+ and one OH^-, there are 10^{-7} mol of H^+ and 10^{-7} mol of OH^- per liter.

The acidity or alkalinity of a solution refers to the molar concentration of hydrogen ions (denoted by $[\text{H}^+]$) in the solution. The higher the $[\text{H}^+]$, the more acidic the solution. The molar concentration of hydrogen ions is more conveniently expressed in terms of *pH* (potential of Hydrogen), which is defined as follows:

$$\text{pH} = -\log_{10}[\text{H}^+]$$

Since pure water has a $[\text{H}^+]$ of 10^{-7} *M*, its pH is $-\log_{10} 10^{-7} = -(-7)$, or 7. This pH represents neutrality, which means that it is neither acidic nor alkaline. Vinegar has a $[\text{H}^+]$ of 10^{-3} *M* (0.001 *M*), so that it is acidic and its pH is 3. On the other hand, if the $[\text{H}^+]$ is less than 10^{-7} *M*, the solution is alkaline. Milk of magnesia has a $[\text{H}^+]$ of 10^{-10}, making it alkaline with a pH of 10.

For practical purposes the pH scale extends from 0 to 14 [FIGURE 1.9]. It is important to understand that this scale is a *logarithmic* scale. On this scale pH 5 represents *10 times* greater acidity than pH 6; pH 4 is *100 times* more acidic than pH 6.

Acids

Substances that are *acids* ionize in water and liberate a hydrogen ion. For example, hydrochloric acid (stomach acid) ionizes in the following manner:

$$\text{HCl} \rightarrow \text{H}^+ + \text{Cl}^-$$
$$\text{Hydrochloric acid} \qquad \text{Hydrogen ion} \quad \text{Chloride ion}$$

Acetic acid (vinegar acid) also ionizes to free a hydrogen ion:

$$\text{CH}_3\text{COOH} \rightarrow \text{H}^+ + \text{CH}_3\text{COO}^-$$
$$\text{Acetic acid} \qquad \text{Hydrogen ion} \quad \text{Acetate ion}$$

Some acids, such as HCl, are *strong acids*, because they are almost completely ionized in water, thus liberating many hydrogen ions. Others, such as acetic acid, are *weak acids*, because they only partially ionize in solution.

Bases

A *base* (or alkaline material) is a substance that, when

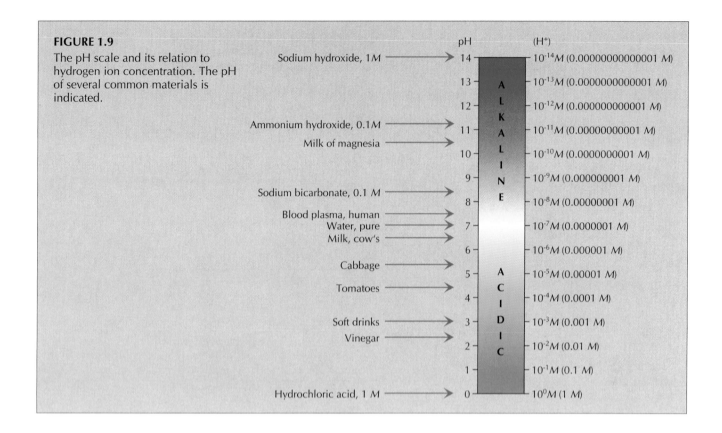

FIGURE 1.9
The pH scale and its relation to hydrogen ion concentration. The pH of several common materials is indicated.

ionized, releases a negatively charged ion that accepts a hydrogen ion. If NaOH (sodium hydroxide, also known as caustic soda) is dissolved in pure water, it ionizes in the following way to form hydroxyl ions:

$$\text{NaOH} \quad \rightarrow \quad \text{Na}^+ \quad + \quad \text{OH}^-$$

Sodium hydroxide   Sodium ion   Hydroxyl ion

The pure water to which the NaOH was added initially contained 10^{-7} M hydrogen ions (pH 7). However, some of these hydrogen ions are now removed to form more water molecules with the free hydroxyl ions from NaOH:

$$\text{OH}^- \quad + \quad \text{H}^+ \quad \rightarrow \quad \text{H}_2\text{O}$$

Hydroxyl ion   Hydrogen ion   Water

The result is an increase in pH, and a solution that is more basic, or alkaline. NaOH is a *strong base*, because the hydroxyl ions that result from its ionization have a great ability to take up hydrogen ions. In a 1.0 M solution of NaOH, the concentration of hydrogen ions is only 10^{-14} M, and the solution has a pH of 14 [FIGURE 1.9].

Salts

If an ionic compound does not contain either H$^+$ or OH$^-$, it is a *salt*. One example is NaCl, which ionizes in water to yield sodium ions and chloride ions. NaCl is neither an acid nor a base, but some salts, such as sodium acetate, may act as bases. Sodium acetate is a salt because an Na$^+$ has replaced the H$^+$ on acetic acid. It ionizes in the following way:

$$\text{CH}_3\text{COONa} \rightarrow \text{CH}_3\text{COO}^- + \quad \text{Na}^+$$

Sodium acetate   Acetate ion   Sodium ion

Because of their negative charge, some of the acetate ions can bind to hydrogen ions:

$$\text{CH}_3\text{COO}^- + \quad \text{H}^+ \quad \rightarrow \text{CH}_3\text{COOH}$$

Acetate ion   Hydrogen ion   Acetic acid

Therefore, although acetic acid ionizes to liberate hydrogen ions and thus is an *acid*, sodium acetate ionizes into acetate ions that can take up hydrogen ions and thus act as a *base*. Indeed, for every weak acid there is a corresponding salt that is a conjugate base.

Such a salt is a *weak base*, because the anions that result have only a weak ability to take up hydrogen ions. A 0.1 M solution of sodium acetate has a pH of 8.0, whereas a 0.1 M solution of the strong base sodium hydroxide has a pH of 13—about 100,000 times more alkaline.

Buffers

Most microorganisms grow best at pH values between 6.5 and 7.5, and few grow below pH 5 or above pH 9. But many microorganisms produce acidic or alkaline waste products that can alter the pH of their environment so that it becomes unfavorable for growth. In nature these waste products may be removed by flowing water or neutralized by chemicals inside cells. In laboratory cultures a *buffer* is usually added to the growth medium to maintain a desired pH.

A buffer is a chemical mixture that causes a solution to resist change in pH. More specifically, a buffer is a mixture of a weak acid and one of its salts—such as acetic acid and sodium acetate. Each buffer resists pH change within a particular range. For example, an acetic acid–sodium acetate buffer is effective between pH 3.5 and 5.5, but has little buffering capacity at pH 7. Therefore this buffer would be inadequate in most microbial culture systems. One buffer commonly used by microbiologists is a mixture of a weak acid called potassium dihydrogen phosphate (KH_2PO_4) and its salt dipotassium hydrogen phosphate (K_2HPO_4). This mixture has a strong buffering capacity between pH 6 and 8.

Buffering capacity in a biological system can be crucial to life. In animals, the pH of blood cannot vary much outside a narrow range, or the organism is in danger. If your stomach did not stay acidic, food would not be properly digested; but if it becomes too acidic, you are uncomfortable. The chemical activities of aquatic microorganisms contribute to the stability of pH in lakes and streams. However, if water becomes too acidic through pollution, organisms living there may die.

ASK YOURSELF

1 If the sugar glucose has a molecular weight of 180, how would you make a 1 *M* solution of glucose? A 1% (w/v) solution of glucose?

2 What is the relation between the molar concentration of hydrogen ions in a solution and the pH of that solution?

3 What is the difference between acids, bases, and salts? What property makes hydrochloric acid a strong acid? Acetic acid a weak acid? Sodium acetate a weak base?

4 What are buffers, and how are they used in microbiology?

IMPORTANT BIOLOGICAL COMPOUNDS

The cells of all living organisms, from microbes to humans, are composed of chemical compounds. Various inorganic compounds are found in all organisms, but organic compounds have the most biological significance. There are thousands of these organic compounds, most of which can be grouped into one of four main categories—carbohydrates, lipids, proteins, and nucleic acids.

Carbohydrates

Sugars and starches are carbohydrates, the primary source of energy in cells. Some carbohydrates are also found in microbial cell walls, while others serve as food storage, and act as building blocks for proteins, lipids, and nucleic acids. Carbohydrates have the general formula $(CH_2O)_n$, where *n* is any whole number. They can be quite simple in structure, or contain a large number of molecules arranged in complex ways.

The simplest carbohydrates are *monosaccharides*, or simple sugars [FIGURE 1.10]. The simplest of these have only three carbon atoms per molecule and are called *trioses; glyceraldehyde* is an example. Monosaccharides with four carbons are *tetroses* (e.g., *erythrose*), those with five carbons are *pentoses* (e.g., *ribose* and *deoxyribose*), and those with six carbons are *hexoses* (e.g., *glucose, galactose, mannose,* and *fructose*). Glucose is of special interest to biochemists because it is the major source of carbon and energy for many living organisms. Monosaccharides with more than seven carbon atoms rarely occur in nature, although one (sedoheptulose) is important in metabolism. Molecules of monosaccharides can exist as linear structures, but when dissolved in water, many of them have a ring structure [FIGURE 1.10].

Carbohydrate molecules larger than monosaccharides are formed by linking two or more monosaccharides together. A molecule of *lactose*, the sugar found in milk, is made of two monosaccharides, galactose and glucose [FIGURE 1.11]. Glucose and fructose combine to form sucrose, or table sugar. Both sucrose and lactose are *disaccharides*.

When a large number of monosaccharides are linked together, as in a molecule of starch, the result is called a *polysaccharide*. These compounds frequently are not soluble in water, but they are important in cell structure and energy storage. Examples are dextran, made by bacteria and used in a blood plasma substitute, and cellulose, found in cell walls of plants and most algae.

FIGURE 1.10
Some examples of monosaccharides, or simple sugars.

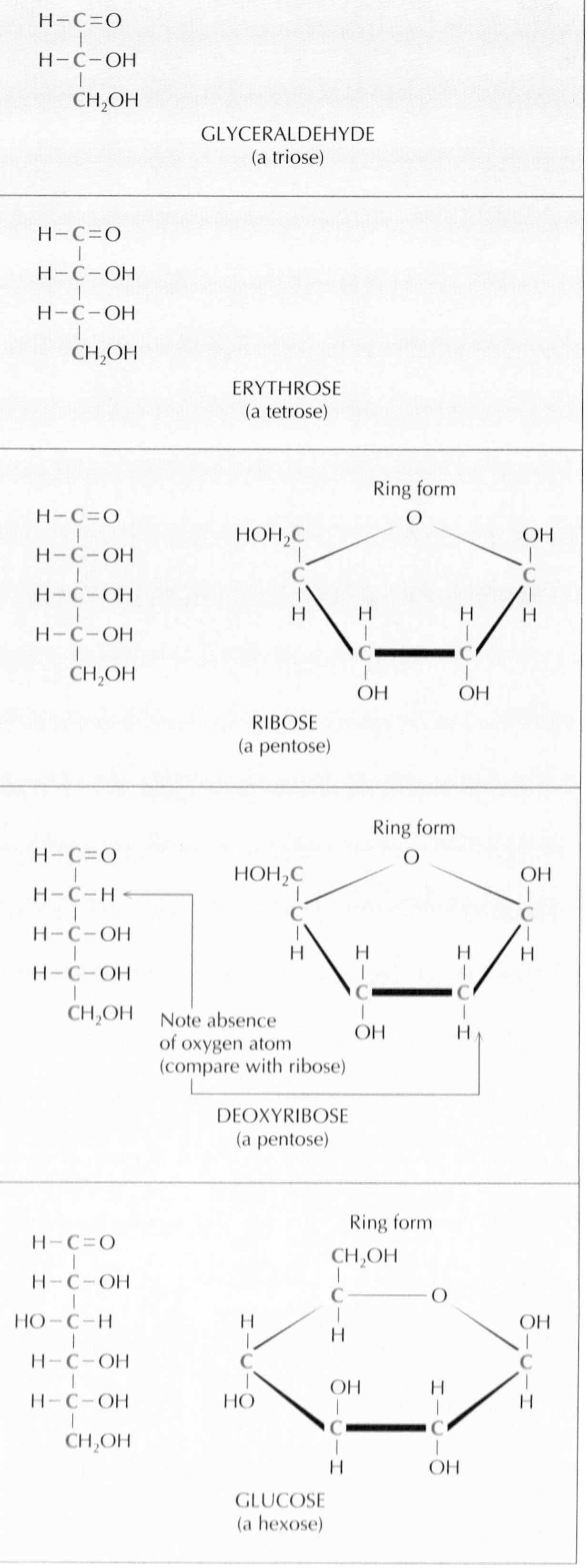

GLYCERALDEHYDE
(a triose)

ERYTHROSE
(a tetrose)

RIBOSE
(a pentose)

Ring form

DEOXYRIBOSE
(a pentose)

Note absence
of oxygen atom
(compare with ribose)

Ring form

GLUCOSE
(a hexose)

Ring form

FIGURE 1.11
The monosaccharides galactose and glucose differ only in the arrangement of the −H and −OH groups (shown in red) about one carbon atom. Lactose, or milk sugar, is a disaccharide composed of a molecule of galactose and a molecule of glucose; the linkage between the two monosaccharides is formed by removing a molecule of water.

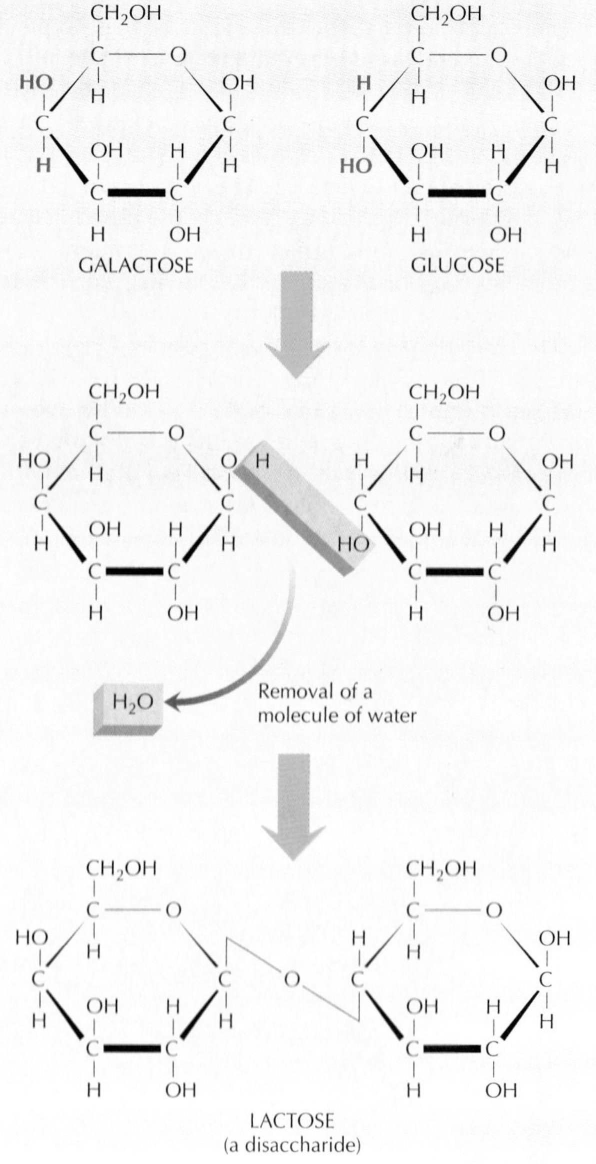

GALACTOSE   GLUCOSE

H_2O Removal of a
molecule of water

LACTOSE
(a disaccharide)

Optical Isomers. The general term *isomers* applies to compounds that have the same number and kinds of atoms but differ in the spatial arrangement of the atoms. Isomers do not necessarily have the same chemical properties. For instance, the monosaccharides glucose and fructose are isomers because they have the same composition, $C_6H_{12}O_6$. But the arrangement of the atoms in glucose differs from that in fructose, and the two compounds have different chemical properties. On the other hand, *optical isomers* (often called **D** and **L** *isomers*) are two forms of a compound each of which is the mirror image of the other. Because this is the only difference, the two forms have the same chemical properties. Optical isomers can occur when one of the carbon atoms of a compound is *asymmetric*, which means that it has four different chemical groups linked to it. For instance, in a molecule of glyceraldehyde, the middle carbon atom has the following chemical groups linked to it: —OH, —H, —CHO, and —CH$_2$OH. Thus glyceraldehyde can exist as either **D**-glyceraldehyde or **L**-glyceraldehyde, each being the mirror image of the other [FIGURE 1.12]. Moreover, if the **D** and **L** isomers of a compound are allowed to form crystals, the crystals of the **D** isomers are mirror images of those formed by the **L** isomers. This phenomenon was first discovered by Louis Pasteur during his studies of tartaric acid [DISCOVER 1.1].

The difference between **D** and **L** isomers may seem small, but it is similar to the difference between a left hand and a right hand. Cells can tell this difference—living organisms in general preferentially synthesize *one or the other optical isomer of a compound but not both*. For example, if glyceraldehyde is made in a chemical laboratory, the product is a mixture of equal amounts of

D and **L** isomers. But when a living organism makes this compound, it makes only one of the optical isomers.

Lipids

Organic substances are grouped as **lipids** if they are soluble in nonpolar solvents such as acetone, chloroform, ether, or benzene. Thus most lipids are insoluble in water. They are composed mainly of hydrogen and carbon atoms, with lesser amounts of other elements such as oxygen, nitrogen, and phosphorus. There are three major categories of biologically important lipids based on differences in structure: fats, phospholipids, and sterols.

Fats. Fats are simple lipids made of two kinds of building blocks: *glycerol* and *fatty acids* [FIGURE 1.13A]. Glycerol molecules contain three carbon atoms:

$$H_2C—OH$$
$$HC—OH$$
$$H_2C—OH$$

The hydroxyl groups (—OH), which are polar groups, make the glycerol water-soluble. Fatty acids have the general formula CH$_3$—(CH$_2$)$_n$—COOH, where *n* is usu-

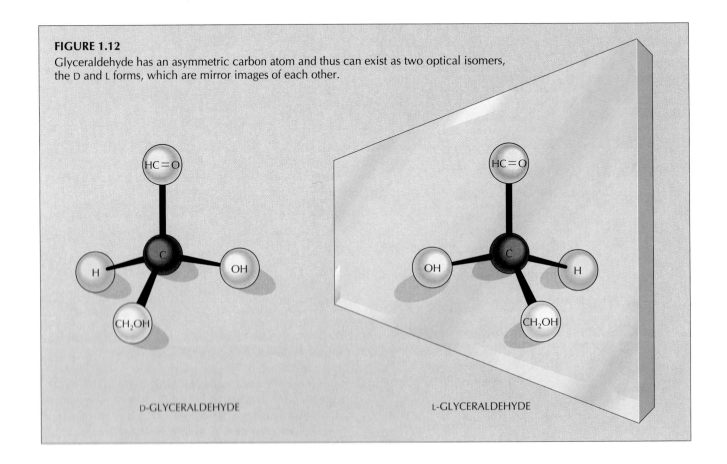

FIGURE 1.12
Glyceraldehyde has an asymmetric carbon atom and thus can exist as two optical isomers, the D and L forms, which are mirror images of each other.

D-GLYCERALDEHYDE   L-GLYCERALDEHYDE

FIGURE 1.13

[A] Glycerol molecules and fatty acid molecules are the building blocks of fats. [B] Three fatty acid molecules are linked to one molecule of glycerol by removing three molecules of water, to form one molecule of fat, i.e., a triglyceride.

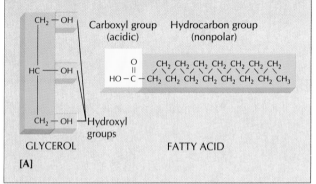

[A]

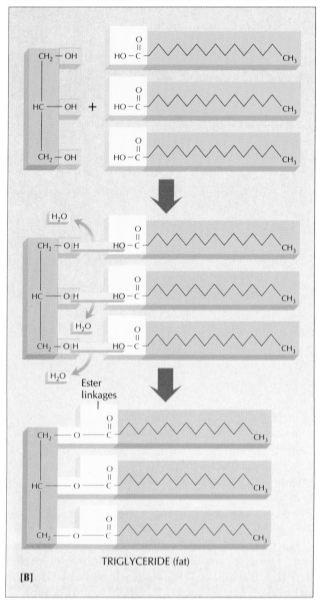

TRIGLYCERIDE (fat)

[B]

ally an even number. For example, in the formula for palmitic acid, $n = 14$:

$$CH_3—CH_2—CH_2—CH_2—CH_2—CH_2—CH_2—CH_2—$$
$$CH_2—CH_2—CH_2—CH_2—CH_2—CH_2—CH_2—COOH$$

When n is large, as in palmitic acid, the fatty acid is called a *long-chain fatty acid*. A molecule of fat forms when three fatty acid molecules are attached by an enzyme to one molecule of glycerol [FIGURE 1.13B]. Thus fats are often called *triglycerides*.

Phospholipids. The complex lipids known as *phospholipids* are important components of cell membranes. For example, a single cell of the bacterium *Escherichia coli* contains 22,000,000 phospholipid molecules in its membrane. Phospholipids differ from fats in two respects: (1) only two fatty acid molecules are linked to a molecule of glycerol, and (2) a phosphate group is linked to the glycerol [FIGURE 1.14A]. The simplest phospholipids have no additional components, but others have an additional chemical group linked to the phosphate group. The names of these phospholipids reflect this additional group. For example, *phosphatidylserine* has a serine group attached.

In any phospholipid, the phosphate group is hydrophilic, because it has a negative charge when ionized ($—PO_3H_2 \rightarrow —PO_3H^- + H^+$). However, the long hydrocarbon chains of the fatty acid portion are nonpolar, hydrophobic groups. Thus a phospholipid molecule is an amphipathic molecule. This amphipathic nature accounts for the characteristic behavior of phospholipids when they are placed in water. They form a *phospholipid bilayer*, in which the ionized hydrophilic phosphate groups face outward toward the water and the nonpolar, hydrophobic hydrocarbon chains of the fatty acids face inward [FIGURE 1.14B]. *This bilayer forms the fundamental structure of cell membranes.* Antibiotic development frequently relies on finding chemicals that disrupt these bilayers and consequently destroy microorganisms. Polymyxin B is an example of an antibiotic that attaches to the phospholipids of a cell membrane and fatally injures the cell.

Sterols. A sterol molecule is highly nonpolar and consists mainly of several interconnected rings made of carbon atoms. Animals use them to synthesize vitamin D and steroid hormones, and they are found in the membranes of eucaryotic cells and a few bacteria. The compound *cholesterol*, a normal component of some membranes, is a member of this group of lipids [FIGURE 1.15A]. Certain antifungal drugs combine with the sterols in membranes of fungal cells, eventually killing the cells.

FIGURE 1.14
[A] The simplest kind of phospholipid is composed of one glycerol molecule, two fatty acid molecules, and one molecule of phosphate. [B] When placed in water, the amphipathic phospholipid molecules form a bilayer, with the nonpolar hydrocarbon chains of the fatty acids facing inward and the negatively charged phosphate groups facing outward.

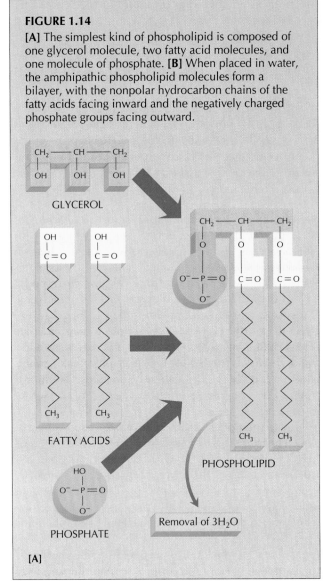

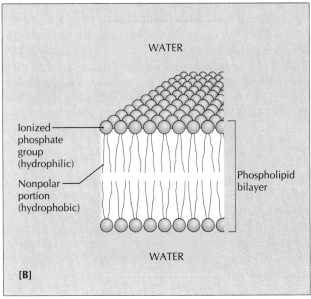

FIGURE 1.15
[A] Cholesterol is a lipid characterized by a series of interconnected rings. [B] Poly-ß-hydroxybutyrate is a chain of many molecules of ß-hydroxybutyric acid linked together by removal of water molecules; only a small portion of the entire chain is shown.

CHOLESTEROL

[A]

β-HYDROXYBUTYRIC ACID

POLY-β-HYDROXYBUTYRATE

[B]

Other Lipids. In addition to the three main groups of lipids, other lipids are found in microorganisms. Among these are the lipids in chlorophyll, those in the cell walls of the bacterium that causes tuberculosis, and those that provide the red and yellow pigments of some microorganisms. A lipid called *poly-β-hydroxybutyrate*, or *PHB*, occurs only in certain bacteria as a reserve source of carbon and energy. It is insoluble not only in water but also in many nonpolar solvents, including alcohol and ether. It is, however, soluble in hot chloroform. Molecules of PHB consist of hundreds of molecules of β-hydroxybutyric acid joined together [FIGURE 1.15B].

1.1 A SURPRISING DISCOVERY OF BIOLOGICAL "MIRROR IMAGES"

In 1844 Louis Pasteur solved a mystery and discovered an important principle involved in the chemical processes of living organisms. Other chemists had been puzzled by an organic compound called tartaric acid. The acid had two types of crystalline salts, one naturally occurring, the other made in the laboratory. *Tartrate* formed as a crusty material in wine fermentation barrels, while chemical experiments resulted in *paratartrate*. The two had exactly the same chemical composition and the same chemical properties. However, there was one difference: when a beam of polarized light was passed through a solution of tartrate, the beam was rotated to the right, but when passed through a paratartrate solution it showed no rotation. Chemists at the time could not understand how two compounds could be identical in every respect other than their effect on polarized light.

When Pasteur used his microscope to study paratartrate crystals, he noticed something extraordinary. Some crystals differed from others in their shape. In fact, there seemed to be two kinds of crystals, each the mirror image of the other (see the illustration). Pasteur painstakingly separated a pile of crystals into two portions, each having only one type of crystal. When he dissolved one portion in water and passed a beam of polarized light through the solution, the beam rotated to the left. However, a so-lution of the second type rotated the beam to the right, just as tartrate did. A mixture of equal amounts of the two types of crystal behaved just like the original paratartrate: it did not affect the light. Pasteur later found that a number of other biological compounds, such as amino acids, could also exist in "left" and "right" forms.

In his studies on microbial fermentation, Pasteur discovered that microorganisms given paratartrate used only one of the two forms, leaving the other untouched. This led to the realization that many biochemical processes were far more discriminating than anyone had thought. It is now clear that this specificity is dictated by the enzymes that catalyze chemical reactions. A molecule fits into a cavity on the surface of an enzyme much as a hand fits into a glove. If the cavity is designed for the "left" form of a molecule, the "right" form will not fit, just as a left hand will not fit into a right-hand glove. The opposite is also true, making it possible for enzymes to recognize which mirror image is which.

The "left" and "right" crystals of paratartrate based upon Pasteur's sketches.

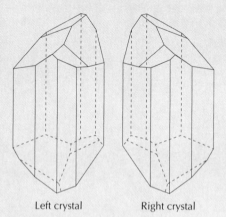

Left crystal   Right crystal

Proteins

In terms of weight, proteins surpass lipids and carbohydrates in a cell. In terms of function, they have a multitude of chores. Some may be enzymes, the catalytic agents that control all biochemical processes. Others may be part of cell structures such as flagella, or they may control nutrient transport through membranes. Toxins released by bacterial cells are proteins. Proteins are composed of many molecules of **amino acids** linked together in a chain. In order to understand the chemical nature of proteins, it will help to understand the nature of amino acids, the building blocks of proteins.

All 20 amino acids from which proteins are formed consist of four chemical groups attached to a carbon atom [FIGURE 1.16]. The four groups are: (1) an amino group ($—NH_2$), which can take up a hydrogen ion and thus is a basic group; (2) a carboxyl group ($—COOH$), which can release a hydrogen ion and is an acidic group; (3) a hydrogen atom; and (4) an "R" group, which varies with each kind of amino acid [FIGURE 1.17].

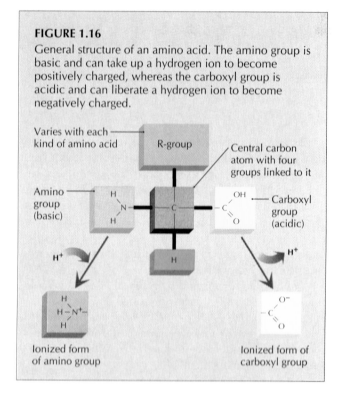

FIGURE 1.16
General structure of an amino acid. The amino group is basic and can take up a hydrogen ion to become positively charged, whereas the carboxyl group is acidic and can liberate a hydrogen ion to become negatively charged.

FIGURE 1.17

The 20 kinds of amino acids from which proteins are formed all have one part of their structure in common (lower, purple boxes) but differ in their R groups (upper, magenta boxes). The standard abbreviation for the name of each amino acid is indicated. The central carbon is asymmetric if the four groups linked to it differ from one another, as is the case for most amino acids.

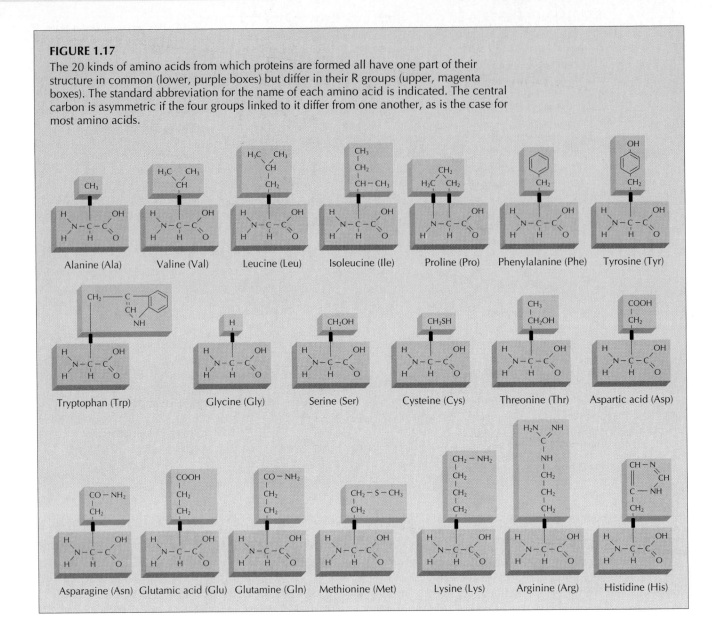

In most of these 20 amino acids, the carbon atom is an asymmetric carbon, since the four groups differ from one another. The only exception is the amino acid *glycine*, in which two of the groups are hydrogen atoms [FIGURE 1.17]. Because of the asymmetric carbon atom, an amino acid can exist as either of two optical isomers. Living organisms usually make only the L isomer. D-Amino acids are rare in nature, although certain ones do occur in the cell walls of bacteria.

Peptide bonds, formed by removal of a water molecule [FIGURE 1.18A], tie together amino acids to form a long chain called a *polypeptide chain* [FIGURE 1.18B]. Proteins consist of one or more of these polypeptide chains, which may range in length from fewer than 100 amino acids to more than 1000.

Levels of Protein Structure. A living cell contains 1000 or more different kinds of proteins, and each kind has its own unique sequence of amino acids. This amino acid sequence is called the *primary structure* of the protein. For example, the sequence of amino acids in the enzyme ribonuclease contains 124 amino acids in a specific order [FIGURE 1.19].

A polypeptide chain can fold into a specific shape, much like a ribbon. Some portions of the chain may form a coil, while others may form side-by-side arrangements or other configurations. These forms constitute the *secondary structure* of the protein and are due to hydrogen bonding between the polar —C=O and —NH groups along the chain [FIGURE 1.20A].

The *tertiary structure* of a protein refers to the overall folding of the molecule into a specific shape, much like a tangled ribbon [FIGURE 1.20B]. This shape is caused by interactions between different parts of the polypeptide chain. For instance, *disulfide bridges*, or bonds between sulfur ions, contribute to the tertiary structure by connecting cysteine molecules located in different regions of the polypeptide chain:

FIGURE 1.19 shows the location of disulfide bridges in the enzyme ribonuclease. Some proteins contain two or more polypeptide chains for their proper activity [FIGURE 1.20C]. This combination of polypeptide chains constitutes the *quaternary structure* of the protein. For example, the blood protein hemoglobin contains four polypeptide chains.

$$H_2N-\underset{\underset{COOH}{|}}{\overset{\overset{H}{|}}{C}}-CH_2-SH \ + \ H_2N-\underset{\underset{COOH}{|}}{\overset{\overset{H}{|}}{C}}-CH_2-SH \ + \ \tfrac{1}{2}O_2 \ \rightarrow \ H_2N-\underset{\underset{COOH}{|}}{\overset{\overset{H}{|}}{C}}-CH_2-S-S-CH_2-\underset{\underset{COOH}{|}}{\overset{\overset{H}{|}}{C}}-NH_2 \ + \ H_2O$$

Cysteine   Cysteine   Bridge formation

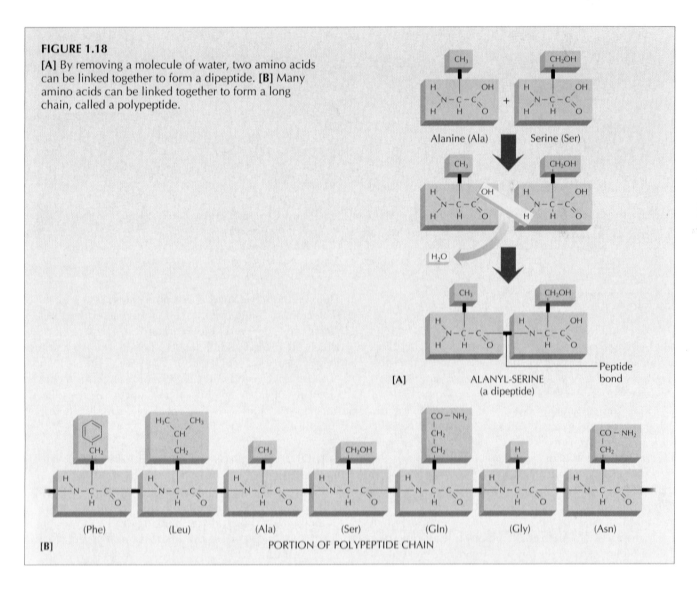

FIGURE 1.18

[A] By removing a molecule of water, two amino acids can be linked together to form a dipeptide. **[B]** Many amino acids can be linked together to form a long chain, called a polypeptide.

Alanine (Ala)   Serine (Ser)

H₂O

[A]   ALANYL-SERINE (a dipeptide)   Peptide bond

(Phe)   (Leu)   (Ala)   (Ser)   (Gln)   (Gly)   (Asn)

[B]   PORTION OF POLYPEPTIDE CHAIN

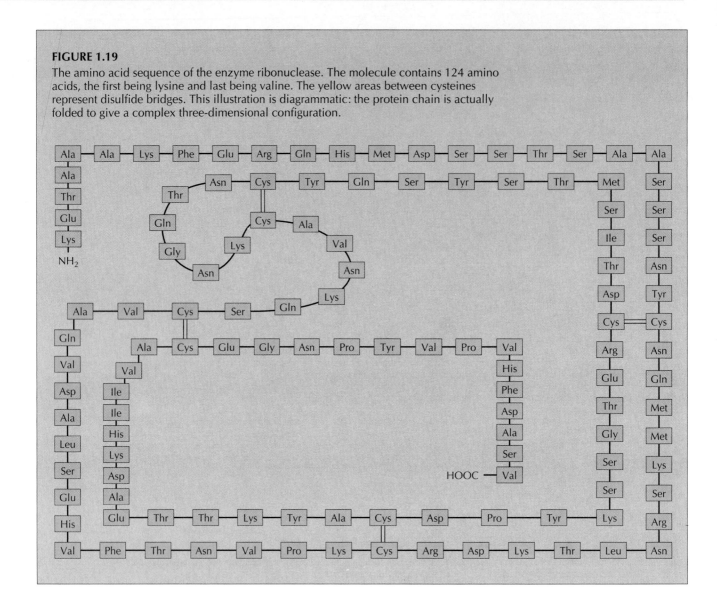

FIGURE 1.19
The amino acid sequence of the enzyme ribonuclease. The molecule contains 124 amino acids, the first being lysine and last being valine. The yellow areas between cysteines represent disulfide bridges. This illustration is diagrammatic: the protein chain is actually folded to give a complex three-dimensional configuration.

Nucleic Acids

Discovery of the chemical substance that carries genetic information in cells was one of the most exciting findings of the twentieth century. In 1944 the American microbiologists Oswald Avery, Colin MacLeod, and Maclyn McCarty were the first to identify *deoxyribonucleic acid (DNA)* as the substance responsible for the inheritable characteristics of living organisms. Within a decade, work by James Watson, Francis Crick, Rosalind Franklin, and Maurice Wilkins led to an understanding of the physical appearance of DNA, as well as how it works. DNA and another substance first found in nuclei of cells, *ribonucleic acid (RNA)*, are called *nucleic acids*. DNA is the substance that contains the hereditary information of a cell, whereas RNA is usually involved in deciphering the hereditary information in DNA and carrying out its instructions.

Deoxyribonucleic Acid. DNA molecules are the longest molecules in living cells. A cell of the bacterium *Escherichia coli*, for example, contains a DNA molecule which, if extended full length, would be 1000 times longer than the cell itself. It fits within the cell only because it is twisted into a highly compact form. A single molecule of DNA contains a vast library of hereditary information, but it has a relatively simple chemical structure:

1 A DNA molecule is composed of molecules called *nucleotides* [FIGURE 1.21].
2 Each nucleotide is constructed of three parts:
   (a) One molecule of a class of nitrogen-containing compounds called *nitrogenous bases*
   (b) One molecule of the pentose sugar *deoxyribose* [see FIGURE 1.10]
   (c) One phosphate group

FIGURE 1.20

[A] Secondary structure of a protein. Portions of the polypeptide chain form an alpha helix due to hydrogen bonding (● ● ● ●) between −C=O and −NH groups of the peptide bonds. (For simplicity, only the hydrogen atoms actually involved in the hydrogen bonding are shown.) The R groups of the amino acids in the chain project outward from the helix. **[B]** The tertiary structure of a protein is determined by interactions between different portions of the chain. **[C]** Quaternary structure of a protein. The protein shown here is composed of two identical polypeptide chains, but some proteins are composed of several different kinds of chains.

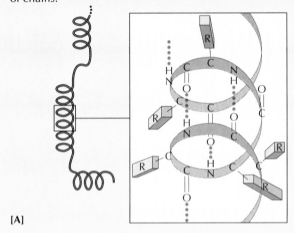

[A]

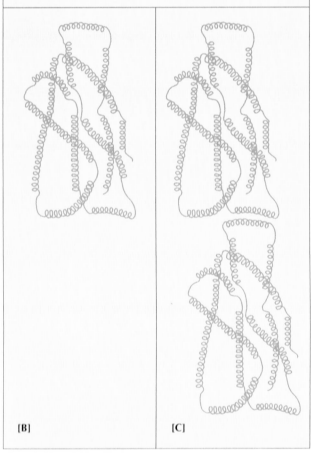

[B]   [C]

3 By using energy from food sources, a cell links these three parts to form a nucleotide.

4 Four kinds of nitrogenous bases occur in DNA [FIGURE 1.22A]. Two are *adenine* and *guanine*, which are called *purines*. The other two are the *pyrimidines*—*cytosine* and *thymine*. Thus there are four kinds of nucleotides in DNA, each having a particular purine or pyrimidine base [FIGURE 1.22B].

5 A cell puts together thousands of nucleotides to form a single strand of DNA [FIGURE 1.22C]. Two things are interesting about this strand: each phosphate is attached to two deoxyriboses, and the deoxyriboses and the phosphates alternate to form a "backbone" from which project the purines and pyrimidines.

6 Finally, two strands are cross-linked by means of the projecting purine and pyrimidine bases to form double-stranded DNA [FIGURE 1.23]. Hydrogen bonds link the bases on one chain with those on the other chain. Two bases attached in this manner are called a *complementary base pair.* Only two kinds of complementary base pairs are found in double-stranded DNA:

Adenine (A) linked to thymine (T)
Guanine (G) linked to cytosine (C)

Thus the ratio of A to T, or G to C, in double-stranded DNA is always 1 : 1.

The complementarity of the purines and pyrimidines means that the sequence of bases on one strand dictates the sequence on the other. This is of critical

FIGURE 1.21

Nucleotides are the building blocks of nucleic acids. In deoxyribonucleic acid (DNA), a nucleotide is composed of one molecule of a nitrogenous base, one molecule of the sugar deoxyribose, and one molecule of phosphate.

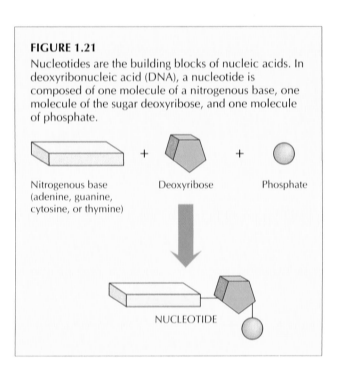

Nitrogenous base
(adenine, guanine,
cytosine, or thymine)   Deoxyribose   Phosphate

NUCLEOTIDE

FIGURE 1.22

[A] Four kinds of nitrogenous bases occur in DNA. Two of them, adenine (A) and guanine (G), are purines; the other two, thymine (T) and cytosine (C), are pyrimidines. [B] Four kinds of nucleotides can be constructed using deoxyribose (pentagons), phosphate (spheres), and the four nitrogenous bases. [C] Nucleotides can be joined to form a single polynucleotide strand of DNA. Only a small portion of a DNA strand is shown; a complete strand would contain thousands of nucleotides. Note that the deoxyriboses and phosphates form a "backbone" from which the purine and pyrimidine bases project.

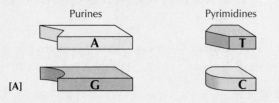

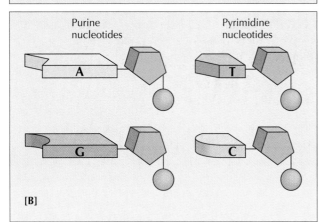

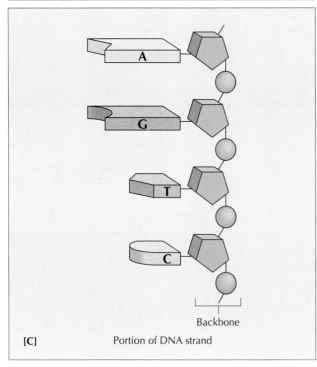

[C] Portion of DNA strand

FIGURE 1.23

Portion of a double-stranded DNA molecule showing the two polynucleotide chains linked by hydrogen bonds (••••). Note that pairing always occurs between complementary purine and pyrimidine bases, i.e., between adenine (A) and thymine (T), and between guanine (G) and cytosine (C).

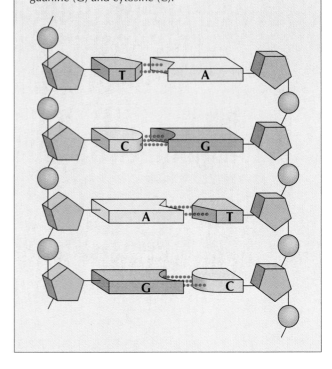

importance in the synthesis of new strands of DNA during cell division, because *it is the sequence of bases in DNA that represents the hereditary information of the cell.* There is a different sequence for each species of living organism.

7 In a double-stranded DNA molecule, the two strands are not straight but are wound around each other to form a *double helix* [FIGURE 1.24]. As already mentioned, the two strands in a double helix are held together by hydrogen bonds between the complementary bases.

Ribonucleic Acid. An RNA molecule is also composed of a chain of nucleotides. But it differs from DNA in certain respects [FIGURE 1.25]:

1 The sugar component of RNA is *ribose*, not deoxyribose. (The prefix *deoxy-* means "lacking oxygen," and ribose has one more oxygen atom than does deoxyribose.)

2 Instead of the pyrimidine thymine, RNA contains the pyrimidine called *uracil*.

3 Unlike double-stranded DNA, RNA is *single-stranded*. This means that there is no complementary

FIGURE 1.24

In double-stranded DNA, the two strands are wound about each other in the form of a double helix and are held together by hydrogen bonds between complementary purine and pyrimidine bases. P, phosphate; S, the sugar deoxyribose.

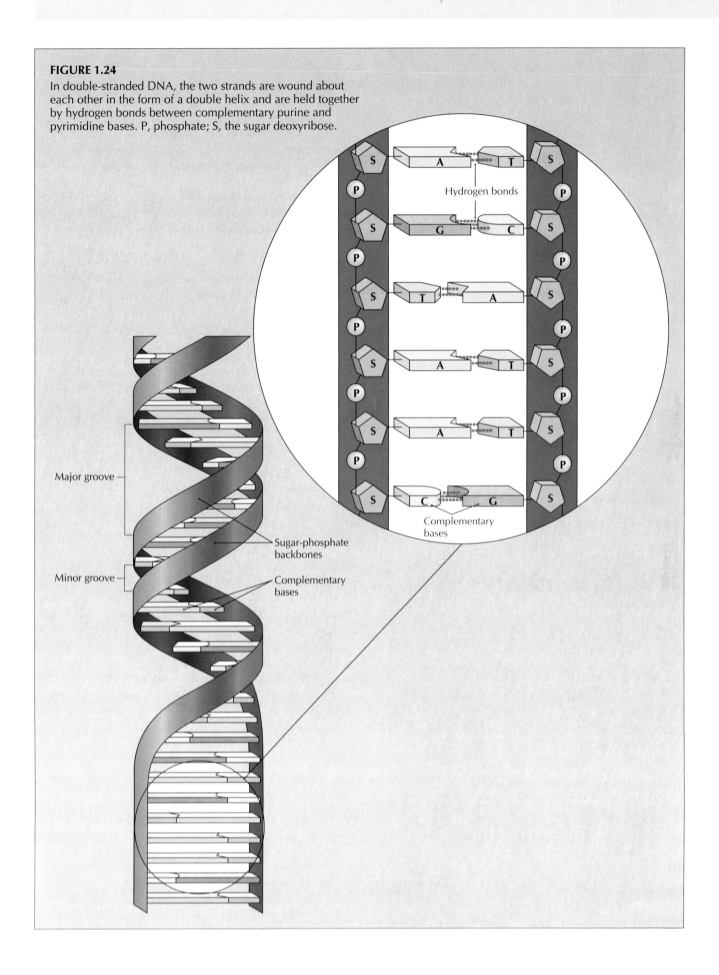

FIGURE 1.25
The structure of RNA. RNA differs from DNA by having the sugar ribose instead of deoxyribose, and the pyrimidine uracil (U) instead of thymine. The other three bases (A, adenine; G, guanine; and C, cytosine) occur in both RNA and DNA. Unlike DNA, RNA is single-stranded.

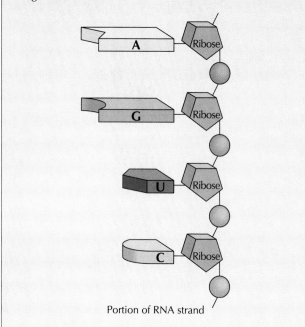

Portion of RNA strand

second strand paired with it. Thus the ratio of A to U, or G to C, in RNA can vary among different RNA molecules and is not necessarily 1:1 as seen in DNA.

ASK YOURSELF

1 What are the four classes of biologically important compounds, and what are their major characteristics?

2 In what way do the optical isomers of a compound differ from one another? Can living organisms tell this difference?

3 What compounds are the building blocks for polysaccharides, fats, phospholipids, proteins, DNA, and RNA?

4 How do phospholipids form the fundamental structure of cell membranes?

5 What role do complementary base pairs play in the structure of DNA?

INTRODUCTION TO CHEMICAL REACTIONS

A *chemical reaction* is the interaction of molecules, atoms, or ions resulting in the formation of one or more new substances. It involves the making and breaking of chemical bonds. Examples include the photosynthetic reactions that convert CO_2 and water to plant matter, and the production of alcohol by yeast. A living organism must be capable of carrying out a multitude of chemical reactions in order to stay alive, grow, and reproduce. Although chemical reactions important to microorganisms will be more fully discussed in later chapters, it is important to understand the fundamental characteristics of chemical reactions common to all living things.

Chemical Reactions

Some chemical reactions involve a single compound that undergoes some change in its molecular structure, resulting in a new compound:

Compound A $\rightleftharpoons$ compound B

Other reactions may involve two compounds:

Compound V + compound W $\rightleftharpoons$

compound X + compound Y

All chemical reactions are reversible. The two arrows in each of the two reactions cited signify the forward reaction and the reverse reaction of chemical changes. Any chemical reaction, if given sufficient time, will reach a state of *chemical equilibrium*, where the rates of the forward reaction and the reverse reaction are equal. There will no longer be any net change in the levels of the reactants or of the products. For example, in the second reaction, the net amounts of V, W, X, and Y will no longer change. This is because, although V and W still continue to react to form X and Y, X and Y also react to form V and W at exactly the same rate. However, this does not mean that the *final concentrations of the reactants* will be equal at equilibrium.

Enzymes

All chemical reactions strive to reach equilibrium, but the rate is often exceedingly slow. To speed these reactions, cells contain substances called *enzymes* (usually proteins) that act to expedite chemical reactions. Enzymes serve as *catalytic* agents, and they are specific to particular chemical reactions. Some are capable of increasing the rate of a chemical reaction millions of times over that of the spontaneous reaction. Sensitive to their surroundings, enzymes can also be inhibited in various ways, as you will see in the discussion of enzyme inhibition later in this section.

Catalysts are substances that, even in small amounts, have the ability to increase the rate of a chemical reaction. However, a catalyst is not consumed or destroyed during the reaction it catalyzes. For example, hydrogen gas and oxygen gas can react to form water, but the reaction is so slow under normal atmospheric conditions that it would take a very long time to form appreciable amounts of water. But if finely powdered platinum metal is added to the gas mixture, the gases react instantly to produce water. Platinum therefore acts as a catalyst in this example, because it greatly increases the speed of chemical interactions without being used up by the reaction.

Unlike inorganic catalysts like platinum, enzymes are organic substances produced by living cells. Until recently, all enzymes were thought to be proteins. However, in 1989 Sidney Altman of Yale University and Thomas Cech of the University of Colorado received the Nobel Prize in chemistry for their discovery that RNA can also catalyze certain chemical reactions in cells. This discovery has revolutionized the ideas held by biochemists about the origin and nature of enzymes.

Enzymes also differ from inorganic catalysts because they exhibit specificity; that is, a particular enzyme catalyzes only a certain type of chemical reaction. In contrast, each inorganic catalyst speeds up many different kinds of chemical reactions.

Some enzymes are pure proteins, but many consist of a protein combined with a much smaller nonprotein molecule called a *coenzyme*. The coenzyme assists the protein portion, called the *apoenzyme*, by accepting or donating atoms when needed. When united, the two portions form a complete enzyme, the *holoenzyme:*

Apoenzyme   +   coenzyme   →   holoenzyme

Inactive by itself   Inactive by itself   Active
Protein   Nonprotein
High molecular weight   Low molecular weight

A *vitamin* may be a coenzyme or the principal component of a particular coenzyme. Vitamins are organic substances that occur naturally in very small amounts but are essential to all cells. Those vitamins that an organism cannot synthesize must be supplied in the diet. TABLE 1.3 lists some coenzymes that contain vitamins. Metal ions such as magnesium ions (Mg^{2+}) and zinc ions (Zn^{2+}) also may be needed to activate certain enzymes. Such ions are regarded as inorganic coenzymes, or *cofactors*. Sometimes both a cofactor and a coenzyme are required before an enzyme is able to act as a catalyst.

The general characteristics of enzymes are similar, whether they are produced by the cells of microorgan-

TABLE 1.3 Some Coenzymes and Their Constituent Vitamins	
Coenzyme	**Vitamin**
Coenzyme A (CoA)	Pantothenic acid
Cocarboxylase (thiamine pyrophosphate, TPP)	Thiamine (B$_1$)
Flavin adenine dinucleotide (FAD)	Riboflavin (B$_2$)
Nicotinamide adenine dinucleotide (NAD) and nicotinamide adenine dinucleotide phosphate (NADP)	Niacin (nicotinic acid)
Pyridoxal phosphate	Pyridoxal (B$_6$)
Tetrahydrofolic acid (THF)	Folic acid

isms, humans, or other forms of life. In fact, cells from widely different organisms may contain some enzymes with similar or identical functions, even though the amino acid sequences of the different enzymes are not the same. For example, many of the chemical reactions taking place in a yeast cell are identical to those in a human muscle cell, and thus are catalyzed by functionally similar enzymes.

Although there are thousands of kinds of enzymes, they can be grouped into six major classes, depending on the general type of reaction they catalyze [TABLE 1.4]. The name of any enzyme always has the suffix *-ase* and is usually based on the particular chemical reaction it catalyzes. An example is the enzyme that removes hydrogen atoms from lactic acid: *lactic acid dehydrogenase.*

Enzyme-Substrate Complex. In a chemical reaction, the compound acted on by an enzyme is called the *substrate*. This is converted to another compound called the *product*. The enzyme and substrate combine as an *enzyme-substrate complex*, which then breaks apart to yield the product:

En   +   S   →   En—S   →   En   +   P

Enzyme   Substrate   Enzyme-substrate   Enzyme   Product
                                    complex

After the reaction occurs, the enzyme is released for reaction with another substrate molecule. This process is repeated many times until the reaction reaches equilibrium. Typically, one enzyme molecule can catalyze the conversion of 10 to 1000 molecules of substrate to product in one second. Enzyme-catalyzed reactions may be from several thousand to 1 billion times faster than the

TABLE 1.4
Major Classes of Enzymes

Class number	Class name	Catalytic reaction	Example of enzyme and the reaction it catalyzes
1	Oxidoreductases	Electron-transfer reactions (transfer of electrons or hydrogen atoms from one compound to another)	Alcohol dehydrogenase: Ethyl alcohol + NAD $\rightarrow$ acetaldehyde + $NADH_2$
2	Transferases	Transfer of functional groups (such as phosphate groups, amino groups, methyl groups)	Hexokinase: D-Hexose + ATP $\rightarrow$ D-hexose-6-phosphate
3	Hydrolases	Hydrolysis reactions (addition of a water molecule to break a chemical bond)	Lipase: Triglyceride + H_2O $\rightarrow$ diglyceride + a fatty acid
4	Lyases	Addition to double bonds in a molecule as well as nonhydrolytic removal of chemical groups	Pyruvate decarboxylase: Pyruvate $\rightarrow$ acetaldehyde + CO_2
5	Isomerases	Isomerization reactions (in which one compound is changed into another having the same number and kinds of atoms but differing in molecular structure)	Triosephosphate isomerase: D-Glyceraldehyde-3-phosphate $\rightarrow$ dihydroxyacetone phosphate
6	Ligases	Formation of bonds with cleavage or breakage of ATP (adenosine triphosphate)	Acetyl-coenzyme A synthetase: ATP + acetate + coenzyme A $\rightarrow$ AMP + pyrophosphate + acetyl-coenzyme A

same reactions without enzymes. Calculations have shown that, if enzymes were absent, the breakdown of proteins in human digestive processes would take more than 50 years instead of a few hours!

Enzyme Specificity. As indicated earlier, a striking characteristic of enzymes is their high degree of specificity for substrates. A single enzyme may react with only a single substrate or, in some instances, with a group of very closely related substrates. This means that a cell typically produces a different enzyme for every compound it uses. Furthermore, each enzyme causes a one-step change in the substrate. Most biological processes thus require a form of cooperation among groups of enzymes, rather like a relay team running a long race. For instance, when yeasts change glucose to alcohol and carbon dioxide, the process really is a series of 12 individual steps, each catalyzed by a different enzyme. Together these enzymes constitute an *enzyme system*.

Enzyme specificity is based to a great extent on the three-dimensional structure of the *active site* on the enzyme molecule. An active site is the area on the enzyme surface into which the substrate molecule fits. The specificity of an active site extends even to a particular optical isomer of a compound—the L isomer of a substance

might fit well onto an enzyme while the D isomer does not; the reverse may also be true. Trying to fit the wrong optical isomer onto the active site is like trying to fit the left hand into a right-hand glove. But once a substrate molecule fits into the active site, it is converted to a product. The product is then released from the active site and the enzyme is free to combine with more substrate to repeat the action [FIGURE 1.26].

Enzyme Inhibition. Although enzymes are extremely efficient in accelerating chemical reactions, their efficiency is highly vulnerable to various environmental factors. Activity may be significantly diminished or even destroyed by a variety of physical or chemical conditions, such as excessive heat, treatment with alcohol, or pH changes. Some enzymes are much more sensitive than others to inhibition by minor environmental changes.

Another way to inhibit enzyme activity is to block the active site. A compound that closely resembles the substrate of a particular enzyme may bind to the active site of that enzyme and thus prevent the real substrate from binding. The enzyme *succinic dehydrogenase*, for which succinic acid is the substrate, is inhibited by malonic acid, which is structurally similar to succinic acid [FIGURE 1.27]. When the active site binds malonic acid, the succinic acid molecule cannot attach to the enzyme and there is no reaction. This type of inhibition is called **competitive inhibition,** because there is competition for the same active site by two different molecules. This concept has been used in designing chemicals that inhibit microbial enzymes by mimicking their substrates.

Noncompetitive inhibition of an enzyme can also occur. Here the inhibitor does not compete with the substrate for the active site. Instead, it frequently binds to some other component of the enzyme. Cyanide inhibits enzymes that have iron atoms as cofactors, because it combines with iron and prevents the metal from aiding the enzymes. The ions of certain heavy metals may inhibit enzymes by altering the shape of the enzyme and rendering it useless. Mercuric ions (Hg^{2+}) act as inhibitors in this way when they attach to the sulfur atoms of cysteine.

Sometimes enzyme activity is slowed or stopped when there is enough product produced, at least temporarily. This *feedback inhibition* is found in many biochemical systems. In this process, the final product of a synthetic pathway inhibits some enzyme earlier in the pathway. This happens because of *allosteric inhibition*, a noncompetitive inhibition in which an inhibitor (in this case the product molecule) binds to the enzyme at some place other than the active site. This distorts the active site so that the substrate no longer fits into it [FIGURE 1.28]. Allosteric inhibition is a type of regulation used by microorganisms to control their production of amino acids, purines, pyrimidines, and vitamins.

Enzymes and their activities are good examples of how biochemical processes work together to maintain life. In this chapter you have learned how ions, atoms, and molecules combine to form elements and compounds. Likewise, different building blocks such as monosaccharides, fatty acids, or amino acids are arranged into complex substances such as polysaccharides, phospholipids, or proteins. Their synthesis and utilization are ultimately controlled by the information in DNA and RNA, compounds that are also assembled from smaller structures.

ASK YOURSELF

1 What are enzymes, and what vital function do they perform in living organisms?

2 What is the relation of a coenzyme or a cofactor to an enzyme? What relationship exists between vitamins and coenzymes?

3 What is the active site of an enzyme?

4 How does competitive inhibition of an enzyme-catalyzed reaction differ from noncompetitive inhibition?

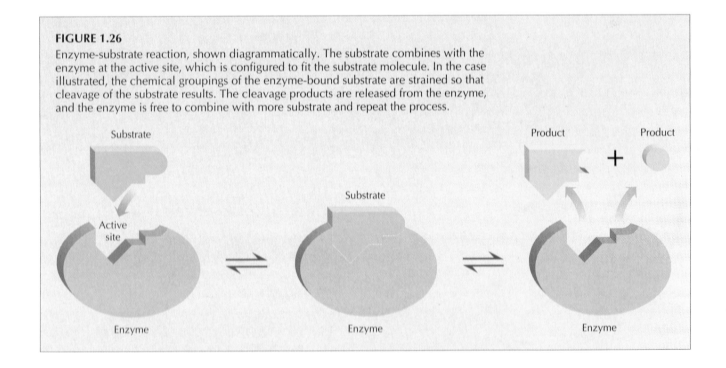

FIGURE 1.26
Enzyme-substrate reaction, shown diagrammatically. The substrate combines with the enzyme at the active site, which is configured to fit the substrate molecule. In the case illustrated, the chemical groupings of the enzyme-bound substrate are strained so that cleavage of the substrate results. The cleavage products are released from the enzyme, and the enzyme is free to combine with more substrate and repeat the process.

FIGURE 1.27

Competitive inhibition (schematic diagram) of the enzyme succinic dehydrogenase by malonic acid. Malonic acid has a structure that is similar to that of the substrate, succinic acid, allowing it to compete with the substrate for attachment to the active site on the enzyme surface. If malonic acid occupies the site, further enzyme activity is blocked, as malonic acid is not changed by this enzyme.

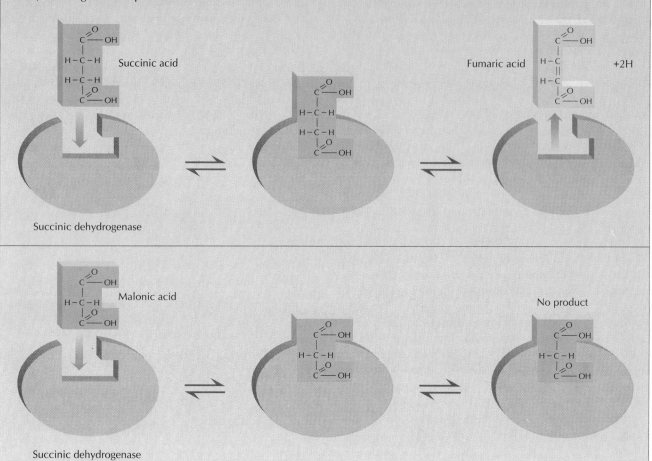

FIGURE 1.28

Allosteric inhibition of an enzyme. **[A]** An allosteric site is located at a region on the enzyme other than the active site. When the allosteric site is unoccupied, the substrate for the enzyme can fit into the active site. **[B]** When a specific inhibitor occupies the allosteric site, the active site is distorted and the substrate no longer fits.

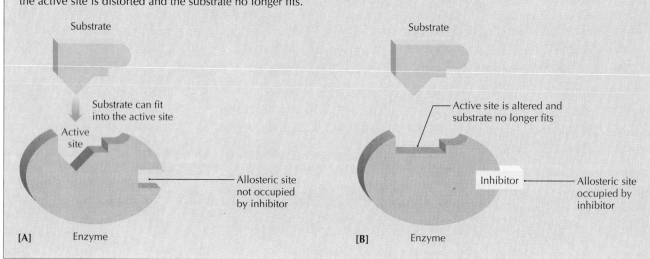

SUMMARY

1 Atoms, the smallest units of matter that have unique chemical properties, are composed of electrons, protons, and neutrons. There are 92 naturally occurring kinds of atoms. Each kind is called an *element* and is defined by its atomic number.

2 Molecules are formed by linking atoms together; a compound is a substance made of a single kind of molecule. Chemical bonds may be ionic bonds, covalent bonds, or hydrogen bonds. Molecules that have ionic or polar groups are hydrophilic and water-soluble, whereas nonpolar molecules are hydrophobic and water-insoluble. Some molecules are amphipathic and tend to form micelles or bilayers in water.

3 A one molar (1 *M*) solution of a compound contains one gram molecular weight (one mole) of the compound in each liter of solution. The concentration of hydrogen ions in pure water is 10^{-7} mol per liter, so that the pH of pure water is 7. In solution, acidic substances liberate hydrogen ions, while basic substances take up hydrogen atoms. A mixture of a weak acid and its conjugate base (e.g., acetic acid and acetate) acts as a buffer to resist pH changes.

4 Carbohydrates have the general formula $(CH_2O)_n$. The simplest carbohydrates are monosaccharides; the most complex are polysaccharides. Monosaccharides contain at least one asymmetric carbon atom and thus can occur in two forms called *optical isomers*. Living organisms ordinarily use only one of these two forms.

5 Lipids dissolve in nonpolar solvents such as ether, but not in water. There are several types of lipids important to living organisms. Fats are nonpolar, whereas phospholipids are amphipathic and tend to form bilayers when placed in water. Sterols are lipids made of several interconnected rings of carbon. Other types of lipids can be found in certain organisms.

6 Proteins are composed of 20 different kinds of amino acids linked by peptide bonds. Each kind of protein has a characteristic amino acid sequence, called the *primary structure*. A protein also has secondary, tertiary, and sometimes quaternary structure.

7 Purines and pyrimidines form part of the structure of DNA and RNA, the compounds needed to transfer hereditary information from cell to cell. The base sequence of DNA represents the hereditary information of a cell; RNA helps convert this information into a form usable by the cell. DNA consists of deoxyribose, phosphate, and four kinds of nitrogen-containing bases (adenine, guanine, cytosine, and thymine). Two DNA strands form a double helix structure when they are joined by hydrogen bonds between their complementary bases (adenine-thymine or guanine-cytosine). RNA differs from DNA by containing ribose instead of deoxyribose and uracil instead of thymine, and by being single-stranded instead of double-stranded.

8 Enzymes are highly specific biological catalysts that speed the rate at which a chemical reaction reaches equilibrium. Nearly all enzymes are proteins. Enzymes are vulnerable to various environmental factors such as temperature changes. Enzyme activity can be inhibited by compounds that mimic the normal substrate, by compounds that inactivate cofactors or coenzymes, or by the products themselves.

KEY TERMS

acids
amino acids
amphipathic
anion
atoms
base
biochemistry
buffer
cation
chemical reaction
chemistry
competitive inhibition
complementary base pair
compounds
covalent bond
deoxyribonucleic acid (DNA)
element
enzymes
feedback inhibition
hydrogen bond
hydrolysis
inorganic compounds
ion
ionic bond
lipids
mole
molecules
noncompetitive inhibition
nonpolar compounds
nucleotides
nucleus
optical isomers (D and L isomers)
organic compounds
pH
polar molecules
ribonucleic acid (RNA)
salt
solutes
solvent

ATOMS AND MOLECULES

1 Of the three major kinds of elementary particles of an atom, the one that bears a positive electric charge is the **(a)** neutron; **(b)** proton; **(c)** intron; **(d)** electron; **(e)** none of these.

2 The maximum allowable numbers of electrons in the K and L energy levels of an atom are, respectively, **(a)** 2 and 8; **(b)** 1 and 4; **(c)** 8 and 2; **(d)** 2 and 4; **(e)** 2 and 16.

3 Each element is defined by its atomic _____.

4 A heavier isotope of a naturally occurring element would contain more of which subatomic particles in its nucleus? **(a)** electrons; **(b)** protons; **(c)** neutrons; **(d)** ions; **(e)** electrons and protons.

5 If an atom gains or loses an electron it becomes a(n) _____.

6 Substances composed of a single kind of molecule are called

_____.

7 The type of bond that occurs between the sodium and chlorine atoms in NaCl is: **(a)** ionic; **(b)** covalent; **(c)** hydrogen; **(d)** hydrophobic; **(e)** polar covalent.

8 Match each definition on the right with the appropriate item on the left.

_____ molecule

_____ ion

_____ covalent bond

_____ neutron

_____ hydrogen bond

(a) The product formed by linking two or more atoms together

(b) Uncharged particle found in the nucleus of most atoms

(c) The bond formed when two atoms share electrons

(d) The weak bond formed from the electrostatic interaction between two polar molecules

(e) An atom that possesses either a net positive or negative charge

9 *Organic* compounds are compounds that contain **(a)** hydrogen; **(b)** nitrogen; **(c)** oxygen; **(d)** carbon; **(e)** phosphorus.

SOLUBILITY OF COMPOUNDS

10 When a crystal of NaCl is placed in water, each sodium and chloride ion

becomes surrounded by a shell of oriented _____.

11 When sodium acetate is dissolved in water, it dissociates into a(n)

_____ ion and a(n) _____ ion.

12 Glucose does not ionize in water but it is soluble because it contains —OH groups, which are (indicate the *two* correct answers): **(a)** ionic groups; **(b)** nonpolar groups; **(c)** polar groups; **(d)** hydrophilic groups; **(e)** hydrophobic groups.

13 The tendency of nonpolar molecules to aggregate in water is termed

_____ bonding.

14 Match each description on the right with the appropriate item on the left.

_____ amphipathic

_____ nonpolar

_____ solvent

_____ crystal

_____ micelle

(a) A compound in which other substances can be dissolved

(b) A solid material having a regularly repeating arrangement of its atoms or molecules

(c) Compounds that neither ionize nor have polar groups

(d) Compounds that contain polar or ionized groups at one end of the molecule and a nonpolar region at the opposite end

(e) A spherical cluster of molecules that form when a soap is placed in water

CONCENTRATION OF
COMPOUNDS IN
SOLUTION

15 If we have 5 g of glucose in every 100 g of solution, the glucose concentration is
_____ percent (____/____).

16 If we have 5 g of glucose in every 100 ml of solution, the glucose concentration is
_____ percent (____/____).

17 The molecular weight of a glucose molecule is 180. If we have 18 g of glucose, we have **(a)** 1 mol of glucose; **(b)** 0.1 mol of glucose; **(c)** 10 mol of glucose; **(d)** 0.5 mol of glucose; **(e)** 18 mol of glucose.

18 Match each definition on the right with the appropriate item on the left.

_____ 1 molar solution

_____ 1% NaCl solution (w/w)

_____ mole

_____ molecular weight

_____ 1% NaCl solution (w/v)

(a) One gram of NaCl per 100 g of solution
(b) The sum of the atomic weights of all the atoms in a molecule of compound
(c) The weight of a compound in grams equal to the numerical value of its molecular weight
(d) One gram of NaCl per 100 ml of solution
(e) One mole of a compound per liter of solution

ACIDS, BASES,
AND pH

19 If the pH of a solution is 9, the hydrogen ion concentration in the solution is (pick the *two* correct answers): **(a)** 10^9 M; **(b)** 9 M; **(c)** 90 M; **(d)** 10^{-9} M; **(e)** 0.000000001 M.

20 A solution having a pH of 4 is _____ times more acidic than one having a pH of 6.

21 A substance that can ionize in water to liberate a hydrogen ion is called a(n)

_____.

22 A substance that can ionize in water to form an anion that can accept a hydrogen ion is called: **(a)** acid; **(b)** base; **(c)** cation; **(d)** isotope; **(e)** amphipathic.

23 Match each description on the right with the appropriate item on the left.

_____ buffer

_____ salt

_____ weak acid

_____ pH

_____ strong base

_____ strong acid

(a) NaOH
(b) An ionic compound that does not contain either H^+ or OH^-
(c) $-\log_{10} [H^+]$
(d) A chemical mixture that causes a solution to resist change in pH
(e) CH_3COOH
(f) HCl

IMPORTANT
BIOLOGICAL
COMPOUNDS

24 Carbohydrates have the general formula **(a)** $(CH_2O)_n$; **(b)** $(CHO)_n$; **(c)** $(C_2H_5O_2)_n$; **(d)** $(CH_2)_n$; **(e)** none of these.

25 A hexose is a monosaccharide that contains **(a)** 7 carbon atoms; **(b)** 5 carbon atoms; **(c)** 6 carbon atoms; **(d)** 12 carbon atoms; **(e)** 6 oxygen atoms; **(f)** 6 hydrogen atoms.

26 Molecules that are mirror images of each other are called _____.

27 To exist as optical isomers, the molecules of a compound must contain a(n)

_____ carbon atom.

28 A molecule of a polysaccharide contains many _____ that are linked together.

29 A lipid is an organic substance that is insoluble in water but is soluble in **(a)** anionic solvents; **(b)** polar solvents; **(c)** nonpolar solvents; **(d)** cationic solvents.

30 A molecule of fat is composed of one molecule of _____

and three _____ molecules.

31 The simplest kind of phospholipid is composed of one molecule of phosphate, two fatty acid molecules, and one molecule of **(a)** nitrogen; **(b)** glycerol; **(c)** fat; **(d)** glucose; **(e)** ammonia.

32 Match each definition on the right with the appropriate item on the left.

_____ disulfide

_____ deoxyribose

_____ bilayer

_____ nucleotides

_____ glycine

_____ primary structure

_____ amino acids

(a) The structure formed when molecules of a phospholipid are placed in water
(b) The building blocks of proteins
(c) The one amino acid that lacks an asymmetric carbon atom and thus does not have D and L forms
(d) The amino acid sequence of a protein
(e) Bridges that occur in the secondary structure of a protein
(f) The building blocks of DNA
(g) The sugar component of a nucleotide of DNA

33 Base pairing between two DNA strands occurs between the following nitrogenous

bases: _____ and thymine, and _____ and cytosine.

34 The hereditary information of a DNA molecule is represented by the sequence of: **(a)** riboses; **(b)** deoxyriboses; **(c)** phosphates; **(d)** nitrogenous bases; **(e)** hydrogen bonds.

35 In RNA, the nitrogenous base _____ occurs instead of

thymine, and the sugar _____ occurs instead of deoxyribose.

INTRODUCTION TO CHEMICAL REACTIONS

36 When a chemical reaction reaches equilibrium, the rate of the forward reaction

equals the rate of the _____ .

37 Match each description on the right with the appropriate item on the left.

_____ competitive

_____ substrate

_____ noncompetitive

_____ coenzyme

_____ enzymes

_____ vitamin

(a) Organic catalysts
(b) A small nonprotein organic molecule that is combined with an apoenzyme to form an active holoenzyme
(c) The integral part of some coenzymes
(d) The compound acted on by an enzyme
(e) Inhibition of an enzyme in which the inhibitor owes its activity to a close resemblance to the substrate
(f) Inhibition of an enzyme in which the inhibitor does *not* bind to the active site

38 An active site on an enzyme is an area of the enzyme into which the

_____ fits.

39 The name of an enzyme ends with the suffix **(a)** *-ide*; **(b)** *-ase*; **(c)** *-ing*; **(d)** *-or*; **(e)** *-ose*.

REVIEW QUESTIONS

1 How did Pasteur discover the existence of optical isomers?

2 Many compounds of biological importance are formed from smaller molecules that become linked as the result of removing water molecules, for example, as in the linking of amino acids to form a polypeptide chain. In what other compounds discussed in this chapter does linking result from the removal of water molecules?

3 What is the importance of hydrogen bonding in a molecule of double-stranded DNA?

4 In what ways can one kind of protein differ from another?

5 In what ways does DNA differ from RNA?

6 What are the main differences between phospholipids and fats?

7 How are enzymes essential for living organisms?

DISCUSSION QUESTIONS

1 A carbon atom has six protons, six neutrons, and six electrons. Another atom has six protons, eight neutrons, and six electrons. What relation does this second atom have to a carbon atom? If the second atom is radioactive, how might you make use of it in biochemical research? For instance, how might you use it to determine whether or not glucose is taken into the cells of the bacterium *Escherichia coli* and used as a nutrient?

2 Suppose you need to prepare a 0.15 *M* solution of NaCl and you need only 200 ml of this solution. How exactly would you do it without making a whole liter of 0.15 *M* solution and then discarding part of it? How would you describe this same solution in terms of percent NaCl (w/v)?

3 Suppose you are traveling in a spacecraft to a faraway galaxy. Just as your food supply is getting low, you find a planet where animals and plants abound. The animals and plants there look much like those back on Earth, but their proteins consist entirely of D-amino acids. Why will you probably starve to death if you stay on this planet?

4 Suppose you are growing a microbe in your laboratory in a beef broth at pH 7, but you find that the organism produces an acidic chemical as it grows. This causes the pH to decrease from 7 to 5, causing the cultures to die within 24 hours. When you add a small amount of a base such as potassium hydroxide (KOH) every hour to the culture to restore the pH to 7, you find that the organisms can continue to grow for several days. How might you achieve a similar result without having to add base every hour?

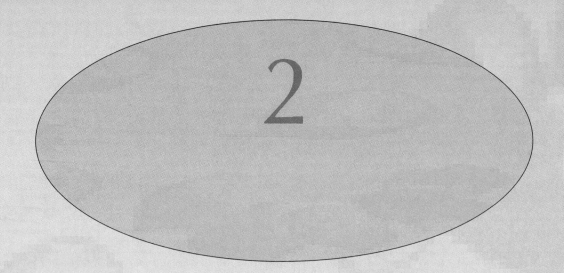

2

The Scope of Microbiology

OBJECTIVES

After reading this chapter, you should be able to

1 Explain why cells are considered the structural units of life.

2 Describe how microorganisms are classified with respect to other forms of life.

3 Distinguish between a eucaryotic cell and a procaryotic cell.

4 Summarize the major differences between the Whittaker and Woese systems of classification.

5 Characterize the major groups of eucaryotic microbes.

6 Characterize the major groups of procaryotic microbes.

7 Distinguish between eubacteria and archaeobacteria.

8 Explain why viruses are studied with microorganisms.

9 Give an example of the role of microbes in the natural environment.

10 Distinguish between basic microbiology and applied microbiology, and give examples.

OVERVIEW

Look in any direction, and you will see signs of microorganisms at work. Bacteria help some plants grow by capturing nitrogen from the air. Bacteria and fungi degrade waste such as dead plants, oil from spills, sewage, and discarded food. Food production, drug manufacturing, and other industries frequently utilize microorganisms or their by-products. Found nearly everywhere, microorganisms are the most widely distributed group of organisms on earth. See yourself in a mirror, and you see a home to roughly 100 trillion microorganisms. They are on your skin and hair, in the tartar on your teeth, along your intestine, and elsewhere on body surfaces. Every gram of waste material your body discharges from the large intestine contains 10 billion microorganisms, which are quickly replaced by others.

No other organisms have the ability to chemically alter substances in as many ways as do microorganisms. Chemical changes caused by microorganisms are called biochemical changes, because they involve living organisms. Some of these biochemical reactions are the same as those in other forms of life, including humans. Such similarities, coupled with the convenience of studying microbes, make these organisms important in research. Chemists, physiologists, geneticists, and others frequently use microbes to explore the fundamental processes of life.

Microbiology is concerned with all aspects of microorganisms: their structure, nutrition, reproduction, heredity, chemical activities, classification, and identification. It examines their distribution and activities in nature, their relationships to each other and to other organisms, and their ability to cause physical and chemical changes in the environment. As you learned in the Prologue of this book, the study of microorganisms seeks an understanding of how they affect the health and welfare of all life on earth.

CELLS AS THE STRUCTURAL UNITS OF LIFE

Cells are considered the basic units of any organism, from single-celled microorganisms to life forms with specialized tissues and complex organ systems. The word *cell* first appeared in 1665, when an Englishman, Robert Hooke, used it to describe plant materials he saw through his microscope [FIGURE 2.1A]. Looking at thin slices of cork, he noted the honeycomblike structures formed by the walls of once-living cells [FIGURE 2.1B]. On the basis of this and other observations, the German scientists Matthias Schleiden and Theodore Schwann developed the *cell theory* in 1838–1839. They suggested that cells are the basic structural and functional units of all organisms.

As the cell theory gained acceptance, investigators speculated about the substance within the cell, the *protoplasm* (Greek *proto*, "first"; *plasm*, "formed substance"). Protoplasm is a complex, gelatinous mixture of water and proteins, lipids, and nucleic acids. It is enclosed by a flexible membrane, and sometimes by a rigid cell wall as well.

Within every cell is a region that controls cell function and inheritance. In some cells, this is the structure called a *nucleus;* it is surrounded by a *nuclear membrane.* In some simpler cells, there is similar material that is not physically separated by a membrane from the rest of the cell. This is referred to as a *nucleoid.* In either type of cell, the nucleus or nucleoid contains genetic information, the coded instructions that allow an organism to transmit its hereditary characteristics to its offspring. The remainder of the protoplasm, the nonnuclear area, is called the *cytoplasm.* FIGURE 2.2 shows typical structures for procaryotic (bacterial) and eucaryotic (animal and plant) cells.

In a *unicellular,* or single-celled, organism, all the life processes take place within that cell. If an organism contains many cells, it is *multicellular.* In higher forms of life, such as plants and animals, these cells are arranged into structures called *tissues* or *organs,* each with a specific function. All organisms, whether unicellular or multicellular, have the following characteristics:

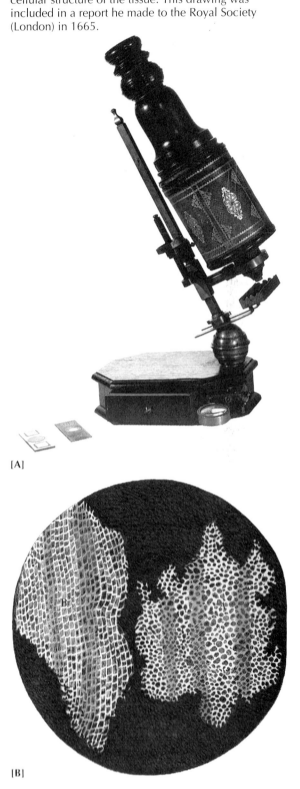

FIGURE 2.1

[A] The microscope used by Robert Hooke in the 1600s to examine thin slices of plant tissue. [B] Robert Hooke's drawing of a thin slice of cork showing the cellular structure of the tissue. This drawing was included in a report he made to the Royal Society (London) in 1665.

[A]

[B]

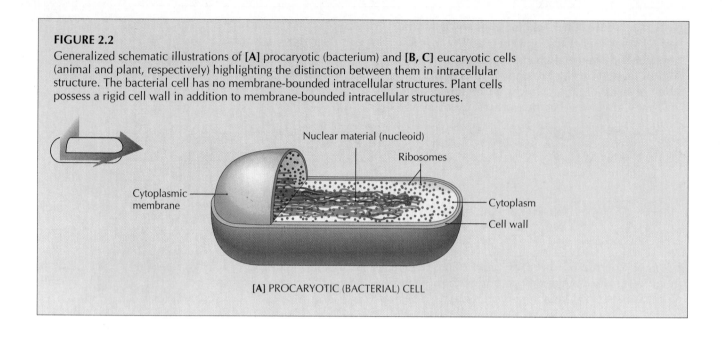

FIGURE 2.2
Generalized schematic illustrations of [A] procaryotic (bacterium) and [B, C] eucaryotic cells (animal and plant, respectively) highlighting the distinction between them in intracellular structure. The bacterial cell has no membrane-bounded intracellular structures. Plant cells possess a rigid cell wall in addition to membrane-bounded intracellular structures.

Nuclear material (nucleoid)

Ribosomes

Cytoplasmic membrane

Cytoplasm

Cell wall

[A] PROCARYOTIC (BACTERIAL) CELL

1 They reproduce.
2 They use food as a source of energy.
3 They synthesize cell substances and structures.
4 They excrete wastes.
5 They respond to changes in the environment.
6 They mutate, through infrequent, sudden changes in their hereditary characteristics.

ASK YOURSELF

1 What is the cell theory?

2 What is meant by the term *protoplasm?*

3 What is the role of the nucleus of the cell? How does a nucleoid differ from a nucleus?

CLASSIFICATION OF LIVING ORGANISMS

There are about 10 million species of living organisms in the world, including thousands of microbial species. The need to make order out of this great number and variety of organisms is characteristic of the human mind. Scientists thus attempt to place them into groups based on their similarities.

The science of **taxonomy** includes the *classification* (arrangement), *nomenclature* (naming), and *identifica-tion* (description and characterization) of living organisms. Biologists place organisms that share certain common characteristics into taxonomic groups called **taxa** (singular, **taxon**). The basic taxon is the **species,** which is a collection of strains with similar characteristics—especially similarity in their hereditary material. (A *strain* is made up of the descendants of a single colony from a pure culture.) Other features used to place organisms into species include morphology and nutritional requirements. Closely related species are grouped into **genera** (singular, **genus**), genera into *families*, families into *orders*, orders into *classes*, classes into *phyla* (singular, *phylum*) or *divisions*, and phyla or divisions into *kingdoms.*

TABLE 2.1 shows the classification schemes for three species: a bacterium, an alga, and an animal. Note that the name of a species is always given as a two-part Latin combination *(binomial)*, consisting of the genus name and a specific name that denotes the species. For instance, humans belong to the species *Homo sapiens*, while the bacterium that causes Lyme disease belongs to the species *Borrelia burgdorferi.*

Because of different traditions among the various biological sciences, there is no consensus on the nomenclature and classification of every taxon. For example, zoologists and botanists agree, with few exceptions, on the arrangement of animals and plants into phyla (botanists prefer the term *division*). On the other hand, microbiologists have not established phyla that satisfy bacteriologists, phycologists, protozoologists, and others. Partly because of this lack of agreement, the genus and the species remain the two most important taxa among bacteria.

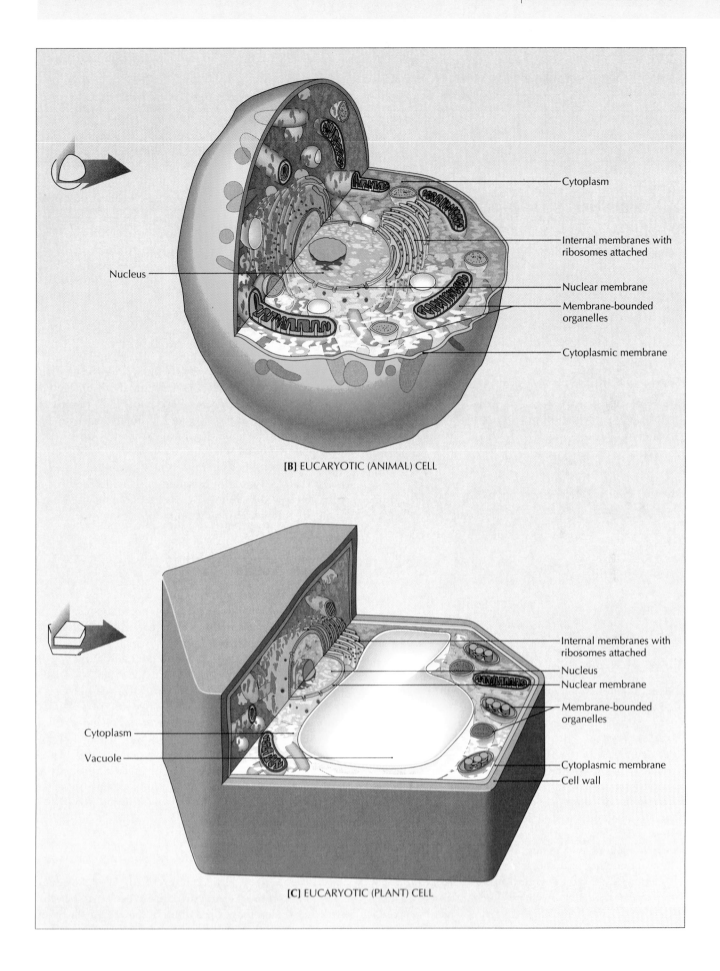

[B] EUCARYOTIC (ANIMAL) CELL

[C] EUCARYOTIC (PLANT) CELL

TABLE 2.1
Some Examples of the Classification of Organisms

Taxa (categories)	ORGANISM		
	Cat	Alga	Bacterium
Kingdom or major group	Animal	Plant	Eubacteria
Division		Chlorophyta	Gracilicutes
Phylum	Chordata		
Subphylum	Vertebrata		
Class	Mammalia	Chlorophyceae	Scotobacteria
Subclass	Eutheria		
Order	Carnivora	Volvocales	Spirochaetales
Family	Felidae	Chlamydomonadaceae	Leptospiraceae
Genus	*Felis*	*Chlamydomonas*	*Leptospira*
Species	*F. domesticus*	*C. eugametos*	*L. interrogans*

ASK YOURSELF

1 What is the function of each of the three branches of taxonomy?

2 What is the basic taxonomic unit?

3 What is the relation between strain, species, genus, family, order, class, phylum or division, and kingdom?

4 How do you write the scientific name of an organism?

CLASSIFICATION OF MICROORGANISMS

During the mid-eighteenth century, all living organisms were placed into one of two kingdoms, Plantae or Animalia, by Carolus Linnaeus. A Swedish physician and botanist, Linnaeus developed the *binomial system* of species names described in the preceding section. Although Linnaeus' pioneering work was a great scientific contribution, his and other early systems of classification often were misleading or just plain wrong because they were based on inaccurate information. Today, systems of classification, particularly those for microorganisms, are still evolving as researchers discover more about the physical and chemical characteristics of organisms.

Examples of the dynamic aspect of classification are *Streptococcus pneumoniae* (once a member of the genus *Diplococcus*) and *Pneumocystis carinii*, which is considered a fungus by some scientists and a protozoan by others. Changes in classification are based on results generated by powerful analytical research tools, like those that determine the composition and structure of an organism's most fundamental chemical substance—the hereditary material DNA. Despite being based on more scientific information, however, current systems are rooted in more than 200 years of taxonomy. Principal features of the classification schemes discussed in the following sections are summarized in TABLE 2.2.

Kingdom Protista

Under his two-kingdom scheme, Linnaeus put protozoa in the animal kingdom, and other microorganisms with the plants. However, this simple concept was impractical for microorganisms, some of which are predominantly plantlike, others animal-like, and others with characteristics of both. In 1866 Ernst H. Haeckel, a German zoologist and student of Charles Darwin, proposed that a third kingdom be established to solve the dilemma. This kingdom, called *Protista,* included those microorganisms having features of both plants and animals. According to Haeckel, it included bacteria, algae, yeasts, and protozoa. But as more information became available about the internal structures of microbes, the validity of the kingdom Protista was questioned.

Procaryotic and Eucaryotic Microorganisms

Advances in electron microscopy in the 1940s exposed much more of the internal structure of cells than possible with light microscopes [FIGURE 2.3]. A particularly im-

TABLE 2.2

Major Schemes of Classification of Living Organisms

Classification scheme	Kingdoms	Organisms included
Linnaeus (1753)	Plantae	Bacteria, fungi, algae, plants
	Animalia	Protozoa and higher animals
Haeckel (1865)	Plantae	Multicellular algae and plants
	Animalia	Animals
	Protista	Microorganisms, including bacteria, protozoa, algae, molds, and yeasts
Whittaker (1969)	Plantae	Multicellular algae and plants
	Animalia	Animals
	Protista	Protozoa and single-celled algae
	Fungi	Molds and yeasts
	Monera	All bacteria (procaryotes)
Woese (1977)	Archaeobacteria	Bacteria that produce methane gas, require very high levels of salt, or require very high temperatures
	Eubacteria	All other bacteria, including those most familiar to microbiologists, such as disease-causing bacteria, soil and water bacteria, and photosynthetic bacteria
	Eucaryotes	Protozoa, algae, fungi, plants, and animals

FIGURE 2.3

[A] The bacterium *Escherichia coli,* a typical procaryotic cell. Here we see a bacterial cell that has just about completed dividing into two cells. Note the absence of any discrete intracellular structures. The light central area represents nuclear material; the dark area is cytoplasm. Many ribosomes are also visible. **[B]** Electron micrograph of the alga *Chlamydomonas reinhardii,* a eucaryotic cell. Note the well defined nucleus and numerous intracellular structures.

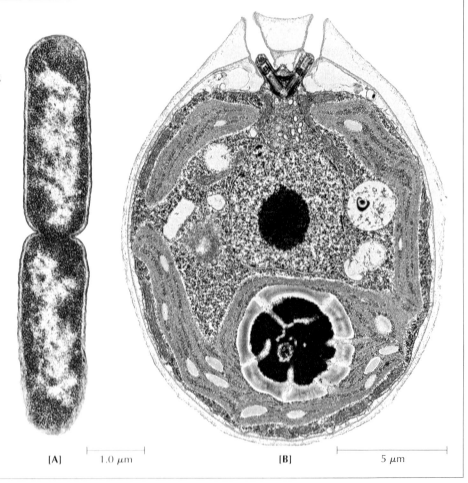

[A]   1.0 μm   [B]   5 μm

portant discovery in terms of taxonomy was that microbial cells could be divided into two categories based on how the nuclear substance exists within the cell: *eucaryotic cells* have a nucleus separated from the cytoplasm by a nuclear membrane, where *procaryotic cells* have nuclear material not enclosed within a membrane. This difference is the basis for separation of bacteria from other kinds of microorganisms and from all other cells, plant or animal. Bacteria have a procaryotic cell structure and are **procaryotes**. Other cells, including algae, fungi, protozoa, and cells of plants and animals, have a eucaryotic cell structure and are **eucaryotes** [TABLE 2.3].

The Five-Kingdom Concept of Classification

Ways in which organisms obtain nutrition from their food are the basis of a five-kingdom system of classification proposed in 1969 by Robert H. Whittaker. He expanded Haeckel's system of classification and suggested that three levels of cellular organization have evolved to accommodate three principal modes of nutrition: (1) **photosynthesis**, the process whereby light supplies energy to convert carbon dioxide and water to sugars; (2) **absorption**, the uptake of chemical nutrients dis-

TABLE 2.3
Some Differential Characteristics of Procaryotes and Eucaryotes

Characteristic	Procaryotes	Eucaryotes
Genetic material separated from cytoplasm by a membrane system	No	Yes
Usual cell width or diameter	0.2 to 2.0 μm	> 2.0 μm
Mitochondria	Absent	Present
Chloroplasts (in photosynthetic species)	Absent	Present
Endoplasmic reticulum and Golgi complex	Absent	Present
Gas vacuoles	Formed by some species	Absent
Poly-β-hydroxybutyrate inclusions	Formed by some species	Absent
Cytoplasmic streaming	Absent	Often present
Ability to ingest insoluble food particles	Absent	Present in some species
Flagella, if present:		
Diameter	0.01 to 0.02 μm	Ca. 0.2 μm
Cross section shows "9 + 2" arrangement of microtubules	No	Yes
Heat-resistant spores (endospores)	Formed by some species	Absent
Polyunsaturated fatty acids or sterols in membranes	Rare	Common
Muramic acid in cell walls	Common	Absent
Ability to use inorganic compounds as a sole energy source	Present in some species	Absent
Ability to fix atmospheric nitrogen	Present in some species	Absent
Ability to dissimilate nitrates to nitrogen gas	Present in some species	Absent
Ability to produce methane gas	Present in some species	Absent
Site of photosynthesis, if it occurs	Cytoplasmic membrane extensions; thylakoids	Grana of chloroplasts
Cell division occurs by mitosis	No	Yes
Mechanisms of gene transfer and recombination, if they occur, involve gametogenesis and zygote formation	No	Yes
Chromosomes:		
Shape	Circular	Linear
Number per cell	Usually 1	Usually > 1
Ribosomes:		
Location in cell	Dispersed throughout cytoplasm	Attached to endoplasmic reticulum
Sedimentation constant (in Svedberg units)	70 S	80 S*

*Except in mitochondria and chloroplasts, which have ribosomes of the procaryotic type (70 S).

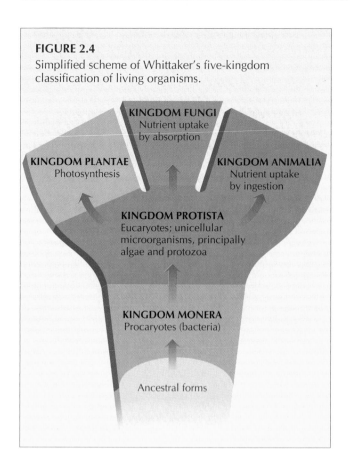

FIGURE 2.4
Simplified scheme of Whittaker's five-kingdom classification of living organisms.

KINGDOM FUNGI
Nutrient uptake by absorption

KINGDOM PLANTAE
Photosynthesis

KINGDOM ANIMALIA
Nutrient uptake by ingestion

KINGDOM PROTISTA
Eucaryotes; unicellular microorganisms, principally algae and protozoa

KINGDOM MONERA
Procaryotes (bacteria)

Ancestral forms

ASK YOURSELF

1 Into what two kingdoms did Linnaeus classify organisms?

2 Into what three kingdoms did Haeckel classify organisms? Which one contained microorganisms?

3 What is the difference between eucaryotic and procaryotic microorganisms? Into which kingdom did Whittaker place procaryotic microorganisms?

solved in water; and (3) **ingestion,** the intake of undissolved particles of food.

In this scheme [FIGURE 2.4], *procaryotes* form the kingdom ***Monera,*** which until recently was considered the most primitive kingdom and thought to be the ancestors of the eucaryotes. Procaryotes normally obtain nutrients only by absorption, and cannot ingest or photosynthesize food. The kingdom *Protista* includes the unicellular *eucaryotic* microorganisms, which represent all three nutritional types: algae are photosynthetic, protozoa can ingest their food, and slime molds (the lower fungi) only absorb nutrients. Higher eucaryotic organisms are placed in the kingdom ***Plantae*** (photosynthetic green plants and higher algae), ***Animalia*** (animals, which ingest food), and ***Fungi,*** organisms that have cell walls but lack the photosynthetic pigment chlorophyll found in other plants and thus absorb their food.

Thus microorganisms were placed in three of the five kingdoms: Monera (bacteria), Protista (protozoa and microscopic algae), and Fungi (the microscopic fungi called *yeasts* and *molds*). Whittaker's system puts all bacteria in the kingdom Monera and suggests a common ancestry for all members of this kingdom. However, results of extensive research during recent decades suggest a different ancestral pattern among microorganisms, as described in the following section.

Archaeobacteria, Eubacteria, and Eucaryotes

Before 1977 scientists thought procaryotes were the most primitive of all organisms. The prefix *pro-*, meaning "earlier than," implied that these organisms, because of their simple structure, were the ancestors of the more complex eucaryotes. Then Carl Woese and his co-investigators at the University of Illinois discovered that neither group had developed from the other. They found instead that procaryotes and eucaryotes apparently had evolved by completely different pathways from a common ancestral form.

Evidence to support this idea came from studies of *ribosomal ribonucleic acid*, or *r*RNA, which is essential for protein synthesis and thus cell survival. Found in ribosomes of all living organisms, *r*RNA is composed of many smaller units called *ribonucleotides*. There are four kinds of ribonucleotides, arranged in various combinations to form a single, long chain of several hundred units. The *r*RNA from any particular organism has a distinctive arrangement of ribonucleotides, or a specific *nucleotide sequence* [see FIGURE 1.25].

The genes that control the nucleotide sequence of *r*RNA slowly change during millions of years of evolution. Because one can compare these changes in different organisms, *r*RNA can serve as an indicator of how closely organisms are related. Some portions of the *r*RNA molecules of all living organisms have remained almost the same, despite 3.5 to 4 billion years of evolution. This constancy supports the idea that all organisms have developed from a common ancestral form.

At the same time, the amount of difference among the other portions of *r*RNA can be used to measure the degree of relatedness between organisms. For example, if the ribonucleotide sequences of two kinds of organisms differ greatly, they are only distantly related; that is, the organisms diverged a long time ago from a common ancestor. However, if sequences show much more similarity, organisms are closely related and have a relatively recent common ancestor.

Using these techniques, Woese found that *r*RNA molecules in groups of organisms differ in the arrangement, or sequence, of their nucleotides. Eucaryotes possess one general type of sequence and procaryotes a second type. But he also discovered that *some procaryotes have a third kind of rRNA*. This *r*RNA arrangement differs as much from that of other procaryotes as it does from that of eucaryotes. In other words, *there are two major kinds of bacteria*. It is now clear that these two kinds of bacteria, designated **archaeobacteria** and **eubacteria,** are as different from each other as they are from the eucaryotes.

The most reasonable explanation is that archaeobacteria, eubacteria, and eucaryotes evolved through separate pathways from a common ancestor [FIGURE 2.5]. Within the eubacterial branch, there are at least 10 different lines of evolutionary descent; within the archaeobacterial branch, at least three. Woese proposed that archaeobacteria, eubacteria, and eucaryotes represent the three primary kingdoms of life, a concept that is gaining support among scientists.

There also is considerable evidence that bacteria may have played an unexpected role in the evolution of eucaryotic cells. Present-day eucaryotic cells differ in

FIGURE 2.5

A depiction of the pathways by which living organisms evolved, as deduced from comparative studies of ribosomal RNA. The three major evolutionary branches are shown leading to present-day archaeobacteria, eubacteria, and eucaryotes. Within the eubacterial branch, at least 10 distinct lines of descent occurred; in the archaeobacterial branch, at least three distinct lines of descent occurred. In the case of eucaryotes, there is evidence that certain Gram-negative eubacteria invaded a primitive form of eucaryotic cell and evolved as specialized intracellular organelles called *mitochondria*. Chloroplasts, the photosynthetic organelles of plant cells, appear to have evolved in a similar manner from cyanobacteria.

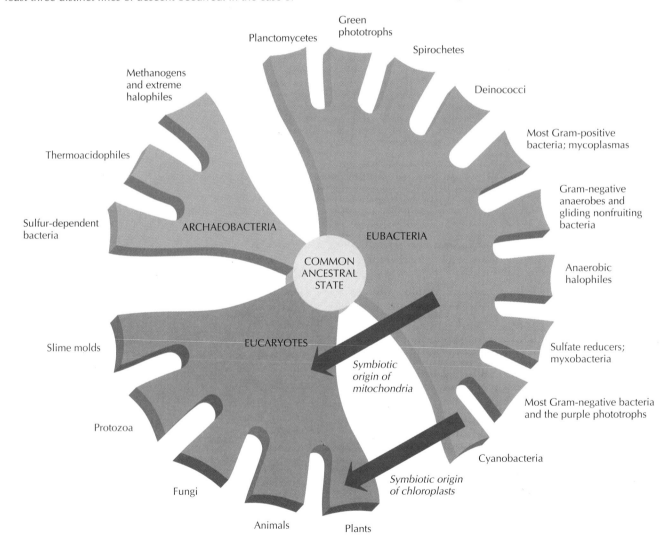

structure from primitive eucaryotic cells—they contain self-replicating *organelles* their ancestors did not have. (Organelles are structures within cells that perform specific functions.) The organelles called *chloroplasts* and *mitochondria* have their own genes and ribosomes. Moreover, in light of comparative studies of the structural and biochemical properties of these organelles and eubacteria, mitochondria and chloroplasts appear to have been derived from eubacteria. Particularly strong support for this idea comes from *r*RNA nucleotide sequence analyses done since 1980. It is thought that at some stage in evolution bacteria invaded a primitive eucaryotic cell. Instead of causing harm, the bacteria provided respiratory and photosynthetic abilities previously lacking in the cell. Both benefited from this association, and each gradually became dependent on the other. The bacteria eventually changed to become mitochondria and chloroplasts, which are responsible for respiration and photosynthesis, respectively. The idea of a procaryotic origin for eucaryotic organelles is known as the *endosymbiotic theory* [FIGURE 2.6].

ASK YOURSELF

1 What is the basis for distinguishing eubacteria from archaeobacteria?

2 What is the endosymbiotic theory of the origin of mitochondria and chloroplasts in eucaryotic cells?

DISTINCTIVE CHARACTERISTICS OF THE MAJOR GROUPS OF MICROORGANISMS

Like any collection of organisms, microbes can be arranged in major groups based on certain traits. Just as the various cat or insect species resemble each other in some way, microorganisms share features with others of their kind. The major groups of microorganisms are protozoa, fungi, algae, and bacteria. Viruses, while not considered to be living, have some characteristics of living cells; they also cause diseases of humans, animals, and plants, and are studied very much like microorganisms. Although these groups are described in detail in later chapters, the following discussion reveals their major similarities and differences.

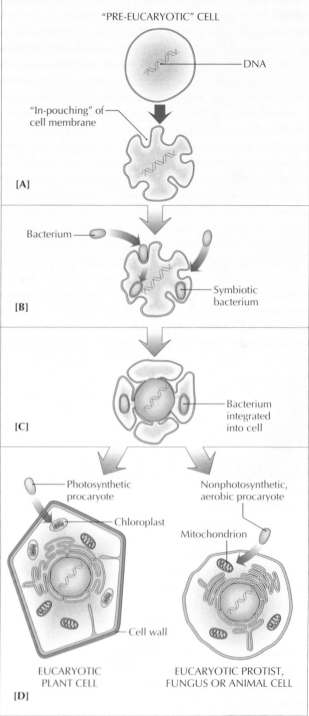

FIGURE 2.6

The endosymbiotic theory, which proposes the manner in which eucaryotic cells may have evolved. This theory suggests that a "pre-eucaryotic" cell developed an "in-pouching" of the cell membrane [A]. Bacteria entered the "in-pouched" area as symbionts [B] and became an integral part of the cell [C]. When the bacterial symbiont was a photosynthetic procaryote, it functioned as a chloroplast and a plant cell evolved. When the bacterial symbiont was a nonphotosynthetic aerobe, it functioned as a mitochondrion (providing energy) and an animal or protist type of cell evolved [D].

"PRE-EUCARYOTIC" CELL

DNA

"In-pouching" of cell membrane

[A]

Bacterium

Symbiotic bacterium

[B]

Bacterium integrated into cell

[C]

Photosynthetic procaryote

Chloroplast

Nonphotosynthetic, aerobic procaryote

Mitochondrion

Cell wall

EUCARYOTIC PLANT CELL

EUCARYOTIC PROTIST, FUNGUS OR ANIMAL CELL

[D]

Protozoa

Protozoa are single-celled, eucaryotic microorganisms. They are animal-like in that they ingest particulate food, lack a rigid cell wall, and do not contain chlorophyll. Some can swim through water by the beating action of short, hairlike appendages called *cilia* [FIGURE 2.7A], or long, whiplike appendages called *flagella* [FIGURE 2.7B]. It is their rapid, darting movement in a specimen of pond water that attracts your attention when you look at them through the microscope.

Other protozoa, called *amoebas*, do not swim, but can creep along surfaces by extending a portion of the cell (a pseudopod) and then allowing the rest of the cell to flow into this extension [FIGURE 2.7C]. This form of locomotion is called *amoeboid movement*. Another type of protozoa are called *sporozoans* because they form resting bodies called *spores* during one phase of their life cycle; they are usually not motile in this phase.

Protozoa occur widely in nature, particularly in aquatic environments. Some cause animal and human disease, such as coccidiosis in chickens and malaria in humans. Some protozoa are beneficial, such as those found in the stomachs of cattle, sheep, and termites that help digest food.

FIGURE 2.7
Schematic illustrations of several types of protozoan cells: **[A]** ciliate protozoan, **[B]** flagellate protozoan, and **[C]** amoeba. Protozoa are microscopic organisms with animal-like characteristics.

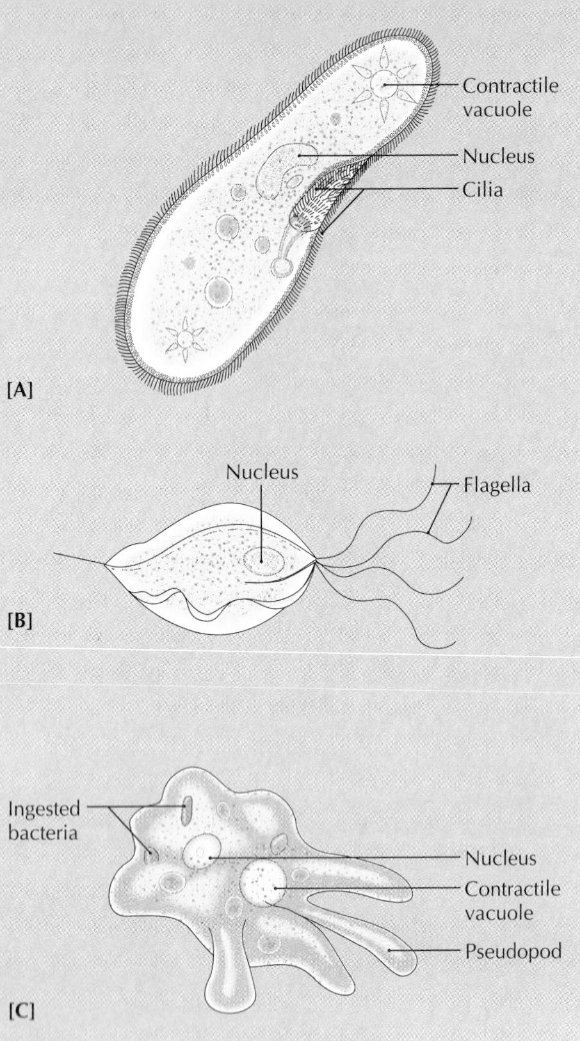

Algae

Algae are considered plantlike because they contain the green pigment chlorophyll, carry out photosynthesis, and have rigid cell walls. These eucaryotes may be unicellular and microscopic in size, or multicellular and up to several meters in length. As shown in FIGURE 2.8, species of algae have a wide range of sizes and shapes. These organisms grow in many different environments, though most are aquatic and a food source for aquatic animals. They cause problems by clogging water pipes, releasing toxic chemicals into bodies of water, or growing in swimming pools. But extracts from specific algal species also have important commercial uses: as thickeners and emulsifiers for foods such as ice cream and custards; as anti-inflammatory drugs for ulcer treatment; and as a source of *agar*, which is used to solidify nutrient solutions on which microbes are grown.

Fungi

Fungi are eucaryotic organisms which, like algae, have rigid cell walls and may be either unicellular or multicellular. Some may be microscopic in size, while others are much larger, such as the mushrooms and bracket fungi growing on damp logs or soil. Unlike algae, fungi do not contain chlorophyll and thus cannot carry out photosynthesis. Fungi do not ingest food, but must absorb dissolved nutrients from the environment. Of the fungi that are classified as microorganisms, those that are multicellular and produce filamentous, microscopic structures are frequently called *molds*, while *yeasts* are unicellular fungi.

In molds, cells are cylindrical in shape and are attached end to end to form threadlike filaments called *hyphae* that may bear spores [FIGURE 2.9A and B]. Individually, hyphae are microscopic in size. However, when large numbers of hyphae accumulate on a slice of bread, for example, the moldy mass called the *mycelium* is visible to the naked eye [FIGURE 2.9C]. Molds have considerable value; they are used to produce the antibiotic penicillin, soy sauce, Roquefort and Camembert

FIGURE 2.8
Schematic illustrations and light micrographs of several types of microscopic algae:
[A] *Chlamydomonas*; **[B]** *Spirogyra*; **[C]** *Euglena*.

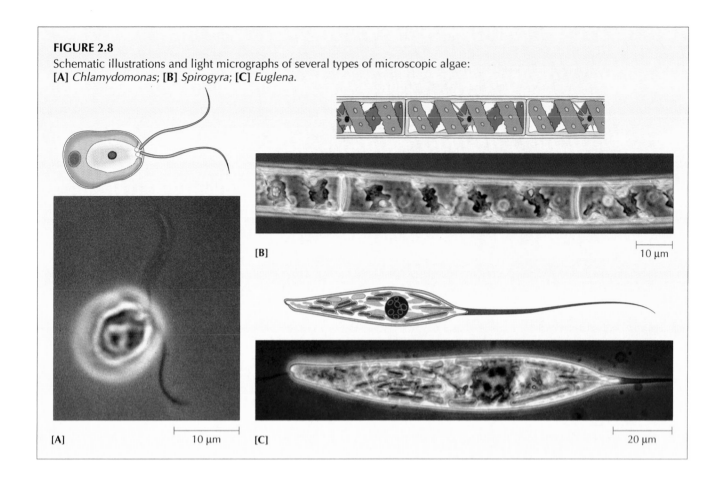

cheeses, and many other products. But they also are responsible for deterioration of materials such as textiles and wood, and the unsightly growth in your shower or bath. They cause diseases of humans, animals, and plants, including athlete's foot and the moldy spoilage of peanuts.

The unicellular yeasts have many shapes—spherical to ovoid, ellipsoidal to filamentous [FIGURE 2.10]. Like the molds, yeasts are both beneficial and detrimental. They are widely used in the baking industry, where they produce gas that makes dough rise. Because of their ability to produce alcohols, yeasts are essential for the production of all alcoholic beverages. On the other hand, they cause food spoilage and diseases such as vaginitis and thrush (an oral infection).

Bacteria

Unlike the previously described microorganisms, *bacteria* are procaryotes, lacking the nuclear membrane and other organized intracellular structures seen in eucaryotes. On the basis of research discussed earlier, bacteria are divided into two major groups, the *eubacteria* and the *archaeobacteria*.

Eubacteria have a variety of shapes, especially spheres, rods, and spirals [FIGURE 2.11A–C]. They are unusual in that the individual cells range in width from 0.5 to 5.0 micrometers (μm; 1 micrometer = 1/25,400 inch). Although unicellular, eubacteria often appear in pairs, chains, tetrads (groups of four), or clusters. Those with flagella can swim rapidly through liquids. Of great importance both in nature and in industry, eubacteria are essential in recycling wastes and in the production of antibiotics such as streptomycin. Infections caused by eubacteria include streptococcal sore throat, tetanus, plague, cholera, and tuberculosis.

Through a microscope the archaeobacteria look much like eubacteria. But there are important differences in their chemical composition and activities, and in the environments in which they thrive. Many archaeobacteria are noted for their ability to survive unusually harsh surroundings, such as those with high levels of salt or acid, or high temperatures. They live in salt flats and thermal pools, for example. Some are capable of a unique chemical activity—the production of methane gas from carbon dioxide and hydrogen. Methane-producing archaeobacteria live only in environments with no oxygen, such as deep in swamp mud, or in the intestines of ruminants such as cattle and sheep.

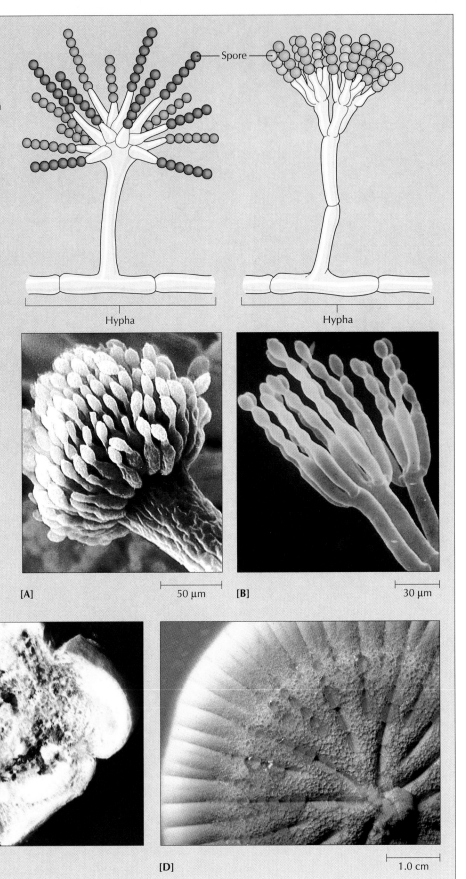

FIGURE 2.9
Types of fungi referred to as *molds* produce a mat of filamentous growth. The individual filaments, called *hyphae*, may bear spores, which are reproductive bodies. Each spore can give rise to new growth. **[A]** *Aspergillus* sp.; **[B]** *Penicillium* sp., the organism that produces penicillin; **[C]** *Rhizopus* sp., the common bread mold. **[D]** The mass of "wool-like" growth, the mycelium, is made up of thousands of hyphae.

Spore

Hypha

Hypha

[A]   50 µm

[B]   30 µm

[C]

[D]   1.0 cm

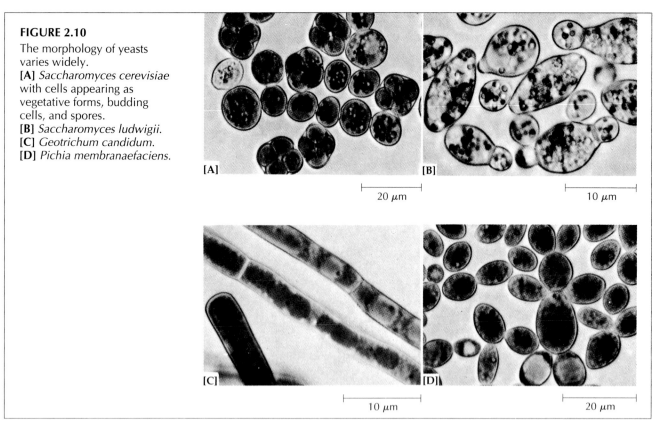

FIGURE 2.10
The morphology of yeasts varies widely.
[A] *Saccharomyces cerevisiae* with cells appearing as vegetative forms, budding cells, and spores.
[B] *Saccharomyces ludwigii.*
[C] *Geotrichum candidum.*
[D] *Pichia membranaefaciens.*

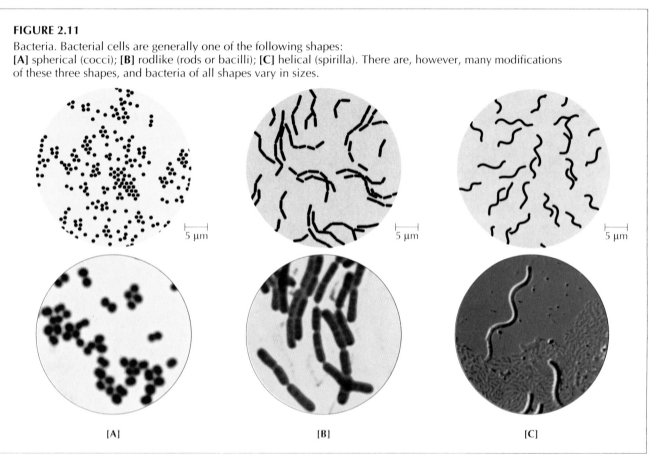

FIGURE 2.11
Bacteria. Bacterial cells are generally one of the following shapes:
[A] spherical (cocci); **[B]** rodlike (rods or bacilli); **[C]** helical (spirilla). There are, however, many modifications of these three shapes, and bacteria of all shapes vary in sizes.

2.1 HOT SPOTS (HYDROTHERMAL VENTS) ON THE OCEAN FLOOR PROVIDE HOME FOR MICROBES

Although the surface waters of the ocean contain many bacteria, it was long thought that few bacteria existed on the ocean floor. Life there is difficult because of the cold temperature (2 to 4°C), the scarcity of nutrients, the absence of light to provide energy for growth of photosynthetic bacteria, and the enormous pressure (e.g., 5600 lb/in^2 at 3800 m). Life is indeed sparse in most regions of the ocean floor, but in the late 1970s, some startling exceptions were revealed by explorations of the ocean floor by a manned submersible vehicle called *Alvin* [A]. Scientists in the research submarine found deep-sea hydrothermal "vents" (hot submarine springs) located along submarine tectonic rifts and ridges of the ocean floor. One form of hydrothermal vent has a spectacular appearance. Cone-shaped and 3 to 10 m in height, it shoots out superheated (350 to 400°C) water in large quantities. Because the water contains iron sulfides, it is frequently black in color. Vents spewing out this water are called *black smokers*. In the areas surrounding the vents, living organisms were discovered in amazing and unexpected abundance, ranging from bacteria to animals such as giant clams and bright-red tube worms 6 ft long [B].

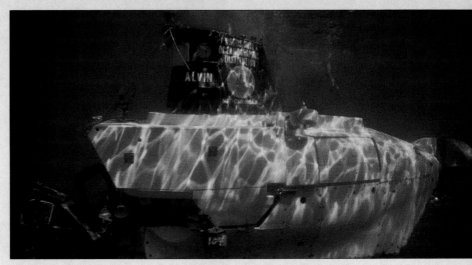

[A]

[A] The research submersible vessel *Alvin* celebrated its fiftieth anniversary in 1989. The vessel carries a crew of three, two scientists or observers and an operator, and has a maximum diving depth of approximately 13,000 ft. Work with *Alvin* has resulted in many discoveries in the field of oceanography including discoveries in deep-sea microbiology. [B] Scientists diving in *Alvin* to the Galápagos rifts in 1977 and 1979 discovered an array of animal life like this (worms, shrimp, mussels, and more) around hydrothermal vents. [C] Tube worm from a hydrothermal vent which has been broken open and examined by scanning electron microscopy reveals a large population of bacteria within the tube.

This proliferation of life is accounted for in part by the relatively high temperature of the water in the regions surrounding the vents (10 to 20°C above the normal seawater temperature of 2.1°C). But this did not answer the question of the source of the carbon and energy on which all of this life depends.

Viruses

Structures called *viruses* represent the borderline between living and nonliving things. They are not cells, unlike the microbes discussed thus far. They are much smaller (20 to 300 nanometers, or nm, in diameter; nm = $\frac{1}{1000}$ μm) and much simpler in structure than bacteria, yet they can insert themselves into the genetic material of cells and do great damage. AIDS is caused by the human immunodeficiency virus (HIV). The common cold, genital herpes, poliomyelitis, and hepatitis are viral diseases, as are tobacco mosaic (a disease of the tobacco plant) and foot-and-mouth disease of animals. Viruses have also been implicated in the growth of some malignant tumors.

Unlike cells, viruses contain only one type of nucleic acid, either RNA or DNA, which is surrounded by a protein envelope, or coat. Because they lack the cellular components necessary for metabolism or independent reproduction, viruses can multiply only within living cells. After invading a plant or animal cell, or a microorganism, a virus has the ability to force the host cell's genetic machinery to make many copies of the virus. Despite their simple structure, viruses exist in several shapes [FIGURE 2.12].

ASK YOURSELF

1 What are the major groups of microorganisms?

2 What are the distinguishing features of protozoa, algae, fungi, and bacteria?

3 Why are viruses studied with microorganisms?

[B]

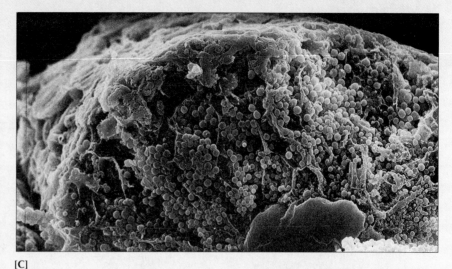

[C]

The answer came with the discovery that the vents discharged water rich in geothermally produced hydrogen sulfide (H_2S) and other reduced inorganic compounds. Moreover, geological and geochemical evidence indicates that oxygen-containing seawater percolates through nearby porous lava and mixes with the heated water spouting from the vents. This supply of H_2S and oxygen allows the growth of bacterial species that use oxygen to oxidize H_2S. Energy is liberated by this oxidation, which then enables bacteria to use available carbon dioxide (CO_2) as their carbon source to make organic material. The bacteria in turn represent the primary source of nutrients and energy for the marine animals living near the vents. Some microbial species live inside the gill cells of the giant clams, while others fill the body cavity of the large tube worms [C]. Indeed, the tube worms seem to have lost all trace of the mouth, stomach, and intestinal tract found in ordinary tube worms. They depend entirely on the bacteria, which take the place of these organs.

In addition to the discovery of the cardinal role of bacteria as the primary source of nutrients in the biological community of the hydrothermal vent, another discovery is the isolation of new bacterial species which grow at temperatures near and above 100°C.

The unexpected abundance of life in these unusual regions of the earth sounds like something that might have been imagined by Jules Verne in his novel *Twenty Thousand Leagues under the Sea*. Yet, it has opened an entirely new and exciting area for research.

FIGURE 2.12

Viruses are of many morphological appearances ranging from needle-like filaments to various geometric patterns. The high magnification of the electron microscope is required to observe their structure.

Vaccinia virus
(250 nm)

Mumps virus
(100 nm)

Tobacco
mosaic virus
(280 nm × 15 nm)

Polio virus
(12 nm)

MICROORGANISMS AND THE ENVIRONMENT

Microorganisms are everywhere. Air currents carry them from the earth's surface to the upper atmosphere, and from continent to continent. Microbes inhabit all marine environments, from the surface waters to the bottom of ocean trenches [DISCOVER 2.1]. There may be billions of them in just a teaspoonful of fertile soil. Only extreme measures can eliminate all microbes from an environment.

It has been estimated that the total mass of microbial cells on earth is approximately 25 times the total mass of animal life. Animals carry large populations of microbes on their body surfaces, in the intestinal tract, and in their body openings. The human body, for example, contains 10 trillion cells and 100 trillion microorganisms—

FIGURE 2.13

A schematic illustration of the role of microorganisms in the recycling of compounds and elements (natural resources) in nature. Elements bound in complex organic molecules are released by the metabolic activities of microorganisms and made available as plant nutrients. The process of breaking down organic compounds into their constituent elements is called *mineralization*.

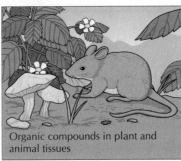

Organic compounds in plant and animal tissues

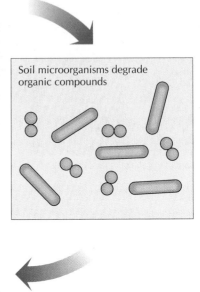

Soil microorganisms degrade organic compounds

Elements and their inorganic compounds serve as plant nutrients

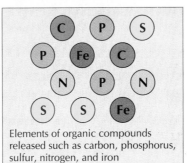

Elements of organic compounds released such as carbon, phosphorus, sulfur, nitrogen, and iron

10 microorganisms for each human cell. Bacteria aid digestion and account for more than 50 percent of the weight of human and animal feces.

Of the many thousand bacterial species known, relatively few can cause human disease. However, those that cause disease have created the impression that all microorganisms are germs and thus are harmful. This is far from the truth. Both animal and plant life depend on the chemical changes brought about by microorganisms throughout the environment.

Microorganisms play the key role in the recycling of elements in nature. In the food chain, animals eat plants and other animals, and plants use animal waste for nutrients. But microbes must in a sense act as translators in this process, by converting chemicals to forms either plants or animals can use. In general, plants use elements, which are inorganic; they cannot use elements that are part of organic molecules (i.e., combined with carbon). But humans and other animals require organic compounds, and excrete organic waste.

A scenario for the essential role played by microorganisms in recycling substances in nature—from complex compounds to elements and back again—is shown in FIGURE 2.13. Elements bound in organic molecules such as carbohydrates, fats, and proteins, which come from plants and animals, are released by the action of microorganisms. These elements serve as plant food, and the plants in turn serve as food for animals. Ultimately, plants and animals, and their wastes, find their way into the soil, and the process is repeated.

Degradation, or decomposition, of waste is part of the nitrogen cycle and similar processes. It is also central to arguments about the environment. Without bacteria and other microorganisms at work, life on earth would be destroyed by its own natural processes. Fallen branches and dead leaves would keep accumulating, as would animals that have died. Materials that can be decomposed through natural processes are described as *biodegradable*. Today there is concern that nonbiodegradable products, such as most plastics, are polluting the environment. Responding to this concern, scientists are developing materials that are more easily degraded by microorganisms and new varieties of microorganisms that can decompose a broader range of materials.

ASK YOURSELF

1 What is the magnitude of the microbial population of the human body?

2 Are all bacteria harmful?

3 What important functions do bacteria perform in nature?

4 How do nonbiodegradable products pose a threat to the environment?

MICROBIOLOGY AS A SCIENCE

There are two major areas of study in the field of microbiology: *basic microbiology,* where the fundamental nature and properties of microorganisms are studied, and *applied microbiology,* where information learned from basic microbiology is employed to control and use microorganisms in beneficial ways.

Basic Microbiology

Basic microbiology encompasses the scientific discoveries that lead to fundamental knowledge about microbial cells and populations. The subjects of basic research in microbiology are discussed in other chapters and can be summarized as follows:

1 *Morphological characteristics:* the shape and size of cells, and the chemical composition and functions of their internal structures

2 *Physiological characteristics:* for example, the specific nutritional requirements and physical conditions needed for growth and reproduction

3 *Biochemical activities:* how the microbe breaks down nutrients to obtain energy, and how it uses that energy to synthesize cellular components

4 *Genetic characteristics:* the inheritance and the variability of characteristics

5 *Disease-causing potential:* presence or absence, for humans, other animals, and plants; includes the study of host resistance to infection

6 *Ecological characteristics:* the natural occurrence of microbes in the environment and their relationships with other organisms

7 *Classification:* the taxonomic relationships among groups in the microbial world

Microorganisms have become the experimental organism of choice in *molecular biology,* which is research on biochemical processes at the molecular level. This is because microbes are easy to manipulate in the laboratory, compared with animals or plants. Many fundamental biochemical processes, such as the form and function of DNA, are the same in all forms of life. Much of the present-day understanding of mammalian genetics, for example, has been learned from research with microorganisms.

Combined with other laboratory procedures, such as experiments with live animals or with animal cell cultures, microorganisms have helped explain the nature of diseases such as cancer. Bacteria such as *Escherichia coli,* in particular, are considered essential in biological research because they provide clues to the metabolic and genetic characteristics of life in general. Building on this type of research, scientists can go beyond the basic principles of microbiology and apply microbes to their own specific purposes.

Applied Microbiology

Useful applications of microbiology are unlimited in their scope and variety. The major applied fields of microbiology include those that focus on either medicine, food and dairy products, agriculture, industry, or the environment. Frequently microbiology provides the best solution to a problem, whether it is a less expensive method to make vaccines or a more efficient process for the treatment of sewage.

Microorganisms make a variety of chemical substances, from relatively simple compounds such as citric acid to the more complex antibiotics and enzymes. The production of these on a large scale is an example of industrial microbiology. Some microorganisms are grown in large quantities and harvested for animal feed or for a human food supplement called *single-cell protein* *(SCP).* Carbohydrates from algae are used widely in the pharmaceutical and food industries. These relatively inexpensive sources of nutrients are attractive in areas of the world with inadequate food resources.

Certain microorganisms are capable of fermenting human and animal wastes, producing methane gas that can be collected and used as fuel. In developing countries, methane-generating systems are used in individual homes to supply heat and light. A tank of wastes buried outside the house serves as a fermentation vessel in which archaeobacteria produce methane, which is piped into the house. At some modern sewage disposal plants, thousands of cubic feet of methane are produced daily, much of it used to heat and operate the plant. Scientists are now looking at bacteria that can convert coal into methane to be used in industrial plants.

Outside the factory, microorganisms are used to alter specific environments. For example, biometallurgy exploits the chemical activities of bacteria to extract minerals such as copper and iron from low-grade ores. Soil microbiologists are looking for microorganisms that can degrade specific pollutants such as herbicides and insecticides. Some microbial products could improve the stain-removing capabilities of household detergents.

In an approach called *biocontrol*, microorganisms are being used as "microbial insecticides" in place of chemicals. Rather than use toxic chemicals to control insects that damage crops, farmers will be able to spray plants with microorganisms that infect and destroy the insects. Another method being developed is the insertion of bacterial genes (such as those from *Bacillus thuringiensis*) into the genetic material of plants. These bacterial genes code for insect-killing proteins, which are then made by the genetically altered plants. The plants thus have an internal insecticide, courtesy of a microorganism. Other microbes, after being genetically altered, will eventually help protect plants from freezing. Such developments in molecular biology and genetic engineering greatly extend the use of microbes for the benefit of society.

In recent years, some of the most dramatic applications of microbiology have been in medicine. These discoveries have helped health professionals understand, diagnose, and treat previously misunderstood diseases. It is now clear that certain conditions, such as tooth decay and some types of ulcers, are related to the actions of microorganisms. This knowledge will lead to better treatments, new methods of diagnosis, and perhaps even a vaccine against ulcers. Through microbiology, better treatments will likely be found for newly described diseases—including AIDS, Lyme disease, and Legionnaires' disease—that are caused by microorganisms. Some leukemias and other types of cancer appear to be caused, at least in part, by microorganisms as well and may some day be treated as microbial diseases.

Genetic engineering and medical microbiology have joined to produce bacterial enzymes that dissolve blood clots, human vaccines made using insect viruses, and rapid laboratory tests for diagnosis of viral infection. Drugs and vaccines already in use are being improved through microbiology. At the front edge of medical research is the use of viruses to insert normally present mammalian genes into individual animals missing those genes. This is an example of basic microbiology on the verge of becoming applied microbiology.

It is important to remember that basic microbiology supplies the fundamental principles used by applied microbiology, and that application of these principles frequently serves as the impetus for discovering more basic information. Both approaches contribute to an understanding of a complex world of life that literally covers the earth. Whether they are valued for their industrial products, feared because they cause disease, or simply ignored because they cannot be seen, microorganisms are always with us. To quote Louis Pasteur, "The microbe will have the last word."

ASK YOURSELF

1 What is the difference between basic microbiology and applied microbiology?

2 What are the areas included in basic microbiology?

3 Why are bacteria considered to be important experimental tools in biological research?

4 What practical use is made of microorganisms in industrial processes, fuel production, pest control, and waste disposal?

SUMMARY

1 The cell is the basic structural and functional unit of all organisms. Many microorganisms are unicellular, consisting of only a single cell, while others are multicellular.

2 All living organisms, unicellular or multicellular, share the ability to reproduce, to ingest or otherwise obtain food that serves as an energy source and as building blocks for cell structures, and to excrete wastes. They are also subject to mutation.

3 Because there are many species of microorganisms, it is helpful to arrange them into groups based on their similarities. The science of taxonomy involves the classification, nomenclature, and identification of species.

4 Early systems of classification placed all living species in either the plant or the animal kingdom. It later became apparent that microorganisms did not fit into this scheme. Haeckel suggested that they be placed into a third kingdom, Protista. However, more recent studies revealed fundamental differences among various microorganisms. Whittaker placed those that were procaryotes into the kingdom Monera, and those that were eucaryotes into either the kingdom Protista or the kingdom Fungi.

5 It was generally assumed that eucaryotes evolved from procaryotes. But studies of ribosomal ribonucleic acid (rRNA) showed that neither group had evolved from the other. Instead, both had evolved separately from a common ancestral form. Woese found that procaryotes themselves had evolved by two distinctly different pathways from the common ancestral form, one leading to the eubacteria and the other to the archaeobacteria. Therefore his studies indicated that there are three primary kingdoms: archaeobacteria, eubacteria, and eucaryotes.

6 Microorganisms are widely distributed. Their biochemical activities in various environments are essential for the continuity of life on earth.

7 In a broad sense, the science of microbiology can be divided into two main areas: the study of the biology of microorganisms, called *basic* microbiology; and the study of how microorganisms can be controlled or used for various practical purposes, called *applied* microbiology. In applied microbiology, microbes are part of many industrial processes (for example, food and drug manufacture, fuel production, mining of minerals, and waste disposal). They can also be used to protect plants from destruction by insects and to better understand plant and animal diseases.

KEY TERMS

absorption
algae
Animalia
applied microbiology
archaeobacteria
bacteria
basic microbiology
binomial system
biochemical
cell
cell theory
cytoplasm
eubacteria
eucaryotes
Fungi
genus (plural, genera)
hyphae
ingestion
molecular biology
Monera
multicellular
nuclear membrane
nucleoid
nucleus
organelles
photosynthesis
Plantae
procaryotes
Protista
protoplasm
protozoa
species
taxa (singular, taxon)
taxonomy
unicellular
viruses

REVIEW GUIDE

CELLS AS THE STRUCTURAL UNITS OF LIFE

1 The word *cell* was introduced by _____ to describe the microscopic structure of _____ and other plant materials.

2 The cell theory states that cells are the _____ and functional units of all organisms.

3 The material that makes up the internal substance of a cell is called

_____.

4 Protoplasm consists largely of water and three kinds of chemical substances called

_____, lipids, and _____ acids.

5 The cell structure called the _____ or

_____ contains the genetic information of the cell.

6 The ability to reproduce is one of the characteristics of all

_____.

7 Which of the following statements is not true for cells of all forms of life, unicellular *and* multicellular?

(a) They reproduce.

(b) They excrete wastes.

(c) They are not subject to mutation.

(d) They synthesize substances and structures.

(e) They respond to environmental changes.

CLASSIFICATION OF LIVING ORGANISMS

8 The basic taxonomic group in the classification of living organisms is the

_____.

9 The highest level of taxonomic group, representing one of the categories into which

all forms of life are divided, is called a(n) _____.

10 A group of related strains is called a(n) _____.

11 The system for naming microorganisms is called a(n)

_____ nomenclature.

12 Arrange the following taxonomic levels in the order of increasing similarity (from least to most) of the microorganisms in each taxonomic group: **(a)** family; **(b)** genus; **(c)** kingdom; **(d)** order; **(e)** species.

CLASSIFICATION OF MICROORGANISMS

13 Until the eighteenth century all living organisms were classified in either the

_____ kingdom or the _____ kingdom.

14 E. H. Haeckel proposed the kingdom _____ for unicellular microorganisms that were typically neither plants or animals.

15 Whittaker's five-kingdom classification is based on three levels of cellular organization which evolved to accommodate three modes of nutrition, namely,

_____, _____, and

_____.

16 In the five-kingdom system of classification, bacteria are placed in the kingdom

_____, whereas protozoa and microscopic algae are placed

in the kingdom _____.

17 Prior to the work of Carl Woese it was thought that eucaryotes had evolved from

_____.

18 The evidence for a separate evolutionary origin of eubacteria, archaeobacteria, and eucaryotes is based largely on comparative studies of the

_____ sequences of the _____ of

microorganisms.

19 Using Whittaker's system of classification, identify the kingdom to which each of

the following groups of microorganisms belongs: **(a)** bacteria _____;

(b) algae _____; **(c)** yeasts _____;

(d) molds _____; **(e)** protozoa _____.

20 From a common ancestral state, living organisms have evolved along which three main lines?

(a) Gram-positive bacteria, Gram-negative bacteria, and archaeobacteria

(b) Gram-negative bacteria, Gram-positive bacteria, and protozoa

(c) bacteria, viruses, and plasmids

(d) eubacteria, archaeobacteria, and eucaryotes

(e) archaeobacteria, eubacteria, and viruses

21 Two kinds of organelles of eucaryotic cells, namely, _____

and _____, are believed to have evolved from the invasion of the eucaryotic cells by bacteria.

22 Protozoa are single-celled _____-like microorganisms.

23 Protozoa can swim by means of the beating of short, hairlike appendages called

_____ or by long, whiplike appendages called

_____.

24 Algae contain the green pigment _____, and unlike pro-

tozoa they have a rigid _____.

25 Microscopic fungi called _____ form threadlike fila-

ments called _____.

26 Microscopic fungi called _____ are widely used in the baking and fermentation industries.

27 On the basis of the nature of their *r*RNA genes, bacteria can be divided into two

major groups, namely _____ and _____.

28 The three major characteristic shapes of bacterial cells are

_____, _____, and

_____.

DISTINCTIVE
CHARACTERISTICS
OF THE MAJOR
GROUPS OF
MICROORGANISMS

29 Bacteria that produce methane gas from carbon dioxide and hydrogen belong to the major bacterial group known as the _____.

30 Viruses can multiply only within a(n) _____.

31 Match each description on the right with the appropriate item on the left.

_____ viruses   **(a)** Contain chlorophyll

_____ archaeobacteria   **(b)** Grow at extremely high temperatures

_____ protozoa   **(c)** Single-celled fungi

_____ yeasts   **(d)** Contain one kind of nucleic acid

_____ algae   **(e)** Ingest particulate food

32 Indicate whether each of the following statements is true **(T)** or false **(F)**.

(a) _____ Viruses cannot multiply outside of a living cell.

(b) _____ Archaeobacteria can grow in very harsh environments, such as high temperatures, acid conditions, and no oxygen.

(c) _____ Yeasts are a category of fungi.

(d) _____ Fungi contain organelles called *chloroplasts*.

(e) _____ Algae are a source of the compound agar, which is widely used in microbiological media.

MICROORGANISMS
AND THE
ENVIRONMENT

33 Microorganisms account for as much as _____ percent of human and animal feces.

34 What generalization can be made as to the microbial content of a teaspoonful of fertile soil? _____

35 What single word best describes the occurrence of microorganisms in nature?

_____

36 Microorganisms are germs, and most of them are responsible for diseases of humans, animals, and plants: true **(T)** or false **(F)**?

37 A key role of microorganisms in nature is the _____ of elements.

MICROBIOLOGY AS A
SCIENCE

38 Microbiology is divided into two major areas: _____ microbiology and _____ microbiology.

39 Which of the following areas of study would be characterized as applied microbiology?

(a) biochemical characteristics of a species

(b) the chemical composition of cells

(c) biometallurgy

(d) single-cell protein (SCP)

(e) microbial spoilage of food

40 Microorganisms are the organisms of choice in studying biochemical processes at the molecular level: true **(T)** or false **(F)**? Give two reasons for your answer.

_____

_____

REVIEW QUESTIONS

1 Identify the structures that are present in a typical cell.

2 Who proposed the term Protista? What are protists?

3 Distinguish between procaryotic and eucaryotic cells.

4 Are viruses cells? Why are they included in the science of microbiology?

5 List several biological activities performed by all cells, including microorganisms.

6 What are the essential features of Whittaker's five-kingdom system of classification? Name the five kingdoms.

7 Briefly describe eucaryotic protists; procaryotic protists.

8 What new lines of evolutionary development have been identified from a comparative study of the ribosomal ribonucleic acid (rRNA) genes of different organisms?

9 Compare archaeobacteria with eubacteria.

10 What explanation is offered for the occurrence of chloroplasts and mitochondria in eucaryotic cells?

11 Describe the occurrence of microorganisms in nature.

12 Describe the importance of microorganisms in several areas of applied microbiology.

13 Enumerate the areas of study in basic microbiology.

DISCUSSION QUESTIONS

1 A microorganism has been isolated from a pond and there is a difference of opinion among the staff of the laboratory whether it should be classified with the algae or the protozoa. How might you justify the different points of view?

2 If you referred to the several editions of *Bergey's Manual of Determinative Bacteriology* (the standard reference for the classification and identification of bacteria), you would find that the first edition (1923) listed 75 species of the genus *Bacillus* whereas the eighth edition (1974) listed only 22 species of this genus. On the other hand, the sixth edition (1948) listed 73 species of the genus *Streptomyces* and the eighth edition listed 415 species of this genus. How might you account for these fluctuations in numbers of recognized species over time?

3 Variations in environmental conditions can greatly influence the numbers and kinds of microorganisms which exist in the atmosphere. Identify several environmental scenarios and explain the resulting impact upon the microbial population of the atmosphere.

4 Studies in basic microbiology and applied microbiology can be regarded as an interactive system—each benefits from the other. Give evidence to support this concept.

Characterization of Microorganisms

OBJECTIVES

After reading this chapter you should be able to

1 Describe methods for the isolation of microorganisms in pure cultures.

2 Name several techniques using the light microscope and identify the advantage(s) of each technique.

3 Distinguish between magnification and resolving power in microscopy.

4 Identify the advantages and the limitations of electron microscopy compared with light microscopy.

5 Distinguish between a simple stain and a differential stain and give examples.

6 Identify the steps in the Gram stain procedure.

7 List the major categories of microbial characteristics used to identify microorganisms. Explain why some of these give more specific information for identification than others.

OVERVIEW

Under natural conditions microbial populations contain many different species—not only different species of bacteria, but also species of yeasts, molds, algae, and protozoa. There may be several kinds of viruses present as well. Frequently it is important to identify how many and what kinds of microorganisms are present in a particular environment. For example, microbiologists base one of the tests routinely used to determine the safety of public drinking water on the presence or absence of the bacterium *Escherichia coli*. Safe drinking water does not contain this organism, which is part of the normal microbial population living in the intestine. Likewise, you may want to determine the total number and kinds of species in a sample of stream water, in order to understand how populations of microorganisms interact in an aquatic environment. Another common example is separating disease-causing bacteria, such as those responsible for strep throat, from the many harmless microorganisms that live in the human body. Finding these microorganisms is part of proper medical diagnosis and treatment. For these reasons microbiologists must be able to isolate, enumerate, and identify the microbes in a sample of material. This chapter will describe some of the methods used to characterize and identify microorganisms.

PURE CULTURE TECHNIQUES

Before you can determine the characteristics of a micro-organism, it should be in *pure culture,* where all cells in the population are identical in the sense that they came from the same parent cell. Microorganisms in nature normally exist in a *mixed culture,* with many different species occupying the same environment [FIGURE 3.1]. Therefore you must first separate, or isolate, the different species contained in a specimen.

Isolation and Cultivation of Pure Cultures

Laboratory workers cultivate, or grow, microorganisms on nutrient materials called *culture media* (singular, *medium*). Walking into a laboratory where media are selected and made is like entering a kitchen lined with jars of food for specialized diets. Some laboratories make their own media from dry powders, while others purchase prepared (ready-to-use) media in Petri dishes or test tubes [FIGURE 3.2]. A long shopping list of media is available, and the kind used depends on many factors. These factors include consideration of the source of the sample being tested, the species thought to be in that

FIGURE 3.1
Colonies of microorganisms that have grown on a nutrient agar plate after being exposed to room air.

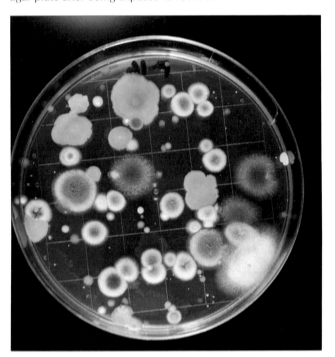

FIGURE 3.2
Commercially prepared media. **[A]** Media that vary in ingredients and in the manner in which they are dispensed (Petri dishes, test tubes, or bottles) are available from many commercial sources. **[B]** Commercially prepared agar medium, in Petri dishes, being inspected for quality.

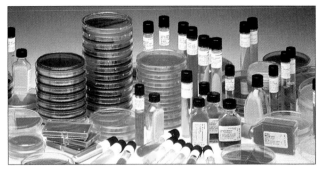

[A]

[B]

sample, and the nutritional requirements of the organisms themselves. Nutrient agar made of meat extract and digested protein (peptone) is one kind of medium. More specific media may contain chemicals or substances such as bile or blood that either inhibit or enhance microbial growth. Like good detectives solving a mystery, microbiologists use media in combinations that help reveal the identity of microorganisms.

FIGURE 3.3

Plate culture techniques for isolation of microorganisms in pure culture. **[A]** Streak-plate method. The specimen is streaked onto the surface of the agar medium with a loop needle to thin out the population so that on some regions of the medium individual cells will be depicted. These cells will later grow into isolated colonies. **[B]** Spread-plate method. A drop of diluted sample of the specimen is placed on the surface of an agar medium, and this drop is spread over the entire surface using a sterile bent glass rod. **[C]** Pour-plate method. The specimen, in this instance a culture of *Serratia marcescens*, is diluted by addition to tubes of melted (cooled) agar media. After thorough mixing, the tubes of inoculated media are poured into sterile Petri dishes; after solidification they are incubated. In this procedure colonies will grow both on and below the surface (subsurface colonies), since some cells are trapped within the agar medium when it solidifies. In each of these techniques **[A, B, C]** the objective is to thin out the microbial population so that individual cells are located at a distance from other cells. The individual cells, if far enough apart, will produce a colony that does not touch other colonies. All the cells in a single colony have the same parentage. To isolate a pure culture, a transfer is made from an individual colony onto a medium in a test tube.

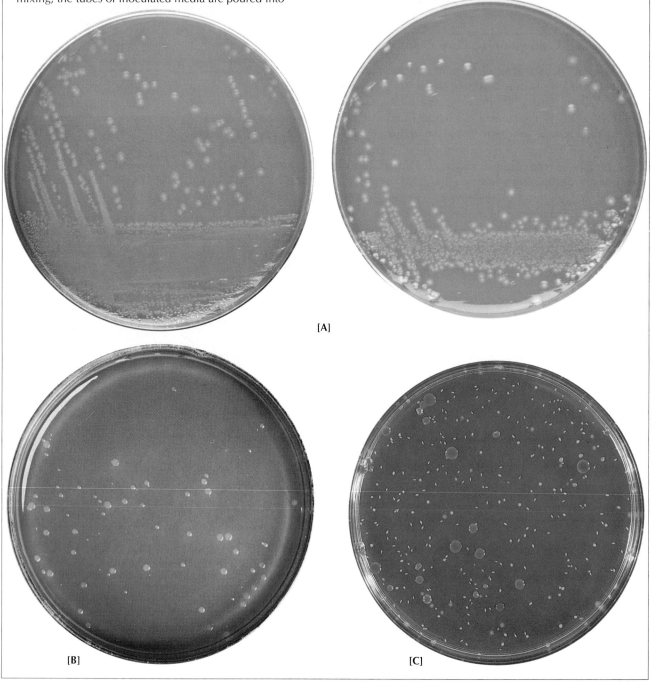

[A]

[B]

[C]

Suppose you want to isolate pure cultures from a mouth. You can either collect saliva in a sterile container or, as medical laboratories normally do, use a sterile cotton swab wiped across some part of the mouth or throat. With either the swab or a sterile wire called a *transfer needle* or an *inoculation loop*, the saliva is streaked across the surface of the agar medium so that individual cells become separated from one another. The material placed onto the medium is called the *inoculum.* The inoculation procedure can be done with the *streak-plate method* [FIGURE 3.3A] just described, by streaking the material across the medium surface with a transfer needle or loop; or with the *spread-plate method* [FIGURE 3.3B], by spreading the inoculum over the surface with a bent glass rod. Another approach is the *pour-plate method* [FIGURE 3.3C], in which the inoculum is mixed into a melted agar medium that has been cooled to 45°C and is poured into a sterile Petri dish (agar must be heated to boiling before it liquefies).

During incubation of the inoculated medium, individual cells multiply and produce a large number of cells that together form a *colony.* Visible to the naked eye, each colony is a pure culture with a single ancestor. Colonies do not look the same for all species. For example, some species of microorganisms may form a sticky, raised colony, while others form flat, dry colonies. In the case of saliva, there will be many types of colonies growing on or in the agar medium, unless you use special media that allow only certain types of microorganisms to grow. In addition to using different media recipes, you can manipulate microbial growth by varying the incubation temperatures, the gaseous atmosphere, and other conditions.

Preservation of Pure Cultures

Once microorganisms have been isolated in pure cultures, it is necessary to keep the cultures alive for some period of time in order to study them. If the culture is kept for only a short time (days to months, depending on the microorganism's hardiness), it can be stored at refrigeration temperatures (4 to 10°C). Some microorganisms, such as *Haemophilus influenzae,* may have to be transferred to new media daily if they are not put in long-term storage. For long-term storage, cultures are kept in tanks of liquid nitrogen at −196°C or in freezers at −70 to −120°C, or are frozen and then dehydrated and sealed under vacuum in a process called *lyophilization* [FIGURE 3.4]. Widely used in laboratories, lyophilization (also known as *freeze-drying*) maintains culture viability for many years and is a key element in building reference collections of microorganisms [DISCOVER 3.1].

Once you have isolated a microorganism in pure culture, you are ready to perform those laboratory tests

FIGURE 3.4

Lyophilization process for preservation of microorganisms. **[A]** Small cotton-plugged vials containing frozen suspensions of microorganisms are attached to a condenser and a high-vacuum pump. This system dehydrates the specimen while it is in the frozen state. **[B]** After the specimen is dehydrated, the tubes containing the vials are sealed while still under vacuum. Details of an individual lyophilized specimen are shown enlarged. This lyophilized culture of microorganisms will remain viable for years.

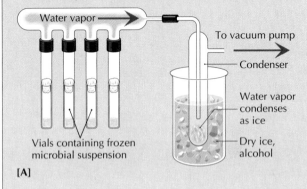

Under high vacuum, ice changes directly to water vapor, leaving microbes dry.

Water vapor

To vacuum pump

Condenser

Water vapor condenses as ice

Dry ice, alcohol

Vials containing frozen microbial suspension

[A]

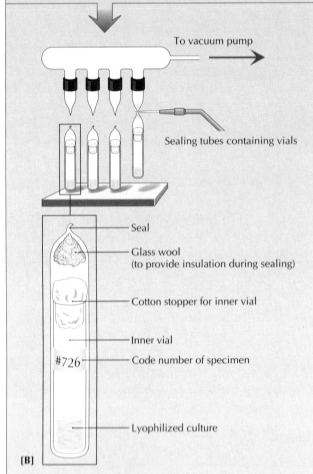

To vacuum pump

Sealing tubes containing vials

Seal

Glass wool (to provide insulation during sealing)

Cotton stopper for inner vial

Inner vial

#726 Code number of specimen

Lyophilized culture

[B]

3.1 BANKING MICROBES FOR THE FUTURE

How do researchers decide whether a mutant microorganism is really the bacterium they think it is? How do courts settle a legal dispute over ownership of a newly developed type of research cell culture? How do you correctly identify an unusual type of protozoan or virus just isolated from a patient? To resolve these challenges it is helpful to have a "standard" set of microorganisms with which to compare your own specimens— a set of reference cells from a ***type culture collection.*** In the United States, the American Type Culture Collection (ATCC) is housed in a building near Washington, D.C. It is a unique bank of microorganisms and other cells for use by research scientists, teachers, patent investigators, and whomever might need to study a particular microbe type. Cells are frozen in vats of liquid nitrogen (see photo) or lyophilized to resist any changes that might destroy the identity of the original cell. An independent, nonprofit organization, the ATCC was founded in 1925 to serve as a central storage area, essentially a place to preserve algae, bacteria, cell lines, DNA, viruses, plant tissues, protozoa, and oncogenes (cancer-causing genes).

Like any bank, the ATCC accepts deposits and authorizes withdrawals. Currently it maintains approximately 50,000 strains of 9500 species, submit-

Microorganisms and various eucaryotic cell lines are stored in individual, labeled vials that are kept frozen in large containers filled with liquid nitrogen.

ted over many years by scientists. It is the repository for genetic material used in research by members of 19 scientific societies. Since 1981, it has also served as the international patent culture center. When researchers discover a new kind of microorganism, for example, they send samples to ATCC; information about a particular sample is kept confidential until the patent is issued. Also

kept in the collection are such materials as frozen embryos of a mouse recently developed as a cancer model by Harvard University. However, the largest share of ATCC inventory is unpatented microorganisms and other cells that can be ordered from the ATCC catalog. Each year more than 90,000 cultures are distributed to industry and scientists worldwide.

needed to identify that microorganism. These tests usually include the use of different media and different chemical reactions, but one of your most powerful detective tools will be the microscope.

ASK YOURSELF

1 What is a pure culture?

2 In terms of species present, how would you characterize the microbial population of a natural environment such as garden soil?

3 How are pure cultures isolated? How are they preserved?

MICROSCOPES

In the Prologue, you learned about the invention and early evolution of the microscope, an optical instrument that produces a magnified image of a small object. The microscope frequently is the most often used instrument in a laboratory that studies microorganisms. Using a system of lenses and illumination sources, it makes a microscopic object visible. Microscopes can magnify from 100 times to hundreds of thousands of times the original size, revealing the simple symmetry of viruses or the more complex internal structures of protozoa.

The size of microbial cells and viruses is expressed in units of measurement called the ***micrometer (μm)*** and the *nanometer (nm).* (Size comparisons of different microorganisms are shown in FIGURE 3.5.) Although the first thing you may want to see is the entire microorganism, with additional help from dyes and special illumination systems the microscope can detect interior structures such as membranes, nuclei, and other intracellular bodies.

There are two main categories of microscopes currently in use: *light microscopes* and *electron microscopes.* These differ in the principle on which magnification is produced. To magnify an object, modern light microscopes use a system of lenses to manipulate the path a light beam travels between the object being studied and the eye. Rather than use a light source and a set of lenses, the electron microscope uses a beam of electrons controlled by a system of magnetic fields.

The Light Microscope

Light, or optical, microscopes extend the power of the magnifying glass. The principal parts of a light microscope and the path that light rays follow to magnify the object are shown in FIGURE 3.6. Microscopes of this type generally produce a maximum useful magnification of about 1000 times the original size. By *useful magnification,* microscopists mean a level at which structures are still clearly distinguishable, rather than blurred. With some modifications, including higher-powered eyepieces, an instrument's maximum magnification can be increased. Even with these adjustments, the limit of useful magnification with a light microscope is about 2000 times.

As you can see from FIGURE 3.6, there are lenses in

FIGURE 3.5

[A] A comparison of sizes of selected microorganisms. [B] A table of equivalents in the metric system for units used to express dimensions of microbial cells.

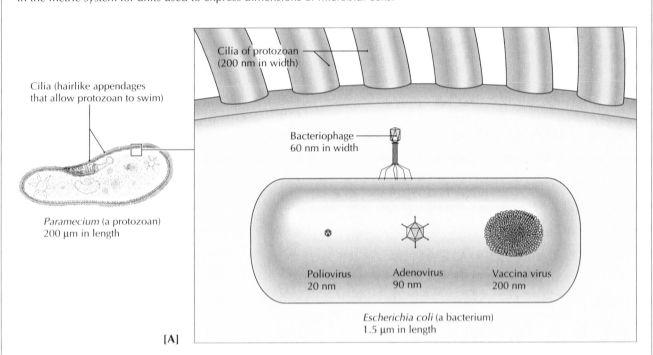

[A]

Unit of length	Meter (m)	Centimeter (cm)	Millimeter (mm)	Micrometer (μm)	Nanometer (nm)
Micrometer (μm)	0.000001 10^{-6}	0.0001 10^{-4}	0.001 10^{-3}	1	1000 10^3
Nanometer (nm)	0.000000001 10^{-9}	0.0000001 10^{-7}	0.000001 10^{-6}	0.001 10^{-3}	1
Angstrom (Å)	0.0000000001 10^{-10}	0.00000001 10^{-8}	0.0000001 10^{-7}	0.0001 10^{-4}	0.1 10^{-1}

[B]

FIGURE 3.6
A modern compound light microscope. **[A]** Identification of parts. **[B]** Cutaway sketch of student microscope showing optical parts and path of light.

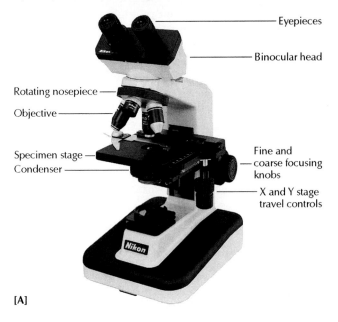

- Eyepieces
- Binocular head
- Rotating nosepiece
- Objective
- Specimen stage
- Condenser
- Fine and coarse focusing knobs
- X and Y stage travel controls

[A]

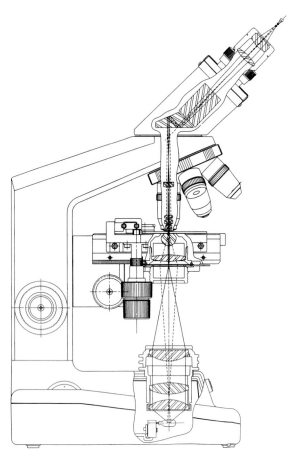

[B]

the *condenser*, the *objective(s)*, and the *eyepiece (ocular)*. The condenser lens focuses light on the specimen. Some of the light rays pass directly into the objective lens, while other rays strike the specimen and are bent. These are brought into focus by the objective lens to form an image of the object being studied.

Microscopes commonly used in microbiology are equipped with three objectives called *low-power, high-power,* and *oil-immersion* objectives—each with a lens that gives different magnification. They are mounted on a "nosepiece" that can be rotated to move any one of them into alignment with the condenser.

In using the oil-immersion objective, a drop of special oil is placed on the specimen slide, and the bottom of the objective is immersed in the oil. The image is brought into focus, with contact maintained between the oil and the front lens of the objective. The oil helps keep the light rays together as they pass between the specimen and the objective lens (i.e., the refractive index of the glass and the oil are the same); this allows the lens to form a clearer, more detailed image, resulting in the highest possible magnification with a given microscope. The oil-immersion objective is commonly used for the examination of microorganisms because of their small size.

The image formed by the objectives is further enlarged by the ocular lens. Thus it is the combination of the objective lens system and the ocular lens system that gives the magnification. The total magnification obtainable with any one of the objectives is determined by multiplying the magnifying power of the objective by the magnifying power of the eyepiece (generally 10 times), as the following demonstrates:

Objective designation	Objective magnification	Eyepiece magnification	Total magnification
Low power	10	10	100
High power (high dry)	40	10	400
Oil immersion	100	10	1000

Resolving Power. A microscope's useful magnification is limited by its **resolving power,** or its ability to distinguish images of two close objects as separate, distinct entities. The resolving power is a function of the wavelength of light and the numerical aperture of the lens system. Greater resolving power means better visualization of the specific structural features of cells such as nuclei and cell walls. However, the maximum resolving power of a microscope is fixed by the wavelength of light used and by the optical properties of the lenses. Light microscopes, by using visible light, have a resolving

FIGURE 3.7
A digital, scanning electron microscope. Note the microscope column on the left and the monitors on the right.

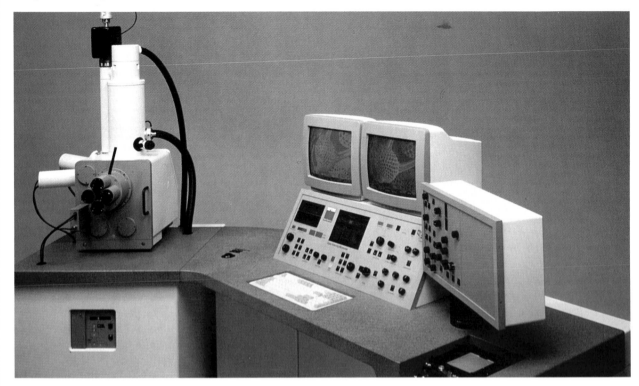

power of approximately 0.25 μm, which means that particles of a smaller size cannot be distinguished from one another. Newer advances in microscope technology, such as the electron microscope, have improved the resolving power available to microbiologists.

The Electron Microscope

Because of its greater resolving power, the electron microscope permits greater magnifications than can be obtained with light microscopes. It can do so because of the very short wavelengths of the electron beams used instead of light. These beams have wavelengths in the range of 0.005 to 0.0003 nm, very short compared with wavelengths of visible light. Therefore, the resolving power is several hundred times that of the light microscope. It is possible by using an electron microscope to resolve objects separated by a distance of 0.003 μm, compared with 0.25 μm with a light microscope. Magnifications approaching 1 million times can be achieved by photographing the magnified image and then enlarging the photograph. A high-resolution electron microscope is shown in FIGURE 3.7. Compare the pictures of the bacterium *Escherichia coli* taken through a light micro-

scope, a transmission electron microscope, and a scanning electron microscope [see FIGURE 3.11].

To prepare microorganisms for examination by an electron microscope, a sample is first dried onto an extremely thin plastic film supported by a screen grid. The specimen is then placed into the instrument at a point between the magnetic condenser and the magnetic objective, which are comparable to the condenser and the objective of the light microscope. You can then view the magnified image on a fluorescent screen or record it on photographic film using an attached camera.

ASK YOURSELF

1 How does the maximum useful magnification obtainable with a light microscope compare with that of the electron microscope? What accounts for this great difference?

2 What is "resolving power," and how is it related to maximum useful magnification?

MICROSCOPY

As a beginning microbiology student, you will develop basic microscopy skills that have been used for years by microbiologists. Put simply, *microscopy* is the use of microscopes in all their various forms. Although you will perform most, if not all, of your examinations using bright-field microscopy, it is possible to use light microscopes to perform different functions, such as bright-field, dark-field, fluorescence, and phase-contrast microscopy. Scientists continue to refine and develop light microscope techniques that perform additional specialized functions, such as measuring biochemical processes as they occur within a living cell.

Beyond light microscopy are the different uses of the electron microscope. When it was developed, this microscope showed scientists parts of the cell that had been hidden from view. There are more recent advances in microscopy as well, like those that utilize computers, other sources of illumination, or new staining techniques. Techniques learned in the years since Leeuwenhoek, tied to increasing knowledge about the chemistry of cells, now offer microbiologists an exciting selection of microscopy methods for studying microorganisms. TABLE 3.1 summarizes the essential features and applications of the different types of microscopy.

Bright-Field Microscopy

Bright-field microscopy uses a direct light source, either a light bulb or daylight, that illuminates the entire specimen field. As previously mentioned, the light rays that strike an object in the specimen are bent and then refocused by the objective lens. Since microorganisms are transparent, they do not stand out distinctly with this type of microscopy. Therefore, microbiologists usually stain, or color with dye, those microorganisms viewed with bright-field microscopy. Because most staining techniques also kill microorganisms, this approach has some limitations.

Dark-Field Microscopy

Dark-field microscopy uses a light microscope equipped with a special condenser and objective to brightly illuminate the microorganisms in the specimen against a dark background. What you see through the eyepiece looks rather like a dancer in a spotlight on a stage, standing against a black curtain. The dark-field condenser directs the rays of light into the specimen field at such an angle that only the rays striking an object in the field are bent, or refracted, into the objective [FIGURE 3.8]. This method is particularly valuable for the examination of unstained living microorganisms. For example, it is use-

TABLE 3.1
A Comparison of Different Types of Microscopy

Type of microscopy	Maximum useful magnification	Appearance of specimen	Useful applications
Bright-field	1000–2000	Specimens stained or unstained; bacteria generally stained and appear color of stain	Gross morphological features of bacteria, yeasts, molds, algae, and protozoa
Dark-field	1000–2000	Generally unstained; appears bright or "lighted" in an otherwise dark field	Microorganisms that exhibit some characteristic morphological feature in the living state and in fluid suspension, e.g., spirochetes
Fluorescence	1000–2000	Bright and colored; color of the fluorescent dye	Diagnostic techniques where fluorescent dye fixed to organism reveals the organism's identity
Phase-contrast	1000–2000	Varying degrees of "darkness"	Examination of cellular structures in living cells of the larger microorganisms, e.g., yeasts, algae, protozoa, and some bacteria
Electron	200,000–400,000	Viewed on fluorescent screen	Examination of viruses and the ultrastructure of microbial cells

FIGURE 3.8

[A] Sunlight streaming through the window of a dark room shows dust specks floating in the air. A similar principle is used in dark-field microscopy to see live bacteria in a wet mount. [B] Path of light through a dark-field microscope system. Some light rays are blocked from entering the bottom of the condenser. Those that do enter the condenser are reflected at the air-glass interfaces to form a hollow cone of light which reaches the specimen. Only those rays that are deflected by the specimen can enter the objective lens and reach the observer's eye. [C] Dark-field photomicrograph of a pure culture of spirochetes, *Treponema* sp.

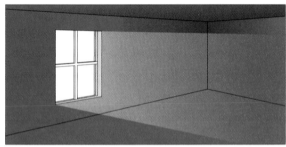

[A]

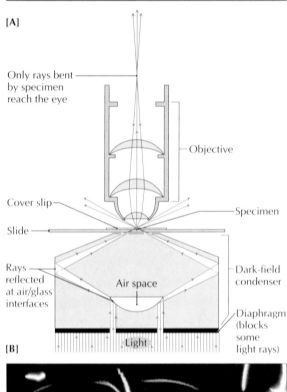

Only rays bent by specimen reach the eye

Objective

Cover slip

Specimen

Slide

Rays reflected at air/glass interfaces

Air space

Dark-field condenser

Diaphragm (blocks some light rays)

[B]   Light

[C]   10 μm

ful for the identification of the syphilis bacterium, which has a characteristic shape and movement when alive [FIGURE 3.8C].

Fluorescence Microscopy

Fluorescence microscopy is a light-microscope technique used widely in hospital and clinical laboratories because it can be adapted to rapid tests that identify disease-causing microorganisms. A specimen is stained with a fluorescent dye that absorbs the energy of short light waves like those in blue light. The dye then releases, or emits, light of a longer wavelength, such as green light. This phenomenon is called *fluorescence*, and its use is increasing in microbiology laboratories.

One common laboratory procedure using this principle is called the *fluorescent antibody*, or *immunofluorescence*, technique. An *antibody* is a protein which develops in the blood after an animal is exposed in some manner to foreign matter such as microorganisms. Antibodies appear following infections such as measles and hepatitis, for example. An antibody reacts, or combines, specifically with whatever stimulated its production. For the fluorescent antibody test, a fluorescent dye is attached to an antibody that is known to specifically react with certain microorganisms. This antibody-dye complex is mixed with unknown microorganisms and examined through a microscope. If the antibody has attached itself to any microorganisms in the specimen, those microorganisms will fluoresce and thus be identified [FIGURE 3.9]. The use of antibodies makes the identification of microorganisms more specific and more rapid than possible with culture techniques.

FIGURE 3.9

Fluorescent stain of *Chlamydia* bacteria elementary bodies, which appear as small, circular, greenish objects. The large, red bodies are epithelial cells.

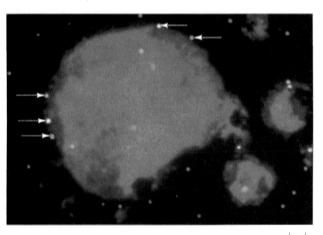

0.5 μm

FIGURE 3.10

The same specimen of protozoa as seen by three methods of microscopy: [A] phase-contrast, [B] dark-field, and [C] bright-field. Note the differences in the appearance of intracellular structures revealed by each type of microscopy.

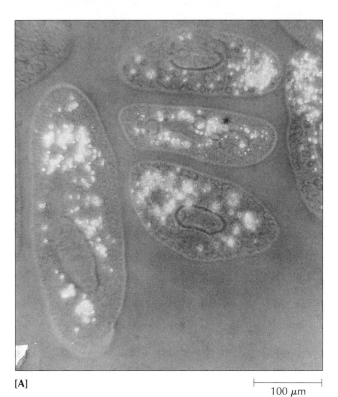

[A] 100 μm

[B] 100 μm

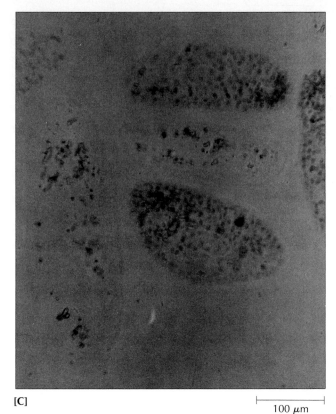

[C] 100 μm

Phase-Contrast Microscopy

Phase-contrast microscopy uses a modified light microscope that permits greater contrast between substances of different thickness or of different density. A special condenser and objective control the illumination in a way that accentuates these differences, by causing light to travel different routes through the various parts of a cell. The result is an image with differing degrees of brightness or darkness collectively called *contrast* [FIGURE 3.10]. With this method, denser materials appear bright, while parts of the cell that have a density close to that of water (e.g., the cytoplasm) appear dark. An advantage of this technique is its ability to show cell structure without using dyes or killing the organism.

Electron Microscopy

With its ability to make viruses and minute structures visible, the electron microscope frequently is the most important piece of equipment in a modern research laboratory [FIGURE 3.11]. There are several techniques available for this microscope, including staining methods using heavy metals and radioactive substances. Which method is used depends in part on the type of electron microscope available, as well as the purpose of the examination.

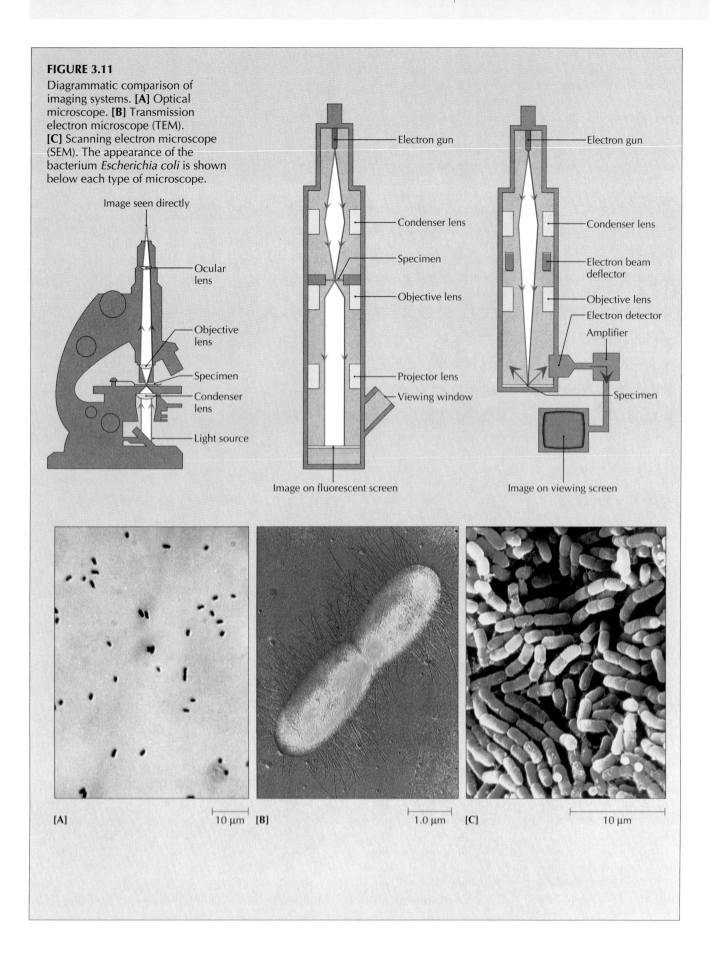

FIGURE 3.11

Diagrammatic comparison of imaging systems. **[A]** Optical microscope. **[B]** Transmission electron microscope (TEM). **[C]** Scanning electron microscope (SEM). The appearance of the bacterium *Escherichia coli* is shown below each type of microscope.

Techniques using stains, or those that slice microorganisms into thin sections, are applicable to *transmission electron microscopy (TEM).* Here the electron beam passes through the specimen, and the scattering of the electrons forms an image like those described earlier [FIGURE 3.11B]. Heavy metals can be used as stains, making some parts of cells appear dark because electrons cannot pass through them. In another technique, the electron microscope can be modified to use a narrow electron beam that moves back and forth over the surface of microorganisms coated with a thin film of metal. The patterns of electrons are detected by a device similar to a television camera. This *scanning electron microscopy (SEM)* provides three-dimensional views of the cell surface [FIGURE 3.11C]. These images give scientists an idea of certain physical aspects of microorganisms, such as the attachment of bacterial cells to objects.

Newer Microscopy Techniques and Microscopes

Since the development of the electron microscope, scientists have kept pushing microscopy to the limits of known technology. They have used computers, electronics, and chemistry to improve the images they see and to understand cell activities at a molecular level. The following is a brief description of some of the more recent innovations; however, new discoveries are being reported with considerable frequency. Although some of these technologies are currently being used primarily on eucaryotic cells, additional applications will include the study of procaryotes.

Two of the newer light microscopy methods have added both cameras and computers to their lenses and light sources. *Video-enhanced contrast microscopy* shows more detail than ordinary light microscopes because multiple images are captured on videotape. A computer then improves contrast by combining those images and subtracting the nonessential "information" also present in the specimen. *Low–light dose microscopy* uses weakly fluorescent marker dyes that attach to specific parts of a cell, and a computer that enhances the fluorescent signals given off as biochemical processes take place in the cell. For example, if a chemical used as a marker fluoresces differently at different pH values, researchers can detect pH-changing metabolic activity inside cells.

A method called *immunoelectron microscopy* borrows some of the technology used in fluorescent antibody techniques [FIGURE 3.12]. Antibodies attached to particles of gold are mixed with cells; if they attach either to cell surfaces or to other antibodies already fastened to cells, these gold particles appear as black dots within or on cells when seen through an electron microscope. By

FIGURE 3.12
Immunogold labeling of 0.5 µm microspheres coated with staphylococcus enterotoxin B antigen [A, B, C] or a cell lysate of herpes simplex virus [D, E, F]. [A, B] and [C] show spheres coated with staphylococcus enterotoxin B antigen and incubated with normal rabbit preimmune serum [A], and with rabbit staphylococcus enterotoxin antiserum [B, C]. [C] is an enlargement of one of the immunogold-labeled spheres shown in [B]. [D, E] and [F] show microspheres coated with herpes simplex antigen and incubated with normal rabbit preimmune serum [D] or rabbit antiserum to Herpes simplex virus antigen [E, F]. [F] is an enlargement of a sphere from [E]. In all cases, the spheres exposed to the primary rabbit sera were subsequently treated with gold-labeled goat anti-rabbit antibodies for immunolabeling.

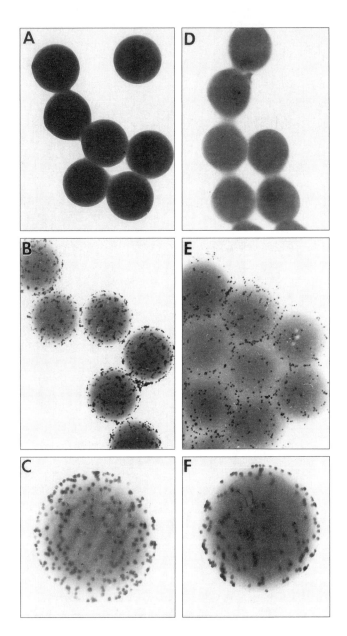

choosing specific antibodies, investigators can detect which structures within microorganisms are producing certain chemicals. This is because specific antibodies can bind to specific cell structures or to specific cell products, such as certain enzymes. The technique can also distinguish dangerous types of a particular microorganism from those types that are less likely to cause disease. For example, some *Candida albicans* types are more often associated with disease than others, and immuno-electron microscopy can differentiate between these two groups of yeast on the basis of the chemicals they produce.

The *scanning-tunneling microscope* also uses electrons rather than light, but they are used somewhat differently from those in TEM and SEM. An extremely sharp needle rides above the surface being scanned, much like a phonograph needle on a record. Electrons move between the surface and the needle, and researchers obtain an image by measuring the current necessary to keep the needle a constant height above the specimen. Rather than give images of whole microorganisms or other materials, this technology locates individual atoms on surfaces. Related to this microscope is the *atomic-force microscope*, which applies a force between the needle and the surface.

Some of the latest microscopy techniques use neither electrons nor light waves. In 1988 scientists published the first image from a *transmission positron microscope*. Still experimental, this microscope uses a beam of positrons (atomic particles emitted by some radioactive material) rather than electrons to create an image. Also in 1988, researchers invented a microscope that shows the viewer moving objects while blocking the images of stationary objects—a technique useful for finding motile microorganisms such as protozoa among nonmotile microorganisms and debris. The microscope uses laser light to produce holograms of the moving objects, with each successive hologram creating a "trail" as it is recorded.

Just as knowledge from microbiology has been applied to medicine, techniques now common in medicine are being adapted to microbiology. Now microbiologists perform "microsurgery" on cells, by using microscopes equipped with microinstruments to manipulate single cells [FIGURE 3.13].

Imaging techniques used in hospitals and medical clinics to take pictures of internal organs are being turned into microscopy tools. *X-ray microtomography* uses x-rays to produce three-dimensional images of objects that are only micrometers in size. However, the necessary concentration of x-rays kills living organisms, and so the technique is somewhat limited. Another technique that may be more promising is based on principles of magnetic resonance imaging, in which magnetic fields

FIGURE 3.13
A micromanipulator apparatus which enables the microbiologist to perform "microsurgery" on cells or to select (isolate) individual cells. The attachments to the stage of the microscope provide probes of microscopic dimensions that can be manipulated to contact individual cells.

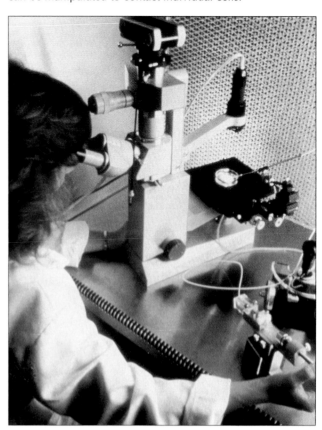

force electrons in living tissue to shift position. When they return to their original location, computers help create images based on the patterns of energy they release.

ASK YOURSELF

1 What are the different types of microscopic examinations that can be performed with the light microscope? What is the special advantage of each method?

2 What is the essential difference between the images produced when a specimen of microorganisms is observed by transmission electron microscopy (TEM) as compared with scanning electron microscopy (SEM)?

3 What are some of the newer types of microscopy that have recently been introduced?

TABLE 3.2
Summary of Preparations for Examination by Light Microscopy

Technique	Preparation	Application*
Wet mount and hanging drop	Drop of fluid containing the organisms on glass slide or cover slip	Study morphology, internal cell structures, motility, or cell changes
Staining procedure	Suspension of cells fixed to slide as a film, usually by heat	Various staining procedures
Simple stain	Film stained with a single dye solution	Shows size, shape, and arrangement of cells
Differential stains:	Two or more reagents used in staining process	Difference observable between cells or parts of cells
Gram	Primary stain (crystal violet) applied to film and then treated with reagents and counterstained with safranin	Characterizes bacteria in one of two groups: 1. Gram-positive—deep violet 2. Gram-negative—red
Acid-fast	Film stained with carbolfuchsin, decolorized, and counterstained with methylene blue	Separate acid-fast bacteria, those not decolorized when acid solution is applied (e.g., mycobacteria), from non-acid-fast bacteria, which are decolorized by acid
Giemsa	Stain applied to blood smear or film of other specimens	Observation of protozoa in blood smear; rickettsia (small parasitic bacteria) in certain cells of the host; nuclear material in bacteria
Endospore	Primary stain (malachite green) applied with heat to penetrate spores; vegetative cells counterstained with safranin	Endospores can be seen in *Bacillus* and *Clostridium* species
Capsule	Smear stained following treatment with copper sulfate	Capsule can be observed as a clear zone surrounding cells of capsulated microorganisms
Flagella	Mordant acts to thicken flagella before staining	Observe flagella on bacteria
Negative staining	Specimen mixed with India ink and spread into thin film	Study morphology; staining procedure and reagents are very mild in their effect on the microorganism; called a negative stain because the microorganism is unstained and is made visible because the background is dark

*The bacterial structures referred to are described in Chapter 4.

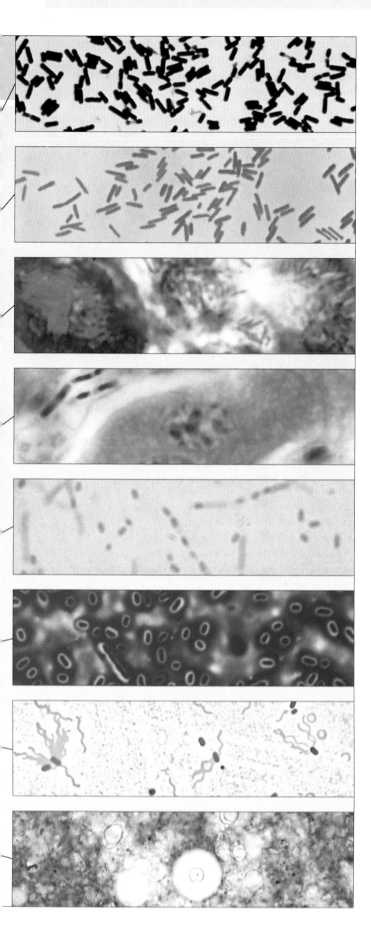

PREPARING MICROORGANISMS FOR LIGHT MICROSCOPY

There are two general methods used to prepare microbiological specimens for observation by light microscopy. One suspends living microorganisms in a drop or film of liquid. The other dries and then stains a thin layer of the specimen, so microorganisms are attached to a surface and colored for easy viewing. The different techniques of both kinds are summarized in TABLE 3.2.

Wet-Mount and Hanging-Drop Techniques

Microbiologists use *hanging-drop* and *wet-mount preparations* to examine living organisms with bright-field, dark-field, or phase-contrast microscopy. Wet-mount preparations are made by placing a drop of the fluid containing the organisms on a glass slide and covering the drop with a very thin piece of glass called a *cover slip*. To reduce the rate of evaporation and to exclude air currents, the cover slip can be sealed around the edges with petroleum jelly or a similar material. Special slides with a concave area in the center are available for making hanging-drop preparations [FIGURE 3.14]. Wet-mount preparations are especially useful when the structure of a microorganism may be distorted by heat or chemicals, or when the microorganism is difficult to stain. They are also the methods of choice when such processes as motility or particulate food ingestion are being observed.

Staining Techniques

The colored organic compounds, or dyes, used to stain microorganisms could fill an artist's palette and more. There are dyes that attach only to specific chemicals in cells, dyes that fluoresce, dyes that turn color in the presence of chemical reactions, and dyes that work together to produce an image. Microbiologists use staining procedures *to show the overall structure of microorganisms, to identify their internal structures*, and *to help identify and separate similar organisms*.

Major steps in preparing a stained microbial specimen for microscopic examination are:

1 Placing a *smear*, or thin film of specimen, on a glass slide
2 Fixing the dried smear onto the slide, usually with heat, to make the microorganisms stick to the glass
3 Staining with one or more dyes

Simple Staining. The coloration of bacteria or other microorganisms with a single solution of stain is called *simple staining*. The fixed smear is flooded with the dye

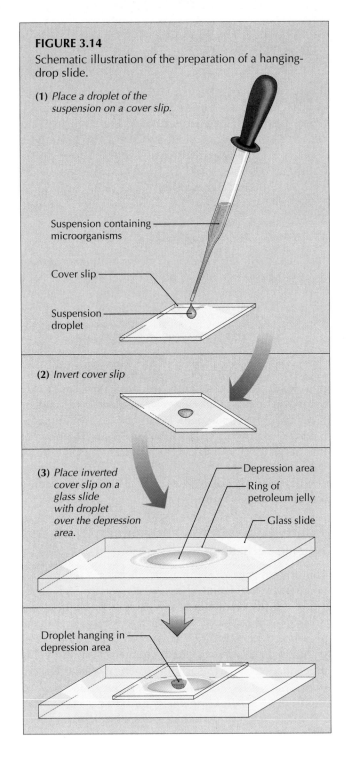

FIGURE 3.14
Schematic illustration of the preparation of a hanging-drop slide.

(1) *Place a droplet of the suspension on a cover slip.*

Suspension containing microorganisms

Cover slip

Suspension droplet

(2) *Invert cover slip*

(3) *Place inverted cover slip on a glass slide with droplet over the depression area.*

Depression area

Ring of petroleum jelly

Glass slide

Droplet hanging in depression area

Differential Staining. Differences between microbial cells or parts of cells can be seen with *differential staining* techniques. These involve more than one dye solution; the dyes may be added one after another. An example of a differential stain is the acid-fast stain for the bacterium that causes tuberculosis. Fatty material in the cell walls makes this microorganism difficult to detect with simple staining, and so special measures must be taken to force dye inside the bacterial cells. Such staining also distinguishes this pathogenic bacterium by color (red, by the first stain) from the myriads of other bacteria (blue, by the second stain) found in samples such as saliva and sputum.

Gram Staining. One of the most important and widely used differential staining techniques for bacteria is *Gram staining.* The technique was first described in 1884 by Christian Gram of Denmark. He developed this procedure while searching for a way to show the pneumococcus bacterium in the lung tissue of patients who had died of pneumonia.

In this process the bacterial smear is flooded with the following, in the order listed: the purple dye *crystal violet, iodine solution* (a mordant, which means that it fixes the dye inside the cell), *alcohol* (a decolorizer that removes dye from certain bacteria), and the red dye *safranin.*

Bacteria stained by the Gram method fall into two groups: the *Gram-positive* bacteria, which retain the crystal violet dye and appear deep violet in color; and *Gram-negative* bacteria, which lose the crystal violet when washed with alcohol. Gram-negative bacteria are stained with the red dye safranin and appear red. The steps in the procedure, as well as the appearance of cells at each stage, are summarized in FIGURE 3.15.

Why do some bacteria stain purple and others red? The answer appears to be related to the differences in thickness and structure of their cell walls. The reasons for this staining reaction will be discussed in later chapters, after you have had an opportunity to learn more about the structure and chemical makeup of bacterial cells. But regardless of the mechanism involved, the Gram stain is particularly valuable in the hospital diagnostic laboratory.

For example, Gram-negative spherical bacteria found in a spinal fluid specimen strongly suggest meningitis caused by the meningococcus bacterium. Gram-positive cells of the same shape, arranged in short chains in a blood smear, would indicate an infection by streptococci. Such information, useful in selecting an antibiotic (or other treatment) for the patient, is available before results of culture tests have identified the microorganism.

solution for a specified period of time, and then rinsed with water and dried. Cells usually stain uniformly with this procedure. Some structures inside cells can also be stained with a single stain—for example, methylene blue is used to detect metachromatic granules in *Corynebacterium diphtheriae*, and iodine is used to stain glycogen granules.

FIGURE 3.15

The color appearance of bacterial cells at each step of the Gram stain procedure.

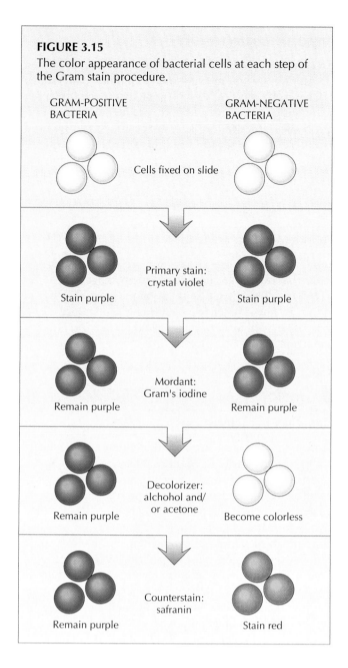

GRAM-POSITIVE BACTERIA		GRAM-NEGATIVE BACTERIA
	Cells fixed on slide	
Stain purple	Primary stain: crystal violet	Stain purple
Remain purple	Mordant: Gram's iodine	Remain purple
Remain purple	Decolorizer: alchohol and/ or acetone	Become colorless
Remain purple	Counterstain: safranin	Stain red

Other procedures are available to stain specific cell structures, such as flagella and capsules [TABLE 3.2].

ASK YOURSELF

1 What is the purpose of staining microorganisms prior to microscopic examination?

2 Name several differential staining techniques.

3 What is the function of alcohol as a reagent in the Gram stain technique?

INFORMATION USED TO CHARACTERIZE MICROORGANISMS

Laboratory techniques for characterizing microorganisms range from relatively simple microscopy to the analysis of genetic material found in a cell. The major categories of information available in the laboratory are briefly described in this section; each will be discussed in more detail in subsequent chapters. An example of the kind of data used to characterize a bacterial species is shown in TABLE 3.3. Different collections of data are used to characterize different species.

Morphological Characteristics

The size, shape, and arrangement of cells can be determined with various microscopes and with different staining methods. Structures of both whole cells and internal components can be studied.

Nutritional and Cultural Characteristics

Knowledge about the nutritional requirements of microorganisms and the physical conditions needed for their growth helps identify them and place them into taxonomic groups. Some are able to thrive on very simple chemical compounds, while others require an elaborate assortment of nutrients. Physical conditions such as temperature, light, and atmosphere are also important to support the life of microorganisms. For example, microorganisms from the human body are grown at 35°C, and those from the open ocean at temperatures between 4 and 20°C.

Metabolic Characteristics

Microorganisms perform a great variety of chemical changes. Some result in the conversion of nutrients to cellular substances, where relatively simple chemical compounds become large, complex molecules. Other changes break down large molecules into smaller molecules. The total of these biochemical changes is known as the **metabolism** of the microorganism. There are numerous laboratory tests that can determine an organism's metabolic activities. A record of changes performed by a microbial species is useful and many times essential for its identification, as shown in TABLE 3.3.

TABLE 3.3
General Characteristics of Two Species of Bacteria—
Pseudomonas diminuta and *Pseudomonas vesicularis*

Characteristics	P. diminuta	P. vesicularis
Cell diameter, μm	0.5	0.5
Cell length, μm	1.0–4.0	1.0–4.0
Number of flagella	1	1
Flagellar wavelength, μm	0.6–1.0	0.6–1.0
Soluble pigment production	–	–
Yellow or orange cellular pigments	–	+
Organic growth factor requirements	+[a]	+[b]
Autotrophic growth with H_2	–	–
Oxidase reaction	+	W[c]
Nitrate used as a nitrogen source	–	–
Poly-β-hydroxybutyrate accumulation	+	+
Accumulation of glucose polysaccharide	–	+
Gelatin liquefaction	–	–
Lecithinase (egg yolk)	–	–
Lipase (Tween 80 hydrolysis)	–	–
Extracellular poly-β-hydroxybutyrate hydrolysis	–	–
Starch hydrolysis	–	–
Denitrification	–	–
Reduction of NO_3^- to NO_2^-	±	–
Growth at 4°C	–	–
Growth at 41°C	±	–
mol% G + C of DNA	66.3–67.3	65.8

[a]Pantothenate, biotin, and cyanocobalamin required.
[b]Pantothenate, biotin, cyanocobalamin, and cystine or methionine required.
[c]W, weak reaction.
SOURCE: N. R. Krieg and J. G. Holt, eds., *Bergey's Manual of Systematic Bacteriology*, vol. 1, Williams & Wilkins, Baltimore, 1984.

Antigenic Characteristics

An *antigen* is a substance that stimulates the production of antibodies when injected into an animal. A microbial cell has many physical structures on its surface which can act as antigens to cause antibody production in this way. Antibodies produced in laboratory animals can be used to detect the presence of unique antigens in bacterial cultures, and are used to characterize microorganisms.

Pathogenic Characteristics

Some microbes cause disease and are called *pathogens;* those that do not are designated nonpathogens. The infected organism (plant, animal, or microbe) is referred to as the *host.* When characterizing a microorganism, it is important to determine whether it is or is not a pathogen.

Genetic Characteristics

More microbiologists are now relying on genetic analyses to either classify or identify microorganisms or understand how they work. Much of the current work to develop vaccines against AIDS depends on this type of information. New analytical methods in molecular biology have made genetic studies of bacteria simpler and more practical. The *DNA probe* is an example of a rapid, widely used procedure using genetics. A strand of DNA from a known species is mixed with a strand from an unidentified species. If the microorganisms are the same species, the two DNA strands will combine, or join together. This combination appears as a double strand of DNA with a marker attached [FIGURE 3.16]. This technology is being "packaged" into test kits and sold for research and diagnostic purposes. An example now on the market is a kit to detect the salmonella bacteria that cause food poisoning.

ASK YOURSELF

1 What are the major categories of characteristics used to describe and identify microorganisms?

2 What is a DNA probe, and how is it used?

FIGURE 3.16
Schematic illustration of the principle of the DNA probe technique for the identification of bacteria.

A piece (strand) of DNA is isolated from a "known" species of bacteria. If the nucleotide sequence of this strand of DNA is unique to the species, the strand can be used as a DNA probe.

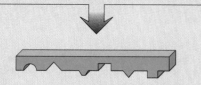

The DNA strand is labeled with a radioactive element or other substance that can be readily detected.

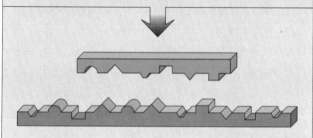

The probe is mixed with a DNA strand that has been isolated from an unknown bacterium under specified conditions.

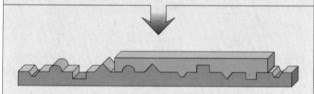

If the DNA probe and strand combine to form a duplex (double-stranded DNA), the unknown bacterium is of the same species as that from which the probe was isolated.

AUTOMATED TECHNOLOGY

Automated testing in the laboratory has become necessary as microbiologists try to respond to an increased demand for more answers more quickly. There are growing numbers of specimens to study, more pressure to obtain results quickly, and a growing amount of available data that must be analyzed to identify a microorganism or its actions. The size of a microorganism, for example, may be determined not only by looking at it through a microscope, but by spinning it in a centrifuge or passing it through a laser beam used to measure width.

Cell counts can be determined by shining light beams through liquid cultures, to measure turbidity and therefore cell numbers. By adding certain chemicals to microbial cultures and then using computer programs to collect data on the resulting metabolic reactions, scientists can quickly separate and identify species. One such technique developed for the rapid identification of microorganisms is shown in FIGURE 3.17. In this procedure a microorganism is characterized on the basis of its ability to utilize 96 different carbon compounds. In each instance when a carbon compound is used, the color of the fluid in the well turns purple. After incubation, the microplate is automatically "read" and the pattern of results is compared with that of known species for identification. Another type of automated laboratory system is used to test large numbers of bacteria for their susceptibility to antibiotics. It employs similar procedures to help identify the species being analyzed. This system can automatically and simultaneously inoculate as many as 240 wells in plastic test-kit trays (Chapter 21).

Whether automated or conventional, laboratory techniques discussed in this chapter are essential aspects of microbiology. Identification of different microorganisms is not merely a matter of scientific curiosity. Diagnosis and treatment of disease, the manufacture of wine and milk products, and the treatment of sewage are just some of the everyday examples where some microorganisms are desirable and others are not. Knowing which microorganisms are present is the first step in microbiological analyses.

ASK YOURSELF

1 Why is automated technology an important development for microbiological testing?

2 Describe an automated microbiological technique.

FIGURE 3.17

Automated technology and equipment for the rapid identification of microorganisms. **[A]** Schematic overview of the procedure. **[B]** The appearance of a microplate after inoculation and incubation. **[C]** The equipment.

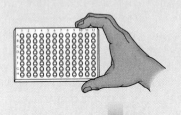

Plastic microplate with 96 wells. Different chemical nutrients (carbon compounds) have been dried into each well.

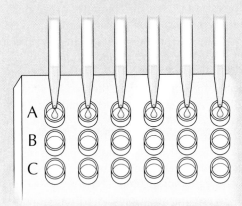

Each well is inoculated with the bacterium to be identified. Then the plate is incubated for 24 h.

[A]

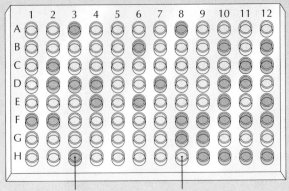

If a nutrient (carbon compound) is used by the bacterium, a chemical indicator turns purple.

If a nutrient is not used, the indicator remains colorless.

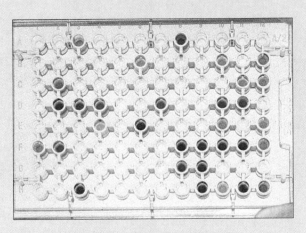

[B]

[C]

SUMMARY

1 In nature, microorganisms exist in mixed cultures. Before you can identify individual species of mixed microbial populations, it is necessary to isolate the different species in pure culture. Once pure cultures are obtained, laboratory techniques can determine the identifying characteristics of microorganisms.

2 Microscopy is one of the major techniques used for characterizing microorganisms. Most microscopes are of two types: light microscopes and electron microscopes. Modifications of light microscopy are available, such as phase-contrast and dark-field microscopy. These and other special microscopy methods provide their own special features for improved examination of microbial cells.

3 Specimens of microorganisms can be seen through a microscope in a living condition by suspending them in a liquid (hanging-drop and wet-mount techniques). They also may be examined by using a stained film preparation.

4 There are two basic types of microbial staining procedures: simple and differential. Simple stains merely "color" the cell or its inclusion granules, while differential stains distinguish among major groups of microorganisms or parts of the microbial cell. One of the most widely used differential stains is the Gram stain. In general, bacteria are either Gram-negative or Gram-positive.

5 The major properties of a microorganism can be categorized under the following characteristics: morphological, nutritional and cultural, metabolic, antigenic, pathogenic, and genetic. Some or all of these characteristics are used to identify species of microorganisms.

6 Electronic instrumentation has been adapted to laboratory procedures, providing results faster and more efficiently. Many of the procedures that once took days to complete can now be accomplished within a very short time.

KEY TERMS

antibody
antigen
bright-field microscopy
colony
culture medium (plural, media)
dark-field microscopy
differential staining
DNA probe
electron microscopes
fluorescence microscopy
Gram-negative
Gram-positive
Gram staining
hanging-drop preparation
host
inoculum
light microscopes
lyophilization
metabolism
micrometer (μm)
microscopy
mixed culture
nanometer (nm)
pathogens
phase-contrast microscopy
pour-plate method
pure culture
resolving power
scanning electron microscopy
   (SEM)
simple staining
smear
spread-plate method
streak-plate method
transmission electron microscopy
   (TEM)
type culture collection
wet-mount preparation

REVIEW GUIDE

PURE CULTURE
TECHNIQUES

1 Microorganisms in natural environments usually occur in _____ culture.

2 Before one can characterize and identify a species of microorganism, it must be isolated as a(n) _____ .

3 A culture of microorganisms in which all the cells have been derived from the same parent cell is called a(n) _____ culture.

4 A specimen of cells that is planted on an agar surface is called a(n)

_____ .

5 A mass of cells growing on a solid surface and becoming visible to the naked eye is called a(n) _____ .

6 Two methods of isolating pure cultures by inoculating the surface of an agar plate are known as the _____ and _____ methods.

7 A collection of cultures maintained as a reference collection is called a(n)

_____ collection.

8 A process for maintaining cultures that involves freezing and drying of the culture specimen is called _____ .

9 A patient's throat is swabbed and the swab is inoculated onto the surface of an agar medium. The inoculated medium is incubated and then observed. Which of the following statements is (are) *not* true?

(a) Colonies will develop on the medium.

(b) The colonies collectively represent a mixed culture.

(c) The colonies most likely represent several species.

(d) Individual colonies represent pure cultures.

(e) The total growth is likely to be a pure culture.

10 Lyophilization is a method for characterizing microorganisms: true **(T)** or false **(F)**?

MICROSCOPES

11 The limit of useful magnification is determined by a characteristic of the microscope called _____ power.

12 A student-type light microscope used in microbiology has three objectives:

(a) _____ ; **(b)** _____ ; and

(c) _____ .

13 The eyepiece of the microscope provides magnification of _____×.

14 The resolving power of a microscope is determined by two factors:

_____ and _____ .

15 The maximum useful magnification obtained with light microscopy is _____×.

16 The optical microscope objective that gives the greatest magnification is generally of the _____ type.

17 Compared with the wavelength of the electron beams used in electron microscopy, how many times longer is the wavelength of light used in light microscopy?

(a) 10,000   **(b)** 1 million   **(c)** 1000

18 The resolution obtainable with the electron microscope is in the range of:

(a) 0.3 μm   **(b)** 0.03 μm   **(c)** 0.003 μm

MICROSCOPY

19 In which type of microscopy is the specimen (microorganism) likely to show varying degrees of darkness within the cell?

(a) bright-field   **(b)** dark-field   **(c)** electron   **(d)** phase-contrast   **(e)** light-field

20 Which of the following types of microscopy is (are) performed with a light microscope?

(a) bright-field   **(c)** dark-field   **(e)** all of the above
(b) phase-contrast   **(d)** fluorescent

21 Dark-field and phase-contrast microscopy are particularly useful for examining

_____ cells.

22 The examination of a specimen using the electron microscope whereby the electron beam passes through the specimen is called _____ electron microscopy; the technique whereby the electron beam moves back and forth over the surface of the cells is called _____ electron microscopy.

23 Scanning electron microscopy will produce a three-dimensional view of microbial cells: true **(T)** or false **(F)**?

24 Despite the microscopic dimensions of microbial cells, they can be sliced into thin sections for observation by electron microscopy: true **(T)** or false **(F)**?

25 Electron microscopy is used only for examination of viruses: true **(T)** or false **(F)**?

PREPARING
MICROORGANISMS
FOR LIGHT
MICROSCOPY

26 The hanging-drop technique allows microorganisms to be observed in a(n)

_____ condition.

27 A thin film of a specimen on a microscope slide is called a(n)

_____ .

28 The coloration of bacteria by applying a single dye to the preparation on a slide is called a(n) _____ stain.

29 The Gram stain is classified as a(n) _____ stain.

30 Bacteria, after being stained by the Gram stain, will appear either

_____ or _____ in color.

31 The color of Gram-negative bacteria, after being stained by Gram's method, will be seen as _____ .

32 The acid-fast stain, like the Gram stain, is a(n) _____ stain.

33 The decolorization of bacteria in the Gram stain technique is accomplished with

_____ .

34 Examination of stained smears of bacteria is best done with

_____ microscopy.

35 Which of the following is not a differential stain?

(a) Gram stain

(b) acid-fast stain

(c) Giemsa stain

(d) crystal violet stain

(e) capsule stain

INFORMATION USED
TO CHARACTERIZE
MICROORGANISMS

36 Match each description on the right with the major category it best fits on the left.

_____ genetic

_____ morphology

_____ biochemical

_____ nutritional

_____ cultural

(a) Gram reaction

(b) Growth at 37°C

(c) DNA probe

(d) Metabolism

(e) Simple medium

37 There is no significant distinction among microorganisms when they are character-ized according to the temperature required for growth: true **(T)** or false **(F)**?

38 All of the biochemical activities of a microorganism are termed

_____ .

39 In terms of disease-producing capability, microorganisms can be divided into two

groups, _____ and _____ .

40 A major characteristic of microorganisms that is associated with the ability of a microbe (or part of the microbe) to produce substances in an animal called *antibodies*

is its _____ characteristics.

41 Molecular biology techniques are generally associated with the

_____ characteristics of microorganisms.

AUTOMATED
TECHNOLOGY

42 Which of the following statements is (are) *not* true in reference to the advantages of using automated technology?

(a) Results are available more quickly.

(b) Large numbers of specimens can be examined.

(c) Less complex equipment is needed.

(d) Results are analyzed by a computer program.

(e) Multiple specimens can be examined simultaneously.

43 The wells in the plastic trays in an apparatus designed to perform automated char-acterization of microorganisms are preloaded with _____ .

44 The automated reading of results from reactions in the inoculated well of a plastic

tray in automated equipment is done by _____ .

REVIEW QUESTIONS

1 Distinguish between a pure culture and a mixed culture.

2 Describe how pure cultures can be isolated.

3 What is the role of the American Type Culture Collection?

4 What characteristics of a microscope determine its maximum useful magnification?

5 Compare the magnifications obtainable with the light microscope with those obtainable with the electron microscope.

6 What is the function of oil when used with the oil-immersion objective?

7 Assume that a yeast cell is examined by **(a)** bright-field, **(b)** phase-contrast, and **(c)** dark-field microscopy. Describe the likely differences in the appearance of the cell when viewed by these methods.

8 Why are microorganisms stained?

9 Name several different staining techniques, and describe the type of information each provides.

10 Compare the kind of image obtained with scanning electron microscopy with that obtained using transmission electron microscopy.

11 What are the major categories under which the properties of a microorganism can be grouped? Briefly identify each.

DISCUSSION QUESTIONS

1 Assume that you have isolated a new species of bacteria. How would you preserve this specimen for a period of a few months? For a few years?

2 Identify a situation where dark-field microscopy would be most appropriate for examination of the specimen. Why would it be?

3 Which one of the several differential staining techniques provides the most information about a bacterial specimen? Explain.

4 Compare transmission electron microscopy (TEM) with scanning electron microscopy (SEM) in terms of the kind of information that each reveals about the nature of microorganisms.

5 Information from several different categories is used to characterize and identify microorganisms. Which category of information is most general? Most specific? Explain.

6 Outline a scheme which illustrates the essential features of an automated laboratory technique.

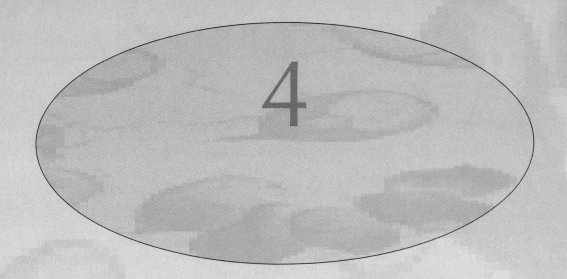

4

Procaryotic and Eucaryotic Cell Structures

OBJECTIVES

After reading this chapter you should be able to

1 Recognize the size, shape, and arrangement of bacterial cells, and compare them with the gross morphology of eucaryotic microorganisms.

2 Describe the structure and function of the bacterial flagellum, and compare it with the eucaryotic flagellum and cilium.

3 Explain what is meant by the glycocalyx and what it does for the bacterial cell.

4 List the differences between the Gram-negative and the Gram-positive eubacterial cell wall.

5 Compare the structure and functions of the eucaryotic and procaryotic cell wall and cytoplasmic membrane.

6 Describe some of the different inclusions that may occur in the bacterial cytoplasm.

7 Discuss the structure and function of the various cellular organelles found inside eucaryotic microorganisms.

8 List the unique properties of bacterial endospores and explain how they differ from other dormant forms of microorganisms.

OVERVIEW

Looking at microorganisms through a microscope reveals their gross morphology—their size, their shape, and their cellular arrangement. If you move closer to the surface and even inside the cell, there are more detailed structures to explore. Knowing what these different structures do for the microbial cell will enhance understanding of how the cell functions. This chapter discusses the structures of procaryotic and eucaryotic microorganisms.

Scientists have taken microorganisms apart in order to examine their structures and analyze their chemical composition. Techniques, such as treating cells with high-frequency sound waves, have been developed to disintegrate cell walls and isolate the various cell components. Such studies are not just of interest to researchers curious about the interior of cells. The presence or absence of certain structures is used to classify microbes; knowing how they function is used to design antimicrobial drugs that attack specific cell components.

As you will see, the morphology of cells affects how they respond to their environment. Structures found on the outside of cells make some microorganisms more pathogenic. Examples are those structures that allow the bacterium that causes syphilis to burrow into tissues and those that protect invading bacteria from the immune system. Other cell components cause fever and shock.

GROSS MORPHOLOGICAL CHARACTERISTICS OF PROCARYOTIC MICROORGANISMS

As you have learned, bacteria are procaryotic microorganisms. Mostly single-celled, they have retained a simplicity of form in spite of the 3.5 to 4 billion years during which they have evolved. This simplicity is apparent if we look at the size, shape, and arrangement of bacterial cells with an ordinary light microscope. However, this seeming simplicity is deceptive, much as the smooth lines of a spacecraft hide the highly complex instrumentation and machinery inside. In a sense, a bacterial cell is like a microscopic spacecraft existing in a watery universe. If we use modern electron microscopy to examine closely the external and internal parts of a bacterial cell, we find an amazing complexity and detail of structure that could scarcely have been imagined by early microbiologists.

Morphology of Bacteria

Size. Invisible to the human eye, bacteria are usually measured in micrometers (μm), which are equivalent to 1/1000 mm (10^{-3} mm, or 1/25,400 in). Bacterial cells vary in size depending on the species, but most are approximately 0.5 to 1 μm in diameter or width [FIGURE 4.1]. For example, staphylococci and streptococci are spherical bacteria with diameters ranging from 0.75 to 1.25 μm. The cylindrical typhoid and dysentery bacteria are 0.5 to 1 μm in width and 2 to 3 μm in length. Cells of some bacterial species are 0.5 to 2 μm in diameter but more than 100 μm in length. Assuming a diameter or length of 1 μm, 10,000 bacteria lying end to end or side by side would span only 1 centimeter (cm), or about ⅜ in.

It is difficult to appreciate the small size of a bacterium. Calculations show that approximately 1 trillion (1,000,000,000,000, or 10^{12}) bacterial cells weigh a mere 1 gram, or about one-fifth the weight of a nickel. Bacteria are usually viewed by microscopy at a magnification of 1000 times. A common housefly magnified to the same extent would appear to be more than 30 ft long!

If one compares bacterial surface area and cell volume, a distinctive feature of bacterial cells becomes evident. The ratio of surface area to volume for bacteria is very high compared with that of larger organisms of similar shape. In practical terms this means that there is a large surface through which nutrients can enter relative to a small volume of cell substance to be nourished. This characteristic accounts in part for the high rate of metabolism and growth of bacteria. The rapid growth of bacte-

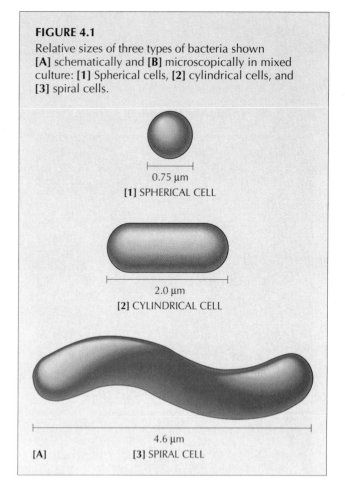

FIGURE 4.1

Relative sizes of three types of bacteria shown [A] schematically and [B] microscopically in mixed culture: [1] Spherical cells, [2] cylindrical cells, and [3] spiral cells.

0.75 µm
[1] SPHERICAL CELL

2.0 µm
[2] CYLINDRICAL CELL

4.6 µm
[A] [3] SPIRAL CELL

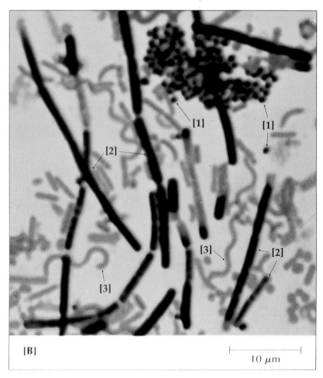

[B] 10 µm

FIGURE 4.2
Bacteria are generally either **[A]** spherical (coccus), **[B]** cylindrical (bacillus), or **[C]** helical (spirillum). However, there are many modifications of these three basic forms. Micrographs show: **[A]** *Staphylococcus aureus*; **[B]** *Klebsiella pneumoniae*; and **[C]** *Aquaspirillum itersonii* (negative stain).

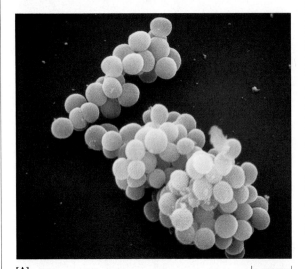

[A]   5 μm

[B]   0.1 μm

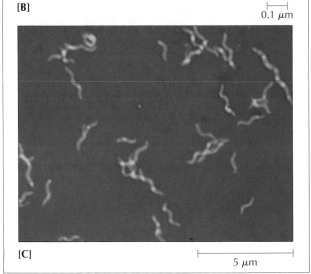

[C]   5 μm

ria is one of the reasons these microorganisms are so frequently used in molecular biology research. The rapid replication of bacterial cells is used in experiments to provide more information more quickly. For example, the bacterium *Escherichia coli* undergoes cell division in about 20 minutes, while a mammalian cell in laboratory culture takes about 13 to 24 hours to divide into two cells.

Shape. Not all bacteria look alike. Individual bacterial cells have one of three basic shapes: they are either *spherical, cylindrical,* or *spiral* [FIGURE 4.2]. Spherical cells are called **cocci** (singular, **coccus**). They are usually round, but they can be ovoid or flattened on one side when they are adhering to another cell. Cylindrical, or rodlike, bacterial cells are called **bacilli** (singular, **bacillus**). There are considerable differences in the length and width of the various species of bacilli. The ends of some are square, others rounded, and still others tapered or pointed. Spiral, or helical, bacteria look like corkscrews, and are called **spirilla** (singular, **spirillum**).

There are many modifications of these three basic forms, as you will see throughout this book. For instance, *Pasteuria* has pear-shaped cells, whereas *Caryophanon* has disk-shaped cells arranged like stacks of coins. Although most bacterial species have cells that are fairly constant in shape, some species can have a variety of cell shapes and are thus termed *pleomorphic*. Pleomorphism in a bacterial species can mislead one into thinking a microbial culture is contaminated with other types of bacteria. *Arthrobacter* is an example of a pleomorphic bacterium, because it changes its shape as the culture ages [FIGURE 4.3].

Arrangement. If you look through a microscope at microbial cells, you will see that they are often attached to each other. While spiral-shaped bacteria usually do occur as single cells, other species of bacteria may grow in characteristic arrangements or patterns. For instance, cocci can grow in several arrangements, depending on the plane of cellular division and whether the daughter cells stay together following cell division [FIGURE 4.4].

Each of these arrangements is typical of a particular species and can be used in identification. When a coccus divides in one plane it forms a *diplococcus*, or two cells joined together. This typifies some species of *Neisseria*, including the one that causes gonorrhea. When a coccus divides in one plane and remains attached after several divisions to form a chain, it has the *streptococcal* arrangement. *Streptococcus* species, like those that cause throat and wound infections, show this pattern during their growth.

If cells divide into more than one plane, or dimension, during growth, cell arrangements become more

FIGURE 4.3

Pleomorphism in *Arthrobacter globiformis*. Note the change in morphology of the culture
(bacillus to coccus) as it ages during its incubation time (shown in hours).

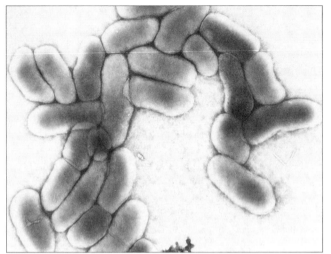

24 h

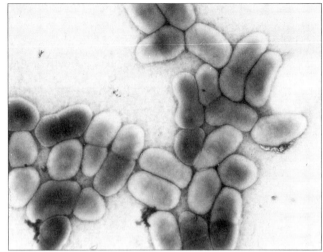

36 h

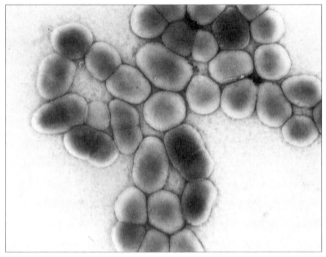

48 h

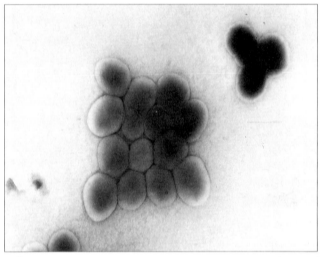

72 h

1.0 μm

complicated. When a coccus such as *Pediococcus* divides at a right angle to the first plane of division, it forms *tetrads*, or groups of four in the shape of a square. A further division in the third plane can result in cubical packets of eight cells known as *sarcinae*. Obviously, species of *Sarcina* have this arrangement. If division in three planes is in an irregular pattern, however, it forms a grapelike cluster. Species of *Staphylococcus* have this cell pattern.

It should be noted that rarely are all the cells of a given species arranged in exactly the same pattern. It is the predominant arrangement that is important when studying bacteria. Also, some words such as *spirillum* and *bacillus* may be used both as genus names and as morphologic terms to denote shape or arrangement.

Unlike the cocci, bacilli do not generally arrange themselves in a variety of characteristic patterns. But there are exceptions [FIGURE 4.5]; for example, the diphtheria bacillus tends to produce groups of cells lined side by side like matchsticks in a *palisade* arrangement. Cells of the genus *Caulobacter* (aquatic bacilli) grow in *rosette* patterns on rocks and similar surfaces. Within the genus *Bacillus*, some species form chains and are called *streptobacilli*. *Beggiatoa* and *Saprospira* species form *trichomes*, which are similar to chains but have a much larger area of contact between the adjacent cells [FIGURE 4.6].

Together, the size, shape, and arrangement of bacteria constitute their gross morphology, their "outside" appearance. But a closer look at the individual cell structures gives a better idea of how bacteria function in their environment.

FIGURE 4.4

Characteristic arrangements of cocci, with schematic illustrations of patterns of multiplication. **[A]** Diplococci: cells divide in one plane and remain attached predominantly in pairs (scanning electron micrograph). **[B]** Streptococci: cells divide in one plane and remain attached to form chains (scanning electron micrograph). **[C]** Tetracocci: cells divide in two planes and characteristically form groups of four cells. Species shown is *Gaffkya tetragena*. **[D]** Staphylococci: cells divide in three planes, in an irregular pattern, producing "bunches" of cocci. Species shown is *Staphylococcus aureus*. **[E]** Sarcinae: cells divide in three planes, in a regular pattern, producing a cuboidal arrangement of cells.

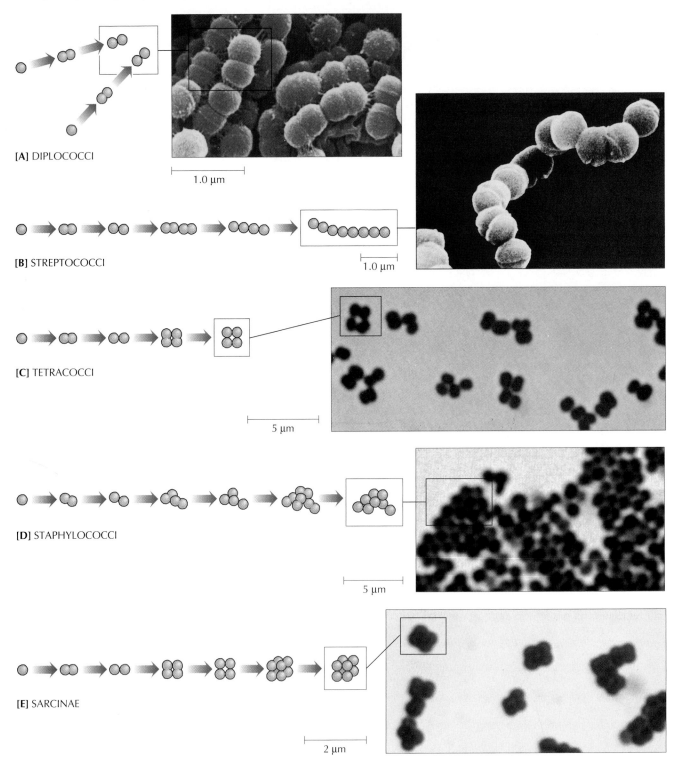

[A] DIPLOCOCCI

1.0 μm

[B] STREPTOCOCCI

1.0 μm

[C] TETRACOCCI

5 μm

[D] STAPHYLOCOCCI

5 μm

[E] SARCINAE

2 μm

FIGURE 4.5
Patterns of arrangements of bacilli. **[A]** Palisade arrangement of *Corynebacterium diphtheriae*. **[B]** Rosette arrangement of *Caulobacter* with enlargement of cell attachment drawn. **[C]** Streptobacilli arrangement of *Streptobacillus*.

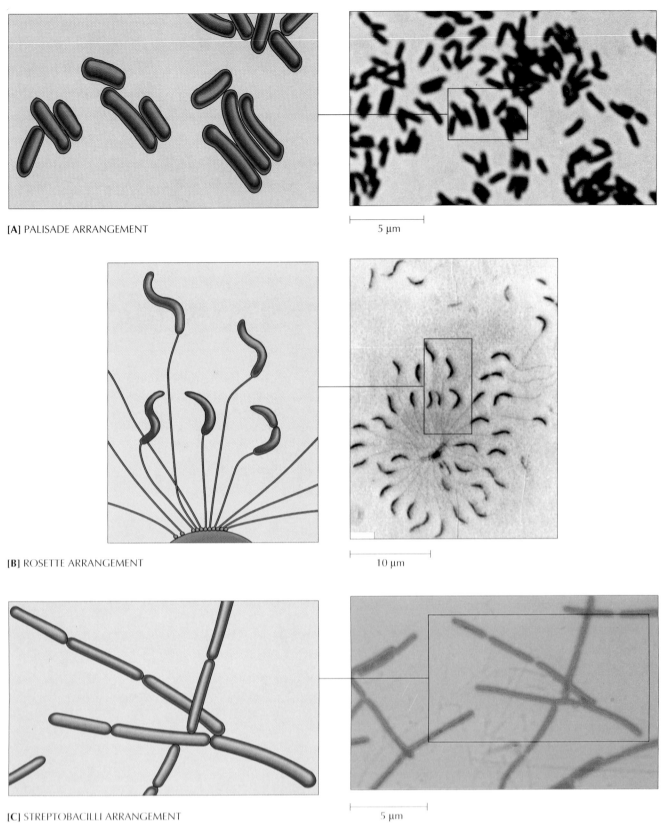

[A] PALISADE ARRANGEMENT

5 μm

[B] ROSETTE ARRANGEMENT

10 μm

[C] STREPTOBACILLI ARRANGEMENT

5 μm

FIGURE 4.6
Photomicrograph of the trichomes of *Saprospira grandis*, composed of individual bacillus cells that are 1 to 5 μm long and closely attached to one another.

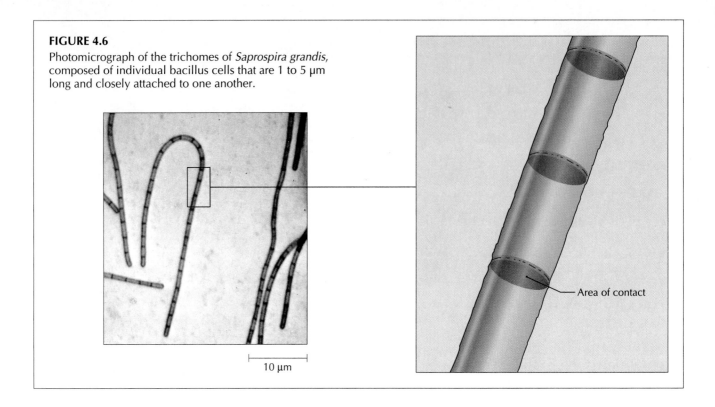

10 μm

Area of contact

ULTRASTRUCTURE OF PROCARYOTIC MICROORGANISMS

Microscopy techniques reveal that a bacterial cell is really a diversity of structures functioning together. Some of these structures are found attached to the outside of the cell wall, while others are inside. Some structures are common to all cells, such as the cell wall and the cytoplasmic membrane. But other cell components are present only in certain species or only under certain environmental conditions. By combining the structures found most often in and on bacteria, it is possible to draw the structure of a "typical" bacterial cell [FIGURE 4.7].

Flagella and Pili

Some structures of bacterial cells are found outside the cell wall. Some are used for swimming and allow bacteria to move toward a more favorable environment. Others allow bacteria to attach to the surfaces of various objects. Biochemical reactions that help move or build these structures have been studied extensively by microbiologists.

Flagella. Bacterial *flagella* (singular, *flagellum*) are thin, hairlike filaments with a helical shape that extend from the cytoplasmic membrane and through the cell wall [FIGURE 4.7]. Flagella propel bacteria through liquid, sometimes as fast as 100 μm per second—equivalent to about 3000 body lengths per minute! The cheetah, one of the fastest animals, has a top speed of only 1500 body lengths per minute.

A flagellum has three parts: the *basal body;* a short,

FIGURE 4.7

Diagrammatic representation of the general structure of a typical procaryotic (bacterial) cell (see FIGURE 4.8C for more detail of flagellum attachment).

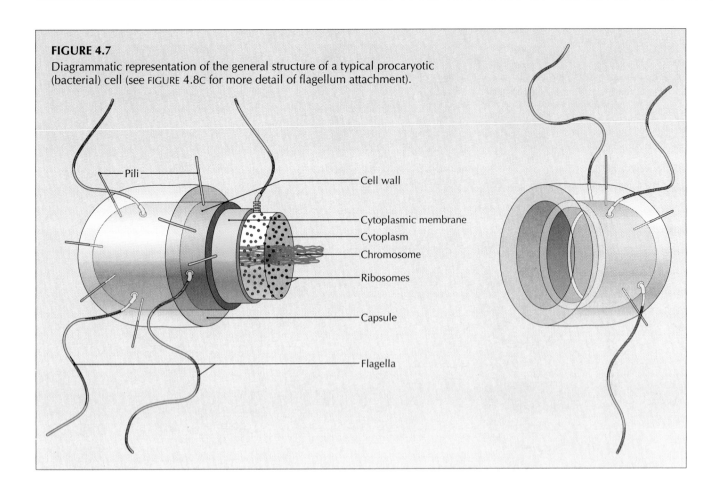

Pili

Cell wall

Cytoplasmic membrane

Cytoplasm

Chromosome

Ribosomes

Capsule

Flagella

hooklike structure; and a long helical filament [FIGURE 4.8]. The basal body is a fine piece of engineering. Embedded in the cell, it consists of a small, central rod surrounded by a series of rings. Gram-negative bacteria have two pairs of rings, with the outer rings anchored to the cell wall and the inner rings attached to the cytoplasmic membrane. In Gram-positive bacteria, only one pair of rings is present—one ring lies in the cytoplasmic membrane and the other in the cell wall. These rings are ultimately responsible for the movement of bacteria.

Flagella function by rotating in a corkscrewlike fashion, which moves the bacterium through liquid. Because water is a very viscous substance to a bacterium, much like what thick molasses seems to us, microscopic fins or flippers would be useless in such a liquid. However, by rotating the flagellum, a bacterium can move through water much the way a corkscrew can penetrate a piece of cork [DISCOVER 4.1]. The rings of the basal body, through chemical reactions, rotate the flagellum. The hook arising from the basal body positions the filament in such a way that the helical filament spins evenly about its long axis instead of rotating off center, as it would if it came straight out of the cell wall. The filament is composed of molecules of a protein called *flagellin*. These molecules are made within the cell and then passed

along the hollow core of the flagellum to be added to the distal end of the filament. Thus a flagellum grows at its tip rather than at its base.

Flagella are usually several times longer than the cell, reaching 15 to 20 μm in length. But the diameter of a flagellum is only a fraction of the cell's diameter—12 to 20 nanometers (1 nm = 1/1000 μm). Flagella are too thin to be seen directly with the ordinary light microscope, since the resolution of such a microscope is about 0.2 μm, or 200 nm. However, staining procedures that layer a dye precipitate on the surface of flagella make them appear thicker and thus visible by light microscopy.

Not all bacteria have flagella. Cocci rarely have these organelles, for example. But for bacteria that do, including many species of bacilli and spirilla, the pattern of flagellar attachment and the number of flagella are used to classify them into taxonomic groups.

Some bacteria have *polar* flagellation [FIGURE 4.9]. The Gram-negative genus *Pseudomonas* has species characterized by an arrangement called *monotrichous* (Greek *monos*, "single"; *trichos*, "hair") flagellation. Some bacteria, like spirilla, exhibit *amphitrichous* flagellation (at both ends). A cluster of flagella at one pole of the cell, as seen in some pseudomonads, is called

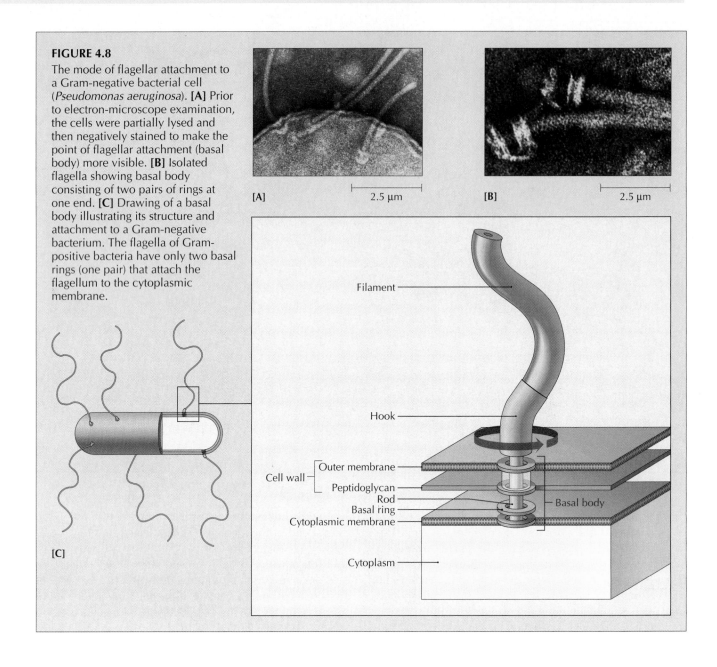

FIGURE 4.8
The mode of flagellar attachment to a Gram-negative bacterial cell (*Pseudomonas aeruginosa*). **[A]** Prior to electron-microscope examination, the cells were partially lysed and then negatively stained to make the point of flagellar attachment (basal body) more visible. **[B]** Isolated flagella showing basal body consisting of two pairs of rings at one end. **[C]** Drawing of a basal body illustrating its structure and attachment to a Gram-negative bacterium. The flagella of Gram-positive bacteria have only two basal rings (one pair) that attach the flagellum to the cytoplasmic membrane.

[A] 2.5 μm

[B] 2.5 μm

Filament

Hook

Cell wall ⎰ Outer membrane
        ⎱ Peptidoglycan
Rod
Basal ring
Cytoplasmic membrane

Basal body

Cytoplasm

[C]

lophotrichous flagellation. Unlike those bacteria with polar flagellation, the genus *Escherichia* has *peritrichous* flagellation (over entire surface) [FIGURE 4.9D].

A group of helical bacteria called *spirochetes* have special flagella called **periplasmic flagella** (also known as *axial filaments*) that arise at the cell poles and wind around the cell body (protoplasmic cylinder) beneath the outer membrane of the cell wall [FIGURE 4.10]. These specialized flagella are responsible for the corkscrewlike motility of the spirochetes [DISCOVER 4.2].

Motile bacteria swim in one direction or another for several reasons. Their movement may be completely random, but often they are moving toward or away from

something in their environment. Swimming bacteria may be seeking light or escaping heat. They also exhibit **chemotaxis,** which is movement in response to chemicals in the environment. For example, bacteria ordinarily swim toward increasing levels of attractants such as nutrients and away from increasing levels of inhibitory substances such as excess salt. Chemotaxis therefore enables a cell to find life-enhancing environments and avoid life-threatening conditions. How bacteria move in response to such stimuli depends on their flagellar arrangement.

Bacteria with polar flagellation swim in a back-and-forth fashion. They reverse their direction by reversing the direction of flagellar rotation. Bacteria with perit-

4.1 HOW DO YOU KNOW BACTERIAL FLAGELLA SPIN IF YOU CAN'T SEE THEM?

Until 1974 it was a matter of great debate which of two theories was correct regarding bacterial flagella. According to the "rotation" theory, flagella were corkscrew-shaped filaments that could rotate on a bearing. However, in the "bending" theory, flagella could not rotate. Instead, corkscrewlike bends were continuously formed along the filament from base to tip. Which theory was correct could not be answered by merely observing the flagella of living bacteria, because the flagella are too thin to be seen under a light microscope. The electron microscope was not helpful because it could be used only for specimens that were dried and in a vacuum. However, in 1974 Michael Silverman and Melvin Simon of the University of California at San Diego found the answer. They used a simple, elegant experiment called the "tethered-cell" system, which has since been repeated in various forms by many other researchers.

It helps to understand the principle of the tethered-cell system by first considering an electric motor. If you set the motor on a table, the shaft spins while the motor body remains stationary. However, if you hold the motor up by the shaft, then the motor body will spin while the shaft is held stationary. If the flagellar rotation theory is correct, a bacterial flagellum is like the shaft of the motor and the bacterial cell is like the motor body. If this is true, then if you can keep the flagellum from spinning, the bacterial cell will rotate. On the other hand, if the bending theory is correct, the cell cannot spin but will only jiggle about. The advantage of this experiment is that the bacterial cell can easily be observed under an ordinary light microscope because it is much larger than a flagellum.

In a typical experiment, the bacteria used have one flagellum per cell. A glass slide is coated with antibodies (specific protein molecules) that can bind to flagella. If you add a drop of water containing the bacteria, the antibodies on the glass slide will stick to the tip of each flagellum and immobilize it. If the rotation theory is correct, the cells should not jiggle but should spin like pinwheels. This is in fact exactly what happens. This phenomenon makes bacterial flagella the only cell structures in biology known to rotate on a bearing!

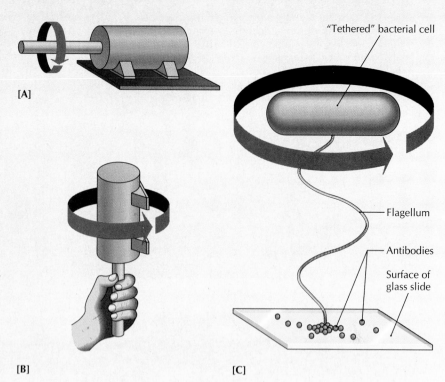

[A]

[B]

[C]

Principle of the tethered-cell experiments that showed that bacterial flagella actually rotate as on a bearing. [A] When an electric motor is set on a table, the shaft rotates while the motor body is stationary. [B] If the motor is held by the shaft, then the motor body will reotate while the shaft is stationary. [C] A bacterial cell with a single flagellum can be tethered to a glass slide that has been coated with antibodies to immobilize the flagellum. Such a cell will spin like a pinwheel, like the motor body in [B].

richous flagella swim in a more complicated manner [FIGURE 4.11]. Their flagella operate in synchrony as a bundle that extends behind the cell; the cell swims along a relatively straight track called a *run*. When the flagellar motors reverse, the bundle of flagella flies apart and the cell *tumbles* wildly. But the bundle soon forms again and the cell sets off on a new run in a different direction. The runs and tumbles alternate, resulting in a swimming path called a *three-dimensional random walk*. In the case of chemotaxis, peritrichous bacteria have longer runs and less tumbling if they are going toward an attractant or away from a repellent. But if the overall conditions are disadvantageous to a cell, there is an increase in tumbling so that the cell can quickly change direction.

FIGURE 4.9

Bacterial flagella as seen by ordinary light microscopy in stained smears. **[A]** Monotrichous flagellation; single flagellum located at the end of the cell. **[B]** Lophotrichous flagellation; a cluster of flagella at one pole of the cell. **[C]** Amphitrichous flagellation; single flagellum or cluster of flagella at each pole of the cell. **[D]** Peritrichous flagellation; random distribution of flagella on the entire surface of the cell.

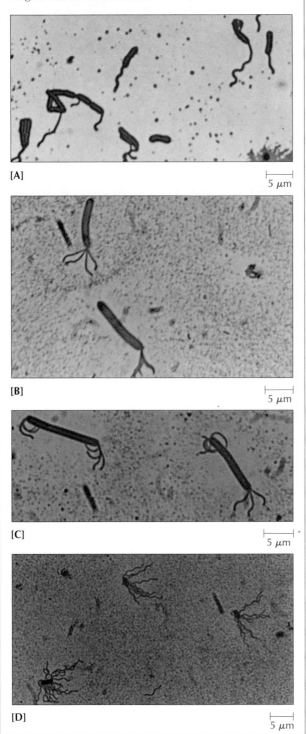

[A]   5 µm

[B]   5 µm

[C]   5 µm

[D]   5 µm

FIGURE 4.10

[A] *Treponema denticola*, a spirochete, exhibits periplasmic flagella beneath the outer membrane as indicated by the arrows. **[B]** Diagrammatic representation of a treponeme, showing three cross-sectional areas, enlarged to show details.

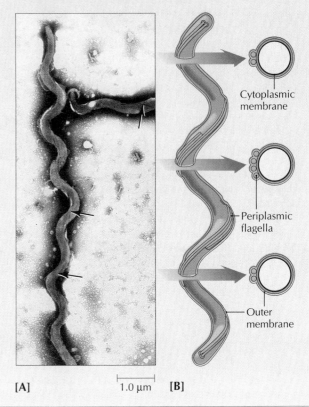

Cytoplasmic membrane

Periplasmic flagella

Outer membrane

[A]   1.0 µm   [B]

Pili (Fimbriae). Many bacteria, particularly those that are Gram-negative, have appendages that have nothing to do with motility. These filamentous structures are hollow like flagella but they are *nonhelical*. They are also thinner (3 to 10 nm in diameter), shorter, straighter, and more numerous than flagella. These structures are called *pili* (singular, *pilus*) or *fimbriae* (singular, *fimbria*).

Their structure, which can be seen only by electron microscopy, is relatively simple [FIGURE 4.12]. They do penetrate the cell wall, but no complex anchoring structures analogous to the flagellar basal bodies have been observed. Individual subunits of a protein called *pilin* are arranged in a spiral fashion around a central space to form the pilus structure. There are a variety of morphological types of pili, and they can range in number from one to several hundred per cell.

Different types of pili are associated with different functions. One type is known as the *F pilus* (or *sex pilus*), which is involved in sexual reproduction of bacteria. Bacteria that have an F pilus are considered donor cells,

4.2 THE INVASIVENESS OF SPIROCHETES IN INFECTION

Some bacteria that cause disease are motile; others are not. Thus it appears that a microbe does not need to be motile to be pathogenic. There is one group of bacteria, however, that seems to use motility to actively invade the body. Spirochetes seem ideally suited to burrow into tissues because of their morphology and mode of locomotion. They are long, thin, and helical, with one or more polar flagella that extend beneath the outer membrane and around the body of the cell. These bacteria gyrate on their ends and are able to flex their coils. They swim by rotating their flagella and rolling about their helical axes. In effect, spirochetes drill their way through a gellike medium much as a corkscrew goes through cork. Observed under dark-field microscopy, their movements appear custom-made for a life spent invading tissue or mucous membranes. This is what happens when the bacterium *Treponema pallidum* causes the disease syphilis.

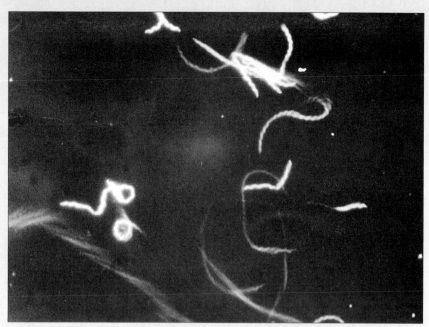

Motility tracks of spirochetes moving through a viscous medium. Dark-field illumination.

5 μm

FIGURE 4.11

Chemotaxis in peritrichously flagellated bacteria is accomplished by alternating between runs and tumbles. After each tumble, the cell swims in a different direction; if it is swimming in the correct direction, e.g., toward an attractant, there is less tumbling, since there is no necessity to change direction. During swimming, the flagella are in the form of left-handed helices and rotate counterclockwise in synchrony to form a bundle. The large arrows indicate the direction of swimming while the small arrows indicate the direction of propagation of helical waves along the flagella. During tumbling, the flagella reverse their rotation, portions of the flagella acquire a short wavelength and right-handed configuration, and the flagellar bundle flies apart.

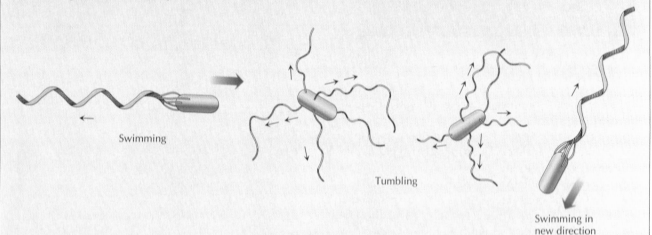

Swimming

Tumbling

Swimming in new direction

FIGURE 4.12
Cell of *Escherichia coli* exhibiting many pili extending from its surface.

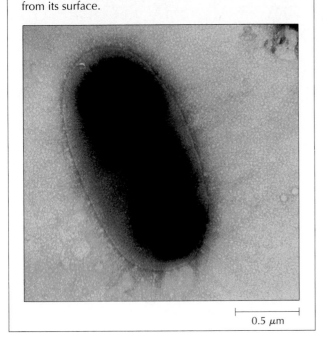

0.5 μm

FIGURE 4.13
Sex pilus holding together a mating pair of *Escherichia coli.* The male cell (on the right) also has pili of another type in addition to the sex pilus. Small RNA bacteriophages adsorbed to the sex pilus appear as dots.

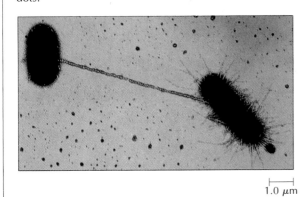

1.0 μm

and those without it are recipient cells. The pili of donor cells recognize and adhere to receptors on the surface of recipient cells, after which genetic material passes into the recipient cell [FIGURE 4.13]. Most other types of pili are involved with adhesion to surfaces.

In infection, pili help pathogenic bacteria to attach to cells lining the respiratory, intestinal, or genitourinary tract, as well as to other host cells. This adhesion prevents the bacterial cells from being washed away by the flow of mucus or other body fluids and permits the start of infection. For example, the pathogen *Neisseria gonorrhoeae*, which causes gonorrhea, possesses pili that recognize and adhere to receptors on certain human cells.

Glycocalyx

Some bacterial cells are surrounded by a layer of viscous material called the **glycocalyx.** Special stains can be used to show this layer [FIGURE 4.14], which can also be seen by suspending cells in a colloidal preparation such as India ink which contains particles in suspension. Because the particles cannot penetrate the viscous layer, the layer appears as a halo when seen through a light microscope.

The glycocalyx is composed of *polymers*, large molecules that are made of hundreds or thousands of repeating units. If the glycocalyx is organized into a defined structure and is attached firmly to the cell wall, it is a **capsule.** But if the glycocalyx is disorganized and without any definite shape, and is attached loosely to the cell wall, it is described as a **slime layer.** The slime layer tends to be soluble in water, so that the medium containing the bacteria becomes highly viscous. Bacteria with highly water-soluble glycocalyx material will produce stringiness in milk, for example.

FIGURE 4.14
Encapsulated cells of the bacterium *Streptococcus pneumoniae.*

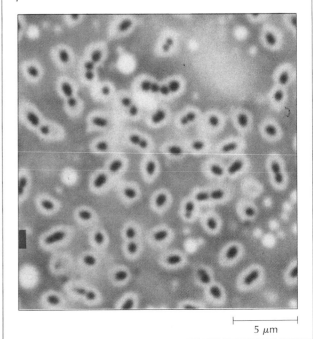

5 μm

The structure of the capsule may be seen by electron microscopy [FIGURE 4.15]. What you see is a mesh or network of fine strands, usually made of polysaccharides. Capsules composed of a single kind of sugar are termed *homopolysaccharide* capsules. The synthesis of glucan from sucrose by *Streptococcus mutans* is an example. The bacterium uses glucan, a glucose polymer, to adhere firmly to smooth tooth surfaces and cause dental caries, or cavities. Without the sticky glucan, the microorganisms might be swept away by flowing saliva.

Other capsules, called *heteropolysaccharide* capsules, contain more than one kind of sugar. Different sugars may be found in different kinds of a particular bacterium. For example, the capsule of *Streptococcus pneumoniae*, type VI, consists of galactose, glucose, and rhamnose. Other types of this pneumonia-causing pathogen contain other sugar combinations. The determination of capsule constituents is often an important step in the identification of certain pathogenic bacteria.

A few capsules are made of polypeptides, not polysaccharides. The capsule of the anthrax organism, *Bacillus anthracis*, is made entirely of a polymer of the amino acid glutamic acid. This polymer is unusual because the glutamic acid is the rare D optical isomer, rather than the L isomer normally found in nature.

The glycocalyx can serve a number of functions, depending on the bacterial species. Adherence is a major role, enabling a bacterium to fasten to various surfaces, such as rocks in fast-moving water, plant roots, and human teeth. Capsules usually have many polar groups and can protect against temporary drying by binding water molecules. They may also serve as a reservoir of stored food. Capsules may prevent attachment and lysis of cells by **bacteriophages,** which are viruses that attack bacteria. Capsules protect pathogenic bacteria from being engulfed by the white blood cells that defend the mammalian body, thus increasing the chance of infection.

Glycocalyxed bacteria can also be a nuisance to industry. They are responsible for the accumulation of slime in manufacturing equipment that can clog filters and coat pipes or other equipment, thus affecting the quality of the final product.

Cell Wall

The cell wall of procaryotic organisms is a rigid structure that maintains the characteristic shape of each bacterial cell. The structure is so rigid that even very high pressure or other severe physical conditions rarely change the shape of bacterial cells. The cell wall prevents the cell from expanding and eventually bursting because of water uptake. (Most bacteria live in environments that

FIGURE 4.15

Bacterial cells treated with special care and technique, such as reaction with specific capsular antibodies that may be labeled with chemicals which are dark in the electron beam (electron-dense chemicals), enable visualization of the capsules under the electron microscope. **[A]** Thin section of *Escherichia coli* cell showing large adhering capsule. **[B]** Thin section of *Streptococcus pyogenes* cell exhibiting capsule.

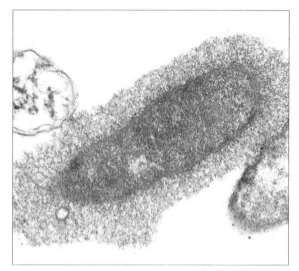

[A]   0.5 μm

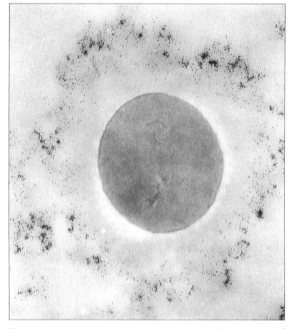

[B]   0.5 μm

FIGURE 4.16

Peptidoglycan in the cell wall of bacteria. **[A, B]** Location of peptidoglycan in Gram-positive and Gram-negative bacteria, respectively. **[C]** The peptidoglycan polymer consists of repeating units of *N*-acetylglucosamine (NAG) linked to *N*-acetylmuramic acid (NAM) with a peptide side chain of four amino acids attached to NAM. Area within colored box is enlarged in **[D]**. This enlargement shows the basic building block of peptidoglycan in *Escherichia coli*. NAM subunits of two neighboring polysaccharide chains are *directly* cross-linked by the peptide chains. Other species of bacteria may have interpeptide bridges, i.e., peptides linking the peptide chains from NAM.

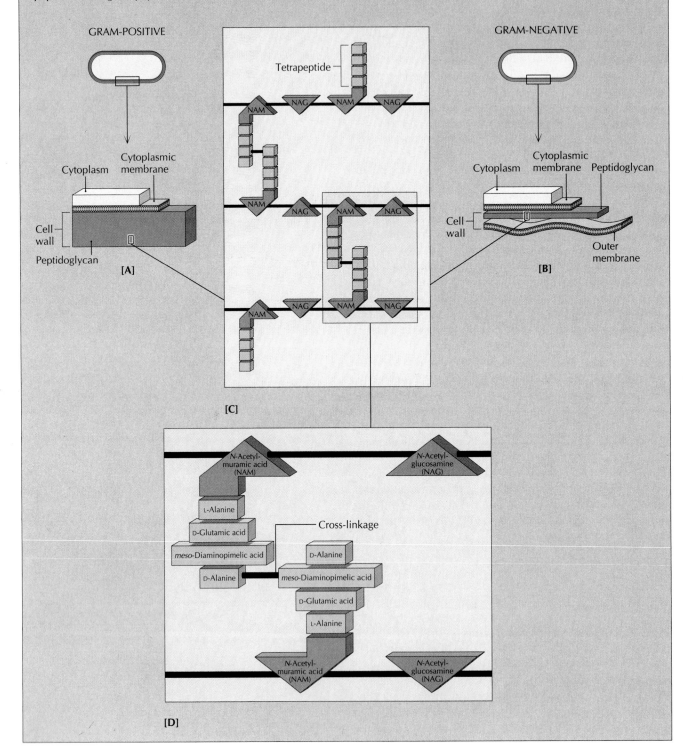

encourage cells to absorb water.) The bacterial cell wall is usually essential for cells to grow and divide; cells whose walls have been removed in the laboratory are incapable of normal growth and division. Depending on the species and the cultural conditions, the cell wall may account for as much as 10 to 40 percent of the dry weight of the cell.

Properties and Chemical Composition of Bacterial Cell Walls. Cell walls are not homogeneous structures, but layers of different substances that vary with the kind of bacteria involved. They differ in thickness, as well as in composition. These differences help identify and classify bacteria. They also help explain some of the characteristic traits of bacteria, such as their response to Gram staining and their ability to make someone ill.

Among the eubacteria, the walls of Gram-negative species are generally thinner (10 to 15 nm) than those of Gram-positive species (20 to 25 nm). The walls of Gram-negative archaeobacteria also are thinner than those of Gram-positive archaeobacteria.

For eubacteria, the shape-determining part of the cell wall is largely **peptidoglycan** (sometimes called *murein*), an insoluble, porous polymer of great strength and rigidity. Found only in procaryotes, peptidoglycan is a single gigantic molecule that surrounds the cell as a network [FIGURE 4.16]. It differs slightly in chemical composition and structure from one species to another, but the basic structure contains three kinds of building blocks: (1) *N-acetylglucosamine (NAG)*, (2) *N-acetylmuramic acid (NAM)*, and (3) a peptide made of four amino acids, or tetrapeptide. This tetrapeptide contains some D-amino acids.

To form a rigid framework around the cell, the tetrapeptides on one peptidoglycan chain are cross-linked with those of another chain [FIGURE 4.16c]. At the same time, portions of this framework must be continually opened by bacterial enzymes called *autolysins* so that new polymer can be added and the cell can grow and divide. Synthesis of the cross-links between the tetrapeptides can be prevented by certain antibiotics, such as penicillin, that inhibit normal cell-wall synthesis.

The cell walls of the archaeobacteria differ from those of the eubacteria in both structure and chemical composition. Archaeobacterial cell walls contain proteins, glycoproteins (molecules composed of both proteins and carbohydrates), or complex polysaccharides, but they lack N-acetylmuramic acid and D-amino acids and therefore do not contain peptidoglycan. The differences in cell-wall chemistry between the two bacterial groups are another piece of evidence that the groups evolved separately.

The cell walls of some bacteria, both Gram-negative and Gram-positive, are covered by a mosaic layer of protein meshwork visible through the electron microscope

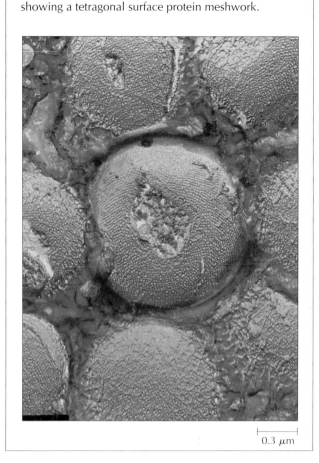

FIGURE 4.17

Freeze-etched cells of *Desulfurococcus mobilis* showing a tetragonal surface protein meshwork.

0.3 µm

[FIGURE 4.17]. The functions of these layers are not well understood, but one known function is to protect Gram-negative bacteria against attack by other predatory bacteria.

Whatever the composition and appearance of a cell wall, it has several functions besides giving the microorganism its distinctive shape. It serves as a barrier to some substances—preventing the escape of certain enzymes, as well as the influx of certain external chemicals and enzymes that could damage the cell. Dyes, some antibiotics, bile salts, heavy metals, and degradative enzymes can be stopped by cell walls. At the same time, desired nutrients and liquids are allowed passage.

The importance of cell walls is understood in part because of experiments using enzymes to remove all or most of the bacterial cell wall. A Gram-positive bacterium's cell wall is nearly completely destroyed by certain enzymes, resulting in a spherical cell called a *protoplast*. Walls of Gram-negative cells are more resistant to such treatment and lose less of their cell wall; but the *spheroplast* produced in this manner is as likely as the protoplast to take in too much water and burst.

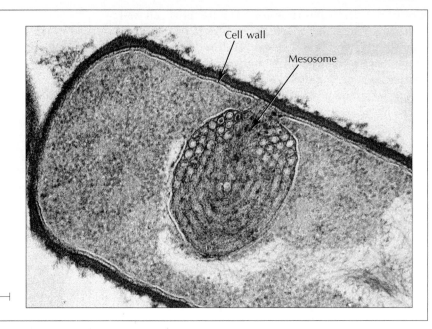

FIGURE 4.18
Thin section of a Gram-positive bacterium showing a uniformly thick cell wall consisting mainly of peptidoglycan. A mesosomal structure, an invagination of the cytoplasmic membrane, is also shown.

0.5 μm

Walls of Gram-Positive Eubacteria. Compared with Gram-negative eubacteria, Gram-positive eubacteria usually have a much greater amount of peptidoglycan in their cell walls, which makes the wall appear very thick [FIGURE 4.18]. The polymer may account for 50 percent or more of the dry weight of the wall of some Gram-positive species, but only about 10 percent of the wall of Gram-negative species. Many Gram-positive eubacteria also contain polysaccharides called *teichoic acids* in their walls [FIGURE 4.19A]. Teichoic acids, which are polymers of glycerol and ribitol phosphates, are attached to the peptidoglycan or to the cytoplasmic membrane. Negatively charged, they may aid in the transport of positive ions into and out of the cell and in the storage of phosphorus.

Walls of Gram-Negative Eubacteria. More complex than Gram-positive cell walls, the walls of Gram-negative eubacteria have an *outer membrane* covering a thin layer of peptidoglycan. As stated earlier, the Gram-negative peptidoglycan layer represents only 5 to 10 percent of the dry weight of the cell wall. It is found in the periplasmic space between the cytoplasmic membrane and the outer membrane. Gram-positive bacteria do not have this space, as they have no outer membrane as part of their cell wall.

But it is the outer membrane, not the peptidoglycan layer, that distinguishes Gram-negative bacteria. Like the thick cell wall of the Gram-positive cell, the outer membrane serves as a selective barrier when it controls the passage of some substances into and out of the cell. It can also cause serious toxic effects in infected animals. The basic structure of the Gram-negative membrane is typical of membranes discussed earlier—it is a bilayered structure containing phospholipids, with their nonpolar ends facing inward away from aqueous environments and the polar ends facing outward. It is anchored to the underlying peptidoglycan by a *lipoprotein,* a molecule composed of both a protein and a lipid [FIGURE 4.19B]. The phospholipids of the outer membrane are similar to those in the cytoplasmic membrane (to be discussed shortly). Besides phospholipids, the outer membrane of the wall contains proteins and *lipopolysaccharides (LPSs).* Lipopolysaccharides are located exclusively in the outer layer of the membrane bilayer, while phospholipids are present almost entirely in the inner layer.

Lipopolysaccharides are characteristic of Gram-negative bacteria; cell walls of Gram-positive bacteria do not contain such substances. Occurring only in the outer membrane, LPSs are composed of three covalently linked segments: (1) *Lipid A,* firmly embedded in the membrane; (2) *core polysaccharide,* located at the membrane surface; and (3) *O antigens,* which are polysaccharides that extend like whiskers from the membrane surface into the surrounding medium [FIGURE 4.19C]. The lipid portion of an LPS is also known as an *endotoxin* and can act as a poison—causing fever, diarrhea, destruction of red blood cells, and potentially fatal shock. Unlike lipids in the cytoplasmic membrane, lipid A is not composed of phospholipids but of saturated fatty acids.

The O antigens consist of repeating carbohydrate units arranged in a variety of combinations. These carbohydrates include common hexoses such as glucose, galactose, mannose, and rhamnose, as well as some unique sugars. These O antigens are responsible for many of the serological properties of LPS-containing bacteria (i.e.,

FIGURE 4.19

Diagrammatic representation of the differences between the fine structure of the Gram-positive cell wall and the Gram-negative cell wall of bacteria. **[A]** Structure of the cell wall of a Gram-positive bacterium (*Bacillus* sp.). **[B]** Structure of the cell wall of a Gram-negative bacterium. Electron micrograph is of a stained thin section of the marine bacterium *Alteromonas haloplanktis*. The organism has the simple ultrastructural characteristics of a typical Gram-negative bacterium. **[C]** Structure of one unit of *Salmonella* cell wall lipopolysaccharide (LPS). This structure may vary slightly from one genus of Gram-negative bacterium to another. However, all cell-wall LPSs contain the three general regions shown: lipid A, core polysaccharide, and O antigen (which extends into the surrounding medium).

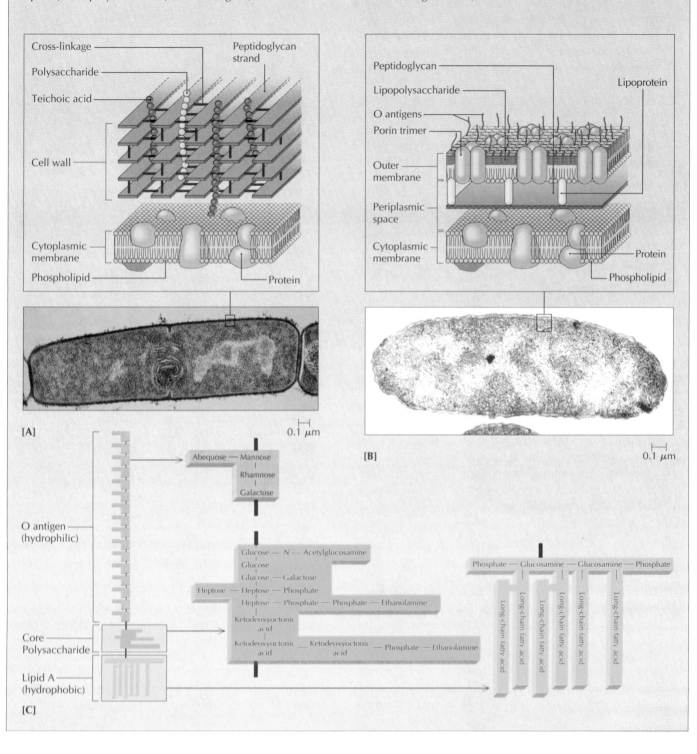

how they react with antibodies in laboratory tests). They can also serve as sites for bacteriophage attachment to bacterial cells.

Although generally a barrier to large molecules such as proteins, the outer membrane is permeable to smaller molecules, such as purines and pyrimidines, disaccharides, peptides, and amino acids. Thus the outer membrane is selectively permeable to molecules on the basis of their electric charge and molecular size. Molecules pass through diffusion channels formed by special proteins called *porins*, which span the outer membrane [FIGURE 4.19B]. Various porins are specific for different kinds or classes of small molecules, and some can allow passage of larger, essential molecules such as vitamin B_{12}.

Some outer-membrane proteins also serve as receptor sites for attachment of bacterial viruses and *bacteriocins*. The latter are proteins produced by some bacteria that inhibit or kill closely related species of bacteria. The general designation for *outer-membrane proteins*, including porins and receptors, is *Omp*.

Mechanism of the Gram Stain. Now that you know the chemical structure and composition of the procaryotic cell wall, it is easy to understand the mechanism of the Gram stain described in Chapter 3. The difference in the staining of Gram-positive and Gram-negative eubacterial cells is due to their relative resistance to decolorization by alcohol. During the Gram staining process, the cells are treated with crystal violet (the primary dye) and then with iodine (a mordant). This results in the formation of a crystal violet–iodine (CVI) complex within the cells. When a Gram-negative bacterium is washed with ethanol, the lipid in the outer membrane is dissolved and removed. This disrupts the outer membrane and increases its permeability. Thus the dye complex can be washed away, decolorizing the Gram-negative bacterium (which can then be stained with the pink counterstain safranin). In the Gram-positive bacterium, ethanol causes the pores in the peptidoglycan to shrink, trapping the CVI dye complex inside.

Cytoplasmic Membrane

Immediately beneath the cell wall is the **cytoplasmic membrane.** As seen by electron microscopy it has the appearance of other bilayer membranes—two dark lines with a light area between them [FIGURE 4.20]. It is the site of specific enzyme activity and the transport of molecules into and out of the cell. In some cases, invaginations of cytoplasmic membrane also extend deep into the cell and participate in cell metabolism and replication.

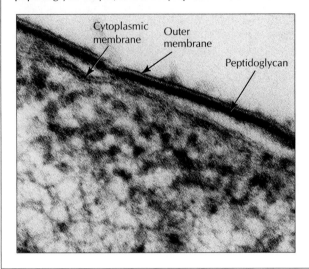

FIGURE 4.20

High magnification of a thin section of an *Escherichia coli* cell showing the outer membrane, the peptidoglycan layer, and the cytoplasmic membrane.

Cytoplasmic membrane · Outer membrane · Peptidoglycan

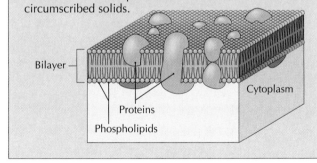

FIGURE 4.21

Schematic interpretation of the structure of the cytoplasmic membrane. Phospholipids are arranged in a bilayer such that the polar portions (spheres) face outward and the nonpolar portions (filaments) face inward. Protein components are shown as circumscribed solids.

Bilayer · Proteins · Phospholipids · Cytoplasm

Structure and Chemical Composition of the Cytoplasmic Membrane. Approximately 7.5 nm thick, the cytoplasmic membrane is composed primarily of phospholipids (20 to 30 percent) and proteins (50 to 70 percent). The phospholipids form a bilayer in which most of the proteins are embedded [FIGURE 4.21]. Each phospholipid molecule contains a charged, polar head (the phosphate end) and an uncharged, nonpolar tail (the hydrocarbon end) [FIGURE 4.22]. In the phospholipid bilayer, the water-soluble, polar ends are lined on the outside, while the water-insoluble, nonpolar ends are on the in-

FIGURE 4.22

Example of a eubacterial phospholipid, showing two unbranched long-chain fatty acids esterified to glycerol. (R is any of several compounds such as ethanolamine, choline, serine, inositol, or glycerol.) The phosphate end is the charged, polar head (soluble in water), while the hydrocarbon end is the uncharged, nonpolar tail (insoluble in water).

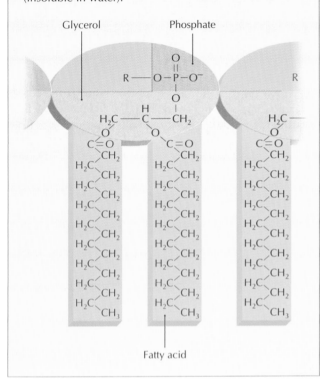

FIGURE 4.23

Mesosome (arrow) seen in a thin section of an *Escherichia coli* cell.

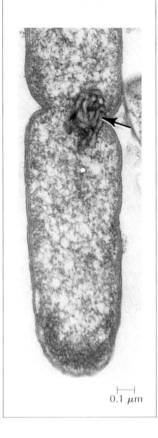

0.1 μm

FIGURE 4.24

Electron micrograph of a thin section of *Bacillus subtilis* showing nuclear material (lighter areas) in addition to the cell wall, cytoplasmic membrane, mesosome, and initial stage of cross-wall formation.

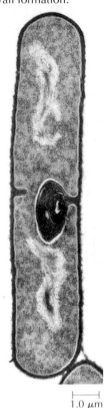

1.0 μm

side. The phospholipids in the membrane make it fluid, allowing the protein components to move around. This dynamic fluidity appears to be essential for various membrane functions. Such an arrangement of phospholipid and protein is called the *fluid mosaic model.*

Unlike the cytoplasmic membranes of eucaryotic cells, most procaryotic cytoplasmic membranes do not contain sterols such as cholesterol, and so they are less rigid than those of eucaryotes. An exception is the mycoplasmas, the only eubacteria without rigid, protective cell walls. The cytoplasmic membrane is the outermost structure of a mycoplasma cell, and the sterols in this membrane help the cell to maintain its integrity.

Function of the Cytoplasmic Membrane. Some processes essential to the cell are located in the cytoplasmic membrane. It is a barrier to most water-soluble molecules, and is much more selective than the cell wall. However, specific proteins in the membrane called *permeases* transport small molecules into the cell. The

membrane also contains various enzymes, some of which are involved in energy production and cell-wall synthesis.

Bacterial cells do not contain membrane-bound organelles corresponding to the mitochondria and chloroplasts of eucaryotic cells (discussed on pages 141–142). Instead, the cytoplasmic membranes of many bacteria extend into the cytoplasm to form tubules called **mesosomes** [FIGURE 4.23]. They are especially prominent in Gram-positive bacteria. Mesosomes may lie near the cytoplasmic membrane or deeper inside the cytoplasm. The deeper, central mesosomes seem to be attached to the cell's nuclear material. They are thought to be involved in DNA replication and cell division [FIGURE 4.24]. Peripheral mesosomes barely penetrate the cyto-

FIGURE 4.25
Electron micrograph of a thin section of a chemoautotrophic bacterium, *Nitrosococcus oceanus*, showing an extensive intracellular membrane system.

0.5 μm

plasm, are not restricted to a central location, and are not associated with nuclear material. They appear to be involved in the secretion of certain enzymes from the cell, such as penicillinases that destroy penicillin.

Elaborate intracellular extensions of the cytoplasmic membrane occur in bacteria that have a metabolism based on the exchange of gases or on the use of light energy. Such membrane systems increase the surface area available for these activities [FIGURE 4.25]. For example, in phototrophic bacteria these membranes are the site of photosynthesis; the infoldings provide a large area to accommodate a high concentration of light-absorbing pigments.

Diffusion and Osmosis across the Cytoplasmic Membrane. When the concentration of a dissolved substance (solute) in water is greater on one side of a biological membrane, such as the cytoplasmic membrane, a *concentration gradient* exists. This means that there is a gradual difference in solute concentration as you move from one point to another. If the solute can cross the selectively permeable membrane, it will move to the more dilute side. *Equilibrium* is reached when the rate of movement from each side to the other is equal. This movement of solutes across a *semipermeable* (selectively permeable) membrane is referred to as **simple diffusion.** It is a passive process because no energy is expended by the cell for this to occur. Cells depend on simple diffusion to transport some small molecules such as dissolved oxygen and carbon dioxide across their cytoplasmic membranes. However, most nutrients must be transported into the cell by permeases in the cytoplasmic membrane. This transport process often requires energy to be expended by the cell.

Solvent molecules, such as water, also move across semipermeable membranes, flowing from a region in which the molecules are highly concentrated to one of low concentration. In other words, solvents go from a solution with a low concentration of solute (high concentration of water) to a solution with a high concentration of solute (low concentration of water). This is called **osmosis,** and the force with which water moves through the membrane is the *osmotic pressure.*

Microbial cells can be exposed to three kinds of osmotic conditions in an aqueous environment: isotonic, hypotonic, or hypertonic. An *isotonic solution* is one in which the overall concentration of solutes (as well as solvent molecules) is the same on either side of the semipermeable membrane; there is no net flow of water into or out of the cell. In a *hypotonic solution* the concentration of solutes in the medium is lower than that inside the cell, so that water enters the cell as a result of the difference in osmotic pressure. Most bacteria thrive in hypotonic media, and the swelling of cells is contained by the rigid cell wall. A *hypertonic solution* has a higher concentration of solutes than inside the cell. Water leaves the cell because of osmotic pressure, causing the cytoplasmic membrane to shrink from the cell wall.

Internal Cell Structures

Enclosed within the cell wall and the cytoplasmic membrane are the internal structures of the cell [FIGURE 4.26]. Material contained within the cytoplasmic membrane may be divided into the following: (1) the cytoplasmic area, which is the fluid portion containing dissolved substances and particles such as ribosomes, and (2) the nuclear material, or *nucleoid*, which is rich in the genetic material DNA. A general description of these will help complete this survey of procaryotic cell structures.

Cytoplasmic Area. In any cell, the cytoplasm is about 80 percent water, along with nucleic acids, proteins, carbohydrates, lipids, inorganic ions, many low–molecular weight compounds, and particles with various functions. This thick fluid is the site of many chemical reactions, such as those involved in the synthesis of cell components from nutrients. Unlike eucaryotic cytoplasm, cytoplasm in procaryotes does not flow around within the cell. Thus far, there is also no evidence that procaryotic cytoplasm has a **cytoskeleton,** a network of fibrils that helps maintain the shape of the cell.

Densely packed throughout the cytoplasm are the particles called **ribosomes,** which are the site of protein synthesis. Ribosomes are found in all cells, both procaryotic and eucaryotic. However, unlike eucaryotic cells, bacterial cells have no internal system of membranes. Some ribosomes are found free in the procaryotic cyto-

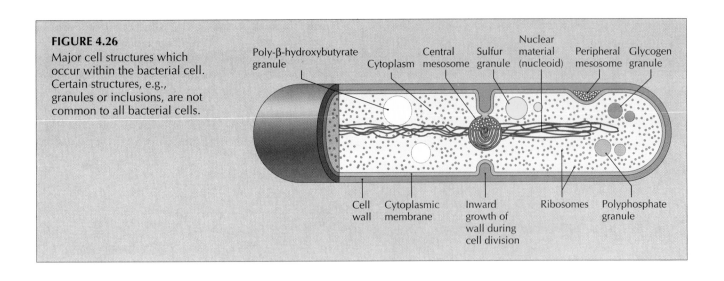

FIGURE 4.26
Major cell structures which occur within the bacterial cell. Certain structures, e.g., granules or inclusions, are not common to all bacterial cells.

Poly-β-hydroxybutyrate granule

Cytoplasm

Central mesosome

Sulfur granule

Nuclear material (nucleoid)

Peripheral mesosome

Glycogen granule

Cell wall

Cytoplasmic membrane

Inward growth of wall during cell division

Ribosomes

Polyphosphate granule

FIGURE 4.27
Thiospirillum jenense showing sulfur globules.

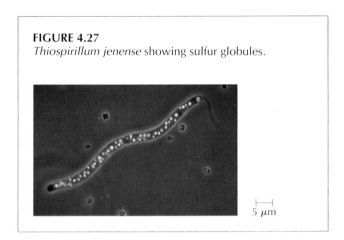

5 μm

plasm, while others, especially those involved with synthesis of secreted proteins, are associated with the inner surface of the cytoplasmic membrane. Ribosomes in bacteria consist of two subunits of different size. The larger subunit is a *50-S subunit* and the smaller is a *30-S subunit*; together they form the 70-S bacterial ribosome. (The "S" refers to the *Svedberg unit*, a measure of how fast a particle settles, or sediments, when a particle suspension is centrifuged at high speed. Since both shape and size determine the rate of sedimentation, the S units do not add up arithmetically; for example, 50 S plus 30 S does not equal 80 S.) Procaryotic ribosomes are the targets of many antibiotics that inhibit protein synthesis, such as streptomycin, neomycin, and the tetracyclines.

Different kinds of chemical substances can accumulate and form insoluble deposits in the cytoplasm called *inclusions*. For example, some species of H_2S–oxidizing bacteria contain large amounts of sulfur in globules [FIGURE 4.27]. These may serve as an energy reserve for the bacteria. **Volutin granules,** also known as *metachromatic granules*, are made of polyphosphate. They stain

an intense reddish-purple color with dilute methylene blue dye, and are used to identify certain bacteria, including the causative agent of diphtheria. With electron microscopy, volutin granules appear as round, dark areas [FIGURE 4.28].

Another substance often found in bacteria is a chloroform-soluble, lipid material called *poly-β-hydroxybutyrate (PHB)*, which acts as a reserve carbon and energy source. PHB granules can be stained with lipid-soluble dyes such as Nile blue. Through an electron microscope, they are clear, round areas [see FIGURE 4.28]. Unlike volutin or PHB granules, *glycogen granules* look like dark granules [see FIGURE 4.28]. Found in some bacteria, they stain brown with iodine for light microscopy, since glycogen is a polysaccharide.

FIGURE 4.28
Thin section of *Pseudomonas pseudoflava* showing polyphosphate (volutin) granules (PP), poly-ß-hydroxybutyrate granules (PHB), and glycogen granules (G).

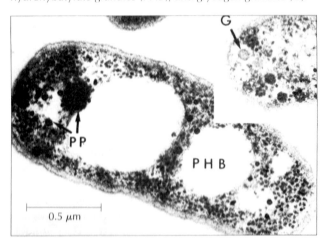

G

PP

PHB

0.5 μm

Nuclear Area. A bacterial cell, unlike the cells of eucaryotic organisms, lacks a distinct membrane-enclosed nucleus. Instead, the nuclear material in a bacterial cell occupies a position near the center of the cell. It seems to be attached to the mesosome-cytoplasmic membrane system [see FIGURE 4.24]. This total nuclear material, called the *nucleoid*, consists of a single, circular **chromosome.** A chromosome is the structure inside cells that physically carries hereditary information from one generation to the next. By electron microscopy the nucleoid appears as a light, fibrillar area [see FIGURE 4.24].

ASK YOURSELF

1 Draw a bacterial cell showing all the typical structures.

2 How does the flagellum propel a bacterial cell? What are the different kinds of flagellation?

3 How do peritrichously flagellated bacteria swim? Do polarly flagellated bacteria swim the same way?

4 What is the difference between flagella and pili in terms of form and function?

5 What is the definition of *glycocalyx*? What are its functions?

6 Of what use is the cell wall to the bacterial cell?

7 What are the differences between the cell walls of Gram-positive and Gram-negative eubacteria? How does the cell-wall composition of archaeobacteria differ from that of the eubacteria?

8 What is the most probable mechanism of the Gram stain?

9 Why can the cytoplasmic membrane be described as a *fluid mosaic model*? As *semipermeable*?

10 What are the different granules found in the bacterial cytoplasm?

DORMANT FORMS OF PROCARYOTIC MICROORGANISMS

Some species of bacteria produce *dormant* forms called *spores* and *cysts* that can survive unfavorable conditions, such as drying or heat. These resting forms are metabolically inactive, which means that they are not growing. However, under appropriate environmental conditions, they can germinate (begin to grow) and become meta-

bolically active *vegetative* cells, which grow and multiply. In the early days of microbiology, these dormant forms confused microbiologists. Some of the first attempts to disprove spontaneous generation failed because experimental conditions did not kill the dormant forms of bacteria and fungi, allowing them to grow in the inadequately treated specimens. In fighting anthrax among farm animals, microbiologists eventually understood that dormant forms of the anthrax bacillus could survive for years in soil.

Spores

Spores that form within the cell, called **endospores,** are unique to bacteria. They are thick-walled, highly refractile (very bright with light microscopy), and highly resistant to environmental changes. It is necessary to use heat when staining an endospore for light microscopy, to make the spore absorb the dye. Produced one per cell, endospores vary in shape and location within the cell [FIGURE 4.29]. They are most common in the genera *Clostridium* and *Bacillus*, and normally appear in cultures that are approaching the end of an active growth phase.

When endospores are freed from the mother cell, or **sporangium,** they can survive extreme heat, drying, and exposure to toxic chemicals such as some disinfectants. For example, the endospores of *Clostridium botulinum*, the cause of the food poisoning called *botulism*, can resist boiling for several hours. Endospore-forming bacteria are a problem in the food industry because they are likely to survive if processing procedures are not adequate. Vegetative cells are killed by temperatures above 70°C, but most endospores can withstand 80°C for at least 10 minutes.

What causes this heat resistance has been a subject of intense research for decades, but the explanation is still not clear. Apparently, a dehydration process occurs during sporulation that expels most of the water from the spore. This may contribute to heat resistance. Furthermore, all endospores contain large amounts of *dipicolinic acid (DPA)*, a unique compound not found in vegetative cells that may play a role in heat resistance. DPA accounts for 5 to 10 percent of the endospore's dry weight and occurs in combination with large amounts of calcium. It is probably located in the central part of the spore.

The structural changes that occur during the development of endospores have been extensively studied. Some of the changes are shown in FIGURE 4.30. Under the right conditions, a spore will form a vegetative cell [FIGURE 4.31]. This germination may be triggered by brief exposure to heat or by mechanical forces acting on the spore.

FIGURE 4.29

[A] Location, size, and shape of endospores in cells of various species of *Bacillus* and *Clostridium.* [B] Micrograph showing cells and spores (green) of *Bacillus subtilis.*

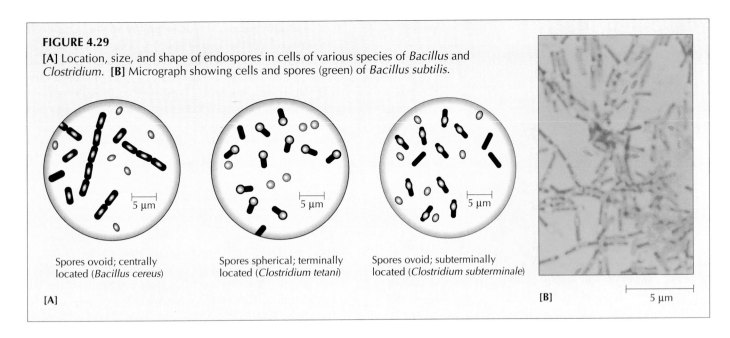

Spores ovoid; centrally located (*Bacillus cereus*)

Spores spherical; terminally located (*Clostridium tetani*)

Spores ovoid; subterminally located (*Clostridium subterminale*)

[A]

[B]

5 μm

FIGURE 4.30

Structural changes in the bacterial cell during sporulation.

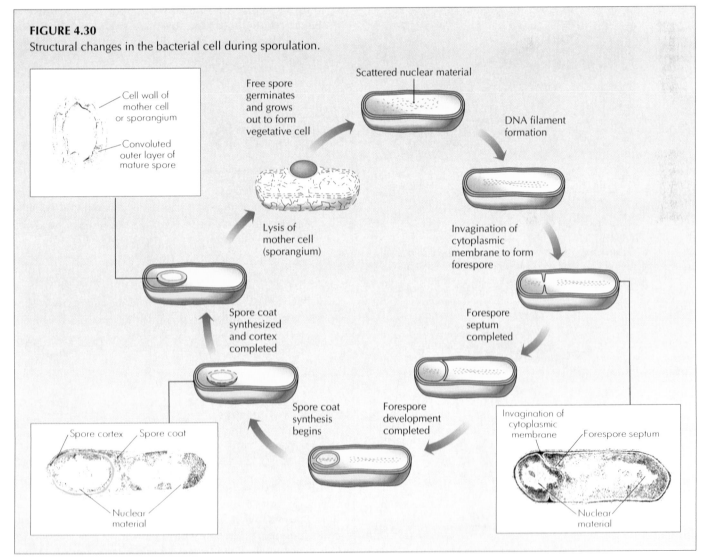

FIGURE 4.31
Outgrowth of spores from cultures of *Bacillus mycoides*: **[A]** grown 2 h at 35°C and **[B]** grown 1.75 h at 35°C. The two halves of the severed spore coat appear at the ends of the vegetative cell.

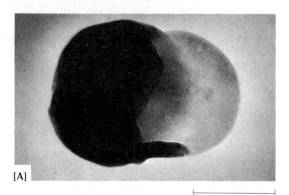

[A]

0.5 µm

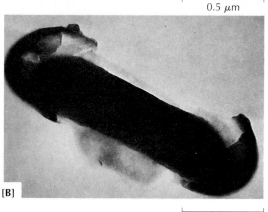

[B]

0.5 µm

FIGURE 4.32
Fine structure of an *Azotobacter* cyst. The exosporium (Ex) and the two layers of exine (CC₁ and CC₂) are visible. In addition, a nuclear region (Nr) and a cytoplasmic region containing ribosomes can be seen within the central body.

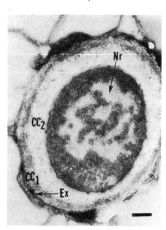

0.5 µm

Another type of spore is produced by a group of bacteria called the *actinomycetes*. The spore, called a *conidium* (plural, *conidia*), is not much more heat-resistant than a vegetative cell, although it is resistant to drying. However, unlike the vegetative cells that produce a single endospore, each actinomycete organism can produce many of these conidia at the tip of a filament. Thus such conidia are used for reproduction, not for protection.

Cysts

Like endospores, cysts are dormant, thick-walled forms that resist drying. They develop from a vegetative cell and can later germinate under suitable conditions. However, their structure and chemical composition are different from that of endospores, and they do not have the high heat resistance. The classic example of a bacterial cyst is the type produced by the genus *Azotobacter* [FIGURE 4.32]. Several other genera of bacteria have been reported to differentiate into cysts, but they seem to lack the degree of complexity seen in azotobacter cysts.

ASK YOURSELF

1 What are the two dormant structures of procaryotic microbes?

2 Which are the bacterial genera associated with endospore formation?

3 What are the unique physiological characteristics of the bacterial endospore?

4 What is the probable functional role of dipicolinic acid in the bacterial endospore?

5 What is the bacterial genus that produces cysts?

GROSS MORPHOLOGICAL CHARACTERISTICS OF EUCARYOTIC MICROORGANISMS

All procaryotic organisms are microorganisms, yet only a few groups of the eucaryotic organisms include microorganisms. These groups—algae, fungi, and protozoa—include a vast diversity of organisms. Among them are species too large to be considered microscopic. Obvious

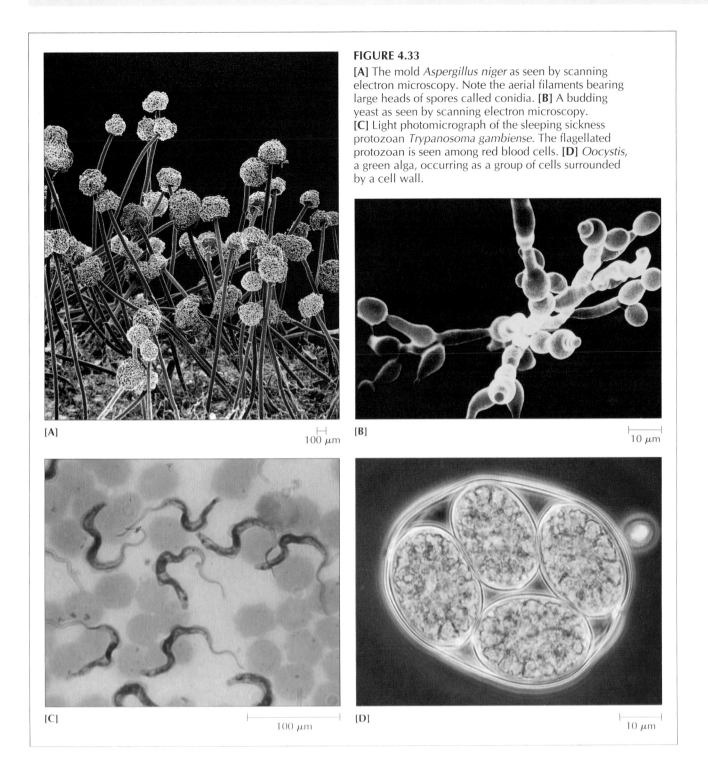

FIGURE 4.33
[A] The mold *Aspergillus niger* as seen by scanning electron microscopy. Note the aerial filaments bearing large heads of spores called conidia. [B] A budding yeast as seen by scanning electron microscopy. [C] Light photomicrograph of the sleeping sickness protozoan *Trypanosoma gambiense*. The flagellated protozoan is seen among red blood cells. [D] *Oocystis*, a green alga, occurring as a group of cells surrounded by a cell wall.

[A]   100 μm

[B]   10 μm

[C]   100 μm

[D]   10 μm

examples are the seaweeds, which are algae, and the mushrooms, which are fungi. However, these are related to the microscopic eucaryotes and are usually included within the scope of microbiology. Other eucaryotes are minute, single cells. The morphological differences among fungi, protozoa, and algae are a reminder of the dramatic structural diversity among microorganisms [FIGURE 4.33].

Morphology of Fungi

Yeasts and molds are fungi, but they differ in their morphology. Single yeast cells are generally larger than most bacteria, ranging widely in size from 1 to 5 μm in width and 5 to 30 μm or more in length. They are commonly oval, but some are elongated or spherical. Each species has a characteristic shape, but even in a pure culture

FIGURE 4.34
Fungal colonies on agar medium. **[A]** Yeast colonies.
[B] Mold colonies. Note the difference in surface
texture between the two groups of fungi: yeast colonies
are smooth and glistening; mold colonies are
filamentous and fuzzy.

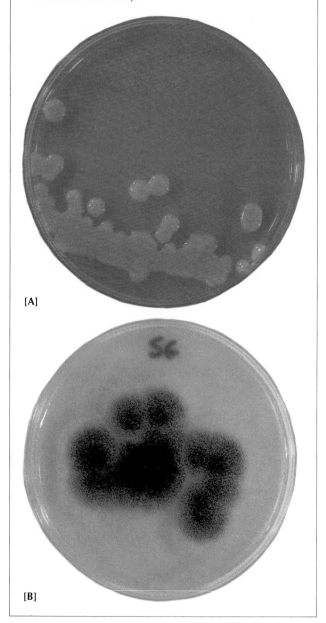

[A]

[B]

FIGURE 4.35
[A] The body (thallus) of the common bread mold,
Rhizopus stolonifer, forms several types of hyphae (a
mass of hyphae is called a mycelium). There are rootlike hyphae (rhizoids), vegetative hyphae which also
penetrate the substrate, and aerial hyphae (sporangiophores) which produce spores within sacs called
sporangia. Stolons are rootlike filaments which connect
individual thalli. Numerous sporangia can be seen in
the micrograph below. **[B]** Nonseptate (coenocytic)
hyphae. Note that there are no crosswalls (septa). **[C]**
Septate hyphae with septa dividing the hyphae into
individual cells.

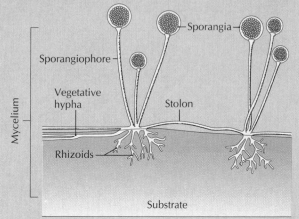

[A]   100 μm

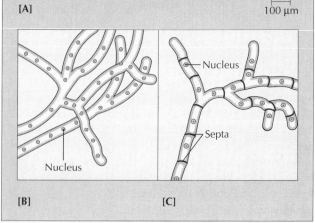

[B]   [C]

there is considerable variation in size and shape of individual cells. Yeasts lack flagella and other means of locomotion. On an agar medium, they form smooth, glistening colonies that resemble those of bacteria. These
colonies are quite different from the spreading, furry, or
filamentous colonies formed by molds [FIGURE 4.34].

Unlike the unicellular yeast cells, molds are multicellular organisms that look like filaments under low

4.3 KILLER FUNGI: NEMESIS OF PLANT PESTS

Plants sometimes die because their root systems are destroyed by tiny worms called *nematodes*. Fortunately, farmers and gardeners have an ally against these invaders—a group of fungi that can switch from a saprophytic form of nutrition to become ferocious carnivores that feed on the microscopic worms!

These predatory fungi have a chilling array of constricting trapping rings along their body that resemble hangman's nooses (see the accompanying illustration). These regularly spaced rings are oriented at right angles to the fungal filament. When a nematode tries to pass through a ring (lured by chemicals secreted by the fungi), the three ring cells inflate to 3 times their normal size. Then they tighten within one-tenth of a second, trapping the worm. This closure is

Nematode-catching fungus. A nematode has been trapped by a hyphal noose.   50 μm

so violent that it immediately disables the worm. Not only do the rings garrot the nematode, but soon hyphae develop that penetrate deep into the worm, unloading poisonous toxins. Then more hyphae grow through the nematode's body, consuming its contents.

Species of such fungi belong to the genera *Dactylella* and *Arthrobotrys*. Obviously, cultivation of these cannibalistic fungi could lead to healthier plants, as well as healthier human beings, since such biological agents can replace noxious pesticides.

---

magnification. With high magnification, molds can look like tiny jungles with many parts [FIGURE 4.35A]. The body, or ***thallus*** (plural, ***thalli***), of a mold consists of the ***mycelium*** (plural, ***mycelia***) and the dormant spores. Each mycelium is a mass of filaments called ***hyphae*** (singular, ***hypha***). Each hypha is about 5 to 10 μm in width and is formed by the joining together of many cells. The rigid walls of hyphae are made of chitins, celluloses, and glucans.

Hyphae may be classified as either *coenocytic* or *septate* [FIGURE 4.35B and C]. Coenocytic hyphae do not have *septa* (singular, *septum*), which are crosswalls between the cells that make up a long filament. Each coenocytic hypha is essentially a long cell containing many nuclei. Septate hyphae have septa that divide the filaments into distinct cells containing nuclei. However, there is a pore in each septum that allows cytoplasm and nuclei to migrate between cells. A hypha grows by elongation at its tip, and each fragment that contains nuclei is capable of growing into a new organism.

Some hyphae are embedded into solid media such as bread or soil to give the thallus support and nourishment. These specialized hyphae are called *rhizoids*, because they are rootlike. *Reproductive hyphae* may grow upward into the air to disseminate the spores they produce. Each spore on germination puts out a *germ tube*, a short, hyphalike extension that soon grows into a thallus [FIGURE 4.36]. Hyphae with no specialized division of labor may simply grow along the surface of a substrate

and are referred to as *vegetative hyphae*. Other hyphae can become organized into large structures to form the so-called fleshy fungi, such as the mushrooms, puffballs, and bracket fungi.

Many pathogenic fungi exhibit *dimorphism*, existing either in a unicellular, yeastlike form or in a filamentous form. The yeast phase is present when the organism is a parasite, and the mold form when the organism is a saprophyte in its natural habitat (such as soil) or on laboratory media incubated at room temperature [FIGURE 4.37]. Demonstrating this dimorphism is often very crucial in laboratory identification of these pathogens.

Morphology of Algae

Algae as a group are a potpourri of sizes and shapes. Species range from single microscopic cells to organisms hundreds of feet long. Single-celled species may be spherical, rod-shaped, club-shaped, or spindle-shaped. Some may be motile [FIGURE 4.38]. Those algae that are multicellular appear in a variety of forms and degrees of complexity. Some are organized as filaments of cells attached end to end; in some species these filaments intertwine into macroscopic, plantlike bodies. Algae also occur in colonies, some of which are simple aggregations of single cells, while others contain different cell types with special functions [FIGURE 4.39].

FIGURE 4.36
Scanning electron micrographs of *Rhizopus stolonifer* spores at sequential stages of germination, with corresponding phase-contrast photomicrographs. **[A]** Ungerminated spore. **[B]** Swollen spore. **[C]** Elongated spore. **[D]** Germ tube emerging. **[E]** Germ tube elongated.

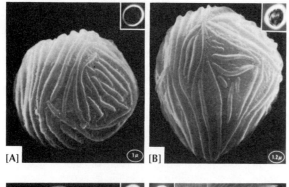

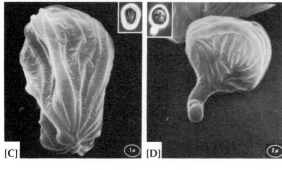

FIGURE 4.37
Dimorphism in a pathogenic fungus, *Blastomyces dermatitidis*. **[A]** Mycelial phase. **[B]** Yeast phase. Phase-contrast illumination.

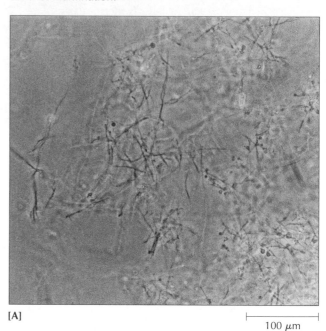

[A]   100 μm

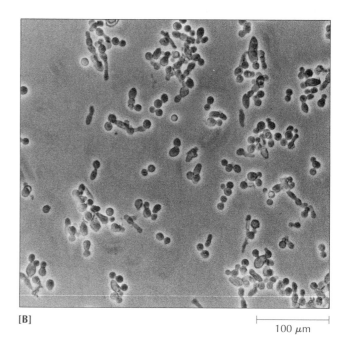

[B]   100 μm

Morphology of Protozoa

Some protozoa are oval or spherical, others elongated. Still others are *polymorphic*, with morphologically different forms at different stages of the life cycle. Cells can be as small as 1 μm in diameter and as large as 2000 μm, or 2 mm (visible without magnification). Like animals, protozoa lack cell walls, are able to move at some stage of their life cycle, and ingest particles of food. Each individual cell is a *complete* organism, containing the organelles necessary to perform all the functions of an individual organism. Consequently, many protozoan cells are more complex than other types of cells.

Some of the general characteristics that distinguish fungi, algae, and protozoa are summarized in TABLE 4.1.

FIGURE 4.38

[A] *Chlamydomonas* in the vegetative and palmelloid states. Usually the cells in the palmelloid state are nonflagellated and are embedded in a gelatinous matrix. Flagella reappear and the cells swim away when favorable environmental conditions return. [B] Organization of a *Chlamydomonas* cell.

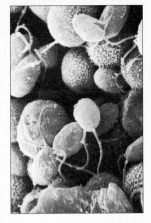

[A]   25 μm

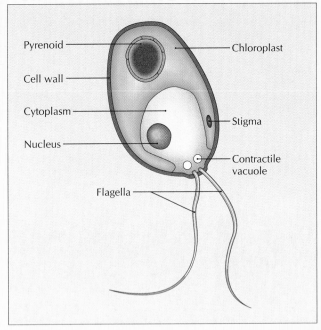

[B]

FIGURE 4.39

[A] Spherical colony of the green alga *Volvox* sp. Each colony may become as large as 500 μm in diameter and may be visible to the unaided eye. Each colony may contain up to 50,000 single-celled flagellates embedded in a gelatinous matrix and organized into a hollow sphere. The individual cells are joined by cytoplasmic threads. Each cell has two flagella directed outward from the surface of the sphere. Through coordinated action of these cells, the entire colony can become motile and then roll smoothly through the water. As shown, each parental colony has a number of developing progeny colonies, which are formed by repeated division of a few specialized reproductive cells. Eventually, progeny colonies are released through disintegration of the parental colony. [B] Diagrammatic representation of a volvox colony.

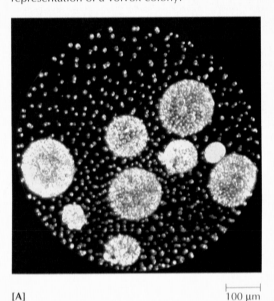

[A]   100 μm

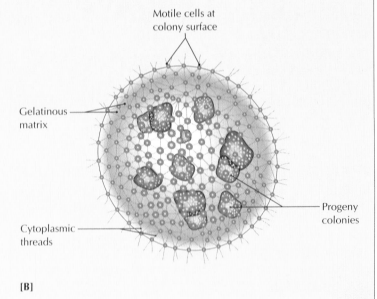

[B]

TABLE 4.1
Major Distinguishing Characteristics of the Eucaryotic Protists

Protist	Cell arrangement	Mode of nutrition	Motility	Miscellaneous
Fungi	Unicellular or multicellular	Chemoheterotrophic by absorption of soluble nutrients	Nonmotile	Sexual and asexual spores
Algae	Unicellular or multicellular	Photoautotrophic by absorption of soluble nutrients	Mostly nonmotile	Photosynthetic pigments
Protozoa	Unicellular	Chemoheterotrophic by absorption or ingestion of particles of food	Mostly motile	Some form cysts

ASK YOURSELF

1 Are yeast cells motile?

2 How do yeast colonies differ in appearance from mold colonies?

3 What are the terms associated with the gross morphology of molds?

4 What is dimorphism? What is its practical implication in the microbiology laboratory?

5 What is the size range of algae?

6 What are the several forms of multicellular algae?

7 Why are some protozoa described as *polymorphic*?

8 Can all algae move? Why, or why not?

ULTRASTRUCTURE OF EUCARYOTIC MICROORGANISMS

Eucaryotic cells are generally larger and structurally more complex than procaryotic cells. *The outstanding feature of the eucaryotic cell is the membrane-bounded nucleus with linear chromosomes, which is not found in procaryotes.* But the nucleus is only one of many structures that characterize the eucaryotic fungi, algae, and protozoa. The morphology of these microorganisms can include appendages, cell walls, membranes, and various internal structures. The greater complexity of the eucaryotic cell over the procaryotic cell is evident when the schematic diagram of a eucaryotic cell [FIGURE 4.40] is compared with that of a procaryotic cell [see FIGURE 4.7].

Flagella and Cilia

Like the bacteria, many eucaryotic cells have thin structures used for locomotion. Called flagella and *cilia* (singular, *cilium*), they originate from a basal body lying beneath the membrane that encloses the cell. Many single-celled protozoa and algae possess flagella, which beat with a whiplike motion and propel the cell through fluid environments [FIGURE 4.41]. In some cases, only the presence of chlorophyll distinguishes a motile alga from a protozoan. Eucaryotic cilia are identical to eucaryotic flagella in structure, but they are usually shorter and more numerous. They ordinarily are arranged in groups or rows on the cell surface. Unlike the whipping motion of flagella, cilia beat with a coordinated rhythmic motion. With high magnification, a cell covered with cilia looks like a porcupine; a large number of the protozoan species have this appearance [FIGURE 4.42].

Eucaryotic flagella and cilia are structurally and functionally more complex than their procaryotic counterparts. They are composed of thin, hairlike *microtubules:* nine pairs of these proteinaceous tubules encircle a central pair in an arrangement called "9 + 2." The shaft formed by the microtubules is wrapped in a membrane [FIGURE 4.43]. Movement of eucaryotic appendages is powered by the hydrolysis of the chemical compound ATP. On the other hand, the energy to move procaryotic flagella comes from the *protonmotive force* (the movement of hydrogen ions across the cytoplasmic membrane). The two types of flagella also differ in the way they move the cell. The eucaryotic flagellum propels the cell by acting like a whip, bending and twisting against the liquid environment. However, as you learned earlier, the procaryotic flagellum moves the cell by rotating like a corkscrew.

Some protozoa have flagella; others have cilia. But another group of protozoa has its own mode of locomotion—specialized structures called *pseudopodia* (singular, *pseudopodium*). A pseudopodium is a temporary

FIGURE 4.40
Schematic diagram of the general structure of a typical eucaryotic (animal) cell.

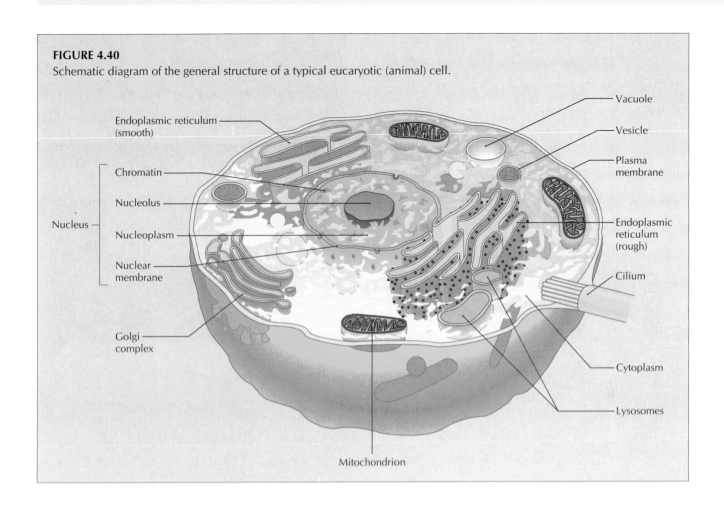

FIGURE 4.41
Scanning electron micrograph of flagellated trophozoites, or growing cells, of *Giardia lamblia*. Each cell has eight trailing flagella. *G. lamblia* is a common parasite of humans and resides in the upper small intestine. Infection is usually asymptomatic; however, heavy infection with this protozoan causes gastrointestinal disturbances and diarrhea.

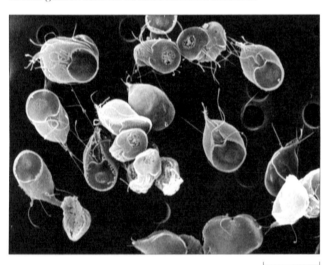

25 μm

FIGURE 4.42
Scanning electron micrograph of a ciliated growing cell, or trophozoite, of *Balantidium coli*, the only ciliated protozoan that is of medical importance. The trophozoites are oval and measure between 40 μm and 150 μm in length. They are highly motile, and the surface is covered with cilia. It is the coordinated beating of these cilia which propels the cell. (Crystalline structures at the periphery are starch granules.)

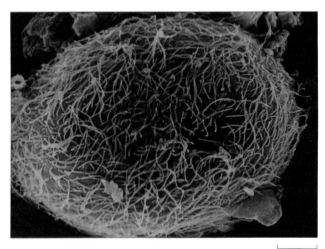

30 μm

FIGURE 4.43

[A] Transverse section of an infective form of *Trypanosoma brucei* showing the uniform, electron-dense surface coat covering the cell body and the flagellum (with the typical "9 + 2" structure). SC, surface coat; F, flagellum; MT, microtubules. [B] Diagram of a cross section through a flagellum showing the microtubules in their "9 + 2" arrangement.

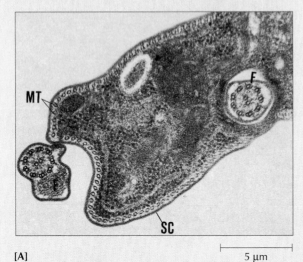

[A]

5 μm

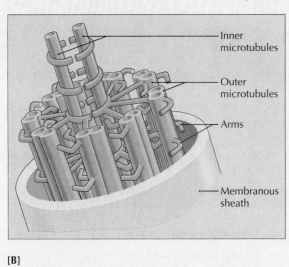

Inner microtubules

Outer microtubules

Arms

Membranous sheath

[B]

FIGURE 4.44

[A] An amoeba approaching a food particle as seen by scanning electron microscopy. Note the pseudopodia projecting from the cell. [B] Diagrammatic representation of the anatomy of an amoeba showing internal structures.

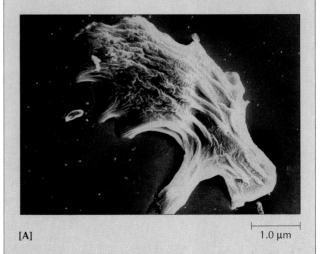

[A]

1.0 μm

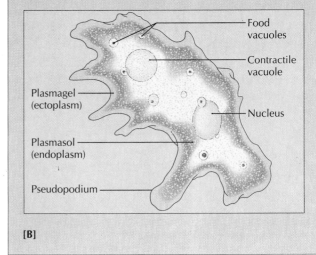

Food vacuoles

Contractile vacuole

Plasmagel (ectoplasm)

Nucleus

Plasmasol (endoplasm)

Pseudopodium

[B]

Cell Wall

Plants, algae, and fungi have cell walls, while other eucaryotic cells do not. The cell wall maintains the shape of

projection of part of the cytoplasm and cytoplasmic membrane, which is caused by *cytoplasmic streaming*. Pseudopodia are characteristic of the amoebas [FIGURE 4.44] and may be used to capture food particles.

cells and prevents them from bursting through osmotic pressure. (For animal cells and most protozoa, the absence of cell walls makes the cytoplasmic membrane the outermost structure.)

Cell walls of plants, algae, and fungi differ from one another and from bacterial cell walls in chemical composition and physical structure. For example, eucaryotic cell walls do not contain peptidoglycan, a major constituent of bacterial cell walls. In plants the cell wall is rigid; it is composed mainly of polysaccharides such as cellulose and pectin. The filamentous fungi have cell walls containing chitin and cellulose, while the unicellular yeasts have walls of the polysaccharide mannan, a polymer of the monosaccharide mannose. Depending on the type of algae, the algal cell wall is composed of varying amounts of cellulose, other polysaccharides, and calcium carbonate. The walls of algae called *diatoms* are impregnated with silica, making them thick and very rigid. Diatom surfaces are often delicately sculptured with intricate designs characteristic of the species.

Even though protozoa lack a cell wall, some are surrounded by a layer of shell-like material. This may fit tightly or may form a loose chamber, in which the organism moves. Scales or spines may also be present. The shells have an organic matrix reinforced by inorganic substances, such as calcium carbonate, silica, or even grains of sand.

Cytoplasmic Membrane

Whether or not a eucaryotic cell has a cell wall, it has a cytoplasmic membrane that encloses the main body of the cell [see FIGURE 4.40]. The semipermeable membrane is a lipid bilayer with inserted proteins that may protrude on one side or the other of the membrane. Some proteins traverse the entire width of the membrane, often creating pores through which nutrients enter into the cell. They serve as *permeases* that actively transport specific nutrients across the membrane. The basic principles of diffusion and osmosis described earlier for procaryotes also apply to eucaryotic cytoplasmic membranes. Thus the eucaryotic cytoplasmic membrane morphologically and functionally resembles that of procaryotic cells.

However, there are differences between procaryotic and eucaryotic cytoplasmic membranes. The eucaryotic cytoplasmic membrane contains sterols (mainly cholesterol), while the procaryotic membrane generally does not. The sterols interweave into the lipid bilayer and add strength to the membrane. In those eucaryotic microorganisms that lack cell walls, the cytoplasmic membrane is reinforced by microtubule fibers made of the proteins actin and myosin. Also in contrast to procaryotes, there are no enzymes involved in metabolic energy generation located in the eucaryotic cytoplasmic membrane.

Cellular Organelles

Inside the cytoplasmic membrane is the *protoplasm*, which is divided into the *karyoplasm* and the *cytoplasm*. Karyoplasm is the material inside the nuclear membrane (discussed in the following paragraphs), while cytoplasm is the material between the nuclear membrane and the

cytoplasmic membrane. Rich in chemicals, the latter forms the bulk of the cell and is home to the cellular *organelles*. Organelles are membrane-bound structures that perform special functions, such as photosynthesis and respiration. Unlike procaryotic cytoplasm, the eucaryotic cytoplasm has an extensive network of microtubules and protein structures that constitute the cytoskeleton of the cell. The cytoskeleton provides shape and support, and serves as a framework along which organelles move through the cytoplasm.

Nucleus. The characteristic feature of the eucaryotic nucleus is the **nuclear membrane.** This double-membrane envelope, which resembles two cytoplasmic membranes together, distinguishes the *eucaryotic* cell from the *procaryotic* cell. The nuclear membrane contains numerous large pores through which substances such as proteins and RNA can pass [FIGURES 4.45 and 4.46]. This membrane often gives rise to, or is continuous with, the **endoplasmic reticulum,** a network of intracellular membranes where proteins are synthesized (as discussed under "Endoplasmic Reticulum" on page 140).

Usually spherical or oval, the nucleus is the largest organelle in the eucaryotic cell. It contains the cell's hereditary information in the form of DNA. In the nondividing karyoplasm, the DNA is combined with basic proteins, such as histones, that give it a fibrillar appearance [see FIGURE 4.45]. These threads of combined DNA and protein are called *chromatin*. During cell division, the chromatin condenses into chromosomes, the large, discrete DNA molecules that become visible under the light microscope.

Within the karyoplasm is the electron-dense **nucleolus,** which appears very dark with electron microscopy [see FIGURE 4.45]. About 5 to 10 percent of the nucleolus is RNA, with the remainder primarily protein. This structure is the site of synthesis of ribosomal RNA, an essential component of ribosomes. Protein components of ribosomes in the cytoplasm enter the nucleus through nuclear pores to combine with newly made ribosomal RNA. Together the proteins and RNA form the large and small subunits of the ribosomes. These subunits then leave the karyoplasm via the pores and become fully functional in the cytoplasm. Eucaryotic ribosomes are larger (80 S) than procaryotic ribosomes (70 S). This is because each eucaryotic ribosome consists of a 60-S subunit and a 40-S subunit, rather than a 50-S subunit and a 30-S subunit.

Many protozoa have multiple nuclei throughout the greater part of their life cycle. In those with cilia, there are one large nucleus (macronucleus) and one small nucleus (micronucleus). The macronucleus controls metabolic activities, growth, and regeneration; the micronucleus controls reproductive activities.

FIGURE 4.45
Thin sections of the euglenoid (an alga) *Astasia longa*
seen by transmission electron microscopy at two
magnifications. **[A]** The cell is flagellated and is
surrounded by a convoluted pellicle, or cell covering.
[B] Other internal structures seen are the nucleus,
nucleolus, mitochondrion, Golgi complex,
endoplasmic reticulum, and the paramylon, a
carbohydrate reserve granule.

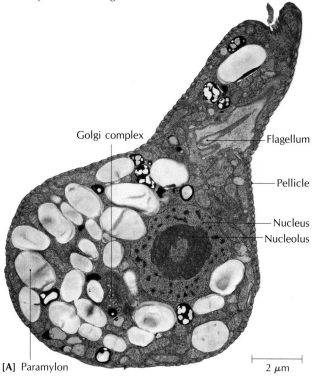

Golgi complex

Flagellum

Pellicle

Nucleus
Nucleolus

[A] Paramylon

2 µm

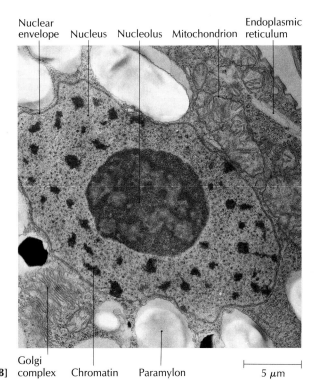

Nuclear
envelope Nucleus Nucleolus Mitochondrion Endoplasmic
reticulum

[B] Golgi complex Chromatin Paramylon

5 µm

FIGURE 4.46
Diagrammatic representation of the nucleus of a
eucaryotic cell.

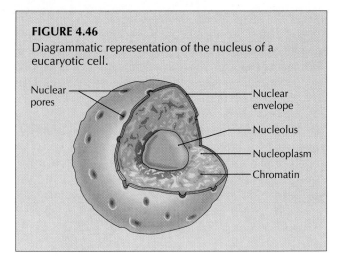

Nuclear
pores

Nuclear
envelope

Nucleolus

Nucleoplasm

Chromatin

FIGURE 4.47
Diagram of the rough endoplasmic reticulum.

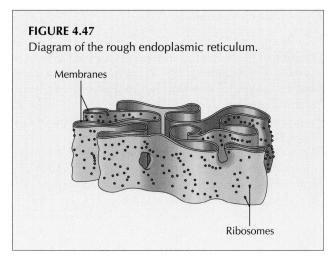

Membranes

Ribosomes

Endoplasmic Reticulum. The endoplasmic reticulum
(ER) is a membranous network of flattened sacs and tubules that are often connected to both the nuclear membrane and the cytoplasmic membrane. This elaborate
system of membranes is not present in procaryotes.
There are two forms of endoplasmic reticulum—*rough*
and *smooth*. The rough ER is studded with ribosomes
[FIGURE 4.47], while the smooth ER is not. Proteins
manufactured by the ribosomes on rough ER either are
released into the cytoplasm or pass across the ER membrane into the channels of the ER, where they are
moved to various parts of the cell.

Instead of protein synthesis, the smooth ER is involved in glycogen, lipid, and steroid synthesis. The
amount and function of the smooth ER found in a cell
depend on the kind of cell; for example, it is more abundant in steroid-producing cells than in those that primarily synthesize protein. The channels of smooth ER also
aid in the distribution of synthesized substances
throughout the cell.

FIGURE 4.48
Diagram of the Golgi complex.

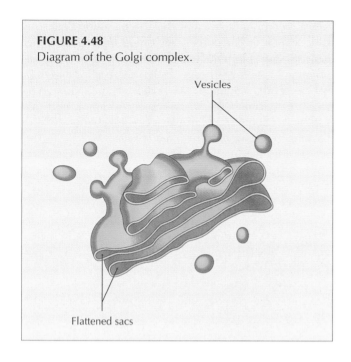

Vesicles

Flattened sacs

Mitochondria. Activities in a cell require energy, whether for macromolecular synthesis or for transport of substances through or out of the cytoplasm. *Mitochondria* (singular, *mitochondrion*) are cytoplasmic organelles where the energy-rich molecules of adenosine triphosphate (ATP) are generated during a biochemical process called *aerobic respiration.* Because of this function, the mitochondria are called the "powerhouses" of the eucaryotic cell.

A typical mitochondrion measures about 0.5 to 1.0 μm in diameter and several micrometers in length. Despite its small size, this organelle is an efficient energy producer. The inner membrane is highly invaginated [FIGURE 4.49], much like the surface of a natural sponge. Energy conversion takes place on the inner membrane of the mitochondrion, a function similar to that of the cytoplasmic membrane of the procaryotic cell. The infoldings in the inner membrane, called *cristae,* increase the surface area available for respiratory activity.

Although mitochondria are organelles of eucaryotic cells, they resemble procaryotic cells in several ways. For instance, they contain their own ribosomes, which

Golgi Complex. The *Golgi complex* is composed of flattened membranous sacs that have spherical vesicles at their tips [FIGURE 4.48]. This organelle was first described by Camillo Golgi in 1898. It is the *packaging center* of eucaryotic cells, responsible for safe transport of synthesized compounds to the cell's exterior and protection of the cell from its own enzymes. Part of its role is as a distribution center for the cell. The Golgi complex is connected to the cell's cytoplasmic membrane and fuses with it in order to release the contents outside the cell, a process called *exocytosis.*

Another function of the Golgi complex is to package certain enzymes synthesized by the rough ER into organelles called *lysosomes.* These enzymes catalyze hydrolytic reactions, reactions in which water is used to split chemical compounds. They include proteases, nucleases, glycosidases, sulfatases, lipases, and phosphatases. The contents of lysosomes are not excreted but remain in the cytoplasm and participate in cytoplasmic digestion of materials ingested or absorbed by the cell. Containment of the hydrolytic enzymes within lysosomes also protects the cell from the damaging action of its own enzymes.

In addition, the Golgi complex usually contains glycosyltransferase enzymes that attach carbohydrate molecules such as glucose to certain proteins to make glycoproteins. The carbohydrate molecules are needed to make these proteins function properly in the cell. Proteins made on the rough ER are brought into the Golgi complex, where sugars are added to produce glycoproteins.

FIGURE 4.49
In bacterial cells the electron-transport system occurs in the cytoplasmic membrane. In eucaryotic cells the electron-transport system is located within small organelles called *mitochondria*, which are about 1 to 3 μm long (the same size as many bacteria). A mitochondrion has two membranes; the inner one contains the electron-transport system and has numerous infoldings.

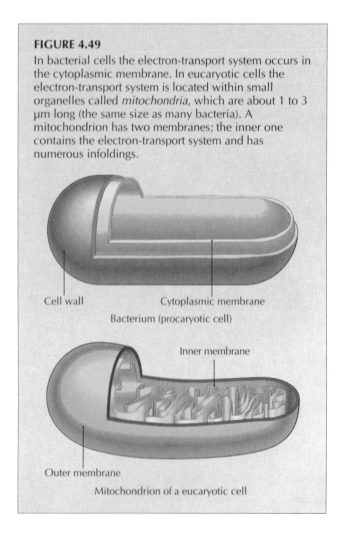

Cell wall

Cytoplasmic membrane

Bacterium (procaryotic cell)

Inner membrane

Outer membrane

Mitochondrion of a eucaryotic cell

are of the procaryotic type (70 S) rather than the eucaryotic type (80 S). They also contain their own DNA, which, like procaryotic DNA, is a single circular, double-stranded molecule. The exact size of this DNA depends on the eucaryotic species, but it is about 1/200 the size of procaryotic DNA. It carries the genetic instructions for making a limited number of proteins, which are produced on the mitochondrial ribosomes. Finally, mitochondria divide to form new mitochondria in much the same way that a procaryotic cell divides, and they divide independently of the cell's nucleus. (However, they are unable to divide if they are removed from the cytoplasm.)

Chloroplasts. In addition to the mitochondrion, algae have another energy-generating cytoplasmic organelle called the *chloroplast* [FIGURE 4.50]. This is the site of photosynthetic reactions, in which light is used as the energy source for the cell. This energy is used to convert carbon dioxide to sugars, and to convert the oxygen atoms in water to molecules of gaseous oxygen. The chloroplast is a cucumber-shaped body (2 to 3 μm wide, 5 to 10 μm long) surrounded by a double membrane. Its interior is called the *stroma*, where DNA (circular, like procaryotic DNA) codes for proteins on the chloroplast ribosomes (70 S, like procaryotic ribosomes) and for the enzymes needed to use carbon dioxide from the air. The

inner membrane folds into the stroma to form stacks of disk-shaped or ribbonlike sacs called *thylakoids*, which contain the chlorophyll and carotenoid pigments that function in photosynthesis. Each stack is called a *granum* (plural, *grana*). Some of the thylakoids on a granum attach to thylakoids on other grana, forming a network. Like mitochondria, chloroplasts are capable of dividing by binary fission within the cytoplasm.

The similarities of both mitochondria and chloroplasts to procaryotic microorganisms are in accord with the endosymbiotic theory of the origin of these organelles (see Chapter 2).

ASK YOURSELF

1 In what ways is the eucaryotic cell more complex morphologically than the procaryotic cell?

2 What is meant by the "9 + 2" structure of eucaryotic flagella and cilia? What kind of energy powers the movement of these appendages?

3 How do amoebas move?

4 What can be said about the general composition of the cell walls of fungi and algae? In what way are they different from procaryotic cell walls?

5 How is the cytoplasmic membrane of eucaryotes different from that of procaryotes?

6 What is the difference between the *karyoplasm* and the *cytoplasm*?

7 What are the functions of the various organelles (such as the nucleus, endoplasmic reticulum, Golgi complex, mitochondria, and chloroplasts) in the eucaryotic cell?

DORMANT FORMS OF EUCARYOTIC MICROORGANISMS

As described earlier in this chapter, some microorganisms can produce dormant forms called *spores* and *cysts* that can withstand unfavorable conditions. Both fungi and protozoa include species that use such resting structures for protection and reproduction. Algae also form spores but their main function is for reproduction. Algae do not form cysts.

Spores

Fungi produce both *sexual* and *asexual* spores. Sexual spores are produced as a result of the fusion of two spe-

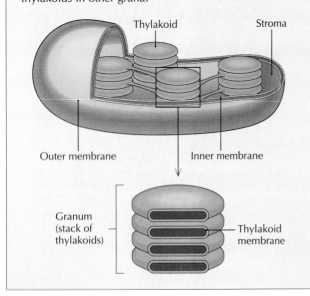

FIGURE 4.50
In eucaryotic cells, thylakoids occur within special organelles called *chloroplasts*, which are larger than mitochondria. In the chloroplasts of plant cells the thylakoids are flattened, disk-shaped sacs arranged in stacks; each stack is called a *granum* (plural, *grana*). Some of the granum thylakoids are connected to thylakoids in other grana.

Thylakoid

Stroma

Outer membrane

Inner membrane

Granum (stack of thylakoids)

Thylakoid membrane

FIGURE 4.51

Types of asexual spores in the fungi.

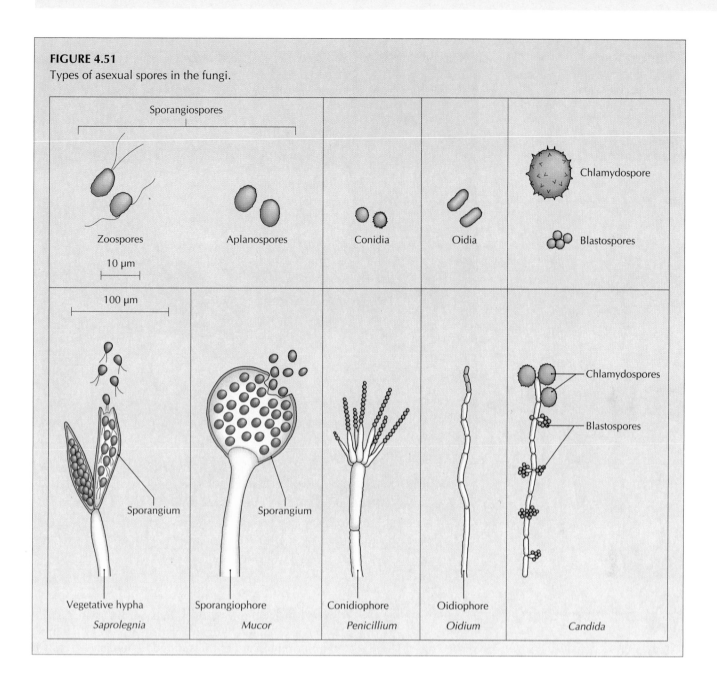

cialized reproductive cells called *gametes* into one fertilized cell. The formation of asexual spores does not involve the fusion of gametes. Each thallus can produce hundreds of thousands of asexual spores, which are produced by the aerial hyphae. Their purpose is to disseminate the species, and they are specially structured for dispersion from the mother thallus. Spores of aquatic fungi may be motile in water; spores of soil fungi may have thick coats to withstand drying or may be light enough to travel on air currents. Asexual spores are usually white when first produced, but they turn a characteristic color with age. For example, spores of *Penicil-*

lium notatum colonies are typically blue-green, while those of *Aspergillus niger* are black. There are many kinds of asexual spores found among the fungi [FIGURE 4.51].

Sexual spores are produced less frequently and in smaller numbers than asexual spores. FIGURES 4.52 to 4.55 illustrate in more detail the formation of different types of sexual spores. Although a single fungus may produce both asexual and sexual spores by several methods at different times, spore structures are sufficiently constant that they can be used in fungal identification and classification.

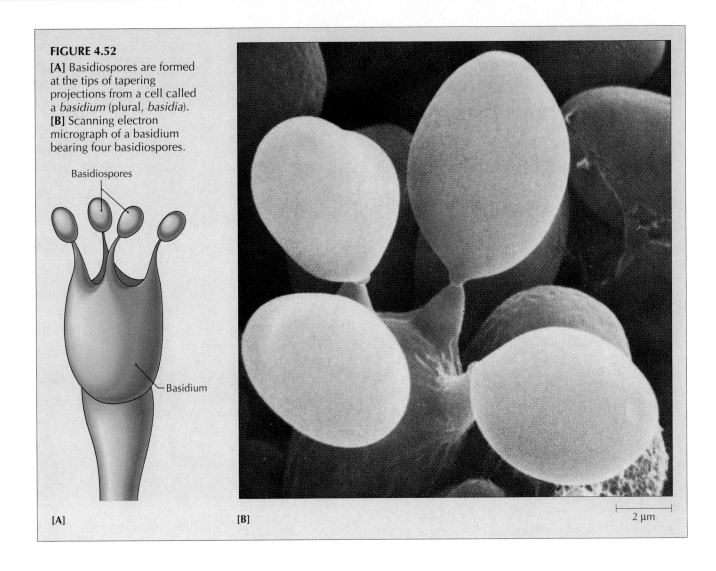

FIGURE 4.52
[A] Basidiospores are formed at the tips of tapering projections from a cell called a *basidium* (plural, *basidia*). [B] Scanning electron micrograph of a basidium bearing four basidiospores.

Basidiospores

Basidium

[A]　　　　[B]

2 μm

Cysts

Many protozoa produce resting forms called *cysts*. There are two possible forms of protozoan cysts: *protective* cysts and *reproductive* cysts. The vegetative forms of protozoa, or **trophozoites,** synthesize protective cysts that are resistant to drying, lack of food, lack of oxygen, or acidity in the host's stomach. When conditions once again become favorable, the cysts form trophozoites that feed and grow. By contrast, reproductive cysts are not induced by adverse environmental conditions. They are often thin-walled and lack the resistance of protective cysts.

Parasitic species of protozoa often move from host to host as cysts, making these structures important as modes of transmission as well. Such cysts form in the intestinal tract and are excreted in the feces, which contaminate water and food ingested by the next host. With many of these parasites, the cyst is the only way the protozoan is able to survive outside the host. *Giardia lamblia*, a causative agent of diarrhea and abdominal cramps in humans, is transmitted to humans by cysts in water supplies contaminated with feces [see FIGURE 4.41].

ASK YOURSELF

1 What groups of eucaryotic microorganisms produce dormant forms?

2 What are the characteristics of asexual spores of fungi? How different are they from sexual spores?

3 When do trophozoites form protective cysts?

4 Are cysts important in the transmission of disease?

FIGURE 4.53

[A] In the formation of ascospores, nuclear fusion (karyogamy) takes place in the ascus. The diploid zygote nucleus divides by meiosis almost immediately after karyogamy, and produces four haploid nuclei. These haploid nuclei divide once more by mitosis, forming the eight ascospores typically produced in each ascus. [B] Photomicrograph of asci containing ascospores.

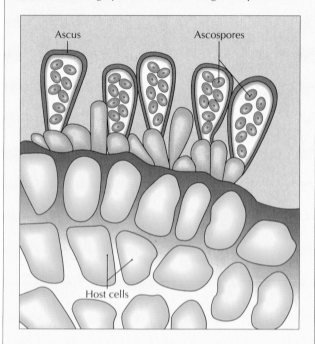

[A]

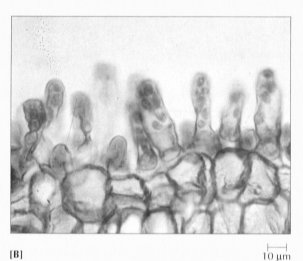

[B]   10 μm

FIGURE 4.54

Formation of zygospores. [A] Zygospore formation starts when two compatible gametangia begin to fuse together. Note the presence also of a sporangium containing sporangiospores. [B] Zygospores in *Mucor hiemalis.* Sexual reproduction occurs when two sexually compatible mating types, + and –, come in contact with each other and produce zygospores. Zygospores of different ages are shown, the oldest being darkest, largest, and roughest.

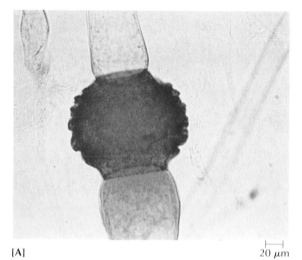

[A]   20 μm

[B]   20 μm

FIGURE 4.55

[A] Female gametes, egg cells called *oospheres*, are formed within a special female structure called an *oogonium* (plural, *oogonia*). Oospores develop when the oospheres are fertilized by male gametes produced in structures called *antheridia* (singular, *antheridium*). [B] Photomicrograph of an *Achlya* species showing many oogonia, each containing several oospheres (dark bodies). [C] Photomicrograph of an oogonium containing three oospheres. Two antheridia are in contact with the lower portion of the oogonium. Note the bumplike protrusions that occur along the wall of the oogonium. [D] Scanning electron micrograph of an oogonium of *Achlya recurva*, showing antheridia (threadlike structures) lying in close contact with the oogonium. Knoblike protrusions along the oogonium surface give the oogonium a sea minelike appearance. Oospheres are not visible within the oogonium.

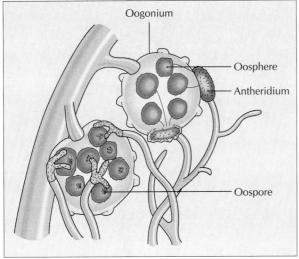
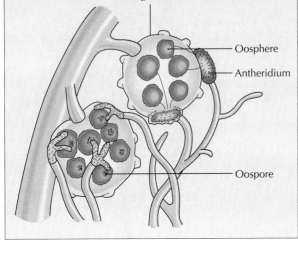

[A]

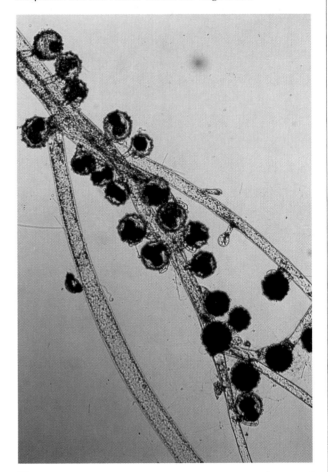

[B]

90 μm

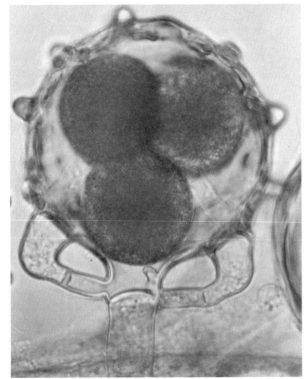

[C]

15 μm

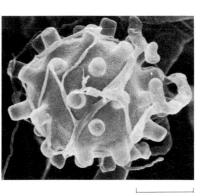

[D]

20 μm

SUMMARY

1 Bacteria are small procaryotic cells that average 0.5 to 1.0 μm in diameter or width. There are three basic shapes of bacteria: spherical, cylindrical, and helical. Other shapes are less common, but do occur. Certain arrangements of cells, such as pairs or chains, are characteristic of different bacterial species.

2 Many bacteria have flagella for locomotion; different species of motile bacteria exhibit characteristic numbers and arrangements of flagella. Pili help the cell attach to a surface or to bring cells into contact for the exchange of genetic material from one cell to another.

3 The glycocalyx helps cells adhere to surfaces, but it can also serve as energy storage and as a coat that defends the bacterium against attack by other cells.

4 The cell wall gives shape to the cell and protects it from forces such as osmotic pressure. There are two main types of eubacterial cell walls: the Gram-positive and the Gram-negative. They are distinctly different in structure and in chemical composition, and the Gram reaction is based on these differences.

5 The cytoplasmic membrane of procaryotes is composed mainly of phospholipids and protein components arranged in a bilayer. Its main function is to regulate permeability and transport into and out of the cell. It is also the site of energy production.

6 Ribosomes and DNA are the primary structures found inside a procaryotic cell. The ribosomes function in protein synthesis, while DNA is the genetic system of the cell. Various kinds of inclusions are also found within the procaryotic cytoplasm, many of them accumulations of different molecules that serve as a reserve source of nutrients.

7 Some bacteria differentiate into metabolically dormant bodies, such as endospores, conidia, and cysts, which are resistant to adverse environments.

8 Eucaryotic microorganisms show even more diversity in size, shape, and arrangement than the procaryotes. They can form elaborate structures.

9 Eucaryotic flagella and cilia are structurally and functionally more complex than their procaryotic counterparts. The eucaryotic appendages are made of microtubules in clusters; they obtain energy and move in a manner different from procaryotic structures.

10 Cell walls and cytoplasmic membranes of eucaryotic organisms differ from those of procaryotes and from each other in structure and composition.

11 Eucaryotes are distinguished from procaryotes primarily by their membrane-enclosed nucleus. Eucaryotes contain other cellular organelles, such as the endoplasmic reticulum, the Golgi complex, mitochondria, and chloroplasts.

12 Like bacteria, the eucaryotic microorganisms produce dormant bodies that help protect them from adverse conditions. Some of these structures are also used to disseminate the species.

KEY TERMS

bacilli (singular, bacillus)
bacteriophages
capsule
chemotaxis
chloroplast
chromosome
cilia (singular, cilium)
cocci (singular, coccus)
conidium (plural, conidia)
cristae
cysts
cytoplasmic membrane
cytoskeleton
endoplasmic reticulum
endospores
flagella (singular, flagellum)
glycocalyx
Golgi complex
granum (plural, grana)
hyphae (singular, hypha)
lipopolysaccharides (LPSs)
lipoprotein
lysosomes
mesosomes
mitochondria (singular, mitochondrion)
mycelium (plural, mycelia)
nuclear membrane
nucleolus
osmosis
peptidoglycan
periplasmic flagella
pili (singular, pilus)
pseudopodia (singular, pseudopodium)
ribosomes
simple diffusion
slime layer
spirilla (singular, spirillum)
sporangium (plural, sporangia)
spores
teichoic acids
thallus (plural, thalli)
thylakoids
trophozoites
volutin granules

OVERVIEW

1 Treating bacterial cells with high-frequency sound waves will _____ their cell walls.

2 Structures found on the outside of cells make some microorganisms more _____.

GROSS MORPHOLOGICAL CHARACTERISTICS OF PROCARYOTIC MICROORGANISMS

3 Most bacteria are approximately _____ to _____ μm in width or in diameter.

4 Helical bacteria are called _____.

5 Cocci are _____ cells.

6 *Pasteuria* has _____ cells, whereas *Caryophanon* has _____ cells.

7 For bacterial cells, the ratio of surface area to volume when compared with that of larger organisms of similar shape is **(a)** higher; **(b)** lower; **(c)** the same.

8 Cocci dividing in one plane and remaining attached to form chains are described as _____.

9 The pattern of arrangement of *Caulobacter* species is described as a(n) _____ arrangement.

10 Which description most accurately fits the cell shape of *Arthrobacter*?
(a) pear-shaped
(b) disks arranged like stacks of coins
(c) pleomorphic
(d) cigar-shaped

ULTRASTRUCTURE OF PROCARYOTIC MICROORGANISMS

11 The basal body of the flagella of Gram-negative bacteria has _____ pairs of rings.

12 The protein molecules that make up the filaments of bacterial flagella are called _____.

13 A bacterial cell with a tuft of flagella at one pole is said to be _____.

14 Flagella of spirochetes are called _____ flagella.

15 The swimming path of a peritrichous bacterium is called a(n) _____.

16 When the motors of the flagella reverse and the flagellum bundle flies apart, the cell is said to _____.

17 Most bacterial pili function to _____ the cell to surfaces.

18 The F pilus is also known as the _____ pilus.

19 If the glycocalyx is organized and is attached firmly to a cell, it is known as a(n)

_____.

20 Bacterial cells whose walls have been *completely* removed are known as

_____.

21 The walls of Gram-negative bacteria are morphologically

_____ than those of Gram-positive species.

22 Another name for peptidoglycan is _____.

23 The three building blocks of a peptidoglycan unit are

_____, _____, and a short peptide.

24 Unlike the eubacterial cell wall, the archaeobacterial cell wall does not contain

_____.

25 _____ acids are polymers of glycerol and ribitol phosphates found in Gram-positive bacterial cell walls.

26 An outer membrane is found in the cell wall of _____ eubacteria.

27 The outer membrane of a Gram-negative bacterium is composed of lipoprotein

and _____.

28 The peptidoglycan layer of Gram-negative bacteria is located in the

_____ space.

29 Lipid A of LPS is also known as _____.

30 The three covalently linked parts of LPS are _____,

_____, and polysaccharide O antigens.

31 Special proteins called _____ in the outer membrane allow selected small molecules to pass across it.

32 Membrane invaginations into the bacterial cytoplasm are known as

_____.

33 A chloroform-soluble, lipidlike inclusion in bacteria is composed of

_____.

34 The nuclear material in a bacterial cell is known as the

_____.

35 Match each statement on the right with the correct adjective describing the medium on the left.

_____ hypertonic   **(a)** Overall concentrations of solutes are the same on either
_____ hypotonic   side of a semipermeable membrane.
_____ isotonic   **(b)** Concentration of solutes is lower outside than inside the cell.
   (c) Concentration of solutes is higher outside than inside the cell.

36 Dormant structures facilitate _____ under unfavorable environmental conditions.

37 By light microscopy, bacterial endospores are seen as highly

_____ structures.

38 Endospores are produced _____ per cell by species of bacteria belonging to the genera *Bacillus* and *Clostridium*.

39 Bacterial endospores can survive extreme _____, desiccation, and toxic chemicals.

40 The genus of eubacteria best known for the production of cysts is

_____.

41 Match the spore form on the right with the bacterium on the left.

_____ *Bacillus*   **(a)** Conidia

_____ *Azotobacter*   **(b)** Endospore

_____ actinomycete   **(c)** Cyst

42 Obvious examples of algae and fungi which are not microscopic are the _____ and the _____, respectively.

43 While the yeasts are generally oval and unicellular in morphology, the molds are _____ and multicellular.

44 Pathogenic fungi that exist either in a unicellular yeastlike form as a parasite or in a filamentous form as a saprophyte are said to exhibit

_____.

45 Protozoa have the following animal-like characteristics: they can move, they lack _____, and they can ingest

_____.

46 The distinctive characteristic of algae that sets them apart from other eucaryotic

protists is that they are _____.

47 Match each organism or cell on the right with the most appropriate cell-wall compound(s) on the left.

_____ peptidoglycan

_____ mannan

_____ cellulose, other polysaccharides, silicon, and calcium carbonate

_____ chitin, cellulose

_____ cellulose, hemicellulose, pectin

(a) Yeasts

(b) Molds

(c) Algae

(d) Bacteria

(e) Plants

48 Match each description on the right with the most appropriate term on the left.

_____ cell's hereditary DNA

_____ semipermeability

_____ protein synthesis

_____ packaging center

_____ "powerhouse"

_____ photosynthesis

_____ "9 + 2"

(a) Property of the cytoplasmic membrane

(b) Fine structure of eucaryotic cilia and flagella

(c) Substance in the nucleus

(d) Function of the rough endoplasmic reticulum

(e) Function of the Golgi complex

(f) Function carried out by the chloroplast

(g) Term for the mitochondrion

DORMANT FORMS
OF EUCARYOTIC
MICROORGANISMS

49 Both fungi and _____ include species that produce spores or cysts that can withstand unfavorable conditions.

50 Asexual spores of *Penicillium notatum* colonies are typically

_____ in color, while those of *Aspergillus niger* are

_____ .

51 _____ spores are produced by the hundreds of thousands by each fungal thallus.

52 Protozoa produce two kinds of cysts: _____ cysts and

_____ cysts.

REVIEW QUESTIONS

1 What are the practical implications to the bacterial cell of having a high surface area to volume ratio?

2 Describe the characteristic and unique cell arrangements of some bacterial species.

3 Draw a bacterial cell and label all its identifiable parts.

4 With the aid of a diagram, explain the meaning of *tumbles* and *runs* in the chemotaxis of a peritrichously flagellated bacterial cell.

5 What are the different forms and functions of the glycocalyx of a bacterial cell?

6 Compare the structure and chemistry of the cell walls of Gram-negative and Gram-positive bacteria.

7 Explain the role of porins in the outer membrane of the Gram-negative bacterial cell.

8 What are mesosomes, and what are their most probable functions?

9 Where do ribosomes occur in the bacterial cell?

10 When ribosomes are the site of antibiotic action, what metabolic process is inhibited?

11 Describe some inclusions in bacterial cells, and indicate how their chemical nature can be determined cytologically.

12 Describe some unique properties of bacterial endospores.

13 Explain why endospore formation in bacteria is not a mode of cell reproduction.

14 What is dimorphism? What microorganisms exhibit it?

15 Describe the morphology of the thallus of a mold.

16 What is meant by polymorphism in the protozoa?

17 What is the outstanding ultrastructural feature of the eucaryotic cell that distinguishes it from the procaryotic cell?

18 Describe the unique arrangement of microtubules that form eucaryotic flagella and cilia.

19 How do amoebas move?

20 What form and function do the following organelles have in the eucaryotic cell? (a) endoplasmic reticulum, (b) Golgi complex, (c) mitochondrion, (d) chloroplast.

21 Describe the different forms of fungal asexual and sexual spores.

DISCUSSION QUESTIONS

1 What properties of spirochetes set them apart from the spirilla?

2 How do the locomotor organelles of procaryotic cells differ from those of eucaryotic cells with respect to mechanisms of energization and of movement?

3 Why do we say that bacteria respond chemotactically to a *temporal gradient*?

4 Explain why the glycocalyx is of importance in the infectious process of pathogenic microorganisms.

5 Explain why the peptidoglycan has been called a "bag-shaped macromolecule."

6 How does the cell-wall chemistry of eubacteria and archaeobacteria reflect in part their separate evolution?

7 Describe the three covalently linked segments of liposaccharide in the outer membrane of Gram-negative bacteria, and discuss their relevance to medicine.

8 Describe the functions of the proteins in the outer membrane of Gram-negative bacteria.

9 What is the generally accepted mechanism for the differential reaction of the Gram stain?

10 How does the chemical composition of the cytoplasmic membrane allow it to have dynamic fluidity?

11 Explain what happens to bacterial cells when they are suspended in media of different tonicities, that is, when the medium is isotonic, hypertonic, or hypotonic.

12 Compare the distribution of ribosomes in the procaryotic and the eucaryotic cell.

13 What is known about the mechanism of heat resistance of the bacterial endospore?

14 In what way is the algal colony different from the bacterial colony?

15 Compare and contrast the procaryotic flagellum with the eucaryotic one in terms of ultrastructure.

16 Discuss the fine structure of the eucaryotic nuclear membrane and the contents it encloses.

17 What properties of the mitochondria and the chloroplasts give rise to the endosymbiotic theory of their origin?

18 How do the dormant forms of protozoa contribute to the transmission of disease?

II

Nutrition and Cultivation
of Microorganisms

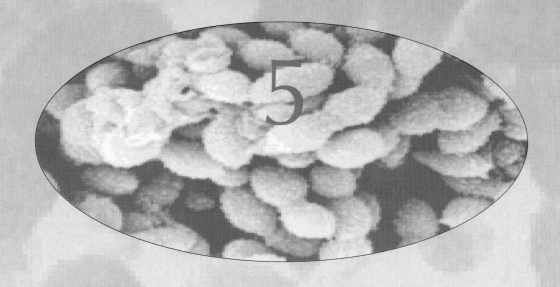

Nutritional Requirements
and Microbiological Media

OBJECTIVES

After reading this chapter you should be able to

1 Discuss the reasons for the laboratory cultivation of microorganisms.

2 Explain in general terms how chemical elements are used for cell growth.

3 Distinguish between autotrophs and heterotrophs and state how these categories are used in the nutritional classification of microorganisms.

4 Explain why nutritional requirements are used to classify bacteria and yeasts into different taxonomic groups.

5 Distinguish between chemically defined and undefined (complex) media, and between solid and liquid media.

6 Determine how and when to use special-purpose media.

7 Discuss the importance of tissue cultures and how they are propagated.

OVERVIEW

Of all living organisms, microorganisms are the most versatile and diversified in their nutritional requirements. Humans and other animals all require certain types of complex carbon-containing compounds as nutrients, while microorganisms may not. Some microbes can grow with just a few *inorganic* substances as their sole nutritional requirements, while other microorganisms are more like higher organisms in their need for complex *organic* compounds. But all living organisms share some common nutritional needs, like the need for carbon, nitrogen, and water. Water is particularly important to microorganisms, because most microorganisms can absorb nutrients only when the chemicals are dissolved in water. These chemical requirements, along with the physical requirements discussed in the next chapter, must be satisfied by an organism's environment in order for it to grow.

Sometimes microorganisms are studied in their natural habitats. Microbiologists do field research in Antarctica, the hot pools and springs of Yellowstone National Park, the ocean floors, and the sewage treatment plants of large cities. However, in order to characterize the morphological, physiological, and biochemical properties of microbes, laboratory cultivation of microbial cells is necessary. Controlling the environment in which microorganisms are growing can be used to make accurate identification of species and measurements of microbial growth.

The cultivation of microorganisms requires the appropriate culture *media* (singular, *medium*). Media are nutrient preparations used for the growth of microbes in the laboratory. Many microbes, as well as cells of both plants and animals, can be grown in vitro (in laboratory vessels) if proper media are used. Some microorganisms have not been cultivated on or in artificial media because their complex nutritional requirements are not understood. Such microbes— for example, the causative agent of leprosy—must be grown in vivo, or in a living host organism. By understanding and manipulating the nutritional sources available in the laboratory setting, microbiologists can select, identify, and study specific microorganisms.

CHEMICAL ELEMENTS AS NUTRIENTS

In order to grow, all organisms need a variety of chemical elements as nutrients. These elements are necessary for both the synthesis and the normal functions of cellular components. They exist in nature in a great variety of compounds, which are either inorganic or organic. Details of microbial metabolism are found later in this book, but basically each microorganism utilizes those compounds present in its natural habitat [DISCOVER 5.1]. When microorganisms are removed from their environment and cultivated in the laboratory, microbiologists use media that simulate or even improve on natural conditions. One of the things that must be done is to provide the proper essential chemical elements. The main elements for cell growth include carbon, nitrogen, hydrogen, oxygen, sulfur, and phosphorus.

Carbon

Carbon is one of the most important chemical elements required for microbial growth. All organisms require carbon in some form. In general, *organic* compounds are those that contain carbon, while *inorganic* compounds are those that do not. (An exception is carbon dioxide, which biologists consider to be like an inorganic compound.) As you learned in Chapter 1 of this book, carbon forms the backbone of three major classes of organic nutrients: carbohydrates, lipids, and proteins. Such compounds provide energy for cell growth and serve as building blocks of cellular material. Those microbes that use organic compounds as their major carbon source are called **heterotrophs.** Heterotrophs obtain such organic molecules by absorbing them from the environment, or by ingesting autotrophs or other heterotrophs.

Microorganisms that use carbon dioxide (the most oxidized form of carbon) as their major or even sole source of carbon are called **autotrophs.** They can live exclusively on relatively simple inorganic molecules and ions absorbed from the environment.

Nitrogen

All organisms also require nitrogen in some form. The element is an essential part of amino acids that together form proteins. Bacteria are particularly versatile in the utilization of nitrogen. Unlike eucaryotic cells, some bacteria can use atmospheric or gaseous nitrogen for cell synthesis through a process called **nitrogen fixation.** Others use inorganic nitrogen compounds such as nitrates, nitrites, or ammonium salts, while some require organic nitrogen compounds such as amino acids or peptides.

Hydrogen, Oxygen, Sulfur, and Phosphorus

Other elements essential to all organisms are hydrogen, oxygen, sulfur, and phosphorus. Hydrogen and oxygen form part of many organic compounds. Sulfur is needed for the biosynthesis of the amino acids cysteine, cystine, and methionine. Phosphorus is essential for the synthesis of nucleic acids and **adenosine triphosphate (ATP)**, a compound that is extremely important for energy storage and transfer. Some of these elements are found in water, as components of various nutrients, or in the gaseous atmosphere of the environment. Inorganic ions such as sulfate (SO_4^{2-}) and phosphate (PO_4^{3-}) can also supply the main elements needed by microorganisms.

Other Elements

Many other essential elements are required, though in smaller amounts than the elements already listed. These may facilitate the transport of materials across cell membranes. For example, Na^+ is required by the permease that transports the sugar melibiose into cells of *Escherichia coli*. Moreover, essential elements are often required as cofactors for enzymes. For example, Fe^{2+} is required for such enzymes as cytochromes, catalase, and succinic dehydrogenase. Microbes differ in the concentration of ions they require. Some "salt-loving" bacteria called *red extreme halophiles* cannot grow with less than 15 percent sodium chloride in the environment.

Other mineral elements are also needed, but usually in extremely small amounts (a few milligrams per liter). Examples of these *trace elements* are zinc (Zn^{2+}), copper (Cu^{2+}), manganese (Mn^{2+}), molybdenum (Mo^{6+}), and cobalt (Co^{2+}). They are required to activate enzymes. For example, Mo^{6+} is required by *nitrogenase*, the enzyme that converts atmospheric nitrogen gas (N_2) to ammonia (NH_3) during nitrogen fixation. They may be added specifically as salts to microbiological media, but they usually occur as impurities in other media compo-

FIGURE 5.1

One way of producing pure water in the laboratory for preparation of media is by distillation. Shown here is a compact still (a still is a distilling apparatus) used in microbiological laboratories for producing distilled water.

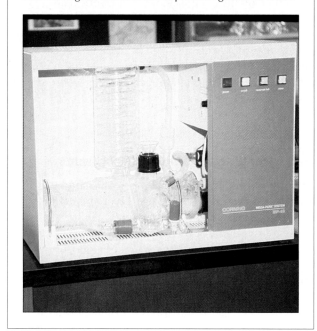

nents. Media and even water must be carefully purified to ensure the absence of contaminating trace elements when the nutritional requirements for trace elements are studied [FIGURE 5.1]. The necessity of trace elements for microbial growth was discovered in the last half of the nineteenth century by a follower of Pasteur, Jules Raulin. Raulin spent 10 years studying the nutritional requirements of a single mold.

ASK YOURSELF

1 Why do organisms need chemical elements as nutrients?

2 What are the main essential elements for cell growth?

3 What is the form of carbon needed by heterotrophs for their nutrition? By autotrophs?

4 Why do all organisms require nitrogen in some form?

5 What are the sulfur-containing amino acids?

6 What function do trace elements serve in cells?

NUTRITIONAL CLASSIFICATION OF MICROORGANISMS

Organisms that use chemical compounds for energy are called *chemotrophs*. Those that depend primarily on radiant energy (light) are designated *phototrophs*. By combining these terms with those concerning principal carbon sources, the following groupings emerge:

1 *Chemoautotrophs*—those organisms that use chemical substances (inorganic) as sources of energy and carbon dioxide as the main source of carbon

2 *Chemoheterotrophs*—those that use chemical substances (organic) as sources of energy and organic compounds as the main source of carbon

3 *Photoautotrophs*—those that use light as a source of energy and carbon dioxide as the main source of carbon

4 *Photoheterotrophs*—those that use light as a source of energy and organic compounds as the main source of carbon

This nutritional classification of microorganisms and examples of each are summarized in TABLE 5.1.

It should be remembered that some species of microorganisms are versatile in their nutritional needs; they cannot be categorized exclusively into one of the four groupings. For example, certain phototrophic bacteria can also grow as chemotrophs. In the absence of oxygen (anaerobic conditions), *Rhodospirillum rubrum* depends on light as its energy source and lives as a photoheterotroph. However, in the presence of oxygen

FIGURE 5.2

Photomicrograph of the intestinal bacterium *Escherichia coli.*

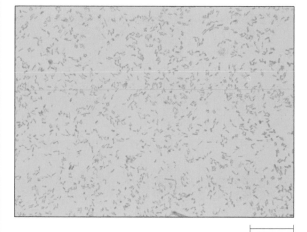

25 μm

5.1 ONE ORGANISM CAN HELP ANOTHER TO GROW

In nature, organisms often compete with one another for available food. But there are also many cases in which one organism helps another to obtain nutrients for growth. One way this happens is when one organism produces a waste product that another organism uses as food. A good example is the relationship of the three species of bacteria—*Streptococcus thermophilus, Lactobacillus bulgaricus,* and *Propionibacterium shermanii*—used in the manufacture of Swiss cheese. The streptococci and lactobacilli ferment the lactose sugar in milk and produce lactic acid as their waste product. The propionibacteria, which do not use lactose, can then grow on the lactic acid

to produce propionic acid as their waste product. The propionic acid gives Swiss cheese its characteristic nutlike flavor. Similarly, in the manufacture of vinegar, yeasts ferment glucose and produce ethyl alcohol as their waste product. Bacteria called *acetobacters* then grow on this ethyl alcohol and produce acetic acid, which gives vinegar its acrid flavor.

Two organisms can benefit equally when each makes an essential nutrient required by the other. For instance, *Bacillus polymyxa* and *Proteus vulgaris* will not grow separately in a laboratory culture medium lacking the vitamins niacin and biotin. However, they can grow together in such a medium as a mixed cul-

ture. This is because the *B. polymyxa* makes the niacin required by the *P. vulgaris,* and the *P. vulgaris* makes the biotin needed by the *B. polymyxa.* Thus the two organisms can grow together under conditions where neither could grow alone. Another example of a mutually beneficial interaction is that between bacteria called *rhizobia* and leguminous plants. The bacteria live within the roots of plants such as soybeans, clover, and alfalfa. There they convert atmospheric nitrogen to ammonia, which is used by the plants as a nitrogen source. As the plants grow, the products of their photosynthesis provide essential carbon sources for the rhizobia.

TABLE 5.1
Nutritional Classification of Bacteria and Other Organisms

Nutritional group	Carbon source	Energy source	Examples
Chemoautotrophs	Carbon dioxide	Inorganic compounds	Nitrifying, hydrogen, iron, and sulfur bacteria
Chemoheterotrophs	Organic compounds	Organic compounds	Most bacteria, fungi, protozoa, and animals
Photoautotrophs	Carbon dioxide	Light	Purple sulfur and green sulfur bacteria, algae, cyanobacteria, and plants
Photoheterotrophs	Organic compounds	Light	Purple nonsulfur and green nonsulfur bacteria

(aerobic conditions), it can grow in the dark as a chemoheterotroph.

The specific nutritional requirements of different bacteria and yeasts are used extensively for taxonomic purposes. In fact, with advances in computer technology and laboratory instrumentation, there now are automated systems that quickly identify species of bacteria or yeasts on the basis of how they use nutrients. Rather than wait for days for results, microbiologists now can identify a microbe within hours using these systems. Specific tests have been designed for particular groups of bacteria and yeasts, such as Gram-negative intestinal bacilli [FIGURE 5.2] and clinically significant yeasts including *Candida.*

ASK YOURSELF

1 Can bacteria be classified on the basis of their nutritional requirements?

2 Why is *Rhodospirillum rubrum* interesting nutritionally?

3 What is the basis for the nutritional classification of bacteria and other microorganisms?

MEDIA USED FOR CULTIVATING MICROORGANISMS

To determine the precise nutritional requirements of a microorganism, **chemically defined media** are used, because the exact composition of such media is known. By deleting or adding a constituent to defined media, you can assess whether that constituent is essential for the growth of the microorganism [FIGURE 5.3]. However, for the *routine* laboratory cultivation and study of heterotrophs, *complex* culture media prepared from natural products are used. Such media are chemically *undefined*, but they are meant to simulate and even to improve on the natural environment of the microorganisms being studied.

Examples of natural products added to media include meat extract (an aqueous beef extract concentrated

FIGURE 5.3

Whether or not a nutritional constituent is essential for the growth of a bacterium may be tested on a chemically defined medium. Such a test is shown in this series of plates. The "control" plate contains a chemically defined minimal medium; the medium has only glucose and salts but no other organic supplement. Organic supplements to the other three plates are indicated as "anthranilic acid," "indole," and "tryptophan." From the bacterial growth obtained by streaking and incubating the plates, one may conclude that bacterial strain 2 (in the sector marked "2") is *prototrophic*, i.e., it does not require any organic supplements, because it can grow on the minimal medium plate marked "control." Strains 1 and 3 are *auxotrophic*; i.e., they need organic supplements in the minimal medium before they can grow (note no growth on the "control" plate). Strain 1 grows when supplemented with tryptophan, while strain 3 grows when supplemented with indole and tryptophan. This means that strains 1 and 3 are blocked at different steps in the synthesis of tryptophan. The simplified scheme for biosynthesis of tryptophan is as follows:

$$\text{Minimal medium ingredients} \xrightarrow{A} \text{anthranilic acid} \xrightarrow{B} \text{indole} \xrightarrow{C} \text{tryptophan}$$

Prototrophic strain 2 is not blocked at any biosynthetic step and can synthesize tryptophan from minimal medium ingredients. Strain 1 is blocked at step C, since it cannot synthesize tryptophan even when supplemented with anthranilic acid and indole. Strain 3 is blocked at step B, since supplementation with anthranilic acid does not support growth but indole supplement permits synthesis of tryptophan. In this general way, mutant auxotrophs have been used to elucidate the biosynthetic pathways of many biochemicals.

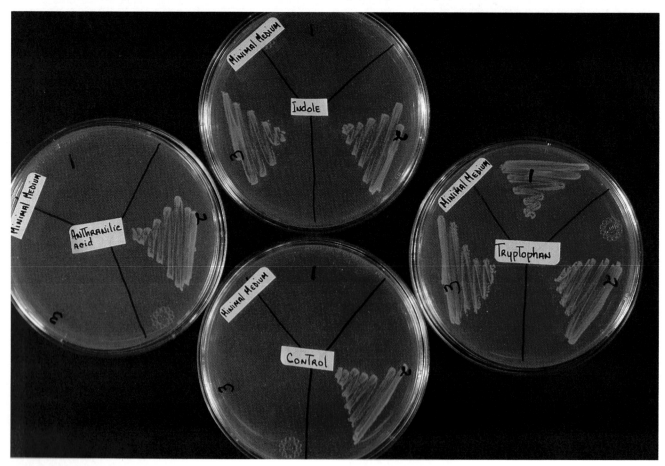

FIGURE 5.4

Different commercially prepared agar media in Petri dishes are shown streaked with bacteria to obtain isolated colonies.

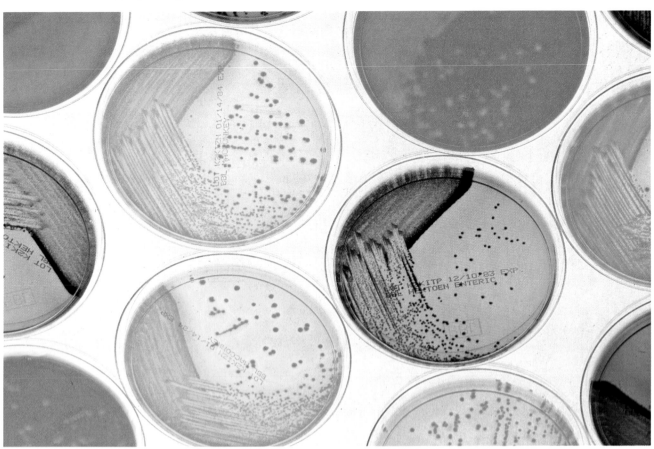

to a paste), peptone (proteins that have been partially degraded by enzymes, such as milk-casein hydrolysate and soybean-protein hydrolysate), yeast extract, blood, serum, milk, soil extract, and bovine rumen fluid. All these materials are complex chemical substances containing sugars, amino acids, vitamins, and salts; their exact composition is unknown. Natural products added to media stimulate growth of a wide variety of heterotrophic microbes. Yeast extract, for example, contains B vitamins that enhance microbial growth.

When a solid medium is necessary for the growth or study of microorganisms, a solidifying agent is added to a liquid medium. Microbiologists normally add *agar*, a complex polysaccharide extracted from marine algae. Agar, which is used at a concentration of about 1.5% (w/v), or 1.5 g/100 ml, has several properties that make it the ideal solidifying agent. It becomes a transparent molten solution at about the boiling point of water (100°C) and then remains liquid down to about 40°C. Because most microorganisms are not killed at 45°C, they can be added to a liquid medium containing molten agar before the medium is poured into tubes or Petri

plates. Once the agar medium cools and solidifies, it will remain solid at the usual incubation temperatures and can be inoculated with microorganisms. Agar is not a nutrient for most microorganisms and is not metabolized during microbial growth.

There are hundreds of different media commercially available [FIGURE 5.4], from those that allow many kinds of microbes to grow to those that allow only one type of microorganism to grow. Some contain dyes to detect pH changes due to metabolism of substrates [FIGURE 5.5]; others encourage microorganisms to produce slime layers or endospores. For rapid identification of microbes in the laboratory, some manufacturers make plastic trays containing many tiny wells, each containing a different dried culture medium [FIGURE 5.6]. When you add a microbial suspension to each well, this rehydrates the dried medium in the well and also inoculates it. Also available are inoculating tools that allow you to place multiple samples of a microbial suspension into these wells in a single step, instead of one by one. Other efficient systems provide a Petri dish that is divided into several compartments, like a pie that has been cut before

FIGURE 5.5
On MacConkey's medium *Escherichia coli* forms red colonies **[A]** while *Shigella sonnei* does not **[B]**. Red coloring is due to reaction of neutral red dye with the acid formed from lactose fermentation by *E. coli*.

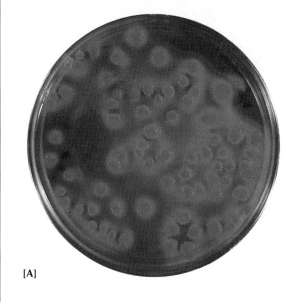

[A]

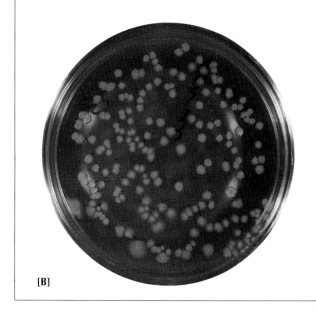

[B]

FIGURE 5.6
Several companies manufacture miniaturized versions of conventional procedures for the identification of bacteria. The API 20E System shown here is for the identification of bacteria in the family *Enterobacteriaceae* and other Gram-negative bacteria. It is a ready-to-use microtube system designed for the performance of standard biochemical tests on isolated colonies of bacteria taken from plating media. The microtubes in the control strip (left) were inoculated with sterile saline solution (0.85% NaCl), while those in the other strip (right) were inoculated with a saline suspension of *Escherichia coli* cells. The dehydrated media were reconstituted upon the addition of saline. During incubation (18 to 24 h at 35 to 37°C), any cells present would react with the contents of the microtubes, causing color changes in the tube.

serving. Each compartment contains a different agar medium, which can be inoculated with a drop of microbial suspension. The results from these media may be evaluated by a computer program that compares them with results obtained with a known microorganism.

Microbiologists can either make their own media from raw materials or dehydrated powders, or buy media ready made from supply firms. Media come in test tubes, Petri plates, bottles, and custom-made plates for automated testing. There are too many microbiological media to discuss each one here, but a survey of general nutritional requirements and the media that satisfy them will show you how microbiologists use media to study microorganisms.

Media for the Growth of Bacteria

Media chosen to cultivate specific bacteria normally imitate the normal habitat of those bacteria. If a bacterium prefers nutrients found in blood, then blood may be added to the medium. If glucose is a common constituent of a bacterial environment, then the sugar is added to the culture medium. Bacteria can be autotrophic or heterotrophic, and the media selected can reflect these characteristics. As mentioned previously, photoautotrophic bacteria require light for energy and only carbon dioxide, water, and some soluble inorganic ions for growth. The chemoautotrophic bacteria have the same nutritional requirements, but they obtain energy from simple inorganic substances rather than light. TABLE 5.2 shows the composition of a typical chemically defined medium for chemoautotrophic bacteria.

The organic compounds required by heterotrophic bacteria vary in kind and number from one group of bacteria to another. Some, such as *Escherichia coli*, can grow very well in media containing only one organic compound such as a sugar plus inorganic ions. The formula of a chemically defined medium for such bacteria is described in TABLE 5.3. At the other extreme, certain heterotrophic bacteria must have as many as 20 amino acids and several vitamins for growth. Microorganisms with demanding nutritional requirements are described

as *fastidious.* Ordinarily, undefined (complex) media are used to cultivate these bacteria, since making the appropriate chemically defined media is a time-consuming and painstaking chore. Complex media contain a great variety of organic substances prepared from natural materials and are therefore not chemically defined. TABLE 5.4 shows the composition of a typical complex medium used for cultivating heterotrophic bacteria.

More fastidious bacteria may require the addition of animal blood or serum. There also are some bacteria that cannot be cultivated in vitro on laboratory media, no matter which media are used. An example is *Treponema pallidum*, the bacterium that causes syphilis. Although

---

TABLE 5.3

Chemically Defined Medium for a Heterotrophic Bacterium

Ingredient	Function	Amount
Glucose	Carbon and energy source	1 g
$NH_4H_2PO_4$	Nitrogen source, buffer, and essential ions	5 g
K_2HPO_4	Buffer and essential ions	1 g
NaCl	Essential ions	5 g
$MgSO_4 \cdot 7H_2O$	Essential ions	0.2 g
Water	Solvent	1000 ml

The above ingredients represent the minimum constituents in a medium for a nonfastidious bacterium such as the wild-type *Escherichia coli*. For a fastidious species, such as *Lactobacillus acidophilus*, additional substances such as amino acids and vitamins have to be added to the medium.

TABLE 5.2

Chemically Defined Medium for a Chemoautotrophic Bacterium

Ingredient	Function	Amount
$(NH_4)_2SO_4$	Nitrogen as well as energy source	0.5 g
$NaHCO_3$	Carbon source in the form of CO_2 in aqueous solution	0.5 g
Na_2HPO_4	Buffer and essential ions	13.5 g
KH_2PO_4	Buffer and essential ions	0.7 g
$MgSO_4 \cdot 7H_2O$	Essential ions	0.1 g
$FeCl_3 \cdot 6H_2O$	Essential ions	0.014 g
$CaCl_2 \cdot 2H_2O$	Essential ions	0.18 g
Water	Solvent	1000 ml

TABLE 5.4

Composition of Nutrient Broth, a Complex Medium for the Growth of Heterotrophic Bacteria

Ingredient	Function	Amount
Beef extract	Water-soluble substances of animal tissue: carbohydrates, organic nitrogen compounds, vitamins, salts	3 g
Peptone	Organic nitrogen, some vitamins	5 g
Sodium chloride	Ions and osmotic requirements	8 g
Water	Solvent	1000 ml

If a solid medium is required, agar (15 g) is added; the medium is then called *nutrient agar.*

this spirochete has been cultivated in rabbits and in cultures of live rabbit cells, it has not been cultivated on a laboratory medium in the absence of host cells [FIGURE 5.7].

Media for the Growth of Fungi

Like bacteria, fungi absorb nutrients and do not ingest them. Absorption is aided by enzymes secreted into the environment, which break down large organic molecules into smaller ones that can pass more readily into the cell. All fungi are heterotrophs. In the laboratory, many fungi can grow in an uncomplicated mixture of a sugar, an inorganic or a simple organic nitrogen source, and a few minerals. Some require a few vitamins as well. Others can grow only on complex media that contain a wide range of organic compounds provided by peptone and meat extract.

In general, media for fungal growth have a higher sugar concentration (4 percent) and a lower pH range (3.8 to 5.6) than media for bacterial growth (generally, pH 6.5 to 7.5). This is seen in more natural settings, particularly when you notice that bacteria frequently contaminate meats and milk, while fungi grow on acidic citrus fruits [FIGURE 5.8], bakery products, and jams and jellies. TABLE 5.5 shows a chemically undefined, general-purpose medium for cultivating many *saprophytic* fungi, those that live on dead organic matter. Note the high concentration of glucose (4%) and the relatively low pH (5.6). This combination favors the growth of fungi,

FIGURE 5.7
Treponema pallidum in fetal liver tissue section from an autopsy specimen. Levaditi's silver stain.

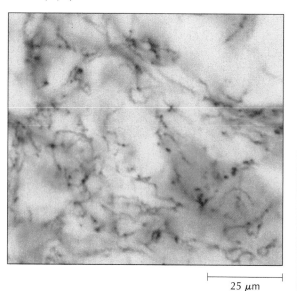

25 μm

FIGURE 5.8
Fungi can grow on acidic citrus fruits. Shown are a healthy orange and tangerine (top); at bottom, what happens when they are overgrown with fungi.

but inhibits the growth of most bacteria. Some *parasitic* fungi, which live in or on a living host, have been cultivated in vitro.

TABLE 5.5
Composition of a General-Purpose Medium, Sabouraud's Agar, for the Isolation and Growth of Fungi

Ingredient	Function	Amount
Peptone	Source of carbon, nitrogen, elements	10 g
Glucose	Carbon and energy source; high concentration favors growth of fungi but inhibits growth of bacteria	40 g
Agar	Solidifying agent	15 g
Water	Solvent	1000 ml
pH	Low pH suppresses bacterial growth but enhances fungal growth	5.6

Media for the Growth of Protozoa

Most protozoa require a pH range of 6 to 8 for optimal growth. Protozoa are aerobic heterotrophs with complex nutritional requirements. Many have not been grown in vitro. Those that can be grown in vitro require a range of amino acids and vitamins, plus carbohydrates. For example, *Tetrahymena pyriformis* can be cultured in a medium containing 10 amino acids, 7 vitamins, the chemicals guanine and uracil, and some inorganic salts. Some amoebas can grow in the relatively simple peptone broth; other protozoa require supplements such as brain tissue emulsion, fetal calf serum, or liver infusion. Some protozoa can grow in nutrient broth or water gelled with agar if they are given bacterial cells to ingest as food.

Media for the Growth of Algae

Algae use light for energy, and require only carbon dioxide, water, and various soluble inorganic ions for growth. Thus they are photoautotrophs. However, certain algae, such as some of the *Euglena* species, are capable of heterotrophic growth in the dark using a narrow range of substrates. Some algae are easier to propagate in vitro than others, especially if chemically undefined media are used. Undefined media for algae usually contain supplements such as soil extract, a rich source of nutrients. Unlike media for bacteria and fungi, there are few commercially available, standardized "packaged" media for algae. Algal media may be prepared from their individual ingredients. In preparing defined media for marine algae, this may be a particularly tedious task if all the salts that make up seawater have to be added individually.

Special-Purpose Media

When microbiologists want to isolate, identify, or count microbes, they use special-purpose media designed to provide specific information about the organism. These include media for microorganisms that grow without oxygen, media that allow only certain organisms to grow, and media that are used to help classify microorganisms on the basis of their growth characteristics.

Media for Anaerobes. For a long time, microbiologists have recognized the existence of some microorganisms called *anaerobes*, organisms that tolerate little or no oxygen and do not use oxygen to obtain energy. In 1885 microbiologists discovered that the anaerobic bacterium *Clostridium tetani* was the cause of tetanus. For years anaerobic bacteria were grown in *agar medium deeps*, or media in tall test tubes. The bacteria could grow in the bottom of these tubes because the top layer of agar excluded atmospheric oxygen [FIGURE 5.9].

Later refinements included the addition of a reducing agent to the media that would remove oxygen, to make what are called **reduced media.** Sodium thioglycolate is a commonly used reducing agent; it chemically combines with oxygen dissolved in the medium and makes it unavailable to microorganisms.

Some anaerobes can tolerate low levels of oxygen, but others, called **strict anaerobes,** cannot tolerate any oxygen at all. The archaeobacteria that produce methane gas are an example. Strict anaerobes can be cultivated only by taking special precautions in preparing media. During media preparation, the culture media are boiled to drive off most of the dissolved oxygen. Oxygen-free nitrogen gas is used to flush the medium-containing vessel, and then a reducing agent must be added (usually cysteine) which removes the last traces of oxygen. Then the media are sterilized by autoclaving (heated under pressure) in the complete absence of oxygen. One

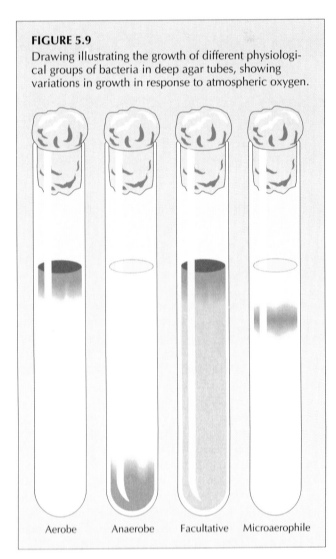

FIGURE 5.9

Drawing illustrating the growth of different physiological groups of bacteria in deep agar tubes, showing variations in growth in response to atmospheric oxygen.

Aerobe   Anaerobe   Facultative   Microaerophile

FIGURE 5.10

Simple flask assembly for the safe and efficient autoclaving of microbiological media in the absence of oxygen. The check valve (CV), fixed to the top of the flask, keeps air from entering the vessel and relieves any pressure changes within the flask during the process of autoclaving.

Check valve

method for autoclaving anaerobe media is to use a check valve on top of the flask to prevent the intake of oxygen [FIGURE 5.10]. In Chapter 6 you will learn about special anaerobic incubators that have simplified the cultivation of anaerobic microorganisms.

Selective Media. *Selective media* are designed to *enhance* the growth of a particular kind of microorganism or *suppress* the growth of other kinds of microorganisms (some may do both). Using such media, therefore, *selects* for a certain microorganism. As shown in TABLE 5.5, Sabouraud's agar selects for fungi because it has a low pH of 5.6 and a high glucose concentration. Selective media are also used widely in clinical and public health laboratories to isolate specific microbes associated with disease. These are particularly helpful when studying specimens containing more than one kind of microorganism, such as feces, saliva, and abscess exudate. An example is brilliant green agar, used to isolate the Gram-negative bacilli in the genus *Salmonella*. Some of these species cause foodborne infections in humans. Brilliant green dye added to agar inhibits Gram-positive bacteria,

common inhabitants of the intestinal tract. On the other hand, phenylethanol agar inhibits the growth of Gram-negative bacteria, but not that of Gram-positive organisms such as streptococci and staphylococci. Today antibiotics are added to some media, making them selective for microbes that are resistant to these antimicrobial agents. For instance, if the antibiotic rifampin is used, the helical bacteria called *spirochetes* can still grow because they are resistant to the antibiotic, while many other kinds of bacteria are inhibited [FIGURE 5.11].

FIGURE 5.11

Use of the antibiotic rifampin in special culture media has facilitated the isolation of oral anaerobic spirochetes. This group of bacteria is relatively resistant to rifampin, while most other oral bacteria are susceptible to its selective antibacterial activity. **[A]** Typical isolated colonies of an oral spirochete. The colonies are subsurface and exhibit fuzzy edges. **[B]** A pure culture of spirochetes as seen with dark-field illumination. Some of the long streaks that are seen are locomoting cells as recorded by time-lapse exposure of the film.

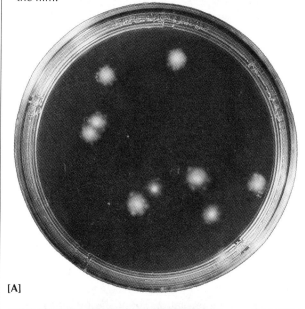

[A]

[B]

25 μm

Differential Media. Microbiologists use *differential media* when they want to differentiate among various kinds of microorganisms on an agar plate. For example, if a mixture of bacteria is inoculated into a blood-containing agar medium (blood agar), some of the bacteria may produce enzymes that lyse (dissolve) the red blood cells, and others may not. Depending on the pattern of lysis surrounding each bacterial colony, one can distinguish between **hemolytic** and nonhemolytic bacteria from the same specimen. Thus a throat swab inoculated on a blood-agar plate will show whether *Streptococcus pyogenes* is present. The cause of strep throat and scarlet fever, *S. pyogenes* produces β hemolysis, or clear zones, around each colony [FIGURE 5.12].

Selective/Differential Media. Some culture media are both selective and differential. They are particularly useful in public health microbiology, in determining water quality, for example, or finding the cause of a food poisoning outbreak. One such medium is MacConkey agar, which contains bile salts and crystal violet dye to inhibit the growth of Gram-positive bacteria and thus allow Gram-negative bacteria to grow. Lactose is also present, and Gram-negative bacteria that produce acid from this sugar can be differentiated from Gram-negative bacteria that do not. Colonies of the bacteria that use lactose are

FIGURE 5.13

A lactose-negative mutant strain of *Escherichia coli* (unable to ferment lactose) is streaked on the differential and selective medium called *MacConkey agar*. Such colonies are colorless. However, this mutant is not very stable and frequently reverts back to the wild-type cells, i.e., undergoes back mutation to the lactose-positive characteristic. These colonies become red or pink in color.

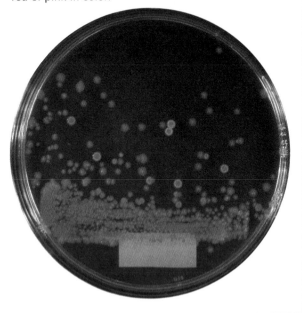

acidic and become reddish in color, since the pH indicator dye neutral red is also part of the medium [FIGURE 5.13]. TABLE 5.6 describes some selective and/or differential media available commercially in a dehydrated form.

Enrichment Media. Natural environments are usually populated by numerous kinds of bacteria or other microorganisms. When a species of special interest is present, but only in very small numbers, microbiologists use an **enrichment medium.** The medium favors the growth of that species, but not the growth of the others present in the mixed population. Enrichment techniques provide an environment, both chemical and physical, that results in increased numbers of an initially scarce species. Unlike a selective medium, no inhibitory agent is used to prevent the growth of unwanted microorganisms. After serial transfers of growth to new media preparations, the desired species emerges as the predominant or enriched population. For example, phenol-oxidizing bacteria can be isolated from soil samples by using an ammonium-salts medium with phenol as the only source of carbon and energy. Only microbes able to oxidize phenol will be present in any large numbers after several serial transfers.

FIGURE 5.12

A streaked plate of the bacterium *Streptococcus pyogenes* on blood-agar medium. Note the clear zones around the colonies; such clear zones are indicative of ß hemolysis of blood cells, a distinguishing characteristic of some bacterial species.

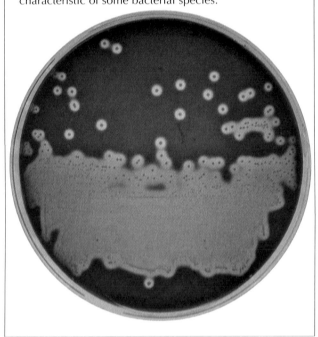

TABLE 5.6
Some Commercially Available Selective and/or Differential Media for Bacteria

Medium	Intended use	Principles of use
MacConkey agar	Differential and selective medium for isolation and differentiation of Gram-negative lactose-fermenting bacteria from non-lactose-fermenting enteric bacteria	Colonies of bacteria able to ferment lactose produce a localized pH drop, which, followed by absorption of neutral red indicator, imparts a red color to the colonies as well as a zone of precipitated bile. Bile salts also inhibit Gram-positive bacteria. Non-lactose-fermenting colonies remain colorless and translucent.
Deoxycholate agar	Differential and selective plating medium for the isolation of Gram-negative enteric bacilli	Coliform colonies (lactose-fermenting) are red; non-lactose-fermenting colonies are colorless. Sodium deoxycholate suppresses Gram-positive bacteria.
Phenylethanol agar	Selective medium for the isolation of Gram-positive staphylococci and streptococci from specimens also containing Gram-negative organisms	Phenylethanol permits the growth of Gram-positive organisms but inhibits the growth of Gram-negative organisms found in the same specimen.
Columbia CNA agar	Selective medium to which blood is added, used for the isolation of Gram-positive cocci	The antimicrobial agents colistin and nalidixic acid in the medium suppress growth of Gram-negative bacteria.

Microbiological Assay Media. Specific microorganisms can be used to measure the concentrations of substances such as antibiotics and vitamins (see Chapter 21). For instance, blood serum or other tissue fluids can be assayed for antibiotics by using microorganisms known to be susceptible to those antibiotics. This type of assay involves the measurement of growth inhibition caused by the antibiotic. Within established limits, the degree of inhibition is proportional to the amount of drug. One of the assay techniques uses wells made in the bacteria-containing agar medium that are filled with sample fluid. As the fluid diffuses out of the wells, zones of microbial inhibition are visible [FIGURE 5.14]. Microbial assays of antibiotics are also made on pharmaceutical products, animal feeds, and other materials.

Microbial isolates from clinical specimens are routinely tested for their susceptibility to selected antimicrobial agents. The result of one assay of this type is called the ***minimum inhibitory concentration (MIC)***, which is the lowest concentration of the test agent to inhibit growth of the microorganism. Results from various sensitivity tests guide the physician in selecting appropriate treatments for infected patients. Standardized microbiological assay media for different chemical agents are commercially available.

ASK YOURSELF

1 Why do microbiologists use chemically defined media?

2 Explain why complex media containing natural materials are chemically undefined.

3 Why is agar an ideal solidifying agent for microbiological use?

4 How do the chemical sources of energy differ between the chemoautotrophs and the chemoheterotrophs?

5 Name two ways in which media for fungal growth differ from media for bacterial growth.

6 Besides inorganic ions, what two ingredients are necessary for the nutrition of algae?

7 How can anaerobic bacteria be cultivated without an anaerobic jar or an anaerobic chamber?

8 What are the differences between *selective* media, *differential* media, *enrichment* media, and *assay* media?

FIGURE 5.14

The assay of an antibiotic (spiramycin) in blood serum. The standard test bacterium used was *Micrococcus luteus*; cells of the organism were suspended in warm molten agar medium prior to being poured into Petri plates. Wells were made in the solid agar medium (now seeded with bacteria) and a small volume of blood serum to be assayed was pipetted into each well. After incubation for 18 h, the susceptible cells grew uniformly in the medium except where antibiotic had diffused into the medium. This is indicated by the clear zones of inhibition. In this illustration, each plate contains the assay for one serum sample tested six times. The numbers indicate the time in hours after ingestion of the antibiotic by a patient, i.e., the times when the blood samples were drawn from the patient. Note that the serum concentration of the drug peaked at about 4 to 6 h after medication; at 24 h the serum concentration of the drug had diminished.

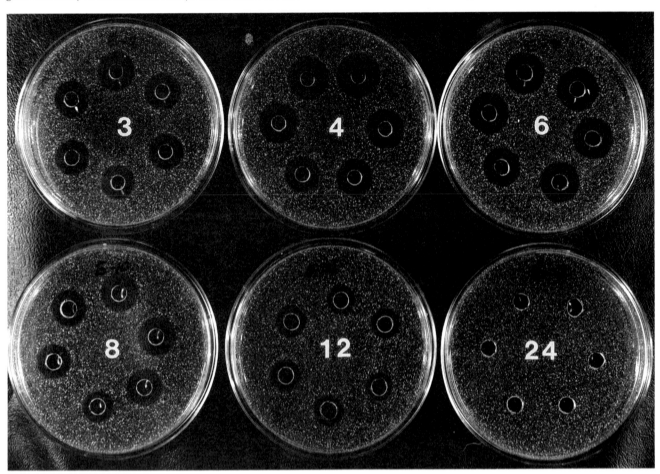

TISSUE-CULTURE MEDIA AND METHODS

Tissue cultures are plant or animal cells grown in the laboratory in specialized media. Tissue culture methods were developed to cultivate viruses in vitro, since viruses can replicate only inside living host cells. Chlamydias, rickettsias, and some spirochetes are also cultivated in tissue cultures. In 1949, John F. Enders and his associates demonstrated that viruses could be regularly propagated to a high concentration in animal cells and tissues growing in culture. Tissue cultures are also used to produce animal or plant products such as hormones. They are usually more convenient and more economical to work with than living animals or plants. However, they also require careful preparation and handling, to avoid contamination with microorganisms that might kill the cells [FIGURE 5.15]. While they have their limitations, tissue cultures are key elements in medical research, where they are used to study viruses such as those that cause acquired immune deficiency syndrome, or AIDS [DISCOVER 5.2].

Animal Cell Cultures

Animal cell cultures were made possible when media were formulated to meet the growth requirements of animal cells. The use of antibiotics facilitated maintaining a bacteria-free environment. Animal cell cultures are started by cutting sterile tissue into small pieces (about

FIGURE 5.15
A microbiologist is shown working in a special hood used to prevent microbiological contamination of animal cell cultures. Aseptic technique is employed as she transfers serum into a tissue-culture flask.

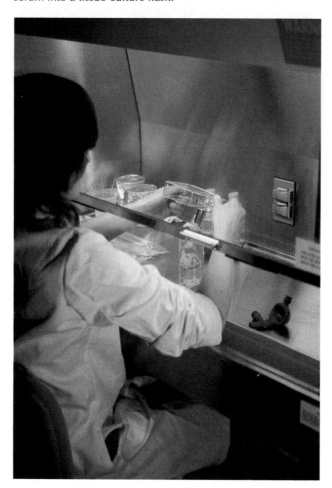

mortalization, which means that the cells can multiply forever in an appropriate laboratory environment with proper physical conditions. Thus the cells can be maintained through an indefinite number of generations. Continuous cell cultures have been established from a wide variety of vertebrates and invertebrates, and from a wide variety of organs and tissues. Sometimes cells from a species are used to grow viruses that normally do not infect that species. An example is the insect cell cultures used to study plant viruses.

Perhaps the most famous cell culture is the HeLa cell line, isolated in 1951 from a woman with cervical cancer. Cancerous HeLa cells are frequently used in research because they are readily available and they support the growth of many human viruses.

FIGURE 5.16
A culture of monkey kidney cells in monolayer. The specimen was stained with Giemsa stain.

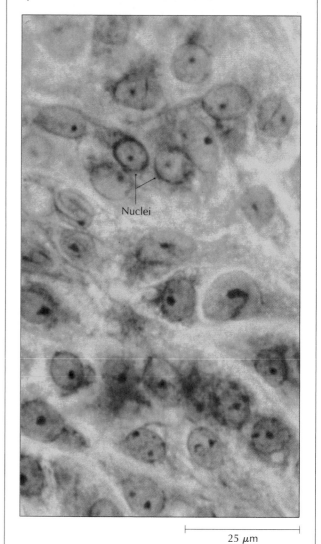

Nuclei

25 μm

0.5 to 2 mm) while the tissue sample is immersed in a sterile *balanced-salt solution*, which is a solution containing glucose and various inorganic salts at concentrations similar to those present in normal tissue fluid. These pieces are called **explants.** They are either placed whole into tissue-culture media, or separated first into individual cells using enzyme treatments. Animal cells tend to adhere to glass or plastic containers and form a monolayer, or single layer, of cells as they reproduce [FIGURE 5.16].

Unfortunately, the **primary cell lines** derived from explants tend to die out after only a few generations. Techniques for the *continuous* culture of cells were first developed in Wilton R. Earle's laboratory in the late 1940s. **Continuous cell lines** consist of **transformed cells,** which have acquired properties distinct from the original cells. (Transformation is one of the earlier stages leading to cancer, but there is no certainty that all transformed cells will become cancer cells.) One such property is *im-*

5.2 DIET, CANCER, AND CELL CULTURE NUTRITION

Since the 1950s microbiology has included the study of animal and plant cells in laboratory cultures. This added dimension of research has contributed immeasurably to human welfare, especially with investigations of viruses and cancer cells. In the mid-1960s, scientists doing routine cell cultures noted that, during cell division, chromosomes broke in a small percentage of healthy human cells. Several years later the Australian geneticist Grant Sutherland reproduced these chromosome breaks by using a culture medium low in the B vitamin folic acid. Folic acid is essential for the synthesis of thymine, one of the pyrimidine components of DNA.

This culture method was repeated by other laboratories, and it is now known that there are 96 fragile sites on human chromosomes that are vulnerable to this type of breakage. These sites are probably rich in thymine. Thirty-eight of these fragile sites have been associated with various cancers. For example, patients with five types of leukemia and lymphoma have an increased number of chromosome breaks in their healthy cells that correspond to the breaks in their cancer cells. These findings suggest that some individuals are more susceptible to chromosome breaks than others, and that such breaks make them more prone to certain types of cancer.

All cells need folic acid for DNA synthesis. If folic acid is in short supply, the chromosomes may break at these fragile sites. Could people found to be more susceptible to chromosome breaks, on the basis of a blood test, cut their risks of developing cancer by taking folic acid supplements? Only further studies and time will tell!

In spite of the success in growing cell cultures, some viruses have still not been cultivated successfully in the laboratory.

Plant Cell Cultures

Plant cell cultures have not been developed to the same extent as animal cell cultures. This is probably because using living plants for the propagation of plant viruses is not as expensive and inconvenient as using living animals for propagating animal viruses. Furthermore, enormous numbers of plant viruses can be obtained from infected plant cells without resorting to plant cell cultures. Unlike many animal cells, infected plant cells can continue to manufacture virus without either lysing or dying.

Plant tissues may be cultured on solid agar or in liquid media. When grown on agar the tissue forms a *callus,* or mass of unorganized cells. Liquid suspension cultures contain single cells or cell clusters. Almost any part of a plant can be induced to produce a callus or a suspension culture. In general, seeds or sections of plant material are first disinfected in 70% ethanol and then in 20% commercial bleach, and then rinsed with water. When placed in media, the seeds germinate and the sections of plant tissue act as explants. Chemically defined media for plant cell growth consist of mineral salts, a carbon source, vitamins, and growth regulators.

Recent progress in cell cultures for plant viruses has gone in two directions: (1) the preparation of plant cell *protoplasts,* which lack cell walls and can be infected in vitro (cell walls block entry of viruses); and (2) the development of monolayer cultures of cells from insect vectors that carry the causative agents of viral diseases from plant to plant.

Propagation of plant viruses is an important use of plant cell cultures, but the use of plant cell cultures in *biotechnology* is even more significant. Biotechnology is the combination of scientific and engineering principles that use biological agents to process materials into commercially valuable products. Not only may plant cell cultures someday produce single-cell protein as a food supplement, but cultured plant cells can also be a source of valuable secondary plant products such as growth hormones.

ASK YOURSELF

1 What was the contribution of John Enders and his associates?

2 What two developments facilitated the cultivation of animal cell cultures?

3 Define *explants, primary cell lines,* and *continuous cell lines.*

4 Do all transformed cells become cancerous?

5 In what way do virally infected plant cells differ from virally infected animal cells?

6 What is a *callus?*

7 What is the promise of cultured plant cells in biotechnology?

SUMMARY

1 Microorganisms are very diversified in their nutritional requirements, but they share with all living cells the need for essential chemical elements as food and/or energy sources.

2 Different groups of microorganisms require different sources of carbon—some are autotrophic, while others are heterotrophic. All microorganisms also require nitrogen, hydrogen, oxygen, sulfur, and phosphorus, along with small quantities of other elements. These elements are needed as precursors of cell structures, as essential components for organelle function, or as coenzymes. Some microbes can use nitrogen from the atmosphere.

3 Some microorganisms use chemical substances as sources of energy, and others use light.

4 Microorganisms can be categorized into nutritional groups based on their energy source and their main carbon source. Nutritional patterns are useful in classifying bacteria and yeasts.

5 Microbiological media used for the cultivation of microbes can be either chemically defined or undefined (complex), and either fluid or solidified with agar. Chemically defined fluid media are used for determining the precise nutritional requirements for microorganisms.

6 There are different media that specifically encourage the growth of bacteria, fungi, protozoa, or algae. Special-purpose media include media for anaerobes, selective media, differential media, enrichment media, and microbiological assay media.

7 Media have also been devised to cultivate cells from animals and plants. Animal cell cultures are used routinely by microbiologists to propagate viruses. Many basic studies are carried out with plant cell cultures, which also have great potential in biotechnology.

KEY TERMS

adenosine triphosphate (ATP)
agar
anaerobes
autotrophs
biotechnology
callus
chemically defined media
chemoautotrophs
chemoheterotrophs
chemotrophs
continuous cell lines
differential media
enrichment media
explants
fastidious
hemolytic
heterotrophs
inorganic
media (singular, medium)
minimum inhibitory concentration (MIC)
nitrogen fixation
organic
parasitic
photoautotrophs
photoheterotrophs
phototrophs
primary cell lines
protoplasts
reduced media
saprophytic
selective media
strict anaerobes
transformed cells

REVIEW GUIDE

OVERVIEW

1 Some bacteria can live with just a few _____ substances as their sole nutritional requirements, whereas other bacteria require complex _____ substances.

2 Water is important in the nutrition of microorganisms because the food of most microorganisms is _____ in water.

3 The cultivation of microorganisms requires the formulation of appropriate culture _____.

4 Growth of microorganisms in laboratory vessels is termed cultivation **(a)** in vitro; **(b)** in vivo; **(c)** in situ; **(d)** in utero.

CHEMICAL ELEMENTS AS NUTRIENTS

5 Chemical elements are necessary for the _____ of cellular components as well as the normal functions of these components.

6 The main chemical elements for cell growth include _____, _____, hydrogen, oxygen, sulfur, and phosphorus.

7 For which microorganisms do many organic compounds serve both as a source of energy and as a source of carbon building blocks of cellular material? **(a)** autotrophs; **(b)** heterotrophs; **(c)** nitrogen fixers; **(d)** halophilic bacteria; **(e)** barophilic bacteria.

8 _____ are organisms that make use of carbon dioxide as their main source of carbon.

9 Which one of the following most accurately represents the major carbon source used by heterotrophs? **(a)** carbon dioxide; **(b)** only sugars; **(c)** only amino acids; **(d)** organic compounds; **(e)** inorganic compounds.

Indicate whether the following statement is true **(T)** *or false* **(F)**; *if false, restate as true.*

10 The process by which some bacteria use gaseous nitrogen as a source of nitrogen for cell material is called *nitrogen fixation*. _____

_____

_____

11 Nitrogen is an essential element of the _____ that make up proteins.

12 Sulfur is needed for the biosynthesis of amino acids such as methionine, _____, and _____.

13 Phosphorus is essential for the biosynthesis of _____, as well as ATP.

14 Trace elements are needed by cells to _____ enzymes.

NUTRITIONAL CLASSIFICATION OF MICROORGANISMS

15 _____ rely on chemical compounds for energy, while phototrophs depend on _____ energy.

16 Microorganisms that use inorganic chemical substances as sources of energy and carbon dioxide as the main source of carbon are called _____.

172

17 _____ use light as a source of energy and carbon dioxide as the main source of carbon.

Indicate whether the following statement is true (T) or false (F); if false, restate as true.

18 Under aerobic conditions, *Rhodospirillum rubrum* depends on light as its energy source and lives as a photoheterotroph. _____

_____

_____

MEDIA USED FOR CULTIVATING MICROORGANISMS

19 If the exact chemical composition of a medium is known, the medium may be described as (a) complex; (b) enriched; (c) selective; (d) chemically defined; (e) differential.

20 _____ is a desiccated product from the degradation of proteinaceous materials such as casein and meat.

21 Yeast extract contains many _____ which enhance the growth of microorganisms.

22 Agar melts at the boiling point of water but remains in the molten state in microbiological media down to about ____°C.

23 Media for fungi have a higher _____ concentration and a lower _____ than media for bacteria.

24 A good general-purpose medium for the growth of fungi is called _____ agar.

25 Nutritionally, the algae are (a) chemoheterotrophs; (b) chemoautotrophs; (c) photoautotrophs; (d) photoheterotrophs.

26 Sodium thioglycolate is a chemical agent added to media for growing _____ bacteria.

27 A check valve may be used in the _____ of media in the absence of oxygen.

28 Media developed to enhance the growth and predominance of a particular type of bacteria and to suppress the growth of unwanted microorganisms are called _____ media.

29 MacConkey agar is both a selective and a _____ medium.

30 Media which encourage the growth of a particular physiological type of microbe but do not encourage the growth of other types present are called _____ media.

TISSUE-CULTURE MEDIA AND METHODS

31 Enders and his associates were the first to demonstrate that viruses could be propagated in _____ or _____.

32 The _____ action of antibiotics has helped in the cultivation of animal cells.

33 Cut-up pieces of animal tissues placed into growth media are called

_____.

34 _____ cell lines tend to die out after only a few generations.

35 Continuous cell lines are _____ cells that can be maintained through an indefinite number of generations.

36 The development of monolayer cultures of susceptible cells from

_____ that are _____ of certain plant virus diseases has been instrumental in the in vitro propagation of plant viruses.

37 A mass of unorganized plant cells on an agar medium is called a(n)

_____.

38 Defined media for growth of plant cultures consist of mineral salts, a carbon source, vitamins, and _____.

REVIEW QUESTIONS

1 Explain why it is useful to study microorganisms in the laboratory and not only in situ in natural habitats.

2 Give one reason why water is required for the nutrition of most microorganisms.

3 Discuss the nutritional utilization of carbon and nitrogen by microorganisms.

4 Describe the growth response of aerobes, anaerobes, facultatives, and microaerophiles in agar medium deeps.

5 Describe the nutritional groupings of microorganisms based on their energy and principal carbon sources.

6 Can all microorganisms be rigidly categorized into a nutritional classification scheme? If not, why not?

7 Compare the uses of chemically defined and chemically undefined media for growing microorganisms.

8 Compare in general the nutritional needs of bacteria, protozoa, fungi, algae, and viruses.

9 Discuss the advantages of using selective and/or differential media in microbiology. Provide specific examples of such media to supplement your answer.

10 When does a microbiologist resort to the use of enrichment media for growing microorganisms?

11 Explain the probable reason why plant cell cultures have not been used in the laboratory as extensively as animal cell cultures.

12 Compare the production of viruses in infected plant cells and in infected animal cells.

13 Cite two developments that contributed in a major way to the successful cultivation of animal cell cultures.

DISCUSSION QUESTIONS

1 Why do we say that microorganisms are more versatile than humans and other animals in their nutrition?

2 Why is the process of nitrogen fixation extremely important in the economy of nature?

3 What nutritional group of organisms does not depend upon other living things to live and grow? Explain.

4 Explain why it is difficult to ascertain with precision the trace-element requirements of microorganisms in the laboratory.

5 Why is it necessary to use nutritional requirements as a taxonomic tool in the classification of bacteria and yeasts?

6 When does one use a chemically defined medium in preference to a complex medium in the laboratory for the study of microorganisms?

7 Compare the advantages of using agar as a solidifying agent for microbiological media as opposed to using other gelling agents.

8 What is the purpose of biotechnology?

9 Why is it useful to be able to cultivate a pathogen on a laboratory medium?

10 Which group of microorganisms would you think most valuable for cultivation in space travel?

11 Explain how differential media are useful in genetic studies.

12 How do some cells become immortal?

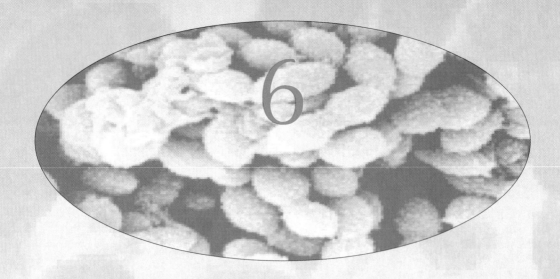

Cultivation and Growth of Microorganisms

OBJECTIVES

After reading this chapter you should be able to

1 Describe the physical conditions required for the successful cultivation of microorganisms.

2 Explain the concept of cardinal temperatures and their relationship to different groups of microorganisms.

3 Specify the kinds of gaseous atmospheres required for growth of various microorganisms.

4 Explain the importance of pH in the growth of microorganisms.

5 Describe the effect of osmotic pressure and hydrostatic pressure on microbial growth.

6 Explain the process of both asexual and sexual reproduction in eucaryotic microorganisms.

7 Describe how procaryotic microorganisms reproduce.

8 Explain the concept of exponential growth and how it can be measured.

9 Describe the growth pattern of cells inoculated into a medium in a flask or tube.

10 Describe how microbial growth is measured.

11 Discuss the use of the chemostat in obtaining continuous cultures.

12 Explain what is meant by synchronous growth.

OVERVIEW

Much of what has been learned in microbiology has come from the cultivation of microorganisms in the laboratory. Scientists have learned to cultivate many types of microorganisms, getting them to grow and to maintain their viability. As you have already learned, microorganisms are cultivated on media, which provide nutrients. In addition, the proper physical environment must be provided for optimal growth. Microorganisms show wide differences with respect to the physical conditions required for growth. Some species grow at temperatures near the freezing point of water; others grow at temperatures as high as 110°C. Oxygen is essential to some, poisonous to others. Most bacteria grow best at or near neutral pH, but the preferred pH for growth among microbes varies from alkaline to acidic. Thus physical conditions must be adjusted in the laboratory to meet the special growth needs of specific species.

Once the chemical and physical requirements are satisfied, it is possible to study the mode of reproduction and growth of a species of microorganism. As you will see in this chapter, eucaryotes and procaryotes differ in their methods of reproduction. For example, eucaryotes have developed elaborate processes to ensure that each daughter cell receives the correct number of chromosomes following sexual reproduction. However, it is important to remember that the behavior of a species in pure culture in the laboratory may not be the same as its growth characteristics in nature. Pure cultures in the laboratory are pampered, because they usually have an overabundance of nutrients and do not have to compete with other microbes for available food. Even some animal cells have been adapted to life in laboratory culture so well that they grow like cultured microorganisms. An example is the HeLa cells derived from human cervical cancer cells. With an understanding of microbial growth requirements, microbiologists can learn how microorganisms grow as individual cells and as communities or cultures.

PHYSICAL CONDITIONS FOR CULTIVATION OF MICROORGANISMS

Four main conditions influence the physical environment of a microbe: temperature, pH, gaseous atmosphere, and osmotic pressure. The successful cultivation of the various types of microorganisms requires a combination of the proper nutrients and the proper physical environment. Microbiologists must know what a specific microbe requires for growth, satisfy those needs, and check the cultures to make certain that the organisms are thriving.

Temperature

Temperature has a great influence on the growth of microorganisms. This is not surprising, since all the processes of growth are dependent on chemical reactions that are affected by temperature. Unlike mammalian cells, which grow within a relatively narrow temperature range (close to 37°C), microorganisms can grow over a rather broad range of temperatures. However, this range may be wider for some than for others. For example, the range for *Bacillus subtilis* is from 8 to 53°C, a 45° range; for *Neisseria gonorrhoeae* it is from 30 to 40°C, a 10° range. At the most favorable temperatures for growth, the number of cell divisions per hour, called the *growth rate*, generally doubles for every temperature increase of 10°C. This growth behavior is similar to that of most enzyme-catalyzed reactions, supporting the principle that growth is the result of a series of integrated, enzyme-based chemical reactions. The temperature at which a species of microorganism grows most rapidly is the *optimum growth temperature.*

For any particular microbe, the three important temperatures are the *minimum, optimum,* and *maximum* growth temperatures [FIGURE 6.1]. These are known as the *cardinal temperatures* of a species of microorganism. Cardinal temperatures of a particular microbial species may vary with the stage in the life cycle of the microorganism and with the nutritional content of the medium. In addition to affecting the growth rate, temperature may also affect the type of reproduction, morphology,

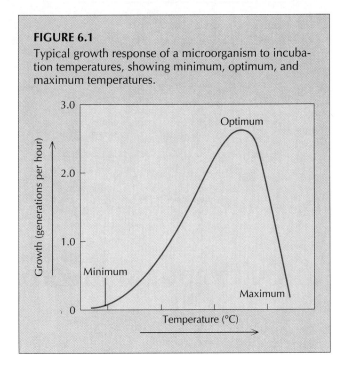

FIGURE 6.1

Typical growth response of a microorganism to incubation temperatures, showing minimum, optimum, and maximum temperatures.

metabolic processes, and nutritional requirements. Therefore, the optimum temperature for growth may not necessarily be the optimum temperature for every cellular activity.

The optimum temperature for a microbial species does not lie midway between the minimum and maximum temperatures. Instead, it is nearer the upper limit of the temperature range, because the rate of enzyme reactions increases with increasing temperature until a point where the enzymes are damaged by heat and cells stop growing. Microorganisms may be divided into three groups on the basis of the temperature range in which they grow best [FIGURE 6.2]:

1 *Psychrophiles,* or cold-loving microbes
2 *Mesophiles,* or moderate-temperature–loving microbes
3 *Thermophiles,* or heat-loving microbes

Psychrophiles. Psychrophiles grow best at temperatures from 15 to 20°C, although they can grow at lower temperatures. Some of these microbes die if they are exposed to room temperature (about 25°C) for a short time. The physiological reasons for the low-temperature requirements of strict psychrophiles are not entirely clear. However, if the temperature is too high, certain enzymes and/or the cytoplasmic membrane may be damaged. Enzymes of psychrophilic cells are more efficient in catalyzing reactions at low temperatures. Such cells are also able to transport solutes across cytoplasmic membranes at cold temperatures.

6.1 ASTOUNDING EXTREME THERMOPHILY AMONG MICROBES

In 1982, German microbiologists were examining samples of water and sulfurous deposits from an undersea volcanic region near Italy. At the time of their collection, the samples had a temperature of between 95 and 103°C, but, from them, the scientists isolated a new genus of archaeobacteria, called *Pyrodictium*. The strange, disc-shaped cells were anaerobic autotrophs that grew in sealed, pressurized bottles of inorganic media containing elemental sulfur, CO_2, and H_2. Their most amazing feature, however, was that they had an optimal growth temperature of 105°C, and they could even grow at 110°C! However, 80°C—a temperature that would rapidly "cook" most other living organisms—was too chilly.

It is difficult to explain how organisms can grow at such high temperatures. However, there are a few clues. (1) Most extreme thermophiles are archaeobacteria, which have membranes that are chemically different from those of eubacteria; for example, the archaeobacterial membranes with their long-chain ether lipids may be more thermostable. (2) The thermophilic archaeobacteria have proteins that function optimally at extremely high temperatures, although the reasons are not yet clear. (3) Double-stranded DNA typically "melts" (separates into two strands) when heated to temperatures of 80 to 85°C. However, archaeobacterial DNA may not unravel so easily, since it has specialized proteins that bind the DNA chains together tightly.

Organisms like *Pyrodictium* have provided microbiologists with a fascinating new research area.

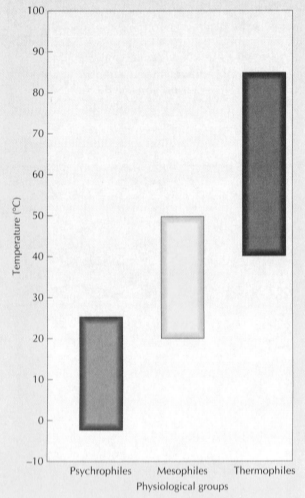

FIGURE 6.2

Approximate temperature ranges for growth of various physiological groups of microorganisms (excluding the extreme thermophilic archaeobacteria).

There are bacteria, fungi, algae, and protozoa that are psychrophilic. They are found in colder waters and soils such as the oceans and the polar regions. Most marine microorganisms belong to this group. At refrigerator temperatures of 4 to 10°C, psychrophilic microbes spoil food stored for prolonged periods. Among the bacteria, many psychrophiles are members of the genera *Pseudomonas*, *Flavobacterium*, and *Alcaligenes*.

Mesophiles. Most microorganisms are mesophiles, growing best within a temperature range of 25 to 40°C. Saprophytic bacteria, fungi, algae, and protozoa grow in the lower part of the mesophilic temperature range. Parasitic microorganisms of humans and animals grow in the upper part of this range. Those that are pathogenic for humans grow best at about body temperature, which is 37°C. The elevated temperature of a fever may inhibit the growth of some pathogens.

Thermophiles. Most thermophiles grow at temperatures from about 40 to 85°C, but they grow best between 50 and 60°C. These hardy microbes may be found in volcanic areas, compost heaps, and hot springs [DISCOVER 6.1]. Most thermophilic microorganisms are procaryotes; no eucaryotic cells are known to grow at temperatures greater than 60°C.

There are several factors that enable thermophiles like *Bacillus stearothermophilus* to grow at elevated temperatures. Foremost is that enzymes of thermophiles are produced more rapidly than the enzymes of mesophiles, so that those damaged by high temperatures are quickly replaced. Among the procaryotes, certain archaeobacteria are able to grow at temperatures above the boiling point of water. For example, *Pyrodictium occultum* can grow at 110°C, *Pyrococcus woesei* at 104.8°C, and *Thermococcus celer* at 103°C. These organisms have been isolated from sediments near vents on the ocean floor that spew forth superheated water. The ribosomes, membranes, and various enzymes in thermophiles function better at high temperatures than at lower temperatures. Loss of function of the cytoplasmic membrane at lower temperatures may be what determines the minimum growth temperature of thermophiles.

ASK YOURSELF

1 How does one define the optimum growth temperature for microorganisms?

2 What is meant by the *cardinal* temperatures of a species of microbe?

3 What cell activities are influenced by temperature?

4 Describe the three groups of microorganisms based on the temperature range within which they grow.

5 What are the factors that permit eubacteria to grow as thermophiles?

6 What are the factors that permit the archaeobacteria to grow as extreme thermophiles?

Gaseous Atmosphere

Microorganisms in their natural habitats require varying amounts of gases such as oxygen, carbon dioxide, nitrogen, and methane. In order to cultivate microbial, plant, and animal cells in the laboratory, the proper gas atmosphere must be present. Some gases are used in cellular metabolism; others may have to be excluded from a culture because they are toxic to the cells. For example, carbon dioxide is used by all cells for certain chemical reactions; however, oxygen is required by some microorganisms, but is toxic to others. Carbon dioxide and oxygen are the two principal gases that affect the growth of microbial cells.

On the basis of their response to gaseous oxygen, microorganisms are divided into four physiological groups: *aerobes, facultative microorganisms, anaerobes,* and *microaerophiles* [see FIGURE 5.9].

Aerobic Microorganisms. Microbes that normally require oxygen for growth and can grow in a standard air atmosphere of 21% oxygen are classified as aerobes. Filamentous molds and the bacterial genera *Mycobacterium* and *Legionella* are examples of aerobic microbes. Aerobes acquire more energy from available nutrients than do microbes that do not use oxygen. Some aerobes may grow more slowly when oxygen is limited, and so care must be taken to provide an adequate supply of the gas. When microorganisms grow on the surface of a solid

FIGURE 6.3

Mechanical shaker. The flasks are fixed firmly on the platform, which rotates in a circular manner. This agitates the fluid medium constantly during incubation, thereby exposing more culture surface to air.

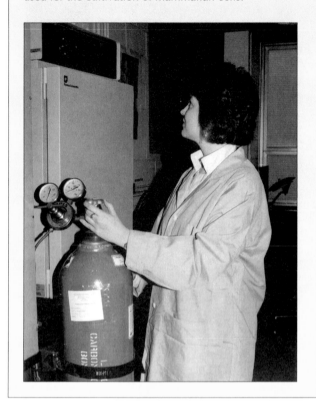

FIGURE 6.4
A microbiologist is shown adjusting the proper level of carbon dioxide flow into a carbon dioxide incubator used for the cultivation of mammalian cells.

medium this is rarely a problem. However, microbes growing in a liquid may rapidly use the oxygen dissolved in the surface layer of medium. To avoid this problem, liquid cultures of aerobic microorganisms are sometimes agitated on a mechanical shaker to increase the supply of dissolved oxygen and produce a larger cell crop within a shorter incubation time [FIGURE 6.3].

Some cells also have specific needs in terms of carbon dioxide. Mammalian cells, which are aerobic, are best cultivated in an incubator with a humid atmosphere and a continuous supply of 5% carbon dioxide [FIGURE 6.4]. There are some groups of microorganisms that require elevated levels of carbon dioxide. For instance, the bacterium that causes gonorrhea, *Neisseria gonorrhoeae*, grows best in an atmosphere enriched to 5 to 10% carbon dioxide. A special incubator can supply this atmosphere, but an apparatus called a *candle jar* will also work in many instances. After inoculated media are placed inside the jar, a candle is lit in the jar and the lid is tightly closed. The candle burns until there is not enough oxygen to maintain combustion; the jar atmosphere then contains a reduced amount of free oxygen (about 17% oxygen) and an increased carbon dioxide concentration (about 3.5%).

Facultative Microorganisms. Facultative microorganisms are those that grow in an air atmosphere and can also grow anaerobically. They do not require oxygen for growth, although they may use it for energy-yielding chemical reactions. Under anaerobic conditions they obtain energy by a metabolic process called *fermentation*. Members of the bacterial family Enterobacteriaceae, such as *Escherichia coli*, are facultative. Many yeasts are facultative as well. An example is *Saccharomyces cerevisiae*, which is common bakers' yeast.

Anaerobic Microorganisms. Anaerobic microorganisms are those which may be poisoned by oxygen, cannot grow in an air atmosphere, and do not use oxygen for energy-yielding chemical reactions. Some anaerobes can tolerate low concentrations of oxygen, but *strict anaerobes* are killed by brief exposure to the gas. It is apparent there is a wide range of oxygen tolerance among anaerobic microorganisms. *Clostridium perfringens* is highly oxygen-tolerant, *Clostridium tetani* is moderately tolerant, and *Methanobacterium* and *Methanospirillum* are strict anaerobes.

The toxicity of oxygen for strict anaerobes is due to certain molecules produced during reactions involving oxygen. Some of these reactions result in the addition of a single electron to an oxygen molecule, forming a *superoxide radical:*

$$O_2 + e^- \rightarrow O_2^{\cdot -} \tag{1}$$

Oxygen   Electron   Superoxide radical

Superoxide radicals may cause damage to cells, but they also give rise to *hydrogen peroxide*, H_2O_2, and *hydroxyl radicals*, OH·, both of which can destroy vital cell components. Hydroxyl radicals are produced from superoxide radicals in two steps. In the first step, two superoxide radicals react with each other to produce hydrogen peroxide, H_2O_2:

$$2O_2^{\cdot -} + 2H^+ \rightarrow O_2 + H_2O_2 \tag{2}$$

In the second step, superoxide radicals react with the hydrogen peroxide in the presence of iron complexes to form hydroxyl radicals:

$$O_2^{\cdot -} + H_2O_2 \xrightarrow{\text{iron complexes}} O_2 + OH^- + OH\cdot \tag{3}$$

Hydroxyl radicals are very short-lived, lasting less than 1/10,000 s. This is because they are among the most reactive chemical substances known. They can damage almost every kind of molecule found in living cells, including the genetic material DNA.

Aerobic microorganisms, facultative microorganisms growing aerobically, and some anaerobic microorganisms have developed various protective mechanisms against these toxic forms of oxygen. One mechanism is

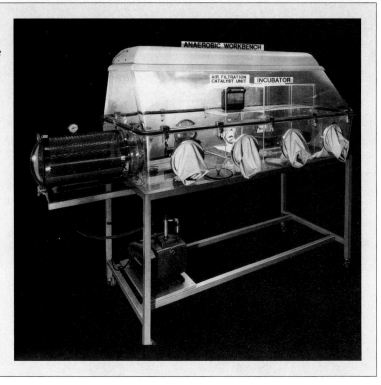

FIGURE 6.5
An anaerobic chamber for the cultivation of anaerobic microorganisms. Manipulation within the chamber is through the glove ports; for this reason, such an incubator is sometimes called a glove box. The enclosure is filled with a gas mixture of nitrogen, carbon dioxide, and hydrogen.

the production of the enzyme *superoxide dismutase,* which eliminates superoxide radicals by rapidly converting them to hydrogen peroxide, as shown in Equation (2). The hydrogen peroxide produced by this reaction can in turn be dissipated by two other enzymes: *catalase,* which converts hydrogen peroxide to molecular oxygen and water; and *peroxidase,* which converts hydrogen peroxide to water. The elimination of both superoxide radicals and hydrogen peroxide means that the reaction in Equation (3) can no longer proceed and hydroxyl radicals will not be formed.

The catalase reaction is used to identify some bacterial species. When a drop of hydrogen peroxide is added to a colony of bacterial cells containing catalase, oxygen bubbles are released immediately. Such bacteria are termed *catalase-positive.* For example, members of the genus *Neisseria* are catalase-positive, including *N. gonorrhoeae* and *N. meningitidis* (the causative agent of epidemic cerebrospinal meningitis). When doing this test, care must be taken to ascertain that other substances in the medium (such as blood, which contains catalase) or other catalase-positive species are not causing the bubble formation.

For the cultivation of anaerobes, oxygen must be eliminated from the atmosphere. An incubator called an *anaerobic chamber,* or *anaerobic glove box,* can be used [FIGURE 6.5]. A technician does work inside the chamber by extending the arms into special gloves attached to

the chamber walls. The atmosphere inside the chamber is a mixture of hydrogen, carbon dioxide, and nitrogen. Culture media are placed inside or removed from the chamber through an air lock that can be emptied and refilled with the oxygen-free gas mixture or with nitrogen. Any residual oxygen in the chamber is removed by its reaction with hydrogen, in the presence of a palladium catalyst: $O_2 + 2H_2 \rightarrow 2H_2O$.

Anaerobes can also be cultivated within an anaerobic jar, which is really a miniature anaerobic chamber [FIGURE 6.6]. Inoculated media are placed in the jar along with an envelope that contains chemicals that generate hydrogen and carbon dioxide. After the jar is sealed, the oxygen present is removed within hours by the same palladium-catalyzed reaction, but this system is inadequate for the cultivation of strict anaerobes. Many medical laboratories use anaerobic jars because they are convenient and because medically important microbes can usually tolerate low levels of oxygen.

Microaerophilic Microorganisms. Microaerophiles are organisms which, like aerobes, can use oxygen for energy-yielding chemical reactions. However, unlike aerobes, they cannot withstand the level of oxygen (21%) present in an air atmosphere and usually grow best at oxygen levels between 1 and 15%. This limited tolerance to oxygen is due to a high susceptibility to superoxide radicals and hydrogen peroxide, which are formed in cultures incubated under aerobic conditions. Special incubation bags with proper gaseous environment are now commercially available for the cultivation of such microaerophiles as *Campylobacter jejuni*, a bacterium that often causes diarrhea in humans. The isolation of *C. jejuni* from fecal samples requires low levels of oxygen.

ASK YOURSELF

1 What are the two principal gases that affect the growth of microorganisms?

2 What are the four physiological groups of microorganisms based on response to gaseous oxygen?

3 Why are facultative microorganisms considered physiologically versatile?

4 Explain the chemical basis for oxygen toxicity.

5 Explain how some microorganisms overcome the toxicity of reactive molecules produced during reactions involving oxygen.

6 How are anaerobic microorganisms cultivated?

pH

In contrast to optimum temperature, the optimum pH for microbial growth lies approximately in the middle of the pH range over which growth will occur. The optimum pH is usually well defined for individual species; different species are adapted to grow at various pH values. But to grow well in an acidic or a basic environment, a microorganism must be able to maintain its intracellular pH at about 7.5, regardless of the external pH. A living cell has the ability, within limits, to keep a constant internal pH by expelling hydrogen ions or by taking hydrogen ions into the cell. Thus the pH of its external environment usually has to change drastically before the inside of the cell is affected.

When you consider the broad variability of pH in nature and the fact that microorganisms are found nearly everywhere, it makes sense that different species of microbes have different pH tolerances. Drainage waters from volcanic soils and from mines may be highly acidic, with a pH between 1 and 3. Alkaline springwaters may have pH values as high as 10, while pH values of 11 can be found in ammonia-rich soils. The oceans have a pH of about 8, and drinking water is about pH 6 because dis-

FIGURE 6.6

Anaerobic jar: GasPak system. **[A]** Media on plates are inoculated and placed in the jar. Water is added to the GasPak generator envelope, causing the evolution of H_2 and CO_2. The hydrogen reacts with oxygen on the surface of the palladium catalyst, forming water and establishing anaerobic conditions. Carbon dioxide aids growth of the anaerobes. An anaerobic indicator strip (a pad saturated with methylene blue solution) changes from blue to colorless in the absence of oxygen. **[B]** Picture of the anaerobic jar with inoculated Petri plates, the GasPak generator envelope, and the anaerobic indicator strip.

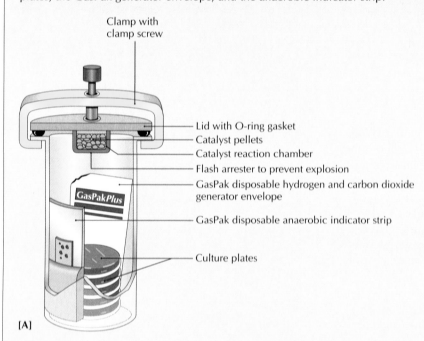

Clamp with clamp screw

Lid with O-ring gasket
Catalyst pellets
Catalyst reaction chamber
Flash arrester to prevent explosion
GasPak disposable hydrogen and carbon dioxide generator envelope

GasPak disposable anaerobic indicator strip

Culture plates

GasPakPlus

[A]

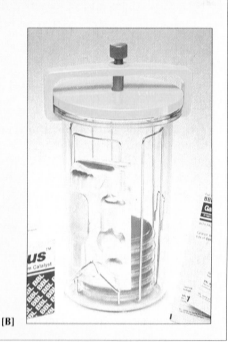

[B]

solved carbon dioxide makes it slightly acidic. Microbes are found in all these environments.

For most bacteria, the pH minimum is about 4, with pH 9 as the maximum for growth. The optimum pH normally lies between 6 and 8. But some species of *Bacillus*, for example, can grow at pH 11, while other bacteria are highly tolerant of acidic conditions. Some *Thiobacillus* species can grow at pH values as low as 0.5 and are found in acidic drainage water from mines where sulfur and iron are present. Foods such as sauerkraut and pickles are preserved by the organic acids resulting from bacterial fermentation, since food spoilage bacteria cannot grow at pH values of 3 to 4.

Molds and yeasts have a broader pH range than do bacteria. In addition, their optimum pH for growth is lower than that of bacteria—about pH 5 to 6. The optimal pH for growth of protozoa is generally between 6.7 and 7.7. Algae have a broader pH range—from 4 to 8.5—for optimal growth.

When actively growing microorganisms are cultivated in a medium, the pH of the medium will change as acidic or alkaline compounds are produced. This shift in pH may be so great that further growth is inhibited; such shifts are prevented by adding a buffer to the medium.

ASK YOURSELF

1 Do different microbial species have different optimal pH for growth?

2 Is the intracellular pH of a microbial cell always the same as the extracellular pH?

3 What is the pH range for growth of most bacteria? Of fungi?

Other Conditions

Temperature, the gaseous environment, and pH are major physical factors that together create the optimum conditions for cellular growth. However, microorganisms may have other requirements. An obvious example is the photosynthetic microbes that must have light. Water, which accounts for 80 to 90 percent of a cell, is another environmental factor that affects microbial growth. Beyond its role in cellular metabolism and nutrition, water influences growth through osmotic pressure and hydrostatic pressure.

As you learned in Chapter 4, *osmotic pressure* is the force with which water moves through the cytoplasmic membrane from a solution containing a low concentration of dissolved substances (solutes) to one containing a

FIGURE 6.7

Effect of osmotic pressure on a microbial cell. **[A]** Cell in isotonic medium. Concentration of solutes in environment is equal to that within the cell. There is no net movement of water into or out of the cell. **[B]** Cell in hypertonic medium. Concentration of solutes in environment is greater than that within the cell. Water flows out of the cell, resulting in dehydration and shrinking of the protoplast. Cell growth is inhibited; cell may die. **[C]** Cell in hypotonic medium. Concentration of solutes in environment is lower than that within the cell. Water flows into the cell. Net influx of water forces the protoplast against the cell wall. If the wall is weak, it may break, allowing the protoplast to swell and eventually burst.

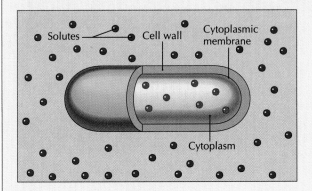

[A]

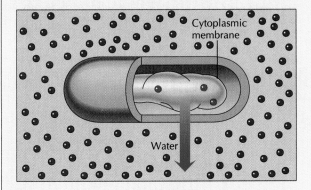

[B]

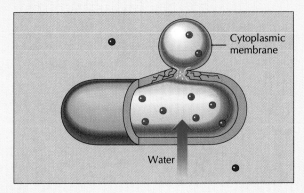

[C]

high solute concentration. When microbial cells are in an aqueous medium, there should not be large differences between solute concentrations inside and outside the cells, or the cells could either dehydrate or lyse [FIGURE 6.7]. In an *isotonic* solution, there is no net flow of water into or out of the cell and the cell grows normally. However, when the external environment is *hypertonic*, with a higher solute concentration than the cell cytoplasm, the cell loses water and growth is inhibited. Salted fish, and fruit in sugar syrup, are preserved by the osmotic withdrawal of water from any microbial cells present. In contrast, when the external solution is too *hypotonic*, with a much lower solute concentration than the cell, water flows in and ruptures the cell.

Hydrostatic pressure may also influence microbial growth. This is the pressure exerted on cells by the weight of the water resting on top of them. Microorganisms have been isolated from ocean floors that are over 2500 m below sea level, where the pressure is more than 250 bars (250 times atmospheric pressure). These organisms will not grow in the laboratory unless the medium is under similar pressure. Pressure-dependent microbes are called **barophiles.** They die in an environment with low hydrostatic pressure because they contain gas vesicles that expand with great force upon decompression and rupture the cells.

ASK YOURSELF

1 How does the solute concentration affect the osmotic pressure on cells?

2 What are barophiles?

3 What is an isotonic solution (medium)?

REPRODUCTION AND GROWTH OF MICROORGANISMS

When microorganisms are inoculated into an appropriate medium and incubated with optimum conditions for growth, a large increase in the number of cells occurs within a relatively short time. With some bacterial species, the maximum population is reached within 24 hours, but most other species of microorganisms require a longer incubation to reach maximum growth. Growth in a microbial culture usually means an increase in the total number of cells due to reproduction of the individual organisms in the culture. Therefore there are two phenomena at work: the growth, or reproduction, of individual cells; and the growth, or increase in population, of a microbial culture.

Reproduction in Eucaryotic Microorganisms

One of the criteria that define life is that an organism has the capacity to produce others of its kind. That is, all living organisms, including microorganisms, reproduce. In nature, reproduction occurs in two forms: *asexual reproduction* and *sexual reproduction*. Asexual reproduction basically results in new cells identical to the original, while sexual reproduction allows for exchange of genetic material and thus unique offspring. Among eucaryotic microorganisms, both types of reproduction occur, but both are preceded by processes that determine the number of chromosomes involved, as explained in the following subsections.

Asexual Reproduction. Asexual reproduction does not involve the union of nuclei, sex cells, or sex organs. It does not provide the opportunity for genetic variation, but it is more efficient than sexual reproduction in propagating a species. In asexual reproduction, new individuals are produced by *one* parent organism, or, in the case of unicellular organisms, by *one* cell. Bacteria reproduce asexually by binary fission, in which a parent cell simply splits into two identical daughter cells. Asexual reproduction of eucaryotic microorganisms is more complicated, because it must be preceded by **mitosis.** Mitosis is a form of nuclear division in which the cell's entire set of chromosomes is duplicated and the two new sets separate to form two identical daughter nuclei. The cell then divides into two daughter cells, each receiving one of the nuclei. In this way each daughter cell has the same number of chromosomes and the same genetic composition as the parent cell. Mitosis is a continuous process, with each phase merging into the next phase.

Between mitoses, cells are said to be in the "resting" stage with respect to nuclear division; this is called the **interphase.** During the interphase the chromosomes are not visible in living cells, but they can be seen in dye-stained preparations as irregular chromatin threads. It is during a particular period in the interphase that the chromosomes are duplicated. However, the two duplicates do not separate until later, after mitosis begins. For descriptive purposes, the process of mitosis may be divided into four phases: *prophase, metaphase, anaphase,* and *telophase* [FIGURE 6.8].

As the cell enters the *prophase,* the chromosomes condense into threadlike structures and become visible through a microscope. But they do not look doubled until mid-prophase, when each chromosome appears as two duplicates lying next to each other, joined at the center by a ring of protein called the **centromere.** The two duplicates may be called daughter chromosomes as long as they remain connected. At the same time, the **centrioles** (cylinders of protein microtubules) migrate to opposite sides of the cell. As these centrioles separate, a

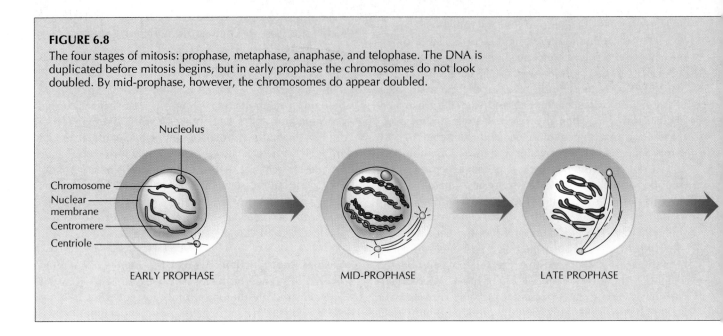

FIGURE 6.8
The four stages of mitosis: prophase, metaphase, anaphase, and telophase. The DNA is duplicated before mitosis begins, but in early prophase the chromosomes do not look doubled. By mid-prophase, however, the chromosomes do appear doubled.

Nucleolus

Chromosome
Nuclear membrane
Centromere
Centriole

EARLY PROPHASE   MID-PROPHASE   LATE PROPHASE

mitotic spindle begins to form between them. This structure consists of a system of microtubules, some of which remain connected to the centromeres. By the end of the prophase the centrioles have moved to opposite poles of the cell, with the spindle between them. During this mitotic phase, the nuclear membrane also begins to disintegrate.

In the *metaphase* the nuclear membrane disappears. Chromosomes appear to be attached by their centromeres to the spindle fibers. The chromosomes are completely condensed and lined up in the equatorial region of the spindle, which now stretches from one pole of the cell to the other. During the metaphase, the centromere of each chromosome divides and the two daughter chromosomes in each set become completely separate. The centromere of each new chromosome then begins to move toward a pole, marking the beginning of the anaphase.

The *anaphase* is usually the shortest stage of mitosis. Here the daughter chromosomes travel to either one side of the cell or the other, using the spindle fibers as guide rails.

Arrival of the two sets of chromosomes at the two poles of the spindle marks the *telophase*. A nuclear membrane forms around the cluster of chromosomes at each pole, and the chromosomes elongate into chromatin threads typical of the interphase. The cytoplasm of the cell then divides in a process called *cytokinesis*.

The mitotic process, followed by cytokinesis, results in two daughter cells from a single parent cell; each daughter cell receives exactly the same number and kind of chromosomes that were present in the parent cell. All the mitosis-derived cells of a eucaryotic organism thus have the same number and kind of chromosomes, and the same number and kind of genes, as their parent cells.

Sexual Reproduction. In sexual reproduction of eucaryotic microorganisms, as well as macroorganisms, a new individual is formed by the fusion of two different sex cells known as *gametes,* which are usually from two parents of different sex or mating type. The fusion of gametes is termed *fertilization,* and the resulting cell is called the *zygote.* Zygotes contain a mixture of genetic material from each of the two gametes. Through mitotic divisions, each zygote becomes a new organism. For instance, an adult human has approximately 60 trillion (6×10^{13}) cells—all of them derived from asexual reproduction, or mitotic divisions, of the single-celled zygote formed when a sperm and an egg fuse!

It follows from this discussion that ordinary (nonsex) body cells, or *somatic* cells, have twice the amount of DNA as the gametes. In other words, a liver cell is a somatic cell and has twice the DNA found in a sperm cell (male gamete) or ovum (female gamete, or egg cell). This is because somatic cells form during mitosis of a zygote that has chromosomes from both gamete cells, giving somatic cells a double set of chromosomes. Somatic cells are therefore *diploid*, with pairs of matched chromosomes that together add up to what is known as the *2n* number. Such paired chromosomes are known as *homologous chromosomes*; they contain identical sequences of genes in their DNA.

Meiosis. Something must occur in the formation of gametes that prevents the somatic cells formed from zy-

At metaphase the chromosomes align themselves in a plane and attach to mitotic spindle fibers. During anaphase the chromosomes separate and move to opposite poles of the cell. By the end of telophase there are two daughter cells, each of which contains a copy of the genetic material of the parent cell.

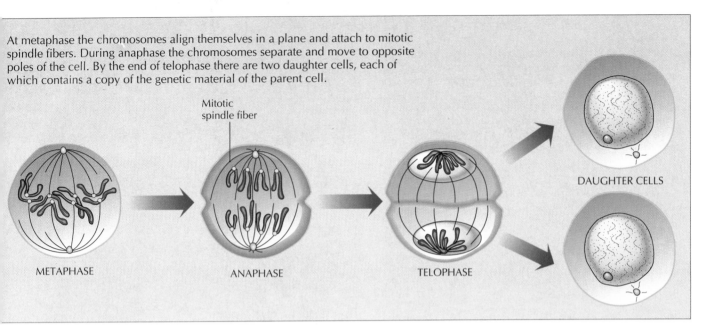

Mitotic spindle fiber

DAUGHTER CELLS

METAPHASE   ANAPHASE   TELOPHASE

gotes from having too many chromosomes. During the life cycle of an organism, somatic cells can undergo another type of cell division, called **meiosis,** to form gametes. Gametes are *haploid*—they contain only one chromosome from each pair of chromosomes present in the somatic cell, a condition referred to as the $1n$ number. For example, for the human the diploid ($2n$) number is 46 and the haploid ($1n$) number is 23. Therefore, a liver cell has 46 chromosomes, while an egg or a sperm cell contains 23, or half that number. Through their gametes, each parent contributes one set of 23 chromosomes containing all the genes necessary for cell activity.

When two gametes fuse during fertilization, each gives one set of chromosomes to the zygote, making it diploid. Therefore each cell of the new progeny that develops from the zygote is also diploid, with two sets of the genetic material, one from the female parent and one from the male parent. In the processes described so far, it is clear that diploid cells in reproductive organs can form haploid gametes by meiosis. When diploid cells alternate with haploid cells during the life cycle of an organism, the process is termed *alternation of generations.*

As discussed previously, the process of *mitosis* ensures that each daughter cell receives exactly the same number and kind of chromosomes as the parent cell had. However, the process of *meiosis* guarantees that, during sexual reproduction, the chromosome number remains the same in successive generations despite the fact that two gametes fuse to form a zygote. This is accomplished by the reduced chromosome number in the gametes [FIGURE 6.9]. In addition, meiosis also allows reassortment and recombination of chromosomes from one gen-

eration to the next, giving each progeny its own unique program of genes.

When there is zygote formation, meiosis occurs only among specialized sex cells found in reproductive organs. Such cells result in haploid cells because they duplicate their entire set of chromosomes once, and then divide twice in succession. Therefore, a single replication of the DNA is followed by two sequential nuclear divisions, producing four haploid gametes from each sex cell. The nuclear divisions are each composed of the same four phases seen earlier in mitosis: prophase, metaphase, anaphase, and telophase. They also involve the same organelles—spindle, centrioles, and centromeres. In the end, meiosis produces four cells, each of which contains half the number of chromosomes found in the single, diploid sex cell that gave rise to it. FIGURE 6.10 illustrates the role of meiosis prior to the fertilization process.

The Eucaryotic Cell Cycle. During their life span, all eucaryotic cells go through a similar *cell cycle*, with the exception of the gametes. The eucaryotic cell cycle is divided into two parts: *interphase* and *mitosis* (M). The interphase is the period between mitoses; it consists of the growth₁ (G_1), DNA synthesis (S), and growth₂ (G_2) phases [FIGURE 6.11]. Therefore, the phases in which neither mitosis nor DNA synthesis occurs are the G_1 (following mitosis) and G_2 (following DNA synthesis) phases. During G_1, the cell grows and synthesizes protein. During the S phase, cell growth continues and DNA synthesis occurs in the nucleus until the amount of DNA doubles. During G_2, cell growth reaches its maximum. During M, the mitotic phase, the synthesis of

FIGURE 6.9
Summary of the main events occurring in meiosis. For simplicity, the parent cell is shown as having only two pairs of chromosomes, one type being shorter than the other. Meiosis may be viewed to occur in two phases, I and II. In meiosis I, the chromosomes of the diploid cell replicate, sets of homologous chromosomes pair, and then the pairs separate. In meiosis II, gametes are formed, each having a haploid set of chromosomes.

Parent cell, 2*n*

Chromosomes replicate

Sets of homologous chromosomes pair

— MEIOSIS I

Homologous sets separate

Gamete formation

— MEIOSIS II

Gametes, 1*n*

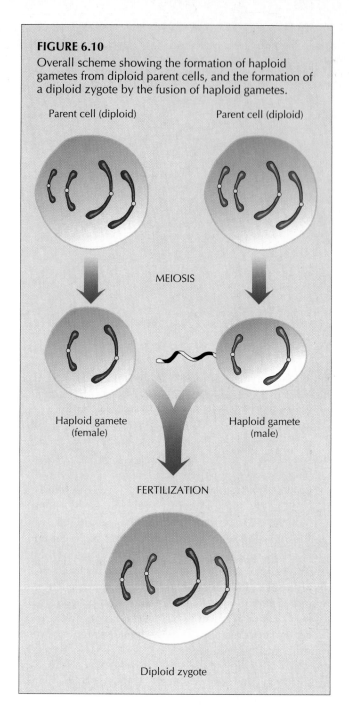

FIGURE 6.10
Overall scheme showing the formation of haploid gametes from diploid parent cells, and the formation of a diploid zygote by the fusion of haploid gametes.

Parent cell (diploid) Parent cell (diploid)

MEIOSIS

Haploid gamete (female) Haploid gamete (male)

FERTILIZATION

Diploid zygote

macromolecules almost ceases and the nucleus undergoes mitosis. Mitosis distributes the genetic material into two equal sets in two daughter nuclei during *karyokinesis*. The entire cell then divides into two daughter cells (through cytokinesis) with one daughter nucleus in each cell.

The duration of the cell cycle varies from cell type to cell type. For example, actively growing cells of the human body may have a cell cycle of 9 h, while that of a yeast cell is about 90 to 120 min.

FIGURE 6.11

The eucaryotic cell cycle. The S phase is started by the initiation of DNA replication; the initiation of mitosis starts in the M phase. Phase G_1 follows mitosis, and phase G_2 follows DNA synthesis.

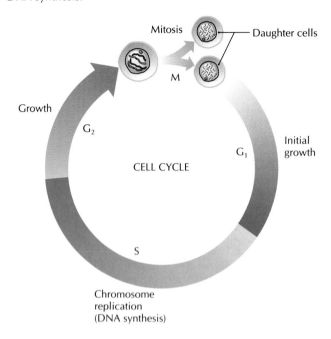

Mitosis

Daughter cells

M

Growth

G_2

Initial growth

G_1

CELL CYCLE

S

Chromosome replication (DNA synthesis)

ASK YOURSELF

1 What two phenomena are at work in the growth of a microbial culture?

2 In living organisms, what two types of reproduction occur?

3 Describe the process of mitosis.

4 What is the significance of meiosis to sexual reproduction?

5 What are the different phases of the eucaryotic cell cycle?

6 Is the duration of the cell cycle the same for all eucaryotic cells?

Reproduction in Procaryotic Microorganisms

Most bacteria multiply by the process of asexual reproduction, a process that involves no sex cells (gametes). Thus new cells arise from just one parent cell. In unicellular microorganisms, each cell divides into two identical

FIGURE 6.12

Bacterial multiplication by transverse binary fission.

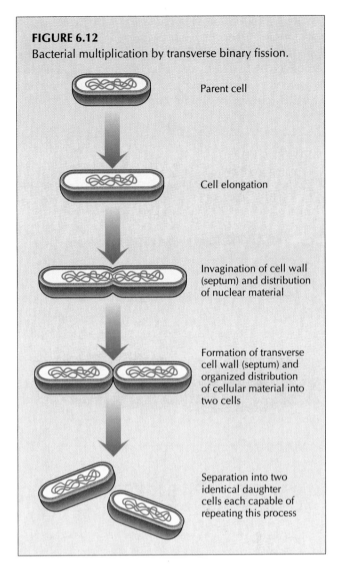

Parent cell

Cell elongation

Invagination of cell wall (septum) and distribution of nuclear material

Formation of transverse cell wall (septum) and organized distribution of cellular material into two cells

Separation into two identical daughter cells each capable of repeating this process

daughter cells [FIGURE 6.12]. In most unicellular procaryotes the mode of asexual reproduction is *transverse binary fission*, in which a single cell divides into two daughter cells of approximately equal size. Prior to cell division, the cell contents roughly double in amount, and the nucleoid is replicated. This conforms to growth in the biological sense, which is an orderly increase in all the chemical constituents of an organism. As the parent cell enlarges, the cytoplasmic membrane extends and the nuclear material becomes separated [FIGURE 6.13A]. Cell division occurs in the zone between the two nucleoids, as the membrane near the center of the enlarged cell pinches inward. At the same time, new cell-wall material grows inward to form a crosswall (septum) between the two daughter cells [FIGURE 6.13B]. Daughter cells may separate completely, but in some species they remain attached to form characteristic pairs, clusters, or chains.

Some procaryotes reproduce asexually by modes of cell division other than binary fission [FIGURE 6.14]. Some bacteria, such as *Rhodopseudomonas acidophila*, reproduce by *budding*, a process in which a small protuberance grows out at one end of the cell. This bud enlarges, eventually becoming a new cell with all the cellular constituents and then separating from the parent. Bacteria that produce filamentous growth, such as *Nocardia* species, reproduce by *fragmentation* of filaments into small rod-shaped or coccoid cells, each of which gives rise to new growth. Species of the genus *Streptomyces* and other actinomycetes produce chains of external spores (exospores), called *conidia*, by developing crosswalls at the hyphal tips. Each conidium can develop into a new organism.

FIGURE 6.13

Septum formation in *Escherichia coli* as seen by electron microscopy of thin sections at different stages [**A** and **B**] of division. Note the nuclear material (white area) partitioned to each half of the cell.

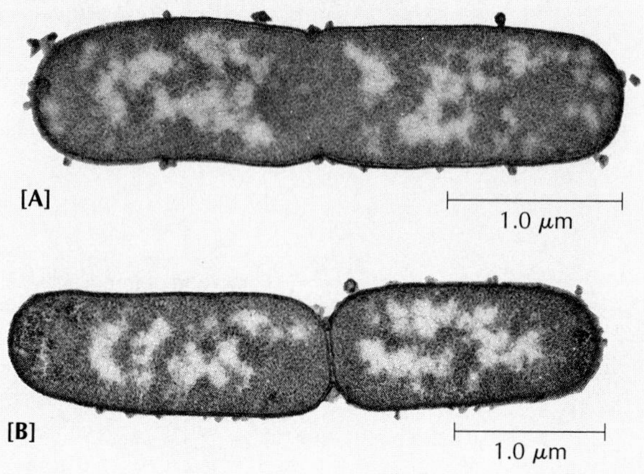

[A]

1.0 μm

[B]

1.0 μm

ASK YOURSELF

1 What is meant by *transverse* binary fission?

2 How do *clusters* or *chains* of bacteria form?

3 Do some bacteria reproduce asexually by modes other than transverse binary fission? What are these alternate modes?

Growth of a Bacterial Culture

If you start with a single bacterium undergoing binary fission, the increase in population numbers in a culture is as follows:

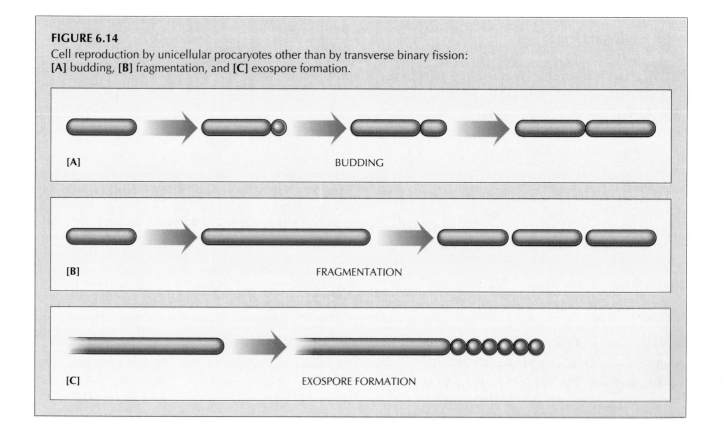

FIGURE 6.14

Cell reproduction by unicellular procaryotes other than by transverse binary fission: [A] budding, [B] fragmentation, and [C] exospore formation.

[A]   BUDDING

[B]   FRAGMENTATION

[C]   EXOSPORE FORMATION

$$1 \rightarrow 2 \rightarrow 4 \rightarrow 8 \rightarrow 16 \rightarrow 32 \rightarrow \cdots$$

That is, one cell divides into two cells, two cells divide to yield four, and so on.

This increase may be expressed as a geometric progression in the following manner:

$$1 \rightarrow 2^1 \rightarrow 2^2 \rightarrow 2^3 \rightarrow 2^4 \rightarrow 2^5 \cdots \rightarrow 2^n$$

where the exponent n refers to the number of generations. The 2^n is an algebraic expression for the ultimate number of cells produced in a given culture; the 2^n number after active growth of a culture thus represents the total number of cells in the culture (which is called N). During the active growth of a microbial culture (when there is no cell death), populations of cells grow *exponentially*, increasing by geometric progression.

Generation Time. The time interval required for each microbe to divide, or for the population in a culture to double, is known as the **generation time.** Not all species of microorganisms have the same generation time. For *Escherichia coli*, the generation time in a rich medium may be as short as 12.5 min; for *Mycobacterium tuberculosis*, it is 13 to 15 h. Nor is the generation time the same for a particular species of microorganism under all conditions. *Escherichia coli*, for example, will take much longer to divide in a nutritionally poor medium. Generation times are strongly influenced not only by the nutritional composition of the medium, but also by the physical conditions of incubation.

Mathematical Expressions of Growth. Growth of a unicellular species in culture can be characterized in *quantitative* terms. This includes the *number of generations* that has developed over a period of incubation, as well as the generation time and the growth rate (number of generations per hour). These values tell something about the nature of a microbial species. It is known that *Bradyrhizobium japonicum*, a nitrogen-fixing bacterium, is a slow grower compared with *E. coli*, the bacterium commonly used in biochemical and genetic studies. Faster-growing organisms are more useful in many types of research and industrial applications. These growth values allow scientists to predict and to control the amount of growth of any unicellular microbial species. Cells resulting from such controlled growth can be used for fundamental studies of the cell, such as electron microscopy of DNA content, as well as for commercial purposes including vaccine production.

The total, final population N of a microbial culture that begins with *one* cell may be expressed as

$$N = 1 \times 2^n \tag{4}$$

However, in reality the number of bacteria inoculated at

time zero (N_0) is not 1 but many thousands, and so Equation (4) may be rewritten as

$$N = N_0 \times 2^n \tag{5}$$

We can solve Equation (5) for n, the number of generations, by taking the logarithm of the equation:

$$\log_{10} N = \log_{10} N_0 + n \log_{10} 2 \tag{6}$$

$\log_{10}$ is used because inoculation numbers N_0 are usually in the magnitude of thousands, which can easily be changed to a $\log_{10}$ value. Equation (6) can be rearranged to solve for n:

$$n = \frac{\log_{10} N - \log_{10} N_0}{\log_{10} 2} \tag{7}$$

If you substitute the value of $\log_{10} 2$, which is 0.301, in Equation (7), the equation is simplified to

$$n = \frac{\log_{10} N - \log_{10} N_0}{0.301} \tag{8}$$

$$n = 3.3(\log_{10} N - \log_{10} N_0) \tag{9}$$

By using Equation (9), you can calculate the number of generations that have taken place in a culture, if the initial population and the final population numbers are known. For example, if you start with 1000 cells and end up with 100,000,000 cells, the number of generations n will be 3.3 (8 − 3) = 16.5 generations.

The generation time g (the time it takes for the population to double) can be determined from the number of generations n that occurs in a particular time interval t, simply by dividing t by n:

$$g = \frac{t}{n} \tag{10}$$

For example, if 16.5 generations have occurred in 5 h, the generation time g equals 3.3 h. During exponential growth, the growth rate R (in generations per hour) is the reciprocal of the generation time:

$$R = \frac{n}{t} = \frac{1}{g} \tag{11}$$

Continuing with the same example, if the generation time is 3.3 h, the growth rate R would be 0.30 generations per hour.

Growth Curve of Unicellular Microorganisms in a Closed System. Microbial cells growing in a tube or flask of liquid medium are said to be in a **closed system,** because no new nutrients are added to the system and no metabolic waste products are removed. When added to the system, the cells initially divide by binary fission and the cell numbers increase for a period of time. However, this increase eventually stops when the nutrients are used up or when enough metabolic waste products accumulate to halt further growth.

During the period of active growth, the population increases at a constant rate. For example, FIGURE 6.15 illustrates the growth of an organism with a generation time of 30 min. Note that the data can be plotted in two ways: arithmetic number of cells versus time, and logarithmic number of cells versus time. When the arithmetic scale is used on the ordinate of the graph, the plotted line curves upward at a progressively increasing rate. But when the logarithm of the cell numbers is used on the ordinate, a straight line results (during the logarithmic phase, which will be explained in the following paragraphs), showing the exponential nature of growth.

Each species of microorganism has its particular generation time, assuming optimum environmental conditions for growth. For example, in a particular medium, an *E. coli* cell may divide into two cells every 15 to 20 min. After 4 h and 12 generations, 4096 cells will have been produced. The consequences of unlimited exponential growth can be illustrated by the following example. If a bacterium the size of an *E. coli* cell divided once every hour, in six days it would produce progeny having a total volume 10,000 times that of the earth.

The exponential growth of a microbial culture, called **balanced growth**, represents only one phase of growth in a closed system. During balanced growth, there is an orderly increase in all the chemical constituents of each cell. But after a certain time, maximum population occurs with its crowding, nutrient exhaustion, and toxicity from waste products. Eventually reproduction is inhibited and microbes begin to die. (In a way, the closed system of microorganisms in a flask resembles the earth, with its limited renewable resources and potential overpopulation.)

Taken together, the various phases of growth in a microbial culture constitute a typical growth curve [FIGURE 6.16]. This curve can be drawn if you inoculate a medium with a known number of cells, determine the microbial population at time intervals, and then plot the logarithmic values of the number of *viable* cells versus time. This curve shows that there are four distinct phases, which are characterized in TABLE 6.1. There is an initial period in which there appears to be no growth in terms of increase in cell numbers (the **lag phase**). Although cells are not dividing during the lag phase, they are still metabolically active, repairing cellular damage and synthesizing enzymes. The lag phase is followed by a period of rapid balanced growth (the **logarithmic**, or **exponential, growth phase,** commonly called the *log phase*). Next is a **stationary phase,** during which no new growth is apparent; and finally there is a decline in the viable population until all microbial cells die (the **decline,** or **death, phase**). Between each two of these phases is a transitional period (the curved sections on the graph in FIGURE 6.16). This represents the time that elapses before all the cells enter the new phase.

FIGURE 6.15

Hypothetical bacterial growth curve, assuming that one bacterial cell is inoculated into a medium and divisions occur regularly at 30-min intervals (generation time).
—— = logarithm of number of bacteria versus time;
—— = arithmetic number of bacteria versus time.

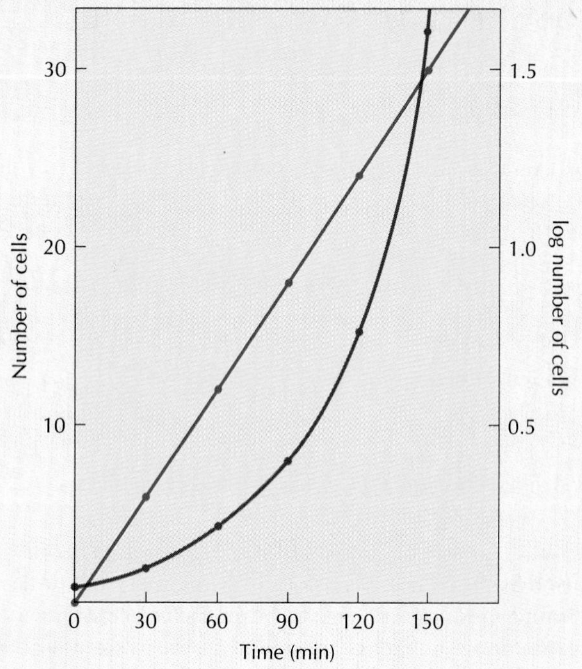

FIGURE 6.16

Typical bacterial growth curve: *a*, lag phase; *b*, log (logarithmic), or exponential, phase; *c*, stationary phase; *d*, death, or decline, phase.

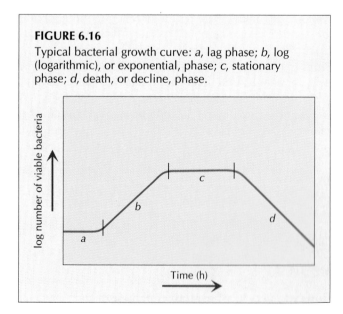

TABLE 6.1

Characteristics of Growth of a Unicellular Microbial Culture in Each Phase of the Typical Growth Curve

Growth phase	Growth rate	Characteristics
Lag	Zero	No increase in cell number. Individual cells increase in size. Cells physiologically active and synthesizing new enzymes to adapt to new environment.
Exponential, or log	Maximal and constant	Condition of balanced growth. Cells most nearly uniform in terms of chemical composition and metabolic and physiological activities. Peak time of physiological activity and efficiency.
Stationary	Zero	Accumulation of toxic metabolic products and/or exhaustion of nutrients. Some cells die while others grow and divide. Number of viable cells levels off.
Death	Negative	Further accumulation of inhibitory metabolic products and depletion of essential nutrients. Death rate accelerates. Number of viable cells decreases exponentially. Depending on species, a very few living cells may persist into the tail of the curve, forming what may be called a *senescent* phase. Typically, all cells normally die within days to months.

Measurement of Population Growth. Microbiologists use a variety of techniques to quantify microbial growth, from a microscope slide etched with grids to sophisticated electronic devices that count the number of cells in a suspension. The two most common quantitative methods are those that measure cell numbers and those that measure cell weight. Growth may also be determined by measuring the amounts of various cellular constituents (e.g., RNA, DNA, or protein) present, as well as the amount of certain metabolic products, such as organic acids. Some of these techniques and their applications are summarized in TABLE 6.2. Such methods have been combined with others that identify microbes, such as fluorescent staining, to develop instruments that count the number of pathogens in a specimen in a very short time.

Continuous Culture. Sometimes it is important to keep a microbial population growing continuously at a particular rate in the logarithmic phase. For example, in research one may wish to simulate the environmental habitat of a microbial species to study its genetic stability over time. In industry, maintaining cells in the active logarithmic growth phase will generate the maximum volume of desired products. To ensure continued new growth, the culture volume and the cell concentration are both kept constant by adding fresh, sterile medium at the same rate that used, cell-containing medium is removed. This cultivation system is sometimes known as an *open system,* or a *continuous culture* [FIGURE 6.17]. Under these conditions, the rate at which new cells are

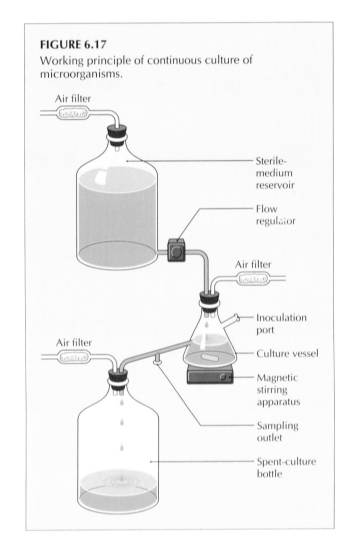

FIGURE 6.17

Working principle of continuous culture of microorganisms.

Air filter

Sterile-medium reservoir

Flow regulator

Air filter

Inoculation port

Air filter

Culture vessel

Magnetic stirring apparatus

Sampling outlet

Spent-culture bottle

TABLE 6.2
Summary of Some Methods for Measuring Microbial Growth

Method	Examples of applications	Manner in which growth is expressed
Microscopic count	Cell number in vaccines, milk, and cultures	Number of cells per ml
Electronic cell count	(Same as for microscopic count)	Number of cells per ml
Plate count	Cell number in vaccines, milk, cultures, soil, foods	Colony-forming units per ml or g
Membrane filter	(Same as for plate count)	Colony-forming units per ml or g
Turbidity	Microbiological assay, estimation of cell mass in broth cultures or other suspensions	Absorbance units
Nitrogen content	Indirect measurement of cell mass	mg nitrogen per ml
Dry weight	(Same as for nitrogen content)	mg cells per ml
Metabolic product	Microbiological assays, indirect measurement of metabolic activity (growth)	Amount of product (e.g., milliequivalents of acid) per ml

produced in the culture vessel is balanced by the rate at which cells are being removed as part of the overflow from the vessel.

The *chemostat* is widely used for continuous cultivation of microorganisms. This apparatus is based on the principle that the concentration of an essential substrate within the culture will control the growth rate of the cells. The concentration of this substrate is in turn controlled by the dilution rate, or the rate at which the medium in the culture vessel is being replaced with fresh medium. Therefore, by adjusting the dilution rate you can control the rate of cell growth.

Synchronous Culture. Cells in a microbial culture do not all divide at the same time. The straight line that characterizes the logarithmic phase of a microbial culture is due instead to random cell divisions [FIGURE 6.18]. However, there are laboratory techniques that manipulate the growth of cultures so that all the cells divide at the same time, or grow synchronously. A population can be synchronized by changing the physical environment or the chemical composition of the medium. For instance, if cells are inoculated into a medium at a suboptimal temperature and kept at that temperature, they will metabolize slowly but will not divide. When the temperature is rapidly increased to that for optimal growth, the cells will undergo synchronized divisions.

Another method to obtain synchronized growth uses differential filtration or centrifugation, because the smallest cells in a log-phase culture are those that have just divided. When separated by size, cells are reason-

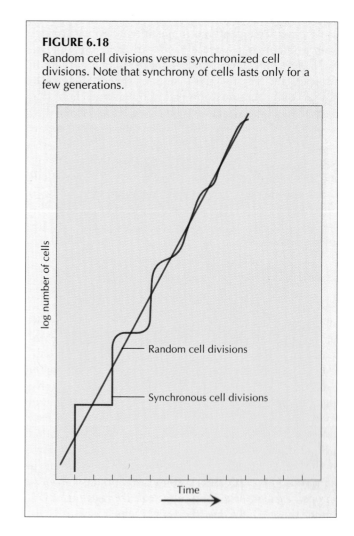

FIGURE 6.18
Random cell divisions versus synchronized cell divisions. Note that synchrony of cells lasts only for a few generations.

log number of cells

Random cell divisions

Synchronous cell divisions

Time

ably well synchronized with each other. Unfortunately, the synchrony of microbial cells usually lasts for only a few generations [FIGURE 6.18]. Even the daughter cells of a single parent cell will soon be out of phase with one another.

Synchronous cultures allow researchers to study microbial growth, organization, and morphogenesis during particular stages of the cell division cycle. It is not practical to analyze a single microbial cell, because of its small size. However, if all the cells in a culture are in the same stage of growth, the information learned from the entire cell population can be extrapolated to provide information applicable to a single cell.

ASK YOURSELF

1 What is meant by *exponential* growth of a bacterial culture?

2 What are the differences between number of generations, generation time, and growth rate?

3 What are the formulas for calculating generation time and the growth rate of a bacterial culture?

4 What is meant by *balanced* growth? *Synchronous* growth?

5 Why is continuous culture of microorganisms described as an open system?

6 How is the rate of cell growth controlled in a chemostat?

SUMMARY

1 Successful cultivation of microorganisms requires both proper nutrients and proper physical conditions. This allows the microbiologist to study processes associated with microbial reproduction and growth in the laboratory.

2 Incubation temperatures influence the growth of cells. The number of cell divisions per hour, called the *growth rate,* is greatest at the optimum growth temperature. The minimum, optimum, and maximum growth temperatures of an organism are its *cardinal* temperatures. With respect to growth within a particular temperature range, microorganisms may be divided into three groups: psychrophiles, mesophiles, and thermophiles.

3 Proper gas atmospheres must also be provided to successfully cultivate microorganisms. Oxygen and carbon dioxide are the two principal gases that affect the growth of microbes. On the basis of their response to free gaseous oxygen, microorganisms may be divided into four physiological groups: aerobes, anaerobes, facultative microorganisms, and microaerophiles. Oxygen toxicity is due to the formation of superoxide radicals, hydrogen peroxide, and hydroxyl radicals. Microorganisms protect themselves from these toxic forms by producing enzymes such as superoxide dismutase, catalase, and peroxidase.

4 Microorganisms must also be cultivated within a pH range suitable for their growth. The optimum pH for many organisms is around 7.0, although others have other pH ranges. Buffers are usually added to media to prevent sudden pH shifts.

5 Other conditions affecting the growth of microorganisms include osmotic pressure and hydrostatic pressure.

6 Growth in a microbial culture is due to the reproduction of individual cells. Eucaryotic cells reproduce by both sexual and asexual reproduction, but in sexual reproduction both mitosis and meiosis must occur to ensure the proper number of chromosomes in daughter cells. Transverse binary fission is the most common process of asexual reproduction in unicellular procaryotes. Other microbial modes of reproduction include budding, fragmentation, and spore formation.

7 Different species of microorganisms have different generation times. The growth of a unicellular microbial species can be characterized in quantitative terms. The number of generations, the generation time, and the growth rate can be calculated for any growing microbial species.

8 When cells are grown in a container such as a tube or flask with a fixed amount of medium, the system is called a *closed system*. During balanced growth in a closed system, there is an orderly increase in all the chemical constituents of a microbial cell. Microorganisms inoculated into a liquid medium exhibit a typical growth curve consisting of four phases: the lag, log, stationary, and death phases.

9 The two principal methods for measuring microbial growth are those that measure cell numbers and those that measure cell mass.

10 By means of a chemostat, microbial cultures can be kept growing continuously in the logarithmic phase at a fixed growth rate. Other laboratory techniques are used to induce synchrony in microorganisms.

KEY TERMS

aerobes
anaerobes
anaphase
balanced growth
barophiles
cardinal temperatures
catalase
centrioles
centromere
chemostat
closed system
continuous culture
decline (or death) phase
facultative microorganisms
gametes
generation time
growth rate
hydrostatic pressure
hydroxyl radicals
interphase
lag phase
logarithmic (or exponential)
  growth phase
meiosis
mesophiles
metaphase
microaerophiles
mitosis
mitotic spindle
open system
optimum growth temperature
peroxidase
prophase
psychrophiles
stationary phase
superoxide dismutase
superoxide radical
telophase
thermophiles
zygote

REVIEW GUIDE

OVERVIEW

1 Microorganisms are cultivated on _____, which provide nutrients.

2 Microorganisms show wide differences with respect to the physical conditions required for _____ .

3 Eucaryotes have developed elaborate processes to ensure that each daughter cell receives the correct number of _____ following sexual reproduction.

4 Which word aptly describes the situation with respect to the supply of nutrients to pure cultures grown in the laboratory?
(a) complex   **(b)** overabundance   **(c)** deficient

PHYSICAL
CONDITIONS FOR
CULTIVATION OF
MICROORGANISMS

5 Within the temperature range of growth of a microorganism, the

_____ generally doubles for every 10°C of temperature increase.

6 At which of the following growth temperatures is the growth rate the greatest?
(a) optimum   **(b)** minimum   **(c)** maximum   **(d)** cardinal

7 The minimum, optimum, and maximum temperatures for growth of microorganisms are known as _____ temperatures.

8 Microorganisms may be divided into three groups on the basis of their temperature requirements for growth: _____,

_____, and _____ .

9 Psychrophiles grow best within the range _____ to

_____ °C.

10 Saprophytic microorganisms grow in which part of the mesophilic temperature range?
(a) upper   **(b)** middle   **(c)** lower   **(d)** entire

11 Microorganisms pathogenic for humans and other warmblooded animals grow best at about _____ °C.

12 _____ is a gas used by all cells.

13 Microorganisms may be divided into four physiological groups based on their response to the gas _____ .

14 The addition of a single electron to an oxygen molecule can result in the formation of a(n) _____ radical.

15 The enzyme _____ eliminates the radicals described in question 14 by converting them to hydrogen peroxide.

16 The gaseous atmosphere in an anaerobic glove box contains all of the following gases *except:* **(a)** oxygen; **(b)** nitrogen; **(c)** carbon dioxide; **(d)** hydrogen.

17 To survive effectively in an acidic or a basic environment, a microorganism must be able to maintain its intracellular pH at about _____ .

18 The optimum pH for growth of fungi is generally _____ than that for most bacteria.

19 Shifts in pH in laboratory media can be prevented by incorporating a(n) _____ into the medium.

20 Dissolved substances in a solution are termed _____.

21 A solution in which water flows equally into and out of a cell is termed a(n) _____ solution.

22 When the external environment of a cell is hypertonic, the cell undergoes a net _____ of water.

REPRODUCTION AND GROWTH OF MICROORGANISMS

23 The form of reproduction that allows for more efficiency in propagating a species is _____ reproduction.

24 Cell division of eucaryotic organisms must be preceded by _____.

25 The four phases of mitosis are _____, _____, _____, and _____.

26 The system of microtubules connected to the centromeres and the centrioles is called the _____.

27 Since all the cells of a eucaryotic organism are formed by mitosis from the zygote, each cell has the same number and kind of _____.

28 The zygote is formed from the fusion of gametes during _____.

29 Diploid cells undergo _____ to form haploid gametes.

30 The process in which the diploid cells alternate with haploid cells in the life cycle is termed _____.

31 Which stage or stages are not considered part of mitosis?
(a) prophase   **(b)** metaphase   **(c)** telophase   **(d)** interphase   **(e)** anaphase

32 A zygote results from this process:
(a) alternation of generations   **(b)** mitosis   **(c)** synapsis   **(d)** meiosis   **(e)** fertilization

In questions 33 to 36, indicate whether the statement is true **(T)** *or false* **(F)**. *If the statement is false, rewrite it as true.*

33 In cytokinesis the whole cell divides into two daughter cells with one nucleus going into each progeny cell. _____

_____

34 The anaphase stage is usually the shortest phase of mitosis. _____

_____

35 In sexual reproduction, a new individual is formed by the fusion of two different sex cells called *zygotes*. _____

_____

36 The meiotic process is necessary to keep the chromosome number constant from generation to generation. _____

_____

37 The two main parts of the eucaryotic cell cycle are the

_____ and _____ .

38 The interphase consists of the three phases _____ ,

_____ , and _____ .

39 The distribution of genetic material into two equal sets in two daughter nuclei by mitosis is called _____ .

40 The most common process of asexual reproduction in unicellular procaryotes is transverse _____ .

41 Match the bacterial species on the right with the mode of asexual reproduction on the left.

_____ fragmentation   **(a)** *Escherichia coli*

_____ budding   **(b)** *Nocardia* sp.

_____ sporulation   **(c)** *Rhodopseudomonas acidophila*

_____ transverse binary fission   **(d)** *Streptomyces* sp.

42 The time interval required for each cell to divide is known as the _____ .

43 The reciprocal of the generation time is known as the _____ ,

which may be described as the number of _____ per hour.

44 When there is an orderly increase in all the chemical constituents of a cell, the type of growth is characterized as _____ .

45 A direct microscope count of cells in a closed container over time will not show a(n) _____ phase.

46 The growth rate is maximal and constant in which phase of the typical growth curve in a closed system of microbial cultivation?

(a) log   **(b)** lag   **(c)** decline   **(d)** stationary

47 A continuous culture apparatus that works on the principle that the concentration of an essential substrate within the culture vessel will control the growth rate of the cells is called a(n) _____ .

48 When all the cells in a culture are dividing at the same time they are said to be growing in _____ .

49 When the medium used for growing microorganisms is in a stoppered container with no addition of fresh medium during growth, the system of cultivation is said to be a(n) _____ one.

50 The most convenient way to graph great increases of growth in a microbial culture is to employ a(n) _____ scale.

REVIEW QUESTIONS

1 What are the main physical conditions that must be considered in the cultivation of microorganisms?

2 Compare the temperatures at which mesophiles and eubacterial thermophiles grow best.

3 Give some probable physiological factors that are responsible for the low optimum temperatures of psychrophiles.

4 Describe the four physiological groups of microorganisms based on response to free gaseous oxygen.

5 Explain why anaerobic microorganisms cannot tolerate molecular oxygen.

6 How are catalase-positive bacteria identified?

7 What is osmotic pressure, and how does it affect growth of microbial cells?

8 Besides binary fission, what other modes of asexual reproduction take place in bacteria?

9 Explain what is meant by *balanced growth, exponential growth,* and *synchronous growth.*

10 Describe the various phases of a typical growth curve of a microbial culture in a closed container.

11 Draw a diagram to explain the workings of a continuous culture apparatus.

12 Describe the process of mitosis.

13 Explain what is meant by *alternation of generations.*

14 Describe the several phases of the eucaryotic cell cycle.

DISCUSSION QUESTIONS

1 Provide a scientific rationale for the survival of archaeobacterial extreme thermophily.

2 Why must we exercise caution in extrapolating data from studies of pure cultures in the laboratory to the behavior of their counterparts in nature?

3 Why do different species of microorganisms have different cardinal temperatures for growth?

4 What are the advantages and disadvantages of using anaerobic gas jars?

5 Compare the use of anaerobic gas jars and anaerobic chambers (glove boxes) and explain how anaerobiosis is obtained in them.

6 What does the content of superoxide dismutase in the cells of a microbial species tell us about the physiology of those cells?

7 Explain why buffers are used in microbiological media, and describe some buffers that are commonly used in the laboratory for the growth of cells.

8 How does osmotic pressure affect the growth of microbial cells?

9 Why is meiosis important in the life cycle of eucaryotic organisms?

10 Correlate the biosynthesis of macromolecules with different phases of the eucaryotic cell cycle.

11 Explain how the growth rate is controlled in a chemostat.

12 Evaluate the pros and cons of some methods used in obtaining synchronized cells.

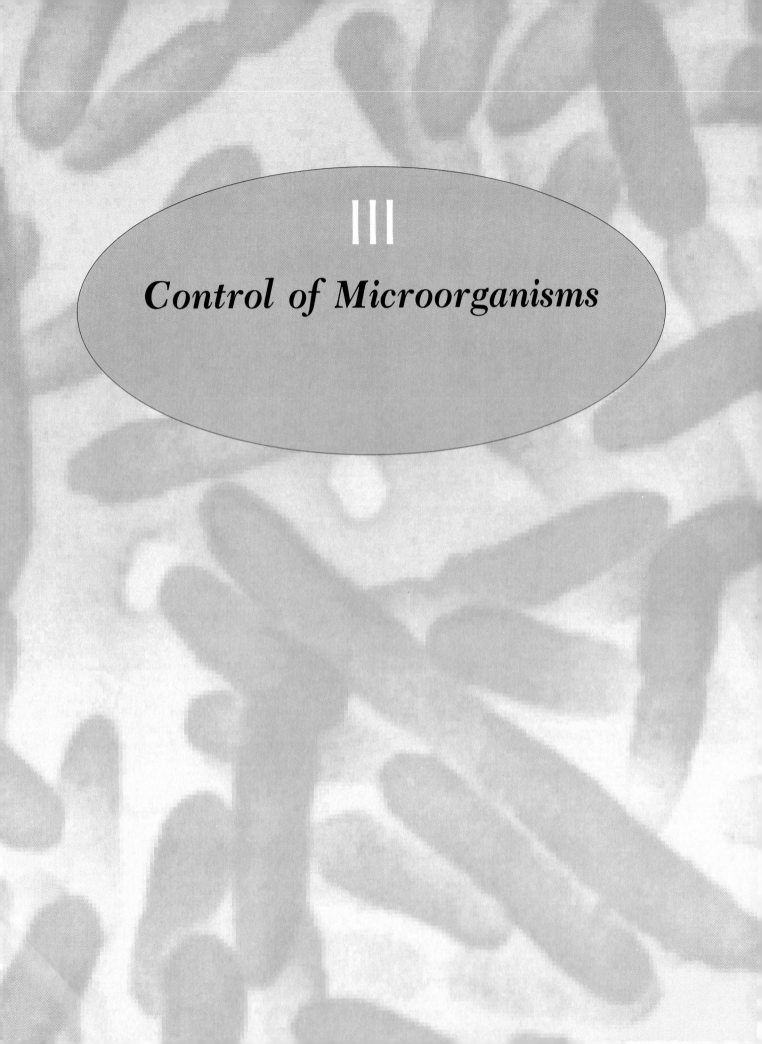

III

Control of Microorganisms

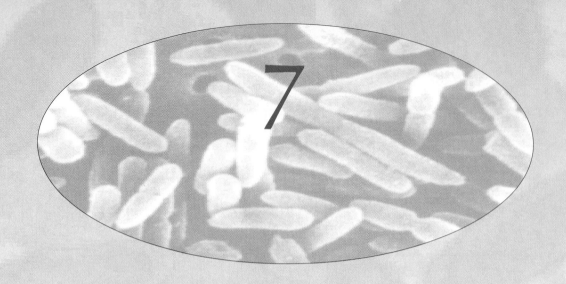

7

Control of Microorganisms:
Principles and Physical Agents

OVERVIEW

Effective management of microorganisms in the laboratory, the home, the hospital, and the industrial setting depends upon a knowledge of how to control (i.e., kill, inhibit, or remove) microorganisms in an environment. This aspect of microbiology is called the "control of microorganisms." Various physical and chemical agents can be used to keep microorganisms at acceptable levels. Selection of the best agent depends in part on whether you want to kill or remove all of the microbes present, kill only certain types, or merely prevent those already present from multiplying.

This chapter describes how physical agents and processes such as heat, low temperature, radiation, filtration, and desiccation can control the number of microorganisms. Which method is selected depends not only on the nature of the agent itself, but also on the type of microbe-containing material being treated. For example, it makes a difference whether the organisms are present in a culture medium, in a pharmaceutical product, on the surface of surgical instruments, in the air of a hospital operating room, or in food for human consumption.

These physical agents, along with the chemical agents described in Chapter 8, are used extensively in industry, in health care, and in the home. Some familiar uses of physical agents to control microorganisms include the thorough cooking of poultry and meat to kill *Salmonella* bacteria, and the pasteurization of milk to destroy bacteria that can cause tuberculosis and typhoid fever.

OBJECTIVES

After reading this chapter you should be able to

1 Describe the general pattern of death in a microbial population following exposure to a microbicidal agent.

2 Identify the conditions that may limit the effectiveness of an antimicrobial agent.

3 Describe the general ways in which antimicrobial agents may kill microorganisms or inhibit their growth.

4 Explain how the autoclave and the hot-air sterilizing oven kill microorganisms and why moist heat is more effective than dry heat.

5 Distinguish between microbicidal and microbiostatic agents.

6 List some situations in which low temperatures are used for the control of microorganisms.

7 Identify the ionizing and nonionizing radiations that can kill microorganisms, describing their practical uses.

8 Explain how microbiological filters and filtration processes are used to remove microorganisms from liquids and air.

9 Explain how desiccation and high osmotic pressure affect microbial growth and survival.

FUNDAMENTALS OF MICROBIAL CONTROL

Although the concepts of microbial physiology are relatively new, food has been preserved by drying and salting for hundreds of years. Along with cooking foods, these preservation techniques are some of the oldest methods of microbial control. From the early bonfires and drying racks, the control of microorganisms has evolved until today there is a variety of methods available. The microbiologist and the food manufacturer can select the control technique that best fits a particular situation, based on principles of microbial physiology learned from modern scientific research.

By the eighteenth century, scientists knew that there were tiny "animals" capable of spoiling food and growing in a natural environment. During the controversy over the theory of spontaneous generation they found that boiling could kill most of these creatures, although bacterial endospores could survive because of their extraordinary heat resistance. Scientists discovered that microbes could also be killed by various chemicals, and that they could be removed from air or liquids by special filters. These early observations were quickly applied to the industrial production of wine, beer, and food products. Cotton filters and high and low temperatures were used to control fermentation and food spoilage; chemical agents such as phenol were used to destroy microbes in air. The same concepts were first implemented in hospitals during the nineteenth century, when a few astute physicians fought for cleaner techniques such as routine hand washing and sterilization of surgical instruments.

Substances that either kill microorganisms or prevent their growth are called *antimicrobial* agents. More specifically, there are *antibacterial, antiviral, antifungal,* and *antiprotozoan* agents, depending on the kind of microorganisms affected.

Those antimicrobial agents that *kill* microorganisms are *microbicidal* agents. The names *bactericidal, virucidal,* and *fungicidal* indicate the type of microorganism killed. Killing *all* the organisms present in a material, including any spores, is called *sterilization.* Agents that merely *inhibit the growth* of microorganisms are called *microbiostatic* agents. Again, more specific names can be used, such as *bacteriostatic* or *fungistatic.*

Antimicrobial agents may be either physical agents or chemical agents. Although this chapter is concerned primarily with physical agents, there are fundamental features that apply to both classes of agents, including (1) the pattern of death of a microbial population after exposure to a microbicidal agent, (2) the conditions that influence the effectiveness of an antimicrobial agent, and (3) the ways in which microbial cells can be damaged by an antimicrobial agent.

Pattern of Death in a Microbial Population

A veterinarian can use various tests to tell whether or not an animal is dead (e.g., it no longer breathes, it has no heartbeat, or it has no blood pressure). Obviously, we cannot apply similar tests to a single microbial cell to see whether it is dead. In microbiology, the criterion of death of a single microorganism is based on a single property: *the ability to reproduce.* As applied to microorganisms, the term *death* is therefore defined as loss of the ability to reproduce. To assess the effectiveness of a microbicidal agent, a sample of the treated specimen is cultured to determine the number of survivors, those that can grow and multiply [DISCOVER 7.1].

Some advertisements for antimicrobial agents claim that they "kill microbes on contact." Technically, this statement is correct because microbial cells do have to come into contact with an agent in order to be killed. But it is misleading in that it implies that all of the microorganisms are killed *instantly* upon contact, which is untrue. *Instead, they die at a constant rate over a period of time.* This characteristic pattern of death is called *exponential death.*

A simple model best illustrates what is meant by exponential death. Suppose that each cell in a large population of bacteria is a target, and that you are shooting bullets at these targets. The bullets are analogous to a chemical or physical microbicidal agent, and the model assumes that a single hit can kill a cell. If you shoot at targets randomly, the probability of hitting a target is directly proportional to the number of targets present.

At first, there are many bacterial cells and there is a good chance of hitting one of them. But as time passes, the number of bacteria not yet hit decreases steadily, making it more difficult to hit the ones that remain. For instance, if there are initially 1 million bacteria and, after one minute of shooting, you manage to hit 90% (900,000) of them, there are only 100,000 left. There now are only one-tenth as many targets as there were in the beginning. After another minute of shooting, during which 90 percent of the 100,000 cells are killed, there are 10,000 survivors. This pattern would continue as follows:

3d min—9000 bacteria killed, 1000 survivors
4th min—900 bacteria killed, 100 survivors
5th min—90 bacteria killed, 10 survivors
6th min—9 bacteria killed, 1 survivor

Notice that it takes just as long to kill the last nine cells as it took to kill the first 900,000 cells. In fact, you can never be certain that the last cell has been killed. All you can do is shoot at the targets long enough that there is a good statistical probability that the last one has been destroyed.

How this model applies to microbicidal agents is illustrated in FIGURE 7.1, which shows the results of ex-

FIGURE 7.1

[A] The arithmetic death curve of bacterial spores exposed to a 5% phenol solution at a constant temperature illustrates that the spores in the population die over a period of time. [B] The logarithmic death curve is based on the same data as the preceding curve. Data expressed in this manner reveal a consistent increment of deaths per unit time.

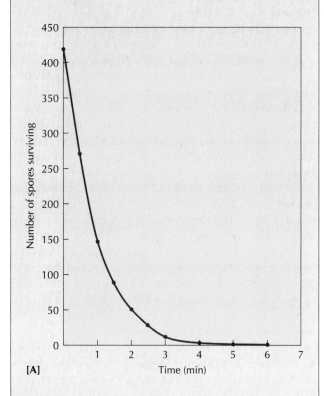

[A]

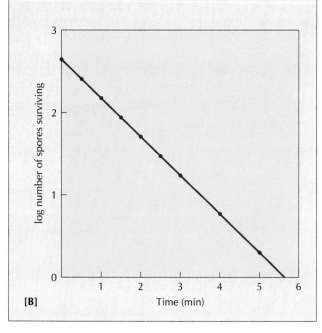

[B]

posing *Bacillus anthracis* spores to 5% phenol. The number of surviving spores is plotted both arithmetically [FIGURE 7.1A] and logarithmically [FIGURE 7.1B], with time of exposure to the phenol on the other axis. In the logarithmic graph, the data points fall on a straight line, indicating that the death rate is constant. The slope of that line is a measure of the death rate. However, precise results like these are obtained only when all the experimental conditions are strictly controlled, including the age and physiological condition of all the microorganisms in the treated population.

Conditions That Affect Antimicrobial Activity

When microbicidal agents are used for some practical application, there can be great variation in the conditions affecting each situation. Some important variables to consider when assessing the effectiveness of a microbicidal agent are:

1 *Size of the microbial population.* Large populations take longer to kill than small populations [FIGURE 7.2].
2 *Intensity or concentration of the microbicidal agent.* The lower the intensity or concentration, the longer it takes to kill a microbial population [FIGURE 7.3].

FIGURE 7.2

Graph showing death rates of three different microbial populations exposed to the same microbicidal agent. Population I is the smallest and is killed in the shortest period of time. Populations II and III each require a longer period of time to be killed because the initial populations are larger.

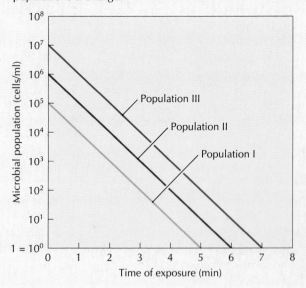

7.1 WHEN IS A MICROBE REALLY DEAD?

There is no way we can put "a finger on the pulse" of a microorganism and declare that it is dead. Nor can we measure the cessation of all vital functions in a microbial cell and say that it is no longer alive. Therefore, we normally choose as the criterion for death of a microorganism something we can measure easily: *its ability to reproduce.* A microbial cell is considered to be alive if it can give rise to a visible colony on an agar medium, produce turbid growth in a liquid medium, or multiply in a host such as an animal or a plant. If it cannot do this, we declare it to be dead.

But this concept of microbial death may be an artificial one that is governed by laboratory conditions. The culture medium that we choose in order to show that the organism can no longer reproduce may not be rich enough to meet the reproduction requirements of the organism. Or the cultural conditions we use, such as temperature, pH, or gaseous atmosphere, may be inadequate for the organism. The organism might possibly be returned to an "alive and well" state if these needs can be satisfied.

For example, a selective medium called *violet-red bile agar* is routinely used to enumerate viable cells of *E. coli* in food products. *Escherichia coli* can normally form colonies on this medium, whereas many other types of bacteria cannot. However, if the *E. coli* cells in the food product have been injured in some way, as by a heat treatment, they often fail to grow on violet-red bile agar, whereas they may still grow on other media such as soybean-casein digest agar. This is because some chemicals in violet-red bile agar are inhibitory for the injured cells, and these chemicals are not present in soybean-casein digest agar. If we use only the violet-red bile agar, we would call the cells "dead." If we use the soybean-casein digest agar, we may find that many of the cells are still alive.

This example shows that the question of life and death of a microbe is one that is not always answered easily. We need to be very careful before declaring that a particular microbe has been "killed" by a heat treatment such as pasteurization, or by a certain antibiotic that is being used to treat a hospital patient, or by some other means. If the microbe happens to be a disease-causing organism, a mistaken conclusion about whether the microbe is dead or not could have important consequences for our own lives.

---

3 *Time of exposure to the microbicidal agent.* The longer the time, the greater the number of cells killed.
4 *Temperature at which the microorganisms are exposed to the microbicidal agent.* In general, the higher the temperature, the more quickly a population is killed [FIGURE 7.4].
5 *Nature of the material containing the microorganisms.* Various characteristics of the material can affect

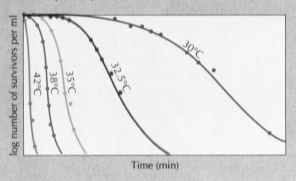

FIGURE 7.4
An increase in temperature decreases bacterial survival when the concentration of the antimicrobial agent remains the same. In this experiment, *Escherichia coli* was exposed to phenol at a concentration of 4.62 g/liter at temperatures between 30 and 42°C. The number of survivors, expressed logarithmically, is plotted against time. *(From R. C. Jordan and S. E. Jacobs, J. Hyg. 44:210, 1945, courtesy of Cambridge University Press.)*

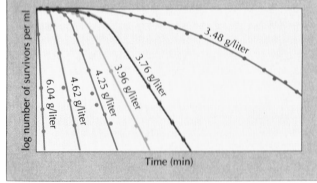

FIGURE 7.3
Effect of concentration of an antimicrobial agent on bacterial death. In this experiment, *Escherichia coli* was exposed to various concentrations of phenol at 35°C. The number of survivors, expressed logarithmically, is plotted against time. *(From R. C. Jordan and S. E. Jacobs, J. Hyg. 43:279, 144, courtesy of Cambridge University Press.)*

the rate of cell death caused by a microbicidal agent. For example, if moist heat is used to sterilize a culture medium, a shorter exposure time is needed if the medium is fluid instead of viscous, or has a pH of 5 instead of 7. Canning of sauerkraut and berries (high-acid foods) requires lower temperatures and shorter times than those required for corn and meats (low-acid foods).

6 *Characteristics of the microorganisms which are present.* Microorganisms vary considerably in their resistance to physical and chemical agents. For example, many Gram-positive species are more resistant to heat than are Gram-negative species; some chemicals are more effective against Gram-positive species than they are against Gram-negative species.

Mechanisms of Microbial Cell Damage

Antimicrobial agents act in various ways to inhibit or kill microorganisms. Knowing the mode of action of a particular agent can help predict the conditions under which it will function most effectively. It may also reveal which species of microbes will be most susceptible to that agent.

The possible mechanisms of antimicrobial damage are linked to the major structural features of a bacterial cell shown in FIGURE 7.5. An understanding of how an agent damages microorganisms makes it possible to select the most effective agent.

The cytoplasm of a normal, living cell exists in a colloidal state, containing DNA, ribosomes that synthesize proteins, and hundreds of enzymes. The cytoplasmic membrane surrounding the cell maintains the integrity of the cellular contents, controls the passage of substances into and out of the cell, and holds enzymes involved in cell metabolism. The cell wall provides a protective covering that prevents the cell from bursting after uptake of water. Damage at any one of these sites—alteration of the physical state of the cytoplasm, inactiva-

tion of enzymes, or disruption of the membrane or cell wall—may lead to death of the cell. More detailed information on possible modes of microbicidal action is included in the following descriptions of specific agents.

ASK YOURSELF

1 What suffixes are used after *microbe* to designate killing of cells? Inhibiting of cells?

2 What is the pattern of death of a large bacterial population when exposed to a killing agent?

3 What are the conditions which influence the effectiveness of an antimicrobial substance?

4 Of what value is it to know the mode of action of an antimicrobial agent?

HIGH TEMPERATURES

The use of high temperatures is one of the most effective and widely utilized means of killing microorganisms. Heat may be applied in either a *moist* condition (steam or water) or in a *dry* condition. The most extreme use of high temperatures to kill microorganisms is *incineration* (burning).

Moist Heat

Moist heat is much more effective than dry heat for killing microorganisms [TABLE 7.1]. This is because moist heat causes *denaturation* and *coagulation* of vital proteins such as enzymes, whereas dry heat causes *oxidation* of the organic constituents of the cell (i.e., it causes them to "burn" slowly). Denaturation of cell proteins occurs with lower temperatures and shorter exposure times than those required for oxidation. For example, the endospores of *Bacillus anthracis* are destroyed in 2 to 15 min by moist heat at 100°C, but with dry heat it takes up to 180 min at 140°C to achieve the same result. TABLE 7.1 shows more examples of the longer times and higher temperatures required to kill spores by dry heat.

Bacterial endospores are the most resistant forms of life. On the other hand, the vegetative cells of bacteria are much more sensitive to heat and are usually killed within 5 to 10 min by moist heat at 60 to 70°C. Vegetative cells of yeasts and other fungi are normally killed

---

FIGURE 7.5
Antimicrobial agents inhibit or kill microorganisms by damaging certain structures of the cell, such as the cell wall or the cytoplasmic membrane, or substances within the cytoplasm, such as enzymes, ribosomes, or nuclear material. Knowledge of the mode of action of an antimicrobial agent is of value in making decisions for practical applications.

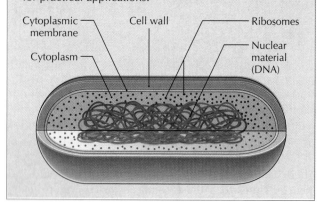

Cytoplasmic membrane — Cell wall — Ribosomes
Cytoplasm — Nuclear material (DNA)

TABLE 7.1

Reported Killing Times of Bacterial Spores by Moist Heat and Dry Heat

Species of bacteria	MOIST HEAT Temperature (°C)	Killing time (min)	DRY HEAT Temperature (°C)	Killing time (min)
Bacillus anthracis	100	2–15	140	Up to 180
	105	5–10	160	9–90
			180	3
Clostridium botulinum	100	300–530	120	50
	110	32–90	130	15–35
	115	10–40	140	5
Clostridium perfringens	100	5–45	120	50
	105	5–27	130	15–35
	115	4	140	5
	120	1		
Clostridium tetani	100	5–90	130	20–40
	105	5–25	140	5–15
			160	12

TABLE 7.2

Temperature of Pure Steam Under Pressure

Steam pressure (lb/in²)	Temperature (°C)
0	100.0
5	109.0
10	115.0
15	121.5
20	126.5

within 5 to 10 min by moist heat at 50 to 60°C. To kill fungal spores in the same time requires temperatures of 70 to 80°C. The susceptibility of protozoa and most viruses to heat is similar to that of most vegetative cells.

Moist heat used to kill microorganisms can be in the form of steam, boiling water, or water heated to subboiling temperatures.

Steam. The use of *pure steam under pressure* is the most practical and dependable way to apply moist heat. In a closed system of constant volume, an increased pressure allows for an increased temperature. Steam under pressure provides temperatures higher than those possible with nonpressurized steam or boiling water, as shown in TABLE 7.2. It also has the advantages of rapid heating and greater penetration. The laboratory apparatus designed to sterilize with pressurized steam is the *auto-*

clave [FIGURE 7.6]. Developed in the nineteenth century, the autoclave is an essential unit of equipment in every microbiology laboratory. Many culture media, solutions, discarded cultures, and contaminated materials are sterilized routinely with this apparatus.

Autoclaves resemble home pressure cookers in that both use steam under pressure, but the temperature and pressure inside an autoclave can be more closely controlled. The double-jacketed chamber of the autoclave is first flushed with free-flowing (nonpressurized) steam to remove any air. It is then filled with pure steam and maintained at a designated temperature and pressure for a specific period of time. It is essential that all the air initially present in the chamber be completely replaced by pure steam. If air is present, it will reduce the temperature. It is the temperature, not the pressure, within the chamber that kills the organisms.

An autoclave is usually operated at a pressure of 15 lb/in², at which the temperature of pure steam is 121°C. The length of time needed to sterilize at this temperature depends on the material being treated. It takes longer for heat to penetrate a viscous or solid material than it does a fluid material. The necessary time also depends upon the volume of material being sterilized [TABLE 7.3]. For example, 1000 test tubes containing 10 ml each of a liquid medium can be sterilized within 10 to 15 min at 121°C, whereas the same amount of liquid (10 liters) in a single container would require 1 h or more at the same temperature. More time is required for the heat to penetrate to the center of bulk material.

TABLE 7.3

Exposure Periods Required for Aqueous Solutions or Liquids in Various Containers Affording a Reasonable Factor of Safety for Sterilization by Autoclaving

Container	Minutes of exposure at 121–123°C (250–254°F)
Test tubes	
18 × 150 mm	12–14
32 × 200 mm	13–17
38 × 200 mm	15–20
Erlenmeyer flasks	
50 ml	12–14
500 ml	17–22
1000 ml	20–25
2000 ml	30–35
Milk-dilution bottle, 100 ml	13–17
Serum bottle, 9000 ml	50–55

SOURCE: J. J. Perkins, *Principles and Methods of Sterilization in Health Sciences*, Charles C Thomas, Springfield, Ill., 1983.

FIGURE 7.6

[A] The laboratory autoclave, a pressure-steam sterilizer. [B] Cross-sectional view of an autoclave illustrating operational parts and path of steam flow.

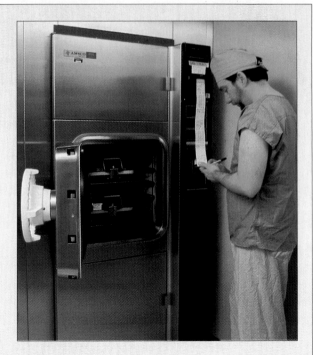

[A]

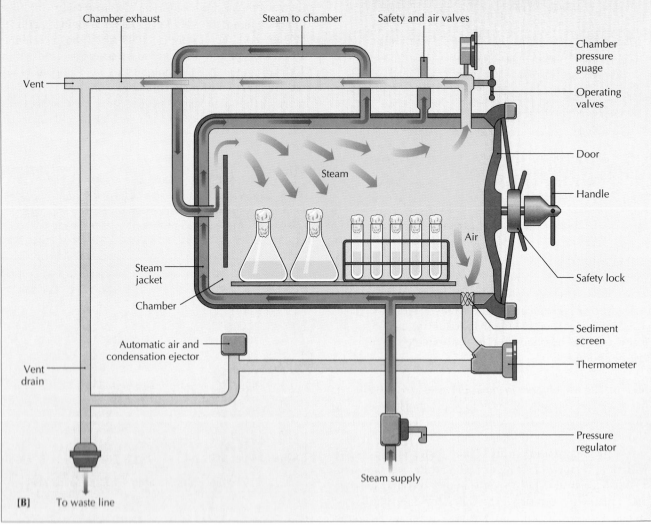

[B]

Boiling Water. Water brought to the boiling point (100°C) will kill vegetative microorganisms present in the liquid. However, contaminated materials or objects exposed to boiling water for several minutes cannot be *sterilized* with certainty. This is because some bacterial endospores can withstand 100°C for more than an hour [TABLE 7.1]. Exposing instruments to boiling water for short periods of time is likely to kill all the vegetative cells present, but it will not necessarily sterilize the instruments. Therefore boiling water is not considered a method of sterilization.

Subboiling Temperatures. Sterilization temperatures have adverse effects on many foods, and alternative treatments must be used to reduce microbial contamination in these materials. In the 1860s, Pasteur used slow heating at lower temperatures to destroy unwanted microorganisms that were spoiling French wines. This controlled heat treatment is now called *pasteurization*. It kills the vegetative cells of most microorganisms but does not sterilize. One method of pasteurizing milk is the batch method, in which milk is held at 62.8°C for 30 min. Another method of pasteurizing milk is done by flowing milk through a heat exchanger, where it is heated to 71.7°C and held for 15 s, and then cooled quickly. Pasteurization eliminates the vegetative cells of disease-causing microorganisms, as well as those of many other microorganisms, and thereby prolongs the keeping quality of the product. Higher temperatures are often avoided in the food industry when they are unnecessary, since they can affect the taste, appearance, or nutritive value of foods such as milk products, fruit juices, and vegetables.

Measurement of Microbial Susceptibility to High Temperatures. The susceptibility of microorganisms to moist heat can be expressed in terms of a time-temperature relationship. Two relationships commonly used by microbiologists are:

1 *Thermal death time (TDT).* This is the shortest period of time required to kill *all* the microorganisms in a sample, when exposed to a specific temperature under standard conditions. During experiments to determine the TDT for a certain microorganism, a specific temperature is selected as the fixed point. The microbial population is then sampled at various time intervals of heat treatment and cultured for growth. This method determines the minimum exposure time capable of destroying all the organisms.
2 *Decimal reduction time (D value).* This is the time required to decrease the microbial population in a sample by *90 percent* (i.e., by a logarithmic value of 1) at a prescribed temperature [FIGURE 7.7]. Refer back to FIGURE 7.1, which illustrates the pattern of death in a population of bacteria. The temperature

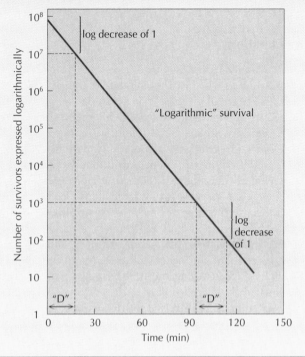

FIGURE 7.7
Graphic illustration of decimal reduction time (D value), or time in minutes to reduce the viable microbial population by 90 percent, or a logarithmic value of 1. In this illustration the D value is approximately 20 min. Note that this value is constant for each logarithmic drop of 1.

serves as the fixed point, and the population is sampled at various intervals. However, unlike TDT measurements, the exposure time that gives 10 percent survival is determined, rather than the time that results in 0 percent survival.

In determining TDTs or D values, factors other than temperature must be rigidly controlled. The nature of the medium, the pH, and the initial concentration of microorganisms can influence their susceptibility to heat.

These measurements are extremely important in the food industry, where optimum processing times and temperatures must be established for various canned foods. Excessive heat exposure is likely to deteriorate the quality of food, and so it is imperative to know the lowest temperature and shortest time that will effectively treat a product.

Dry Heat

Dry heat, or hot air, at sufficiently high temperatures will kill microorganisms. However, this approach is not as effective as moist heat, and much higher temperatures and longer exposure times are necessary. For instance, sterilization of laboratory glassware (such as glass Petri dishes and glass pipettes) in an oven requires a 2-h exposure at 160 to 180°C, whereas sterilization of the same materials with an autoclave requires only 15 min at 121°C. There are situations, however, where a material should not be exposed to moisture, and dry-heat methods are preferred.

Incineration

Destruction of microorganisms by burning *(incineration)* is a routine practice in the laboratory; transfer loops or needles are regularly placed into the flame of a Bunsen burner or into specially designed incinerators located on the laboratory bench. Such "flaming" of loops and needles is an integral part of isolating microbial colonies onto solid medium, of inoculating "tubed" media, and of removing all microbes so that subsequent cultures will not be contaminated [FIGURE 7.8A and B]. Care must be taken when the transfer needle is sterilized, as the heated material may boil and spatter. Droplets that fly off may carry viable microorganisms that can cause disease or contaminate other cultures. Spattering can be minimized by inserting the transfer loop or needle into an electrically heated hollow cone [FIGURE 7.8B].

Incineration is also used for the disposal of contaminated materials such as swabs and sponges, as well as the carcasses of infected laboratory animals. Disposal of medical wastes and other biological materials has become a political and social issue in many communities. Adequate precautions need to be taken to ensure that the exhaust fumes from the incinerator do not carry microbe-containing matter into the atmosphere.

ASK YOURSELF

1 How does moist heat compare with dry heat in terms of temperature and time needed to kill endospores?

2 What are the various methods of using high temperatures to kill microorganisms?

3 In the operation of an autoclave, what is the relationship between pressure and steam temperature?

4 Of what practical value is the information obtained from determinations of *thermal death time* (TDT) and *decimal reduction time* (D value)?

5 What are some of the conditions which may influence the time-temperature conditions when the autoclave is used to sterilize materials?

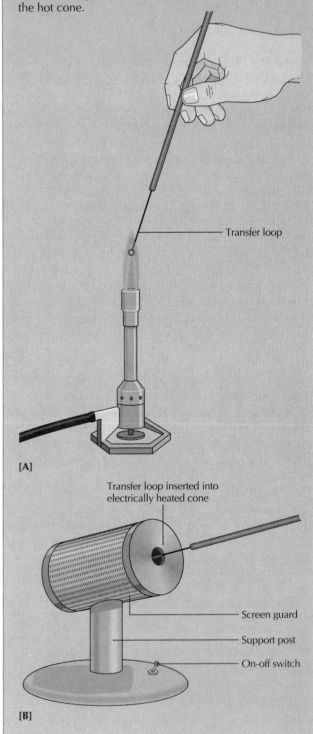

FIGURE 7.8
Sterilization by incineration. **[A]** A transfer loop can be sterilized by placing it in the flame of a Bunsen burner for a few seconds. **[B]** When a transfer loop is placed in the flame, as in part **[A]**, spattering may occur with resultant spread of living organisms. To prevent this, one can sterilize the loop by inserting it into the center of an electrically heated cone for a few seconds. A metal screen prevents accidental contact of hands with the hot cone.

Transfer loop

[A]

Transfer loop inserted into electrically heated cone

Screen guard

Support post

On-off switch

[B]

TABLE 7.4
The Use of Temperature to Control Microorganisms

Method	Temperature	Applications	Limitations
Moist heat			
Autoclave	121.6°C at 15 lb/in^2 pressure, 15–30 min	Sterilizing instruments, linens, utensils and treatment trays, media, and other liquids	Ineffective against organisms in materials impervious to steam; cannot be used for heat-sensitive articles
Boiling water	100°C, 10 min	Killing vegetative cells on instruments, containers	Endospores are not killed; cannot be relied upon to sterilize
Pasteurization	62.8°C for 30 min, or 71.7°C for 15 s	Killing vegetative cells of disease-causing microorganisms and of many other microorganisms in milk, fruit juices, and other beverages	Does not sterilize; see Chap. 30 for more details
Dry heat			
Hot-air oven	170–180°C for 1–2 h	Sterilizing materials impermeable to or damaged by moisture, e.g., oils, glass, sharp instruments, metals	Destructive to materials that cannot withstand high temperatures
Incineration	Hundreds of °C	Sterilization of transfer loops and needles; disposal of carcasses of infected animals; disposal of contaminated objects that cannot be reused	Size of incinerator must be adequate to burn largest load promptly and completely; potential for air pollution exists
Low temperatures			
Freezers	Less than 0°C	Preservation of foods and other materials	Mainly microbiostatic instead of microbicidal
Liquid-nitrogen refrigerators	−196°C	Preservation of microorganisms	High cost of liquid nitrogen

LOW TEMPERATURES

Some psychrophilic bacteria can grow at 0°C, but subzero temperatures will inhibit the metabolism of microorganisms in general. Freezing is commonly used to preserve foods, drugs, and laboratory specimens because it effectively stops microbial growth. (A standard home freezer maintains an approximate temperature of −20°C.) However, subzero temperatures may not kill the microorganisms, and may in fact preserve them along with the materials being frozen. This phenomenon has been used by microbiologists to store microorganisms indefinitely. Stock cultures are frozen at −70°C, or, even better, in tanks of liquid nitrogen at −196°C. These cultures are unlikely to change genetically over time or become contaminated with other organisms. This stability allows researchers to standardize their experiments and to save specific cultures for future experiments.

Both high and low temperatures have their place in the control of microorganisms. TABLE 7.4 summarizes the various applications of temperature discussed in this chapter.

ASK YOURSELF

1 What is the effect of freezing and subfreezing temperatures on the viability of microorganisms? On the metabolism of microorganisms?

2 What application is made of liquid nitrogen in the microbiological laboratory?

RADIATION

Electromagnetic radiation is energy in the form of electromagnetic waves transmitted through space or through a material. Electromagnetic radiation is classified according to its wavelength, with radio waves having the longest wavelength and cosmic rays having the shortest [FIGURE 7.9]. The energy content of the radiation is inversely related to the wavelength: the shorter the wavelength, the greater the energy content. High-energy radiation includes gamma rays, x-rays, and ultraviolet light. These can kill living cells, including microorganisms. Some forms of electromagnetic radiation ionize molecules, while others do not.

Ionizing Radiation

High-energy electron beams, gamma rays, and x-rays have sufficient energy to cause *ionization* of molecules: they drive away electrons and split the molecules into atoms or groups of atoms. For example, water molecules are split into hydroxyl radicals (OH·), electrons, and hydrogen ions (H$^+$), and the hydroxyl radicals are highly reactive and destructive to normal cellular compounds such as DNA and proteins. Ionizing radiation can also act directly on vital cell constituents, including those of microorganisms.

In addition to being microbicidal, high-energy electron beams, gamma rays, and x-rays have the advantage of being able to penetrate packaging and products and sterilize their interiors. Gamma rays are less expensive than x-rays because they are emitted spontaneously from certain radioactive isotopes, such as cobalt-60 (^{60}Co). As a result of nuclear energy research, large quantities of gamma-emitting radioisotopes are available as by-products of atomic fission. However, gamma rays are difficult to control because the isotope emits them in all directions. Moreover, the isotope releases gamma rays constantly and cannot be turned on or off like an x-ray machine.

Despite these disadvantages, high-energy electron beams and gamma rays have been used to sterilize packaged food and medical equipment, and commercial ma-

FIGURE 7.9

The electromagnetic spectrum.

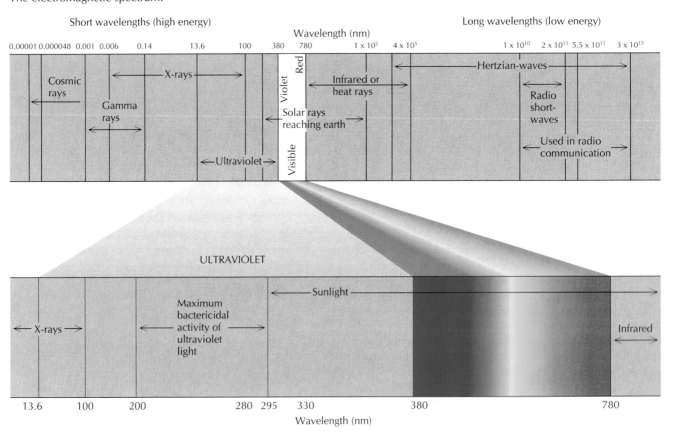

FIGURE 7.10

Industrial sterilization process that employs gamma irradiation.

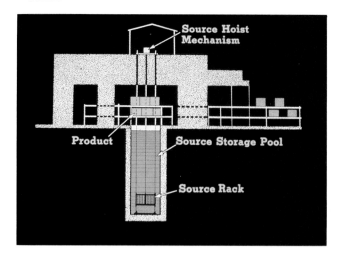

chines have been designed for this purpose [FIGURES 7.10 and 7.11]. Because gamma rays can penetrate materials, a product can be packaged first and then sterilized. Although gamma-ray sterilization of food is used in several countries, it has been approved by the U.S. Food and Drug Administration for only a few food items such as spices. This limited use is due to uncertainties about the effect gamma rays have on product quality, as well as public apprehension about anything connected with radioactivity, even though foods irradiated by gamma rays do not become radioactive (see Chapter 30).

Nonionizing Radiation

Ultraviolet (UV) radiation has a wavelength range of 136 to 400 nanometers (nm). (A nanometer is equal to 1/1000 μm.) Rather than ionize a molecule, UV light excites its electrons, causing the molecule to react differently from nonirradiated molecules. Ultraviolet light is absorbed by many intracellular compounds, but DNA suffers the most damage. The greatest bactericidal action occurs at wavelengths around 260 nm [FIGURE 7.11], which are the wavelengths absorbed most strongly by DNA. After DNA is exposed to UV light, *pyrimidine dimers* form when two adjacent pyrimidines on a DNA strand become bonded together. Unless these dimers are removed by specific intracellular repair enzymes, DNA replication can be inhibited or altered, causing death or mutations.

Ultraviolet light is a component of sunlight, but most of the shorter, more damaging UV wavelengths are filtered out by substances in the atmosphere, such as ozone, water droplets in clouds, and smoke. The UV radiation that actually reaches the surface of the earth is restricted to a wavelength span from about 295 to

FIGURE 7.11

[A] Relative germicidal effectiveness of radiant energy between 200 and 700 nm. (*Courtesy of the General Electric Company, Lamp Division, Publication LD-11.*) [B] Precautions taken by a laboratory worker to prevent contamination during the process of transferring a specimen to a special culture flask. Ultraviolet lights are installed in this "transfer room" to control microorganisms.

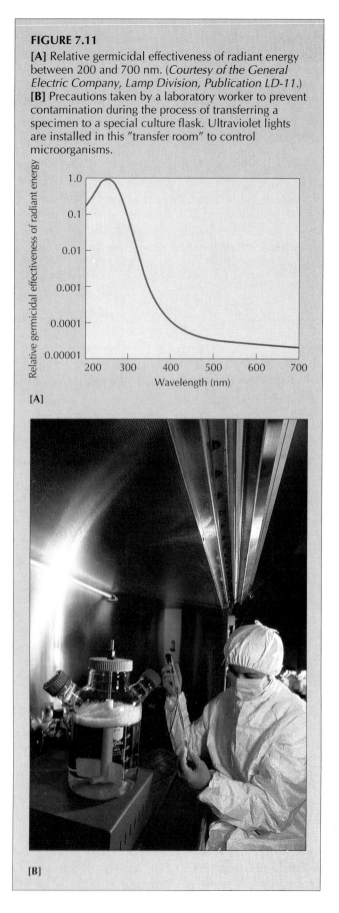

[A]

[B]

400 nm. Therefore, although sunlight itself does have microbicidal properties under certain conditions, it has them only to a limited degree. (Ultraviolet radiation from the sun is thought to be far more important for its role in the development of skin cancer.)

Special lamps that emit high-intensity, microbicidal UV wavelengths are used to kill microorganisms [DISCOVER 7.2]. But UV light has very little ability to penetrate matter, and only microorganisms on the *surface* of an object are likely to be killed by UV radiation. Even a thin layer of glass or water can stop or severely impede UV light. Nonetheless, this form of radiation is commonly used to reduce the number of microorganisms in air and on surfaces of hospital operating rooms, and in aseptic rooms where sterile products are being dispensed into sterile vials or ampules.

ASK YOURSELF

1 What ionizing radiations are used to sterilize materials, and what is their mode of action?

2 What kinds of materials are particularly suitable for sterilization using ionizing radiations? Why?

3 What is the most microbicidal region of UV light?

4 What are the limitations on the use of UV light to control microbial populations inside a room?

FILTRATION

In 1884 Charles Chamberland, developer of the autoclave, described the use of a filter to remove bacteria from drinking water. To purify the water, he used porous porcelain in the shape of a funnel, a technique used in Pasteur's laboratory to separate microorganisms from their culture media. Today microorganisms are frequently removed from liquids and from air by filtration.

Although filtration is not a "physical agent" in the traditional sense like temperature and radiation, it is a "physical process" that in many instances is the sterilization method of choice. Filters are used in the laboratory and in industry to sterilize materials that cannot be sterilized by autoclaving, such as heat-sensitive vitamins or proteins. At first, filters were made from earthenware, asbestos, and sintered glass. Most of these have now been replaced by cellulose membrane filters, commonly referred to as ***membrane filters.***

FIGURE 7.12
[A] A membrane filter assembly used for the filtration of liquids using negative pressure (vacuum pump). **[B]** A sterile membrane filter unit attached to a syringe. The liquid is forced through the filter by positive pressure (i.e., by pushing the plunger of the syringe). In the example shown, sterile liquid media are being added to culture flasks. **[C]** Scanning electron micrograph showing bacterial cells from a water sample that have been trapped on a membrane filter. Note the difference in size of the cells and the filter pores.

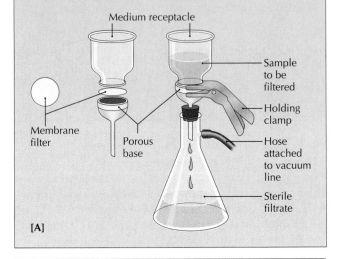

[A]

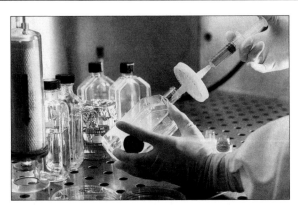

[B]

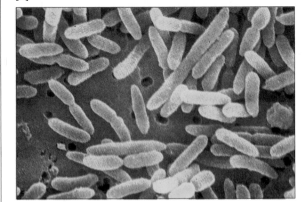

[C]   1.0 μm

7.2 DEPURATION OF SHELLFISH TO CONTROL MICROORGANISMS

Some shellfish, particularly oysters and clams, are eaten raw. This presents a public health problem if the shellfish are harvested from polluted water. A single incident of a person suffering from an infection attributed to eating raw shellfish casts a dark shadow over the entire industry which provides this delicacy to restaurants. Generally speaking, shellfish taken from "clean" water are safe microbiologically. However, the intermittent occurrence of infection from eating raw shellfish has increased public sensitivity to the point that some restaurants have discontinued serving them.

How might living shellfish be treated to provide greater assurance of their freedom from pathogenic microorganisms? One approach to this problem is *depuration*, a process of placing living, harvested oysters in an environment of microbiologically clean seawater. Shellfish are filter feeders: they pump large quantities of water through their system to obtain food. As this pumping process continues in a clean-water environment, the shellfish purge themselves of microorganisms. Some depuration processes may incorporate a step for the treatment of water that passes through the shellfish. The clean seawater can be recirculated over a bed of shellfish, and in the process, the seawater is passed over a source of UV light which kills many of the microbes.

Depuration of shellfish to provide a clean, safe product has been practiced for years in New Zealand, France, Spain, Australia, and other countries. In the United States it has been used mainly by clam processors on the east coast, but there is growing interest in its wider application.

Membrane Filters

Membrane filters are cellulose esters made into extremely thin (about 150-μm) disks with pores small enough to prevent the passage of microorganisms. Membrane filters are superior to older types of filters because (1) the pores of membrane filters are of a uniform, known diameter; (2) the filters can be manufactured with any desired pore size; (3) they absorb very little of the fluid being filtered; and (4) filtration through membrane filters is more rapid than that obtained with older filters. Membrane filters are also disposable, eliminating the need to clean and sterilize reusable filters. Specially designed types of equipment are available to hold membrane filters while liquids pass through them [FIGURE 7.12].

Besides sterilization, membrane filters are used for separating types of microorganisms and for collecting microbial samples. For example, viruses can be separated from other microorganisms by using membrane filters with progressively smaller pore sizes. In fact, one of the earliest clues that viruses actually exist was the observation that removing bacteria with a filter did not necessarily remove the disease-producing capability of a liquid. Membrane filters are also used widely for the microbiological examination of water, in which they function to concentrate microorganisms from large sample volumes.

High-Efficiency Particulate Air (HEPA) Filters

Some laboratory procedures involve working with potentially hazardous materials, such as diseased animal tissue, infectious microorganisms, or genetically engineered microorganisms. In these cases, it is essential that research personnel and any other persons in the area be protected from possible infection. Guidelines from the Centers for Disease Control of the U.S. Public Health Service have established safety procedures for laboratories that work with biological materials. There are four CDC *biosafety levels*, differentiated by the degree of possible danger and characterized by the safety equipment and procedures required. For example, level 1 requires only standard, open-bench laboratory techniques, while level 4 requires maximum containment with special clothing, decontamination procedures, and gastight cabinets.

Special biological safety cabinets have been developed that provide protection from contaminated aerosols. The simplest of these is the biological safety cabinet [FIGURE 7.13]. This chamber has an open front through which air is drawn in and away from the worker. This air then exits the cabinet through a *high-efficiency particulate air (HEPA) filter*, which traps particulate matter such as microorganisms. A HEPA filter consists of cellulose acetate pleated around aluminum foil; it captures 99 percent of the particulate matter from the exiting air.

FIGURE 7.13

The level 1 biological safety cabinet is an open-faced negative-pressure ventilated cabinet that is designed to draw air into it at a controlled rate. The exhaust air is filtered through a high-efficiency particulate air (HEPA) filter. This type of cabinet may be used in three operational modes: with a full-width open front, with an installed front closure panel which is not equipped with gloves, and with an installed front closure panel which is equipped with arm-length rubber gloves.

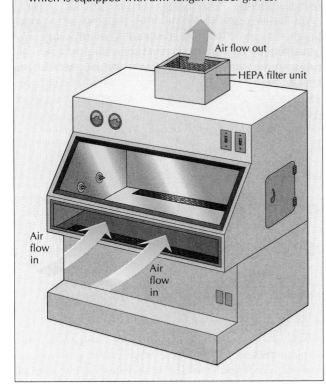

FIGURE 7.14

[A] Biological safety cabinet of a type that provides for all manipulations to be done within a gastight cabinet using arm-length attached rubber gloves. Air is drawn into the cabinet and exhausted from the cabinet through HEPA filters. [B] A laboratory manipulation being performed in a cabinet of the type shown in [A].

[A]

[B]

More elaborate systems (levels 2, 3, and 4) have more stringent requirements. Personnel who work with disease-causing organisms such as the hepatitis virus or with genetically engineered microorganisms may use cabinets equipped with arm-length rubber gloves as shown in FIGURE 7.14. The most rigorous precautions are built into the biosafety level 4 system; the entrance and exit of air in an entire room is controlled and each laboratory worker in the room is completely protected by a full-body suit with its own breathing equipment [FIGURE 7.15]. Biosafety level 4 requires that street clothing be removed and laboratory clothing put on, and that personnel shower when exiting the facility. Numerous other precautions and practices are also required.

FIGURE 7.15
A laboratory facility at the Centers for Disease Control, Atlanta, Georgia, which provides maximum protection to the researchers as well as maximum containment of the agent(s) being experimented with. The researchers are protected completely by an isolation garment equipped with an air supply unit.

ASK YOURSELF

1 What were bacteriological filters made of during the early part of the twentieth century?

2 What is a membrane filter, and what are its advantages over the older types?

3 What are HEPA filters?

4 What are the characteristics of a CDC "biosafety level 4" unit?

DESICCATION

Drying vegetative microbial cells stops their metabolic activity, leading to a decline in the total viable population. This physical process of microbial control was widely used prior to the development of refrigeration. Food producers still utilize this method when they dry fruits, meats (jerky), or bread, and farmers can rely on drying for the preservation of grains such as corn and wheat. The length of time microbes survive after desiccation depends on many factors:

1 The species of the organism
2 The material in or on which the organisms are dried
3 The completeness of the drying process
4 The physical conditions involved, such as light, temperature, and humidity

Species of Gram-negative cocci, such as *Neisseria gonorrhoeae* and *Neisseria meningitidis*, are very susceptible to desiccation; they die in a matter of minutes after being dried. *Streptococcus* species and other Gram-positive cocci are much more resistant and may survive for hours. *Mycobacterium tuberculosis* dried in sputum remains viable for even longer periods of time. Most resistant are the dried endospores of bacteria, which may remain viable indefinitely.

In a process called *lyophilization*, microorganisms are dried quickly at freezing temperatures and then sealed in containers under a vacuum. In this state, the desiccated *(lyophilized)* microorganisms remain alive for many years, and laboratory culture collections of bacteria are often preserved using this method [see FIGURE 3.4].

Materials with high concentrations of sugar or salt, such as jelly and jams and salted fish, have a dehydrating effect on microorganisms much like desiccation and can inhibit microbial growth. This is the result of *osmosis*—the removal of water from the inside of the cell where the concentration of the dissolved substances is less than that outside the cell.

ASK YOURSELF

1 What effect does desiccation have on the viability of microorganisms? On microbial metabolism?

2 Name several everyday materials that are preserved by virtue of being dehydrated (desiccated).

3 What conditions influence the survival of a microbial population?

4 What is lyophilization, and what is its application in microbiology?

SUMMARY

1 Microorganisms can be killed, inhibited, or removed by use of physical agents, physical processes, or chemical agents. Microbicidal agents kill microorganisms, whereas microbiostatic agents inhibit their growth.

2 When a population of microorganisms is exposed to a lethal agent, the entire population does not die instantly. Instead, the microorganisms follow a characteristic pattern of death called *exponential death*.

3 Conditions in the environment—such as temperature and pH—can influence the effectiveness of an antimicrobial agent. Antimicrobial agents can kill or inhibit a microorganism by altering the physical and/or chemical state of its cytoplasm, cell wall, cytoplasmic membrane, enzymes, ribosomes, or nuclear material.

4 Heat is one of the most effective antimicrobial agents. It can be used in the form of moist heat: steam under pressure, free-flowing steam, boiling water, or water at subboiling temperatures. It can also be used as dry heat, as in a sterilizing oven, or as an incinerating agent.

5 While microorganisms can be killed at sufficiently high temperatures, low temperatures are usually microbiostatic. Very low temperatures are frequently used to maintain stock-culture collections.

6 Ionizing radiation (x-rays and gamma rays) and nonionizing radiation (ultraviolet light) are microbicidal, but they have their limitations for practical use.

7 Fluids can be sterilized by using a membrane filter to remove the microorganisms; microorganisms can be removed from air with a HEPA filter. Filters are integral parts of biological containment systems used to prevent the spread of microorganisms in laboratories and hospital environments.

8 Desiccation of microorganisms stops their metabolic activity and is followed by a decline in the total viable population. A special form of desiccation called *lyophilization* is used to preserve culture collections.

KEY TERMS

antibacterial
antifungal
antimicrobial
antiprotozoan
antiviral
autoclave
bactericidal
bacteriostatic
decimal reduction time (D value)
electromagnetic radiation
exponential death
fungicidal
fungistatic
high-efficiency particulate air (HEPA) filter
incineration
membrane filters
microbicidal
microbiostatic
sterilization
thermal death time (TDT)
virucidal

FUNDAMENTALS OF
MICROBIAL CONTROL

1 A substance or process that kills or inhibits microorganisms is called a(n) _____ agent.

2 The suffix _____ refers to agents that kill microorganisms; the suffix _____ refers to agents that inhibit microorganisms.

3 The term *death* as used in microbiology is defined as the irreversible loss of ability to _____.

4 When microorganisms are exposed to a microbicidal agent it is unlikely that the total population is killed _____.

5 If 10 percent of the population of cells is killed by an antimicrobial agent in the first minute of exposure, during the second minute the percentage killed will be _____ percent.

6 In the target concept of action of a microbicide, the probability of hitting a target (bacterial cell) is _____ to the number of targets.

7 When the logarithm of the number of survivors is plotted against the time of exposure to a microbicidal agent, the points will fall on a(n) _____ line.

8 In question 7, the slope of the line is referred to as a measure of the _____ rate.

9 The use of heat to kill bacteria is _____ (more/less) effective under acidic conditions than under neutral pH conditions.

10 An increase in temperature will generally _____ the effectiveness of an antimicrobial agent.

11 If an antimicrobial agent damages the cells' ability to control nutrient uptake, the site of damage is most likely to be the _____.

HIGH TEMPERATURES

12 Moist heat kills microorganisms by _____ protein, whereas dry heat acts by _____ of cellular material.

13 Vegetative cells of bacteria are more susceptible to heat than are _____.

14 *Thermal death time* refers to the _____ required to kill a suspension of bacteria at a given temperature and under specific conditions.

15 The time in minutes required for a heat treatment to reduce a bacterial population by 90 percent is called the _____ time.

16 A device which uses steam under pressure to kill microorganisms is called a(n) _____.

17 The most resistant form of microbial life is the bacterial _____.

18 Three broth cultures of bacteria, *Bacillus* sp., *Pseudomonas* sp., and *Clostridium* sp., are heated in boiling water for 10 min. Which culture is most likely to be sterilized? _____.

19 Exposure of contaminated instruments to boiling water is likely to accomplish _____ but not sterilization.

20 Sterilization of small objects (e.g., test tubes containing culture media) by steam under pressure can be accomplished at _____°C for _____ min.

21 The sterilization of laboratory glassware by dry heat requires a temperature of at least _____°C for _____ min.

22 Pasteurization kills many microorganisms but does not result in _____.

23 Which of the following treatments could be relied upon to sterilize utensils?
(a) boiling water
(b) steam under pressure
(c) liquid nitrogen (−196°C)
(d) pasteurization

LOW TEMPERATURES

24 Some bacteria, called psychrophiles, can grow at temperatures as low as _____.

25 Liquid nitrogen, which has a temperature of _____, is used to preserve cultures of microorganisms.

26 As a general rule, very high temperatures (e.g., 100°C) kill microorganisms; very low temperatures (e.g., −100°C) will _____ microorganisms.

RADIATION

27 One nanometer is equivalent to _____ μm.

28 Radiation that can drive electrons away from molecules is called _____ radiation.

29 Two examples of ionizing radiation are _____ rays and _____ rays.

30 An example of a nonionizing type of radiation which is microbicidal is _____.

31 Ultraviolet light is most germicidal at a wavelength of _____ nm.

32 One limitation of ultraviolet light as a microbicidal agent is that it has poor

_____ ability.

33 Ultraviolet light is strongly absorbed by _____ within a cell.

34 Ultraviolet light causes the formation of _____ between adjacent pyrimidines.

35 Match each description on the right with the appropriate term on the left.

_____ pyrimidine dimers

_____ gamma rays

_____ cobalt-60

_____ ultraviolet rays (UV)

_____ electrons

(a) Source of gamma rays
(b) Microbicidal with ability to penetrate
(c) Bactericidal with little penetrating power
(d) Split off by ionization
(e) Result(s) from UV absorption by DNA

FILTRATION AND DESICCATION

36 Modern microbiological filters (membrane filters) have several advantages over older types of filters. Name four advantages.

(a) _____

(b) _____

(c) _____

(d) _____

37 An essential feature of biological safety cabinets is the

_____ (HEPA) filter.

38 _____ is the process of dehydrating microorganisms while they are in the frozen state.

39 Does desiccation impose **(a)** microbiostatic or **(b)** a microbicidal condition on microorganisms?

40 Solutions of high osmotic pressure, such as concentrated sugar or salt solutions, inhibit microorganisms by _____ .

REVIEW QUESTIONS

1 Distinguish between microbiostatic and microbicidal agents.

2 Describe the death-rate pattern of bacteria when exposed to a microbicidal agent. What is meant by the term *exponential death?*

3 List the conditions which influence the efficacy of an antimicrobial agent.

4 Distinguish between thermal death time and decimal reduction time. What is the significance of this information?

5 Compare the resistance to heat of vegetative cells with that of bacterial endospores. Compare the efficacy of dry heat and moist heat in killing endospores.

6 How are microorganisms affected by zero and subzero temperatures?

7 What advantages are provided by sterilization with gamma rays?

8 List the characteristics of membrane filters. What are HEPA filters, and how are they used?

9 What method of sterilization is appropriate for:

(a) Nutrient agar medium?

(b) Heat-sensitive solution of a vitamin?

(c) Packaged spices?

(d) Dry powder?

(e) Transfer needles?

DISCUSSION QUESTIONS

1 How does the term *death,* as used in microbiology, differ from the assessment of death among higher organisms?

2 Experiments performed in the Pasteur era to prove or disprove the concept of spontaneous generation sometimes produced conflicting evidence. For example, in one instance a broth might be boiled and sealed and remain sterile; another scientist, performing a similar experiment, might observe that the broth "spoiled," that is, it contained microbial growth. How might you reconcile these differences in results?

3 A batch of nutrient broth is prepared and dispensed as follows: 3 liters is dispensed in 20-ml amounts into test tubes (in test tube baskets) and another 3 liters is dispensed in 1-liter amounts into bottles. Would it be satisfactory to sterilize the tubed medium and the bottled medium at the same temperature and time in the autoclave? Explain.

4 The mechanism by which microbes are inhibited by drying and by high concentrations of sugar is essentially the same. Describe this mechanism.

5 Give an example of how an understanding of the mode of action of an antimicrobial agent can be useful in selecting a specific agent.

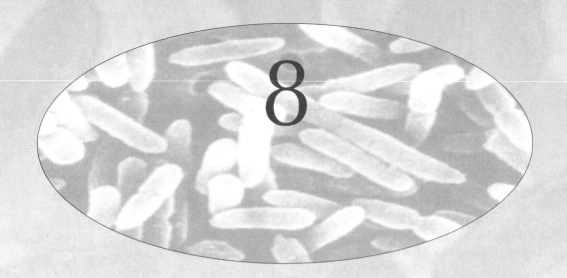

Control of Microorganisms: Chemical Agents

OBJECTIVES

After reading this chapter you should be able to

1 Define each of the terms used to designate chemical antimicrobial agents.

2 Describe the characteristics of an ideal chemical antimicrobial agent.

3 Identify the major groups of chemicals used as antimicrobial agents, and give a specific application of each.

4 Describe the ways in which chemical antimicrobial agents can act on microorganisms.

5 Discuss three methods for assessing the antimicrobial potency of a chemical agent.

6 Distinguish between a chemical sterilant and a disinfectant.

7 Describe the use of ethylene oxide as a sterilant, and give its advantages and disadvantages over other sterilants.

OVERVIEW

Chemicals used to kill or inhibit the growth of microorganisms are called *antimicrobial agents*. There are hundreds of different chemical products available for the control of microorganisms. They are highly advertised and widely used in the home, in schools, and in the workplace. Some antimicrobial chemicals reduce the number of microorganisms on inanimate surfaces such as floors, tabletops, and eating utensils. Others are put on cuts and abrasions of the skin to prevent infection. Still others eliminate disease-causing microbes from drinking and swimming pool water.

Certain antimicrobial chemicals kill microorganisms, while others inhibit their growth. Some can do either, depending on the concentration at which they are used. Some are active against a large number of species and are characterized as having a broad spectrum of activity, while other chemical agents may affect only a few species. There is not a single chemical agent that is optimal for all purposes. Therefore, it is necessary to determine in advance which agent will work best in a particular situation. In this chapter you will learn the major categories of chemical antimicrobial agents, some of their characteristics and practical uses, and how they act against microbes. You will also learn how their antimicrobial potency is measured by laboratory techniques.

TERMINOLOGY OF CHEMICAL ANTIMICROBIAL AGENTS

Before discussing the nature, mode of action, and practical application of individual chemical antimicrobial agents, it is important to understand the general terms used to describe these agents and their activities. In the previous chapter you learned that antimicrobial agents may be divided into those that kill microorganisms (microbicidal agents) and those that merely inhibit their growth (microbiostatic agents) [DISCOVER 8.1]. How this is accomplished varies among the main types of chemical agents, which are described in the following paragraphs. These agents can be purchased at local stores or from industrial supply houses, such as those that service janitorial companies or hospitals.

Sterilant. Sterilization is the process of destroying or removing all forms of microbial life from an object or a specimen. Thus a sterile item is one free of all living microorganisms, and a *sterilant* is a chemical agent that accomplishes sterilization. *Sterile* is an absolute term—an item is either sterile or nonsterile. It cannot be "partly sterile" or "almost sterile."

Disinfectant. A *disinfectant* is a chemical substance that kills the vegetative forms of microorganisms that can cause disease but does not necessarily kill their spores. The term normally refers to substances used on inanimate objects. *Disinfection* is the process of using such an agent to destroy infectious microorganisms.

Germicide. A chemical agent that kills the vegetative forms of microorganisms, but not necessarily their spores, is called a *germicide.* In practice, it is almost synonymous with a disinfectant; however, the microorganisms killed by a germicide are not necessarily disease-producing microbes. As described in Chapter 7, more specific terms such as *fungicide* are sometimes used to indicate the kind of microorganism affected.

Antiseptic. An *antiseptic* is a chemical agent, usually applied to the surface of the body, that prevents microorganisms from multiplying. It may do this either by killing the microorganisms or by inhibiting their growth and metabolic activities. Antiseptics are often used on cuts or abrasions to prevent infection, and drugstore shelves are filled with antiseptic creams, sprays, and liquids.

Sanitizer. Public health guidelines mandate that, in certain settings, microbial populations should not exceed specific numbers. Compliance with these rules is accomplished by using a *sanitizer,* an agent that kills 99.9 percent of microorganisms contaminating an area. Sanitizers are commonly applied to inanimate objects, such as the glasses, dishes, and utensils in restaurants. They are also used in the daily cleansing of equipment in dairy and food-processing plants.

Accuracy in labeling these chemical antimicrobial agents is important because their use may have legal implications. In the United States, a judicial decision under the Pure Food and Drug Act states: "Language used in the label is to be given the meaning ordinarily conveyed by it to those to whom it was addressed." In other words, both the producer and the consumer must interpret a product label in the same way and thus must understand the terminology used. The U.S. Food and Drug Administration and the U.S. Environmental Protection Agency regulate chemical antimicrobial products.

ASK YOURSELF

1 What suffix is used to designate a chemical which kills microorganisms? One which inhibits growth of microorganisms?

2 What is the distinction between a disinfectant and an antiseptic? Sterile and sanitized?

CHARACTERISTICS OF AN IDEAL CHEMICAL AGENT

An "ideal" antimicrobial chemical agent would have characteristics that make it effective under all conditions. Unfortunately, no single chemical substance possesses all these desirable characteristics. Nevertheless, it is useful to recognize the major features that would be found in such an agent. This knowledge helps select the best available product for a specific application. It also serves as a guide for research to formulate better products. The specifications for an ideal chemical agent can be summarized as follows:

1 *Antimicrobial activity.* The ability of the substance to inhibit or, preferably, to kill microorganisms is the foremost requirement. The chemical, at low concentrations, should have a broad spectrum of antimicrobial activity, which means that it should inhibit or kill many different kinds of microbes.

2 *Solubility.* The substance should be soluble in water or other suitable solvents (such as alcohol), to the extent necessary for effective antimicrobial activity.

8.1 BACTERIOSTATIC OR BACTERICIDAL?

Some antimicrobial chemicals are bactericidal at one concentration and bacteriostatic at a much lower concentration. In fact, the bacteriostatic activity may be so great that the small amount carried over in a loopful of material from the medication tube (i.e., the disinfectant and test culture mixture) into the subculture medium may be sufficient to prevent growth. Therefore, the result following incubation can be misleading.

The quaternary ammonium compounds are a good example of this phenomenon. They are bacteriostatic at a dilution of 1000 or more times their bactericidal dilution.

How do we distinguish between bactericidal and bacteriostatic action of compounds that exhibit an extremely wide range between the concentration which kills and the much smaller concentration which inhibits? The answer is provided by incorporating specific substances into the subculture medium that will neutralize the carried-over disinfectant. In the case of the quaternaries the

neutralizing agent is a mixture of lecithin and polysorbate 80 which adsorbs and inactivates the disinfectant. For mercurial disinfectants the neutralizer is thioglycolic acid (a sulfur-containing compound which binds the mercury), and for chlorine disinfectants sodium thiosulfate neutralizes any residual chlorine. As a result of the use of these neutralizers, any residual carryover of the disinfectant is inactivated, permitting the living cells to grow in the subculture medium.

---

3 *Stability.* Storage of the substance for reasonable periods should not result in significant loss of antimicrobial action.

4 *Lack of toxicity.* It should not harm humans or animals.

5 *Homogeneity.* The preparation should be uniform in composition so that active ingredients are present in each application. For instance, the ingredients should not aggregate or settle to the bottom of the container.

6 *Minimum inactivation by extraneous material.* Some antimicrobial chemicals combine readily with proteins or other organic materials found in the substance being treated. This decreases the amount of the chemical available for action against microorganisms.

7 *Activity at ordinary temperatures.* It should not be necessary to raise the temperature beyond that normally found in the environment where the agent is to be used.

8 *Ability to penetrate.* Unless the chemical can penetrate the surface, its antimicrobial action is limited to the site of application. (However, surface action is sometimes all that is necessary.)

9 *Material safety.* The compound should not rust or otherwise disfigure metals, nor should it stain or damage fabrics.

10 *Deodorizing ability.* Ideally, the agent should either be odorless or have a pleasant smell. The ability to deodorize is a desirable attribute as well.

11 *Detergent ability.* An antimicrobial agent that has cleansing properties has the advantage of being able to remove microorganisms mechanically from the surfaces being treated.

12 *Availability and low cost.* The product should be readily available and inexpensive.

ASK YOURSELF

Enumerate the desirable characteristics of an antimicrobial agent.

MAJOR GROUPS OF DISINFECTANTS AND ANTISEPTICS

Historical accounts indicate that both disinfectants and antiseptics were used during the first half of the nineteenth century. Ignaz Semmelweis, a Hungarian physician, is credited with having used chlorine compounds in 1846 in hospital obstetric wards to reduce the incidence of childbed fever, a frequently fatal disease of mothers that developed soon after they gave birth. Medical students in the hospital were required to wash their hands and soak them in a hypochlorite solution before examining patients. This simple procedure proved to be very effective. Such observation led to development of the many antimicrobial chemicals available today. Chemical substances used for disinfection or antisepsis are divided into several major groups: *phenol and phenolic compounds, alcohols,* the halogens *iodine* and *chlorine, heavy metals and their compounds,* and *detergents.*

Phenol and Related Compounds

Phenol, also called *carbolic acid,* has the distinction of being one of the first chemical agents used as an antisep-

FIGURE 8.1

Joseph (Lord) Lister, 1827–1912. Lord Lister was appointed Professor of Surgery at Glasgow in 1860 where he began his experiments in antiseptic surgery. He was aware of Pasteur's studies on the germ theory of fermentation and in this he saw a way of dealing with infections. Accordingly he devised a technique of using a spray of carbolic acid (phenol) solution in the operating room. He also saturated wound dressings with a dilute phenol solution. This practice was published by Lister in 1867 in the British medical journal *Lancet* in a paper entitled "On the Antiseptic Principle in the Practice of Surgery."

TABLE 8.1

Antimicrobial Activity of Phenolic-Type Compounds Compared with Phenol in Terms of Phenol Coefficient*

Name	*Salmonella typhi*	*Staphylococcus aureus*	*Mycobacterium tuberculosis*	*Candida albicans*
Phenol	1.0	1.0	1.0	1.0
o-Cresol	2.3	2.3	2.0	2.0
m-Cresol	2.3	2.3	2.0	2.0
p-Cresol	2.3	2.3	2.0	2.0
4-Ethylphenol	6.3	6.3	6.7	7.8
2,4-Dimethylphenol	5.0	4.4	4.0	5.0

*A phenol coefficient greater than 1.0 means that the compound has greater antimicrobial activity than phenol.

tic. In the mid-1800s, the English surgeon Joseph Lister used phenol to reduce infection in surgical incisions [FIGURE 8.1]. Lister was aware of Pasteur's studies suggesting a germ theory for disease. Accordingly, he initiated the practice of applying a phenol solution to surgical incisions to kill the microorganisms suspected of causing infection. This resulted in a striking reduction in the incidence of postoperative infections.

Phenol is also the standard compound with which other disinfectants are compared. The procedure used to compare the microbicidal activity of a disinfectant with that of phenol is described later in this chapter.

Practical Applications of Phenol and Related Compounds. A 5% aqueous solution of phenol rapidly kills the vegetative cells of microorganisms. However, spores are much more resistant to phenol. Because phenol is toxic and has an unpleasant odor, it is no longer used widely as a disinfectant or antiseptic. It has been replaced by several chemically related compounds that are less toxic to tissues and more active against microorganisms [FIGURE 8.2]. The relative antimicrobial activity of some of these compounds is shown in TABLE 8.1.

Lysol is a proprietary disinfectant made of a soap solution containing phenol-like compounds (*o*-phenyl-

FIGURE 8.2

Phenol and its derivatives. Although all of these compounds have antimicrobial properties, those in series B are more effective than those in series A. *o*, ortho; *m*, meta; *p*, para; *as*, asymmetric.

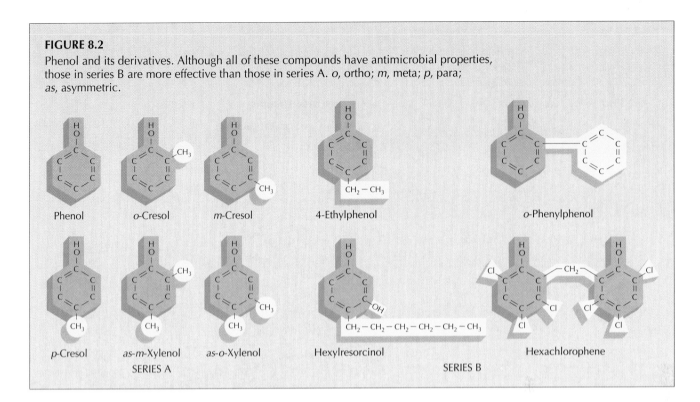

Phenol   *o*-Cresol   *m*-Cresol   4-Ethylphenol   *o*-Phenylphenol

p-Cresol   *as-m*-Xylenol   *as-o*-Xylenol   Hexylresorcinol   Hexachlorophene
SERIES A   SERIES B

phenol, *o*-benzyl-*p*-chlorophenol, xylenols). It is used to disinfect inanimate objects such as floors, walls, and table surfaces, contaminated hospital items such as rectal thermometers, and the excreta and secretions from infected patients.

Hexachlorophene [FIGURE 8.2] acts as a bacteriostat against Gram-positive bacteria, particularly staphylococci. It was formerly incorporated (at a concentration of 3%) into a wide variety of consumer products such as soaps, shampoos, deodorants, toothpastes, ointments, and cosmetics. However, prolonged application of hexachlorophene was shown to be toxic, and so its use and availability are restricted.

Mode of Action of Phenol and Related Compounds. Phenol and phenolic compounds damage microbial cells by altering the normal selective permeability of the cytoplasmic membrane, causing leakage of vital intracellular substances. These chemicals also denature and inactivate proteins such as enzymes. They may be either bacteriostatic or bactericidal, depending on the concentration used.

Alcohols

In concentrations between 70 and 90%, solutions of ethyl alcohol (ethanol), CH_3CH_2OH, are effective against the vegetative forms of microorganisms. But ethyl alcohol cannot be relied upon to sterilize an object, because it does not kill bacterial endospores. For instance, the endospores of *Bacillus anthracis*, the causative agent of anthrax, have been reported to survive in alcohol for 20 years.

Methyl alcohol, or methanol (CH_3OH), is not a useful antimicrobial agent. Sometimes called *wood alcohol*, it is less bactericidal than ethyl alcohol and is highly poisonous. Even the fumes of this compound may produce permanent injury to the eyes.

The bactericidal property of alcohols increases as the length of the carbon chain increases [TABLE 8.2]. However, alcohols with carbon chains longer than that of propyl alcohol and isopropyl alcohol are less water-soluble than ethyl alcohol and so are not commonly used as disinfectants. Propyl alcohol and isopropyl alcohol in concentrations from 40 to 80% are bactericidal for vegetative cells and are frequently used in place of ethyl alcohol.

Practical Applications of Alcohols. Ethyl alcohol (70%) and isopropyl alcohol (90%) are used as a skin antiseptic and as a disinfectant for clinical oral thermometers and certain surgical instruments. Alcohol wipes are the most commonly used method to clean the skin prior to drawing blood samples. Compared with other skin antiseptic solutions, ethyl alcohol is more effective than most in killing bacteria [FIGURE 8.3]. Ethyl alcohol in concentrations between 60 and 90% is effective against viruses. However, the presence of extraneous proteins diminishes its effectiveness against viruses because the alcohol combines with them, preventing it from acting on the viral proteins.

TABLE 8.2
Antibacterial Activity of Some Alcohols Expressed in Terms of Their Phenol Coefficients

| Alcohol | Formula | PHENOL COEFFICIENT | |
		Against *Salmonella typhi*	Against *Staphylococcus aureus*
Methyl	CH_3OH	0.026	0.03
Ethyl	CH_3CH_2OH	0.04	0.039
n-Propyl	$CH_3CH_2CH_2OH$	0.102	0.082
Isopropyl	$CH_3CHOHCH_3$	0.064	0.054
n-Butyl	$CH_3CH_2CH_2CH_2OH$	0.273	0.22
n-Amyl	$CH_3CH_2CH_2CH_2CH_2OH$	0.78	0.63

SOURCE: G. Sykes, *Disinfection and Sterilization*, 2d ed., Lippincott, Philadelphia, 1965.

FIGURE 8.3
Comparative effectiveness of hand washing with various antiseptic solutions. In each test, the calculated bacterial flora immediately before the antiseptic was applied was considered 100 percent. The steeper the curve, the greater the effect. (Note: 1:1000 means 1 part in 1000.) (*Courtesy of P. B. Price, "Skin Antisepsis," in J. H. Brewer, ed., Lectures on Sterilization, Duke University Press, Durham, N.C., 1957.*)

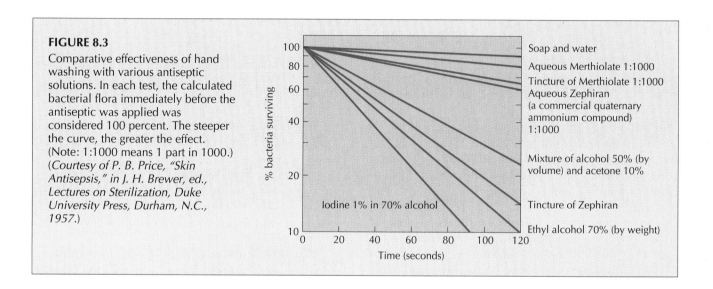

Mode of Action of Alcohols. Alcohols are protein denaturants, which accounts to a large extent for their antimicrobial activity. Alcohols are also lipid solvents, thus damaging the lipid structures within microbial cell membranes. In addition, some of their effectiveness as surface disinfectants can be attributed to their cleansing, or detergent, action, which helps in the mechanical removal of microorganisms.

Halogens

Members of the halogen family of chemical elements, particularly iodine, chlorine, and to a lesser extent bromine, are components of many antimicrobial chemicals. The halogens are strong oxidizing agents and by virtue of this property are highly reactive and destructive to vital compounds within the microbial cell.

Iodine and Iodine Compounds. Iodine is one of the oldest and most effective microbicidal agents. It was recognized by the *United States Pharmacopeia* as early as 1830, and was used to treat wounds during the American Civil War. Pure iodine is a bluish-black crystalline element with a metallic luster. Only slightly soluble in water alone, iodine is readily soluble in ethyl alcohol and in aqueous solutions of potassium iodide (KI) or sodium iodide (NaI). It is traditionally used as an antiseptic agent in a form called *tincture of iodine*. The term **tincture** refers to an alcoholic solution of a medicinal substance. Several preparations are used: 2% iodine plus 2% sodium iodide diluted in 70% alcohol; 7% iodine plus 5% potassium iodide in 83% alcohol; and 5% iodine plus 10% potassium iodide in aqueous solution.

Iodine is also used in the form of substances called **iodophors**, complexes of iodine with compounds that act as carriers and solubilizing agents for iodine. For example, povidone-iodine is a complex of iodine and polyvinylpyrrolidone. Iodophors are germicidal like iodine, but have the additional advantages of being nonstaining and nonirritating to the skin.

Practical applications of iodine and its compounds. Iodine is a highly effective germicidal agent against all kinds of bacteria. It is also sporicidal, fungicidal, virucidal, and amoebicidal. However, the rate at which bacterial endospores are killed by iodine can be decreased by the presence of organic material.

Iodine preparations are used chiefly for the disinfection of skin, where they are often the most effective agent [FIGURE 8.3]. Iodine in its various forms is also used to disinfect small quantities of water and to sanitize food utensils. Iodine vapor is sometimes used to disinfect air.

Mode of action of iodine and its compounds. A strong oxidizing agent, iodine can destroy essential metabolic compounds of microorganisms through oxidation. The ability of iodine to combine with the amino acid tyrosine results in the inactivation of enzymes and other proteins:

Iodine   Tyrosine (active)   Diiodotyrosine (inactive)

Chlorine and Chlorine Compounds. Chlorine, either in the form of a gas (Cl_2) or in certain chemical combinations, is one of the most widely used disinfectants. Compressed chlorine gas in the liquid form is, with few exceptions, the universal choice for purification of municipal water supplies and swimming pools. Chlorine gas is difficult to use unless special equipment is available to dispense it, and so its usefulness is limited to large-scale operations such as municipal water-purification plants.

Many compounds of chlorine are more convenient to use than chlorine gas. Among these are inorganic chlorine-containing compounds called **hypochlorites**, which contain the chemical group —OCl. Two commonly used hypochlorites are *calcium hypochlorite*, $Ca(OCl)_2$, and *sodium hypochlorite*, NaOCl, which is a household bleach. **Chloramines** are organic chlorine-containing compounds in which one or more of the hydrogen atoms in ammonia (NH_3) or an amino group

(—NH_2) are replaced by chlorine. The simplest of these is *monochloramine*, NH_2Cl. Other chloramines have more complex structures, such as chloramine-T and azochloramide:

Monochloramine   Chloramine-T   Azochloramide

One of the advantages of chloramines is their stability; they release chlorine over a much longer period of time than do hypochlorites.

Practical applications of chlorine and its compounds. Liquefied chlorine gas is the agent of choice for the disinfection of drinking water and swimming pool water, and for the treatment of effluents from sewage-treatment plants. To be effective, the chlorine concentration must reach a level of 0.5 to 1.0 parts per million (milligrams per liter). Products containing calcium hypochlorite are used for sanitizing utensils in restaurants and equipment in dairy plants. A solution of 1% sodium hypochlorite is used for personal hygiene and as a household disinfectant. Higher concentrations, such as 5 to 12%, are employed as household bleaches and disinfectants and as sanitizers in dairy and food-processing plants.

Mode of action of chlorine and its compounds. The antimicrobial action of chlorine and its compounds is due to the hypochlorous acid (HClO) formed when free chlorine is added to water:

$$Cl_2 + H_2O \rightarrow HCl + HClO$$
Hydrochloric acid   Hypochlorous acid

When added to water, hypochlorites and chloramines undergo hydrolysis, giving rise to hypochlorous acid. This acid undergoes further change, giving rise to nascent oxygen (O):

$$HClO \rightarrow HCl + O$$
Nascent oxygen

Nascent oxygen is a powerful oxidizing agent that can severely damage vital cellular substances. Chlorine may also combine directly with cellular proteins and destroy their biological activity.

Heavy Metals and Their Compounds

The term *heavy metals* refers to metals such as mercury, lead, zinc, silver, and copper. Ancient peoples made water-storage containers of silver and copper because they noticed that the metal vessels kept water safe to drink. Mercury and compounds containing mercury have a long history of controlling infections, including syphilis. Mercuric chloride ($HgCl_2$) was widely used in the early part of the twentieth century as a general disinfectant, but it has since been replaced by other agents less toxic and corrosive.

The ability of extremely small amounts of certain metals, particularly silver, to exert a lethal effect upon bacteria is termed *oligodynamic action*, from the Greek words *oligos*, meaning "small," and *dynamis*, meaning "power." The phenomenon can be demonstrated in the laboratory by placing a silver coin (previously cleaned) onto the surface of an inoculated agar medium in a Petri dish. After incubation, a zone of inhibition (no growth) surrounds the coin [FIGURE 8.4]. The amount of dissolved metal that brings about this inhibition is vanishingly small and can be expressed in parts per million. The mode of action is believed to be inactivation of certain enzymes that combine with the metal.

Practical Applications of Heavy Metals and Their Compounds.
Some organic mercury-containing compounds have higher antimicrobial activity and lower toxicity than inorganic mercury compounds. Among these organic compounds are merbromin (*Mercurochrome*), thimerosal (*Merthiolate*), and nitromersol (*Metaphen*), which are used for treatment of minor cuts, wounds, and skin infections.

A 1% solution of silver nitrate ($AgNO_3$) was once widely used to disinfect the eyes of infants at birth to prevent gonococcal infections; currently it is sometimes replaced by antibiotics such as penicillin or erythromycin. Compresses (sponges or layers of gauze) impregnated with 0.5% silver nitrate have been used to prevent infections of burns.

Copper sulfate ($CuSO_4$) is effective as an algicide in open bodies of water such as reservoirs and pools. It is also a fungicide and a constituent of Bordeaux mixture, a garden spray used to control fungal infections of plants. Zinc compounds are also fungicidal and are used in ointments and powders to treat athlete's foot.

Mode of Action of Heavy Metals and Their Compounds.
Heavy metals inactivate cellular proteins by combining with some component of the protein. For example, mercuric chloride inactivates enzymes that contain sulfhydryl (—SH) groups:

$$\text{Enzyme} \begin{array}{c} \diagup SH \\ \diagdown SH \end{array} + HgCl_2 \rightarrow \text{Enzyme} \begin{array}{c} \diagup S \\ | \\ Hg \\ | \\ \diagdown S \end{array} + 2HCl$$

Active enzyme   Mercuric chloride   Inactive enzyme

Detergents

Detergents are compounds that make water-repellent surfaces more "wettable." They are also called **surfactants**, which is a contraction of *surface-active agent*. They owe their wetting action to the fact that they are *amphipathic* compounds (see Chapter 1). When a nonpolar substance such as fat is added to an aqueous solution of detergent, the hydrophobic groups of the detergent bind to the substance while the hydrophilic groups create a surface that can be wetted with water.

Soaps are examples of detergents. They are water-soluble sodium or potassium salts of long-chain fatty acids (e.g., sodium oleate; see FIGURE 1.8). When fats are heated with strong bases such as sodium hydroxide or potassium hydroxide, soaps are produced. But soaps have the disadvantage of precipitating easily in acidic or alkaline water. For this reason, new and more efficient cleaning agents called **synthetic detergents** have been developed. They differ in structure from soaps and do not form precipitates.

FIGURE 8.4
In this experiment a clean silver coin was placed upon the surface of an agar medium previously inoculated with a culture of bacteria. Note the clear zone around the periphery of the coin after the plate was incubated; the growth of bacteria near the silver coin was inhibited. This kind of inhibition is called *oligodynamic action*.

Chemically, detergents are classified into three major groups:

1 *Anionic detergents* are those in which the detergent (wetting) property of the compound resides in the anionic, or negatively charged, portion of the molecule. For example,

$$[C_9H_{19}COO]^-Na^+ \qquad [C_{12}H_{25}OSO_3]^-Na^+$$

A soap (left)   Sodium dodecyl sulfate (a synthetic detergent)

2 *Cationic detergents* are those in which the detergent property of the compound resides in the cationic (positively charged) portion of the molecule. For example,

$$\left[\text{⬡}\,N\!-\!C_{16}H_{33}\right]^+ Cl^-$$

Cetylpyridinium chloride (Ceepryn)

3 *Nonionic detergents* are those which do not ionize when dissolved in water. Examples are polysorbate 80 and octoxynol.

Nonionic detergents are not antimicrobial. Most antimicrobial detergents belong to the cationic group, of which *quaternary ammonium compounds* are the most widely used.

Quaternary Ammonium Compounds. The structure of quaternary ammonium compounds is related to that of ammonium chloride, NH_4Cl [FIGURE 8.5]. In a molecule of a quaternary ammonium compound, the R_1, R_2, R_3, and R_4 groups are organic chemical groups linked to the central nitrogen atom.

Quaternaries are bactericidal for both Gram-positive and Gram-negative bacteria, even at very low concentra-

tions. Bactericidal concentrations range from 1 part of a quaternary in a few thousand parts of water to 1 part in several hundred thousand parts of water [TABLE 8.3]. Another important feature of these compounds is that, when they are used at concentrations well below those

TABLE 8.3
Some Bactericidal Concentrations of Three Commercially Available Quaternary Ammonium Compounds: Cetrimide, Ceepryn, and Zephiran

| Organism | LETHAL CONCENTRATIONS* | | |
	Centrimide	Ceepryn	Zephiran
Staphylococcus aureus	1:20,000† 1:35,000 1:218,000	1:83,000 1:218,000	1:18,000 1:20,000 1:38,000 1:50,000 1:200,000
Streptococcus pyogenes	1:20,000	1:42,000 1:127,000	1:40,000
Escherichia coli	1:3000 1:27,500 1:30,000	1:66,000 1:67,000	1:12,000 1:27,000
Salmonella typhi	1:13,000	1:15,000 1:48,000 1:62,000	1:10,000 1:20,000
Pseudomonas aeruginosa	1:3500 1:5000		1:2500
Proteus vulgaris	1:7500	1:34,000	1:1300

*These figures were collected from various published sources; variation among them is due to the use of different testing techniques and experimental conditions.
†Values are expressed as 1 part of quaternary ammonium compound in the stated volume of diluent.
SOURCE: G. Sykes, *Disinfection and Sterilization*, 2d ed., Lippincott, Philadelphia, 1965.

FIGURE 8.5
Chemical structure of quaternary ammonium compounds shown in relation to the structure of ammonium chloride.
[A] Ammonium chloride.
[B] In the general structure of a quaternary ammonium compound, R_1, R_2, R_3, and R_4 are carbon-containing groups, and the X^- is a negatively charged ion such as Br^- or Cl^-. The quaternary ammonium compound CTBA, or cetrimide, is also shown.

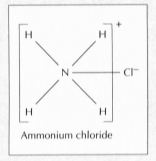
[A] Ammonium chloride

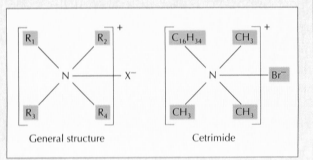
[B] General structure   Cetrimide

TABLE 8.4
Some Commonly Used Disinfectants and Antiseptics

Disinfectant or antiseptic	Concentration	Examples of uses	Level of activity*
Phenolic-type compounds			
Hexylresorcinol, o-phenylphenol, cresols	0.5–3.0% aqueous solution	Disinfection of inanimate objects such as instruments, floor and table surfaces, and (with cresols) rectal thermometers	Intermediate to low
Alcohols			
Ethyl alcohol, isopropyl alcohol	70–90%	Disinfection of skin, delicate surgical instruments, thermometers	Intermediate
Alcohol plus iodine	70% + 0.5–2.0% iodine		
Iodine			
Iodophor (polyvinylpyrrolidone)	1.0%	Disinfection of skin, minor cuts, and abrasions; also used for disinfection of water and swimming pools	Intermediate
Tincture of iodine	2% iodine + 2% sodium iodide + 70% alcohol		
Chlorine compounds			
Hypochlorites and chloramines	0.5–5.0 g available chlorine per liter	Disinfection of water, nonmetal surfaces, dairy equipment, restaurant utensils, household items	Low
Quaternary compounds	0.1–0.2%	Environmental sanitation of surfaces and equipment	Low
Mercurial compounds			
Merthiolate, Mercurochrome	1.0%	Disinfection of skin, instruments; also used as a preservative in some biological materials	Low

*Levels of microbicidal activity: high = kills all forms of microbial life including bacterial spores; intermediate = kills tubercle bacilli, fungi, and viruses but not bacterial spores; low = does not kill bacterial spores, tubercle bacilli, or nonlipid viruses within a reasonable time.

that are bactericidal, they still inhibit bacterial growth. For example, the limit of bactericidal action for a quaternary might be a dilution of 1:30,000, but the compound may be bacteriostatic in dilutions as high as 1:200,000. This underscores the need to distinguish between bacteriostatic and bactericidal activity when measuring the antimicrobial properties of quaternaries.

Practical applications of quaternaries. Besides their germicidal activity and detergent action, the quaternary ammonium compounds are characterized by low toxicity, high solubility in water, high stability in solution, and noncorrosiveness. This combination of properties makes the quaternary compounds especially useful as antiseptics, disinfectants, and sanitizing agents. They are widely applied to floors, walls, and other surfaces in hospitals, nursing homes, and other public places. They are also used to sanitize food and beverage utensils in restaurants, as well as surfaces and equipment in food-processing plants.

Mode of action of quaternaries. The antimicrobial effects of quaternary ammonium compounds come from their denaturation of cell proteins, interference with metabolic processes, and damage to the cytoplasmic membrane.

A summary of the major groups of antiseptics and disinfectants and their uses is given in TABLE 8.4.

ASK YOURSELF

1 Name four major groups of chemicals used to control microorganisms, and give an example of the application of a specific substance from each group.

2 Describe the manner in which substances from these different groups of chemical agents kill or inhibit microorganisms.

3 Besides antimicrobial activity, what additional desirable characteristics do agents from these chemical groups possess?

EVALUATION OF ANTIMICROBIAL POTENCY OF DISINFECTANTS AND ANTISEPTICS

Laboratory techniques are used to assess the antimicrobial potency of chemical agents, making it possible to choose the appropriate disinfectant or antiseptic. However, it should be emphasized that no single laboratory test method can evaluate *all* microbicidal chemicals. A microbiologist must exercise judgment in selecting a test method for a specific chemical agent, in order to ensure meaningful and reproducible results. Although the ultimate criterion for a chemical's effectiveness is its performance under practical conditions, the laboratory test should be able to predict how well it will perform in actual use.

Three widely used laboratory procedures are the **tube-dilution technique**, the **agar-plate technique**, and the **phenol-coefficient technique**. In each procedure the chemical agent is tested against a specified microorganism called the *test organism* (usually *Staphylococcus aureus* or *Salmonella typhi*, which are representative of pathogenic Gram-positive and Gram-negative bacteria).

Tube-Dilution Technique

In the tube-dilution procedure the microbiologist makes several dilutions of the chemical agent and dispenses an equal amount (e.g., 5.0 ml) of each dilution into sterile test tubes. Then a specific amount (e.g., 0.1 ml) of the test organism suspension is added to each tube. At specified time intervals a loopful of material from each tube is transferred to a tube of sterile nutrient broth [FIGURE 8.6A]. The inoculated tubes are incubated for 24 to 48 h and then examined for microbial growth (turbidity). "No growth" (clear broth) indicates the dilution at which the chemical agent has killed the test organism when it is exposed for a particular period of time.

Agar-Plate Technique

Instead of using tubes of liquid media, you can measure antimicrobial potency with solid media that clearly show areas of growth inhibition. A plate of nutrient agar medium is inoculated with the test organism, and the chemical agent is placed at the center of the plate. If the chemical agent is in liquid form, an absorbent paper disk impregnated with the solution can be placed on the agar medium, or a small volume of solution can be held in a hollow cylinder set upon the agar surface. After incubation for 24 to 48 h, the plate is observed for a zone of inhibition (no growth) around the chemical agent [FIGURE 8.6B]. Ointments or salves can be tested by this technique.

In a modification of the agar-plate technique, the chemical agent is incorporated into the nutrient agar before the agar is poured into the plate. The medium is inoculated with the test organism, incubated, and then examined for microbial growth [FIGURE 8.6C].

Phenol-Coefficient Technique

The phenol-coefficient technique is a highly standardized modification of the tube-dilution procedure. Its procedure is prescribed by the Association of Official Analytical Chemists and the U.S. Food and Drug Administration. The *phenol coefficient* may be defined as *the killing power of a disinfectant compared with that of phenol.* Used extensively to test disinfectants, this technique utilizes specific strains of either *Salmonella typhi* or *Staphylococcus aureus*. The proper procedure is illustrated in FIGURE 8.7 and can be summarized as follows:

1 A series of tubes is prepared, each tube containing a 5.0-ml amount of a different dilution of the disinfectant to be tested.
2 A second series of tubes containing various dilutions of phenol is also prepared.
3 The tubes of both series are inoculated with 0.5 ml from a 24-hour-old broth culture of the test bacterium.
4 At intervals of 5, 10, and 15 min a sample is removed from each tube with a transfer loop and inoculated into a tube of sterile growth medium.
5 The tubes of inoculated medium are incubated for 24 to 48 h and examined to see whether the test organism has grown.
6 The greatest dilution of the test disinfectant that kills the test organism in 10 min, but not in 5 min, is divided by the greatest dilution of phenol showing the same result. The number obtained is the phenol coefficient for that particular disinfectant. TABLE 8.5 shows an example of the results obtained in this test.

ASK YOURSELF

1 Outline three methods for evaluating the antimicrobial potential of chemical agents.

2 Which of these techniques would be most suitable for evaluating ointments or salves?

FIGURE 8.6

Schematic illustration of methods to evaluate antimicrobial activity of disinfectants and antiseptic materials. **[A]** A measured amount of a culture of the test bacterium is added to a dilution of the material. At periodic intervals, subcultures are made into sterile nutrient broth; the tubes are incubated and then examined for growth (no antimicrobial activity) or no growth (antimicrobial activity). Note that the lower dilution (dilution 1) of the chemical is more effective than the higher dilution (dilution 2): it killed the organisms exposed to it for 5 min, whereas exposure to the higher dilution for the same time did not kill the organisms. **[B]** Dilutions of the chemical agent are added to the center of a nutrient agar plate which was previously inoculated with the test microorganism. The addition of the chemical can be made by saturating a small paper disk, or it can be placed in a well cut out of the center of the agar medium. After incubation, the plates are examined for zones of inhibition of growth. Note that the lower dilution (dilution 1) causes a distinct zone, whereas the higher dilution (dilution 2) has no effect. **[C]** Dilutions of the chemical agent are incorporated into nutrient agar, which is then inoculated with the test microorganism. Following incubation, the plates are examined for growth (large number of colonies), diminished growth (few colonies), or no growth (no colonies). Note that the lowest dilution (dilution 1) of the chemical prevents growth completely, whereas the highest dilution (dilution 3) has no effect.

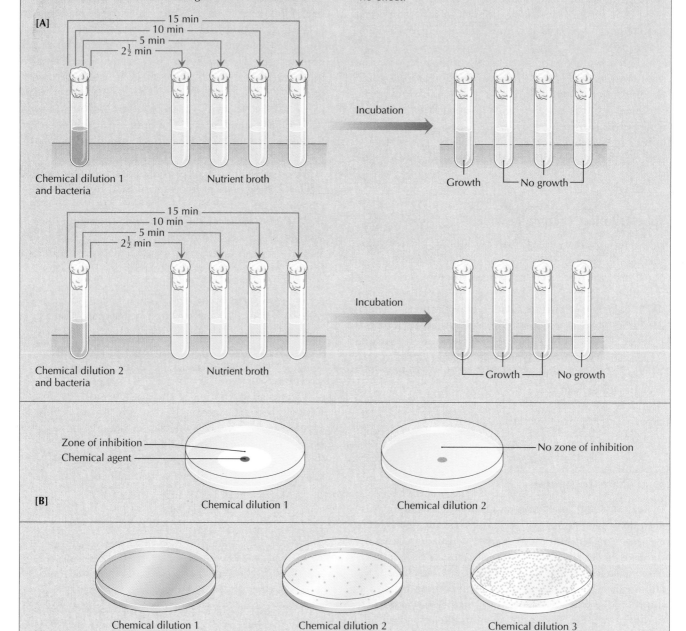

FIGURE 8.7

Schematic illustration of phenol-coefficient technique for evaluation of the antimicrobial potency of a disinfectant. The antibacterial efficacy of several dilutions of the product (disinfectant X) is compared with that of several dilutions of phenol — the standard. Numbers refer to the steps as summarized in the text. Calculation of the phenol coefficient is performed as shown in TABLE 8.5.

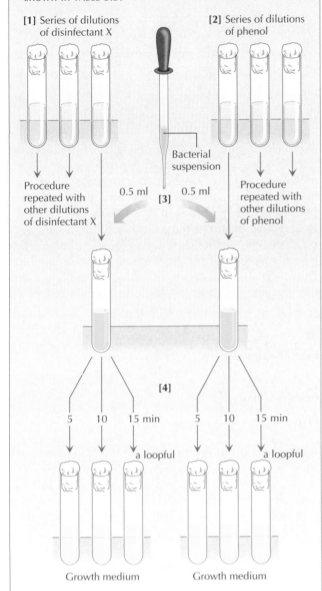

TABLE 8.5

An Example of a Type of Result Obtained in the Phenol-Coefficient Method for Testing Disinfectants—Test Organism *Salmonella typhi**

Disinfectant	Dilution	GROWTH WHEN SUBCULTURED AFTER		
		5 min	10 min	15 min
Disinfectant X	1:100	−	−	−
	1:125	+	−	−
	1:150	+	−	−
	1:175	+	+	−
	1:200	+	+	+
Phenol	**1:90**	+	−	−
	1:100	+	+	+

Phenol coefficient of disinfectant X = 150/90 = 1.6

*Minus sign = no growth; plus sign = growth.

CHEMICAL STERILANTS

Chemical sterilants are particularly useful for the sterilization of heat-sensitive medical supplies, such as plastic blood transfusion or donor sets, plastic syringes, and catheterization equipment. They are also used to sterilize enclosed areas, including the aseptic chambers used for procedures that must be microbe-free. The major chemical sterilants in use are *ethylene oxide, β-propiolactone, glutaraldehyde,* and *formaldehyde.*

Ethylene Oxide

Ethylene oxide is an organic compound with the following cyclic structure:

$$H_2C \overline{\quad\quad} CH_2$$
$$\diagdown \quad \diagup$$
$$O$$

It is a liquid at temperatures below 10.8°C, but above this temperature it becomes a gas. Its vapors are highly irritating to the eyes and mucous membranes, and it is flammable even in low concentrations. This safety problem has been overcome by preparing mixtures of ethylene oxide in carbon dioxide or Freon, which are nonflammable gases. These mixtures retain the microbicidal activity of the ethylene oxide, which kills not only the vegetative cells of microorganisms but also bacterial endospores [FIGURE 8.8].

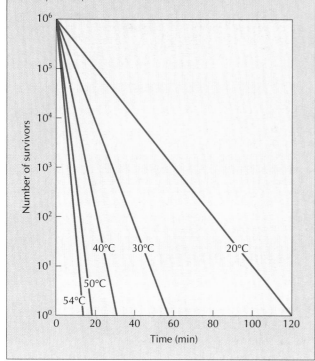

FIGURE 8.8

Decrease in numbers of *Bacillus subtilis* spores on paper strips surviving at various temperatures in gaseous ethylene oxide at 1200 mg/liter and 40 percent relative humidity. *(Courtesy of R. R. Ernst, "Ethylene Oxide Gaseous Sterilization for Industrial Applications," in G. B. Phillips and W. S. Miller, eds., Industrial Sterilization, Duke University Press, Durham, N.C., 1973.)*

Another outstanding and desirable feature of ethylene oxide is its power to penetrate. It will pass through and sterilize large packages of materials, bundles of cloth, and even certain plastics. Such items as medical syringes can be packaged first and then sterilized. However, one disadvantage of ethylene oxide is its comparatively slow rate of action against microorganisms; several hours of exposure (sometimes overnight) is required.

Practical Applications of Ethylene Oxide. Effective usage of ethylene oxide requires precise control of concentration, temperature, and moisture. Some modern autoclaves are equipped to maintain optimal conditions for using ethylene oxide. In addition to being used routinely for sterilizing medical and laboratory materials, ethylene oxide has been used in the space program by both American and Soviet scientists for decontaminating spacecraft components.

Mode of Action of Ethylene Oxide. Ethylene oxide inactivates enzymes and other proteins that have labile hydrogen atoms, such as in sulfhydryl groups. This reaction is called alkylation. The ring in the ethylene oxide molecule splits to form —CH$_2$CH$_2$O—, which inserts itself between the sulfur atom and the hydrogen atom of the sulfhydryl group:

$$H_2C\underset{O}{\diagdown\diagup} CH_2 + \quad R—SH \quad \rightarrow R—S—CH_2CH_2O—H$$

Ethylene oxide   Active enzyme   Inactive enzyme

β-Propiolactone

A colorless liquid at room temperature, β-propiolactone has a high boiling point of 155°C. Its structure is:

$$\begin{array}{ccc} CH_2 & — & CH_2 \\ | & & | \\ O & — & C=O \end{array}$$

β-Propiolactone is not flammable like ethylene oxide, but it has the undesirable feature of causing skin blisters on contact and eye irritation. It is bactericidal, sporicidal, fungicidal, and virucidal. It lacks the penetrating power of ethylene oxide, but it is considerably more active against microorganisms. Only 2 to 5 mg of β-propiolactone per liter is required for sterilization, compared with 400 to 800 mg of ethylene oxide per liter. However, its poor penetration of materials and its alleged cancer-inducing properties have restricted its use as a practical sterilizing agent.

Glutaraldehyde

Glutaraldehyde is a colorless, oily liquid with the following structure:

$$OHC—CH_2—CH_2—CH_2—CHO$$

A 2% aqueous solution of this chemical has a wide spectrum of antimicrobial activity. It is effective against viruses and the vegetative cells and spores of bacteria and fungi. It is used in the medical field to sterilize urological instruments, instruments with lenses, respiratory therapy equipment, and other specialized equipment.

Formaldehyde

Formaldehyde has a simple chemical structure, HCHO. It is a gas that is stable only in high concentrations and at elevated temperatures. It is highly toxic, and its vapors are intensely irritating to mucous membranes. At room temperature formaldehyde gas polymerizes, forming a colorless solid substance called *paraformaldehyde*. When paraformaldehyde is heated it reverts to formaldehyde gas. Formaldehyde is also marketed in aqueous solution as *formalin*, which contains 37 to 40% (w/v)

FIGURE 8.9
Schematic summary of the sites and modes of action of various antimicrobial chemicals.

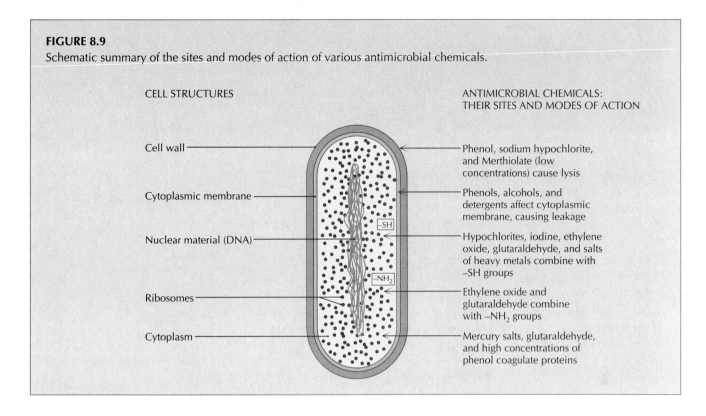

CELL STRUCTURES

ANTIMICROBIAL CHEMICALS: THEIR SITES AND MODES OF ACTION

Cell wall —————— Phenol, sodium hypochlorite, and Merthiolate (low concentrations) cause lysis

Cytoplasmic membrane —————— Phenols, alcohols, and detergents affect cytoplasmic membrane, causing leakage

Nuclear material (DNA) —————— Hypochlorites, iodine, ethylene oxide, glutaraldehyde, and salts of heavy metals combine with –SH groups

–SH

–NH$_2$

Ethylene oxide and glutaraldehyde combine with –NH$_2$ groups

Ribosomes ——————

Cytoplasm —————— Mercury salts, glutaraldehyde, and high concentrations of phenol coagulate proteins

formaldehyde. Methanol is usually included (10 to 15%) to prevent formaldehyde from polymerizing.

Formaldehyde in solution is useful for the sterilization of certain instruments. In the gaseous form, formaldehyde can be used for disinfection and sterilization of enclosed areas. Humidity and temperature affect the microbicidal action of formaldehyde; in order to sterilize an enclosure, the temperature must be approximately 22°C and the relative humidity between 60 and 80 percent. One of the disadvantages of this process is the limited ability of the formaldehyde vapors to penetrate surfaces.

Formaldehyde is an extremely reactive chemical, and its antimicrobial action appears to be due to its ability to inactivate cell constituents such as proteins and nucleic acids. Vegetative cells are killed more quickly by formaldehyde than are spores.

FIGURE 8.9 summarizes the sites and modes of action of various antimicrobial chemicals.

ASK YOURSELF

1 What is a major attractive feature of ethylene oxide for use as a sterilant?

2 How does β-propiolactone compare with other chemical sterilants in antimicrobial potency and other properties?

SUMMARY

1 Antimicrobial chemical agents are designated with a specialized terminology. This terminology may indicate whether the agent kills microorganisms or merely inhibits them, and which groups of microorganisms are affected. It may also describe the likely application of the agent (e.g., antiseptic, disinfectant, sanitizer, sterilant).

2 There is no single chemical agent that is the best choice for every specific application. Knowing the characteristics of an ideal antimicrobial agent is helpful in selecting an agent for a specific purpose and may aid in developing better agents.

3 The manner in which disinfectants and antiseptics cause damage to microbial cells varies with the agent. As examples, phenol damages the cytoplasmic membrane; iodine combines with and inactivates the tyrosine of proteins; hypochlorites give rise to a powerful oxidizing agent; and heavy metals combine with the sulfhydryl groups of proteins.

4 The antimicrobial potency of a chemical agent can be measured by the tube-dilution technique, the agar-plate technique, or the phenol-coefficient technique.

5 A few chemicals can be used as sterilants in either a gaseous form or aqueous solution. Ethylene oxide gas is widely used to sterilize heat-sensitive items. Other chemical sterilants such as β-propiolactone, glutaraldehyde, and formaldehyde have more limited use.

KEY TERMS

agar-plate technique
anionic detergents
antimicrobial agents
antiseptic
cationic detergents
chloramines
detergents
disinfectant
disinfection
germicide
hypochlorites
iodophors
nonionic detergents
phenol-coefficient technique
quaternary ammonium
  compounds
sanitizer
soaps
sterilant
sterile
surfactants
synthetic detergents
tincture
tube-dilution technique

REVIEW GUIDE

TERMINOLOGY OF CHEMICAL ANTIMICROBIAL AGENTS

1 _____ is a process which kills all forms of microbial life.

2 A substance that is usually applied to the body and opposes sepsis, i.e., which destroys organisms or inhibits their growth and metabolism, is called a(n)

_____ .

3 An agent which kills all vegetative cells of disease-producing organisms but not

necessarily spore forms is called a(n) _____ .

4 Which of the following statements contains an incorrectly used term to designate antimicrobial results?

(a) The item is sanitized.

(b) The item is disinfected.

(c) The item is nearly sterile.

5 Which of the following terms is most nearly comparable to _microbicide?_

(a) antiseptic

(b) bactericide

(c) sterilant

(d) germicide

(e) sanitizer

6 What are two distinctive features of the process of sanitization?

(a) _____

(b) _____

7 Which of the following processes is(are) not necessarily sporicidal?

(a) sanitization

(b) disinfection

(c) antisepsis

(d) sterilization

8 Two federal agencies that regulate antimicrobial agents are:

(a) _____

(b) _____

CHARACTERISTICS OF AN IDEAL CHEMICAL AGENT

9 List five characteristics that are desirable in an ideal antimicrobial chemical agent:

(a) _____

(b) _____

(c) _____

(d) _____

(e) _____

10 In general, an ideal antimicrobial chemical agent should have a

_____ spectrum activity.

MAJOR GROUPS OF DISINFECTANTS AND ANTISEPTICS

11 Carbolic acid is another name for _____ .

12 In the 1880s Joseph Lister used _____ as a disinfectant for the purpose of decreasing infections during surgery.

13 Phenolic-type compounds such as *o*-phenylphenol have

_____ antimicrobial power than phenol.

14 Phenol and phenolic compounds kill or inhibit microorganisms by denaturing proteins and damaging the _____ .

15 Ethyl alcohol solutions in a range of _____ to

_____ percent have good antiseptic properties.

16 Methyl alcohol is less attractive as an antimicrobial agent than ethyl alcohol for two reasons: (1) it has lower antimicrobial activity, and (2) it is

_____ to tissue.

17 Iodine and chlorine belong to the class of elements called

_____ .

18 The products released when chlorine (Cl_2) reacts with water (H_2O) are

_____ and _____ .

19 Iodophors are mixtures of iodine with compounds that act as

_____ .

20 In the use of chlorine and chlorine compounds, the concentration of residual free chlorine should be _____ mg/liter.

21 The antimicrobial action of mercuric chloride is through reaction with the

_____ groups of enzymes and other cellular proteins.

22 Copper sulfate is effective as a(n) _____ in swimming pools and reservoirs.

23 The heavy-metal salt that is used to prevent gonococcal infection in the eyes of newborns is _____ .

24 Ceepryn is an example of a(n) _____ detergent, whereas dodecyl sulfate is an example of a(n) _____ detergent.

25 _____ detergents are more germicidal than

_____ detergents.

26 The bacteriostatic effect of quaternary ammonium compounds is considerably

_____ than their bactericidal effect.

27 Match each substance listed on the right with the term on the left that best describes it.

_____ antiseptic

_____ algicide

_____ water purification

_____ sanitizer

_____ disinfectant

(a) 70% isopropyl alcohol
(b) Copper sulfate
(c) Quaternary ammonium compound
(d) Compressed chlorine gas
(e) Lysol

EVALUATION OF ANTIMICROBIAL POTENCY OF DISINFECTANTS AND ANTISEPTICS

28 A liquefied agar medium is inoculated with a culture of test bacteria and is poured into a Petri dish. A paper disk impregnated with a chemical agent is placed on the solidified agar, and the plate is incubated. If the agent has antimicrobial properties, this will be indicated by _____.

29 In the tube-dilution method for testing antibacterial activity, a chemical agent is added to a tube of culture medium and then the tube is inoculated with the test bacteria and incubated. No growth occurs. This could be explained in either of two ways: (1) the agent was a(n) _____ agent, or (2) the agent was a(n) _____ agent.

30 In a phenol-coefficient test, the highest dilution of chemical agent X that killed *Staphylococcus aureus* in 10 min but not in 5 min was 1:200. Under similar conditions the highest dilution of phenol that achieved the same effect was 1:100. Therefore, the phenol coefficient of agent X is _____.

CHEMICAL STERILANTS

31 Two important characteristics of ethylene oxide as an antimicrobial agent are its high _____ and its high _____.

32 Pure ethylene oxide is flammable and explosive. These properties are eliminated by mixing ethylene oxide with _____ or _____.

33 Ethylene oxide exhibits its antimicrobial activity by _____ reactions with compounds such as enzymes and other proteins.

34 One limitation of β-propiolactone for microbiological control is its low _____ ability.

35 Two chemical aldehydes which can be used in solution to sterilize specialized medical equipment are _____ and _____.

REVIEW QUESTIONS

1 Distinguish between the following pairs of terms:

(a) Sterilization and disinfection

(b) Sanitization and disinfection

(c) Germicide and bactericide

(d) Bacteriostat and bactericide

2 Is it correct to say that a substance is "almost" sterile? Explain.

3 Describe several conditions that may influence the efficacy of an antimicrobial chemical when used in a practical situation.

4 List the major categories of antimicrobial chemical agents. Name a specific example for each category and describe a practical use for each substance.

5 Describe several ways by which antimicrobial chemicals may damage (kill or inhibit) microorganisms. Give specific examples.

6 What does a phenol coefficient of 5.0 mean?

7 Name the test organisms used in performing phenol-coefficient tests.

8 What are some of the advantages of using ethylene oxide as a sterilant? Are there any disadvantages? Explain.

9 As a sterilant, how does β-propiolactone compare with ethylene oxide? Explain.

DISCUSSION QUESTIONS

1 Give several reasons why it is highly unlikely that a single chemical agent will ever be produced that will be the best for every practical application.

2 What effect does the presence of organic matter have on the efficacy of halogens when used under practical conditions? Explain why.

3 What are some similarities, and what are the differences, between a chemical that is used as a disinfectant and one that is used as an antiseptic?

4 A new disinfectant is evaluated for its antimicrobial potency by both the tube-dilution technique and the agar-plate technique. Results of the agar-plate technique show very little antimicrobial activity, whereas the results from the tube-dilution technique show a high level of antimicrobial activity. How might this discrepancy be explained?

5 In what ways is the sterilization procedure using ethylene oxide comparable to sterilization using high-energy electron beams or gamma irradiation?

IV

Major Groups
of Microorganisms

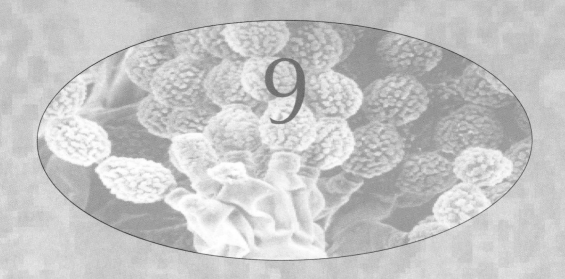

9

The Major Groups of Procaryotic Microorganisms: Bacteria

OBJECTIVES

After reading this chapter you should be able to

1 Describe the two major groups of bacteria.

2 List the major characteristics that differentiate the subgroups of Gram-negative eubacteria.

3 Give the major characteristics that differentiate the various subgroups of Gram-positive eubacteria.

4 Identify the unique characteristics of mycoplasmas.

5 Discuss the differences among the four major groups of archaeobacteria.

OVERVIEW

There are hundreds of genera and thousands of species of bacteria, representing a wide range of morphological and physiological properties. Most bacteria are simple in form, but some have unusual shapes and arrangements. Some are able to live in extreme environments because of their unique metabolic capabilities. You have already learned how ubiquitous and diverse bacteria are, thriving nearly everywhere on earth. The bewildering array of bacteria can be understood by thinking of the organisms in terms of a few major groups and by dealing with typical genera in each group. The bacteria that cause disease have naturally been studied in great detail, but other bacteria are equally interesting because of their shape, strange habitats, nutritional requirements, or interactions with each other and with higher organisms. By emphasizing the distinctive properties of these few genera, this chapter will make it easier for you to understand and remember the various kinds of bacteria, and to appreciate the marvelous diversity of bacterial life.

BERGEY'S MANUAL OF SYSTEMATIC BACTERIOLOGY

Where do microbiologists go for information about a particular bacterial genus or species? Many books and articles have been written that describe the bacteria, but one publication is unique because of its broad scope—*Bergey's Manual of Systematic Bacteriology.* The manual is an international reference work resulting from the cooperative effort of hundreds of microbiologists, each an authority on some group of bacteria. It not only contains descriptions of all established genera and species, but also provides a practical arrangement for differentiating these organisms, together with appropriate classification outlines and tables.

ASK YOURSELF

1 If you wanted the description of a particular genus or species of bacteria, what book would you consult?

2 Why is this book considered the major reference for bacterial classification and identification?

EUBACTERIA AND ARCHAEOBACTERIA

As you learned earlier in this book, there are two major groups of bacteria—the *eubacteria* and the *archaeobacteria* [TABLE 9.1]. A few of the many fundamental differences between these two groups are:

1 The cell walls of eubacteria contain peptidoglycan (whose composition includes muramic acid and D-amino acids), whereas the cell walls of archaeobacteria consist of proteins or polysaccharides.
2 The phospholipids in the cytoplasmic membrane of eubacteria differ markedly in their chemical structure from those in archaeobacteria. Instead of containing long-chain fatty acids, those in archaeobacteria contain long-chain branched alcohols called **phytanols.**
3 Protein synthesis in eubacteria differs significantly from that in archaeobacteria. For instance, in eubacteria the amino acid that is used to begin a protein chain is always formylmethionine, while in archaeobacteria it is always methionine.

TABLE 9.1
Major Groups of Bacteria

EUBACTERIA

Cell wall present	Cell wall absent
Gram-negative:	Mycoplasmas
Spirochetes	
Aerobic or microaerophilic curved rods	
Aerobic rods and cocci	
Facultatively anaerobic rods	
Anaerobes	
Rickettsias and chlamydias	
Anoxygenic phototrophs	
Oxygenic phototrophs	
Gliding bacteria	
Sheathed bacteria	
Budding and/or appendaged bacteria	
Chemolithotrophs	
Gram-positive:	
Cocci	
Endospore formers	
Regularly shaped rods	
Irregularly shaped rods	
Mycobacteria	
Actinomycetes	

ARCHAEOBACTERIA

Methane producers	Thermoplasmas
Red extreme halophiles	
Sulfur-dependent archaeobacteria	

Moreover, archaeobacteria are noted for producing unusual end products of metabolism which eubacteria cannot produce (such as methane gas) or for inhabiting extremely harsh environments which most eubacteria cannot tolerate. Under the classification system proposed by Woese (Chapter 2), each of these constitutes a kingdom in the evolutionary tree.

ASK YOURSELF

1 In which of the two major groups of bacteria does muramic acid–containing peptidoglycan occur?

2 In which of the two major groups of bacteria do the phospholipids contain long-chain branched alcohols instead of fatty acids?

3 In which of the two major groups of bacteria is formylmethionine used to begin the synthesis of a protein chain?

THE EUBACTERIA

Eubacteria can be divided into three main groups on the basis of whether or not they have cell walls and, if so, which type of cell wall is present. Bacteria that form these three groups—the Gram-negative eubacteria, the Gram-positive eubacteria, and the mycoplasmas—are listed in TABLE 9.1. As described earlier in this book, with the Gram stain procedure Gram-negative microorganisms appear pink through a microscope, while Gram-positive microorganisms are purple-violet.

Gram-Negative Eubacteria

Besides their distinctive appearance with the Gram stain, Gram-negative eubacteria have a complex cell wall composed of an outer membrane covering a very thin peptidoglycan layer. Many of the most familiar and well-studied bacterial genera belong to this group. Gram-negative eubacteria can be divided into subgroups based on their morphological and physiological features, such as motility and oxygen requirements [TABLE 9.2].

Spirochetes. Spirochetes are helically coiled, flexible bacteria that twist and contort their shape. Most are so thin that they cannot be easily seen by Gram staining, but they can be seen using wet mounts and dark-field microscopy.

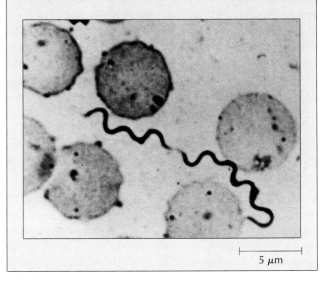

FIGURE 9.2

Giemsa stain of blood from patient with louse-borne relapsing fever, showing the causative agent, *Borrelia recurrentis*. The large round objects are red blood cells.

5 μm

Spirochetes are motile, but they differ from other flagellated Gram-negative bacteria in the location of their flagella. Instead of extending outward from the cells like ordinary flagella, the flagella of spirochetes lie beneath the outer membrane (often called the *outer sheath* in spirochetes). Consequently, they are given a special name, *periplasmic flagella* [FIGURES 4.10 and 9.1].

Some spirochetes, such as the genus *Spirochaeta*, inhabit water, mud, and marine sediments. They are *saprophytes*, which means that they live on inanimate organic matter. Other spirochetes obtain nutrients from living hosts and thus are *parasites*. For instance, the genus *Cristispira* lives only in marine and freshwater mollusks. Some spirochetes cause disease; these pathogens include the causative agent of syphilis, *Treponema pallidum*, and *Borrelia* species, which cause relapsing fever and Lyme disease and are spread by infected ticks or lice [FIGURE 9.2].

Aerobic or Microaerophilic Curved Bacteria. Although some curved aerobic and microaerophilic bacteria are helical like the spirochetes, the cells are rigid, not flexible, and the organisms are called *spirilla* (singular, *spirillum*). Spirilla are motile by means of polar flagella at the ends of the cells [FIGURE 9.3]. *Aquaspirillum* species are common saprophytic inhabitants of freshwater environments. The species *A. magnetotacticum* is remarkable because of its magnetic properties [DISCOVER 9.1].

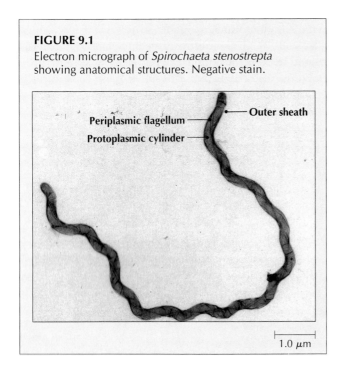

FIGURE 9.1

Electron micrograph of *Spirochaeta stenostrepta* showing anatomical structures. Negative stain.

Periplasmic flagellum
Protoplasmic cylinder
Outer sheath

1.0 μm

TABLE 9.2
Summary of the Major Groups of Gram-Negative Eubacteria

Group	Major characteristics	Representative genera
Spirochetes	Helical; flexible; have periplasmic flagella; live in water and mud, insects, animals, and humans; several are human pathogens	*Borrelia, Cristispira, Leptospira, Spirochaeta, Treponema*
Aerobic or microaerophilic curved rods	Helical, vibrioid, or ring-shaped; motile with polar flagella or nonmotile; live in water or soil or are parasites of animals; some are human pathogens	*Aquaspirillum, Azospirillum, Bdellovibrio, Campylobacter, Flectobacillus, Oceanospirillum, Spirosoma*
Aerobic rods and cocci	Rods or cocci; some live in water or soil; some are pathogens of humans, animals, or plants	*Acetobacter, Agrobacterium, Azotobacter, Bordetella, Brucella, Francisella, Legionella, Methylococcus, Moraxella, Neisseria, Rhizobium, Xanthomonas*
Facultatively anaerobic rods	Straight or vibrioid rods; many inhabit the intestines of humans or animals and some are pathogens; others live in soil or water or on plants	*Enterobacter, Erwinia, Escherichia, Haemophilus, Pasteurella, Proteus, Salmonella, Serratia, Shigella, Vibrio, Yersinia*
Anaerobes	Straight, curved, or helical rods, and cocci; some are environmental and form H_2S; others live in intestinal tracts and cause tissue infections	*Bacteroides, Desulfovibrio, Fusobacterium, Megasphaera, Veillonella*
Rickettsias and chlamydias	Rod-shaped to coccoid; require living hosts in order to grow; many are pathogenic for humans or animals	*Chlamydia, Coxiella, Rickettsia, Rochalimaea*
Anoxygenic phototrophs	Anaerobes that use light as their energy source and do not evolve oxygen; "purple" and "green" bacteria; live in aquatic environments; nonpathogenic	*Chlorobium, Chromatium, Rhodomicrobium, Rhodopseudomonas, Rhodospirillum*
Oxygenic phototrophs	Use light as their energy source and evolve oxygen; commonly called *cyanobacteria*; live in soil and water; nonpathogenic	*Anabaena, Cylindrospermum, Gloeocapsa, Gloeotrichia, Oscillatoria*
Gliding bacteria	Rods or filaments that lack flagella but glide across moist surfaces; some have a complex life cycle and form fruiting bodies; live in soil and water; nonpathogenic	*Beggiatoa, Chondromyces, Cytophaga, Flexibacter, Herpetosiphon, Saprospira, Simonsiella, Stigmatella*
Sheathed bacteria	Rods in chains or filaments, surrounded by a tubular sheath; aquatic saprophytes; nonpathogenic	*Crenothrix, Leptothrix, Sphaerotilus*
Budding and/or appendaged bacteria	Reproduce asymmetrically by budding and/or form prosthecae or stalks; soil and aquatic saprophytes; nonpathogenic	*Ancalomicrobium, Blastocaulis/Planctomyces, Caulobacter, Gallionella, Hyphomicrobium*
Chemolithotrophs	Obtain energy by oxidizing ammonia; nitrite, reduced sulfur compounds, iron, or manganese; most are autotrophs; occur in soil and water; nonpathogenic	*Nitrobacter, Nitrococcus, Nitrosolobus, Nitrosomonas, Siderocapsa, Thiobacillus, Thiospira*

FIGURE 9.3

Electron micrograph of *Aquaspirillum serpens*, a member of the group *Aerobic or Microaerophilic Curved Rods,* showing tufts of polar flagella. Shadowed preparation.

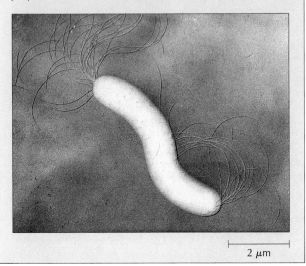

2 μm

FIGURE 9.4

Phase-contrast photomicrograph showing plump vibrioid and straight cells of *Azospirillum brasilense*, a nitrogen-fixing member of the group *Aerobic or Microaerophilic Curved Rods.*

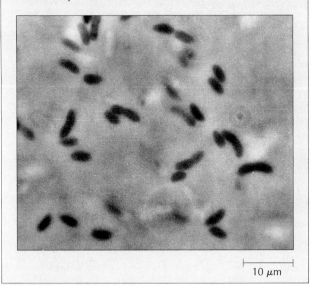

10 μm

The genus *Azospirillum* contains *vibrioid* cells, which look like a twisted comma [FIGURE 9.4]. Azospirilla are microaerophiles that can fix atmospheric nitrogen. They live within the roots of grasses, wheat, corn, and many other kinds of plants. The genus *Campylobacter* also includes microaerophilic vibrioid cells.

FIGURE 9.5

The life cycle of *Bdellovibrio*, a member of the group *Aerobic or Microaerophilic Curved Bacteria*. A bdellovibrio attaches to a host bacterium, penetrates the wall, and grows within the periplasmic space (between the wall and cytoplasmic membrane) as a long, coiled form that eventually fragments into new bdellovibrio progeny. The host cell is destroyed in the process.

Bdellovibrio attaches to and penetrates host-cell wall

Bdellovibrio ——————

Cell wall of ——————
host bacterium

Cytoplasmic membrane ——————
of host bacterium

Cytoplasm ——————

Bdellovibrio growth and fragmentation

Host-cell destruction and release of progeny bdellovibrios

9.1 MAGNETIC BACTERIA

In the early 1970s a graduate student named Richard Blakemore was studying the microbial populations in samples of mud and water collected from a New England swamp. When he observed a drop from a sample under a microscope, he saw that many motile spirilla were present. But then he noticed something remarkable: the spirilla swam in only one geographic direction and eventually accumulated at one edge of the drop. They continued to swim in the same geographic direction even when he turned the microscope around. At first he thought that the bacteria were being attracted toward some light source in the laboratory, but when he covered the microscope with a cardboard box to block any light, the spirilla continued to swim in exactly the same geographic direction.

Blakemore thought that perhaps the spirilla might be responding to the earth's magnetic field. When he brought the end of a bar magnet near the slide, the spirilla instantly turned and rushed away from it. When he tried the opposite end of the magnet the spirilla swam in unison toward the magnet. This end of the magnet was the one that also attracted the north-seeking end of a compass needle.

As Blakemore later wrote, "I wish to emphasize that this was a completely unexpected finding. A research proposal requesting support to search for geomagnetically sensitive bacteria would then have been met by peer review with exactly the same degree of attention as one

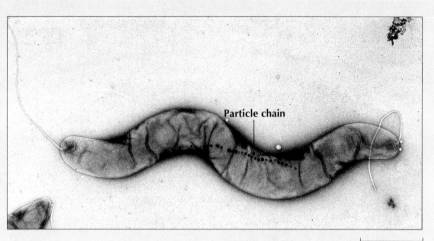

Electron micrograph of a magnetic bacterium, *Aquaspirillum magnetotacticum*, showing a particle chain of highly electron-dense magnetite inclusions within the cell.

submitted today proposing to detect sound production by bacteria."

What caused the bacteria to respond to a magnetic field? When Blakemore and his colleagues looked at the cells under an electron microscope, they found a chain of tiny cubical particles within each cell (see the illustration). Chemical analysis indicated that the main constituent of these particles was magnetic iron oxide, or magnetite (Fe_3O_4). The chain of particles formed an intracellular magnet that caused each cell to become oriented in a magnetic field.

What advantage did being magnetic have for a bacterium? This question became particularly tantalizing when it was discovered that although magnetic

bacteria isolated from New England always swam north, others isolated from Brazil always swam south. The most likely explanation is based on the discovery that magnetic bacteria are micro-aerophilic: although they must have oxygen in order to grow, they cannot tolerate ordinary levels of it, such as those in aerobic surface waters. In the regions where magnetic bacteria have been found, the earth's magnetic field has a vertical as well as a horizontal component; that is, it has a downward declination. Thus magnetic bacteria swim not only north or south but also downward. In aquatic environments, this would cause the bacteria to swim toward deeper, less oxygen-rich areas that are more favorable for growth.

One species, *C. jejuni*, is notable as a major cause of diarrhea in humans. Probably the most unusual genus of vibrioid bacteria is *Bdellovibrio*; these aerobic bacteria are harmless for humans, animals, and plants, but they invade and destroy the cells of many other bacteria [FIGURE 9.5].

Cells of the genera *Spirosoma* and *Flectobacillus* form not only helical spirals and coils but also rings—the cells are so strongly curved that the ends overlap [FIGURE 9.6]. These curved bacteria are saprophytes found in freshwater and marine environments.

Aerobic Rods and Cocci. Many aerobic Gram-negative rods occur in soil and water. A common example is the genus *Pseudomonas* [FIGURE 9.7], well known for the ability to break down many different kinds of complex organic compounds and use them as energy sources. In fact, some *Pseudomonas* species can grow on any of 100 or more different organic compounds. *Azotobacter* and *Rhizobium* are able to fix atmospheric nitrogen. Azotobacters are free-living and fix nitrogen in soil, whereas rhizobia fix nitrogen within the roots of leguminous plants, such as soybeans and alfalfa. The genus *Zoogloea*

FIGURE 9.6

Two ring-forming members of the group *Aerobic or Microaerophilic Curved Rods.* **[A]** Phase-contrast photomicrograph of *Spirosoma* cells showing rings and coils. **[B]** Drawing of cells of *Flectobacillus,* showing rings and coils.

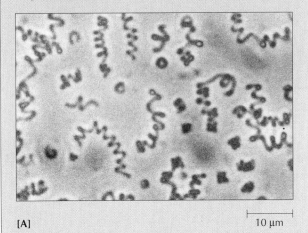

[A]   10 μm

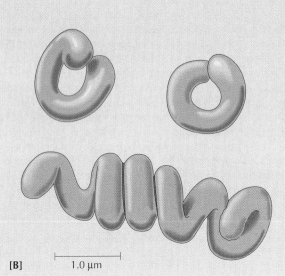

[B]   1.0 μm

FIGURE 9.7

Flagellum stain of *Pseudomonas aeruginosa* showing the characteristic polar flagella. The genus *Pseudomonas* is a member of the group *Aerobic Rods and Cocci.*

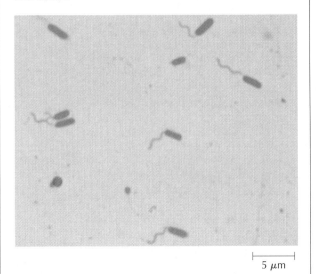

5 μm

FIGURE 9.8

Cells of *Zoogloea ramigera* embedded in a gelatinous matrix. The fingerlike projections of the slimy mass are characteristic of the genus.

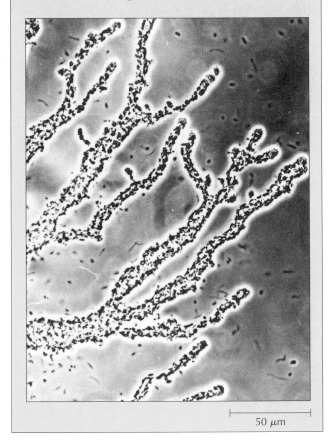

50 μm

is characterized by cells embedded in a gelatinous matrix, forming slimy masses shaped like fingers [FIGURE 9.8]. These bacteria are commonly found coating the rocks on trickling-filter beds in sewage plants, where they oxidize many of the organic substances present in sewage. The genus *Acetobacter* is important commercially for its role in vinegar production. Perhaps the oddest genus of aerobic rods is *Thermus,* which prefers high temperatures. It likes to grow in hot springs at 70 to 75°C, temperatures that kill most other organisms.

Some aerobic Gram-negative rods are pathogenic. Examples are *Brucella* species, which cause abortion in animals and may also infect humans, and *Francisella tularensis,* the causative agent of tularemia. Although

FIGURE 9.9

Sunflower plant showing tumors characteristic of crown gall disease. The tumors are caused by the bacterium *Agrobacterium tumefaciens*, a member of the group *Aerobic Rods and Cocci*.

FIGURE 9.11

Scanning electron micrograph of dividing cells of *Neisseria meningitidis*, showing the characteristic diplococcus arrangement. This species belongs to the group *Aerobic Rods and Cocci*.

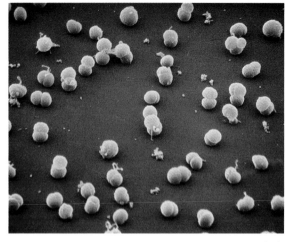

3 μm

not normally pathogenic, some *Pseudomonas* species can cause serious infections in humans whose defense mechanisms against infection have been weakened. For instance, *P. aeruginosa* may cause infection after being introduced into a break in the skin, as in a wound or burn. The genus *Xanthomonas* is pathogenic for plants; in 1984 a variety of *X. campestris* was responsible for a major outbreak of bacterial canker of citrus trees in Florida. Another genus, *Agrobacterium*, is especially interesting because it causes tumors in plants [FIGURE 9.9].

Among the aerobic Gram-negative cocci is *Lampropedia*, a harmless saprophyte in lakes and ponds. These cocci are unusual because they occur in large, flat sheets like trays of muffins [FIGURE 9.10]. Another genus, *Neisseria*, occurs mainly as diplococci [FIGURE 9.11]. Two species are important human pathogens: *N. gonorrhoeae*, which causes gonorrhea, and *N. meningitidis*, the cause of meningococcal meningitis.

FIGURE 9.10

Negatively stained preparation of *Lampropedia hyalina*, a member of the group *Aerobic Rods and Cocci*, showing a sheet of actively growing cells.

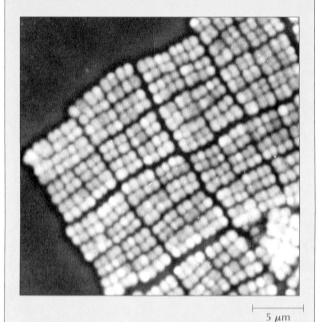

5 μm

Facultative Rods. The facultatively anaerobic rods include both straight and curved rods. Being facultative, they can grow aerobically or anaerobically. When growing anaerobically they obtain their energy by fermentation. Of the facultative rods, the best known group of straight rods is the family **Enterobacteriaceae**, the members of which inhabit the gastrointestinal tracts of humans and other warmblooded animals. Some of the organisms most familiar to microbiologists belong to this family, most notably *Escherichia coli* [FIGURE 9.12A].

FIGURE 9.12

Two members of the family *Enterobacteriaceae* in the group *Facultatively Anaerobic Rods*. **[A]** Drawing of an *Escherichia coli* cell, showing pili and peritrichous flagella. The cutaway portion shows the internal structures. **[B]** Photomicrograph of *Salmonella typhi*, the causative agent of typhoid fever, stained to show the flagella.

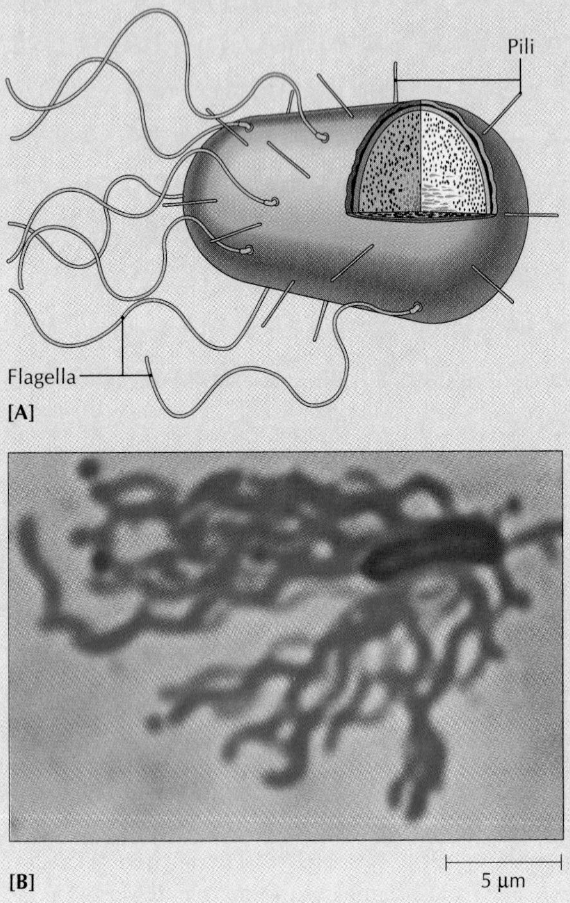

Pili

Flagella

[A]

[B]   5 μm

FIGURE 9.13

The genus *Vibrio* is a member of the group *Facultatively Anaerobic Rods*. The cells are curved rods with polar flagella.

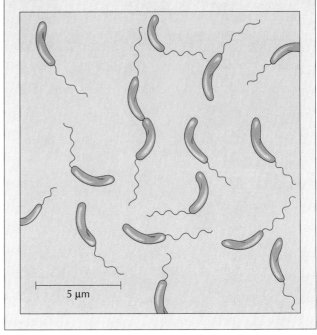

5 μm

Many of the species are indistinguishable under a microscope. Therefore, microbiologists must use a large number of biochemical, physiological, and serological tests to differentiate the organisms. Elaborate schemes of laboratory testing have been developed specifically to characterize and identify the *Enterobacteriaceae*, which are often called *enterics*.

Many human pathogens are enterics; for example, *Salmonella* species [FIGURE 9.12B] cause typhoid fever and gastroenteritis, *Shigella* species cause bacillary dysentery, and *Yersinia pestis* causes plague. Other genera can be pathogenic if they are transferred from the intestinal tract to other areas of the body. For example, *Escherichia*, *Proteus*, *Klebsiella*, *Serratia*, and *Enterobacter* species are common causes of urinary tract infections.

The genus *Erwinia* differs from the other members of the family *Enterobacteriaceae* by being associated mainly with plants, in which it causes soft rots and other diseases.

Facultative anaerobes other than the enterics include *Vibrio cholerae* [FIGURE 9.13], which causes cholera, and *Haemophilus influenzae*, the leading cause of bacterial meningitis in children. (Despite its name, *H. influenzae* does not cause influenza, which is caused by a virus.)

Anaerobes. Among the Gram-negative anaerobic bacteria are straight rods, curved rods, and cocci. This group is divided into two subgroups: those anaerobes that require either sulfate or elemental sulfur, and those that do not.

The anaerobes that require sulfur or sulfate add electrons to the sulfur and reduce it to hydrogen sulfide, a gas that is toxic to humans and has the unpleasant odor of rotten eggs. One common genus, *Desulfovibrio*, has vibrioid cells and inhabits mud in swamps and other aquatic environments. These sulfate- and sulfur-reducing bacteria release tons of hydrogen sulfide into the atmosphere every year. The Gram-negative anaerobes that do not require sulfur or sulfate produce organic acids, and identification is often based on the kinds of acids produced.

FIGURE 9.14

Drawing of cells of *Bacteroides fragilis,* a member of the *Anaerobes* group. The cells are irregularly shaped rods.

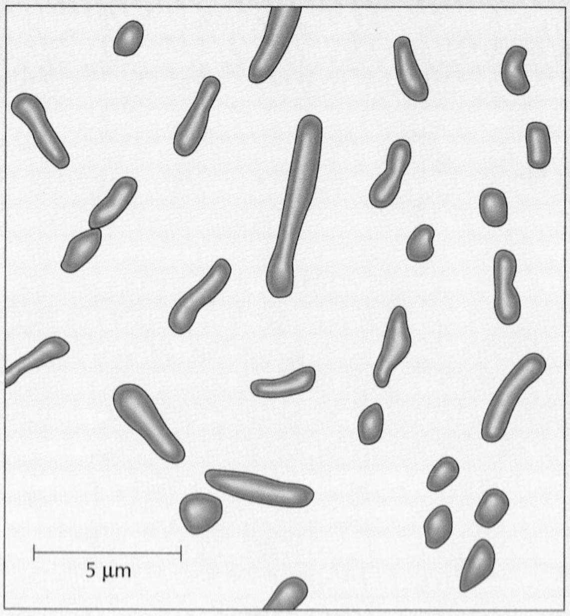

5 μm

FIGURE 9.15

Photomicrograph of numerous rod-shaped cells of *Rickettsia akari* growing in the cytoplasm of an infected mouse cell. The large dark object is the nucleus of the mouse cell.

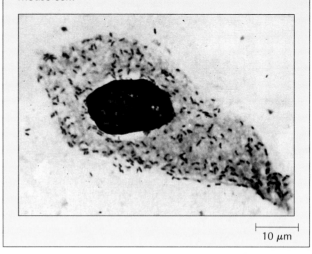

10 μm

Gram-negative anaerobes are the predominant organisms in the human intestine and in the *rumen,* a compartment of the stomachs of cattle and sheep. Some are pathogenic for humans if they gain access to body sites other than the intestine. For instance, *Bacteroides fragilis* [FIGURE 9.14] is the most common anaerobic species isolated from soft-tissue infections in humans.

Rickettsias and Chlamydias. Like viruses, both the rickettsias and the chlamydias are obligate intracellular parasites, which means that they will not grow on cell-free laboratory media. They must be cultivated in tissue-culture systems, in live embryonated chicken eggs, or in a living arthropod or animal host.

Rickettsias are parasitic rod-shaped or oval bacteria that grow within or on the surface of living cells of arthropods or vertebrates [FIGURE 9.15]. *Rickettsia* species cause several diseases of humans, including Rocky Mountain spotted fever (*R. rickettsii*) and epidemic typhus (*R. prowazekii*). Most of them are transmitted to humans by lice, fleas, mites, or ticks, which become infected when they ingest blood from an infected individual.

Unlike rickettsias, the coccoid chlamydias have a unique developmental cycle during which they exist in several forms [FIGURE 9.16]. Also unlike rickettsias, they do not have peptidoglycan in their cell walls and do not require insects for transmission. *Chlamydia* species are

pathogenic: *C. psittaci* causes psittacosis in birds, and *C. trachomatis* causes trachoma (which in the past has been the greatest single cause of blindness in the world), lymphogranuloma venereum, and nongonococcal urethritis, currently the most prevalent sexually transmitted disease in the United States.

Anoxygenic Phototrophic Bacteria. The anoxygenic phototrophs are similar to green plants in one respect: they have the ability to convert the energy of light into chemical energy for growth. However, unlike plants, they do not produce oxygen and thus are *anoxygenic.* Moreover, they contain a type of chlorophyll, *bacteriochlorophyll,* that differs from the chlorophyll of green plants. Bacteriochlorophyll absorbs mainly infrared light (long-wavelength light invisible to the human eye), rather than the shorter-wavelength red light absorbed by plant chlorophyll. The bacterial cells also contain *carotenoids,* water-insoluble pigments that absorb light energy and transmit it to the bacteriochlorophyll. The color of these carotenoids is the basis for dividing anoxygenic phototrophic bacteria into two major groups: the "purple" bacteria (orange to purple-red) and the "green" bacteria (green to brown). Both groups are anaerobic and live beneath the surface of stagnant ponds and salt marsh pools, or at the bottom of lakes.

The anoxygenic phototrophs are rod-shaped, spiral, or coccoid cells. Although many multiply by binary fission, some reproduce by budding. The bud enlarges and eventually develops into a new cell, which then separates from the parent. An example of a phototrophic genus that can reproduce by budding is

FIGURE 9.16

[A] Developmental cycle of *Chlamydia* species. The infectious form of the organism is the *elementary body*, which is taken into the host cell and becomes enclosed in a membrane-bound vacuole. Within the vacuole the elementary body is reorganized to form a *reticulate body* (also called an *initial body*). The reticulate body undergoes binary fission until a number of reticulate bodies are formed, many of which then undergo reorganization into elementary bodies. The total aggregate of reticulate bodies and elementary bodies within the vacuole is visible as an *inclusion* in stained cells; i.e., it appears as a single particle of foreign substance occurring within the host cell. The progeny elementary bodies are eventually liberated from the host cell and proceed to infect other cells. [B] Photomicrograph of iodine-stained tissue cells in which chlamydias have grown. The dark bodies are the host-cell inclusions.

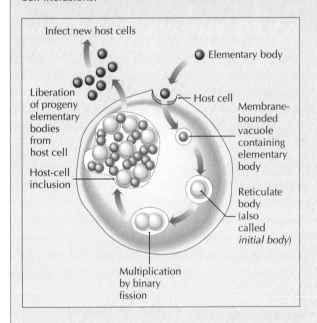

[A]

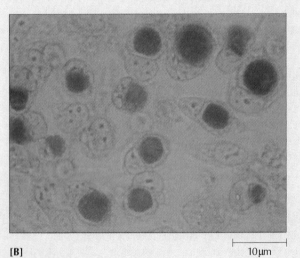

[B]   10μm

FIGURE 9.17

Some species of purple bacteria that belong to the group *Anoxygenic Phototrophs*. [A] *Rhodomicrobium vannielii*, a prosthecate budding species. The buds (arrows) form at the tips of the prosthecae and eventually reach the size of the mother cells. [B] *Rhodopseudomonas acidophila*, a nonprosthecate budding species. The bud (arrow) is formed at the pole of the mother cell and separates by constriction when the bud reaches the size of the mother cell. Some bundles of polar flagella can also be seen in the field. [C] *Rhodopseudomonas palustris*, a nonprosthecate budding species. The cells are narrower than those in part [B]. Phase-contrast microscopy.

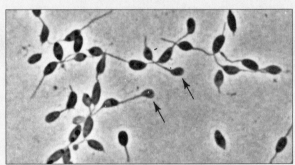

[A]   5 μm

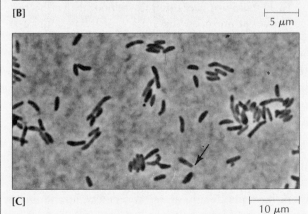

[B]   5 μm

[C]   10 μm

Rhodomicrobium [FIGURE 9.17A]. This organism is particularly interesting because, during growth, a narrow, living extension of the parent cell is formed, called a *prostheca* (plural, *prosthecae*). A bud forms at the tip of the prostheca and develops into a daughter cell. Species of *Rhodopseudomonas* can also reproduce by budding, but the buds are formed directly from the parent cells [FIGURE 9.17B and C].

Oxygenic Phototrophic Bacteria. Unlike the anoxygenic phototrophic bacteria, *oxygenic* phototrophs evolve oxygen as green plants do. Moreover, they contain the *chlorophyll a* found in green plants. Their cells also contain water-soluble protein pigments called *phycobilins*, which can absorb light and transmit the energy to the chlorophyll. Most species contain blue phycobilins, which impart a bluish-green hue to the organisms. Thus the oxygenic phototrophs are often called *cyanobacteria*, meaning "blue bacteria." They have also been called "blue-green algae," but this term is misleading because the microorganisms are now classified as bacteria rather than algae. This change in classification is based on the procaryotic nature of the cyanobacteria. Some oxygenic phototrophs contain red phycobilins and thus are reddish or brownish rather than bluish-green.

Cyanobacteria exhibit a great variety of shapes and arrangements, from unicellular cocci to rods and even long, multicellular filaments [FIGURE 9.18A]. Cyanobac-

FIGURE 9.18

Examples of filamentous cyanobacteria. **[A]** *Oscillatoria limosa*, which has filaments 12 to 18 µm wide. **[B]** *Anabaena planktonica*. The cells are 10 to 15 µm wide and contain gas vacuoles (bright areas). A heterocyst is also shown. **[C]** *Cylindrospermum majus*. The cells are 3 to 5 µm wide, the heterocysts, which are terminal in location, are slightly larger, and the akinetes are much larger. **[D]** *Gloeotrichia echinulata*, showing long and tapering filaments. The heterocysts are 8 to 10 µm wide and the akinetes are 10 to 20 µm wide by 45 to 50 µm long.

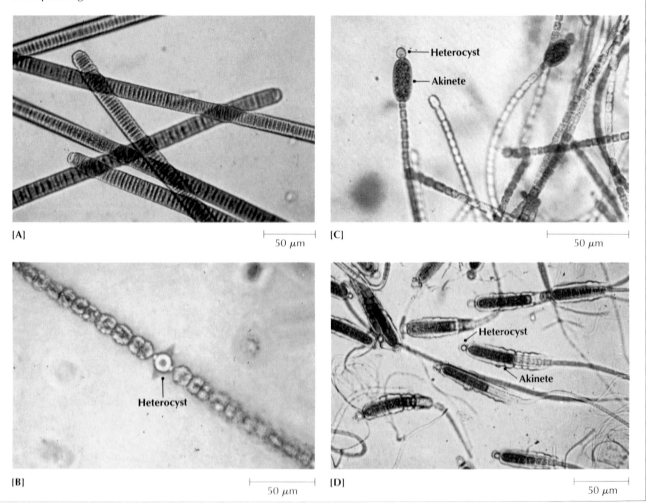

[A] 50 µm

[B] 50 µm

[C] Heterocyst Akinete 50 µm

[D] Heterocyst Akinete 50 µm

teria lack flagella, but the filamentous species usually have *gliding motility* and can migrate across moist surfaces. Specialized cells called *heterocysts* may develop in filamentous species [FIGURE 9.18B through D]. Heterocysts can fix nitrogen because, unlike the other cells in the filament, they do not produce oxygen that could damage the oxygen-sensitive enzyme complex that fixes nitrogen. Some cyanobacteria also form large, thick-walled resting cells called *akinetes* that are highly resistant to drying [FIGURE 9.18C and D].

Cyanobacteria are widespread in soil, freshwater, and marine environments. Some grow in hot springs and are thermophilic. Others can live in intimate association with protozoa, fungi, and green plants. In these partnerships the cyanobacteria provide nutrients through their photosynthetic and nitrogen-fixing processes.

Gliding Bacteria. There are two major kinds of gliding bacteria: those that form specialized spore-producing structures called *fruiting bodies* and those that do not. Those that do form fruiting bodies have some remarkable features. The cells are short rods resembling typical bacteria, except that they are unusually flexible. Although lacking flagella, the cells can glide across moist

FIGURE 9.19

Life cycle of *Stigmatella aurantiaca*, a member of the group *Gliding Bacteria*. During the vegetative cycle the cells multiply by binary fission, but at some stage of growth they swarm together in masses and form desiccation-resistant myxospores, which are contained within the sporangioles of a stalked fruiting body. Under suitable conditions the myxospores can germinate and develop into vegetative cells.

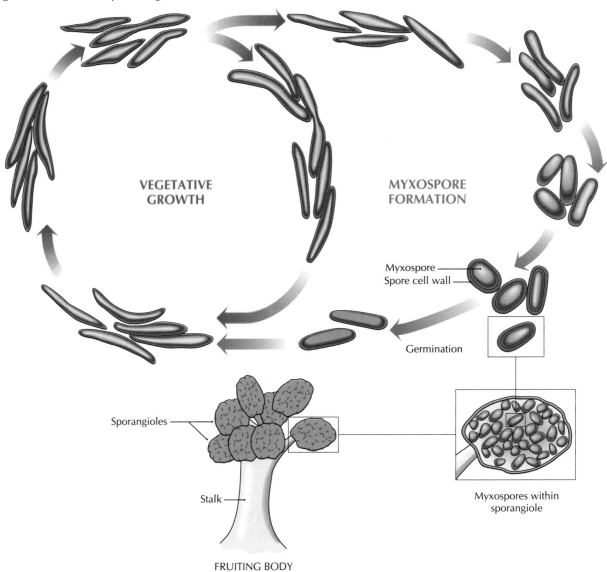

VEGETATIVE GROWTH

MYXOSPORE FORMATION

Myxospore
Spore cell wall

Germination

Sporangioles

Myxospores within sporangiole

Stalk

FRUITING BODY

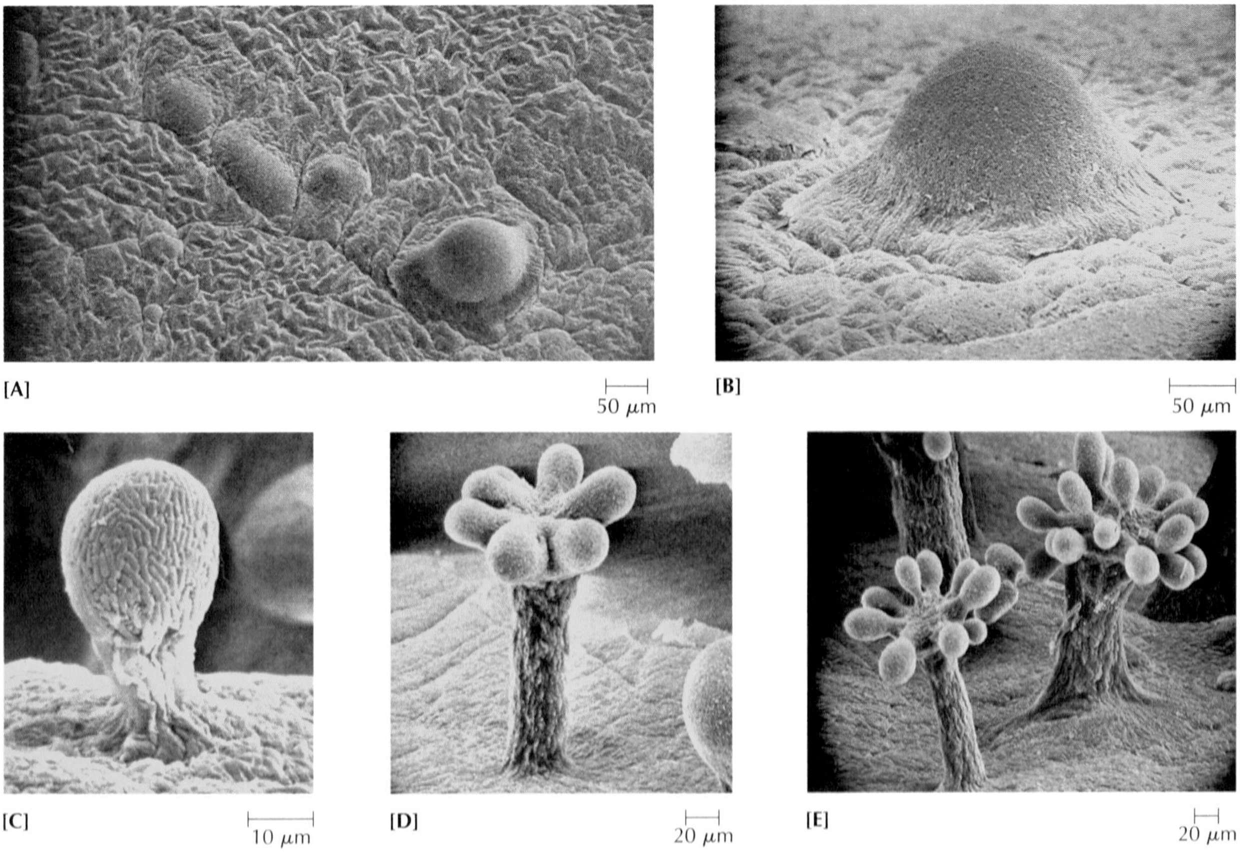

FIGURE 9.20

Stages in fruiting body formation by the myxobacter *Chondromyces crocatus*. Early stages: **[A]** initial stages of vegetative cell aggregation; **[B]** "fried-egg" stage showing orientation of peripheral cells; **[C]** bulb formation and development of stalk. Late stages: **[D]** initial stages of sporangiole formation; **[E]** sporangiole formation after elongation of stalk to maximum length.

[A]

[B]
50 μm
50 μm

[C]
10 μm

[D]
20 μm

[E]
20 μm

surfaces, leaving a trail of slime behind them. This is why they are commonly called *myxobacters*, meaning "slime bacteria."

Another remarkable feature of myxobacters is that at some stage of growth the cells swarm together in masses and form fruiting bodies, which are composed of slime and dormant, desiccation-resistant cells called **myxospores** [FIGURE 9.19]. The fruiting bodies may be simple heaps of myxospores embedded in slime, or they may be much more elaborate, with stalks of slime. On these stalks are walled structures called *sporangioles* that contain the myxospores [FIGURE 9.20]. Fruiting bodies are often brightly colored and large enough to be seen without the aid of a microscope. Myxobacters are aerobic and live in surface layers of soil, compost, rotting wood, and animal dung.

Most gliding bacteria that do not form fruiting bodies are rod-shaped or filamentous (for example, *Flexibacter* and *Herpetosiphon*; FIGURE 9.21) and do not form

myxospores. They are aerobic or microaerophilic organisms that live in soil or water. Like the myxobacters, many species can degrade natural polymers such as cellulose, chitin, pectin, keratin, or even agar.

Sheathed Bacteria. Some rod-shaped bacteria are surrounded by a sheath made of organic substance; a chain of cells looks as though it is contained in a tube. Sheathed bacteria inhabit freshwater and marine environments. One common species, *Sphaerotilus natans* [FIGURE 9.22], often occurs in polluted waters and may cause problems in sewage treatment. Sheaths of this organism are normally colorless, but in iron-containing water the sheaths may accumulate iron hydroxide, giving them a yellow-brown appearance.

Budding and/or Appendaged Bacteria. Among the common inhabitants of soil and water are the budding and appendaged bacteria. These organisms are aerobic, mi-

FIGURE 9.21
Some nonfruiting members of the group *Gliding Bacteria*. **[A]** *Flexibacter polymorphus*. Cells collected on the surface of a membrane filter. **[B]** Filaments of *Herpetosiphon giganteus* on agar, showing "bulbs" (bright spherical enlarged regions).

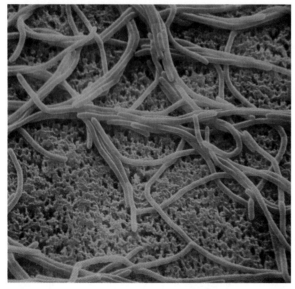

[A] 5 μm

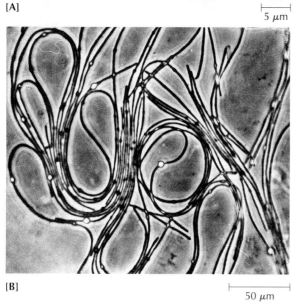

[B] 50 μm

FIGURE 9.22
Sphaerotilus natans, a member of the group *Sheathed Bacteria*. A tubular sheath (arrows) can be seen enclosing the cells.

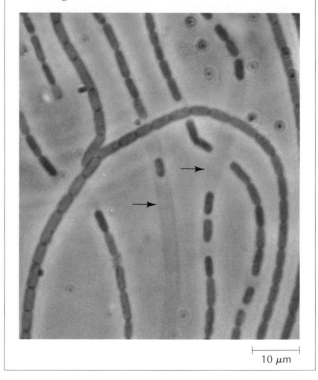

10 μm

None of the bacteria in this group are phototrophic. However, some anoxygenic phototrophic bacteria can also form prosthecae or reproduce by budding.

Chemolithotrophs. Chemolithotrophic bacteria obtain energy by oxidizing inorganic chemical compounds—energy is liberated as they remove electrons from the molecules of these compounds. Many species are autotrophic and can use CO_2 as their major or sole carbon source. Differentiation within the group is based on the kind of inorganic compound oxidized. This differentiation is usually reflected in the names of the genera, as seen in the following:

1 Genera with the prefix *nitro-* obtain energy by oxidizing nitrite to nitrate. Examples are *Nitrobacter* and *Nitrococcus* [FIGURE 9.25].
2 Genera with the prefix *nitroso-* obtain energy by oxidizing ammonia to nitrite. An example is the genus *Nitrosolobus* [FIGURE 9.25].
3 Genera with the prefix *thio-* obtain energy by oxidizing elemental sulfur or reduced sulfur compounds such as hydrogen sulfide, thiosulfate, and sulfite; the end product of this oxidation is sulfate. Examples are *Thiospira* [FIGURE 9.25] and *Thiobacillus*.

croaerophilic, or facultative. Some produce prosthecae; others produce *stalks*, which are nonliving ribbonlike or tubular appendages excreted by the cell. Some species reproduce by binary fission, while others reproduce by budding. Various combinations of these features occur; for example, *Caulobacter* species are prosthecate nonbudding bacteria [FIGURE 9.23], whereas *Blastocaulis/Planctomyces* species are stalked budding bacteria [FIGURE 9.24].

FIGURE 9.23

[A] *Caulobacter*, undergoing binary fission. [B] Life cycle of *Caulobacter*. [1] A cell can attach to a surface by means of a *holdfast*, a region of sticky secreted material. [2] The cell grows longer and forms a flagellum. [3] Binary fission occurs, and [4] the flagellated daughter cell detaches and swims away. [5] Eventually its flagellum is replaced by a prostheca and it can attach to a surface by means of a terminal holdfast. *Caulobacter* cells often occur in a rosette arrangement, as shown here.

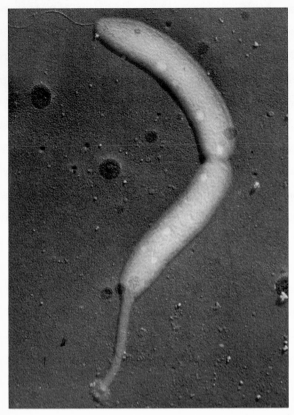

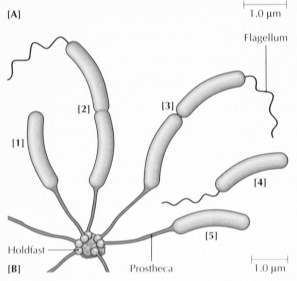

FIGURE 9.24

Electron micrograph of a member of the *Blastocaulis/ Planctomyces* group, morphotype II. The pear-shaped cells secrete stalks, and a bud can be seen developing from a mother cell.

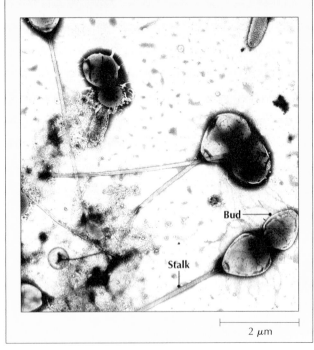

FIGURE 9.25

Drawing of various bacteria that belong to the group *Chemolithotrophs*.

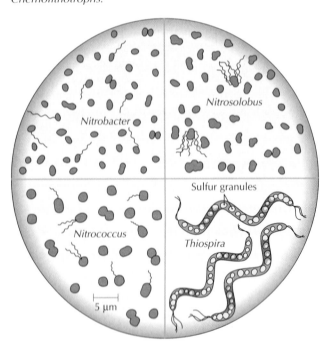

TABLE 9.3
Summary of the Major Groups of Gram-Positive Eubacteria

Group	Major characteristics	Representative genera
Cocci	Aerobic, facultatively anaerobic, or anaerobic; saprophytes or parasites; some are radiation-resistant; some are important human pathogens	*Deinococcus, Micrococcus, Sarcina, Staphylococcus, Streptococcus*
Endospore formers	Rods or cocci that form heat-resistant endospores; aerobic, facultatively anaerobic, or anaerobic; live in soil, water, insects, animals, and humans; some are pathogenic	*Bacillus, Clostridium, Desulfotomaculum, Sporosarcina*
Regularly shaped rods	Aerobic or facultatively anaerobic; live in soil, water, food products, humans, and animals; some cause human disease	*Brocothrix, Caryophanon, Erysipelothrix, Kurthia, Lactobacillus, Listeria*
Irregularly shaped rods	Cells exhibit swellings, are Y- or V-shaped, or have a rod-coccus cycle; aerobic, facultatively anaerobic, or anaerobic; some pathogenic for humans, animals, or plants	*Actinomyces, Arachnia, Arthrobacter, Bifidobacterium, Brevibacterium, Cellulomonas, Corynebacterium, Propionibacterium*
Mycobacteria	Aerobic rods that stain acid-fast; saprophytes or parasites; some pathogenic for humans	*Mycobacterium*
Actinomycetes	Aerobic soil bacteria that form a mycelium composed of branching hyphae; multiply by fragmentation or by production of conidiospores or sporangiospores; some produce antibiotics	*Actinoplanes, Frankia, Micropolyspora, Nocardia, Pseudonocardia, Streptomyces*

4 Genera with the prefix *sidero-* deposit iron or manganese oxides on or in their capsules or slime. They are thought to obtain energy by oxidizing iron or manganese, although this is not yet certain. An example is the genus *Siderococcus*.

Chemolithotrophs occur widely in soil and water and are of great importance to agriculture and to the cycling of nutrients in the environment. Examples include nitrite oxidizers such as *Nitrobacter*, and ammonia oxidizers such as *Nitrosomonas*, which together convert ammonia into nitrate, a form of nitrogen usable by plants. The sulfur-oxidizing bacteria are part of the sulfur cycle.

Gram-Positive Eubacteria

Cell walls of the Gram-positive eubacteria are much thicker than those of the Gram-negative eubacteria, and they lack an outer membrane. As you have already learned, a very high proportion of the Gram-positive wall is peptidoglycan. The Gram-positive eubacteria are divided into groups based on their morphological and biochemical features [TABLE 9.3].

Cocci. Gram-positive cocci are further divided into groups based on differences in their cell arrangement and type of cellular metabolism. One subgroup contains the aerobic cocci. A common genus is *Micrococcus*, in which the cells are arranged in irregular clusters or sometimes in groups of four. *Micrococcus* species are harmless saprophytes that live in soil and fresh water. Perhaps the most remarkable genus is *Deinococcus*. These red-pigmented cocci occur in pairs or groups of four and have an extraordinary capacity to resist high doses of ultraviolet or gamma radiation, doses a thousand times higher than those that kill most other living organisms. What causes this high radiation resistance is still a mystery. Deinococci have been isolated from many environments, most recently from the surface of granite rocks in Antarctica—a region that receives an unusually high level of ultraviolet radiation from the sun.

Another subgroup of Gram-positive cocci contains those that are facultative in terms of oxygen requirements. *Staphylococcus*, with its clustered cells, is one of the most familiar genera [FIGURE 9.26]. Staphylococci live on the skin and mucous membranes of humans and other warmblooded animals. The major pathogenic species is *S. aureus*, which can cause postoperative infections, toxic shock syndrome, and food poisoning in humans. Another familiar genus is *Streptococcus*, whose cells are arranged in pairs or chains [FIGURE 9.26]. *Streptococcus pyogenes* is the most important pathogenic species and causes streptococcal sore throat, scar-

FIGURE 9.26
Drawing of the cells of *Staphylococcus* and *Streptococcus,* which belong to the group *Gram-Positive Cocci.*

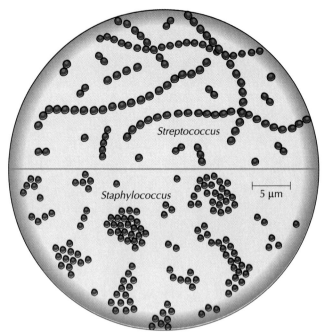

and tetanus, respectively. Some *Bacillus* species are pathogenic for insects and have been widely used as "microbial insecticides" to destroy various insect pests [DISCOVER 9.2].

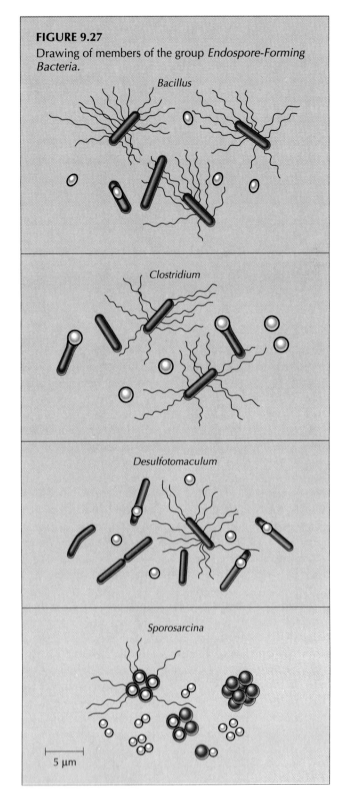

FIGURE 9.27
Drawing of members of the group *Endospore-Forming Bacteria.*

let fever, and rheumatic fever. Another important pathogen is *S. pneumoniae,* which is the major cause of bacterial pneumonia in humans. Other species such as *S. faecalis* are normal inhabitants of the intestinal tract of humans and animals. *Streptococcus lactis* is a harmless contaminant of milk and other dairy products. It is widely used as a "starter culture" in the manufacture of fermented milk products such as cheese.

A third subgroup of Gram-positive cocci contains anaerobic genera such as *Peptococcus, Peptostreptococcus,* and *Coprococcus.* Most species are normal inhabitants of humans or other warmblooded animals.

Endospore-Forming Bacteria. Some bacteria form endospores, which are highly resistant to drying, staining, disinfectants, radiation, and heat. Most endospore formers stain Gram-positive, at least in young cultures, but species of one genus, *Desulfotomaculum,* stain Gram-negative. Endospore formers are rod-shaped, except for the coccoid *Sporosarcina* cells [FIGURE 9.27]. The genera *Bacillus* and *Sporosarcina* are aerobic or facultative, whereas *Clostridium* and *Desulfotomaculum* [see FIGURE 9.27] are anaerobic. Most species are harmless saprophytes in soil, fresh water, or seawater. However, some can cause disease; for example, *Bacillus anthracis* causes anthrax, and *Clostridium perfringens* causes gas gangrene and food poisoning. *Clostridium botulinum* and *C. tetani* secrete powerful nerve poisons (*neurotoxins*) which are responsible for the symptoms of botulism

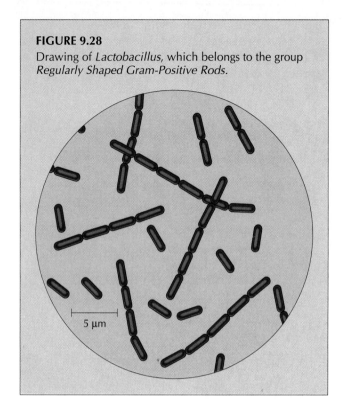

FIGURE 9.28
Drawing of *Lactobacillus*, which belongs to the group *Regularly Shaped Gram-Positive Rods*.

5 μm

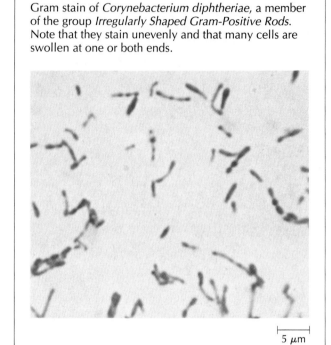

FIGURE 9.29
Gram stain of *Corynebacterium diphtheriae*, a member of the group *Irregularly Shaped Gram-Positive Rods*. Note that they stain unevenly and that many cells are swollen at one or both ends.

5 μm

Regularly Shaped Rods. Among the non-spore-forming rods are a group that have a uniform appearance; that is, they do not exhibit swellings, branching, or other distortions of shape. They are aerobic, facultative, or anaerobic. One genus included in this group is *Lactobacillus* [FIGURE 9.28], facultative saprophytes that occur in fermenting animal or plant products, or as parasites in the mouth, vagina, and intestinal tract of humans and other warmblooded animals. They are generally considered to be nonpathogenic. In fact, certain lactobacilli are widely used in the manufacture of yogurt and cheese. However, some regularly shaped Gram-positive rods are pathogenic. *Listeria monocytogenes*, for example, can be acquired from improperly pasteurized milk or cheese and may cause stillbirth or spontaneous abortion.

Irregularly Shaped Rods. Also non-spore-forming are a group of straight to slightly curved rods that have swellings, club shapes, branching, or other deviations from a regular shape. One unusual genus of aerobic soil bacteria, *Arthrobacter*, exhibits a remarkable *rod-coccus cycle:* the cells grow initially as irregularly shaped rods but later become cocci. When these cocci are inoculated into a fresh medium, they grow again as rods.

The most familiar irregularly shaped rods are members of the genus *Corynebacterium*. Some corynebacteria are saprophytes in soil and water, others are plant pathogens, and still others are animal or human patho-

gens. Of the human pathogens, the major species is *C. diphtheriae* [FIGURE 9.29], the causative agent of diphtheria.

Mycobacteria. There is only one genus of mycobacteria: *Mycobacterium*. The outstanding characteristic of these rod-shaped bacteria is that they are *acid-fast*. This refers to the fact that, after the cells are stained (which usually requires use of a strong dye such as carbolfuchsin, heated to steaming on the slide), it is difficult to decolorize the cells with acidified alcohol [FIGURE 9.30]. Acidified alcohol easily removes dye from stained non-acid-fast bacteria. The acid-fastness of mycobacteria is attributed to certain high–molecular weight lipids called *mycolic acids* found in the cell wall.

Some mycobacteria are harmless saprophytes, but others are pathogenic. Two important pathogenic species are *M. tuberculosis* (tuberculosis) and *M. leprae* (leprosy).

Actinomycetes. The large and very diverse group of bacteria known as *actinomycetes* is characterized by the tendency to form a *mycelium*, a mat of branching filaments called *hyphae* (singular, *hypha*). In some species such as *Nocardia* [FIGURE 9.31], reproduction occurs by *fragmentation*, in which the hyphae break up into many rod-shaped or coccoid cells, each capable of forming a new mycelium. Other species reproduce by forming spores—

9.2 ENDOSPORE FORMERS THAT KILL INSECT PESTS

Several insect-destroying microorganisms have been widely used as microbial insecticides. One of these is the Gram-positive spore former *Bacillus popilliae,* which causes milky disease in the grubs of Japanese beetles. The disease causes the blood of the sick grubs to become filled with bacteria and spores, giving it a milky appearance. The spores are highly resistant to drying, heat, and cold, and they survive in the soil for years. When they are applied to soil where the grubs of the beetles develop, some of the grubs become infected; as the grubs die, more bacterial spores are introduced into the soil. This method has resulted in the virtual elimination of Japanese beetles in areas formerly heavily infested.

Another insect-destroying microbe that is now being studied intensively is a Gram-positive endospore-forming bacterium, *Bacillus thuringiensis.* The cells of this bacillus contain crystals of a protein toxin (Bt toxin) which kills certain insect larvae. When the insects ingest

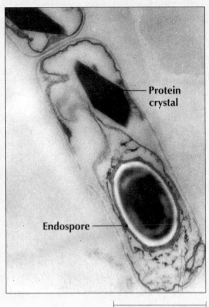

Electron micrograph of a cell of *Bacillus thuringiensis,* showing a protein crystal of Bt toxin and an oval endospore.

Protein crystal

Endospore

1.0 μm

the bacteria, the toxin crystals dissolve and destroy the lining of the insect's intestinal tract. The toxin is not harmful to higher animals or humans. Because it is a protein, it is quickly degraded and does not accumulate in the environment.

Recently, the techniques of genetic engineering have provided a new approach toward making use of Bt toxin. The gene for the toxin, that is, the portion of the DNA containing the coded instructions that allow *B. thuringiensis* to make the toxin, have been transferred from the bacterium to plant tissue cells. This allows the plant cells to make the toxin. The idea is that when insect pests eat the plant tissues, they will consume the toxin and be poisoned. Preliminary experiments with tomato plants have indicated that plants carrying the Bt gene are resistant to attacks by pests such as tomato hornworms and fruitworms. If this technique can be further developed, it may usher in a new era of agricultural pest control.

---

sporangiospores (if they are enclosed in a special sac) or *conidiospores* (if they are not enclosed in a sac). Spores are a major means of multiplication because they are produced in large numbers, each spore having the potential of germinating and growing into a new organism. Although they lack the heat resistance of endospores, conidiospores and sporangiospores are resistant to drying and can aid survival of the species during droughts.

Actinomycetes are mainly harmless soil saprophytes, although a few are pathogenic for humans, animals, or plants. In the soil they have the important function of degrading plant and animal waste. One genus, *Frankia,* is especially interesting because it can fix nitrogen within the roots of nonleguminous woody plants such as alders. Another genus, *Streptomyces* [FIGURE 9.32], is famous for its ability to produce a great variety of antibiotics used to treat human disease, such as tetracycline and streptomycin.

Mycoplasmas

The third major group of eubacteria is the *mycoplasmas.* Their outstanding characteristic is that they are incapable of forming a cell wall, so that they have only a cyto-

plasmic membrane as their outer boundary (thus staining Gram-negative). This lack of a cell wall gives the mycoplasmas some unusual properties not found in most other eubacteria:

1 The cells have plasticity and can assume many different shapes, ranging from spheres to branched filaments [FIGURE 9.33].
2 This plasticity allows many of the cells to slip through the pores of bacteriological filters that retain most other kinds of bacteria.
3 Mycoplasmas swell and burst when the culture is suddenly diluted with water.
4 Mycoplasmas are not inhibited by even very high levels of penicillin—which inhibits cell-wall synthesis and thus has no effect on mycoplasmas. However, mycoplasmas can be inhibited by antibiotics that act upon other metabolic or cellular processes.

Unlike other bacteria, many mycoplasmas have a cytoplasmic membrane that contains a sterol, cholesterol. Normally, only eucaryotic cells contain sterols. Culture media for mycoplasmas contain blood serum to provide cholesterol needed for growth.

FIGURE 9.30

[A] Acid-fast staining of mycobacteria. Once stained with carbol fuchsin, mycobacteria cannot easily be decolorized with acidified alcohol, in contrast to other bacteria that may be present. [B] Acid-fast stain of human sputum showing mycobacteria (red rods) against a non-acid-fast background (blue).

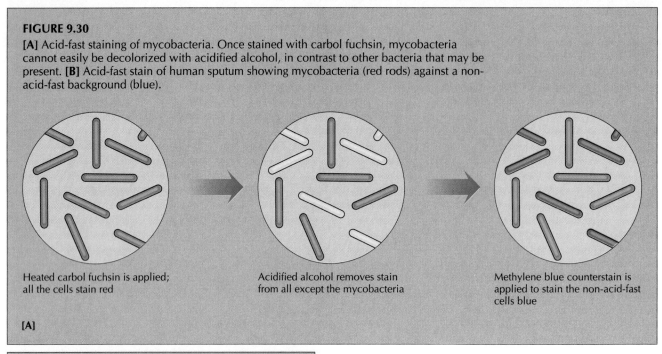

Heated carbol fuchsin is applied; all the cells stain red

Acidified alcohol removes stain from all except the mycobacteria

Methylene blue counterstain is applied to stain the non-acid-fast cells blue

[A]

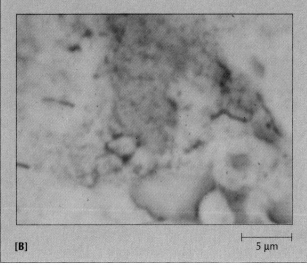

[B]   5 μm

FIGURE 9.31

Cells of *Nocardia*, showing fragmentation of the hyphae.

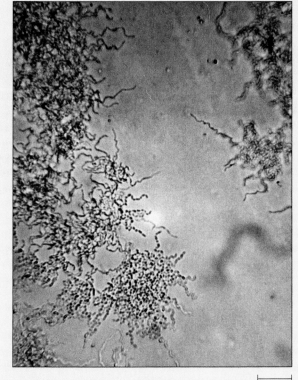

20 μm

Most mycoplasmas inhabit the mucous membranes of humans or other animals. Many species cause animal infections, and some are pathogenic for humans, such as *Mycoplasma pneumoniae*, which causes primary atypical pneumonia, and *Ureaplasma urealyticum*, which causes urethritis.

Members of the genus *Spiroplasma* cause disease in citrus plants and are spread from plant to plant by insects. Spiroplasmas have two very unusual characteristics: (1) the cells are helical, even though they have no cell wall to maintain their shape; and (2) they are motile in liquid media, even though they have no flagella or other apparent means of locomotion. How spiroplasmas can have these features is a mystery that has so far defied explanation.

FIGURE 9.32

Photomicrograph of *Streptomyces viridochromogenes,* showing a hyphal filament bearing long coiled chains of round conidiospores.

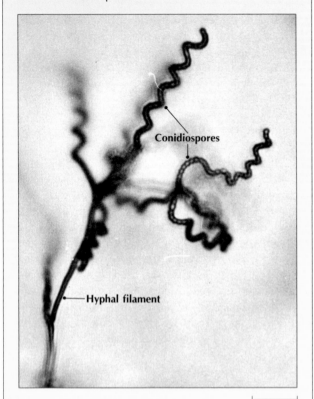

Conidiospores

Hyphal filament

10 μm

FIGURE 9.33

Scanning electron micrograph of *Mycoplasma pneumoniae* from a 6-day culture showing irregular forms, crossing filaments, and piling up of spherical organisms probably representing an early stage of colony formation.

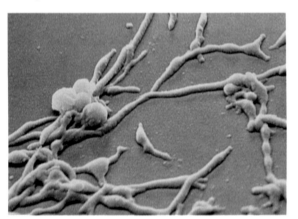

1.0 μm

ASK YOURSELF

1 What are the major features of the subgroups of Gram-negative eubacteria (spirochetes; aerobic and microaerophilic curved bacteria; aerobic rods and cocci; facultatively anaerobic rods; anaerobes; rickettsias and chlamydias; anoxygenic phototrophs; oxygenic phototrophs; gliding bacteria; sheathed bacteria; budding and/or appendaged bacteria; and chemolithotrophs)?

2 What are the major features of the subgroups of Gram-positive eubacteria (cocci, endospore formers, regularly shaped rods, irregularly shaped rods, mycobacteria, and actinomycetes)?

3 What are the distinguishing features of mycoplasmas?

THE ARCHAEOBACTERIA

As a group, the archaeobacteria are morphologically and physiologically diverse. Some have unique properties such as unusual cellular constituents; others live in environments so harsh as to inhibit most other forms of life. At present, four main subgroups of archaeobacteria are recognized. The first three include organisms that have a cell wall: the *methane-producers* (**methanogens**), the *red extreme halophiles* (**halobacteria**), and the *sulfur-dependent archaeobacteria*. The fourth group contains organisms that have no cell wall, the *thermoplasmas.*

Methanogens

The methanogens are anaerobic archaeobacteria that are unique among living organisms in their ability to produce large amounts of methane gas (CH_4). Various kinds of methanogens can be differentiated on the basis of their morphology and Gram reaction. For instance, *Methanosarcina* cells are Gram-positive cocci in clusters, *Methanobacterium* cells are Gram-positive long rods, and *Methanospirillum* cells are Gram-negative wavy filaments [FIGURE 9.34].

Methanogens occur in anaerobic habitats rich in organic matter—marshes, swamps, pond and lake mud, marine sediments, and the rumen of cattle. They also thrive within anaerobic sludge digesters in sewage treatment plants, where they produce many thousands of cubic feet of methane gas each day. This methane can be used as fuel for heating or for power generation.

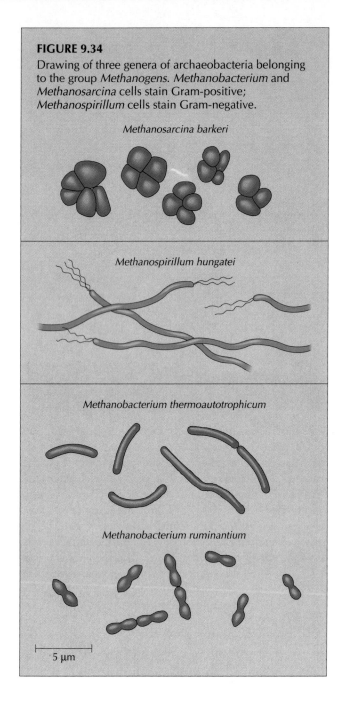

FIGURE 9.34
Drawing of three genera of archaeobacteria belonging to the group *Methanogens*. *Methanobacterium* and *Methanosarcina* cells stain Gram-positive; *Methanospirillum* cells stain Gram-negative.

Methanosarcina barkeri

Methanospirillum hungatei

Methanobacterium thermoautotrophicum

Methanobacterium ruminantium

5 μm

Red Extreme Halophiles

Certain Gram-negative aerobic bacteria are called *halobacteria* ("salt bacteria"), or *red extreme halophiles*, because they require an environment that provides 17 to 23% NaCl for good growth. They cannot grow in solutions less than 15% NaCl; even seawater, which contains approximately 3% NaCl, is not salty enough for halobacteria. Instead, halobacteria live in habitats unsuitable for most other living organisms, such as salt lakes (e.g., the Dead Sea and the Great Salt Lake), industrial plants that produce salt by evaporation of seawater, and foods pre-

served with salt. Colonies are red to orange in color because of the presence of carotenoids, which seem to protect the cells against the damaging effects of sunlight.

Some halobacteria contain a unique purple pigment called **bacteriorhodopsin,** located in the cytoplasmic membrane. Bacteriorhodopsin is photoactive and enables halobacteria to convert the energy of light into chemical energy. In this respect halobacteria are like the phototrophic eubacteria described earlier in this chapter. However, *halobacteria do not contain either bacteriochlorophyll or chlorophyll.*

Sulfur-Dependent Archaeobacteria

In nature, the sulfur-dependent archaeobacteria predominate in acidic hot springs. They can grow at temperatures of 50°C or higher, and sometimes as high as 87°C. Moreover, they prefer acidic conditions; some species cannot grow above pH 4.0 to 5.5. Aerobic genera such as *Sulfolobus* obtain energy by oxidizing elemental sulfur or organic compounds such as sugars or amino acids. Anaerobic genera such as *Thermoproteus* obtain energy by removing electrons from either hydrogen gas or organic compounds, and then using the electrons to reduce elemental sulfur to hydrogen sulfide.

Thermoplasmas

Thermoplasmas resemble the mycoplasmas in that they have no cell wall and are bounded only by the cytoplasmic membrane. However, they differ in their ability to grow at high temperatures under acidic conditions. The optimum temperatures for growth of thermoplasmas are 55 to 59°C, and the optimum pH for growth is 2. In fact, thermoplasma cells actually disintegrate at pH 7. These strange organisms have been isolated from piles of burning coal refuse.

ASK YOURSELF

1 What are the major distinguishing features of methanogens? Of red extreme halophiles? Of sulfur-dependent archaeobacteria? Of thermoplasmas?

2 Which archaeobacteria live in unusually harsh environments?

3 Which archaeobacteria make a metabolic end product not made in significant amounts by any other living organisms?

SUMMARY

1 Detailed information about the characteristics of all genera and species of bacteria can be found in an international reference work called *Bergey's Manual of Systematic Bacteriology.*

2 The two major groups of bacteria are the *eubacteria* and the *archaeobacteria,* which differ in their cell-wall composition, the nature of their membrane phospholipids, and the synthesis of their proteins.

3 The major subgroups of eubacteria are the *Gram-negative eubacteria,* the *Gram-positive eubacteria,* and *eubacteria that lack a cell wall.*

4 Some of the major categories within the Gram-negative eubacteria are differentiated according to morphological features such as cell shape, appendages, and motility. Others are characterized by their relationship to oxygen or by the type of energy source used.

5 The major categories of Gram-positive eubacteria are based on morphological features such as cell shape, occurrence of endospores, acid-fast staining, or formation of a mycelium.

6 Mycoplasmas are pleomorphic bacteria that lack a cell wall and thus are not inhibited by penicillin. Some species require cholesterol for growth.

7 Archaeobacteria are divided into those that have a cell wall and those that do not. Those with cell walls include (1) methane-producing anaerobes, (2) halophiles, and (3) sulfur-dependent organisms. A fourth group lacks a cell wall and grows best at high temperatures and low pH values.

KEY TERMS

anoxygenic
bacteriochlorophyll
bacteriorhodopsin
Bergey's Manual
carotenoids
chlorophyll *a*
cyanobacteria
Enterobacteriaceae
fruiting bodies
gliding motility
halobacteria
heterocysts
methanogens
mycoplasmas
myxospores
oxygenic
phycobilins
phytanols
prostheca (plural, prosthecae)
rod-coccus cycle
stalks

BERGEY'S MANUAL
OF SYSTEMATIC
BACTERIOLOGY

1 Which one of the following statements is *incorrect* with regard to *Bergey's Manual?* **(a)** It is an international reference work. **(b)** It describes only those bacteria that are of medical importance. **(c)** It is the result of the cooperative effort of hundreds of microbiologists. **(d)** It deals with both the classification and identification of bacteria. **(e)** It describes all established genera and species of bacteria.

EUBACTERIA AND
ARCHAEOBACTERIA

2 The cell walls of _____ (eubacteria, archaeobacteria) contain peptidoglycan made of muramic acid and D-amino acids, whereas the cell

walls of _____ (eubacteria, archaeobacteria) consist of proteins or polysaccharides.

3 The phospholipids of archaeobacteria do not contain long-chain fatty acids; instead, they contain long-chain alcohols called **(a)** mycolic acids; **(b)** phenols; **(c)** phytanols; **(d)** butanols; **(e)** pentanols.

THE EUBACTERIA

4 The three major subgroups of the eubacteria are the

_____ eubacteria, the _____

eubacteria, and the eubacteria that lack a(n) _____.

5 Gram-negative eubacteria have a complex cell wall consisting of an outer

_____ and an underlying thin rigid layer of

_____.

6 Which *three* of the following characteristics are possessed by spirochetes? **(a)** a helical shape; **(b)** flagella that extend outward from the cell into the surrounding medium; **(c)** cell rigidity; **(d)** periplasmic flagella; **(e)** flexible cells.

7 Bacteria that derive nourishment from a *living host* are called **(a)** saprophytes; **(b)** pathogens; **(c)** free-living; **(d)** parasites; **(e)** microbes.

8 Bacteria that derive nourishment from *inanimate organic matter* are called **(a)** saprophytes; **(b)** pathogens; **(c)** free-living; **(d)** parasites; **(e)** microbes.

9 Spirochetes are best seen by _____ microscopy.

10 Although spirilla have a helical shape, they differ from spirochetes in that the cells

are _____ and have ordinary bacterial flagella rather than

_____ flagella.

11 The following apply to eubacteria of the groups *aerobic or microaerophilic curved rods* and *aerobic rods and cocci*. Match the description on the right with the name on the left.

_____ *Lampropedia*

_____ *Spirosoma*

_____ *Agrobacterium*

_____ *Neisseria*

_____ *Azospirillum*

_____ *Zoogloea*

_____ *Bdellovibrio*

_____ *Acetobacter*

(a) Vibrioid bacteria that can invade and destroy other bacteria
(b) Vibrioid bacteria that fix atmospheric nitrogen and grow within the roots of corn and wheat
(c) Ring formers
(d) Slime-forming rods noted for their ability to oxidize the organic substances in sewage
(e) Aerobic rods that cause tumors in plants
(f) Bacteria used to make vinegar
(g) Aerobic diplococci that live on the mucous membranes of humans and animals
(h) Cocci that occur in large, flat sheets

12 The following apply to eubacteria of the groups *facultatively anaerobic rods, anaerobes,* and *rickettsias and chlamydias*. Match the description on the right with the name on the left.

(a) The family that contains *E. coli* and other intestinal rods

_____ *Erwinia*

_____ *Desulfovibrio*

_____ *Chlamydia*

_____ *Enterobacteriaceae*

_____ *Vibrio*

_____ *Shigella*

_____ *Bacteroides fragilis*

_____ *Rickettsia*

(b) Facultatively anaerobic rods that cause bacillary dysentery

(c) Facultatively anaerobic rods that cause plant diseases

(d) Genus that contains the bacterium that causes cholera

(e) Vibrioid cells that form large amounts of hydrogen sulfide

(f) The most common anaerobic species isolated from human soft-tissue infections

(g) Parasitic bacteria that reproduce by binary fission and are transmitted to humans by lice, fleas, ticks, or mites

(h) Parasitic bacteria that have a complex developmental cycle

13 The terms "purple" and "green" bacteria refer to _____ phototrophic bacteria.

14 Anoxygenic phototrophic bacteria can convert the energy of light into chemical energy by means of a pigment called _____.

15 The color of the "purple" bacteria and the "green" bacteria is due to water-insoluble pigments called _____.

16 Narrow living extensions of a bacterial cell, such as those formed by *Rhodomicrobium* cells, are called **(a)** stalks; **(b)** flagella; **(c)** prosthecae; **(d)** sheaths; **(e)** carotenoids.

17 Cyanobacteria resemble green plants in that they evolve _____ as an end product of their metabolism.

18 Cyanobacteria contain the photoactive pigment _____; they also contain water-soluble protein pigments called _____, which impart a bluish-green hue to the organisms.

19 In filamentous cyanobacteria, nitrogen fixation occurs in specialized cells called _____.

20 The following apply to eubacteria of the groups *gliding bacteria, sheathed bacteria,* and *budding and appendaged bacteria*. Match the description on the right with the name on the left.

(a) This is left behind as myxobacters glide across moist surfaces

_____ sheath

_____ myxospores

_____ slime

_____ stalk

(b) Desiccation-resistant cells that are components of the fruiting bodies of myxobacters

(c) The tubular structure that encloses a chain of *Sphaerotilus* cells

(d) A nonliving tubular or ribbonlike appendage such as produced by the *Blastocaulis/Planctomyces* group

21 *Nitrosomonas* species obtain energy by oxidizing ammonia to

_____ , whereas *Nitrobacter* species obtain energy by oxi-

dizing nitrite to _____ .

22 *Thiobacillus* and *Thiospira* species obtain energy by oxidizing sulfur compounds such as hydrogen sulfide, thiosulfate, or sulfite to **(a)** dimethyl sulfoxide; **(b)** sulfathiazole; **(c)** sulfoniazide; **(d)** sulfate; **(e)** sulfanilic acid.

23 The cell walls of Gram-positive eubacteria are much

_____ than those of Gram-negative eubacteria and they

lack an outer _____ .

24 Which one of the following best describes the arrangement of the cells of *Staphylococcus*? **(a)** chains; **(b)** pairs; **(c)** cubical packets of four; **(d)** irregular clusters; **(e)** singles.

25 *Deinococcus* is especially noted for its resistance to **(a)** heat; **(b)** freezing; **(c)** nonpolar solvents; **(d)** drying; **(e)** radiation.

26 A species of *Streptococcus* that is widely used in the manufacture of fermented

milk products such as cheese is *S.* _____ .

27 Most endospore formers are rod-shaped bacteria except for the genus

_____ , in which the cells are cocci.

28 The endospore-forming bacterial species that is used to kill Japanese beetle larvae

in soil is called _____ .

29 The genera _____ and _____
contain anaerobic endospore formers.

30 The following apply to eubacteria of the groups *regularly shaped rods, irregularly shaped rods,* and *actinomycetes.* Match the description on the right with the name on the left.

_____ *Arthrobacter*

_____ sporangiospores

_____ *Listeria*

_____ mycelium

_____ *Corynebacterium*

_____ *Mycobacterium*

_____ conidiospores

_____ *Lactobacillus*

_____ *Nocardia*

_____ *Streptomyces*

(a) A genus of regularly shaped rods, some of which are used in the manufacture of yogurt and cheese
(b) A genus of regularly shaped rods that may cause stillbirth or abortion
(c) Soil bacteria that have a rod-coccus cycle
(d) Genus of irregularly shaped rods to which the bacterium that causes diphtheria belongs
(e) Bacteria that stain acid-fast
(f) Actinomycete genus in which reproduction occurs mainly by hyphal fragmentation
(g) Actinomycete spores that are enclosed within a sac
(h) Actinomycete spores that are not enclosed within a sac
(i) A mat of branching hyphae
(j) Organisms especially noted for their ability to make antibiotics

31 The only outer boundary of a mycoplasma cell is the **(a)** capsule; **(b)** outer membrane of the cell wall; **(c)** cytoplasmic membrane; **(d)** lipopolysaccharide layer; **(e)** protein layer.

32 Because mycoplasmas do not have cell walls, they are not inhibited by even very high levels of the antibiotic _____ .

33 The cholesterol that occurs in the cytoplasmic membrane of some mycoplasmas is provided by the _____ in the culture medium.

34 Most mycoplasmas inhabit **(a)** soil; **(b)** freshwater habitats; **(c)** milk and dairy products; **(d)** mucous membranes of humans or animals; **(e)** marine habitats.

35 Which *two* of the following features apply to spiroplasmas? **(a)** They are pathogenic but do not cause disease. **(b)** They are motile but lack flagella. **(c)** They are helical but lack a cell wall. **(d)** They are phototrophic but have no chlorophyll. **(e)** They feed on other bacteria.

THE ARCHAEOBACTERIA

36 Which *two* of the following statements apply to methanogens? **(a)** They are aerobes or facultative anaerobes. **(b)** Some are Gram-positive and others are Gram-negative. **(c)** They are found in anaerobic environments such as the rumen of cattle. **(d)** They live near the surface of lakes and ponds. **(e)** Some species are phototrophic.

37 Halobacteria cannot grow with less than 15% _____ .

38 Some halobacteria possess a photoactive purple pigment called

_____ .

39 Thermoplasmas resemble mycoplasmas in that they **(a)** grow at very high temperatures; **(b)** prefer very acidic environments; **(c)** lack a cell wall; **(d)** are pathogenic for animals or plants; **(e)** produce conidiospores.

40 With regard to their relationship to oxygen, the genus *Sulfolobus* is

_____ and the genus *Thermoproteus* is

_____ .

REVIEW QUESTIONS

1 Describe the kinds of bacteria that are associated with the following characteristics: **(a)** absence of a cell wall, **(b)** pathogenicity for plants, **(c)** photoactive pigments, **(d)** formation of prosthecae, **(e)** production of methane gas, **(f)** ability to fix nitrogen.

2 What is the outstanding morphological feature of each of the following bacteria? **(a)** *Sphaerotilus,* **(b)** *Arthrobacter,* **(c)** *Mycobacterium,* **(d)** *Caulobacter,* **(e)** *Rhodomicrobium.*

3 What is the outstanding physiological feature of each of the following bacteria? **(a)** *Methanobacterium,* **(b)** *Thiospira,* **(c)** *Rhizobium,* **(d)** *Nitrobacter,* **(e)** *Desulfovibrio,* **(f)** cyanobacteria.

4 What hosts do the following bacteria attack? **(a)** *Salmonella,* **(b)** *Erwinia,* **(c)** *Bdellovibrio,* and **(d)** *Bacillus popilliae.*

5 What differences in modes of reproduction occur between *Caulobacter, Hyphomicrobium, Nocardia,* and *Streptomyces?*

6 In what type of environment would you be most likely to find **(a)** *Cristispira,* **(b)** *Thermus,* **(c)** *Neisseria,* **(d)** *Escherichia,* **(e)** myxobacters, **(f)** methanogens, **(g)** *Streptomyces,* **(h)** halobacteria?

DISCUSSION QUESTIONS

1 If you received a bacterial isolate about which you had no prior information, what general approach would you use to identify it? What *primary* characteristics would you determine to help you decide what major group and subgroup the isolate belonged to? What kinds of characteristics would help you subsequently to identify its genus and species?

2 Suppose you were given a mixture of the following organisms: *Thermus aquaticus, Oscillatoria limosa, Clostridium sporogenes, Deinococcus radiodurans, Halobacterium halobium,* and *Thiobacillus thiooxidans.* What general types of treatments, culture conditions, or media could you use that would allow you to grow each organism from this mixture *without growing any of the other organisms?* (*Hint:* You might be able to either kill or suppress all the other organisms, or you might provide either a medium or a culture condition that would allow only the desired organism to grow.)

3 Answer question 2 but for the following mixture of bacteria: *Bacillus cereus, Mycoplasma pneumoniae, Nitrosomonas europea, Azotobacter chroococcum, Sulfolobus acidocaldarius,* and *Xanthomonas campestris.*

10

The Major Groups of Eucaryotic Microorganisms: Fungi, Algae, and Protozoa

OBJECTIVES

After reading this chapter you should be able to

1 List the features that characterize each main group of eucaryotic microorganisms (the fungi, the algae, and the protozoa).

2 Give the criteria used for the classification schemes of fungi, algae, and protozoa.

3 Outline the classification schemes of the fungi, the algae, and the protozoa.

4 Discuss some species of special interest in each group of eucaryotic microorganisms.

5 Diagram the life cycles of representative eucaryotic microorganisms.

OVERVIEW

Like the procaryotic microorganisms, the eucaryotic microorganisms have a vast variety of forms and cellular processes. They can be divided into three major groups: the *fungi,* the *algae,* and the *protozoa.* There are literally thousands of species of eucaryotic microbes. Mycologists, phycologists, and protozoologists have attempted to make order out of this apparent chaos (which can also be called diversity). In doing so, they have constructed specific classification schemes for their respective groups of microbes. These schemes will help you comprehend the diverse forms of the eucaryotic microorganisms, which are the subject of this chapter. Included are representatives from these three major groups. You will see that classification of a particular organism into one category does not necessarily mean that that organism will remain there forever. As a whole, the eucaryotic microorganisms are fascinating for their complex life cycles, their changeable morphology, their alternate methods of reproduction, their effects both as disease-causing microbes and commercially valuable resources, and their role in the environment.

CLASSIFICATION OF THE FUNGI

Fungi are nonphotosynthetic eucaryotic organisms. With some notable exceptions, fungi have cell walls—unlike animal cells. They obtain their food by absorption and do not have chlorophyll. While many fungi are unicellular, some are multicellular and macroscopic. As a group, fungi form spores, which are dispersed by air currents. Some of the more primitive fungi are amoeboid, while others move by flagellation.

The classification of fungi is based primarily on the following criteria:

1 Characteristics of the sexual spores and fruiting bodies present during the sexual stages of their life cycles
2 Nature of their life cycles
3 Morphological characteristics of their vegetative mycelia or cells

However, many fungi produce sexual spores and fruiting bodies only under certain environmental conditions. Those that have known sexual stages are called *perfect fungi;* those that do not are called *imperfect fungi.* In fact, the imperfect fungi are arbitrarily classified and provisionally placed in a special class called *Deuteromycetes.* If their sexual stages are later found, then these fungi are reclassified among the other classes and given new names. TABLE 10.1 contains examples of reclassified imperfect fungi.

Mycologists divide the kingdom Fungi into three major groups: the *slime molds*, the *flagellated lower fungi*, and the *terrestrial fungi*.

TABLE 10.1
Several Genera of Reclassified Members of Imperfect Fungi (Class Deuteromycetes)

Imperfect genus name	Reclassified to class	Perfect genus name*
Aspergillus	Ascomycetes	Sartorya, Eurotium, Emericella
Blastomyces	Ascomycetes	Ajellomyces
Candida	Ascomycetes	Pichia
Cryptococcus	Basidiomycetes	Filobasidiella
Histoplasma	Ascomycetes	Emmonsiella, Gymnoascus
Microsporum	Ascomycetes	Nannizia
Penicillium	Ascomycetes	Talaromyces, Carpenteles
Trichophyton	Ascomycetes	Arthroderma

*Depending on the species.

NOTE: It is difficult to change familiar names. Most microbiologists continue to use the imperfect names out of habit.

The Slime Molds

The slime molds are a biological and taxonomic enigma because they are neither typical fungi nor typical protozoa. During one of their growth stages, they are protozoanlike because they lack cell walls, have amoeboid movement, and ingest particulate nutrients. During their propagative stage they form fruiting bodies and sporangia bearing walled spores like the typical fungi. Traditionally, the slime molds have been classified with the fungi.

There are two groups of slime molds: the *cellular slime molds* and the *acellular slime molds* [TABLE 10.2].

Cellular Slime Molds. During the vegetative (growth) stage, the cellular slime molds are composed of protozoanlike cells; that is, they exist as amoebas, or single

TABLE 10.2
Major Distinguishing Characteristics of the Slime Molds (Division Gymnomycota)

Class	Characteristics	Representative species
Cellular slime molds (Acrasiomycetes)	Amoeboid cells that feed on bacteria and aggregate to form a stalked fruiting body (sporocarp) that bears spores	Dictyostelium discoideum
Acellular slime molds (Myxomycetes)	Multicellular, wall-less plasmodium, which transforms into highly organized sporangia bearing sporangiospores	Physarum polycephalum

cells of irregular and constantly changing shapes. They move and feed heterotrophically by projection of temporary, finger-shaped pseudopodia ("false feet") from their surfaces. They live in fresh water, in damp soil, and on rotting vegetation, especially on fallen logs. The individual protozoanlike cells feed on bacteria.

Under adverse environmental conditions, such as the depletion of food, they aggregate into a slimy mass forming many **pseudoplasmodia.** A *plasmodium* (plural, *plasmodia*) is a multinucleate, amoeboid mass of protoplasm bounded by a cytoplasmic membrane, without definite size or shape. The plasmodia of the cellular slime molds are called *pseudo*plasmodia because the amoebas composing them retain their own cell membranes.

These pseudoplasmodia, wrapped in a slimy sheath, become *slugs* that can migrate and eventually transform into spore-forming fruiting bodies. The scattered spores germinate into amoebas, completing the cycle. FIGURE 10.1 shows the life cycle of a typical cellular slime mold, *Dictyostelium discoideum.*

Acellular Slime Molds. The acellular slime molds (Myxomycetes) are distinguished from the cellular slime molds because the plasmodium of acellular slime molds is not cellular—the nuclei are not separated by cell membranes into individual cells. Therefore, acellular slime molds exist as a *true* plasmodium, or a mass of protoplasm with many nuclei. Like the cellular slime molds, they pass through a vegetative amoeboid stage in which they feed by phagocytosis. In the sporulation stage, they form fruiting structures with stalks that look like stalks of other fungi. However, the acellular slime molds are sexually far more advanced than the cellular slime molds. They show alternation of haploid (having one of each type of chromosome) and diploid (having two of each type of chromosome) generations [FIGURE 10.2], a property not found in the cellular slime molds.

During the growth cycle of acellular slime molds, haploid cells with two flagella are formed. These cells, called **swarm cells,** can readily change into amoeboid cells called **myxamoebas.** Myxamoebas can change just as readily into swarm cells. Both cell types can differentiate into opposite mating types. Either two myxamoebas or two swarm cells can fuse to form a diploid zygote, which divides repeatedly by mitosis to form a plasmodium.

When the environment becomes drier, the plasmodial protoplasm may become concentrated into mounds, from which stalked sporangia grow. Meiosis takes place inside the maturing spores, leading to the haploid cells.

Plasmodia feed by engulfing decaying vegetation. On the other hand, swarm cells and myxamoebas feed on bacteria and absorb dissolved nutrients. About 400 to 500 species of acellular slime molds are known. Characteristics that distinguish between them include the color, shape, and size of the fruiting structure, the presence of a stalk, and the presence of granules on or in the fruiting body.

The Flagellated Lower Fungi

The flagellated lower fungi include all fungi, other than the slime molds, that typically produce flagellated cells at some stage of their life cycle. They also are characterized by an absorptive mode of nutrition—in contrast to the phagotrophic (particle-ingesting) mode exhibited by the slime molds. The great majority of these fungi are filamentous, producing a coenocytic mycelium. But many are unicellular or unicellular with rhizoids. Sexual reproduction within the group is by various means; asexual reproduction is by zoospores.

There are four major groups of the flagellated lower fungi: **Chytridiomycetes, Hyphochytridiomycetes, Plasmodiophoromycetes,** and **Oomycetes.** Their distinguishing features are shown in TABLE 10.3.

Chytridiomycetes. The chytrids are classified together as a group because they all produce motile cells possessing a single, *posteriorly* positioned flagellum of the *whiplash* type. (There are two types of flagella in the fungi—the whiplash and the tinsel. The tinsel flagellum is a feathery structure with lateral hairlike projections on all sides along its entire length; such projections are absent in the whiplash flagellum.)

These fungi are parasitic or saprophytic microorganisms that live in soil or in fresh water. They grow and feed by means of coenocytic hyphae that penetrate into living hosts or dead organic debris. The simplest chytrids grow and develop entirely within the cells of the host. The more complex chytrids produce reproductive structures on the host surface, but the vegetative and feeding parts of the thallus penetrate deeply into the host tissues. The cell walls of the chytrids are made of chitin; some contain cellulose as well.

Some chytrids are unicellular. They have a thallus that is a simple sphere, although some of these species also produce a **rhizomycelium** (a system of branched hyphae that emerge from the posterior of the thallus; FIGURE 10.3). Other chytrids have well-developed branching mycelia. Many of them have complex life cycles with several alternative developmental pathways. This diversity is not unusual, given the complex and varied group of fungi classified as chytrids.

Hyphochytrids. Like the chytrids, the hyphochytrids live in fresh water and in soil and are parasitic or saprophytic. However, unlike the chytrids, they are motile by

FIGURE 10.1

[A] Life cycle of the cellular slime mold *Dictyostelium discoideum*. Amoebas migrate into aggregation centers, becoming associated end to end in chains. They go through several multicellular stages to form a fruiting body. The spores disperse to find a suitable environment before they germinate to form amoebas which begin the life cycle anew.

[B] Photomicrographs illustrating some of the stages of the life cycle. [1] Stage of aggregating amoebas. [2] Aggregation stage. [3] Pseudoplasmodium (*pseudo-* because constituent cells retain their cell membranes) in a well-advanced stage, composed of many amoebas. [4] Pseudoplasmodium becomes slugs and can migrate. [5] Further slug stage. [6] Button stage: early stage of fruiting-body formation with the stalk just beginning to form. [7] Further stage of fruiting-body formation. [8, 9, 10] Sequential stages in the formation of a fruiting body. [11] Spores released from fruiting body; these will germinate to form amoebas to complete the life cycle.

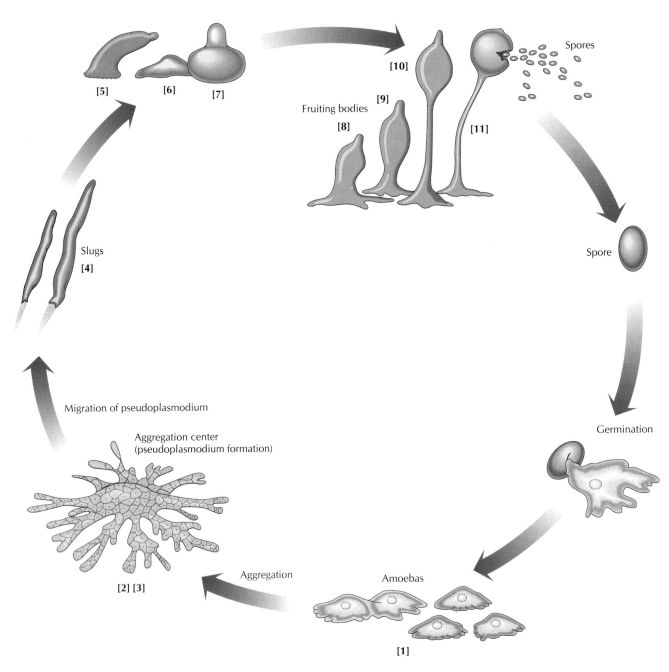

[A]

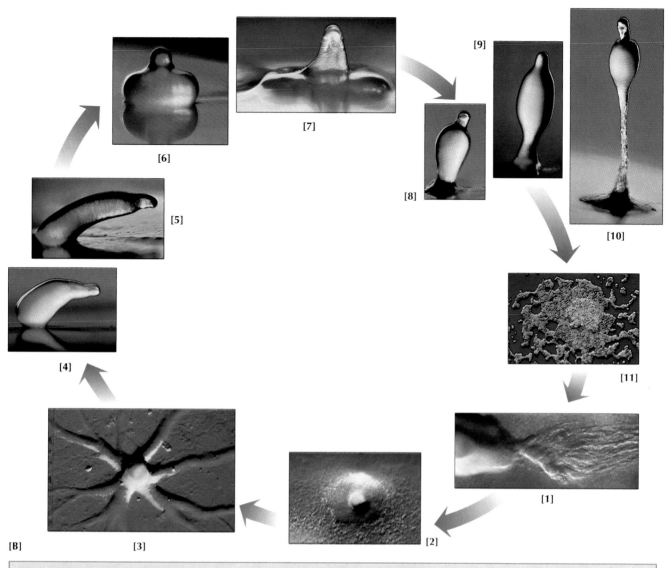

[6] [7] [9] [8] [10] [5] [4] [B] [3] [2] [11] [1]

T A B L E 10.3
Major Distinguishing Characteristics of the Flagellated Lower Fungi (Division Mastigomycota)

Class	Characteristics	Representative species
	Whiplash flagellum Tinsel flagellum	
Chytridiomycetes	Motile cells bearing a single, posteriorly positioned whiplash-type flagellum	*Allomyces macrogynus*
Hyphochytridiomycetes	Motile cells bearing a single, anteriorly positioned tinsel-type, or feathery, flagellum	*Rhizidiomyces arbuscula*, *Hyphochytrium catenoides*
Plasmodiophoromycetes	Obligate parasites on higher plants; vegetative stage a plasmodium; motile cells with two unequal anterior whiplash flagella	*Plasmodiophora brassicae*
Oomycetes	Motile cells with two laterally inserted flagella, one tinsel and anteriorly directed, the other whiplash and posteriorly directed	*Saprolegnia ferax*

FIGURE 10.2
Life cycle of a typical myxomycete, or an acellular slime mold. **[1]** Mature haploid spore;
[2] germinating spore; **[3]** myxamoebas; **[3a]** swarm cells; **[4]** fusing myxamoebas;
[4a] plasmogamy; **[5]** young zygote; **[6]** young plasmodium; **[7]** mature plasmodium;
[8] sclerotium; **[9]** sporulation—sporangial initials; **[10]** young, premeiotic sporangium with
spores; and **[11]** mature, postmeiotic sporangium. Photomicrographs illustrate some stages
in the life cycle of acellular slime molds.

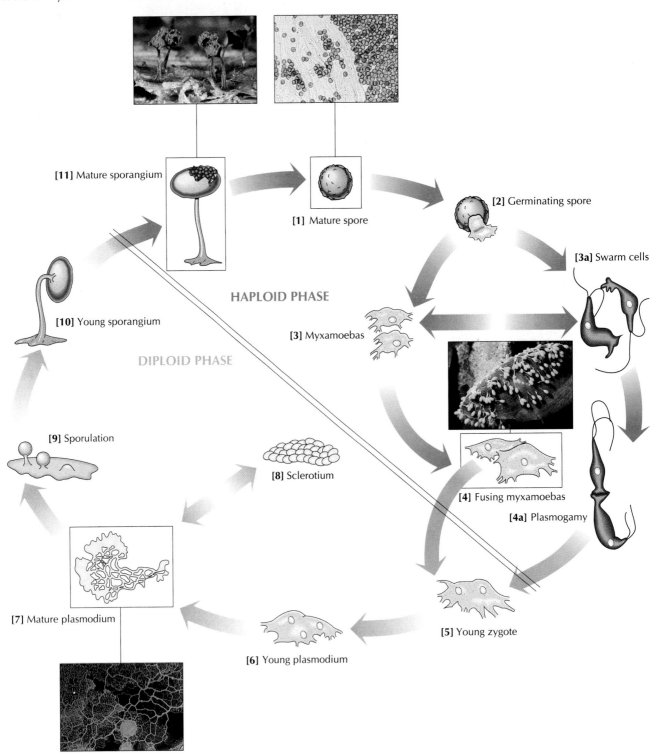

FIGURE 10.3

[A] Scanning electron micrograph of a typical unicellular chytrid, *Chytridium olla*, displaying an extensive rhizoidal system. [B] The asexual life cycle of a chytrid. Zoospores released into the water swim for various periods of time and then encyst. They settle down on a solid surface and eventually germinate, forming new sporangia and rhizoids (or functioning as contributing sexual thalli, not shown here). As development continues, a branching system of rhizoids (rhizomycelium) forms to anchor the fungus to the surface. Growth results in the formation of a spherical zoosporangium that cleaves internally to produce many progeny zoospores. The zoospores either swim through pores in the zoosporangium, or the zoosporangium ruptures to release the zoospores.

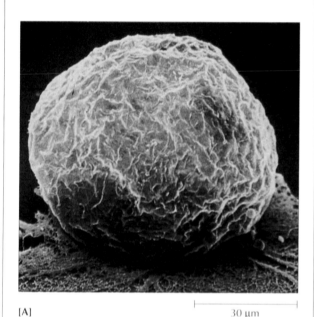

[A]   30 μm

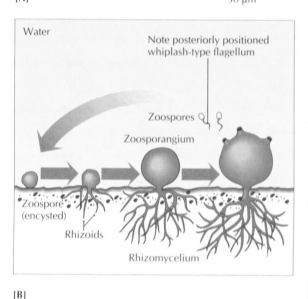

[B]

means of a single *anteriorly* positioned flagellum of the *tinsel* type. All hyphochytrids produce zoospores that emerge through discharge tubes from the zoosporangium. The zoospores swim to new hosts or food substances. Each zoospore can develop into a thallus. All reproduction is asexual, by means of zoospores; no sexual processes are known for this group of microbes.

Plasmodiophoromycetes. The plasmodiophoromycetes are all heterotrophic microorganisms and obligate parasites. Most species grow within vascular plants, algae, and other fungi, where they usually cause an abnormal enlargement of the host cells called **hypertrophy.** They also cause an abnormal multiplication of host cells called **hyperplasia.** Furthermore, since the feeding stage of plasmodiophoromycetes is a multinucleate plasmodium that lacks cell walls, these microorganisms have been called the *endoparasitic slime molds*.

These organisms form zoospores with two anterior whiplash flagella. But the details of their general life cycle are still not entirely understood. Cysts, zoospores, plasmodia, and zoosporangia appear to be present in most species. Most of these microbes live as benign parasites and do no obvious damage to their hosts. However, there are two species of economic importance: *Plasmodiophora brassicae* is the widespread cause of clubroot or finger-and-toe disease of cabbage and related plants, and *Spongospora subterranea* is the cause of powdery scab of potatoes.

Oomycetes. Unlike the other flagellated lower fungi, the oomycetes are usually filamentous, consisting of a coenocytic mycelium. The oomycetes are saprophytic or parasitic. Those with the simplest structure are aquatic fungi either free-living or parasitic on algae, small animals, and other forms of aquatic life. They feed by extending coenocytic hyphae into their host tissues, where they release digestive enzymes and absorb the resulting nutrients. The most complex oomycetes are terrestrial plant parasites that pass their entire life history in the host and depend on air currents to disperse their spores. However, even in these oomycetes, the production of biflagellated zoospores is common; each zoospore bears one whiplash and one tinsel flagellum.

A well-known genus is *Saprolegnia*, which contains the fungi more commonly known as the *water molds*. Common in soil and fresh water, they are saprophytic on plant and animal remains. However, a number of species such as *S. ferax* and *S. parasitica* have been implicated in diseases of fish and their eggs. *Saprolegnia parasitica* causes severe epidemics among fish in the natural environment. It is also commonly seen in freshwater aquariums as a white fuzz on the fins of fish. The life cycle of *Saprolegnia* is illustrated in FIGURE 10.4.

FIGURE 10.4

Life cycle of *Saprolegnia*. The somatic portion of the organism consists of two types of hyphae: the rhizoidal hyphae, which enter the substratum and serve to anchor the organism and to absorb nutrients, and the branched (somatic) hyphae, on which the reproductive organs are formed. Elongated, tapering sporangia are formed at the tips (apex) of somatic hyphae; their nuclei differentiate into zoospores. An opening develops at the tip of the sporangium, and the pear-shaped primary zoospores escape into the surrounding aqueous environment. They swim from a minute to over an hour, then withdraw their flagella and encyst. The cyst, after a period of rest (2 to 3 hours, depending on the species), germinates to release a further, bean-shaped secondary zoospore. The secondary zoospore may swim vigorously for several hours before encysting again. The encysted spore now germinates by sending out a germ tube that develops into a hypha, forming a new colony. When conditions are favorable for sexual reproduction, the somatic hyphae give rise to oogonia and antheridia. Within the oogonium, fertilization gives rise to diploid oospores. Prior to germination, oospores undergo meiosis so that the hyphae generated from the oospores are haploid.

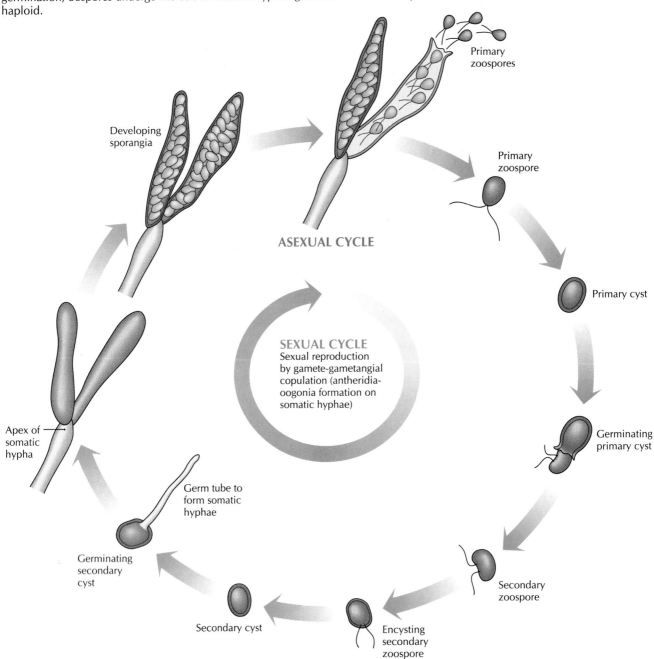

TABLE 10.4

Major Distinguishing Characteristics of the Terrestrial Fungi (Division Amastigomycota)

Class	Characteristics	Representative species
Zygomycetes	Sexual reproduction by gametangial fusion; zygote transformed into a thick-walled zygospore; vegetative reproduction by means of sporangiospores within a sporangium	*Rhizopus stolonifer, Phycomyces blakesleanus, Mucor rouxii*
Ascomycetes	Sexual spores produced endogenously in a saclike ascus typically produced in a well-differentiated ascocarp; vegetative reproduction by conidia	*Saccharomyces cerevisiae, Neurospora crassa*
Basidiomycetes	Sexual spores produced exogenously on clublike cells called *basidia;* basidia formed on well-differentiated basidiocarps	*Agaricus bisporus*
Deuteromycetes	Sexual reproduction unknown; vegetative reproduction by conidia arising from well-defined conidiogenous cells	*Candida albicans, Trichophyton rubra*

Another important species of the oomycetes is *Phytophthora infestans*, which causes the late blight disease of potatoes. During the nineteenth century, this fungus destroyed entire potato crops in Germany and Ireland and forced mass migrations of people from those countries to North America.

The Terrestrial Fungi

The terrestrial fungi are the most familiar species among the fungi. This commonly found group includes the yeasts, common molds, bracket fungi, mildews, cup fungi, rusts, smuts, puffballs, and mushrooms. All are characterized by an absorptive type of nutrition, and with the exception of the yeasts (which are generally unicellular), most produce a well-developed mycelium consisting of septate or coenocytic hyphae. *Motile cells are completely absent in the terrestrial fungi.* Asexual reproduction is by means of budding, fragmentation, sporangiospores, or conidia. Sexual reproduction within this group culminates with the production of zygospores, ascospores, or basidiospores.

There are four major groups of terrestrial fungi: *Zygomycetes, Ascomycetes, Basidiomycetes,* and *Deuteromycetes.* Their primary distinguishing characteristics are shown in TABLE 10.4.

Zygomycetes. The zygomycetes are distinguished by their coenocytic hyphae, which lack crosswalls except for those between reproductive structures and the rest of the hyphal filament. They also are known for the production of a thick-walled sexual spore called a **zygospore.** Asexual reproduction is typically by means of sporangio-

spores that develop within sporangia, which rupture when mature. FIGURE 10.5 shows the life cycle of a typical zygomycete, *Rhizopus stolonifer*, the common black bread mold.

There are about 600 species of zygomycete fungi found worldwide. Many are saprophytic, living on decaying vegetation; some are parasites, living on animals and even fungi (including other zygomycetes). Some zygomycetes have been used to produce valuable commercial products—soy sauce, steroids for contraceptives and anti-inflammatory drugs, and organic acids.

Ascomycetes. Along with the basidiomycetes (discussed later in this section), the ascomycetes are called the *higher fungi*, mainly because they are considerably more complex in structure than other fungi. Well-known examples of the ascomycetes are the ascus-forming mildews, the cup fungi, and the truffles. Diverse and economically important, this large group of fungi comprises tens of thousands of species.

Members of the ascomycetes include yeastlike, mycelial, and dimorphic forms. When present, the mycelium is septate and its cells may contain one or more nuclei. Ascomycetes are distinguished from other fungi by the production of sexual spores called **ascospores** enclosed in **asci** (singular, **ascus**). Typically there are eight ascospores in each ascus. But, depending on the species, anywhere from two to any multiple of eight have been observed. With relatively few exceptions, ascomycetes produce their asci within *sexual* fruiting bodies called **ascocarps.** There are several types of ascocarps, each of which is characteristic of a species. For instance, the *perithecium* type is formed by the common pink bread mold, *Neurospora crassa*. FIGURE 10.6A provides a mi-

FIGURE 10.5

Life cycle of the common black bread mold *Rhizopus stolonifer*. Upon rupture of the sporangial wall, sporangiospores are released. A sporangiospore germinates to develop into a mycelial thallus, rhizoids penetrate into the medium, and sporangiophores develop bearing sporangia. This completes the asexual portion of the life cycle. Sexual reproduction requires two sexually compatible mating types (+ and –). When they come into contact with one another, copulating branches called *progametangia* are formed. They soon fuse, the two protoplasts mix (through *plasmogamy*) and the + and – nuclei also fuse (through *karyogamy*) to form many zygote nuclei. The structure containing the nuclei becomes black and warty, forming the mature, diploid *zygospore*, which lies dormant for 1 to 3 or more months. The zygospore germinates to form a new haploid organism, meiosis having taken place during the germination process.

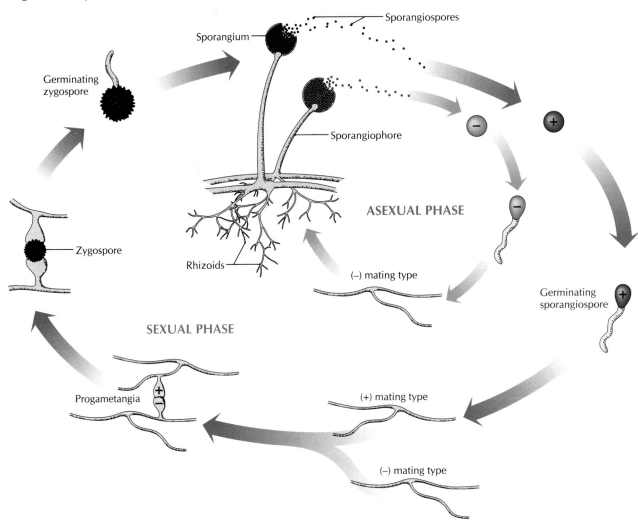

croscopic view of an ascocarp in the ascomycete *Ceratocystis fimbriata*.

The asexual spores (conidia) of the mycelial ascomycetes are produced at the tips of hyphae and are often in chains. Depending on the species, they may be naked or they may be produced inside *asexual* fruiting bodies, such as the *pycnidium* of *Dothiorella ribis* [FIGURE 10.7A] or the *acervulus* of *Marsonina juglandis* [FIGURE 10.7B]. Conidia, like ascospores, are dispersed by wind, water, insects, or animals.

Ascomycetes play an important ecological role in breaking down resistant plant and animal molecules such as cellulose, lignin, and collagen. Pathogenic ascomycetes have decimated such trees as the chestnut and the elm in North America. However, some ascomycetes form beneficial **mycorrhizal** (fungus and plant root) associations with plants. The fungal partner associates only with a particular species of plant. The partnership is a mutualistic one; both benefit because there is a two-way nutrient transfer. Indeed, in many cases there is an ab-

FIGURE 10.6

One type of ascocarp of the ascomycetes that carry ascospores: the perithecium. [A] Longitudinal section of a perithecium of *Ceratocystis fimbriata* seen by scanning electron microscopy. The perithecial wall (W) and hyphae (H) are clearly seen. Other structures seen are ascospores (A) within the perithecial cavity and conidiophores (arrows), which are specialized aerial conidia-bearing hyphae. [B] Diagrammatic representation of a perithecium.

FIGURE 10.7

Asexual fruiting bodies bearing conidia. [A] Section of a pycnidium of *Dothiorella ribis* in apple bark tissue, showing conidia compacted in the mucilaginous matrix. [B] Cross section of a subepidermal acervulus of *Marsonina juglandis* in black walnut leaf. Mature (M) and immature (arrows) conidia are exhibited. The host epidermis (E) is clearly seen. [C] Diagrammatic representation of a pycnidium and an acervulus.

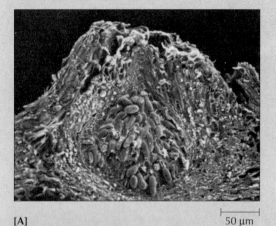

[A]   50 μm

[B]   10 μm

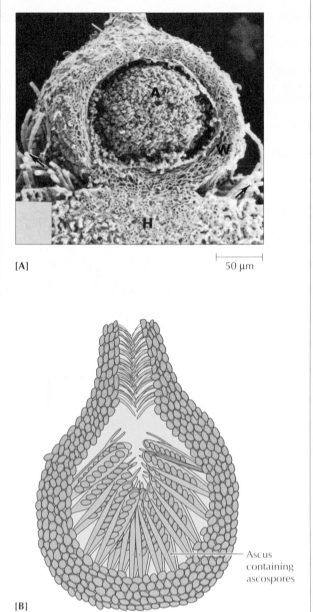

[A]   50 μm

Ascus
containing
ascospores

[B]

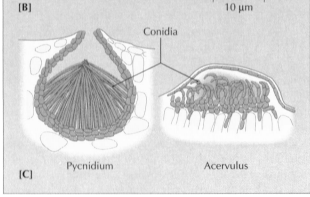

Conidia

Pycnidium   Acervulus

[C]

solute dependence of one or both partners on the association for survival. For instance, most orchids are incapable of germinating and developing unless invaded by a mycorrhizal fungus.

The ascomycete *Claviceps purpurea* produces hallucinogenic alkaloids, including the precursors of LSD, when it infects rye and other cereal grains. This infection of grain is called **ergot**, and eating grains contaminated

FIGURE 10.8

Life cycle of *Neurospora* sp. The female element is represented by the *protoperithecium*. The male elements are the conidia, which can supply nuclei to a protoperithecium. This results in the formation of asci that bear haploid ascospores generated by sexual fusion of nuclei from two different mating strains. *Neurospora* may also reproduce asexually by means of conidia.

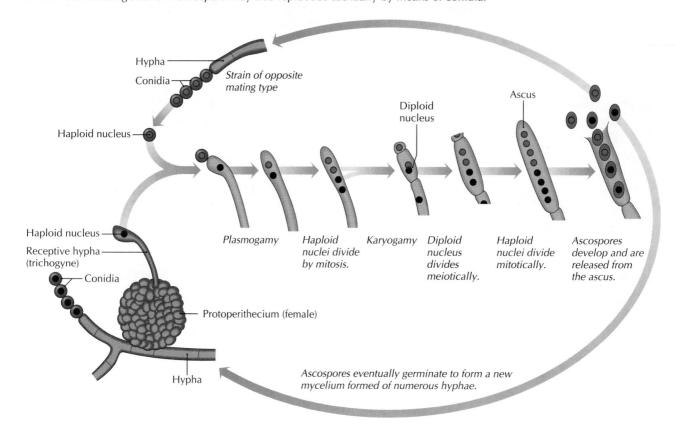

with it causes bizarre behavior, spontaneous abortion, or even death in humans and other animals. This pathological condition is called *ergotism*. Many animal diseases are caused by ascomycetes; most of the dimorphic ascomycetes produce systemic diseases of animals.

The genus *Neurospora* became one of the most important organisms in genetic research when it was used by George Beadle and Edward Tatum in the early 1940s as an experimental model. The two researchers used the fungus to develop their "one gene–one enzyme" hypothesis of gene action, for which they received the Nobel Prize in 1958. This work initiated the era of molecular biology. *Neurospora* is particularly useful for genetic work because, within each ascus, the four products of meiosis divide once to form eight cells that remain fixed in a row in the order in which they were formed. Each ascospore in an ascus can be removed in order and its genetic composition can be determined. This reveals the behavior of chromosomes during a single meiosis and the position of genes on those chromosomes. The life cycle of *Neurospora* is shown in FIGURE 10.8.

Morphologically, *Neurospora* produces a loose network of long strands of septate and aerial hyphae. Conidia, usually oval and pink in color, form branched chains at the tips of the aerial hyphae. Some *Neurospora* species are used in industrial fermentations, and some are responsible for food spoilage, particularly spoilage of starchy food.

Probably the best known of the ascomycetes are the yeasts. Typical of the budding yeasts is *Saccharomyces cerevisiae*. Strains of this species are used in the fermentation process to make alcoholic beverages. In the presence of oxygen, yeasts oxidize sugars to carbon dioxide, seen as "gas bubbles" in bread. Brewers' and bakers' yeasts have been used for thousands of years. Thus *S. cerevisiae* is a yeast of great and longstanding economic importance.

Cells of *S. cerevisiae* are elliptical, measuring about 6 to 8 by 5 μm [FIGURE 10.9A]. They reproduce asexually by budding. During budding, the nucleus divides by constriction and a portion of it enters the bud along with other organelles. The cytoplasmic connection is closed by the synthesis of new cell-wall material. Other yeasts

FIGURE 10.9

[A] The yeast *Saccharomyces cerevisiae* as seen by dark-field microscopy. Note that some cells are in the process of budding. [B] Scanning electron micrograph of *Schizosaccharomyces pombe* exhibiting fission scars.

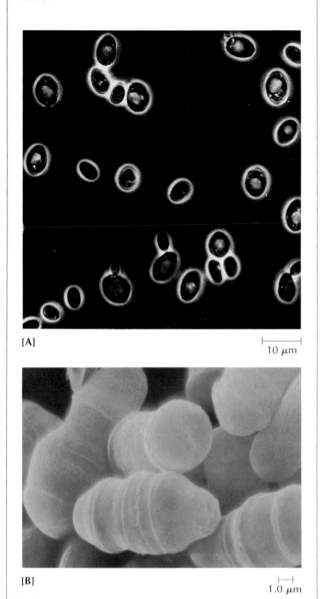

[A]

10 μm

[B]

1.0 μm

meiosis precedes a haploid vegetative stage. It should be noted that yeast life cycles may be quite varied. Variations are due to differences in the timing and location of *plasmogamy* (fusion of protoplasts), karyogamy, and meiosis.

FIGURE 10.10

[A] *Saccharomyces cerevisiae* with cells appearing as vegetative forms, budding cells, and ascospores in tetrahedral arrangement. [B] The life cycle of *Saccharomyces cerevisiae*. Both haploid and diploid vegetative stages may be present. Karyogamy precedes a multiplying diploid vegetative stage; meiosis precedes a multiplying haploid vegetative stage with the formation of ascospores.

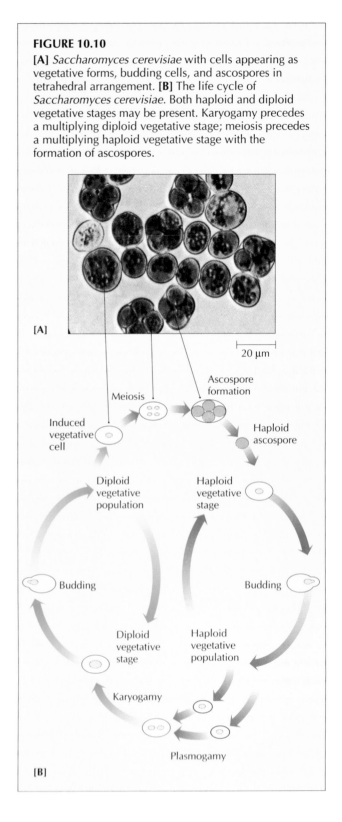

[A]

20 μm

Meiosis

Ascospore formation

Induced vegetative cell

Haploid ascospore

Diploid vegetative population

Haploid vegetative stage

Budding

Budding

Diploid vegetative stage

Haploid vegetative population

Karyogamy

Plasmogamy

[B]

can reproduce asexually by transverse binary fission. They are called *fission* yeasts (as opposed to *budding* yeasts). FIGURE 10.9B shows the fission yeast *Schizosaccharomyces pombe*. Note the fission scars on the cells.

The life cycle of *S. cerevisiae* is diagramed in FIGURE 10.10. In this yeast, both haploid and diploid vegetative stages may be present. *Karyogamy* (fusion of gametic nuclei) precedes the diploid vegetative stage;

FIGURE 10.11
Generalized life cycle of the basidiomycetes.

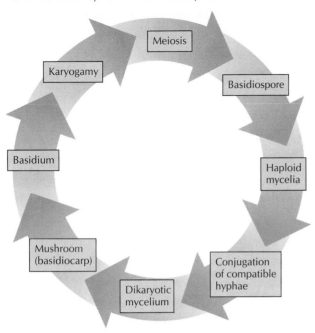

Meiosis

Karyogamy

Basidiospore

Basidium

Haploid
mycelia

Mushroom
(basidiocarp)

Conjugation
of compatible
hyphae

Dikaryotic
mycelium

Basidiomycetes. The basidiomycetes, of which there are more than 25,000 species, include the smuts, rusts, jelly fungi, puffballs, stinkhorns, and mushrooms. Several species devastate crops; for example, smuts cause serious diseases of cereal crops. Others, such as the cultivated mushroom *Agaricus*, are considered delectable food items. The basidiomycetes can be distinguished from all other fungi by the possession of the **basidium** (plural, **basidia**), a microscopic, clublike reproductive structure that is the site of karyogamy and meiosis. Each basidium bears four haploid **basidiospores** produced as a result of meiosis. Thus basidiospores are analogous to ascospores, but they are produced *outside* the basidium instead of being *inside* a structure like the ascus.

The basic life cycle of the basidiomycetes is relatively simple [FIGURE 10.11], although there may be considerable modifications of this cycle in some species. Haploid basidiospores germinate to form haploid mycelia that unite to form a *dikaryotic* mycelium. In the dikaryotic stage, two paired nuclei are found in each cell or segment of the hyphae. Dikaryotic mycelia grow by the simultaneous division of the two nuclei and the for-

FIGURE 10.12
The mushroom is a basidiocarp of the basidiomycetes. Shown is *Agaricus campestris*. On the underside of the cap are found the gills, which contain the basidia, bearing basidiospores.

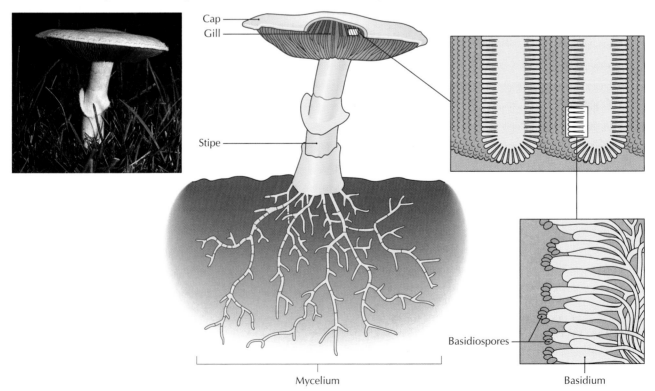

Cap

Gill

Stipe

Basidiospores

Mycelium

Basidium

mation of a new septum. The dikaryotic mycelium differentiates into a **basidiocarp** (fruiting body that bears basidia) or into a basidium-bearing mycelium, depending on the species of basidiomycete. The basidia then produce the basidiospores.

In mushrooms and puffballs (but not rusts and smuts), the basidiocarp is a very conspicuous structure. The common mushroom cap enjoyed by many is the basidiocarp, and the gill surfaces under the cap are packed with microscopic basidia, each bearing basidiospores [FIGURE 10.12]. In the soil, an extensive underground system of mycelia supports the basidiocarp and supplies it with nutrients.

The rusts, like the smuts, are microscopic parasites of cereal grains and some other plants. An example is the wheat rust fungus, *Puccinia graminis* [FIGURE 10.13]. The life cycle of rusts, unlike the simple cycle of smuts, is extremely complex, containing either one or two alternate hosts and as many as five different successive spore stages. It culminates in the formation of basidiospores. The life cycle is linked to seasonal conditions; for example, basidiospores are usually formed in the spring and teliospores in late summer.

Deuteromycetes. Lacking organs for sexual reproduction, the deuteromycetes produce asexual spores, or conidia, which develop into septate mycelia. In this respect they resemble asexual stages of ascomycetes and basidiomycetes, which also produce asexual spores. Indeed, some deuteromycetes are thought to be ascomycetes or basidiomycetes that have lost their potential to form asci or basidia. On the other hand, sexual structures have been discovered in some species originally classified as deuteromycetes. When this happens the

FIGURE 10.14

A culture of *Penicillium* showing numerous typical conidial heads.

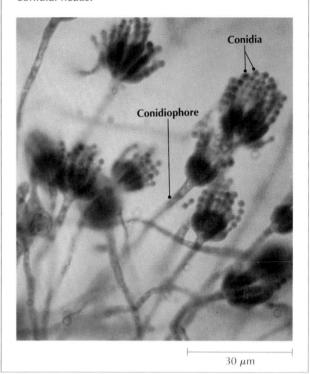

30 μm

species is reclassified as an ascomycete or a basidiomycete [see TABLE 10.1].

Both the genera *Penicillium* and *Aspergillus* contain some species that are designated as ascomycetes and other species that are considered deuteromycetes. Sometimes, even if the sexual stage is discovered for a species and it is renamed, the old name is still used because of habit and because the asexual stage is more common and better known [refer to TABLE 10.1]. For example, species of *Penicillium* with a sexual stage have been renamed as the ascomycetous genus *Talaromyces*. However, most species are still referred to as members of the genus *Penicillium* because their conidial head is so familiar [FIGURE 10.14]. Similarly, the conidial head of *Aspergillus* is well known [FIGURE 10.15].

There are about 25,000 species of deuteromycetes. Some of them are significant for industry and medicine. One of the best known antibiotics, penicillin, is produced by *Penicillium notatum* and *P. chrysogenum*. One of the most common opportunistic pathogens is *Candida albicans* [FIGURE 10.16]. It causes candidiasis, a disease of the mucous membranes of the mouth, vagina, and alimentary tract. More serious candidal infections can involve the heart (endocarditis), the blood (septicemia), and the brain (meningitis).

FIGURE 10.13

Teliospores of *Puccinia graminis*, which have ruptured the epidermis of a wheat leaf.

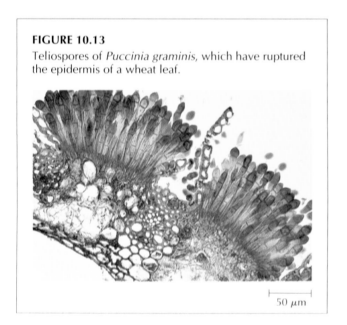

50 μm

FIGURE 10.15
Conidial head of *Aspergillus nidulans* as seen by scanning electron microscopy.

10 μm

FIGURE 10.16
Candida albicans, a yeast pathogenic for humans. **[A]** Note pseudomycelia and blastospores in a urine sample from an infected patient. **[B]** The yeast also forms chlamydospores as well as pseudomycelia and blastospores, when grown on a special medium in the laboratory.

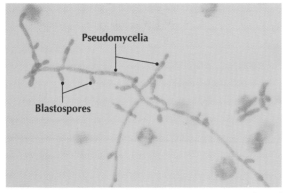

Pseudomycelia

Blastospores

[A]   10 μm

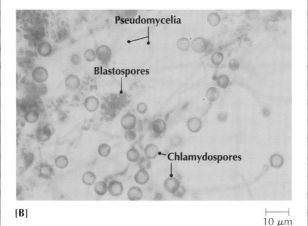

Pseudomycelia

Blastospores

Chlamydospores

[B]   10 μm

ASK YOURSELF

1 What three criteria are used for the classification of fungi?

2 Why are some fungi called *perfect* fungi and others *imperfect* fungi?

3 What are the three major groups of fungi in the kingdom Fungi?

4 Distinguish the acellular slime molds from the cellular slime molds.

5 What are the four major groups of flagellated lower fungi, and how are they differentiated from each other?

6 What single characteristic distinguishes the terrestrial fungi from the flagellated lower fungi?

7 What are the four major groups of terrestrial fungi and their distinguishing characteristics?

CLASSIFICATION OF THE ALGAE

Algae are photoautotrophs, although some also grow heterotrophically. When growing photosynthetically, they produce oxygen and use carbon dioxide as the sole source of carbon. However, unlike photosynthetic higher plants, algae do not need a vascular system to transport nutrients, since every algal cell is photoautotrophic or can absorb dissolved nutrients directly. Many algae are motile or have motile stages during their life cycle.

Even phycologists who specialize in taxonomy do not agree on the details of algal classification. For example, in various classification schemes, the number of major groups (divisions) of the algae have ranged between 4 and 13! However, algae are generally classified on the basis of the following characteristics:

1 Nature and properties of pigments
2 Nature of reserve and storage products
3 Type and number, insertion (point of attachment), and morphology of flagella
4 Chemical composition and physical features of the cell wall
5 Morphology and characteristics of cells and thalli

All these characteristics must be taken into account in assigning the algae to divisions.

TABLE 10.5
Distinguishing Characteristics of the Major Groups of Algae

Division	Habitat	Morphology	Pigments	Reserves	Cell-wall composition
Green algae (Chlorophyta)	Mostly fresh-water, some marine	Uni- to multi-cellular; some microscopic; two or more equal apical or subapical flagella	Chlorophyll a and b, carotenoids	Starch	Cellulose and pectin
Brown algae (Phaeophyta)	Almost all marine	Multicellular and macroscopic; two lateral flagella on zoospores	Chlorophyll a and c, carotenoids	Laminarin and fat	Cellulose with alginic acids
Red algae (Rhodophyta)	Mostly marine, some freshwater	Multicellular and macroscopic; no flagella	Chlorophyll a, d in some; carotenoids; phycobilins	Starch	Cellulose and pectin
Golden-brown algae, diatoms (Chrysophyta)	Mostly marine	Unicellular and microscopic; one or two apical equal or unequal flagella	Chlorophyll a, c; carotenoids	Chrysolaminarin, oils	Pectic compounds with siliceous material
Dinoflagellates (Pyrrophyta)	Marine and freshwater	Unicellular and microscopic; two lateral flagella	Chlorophyll a, c; carotenoids	Starch, oils	No cell wall
Euglenoids (Euglenophyta)	Freshwater	Unicellular and microscopic; one to three apical flagella	Chlorophyll a, b; carotenoids	Paramylon, oils	No cell wall

The major groups of algae and their distinguishing characteristics are shown in TABLE 10.5. Members of some of these algal groups—the euglenoids, the chrysophytes, and the pyrrophytes—are unicellular. The other major groups include genera that are multicellular. In discussing the various groups of algae, this chapter will consider only the microscopic algae; the brown algae (Phaeophyta) and the red algae (Rhodophyta) will not be discussed in detail.

All algae possess chlorophyll a as their primary photosynthetic pigment, as well as accessory carotenoid pigments [TABLE 10.5]. The Rhodophyta contain chlorophyll a and phycobilins; the other algae contain chlorophyll a and either chlorophyll b or c. Members of the Euglenophyta and Pyrrophyta are animal-like; they do not have cell walls. Other algae have cell walls composed of silica, cellulose, other polysaccharides, or organic acids.

Algae are able to store energy reserves in the form of fats, oils, and carbohydrates. Many algae are motile by means of flagella, which vary in structure, number, and point of attachment.

The Green Algae

Green algae as a group are characterized by their possession of chlorophylls similar to those of the terrestrial vascular green plants as well as that of the algae in the division Euglenophyta. However, unlike the euglenoids, the green algae have cell walls. The majority of unicellular green algae contain one chloroplast per cell. Green algae store their food as true starch and have quite rigid cell walls composed of cellulose with pectic substances incorporated into the wall structure.

More than 7000 species of green algae have been described. Most of them are aquatic, although some species are found in a wide variety of habitats, including the surface of snow, in moist soil, in green patches on the trunks of trees, and as symbiotic microbes in lichens and

FIGURE 10.17

Some unicellular green algae: a study in the diversity and beauty of forms. **[A]** Bilaterally symmetrical semicells of *Micrasterias* sp. **[B]** A colony of *Pediastrum* sp. **[C]** Laterally joined cells of *Scenedesmus* sp. **[D]** Coenocytic cells of *Characiosiphon rivularis*. **[E]** Cell in a filament of *Spirogyra* sp. **[F]** Filaments of *Hyalotheca* sp.

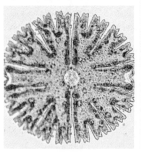

[A]
├─────┤
10 μm

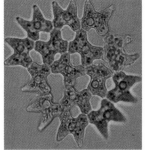

[B]
├─────┤
10 μm

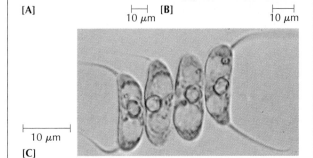

├─────┤
10 μm

[C]

├─────┤
250 μm

[D]

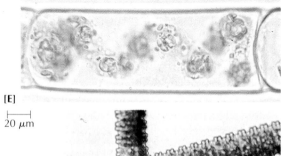

[E]
├─────┤
20 μm

├─────┤
20 μm

[F]

protozoa. The size and shape of the green algae range from that of unicellular freshwater species—which include colonial and filamentous types [FIGURE 10.17]—to that of the large marine species. Many unicellular green algae are motile by means of flagellar action. For reproduction, the green algae utilize sexual means or asexual methods such as fission and zoospores.

Chlamydomonas is a typical unicellular green alga that is motile (except during cell division) by means of two flagella protruding from its anterior pole. It moves very rapidly with a characteristic darting motion, and is found in ponds, streams, and even polluted water. Each round or oval cell (3 to 30 μm in diameter) has a nucleus and a single large chloroplast. Within the chloroplast is a dense region called the *pyrenoid*, which is the site of starch synthesis. There is some evidence that the eyespot in the chloroplast is the site of light perception.

In asexual reproduction the free-swimming *Chlamydomonas* cell becomes nonmotile by withdrawing its flagella and undergoing mitosis to form two, four, or eight daughter protoplasts *within* the parent cell wall. The daughter cells develop two flagella each and synthesize new cell walls. They are then liberated from their parent (called a *sporangium*). This cycle may be repeated indefinitely [FIGURE 10.18]. In some cases the daughter cells do not develop flagella and escape, but keep on multiplying within a more or less gelatinized matrix to form masses of cells. The formation of such cell masses occurs when environmental conditions are favorable to growth but not to motility. Any individual cell, however, can develop flagella and escape from the mass.

Sexual reproduction in *Chlamydomonas* occurs by conjugation of + and − haploid cells to form a diploid zygote. The zygote then divides by meiosis to form two + or two − gametes [FIGURE 10.18].

In addition to motile unicellular algae such as *Chlamydomonas*, *nonmotile* unicellular green algae are widely distributed. One of the most important of these is *Chlorella*. It was the first alga to be isolated in *axenic culture* (culture composed of only one strain of a species). It has served as a useful model for experimental studies in photosynthesis, supplemental food sources, and gaseous exchange (supplying oxygen while utilizing the carbon dioxide exhaled by humans in closed systems such as spacecraft). In nature, *Chlorella* is widespread in both fresh water and saltwater and in soil. Each *Chlorella* cell contains a single cup-shaped chloroplast, with or without a pyrenoid, and a single minute nucleus. The only known method of reproduction is asexual [FIGURE 10.19]. It can produce daughter cells only *within* the mother cell, and these are never flagellated. From 2 to 32 cells are formed at each division. *Chlorella* divides quite rapidly—within 2 h at maximum growth rates.

FIGURE 10.18

Reproduction in *Chlamydomonas*. Conjugation between + and – haploid flagellated cells results in a diploid zygote. The zygote divides by meiosis to form two + and two – zoospores which carry out asexual reproduction by mitosis.

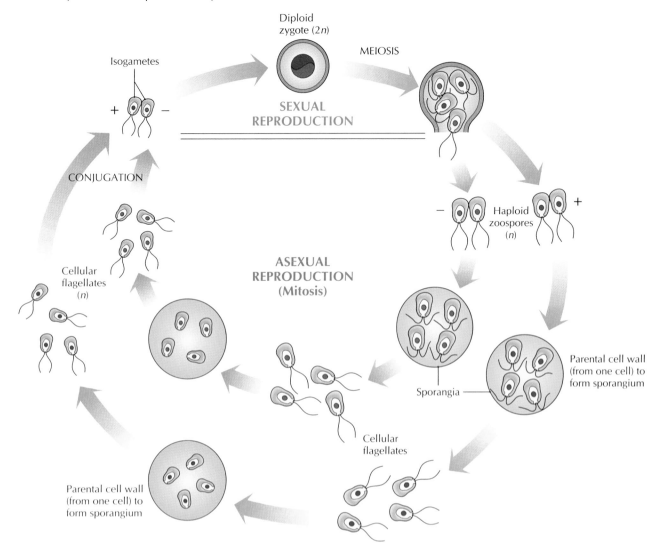

Besides the unicellular forms, green algae can also be filamentous and multicellular. One of these, *Acetabularia*, has a distinctive umbrellalike morphology consisting of a *rhizoidal* (rootlike) system, a stalk, and a cap. The cap has rays that contain cysts [FIGURE 10.20]. Each cyst has about 30 to 40 nuclei and can produce many flagellated gametes of the same mating type. Isogametes of opposite mating types can conjugate to form a new organism.

The Diatoms and Golden-Brown Algae

The diatoms and the golden-brown algae, both of the division Chrysophyta, are microscopic, unicellular mi-croorganisms that are very important components of phytoplankton. As such, the chrysophytes serve as primary sources of food for aquatic animals. They share the same kinds of pigments as the brown algae (Phaeophyta), but the latter are macroscopic and multicellular. In addition, unlike the brown algae, the diatoms and golden-brown algae have a predominance of carotenoids compared with chlorophyll *a* and *c*; this is the reason for their golden color and for their being grouped together in the Chrysophyta. There are 6000 to 10,000 living species in this division.

Diatoms. *Diatoms* are single cells [FIGURE 10.21], which may join to form simple filaments or colonies. There are at least 40,000 valid species of these microorganisms (in-

FIGURE 10.19

Chlorella has a simple life cycle. There is mitotic cell division and release of cells from within the parent cell wall.

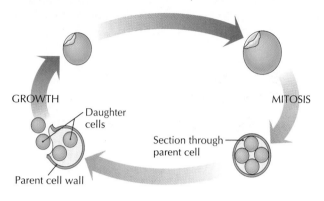

GROWTH

MITOSIS

Daughter cells

Section through parent cell

Parent cell wall

FIGURE 10.20

Cyst formation in the cells of the green alga *Acetabularia*.

1.0 mm

FIGURE 10.21

The diatom *Synedra* sp. seen at two magnifications. The larger magnification shows the opaline silica cell wall with its elaborate pattern.

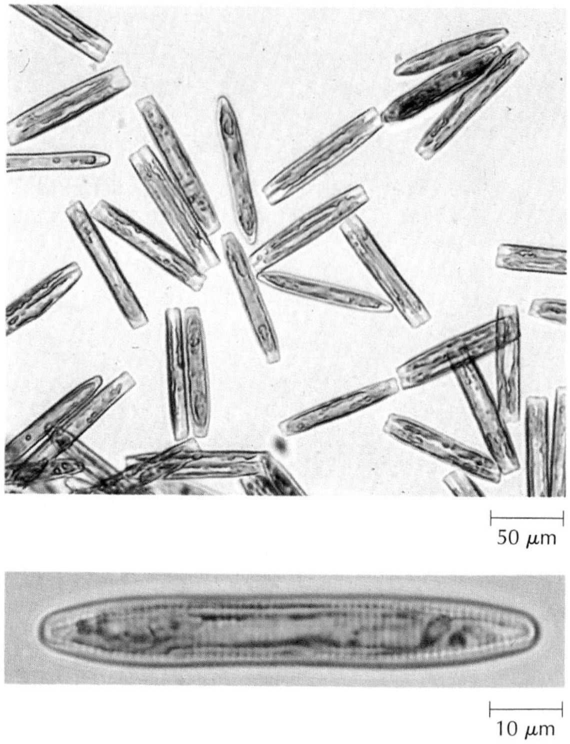

50 μm

10 μm

cluding extinct fossil forms). Found in both fresh water and saltwater and in moist soil, diatoms occur in a wide variety of shapes, like many of the groups discussed thus far in this chapter.

Each diatom cell has a prominent nucleus and massive ribbonlike, or smaller lenslike, plastids. They produce cell walls composed of pectin impregnated with silica; some of these are extremely elaborate and beautiful (see DISCOVER 10.1, with its striking illustration). The cell wall, called a *frustule,* consists of two overlapping halves called *valves* that fit together like a Petri dish. Diatoms lack cilia or flagella, but some forms move by gliding on solid surfaces. This gliding action is due to a

regulated mucous secretion that occurs in response to physical and chemical stimuli. The mucus is released through pores in a longitudinal slit in the cell wall.

Diatoms usually reproduce by mitotic cell division. Each daughter cell retains one valve of the parent cell wall and constructs a second valve. The old valve always forms the top lid of the silica "Petri dish," with the new valve fitting inside it. Consequently, one of the new pair of daughter cells tends to be smaller than the parent [FIGURE 10.22]. In some species the cell walls are expandable and are enlarged by the growing protoplasm within them. In species with more rigid cell walls, the original cell size is regained at the time of sexual reproduction by the formation of the zygote (the *auxospore*), which expands to the full size characteristic of the species. The auxospore synthesizes new frustules with all the intricate surface patterns of the original.

Golden-Brown Algae. Many golden-brown algae are motile by means of two flagella of unequal lengths; some are amoeboid, with pseudopodial extensions of the protoplasm. Except for the presence of chloroplasts, the amoeboid cells are indistinguishable from amoeboid protozoa. Reproduction in the golden-brown algae is largely

10.1 THE BEAUTIFUL DIATOMS AND THEIR MANY USES

Long dead but not forgotten, the skeletons of algae called *diatoms* are an economic treasure. Diatoms are unicellular algae found in fresh and salt water. Their hard, silica-containing cell walls are made of two halves that fit together like the two parts of a laboratory Petri dish. They come in a myriad of shapes, often with beautiful surface designs that rival the carvings of great artisans (see the photograph).

Deposits of the cell walls of dead diatoms accumulate over the centuries as *diatomite*, or *diatomaceous earth*. Although diatomite from prehistoric times is found in Oregon, Nevada, Washington, Florida, and New Jersey in the United States, the world's largest and most productive commercial source is at Lompoc, California.

Diatomaceous earth is used in insulating materials; as filters for juices and other beverages, cane sugar, and swimming pool water; in cosmetic formulas; and as polishing material. It is especially suitable as a filtering material because it is not readily compressed or compacted during use. It is divided into such fine particles that one gram has 100 square

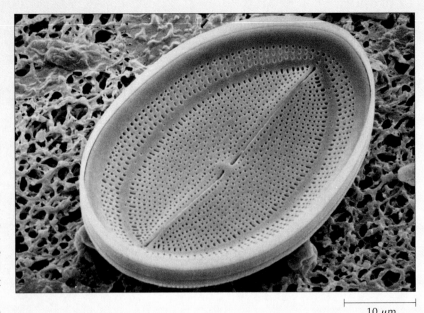

10 µm

Diatoms occur in myriads of shapes, many with beautiful surface designs. Seen here is a scanning electron micrograph of a diatom exhibiting symmetric design.

meters of surface area; yet in use up to 90 percent of the volume of the filter cake is open space. This microbial product is also perfect for polishing delicate surfaces, since the diatom walls collapse under pressure and do not damage surfaces. The elegantly symmetrical markings of diatoms have been used by microscopists for generations to test for optical aberrations in microscope lenses.

FIGURE 10.22

Reproduction in the diatoms.

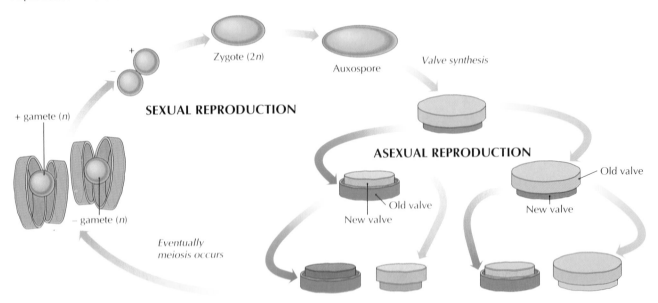

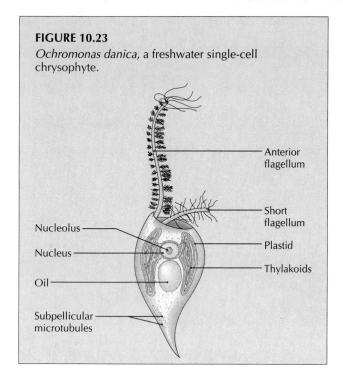

FIGURE 10.23
Ochromonas danica, a freshwater single-cell chrysophyte.

Anterior flagellum

Short flagellum

Nucleolus

Plastid

Nucleus

Thylakoids

Oil

Subpellicular microtubules

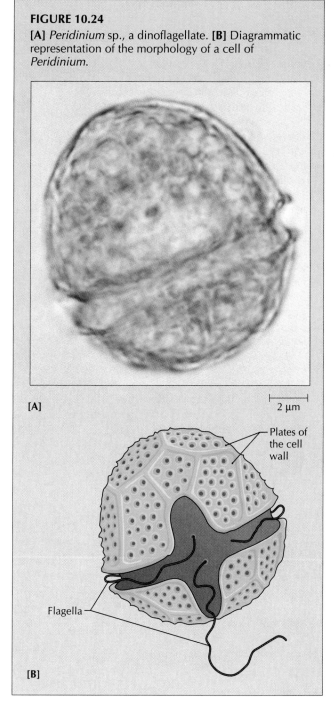

FIGURE 10.24
[A] *Peridinium* sp., a dinoflagellate. [B] Diagrammatic representation of the morphology of a cell of *Peridinium*.

[A]

2 μm

Plates of the cell wall

Flagella

[B]

asexual and involves zoospore formation. The zoospores swim away to establish new colonies.

Ochromonas is an interesting unicellular genus exhibiting unequal flagellation. It is shown diagrammatically in FIGURE 10.23. One species is remarkably versatile in nutrition; it may grow photoautotrophically, heterotrophically, or phagotrophically [DISCOVER 10.2].

The Dinoflagellates

Biflagellated and unicellular, the ***dinoflagellates*** are so named because of their twirling motion rather than their morphology (*dine*, from Greek, means "whirling"). The flagella beat within two grooves—one circles the body like a girdle, and the other is perpendicular to the first. The beating of the hairy flagella in their respective grooves causes the cell to spin like a top as it moves through a liquid. Dinoflagellates can move a distance of 100 times their own length each second! Of the several thousand known species, nearly all are marine planktonic forms, although some occur in brackish and fresh water. These morphologically diverse algae grow heterotrophically or photosynthetically; the heterotrophs can be saprophytic or parasitic.

FIGURE 10.24 shows the morphology of a dinoflagellate. Many marine dinoflagellates appear to have a coat of armor because they are covered by overlapping sculptured cellulose plates. Photosynthetic dinoflagellates contain brownish plastids. Asexual reproduction takes place through longitudinal cell division, with each daughter cell getting one of the flagella and a portion of the cell wall, and then constructing the missing parts in a very intricate sequence. Sexual reproduction is rare among the dinoflagellates.

Marine dinoflagellates frequently exhibit bioluminescence (e.g., *Noctiluca miliaris*, species of "a thousand night-lights"). This property of light emission is the basis for the name of the group: Pyrrophyta, the "fire algae."

10.2 SOME PHOTOSYNTHETIC ALGAE ALSO EAT BACTERIA!

Until recently it was assumed that phytoplankton receive *all* their energy through photosynthesis. This was proved wrong when studies showed that some algae supplement their carbon supply by taking up preformed organic carbon. But it was only in 1986 that two marine biologists at McGill University, D. F. Bird and J. Kalff, discovered that the phagotrophic ingestion of bacteria is also important to these algae. The observed rates of bacterial ingestion by the algae were very similar to those measured for nonphotosynthetic marine flagellates, which are totally dependent on external sources of carbon.

The revealing study was carried out in Lake Cromwell, Quebec, using tracer quantities of bacteria-sized fluorescent latex beads, which were ingested in place of bacteria. The beads were released into a chamber containing phytoplankton. After intervals of time, samples of phytoplankton were filtered onto membrane filters and special instruments measured the amount of fluorescence in the algae. These measurements corresponded to the number of beads ingested. On the basis of these experiments, species of chrysophycean algae (*Dinobryon* species) proved to be the major consumers of bacteria. In fact, they depleted the bacterial populations more than those protozoa considered to be traditional bacterial grazers. Each *Dinobryon* cell ingested about three bacteria every five minutes!

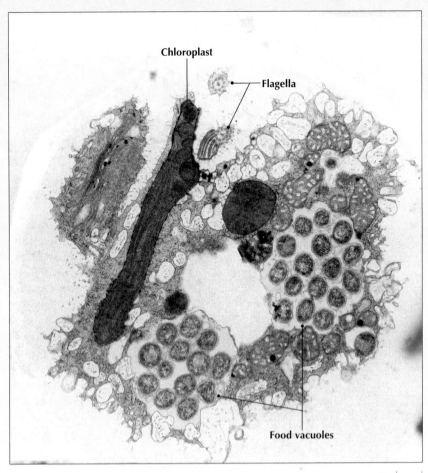

Electron micrograph showing bacterial cells inside the chrysophycean alga, *Dinobryon cylindricum*, from Lake Cromwell. Note food vacuoles containing bacteria, chloroplast, and flagella (in cross section) exhibiting "9 + 2" structure.

Indeed, the nocturnal twinkling of lights in the ocean waves is due to such microorganisms. Dinoflagellates are the only algae that luminesce. Like that of other bioluminescent organisms, the algal luminescence is due to the substrate-enzyme complex of luciferin-luciferase within the cellular cytoplasm.

Perhaps the best-known dinoflagellates are those that produce the "red tides," or blooms, in which the concentration of cells is so great that large areas of the ocean can appear red, brown, or yellow. There may be tens of millions of cells per liter of seawater. Blooms occur almost every summer in the waters off Florida and California, and a bloom of the species *Gonyaulax* occurs yearly in the cold waters off the coast of Maine. Fortunately, these blooms are not always severe.

Many of the dinoflagellates that cause blooms are toxic, producing a poison that can be fatal. They are ingested not only by fish but also by shellfish, which accumulate them because shellfish are filter feeders. The toxin is released in the fish as the dinoflagellate cells disintegrate during passage through the fish gills. As a result, hundreds of thousands of fish can be killed in one bloom. Shellfish are unharmed by the toxin; however, it affects humans when they consume infected shellfish. Depending on the species of dinoflagellate, such shellfish become dangerous to humans. Some species, such as *Gonyaulax catenella* and *G. tamarensis*, produce powerful nerve toxins similar to the nerve poison curare. About 1 percent of poisoned humans die from these toxins, usually from respiratory failure.

FIGURE 10.25

[A] A cell of *Euglena acus*. [B] Diagrammatic representation of a *Euglena* cell. As may be seen, the emergent flagellum is attached at the base of the flask-shaped opening, called the *reservoir*, at the anterior end of the cell. Emptying into the *reservoir* are the contractile vacuoles, which collect excess water from all parts of the cell and discharge it into the reservoir. The cell is delimited by a flexible pellicle.

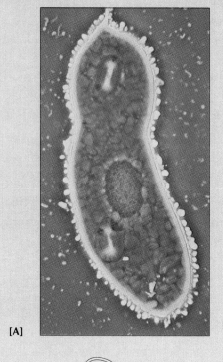

[A]   10 μm

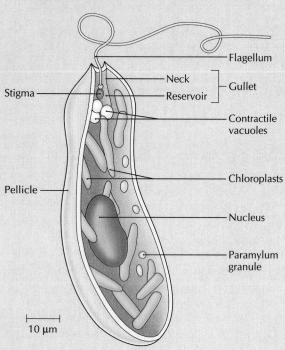

- Flagellum
- Neck — Gullet
- Reservoir
Stigma
- Contractile vacuoles
- Chloroplasts
Pellicle
- Nucleus
- Paramylum granule

10 μm

[B]

The Euglenoids

The unicellular *euglenoids* are distinguished from other algae by the presence of chlorophylls *a* and *b* and the absence of a cell wall. There are more than 800 species, most of which are found in fresh water, especially water rich in organic matter. This is because euglenoids can grow as heterotrophs or as autotrophs. Some biologists even regard the nonphotosynthetic members of the euglenoids as protozoa because they can ingest particulate food matter through a gullet.

In a variety of shapes, euglenoids range in size from 10 μm to more than 500 μm in length. Many species of *Euglena* are elongated [FIGURE 10.25]. The *Euglena* cell is complex and contains numerous small chloroplasts. It has a nucleus and a long flagellum, which is usually held in front of the cell like a spinning lasso. The *pellicle* (cytoplasmic membrane plus protein strips) surrounding the cell is flexible; there is no cell wall. Other cytoplasmic organelles or inclusions include contractile vacuoles, mitochondria, paramylon (a glucose polymer), and an eyespot, or stigma.

Scientists have not observed any sexual reproduction among the euglenoids. Asexual reproduction is by longitudinal binary cell division. Certain genera can encyst to survive adverse environmental conditions.

ASK YOURSELF

1 In what way are the algae different from the higher plants?

2 What characteristics are used for the classification of algae?

3 What are the six major groups of algae and their distinguishing characteristics?

4 What is the primary photosynthetic pigment in *all* algae?

CLASSIFICATION OF THE PROTOZOA

Protozoa are microorganisms with animal-like characteristics, including locomotion, ingestion of food, and lack of a rigid cell wall. Many protozoa absorb dissolved nutrients, but some are predators and eat bacteria and other protozoa. They can be free-living in marine and fresh water and in soil, or they can be symbionts in or on living hosts. Some protozoa have properties they share

TABLE 10.6
The Major Groups of Protozoa of Particular Interest to Microbiologists, and Their Distinguishing Characteristics

Taxonomic group	Characteristics
Flagellates (subphylum Mastigophora)	Asexual reproduction by longitudinal binary fission. Sexual reproduction known in some groups. Autotrophic and/or heterotrophic. Zooflagellates do not have chromatophores. Amoeboid forms, with or without flagella. One to many flagella. Many commensals, symbionts, and parasites. Representative genera: *Leishmania, Trypanosoma, Giardia, Trichomonas.*
Amoebas (subphylum Sarcodina)	Mostly free-living species. Body naked or with external or internal skeleton. Amoeboid movement and feeding by pseudopodia. Asexual reproduction by fission. Sexual reproduction, if present, associated usually with flagellated gametes. Representative genus: *Amoeba.*
Sporozoa (phylum Apicomplexa)	Spore-forming stage in life history. Sexual reproduction by the union of gametes. Asexual reproduction by multiple fission. All species parasitic. Generally nonmotile but locomotion of mature organisms by body flexion, gliding, or undulation of longitudinal ridges. Representative genera: *Toxoplasma, Plasmodium.*
Ciliates (phylum Ciliophora)	Largest phylum. All possess cilia or compound ciliary structures as locomotor or food-acquiring organelles at some time in the life cycle. Most ciliates possess a mouth, or cytostome. Two types of nuclei: the macronucleus (governs metabolism) and the micronucleus (governs reproduction). Fission is transverse; sexual reproduction never involves the formation of free gametes. Widely distributed in both fresh and marine waters and in soil water films. One third of species are parasites; others are free-living. Representative genera: *Didinium, Balantidium, Tetrahymena, Paramecium, Euplotes.*

with the algae or the fungi. For instance, the photosynthetic euglenoids and dinoflagellates are classified as algae by the phycologists and as phytoflagellates by the protozoologists. The amoeboid slime molds are studied by both mycologists and protozoologists.

The diverse forms of protozoa have been classified, but not on the basis of evolutionary relationships. Structural features of the cells (seen through electron microscopes) played a significant role in the new classification scheme developed in 1980. The new scheme includes several groups still claimed by mycologists and phycologists as fungi and algae, respectively. The older classification schemes of the protozoa were based primarily on organelles or modes of locomotion.

TABLE 10.6 describes the major groups of protozoa of interest to microbiologists. They may be separated into the *flagellates*, the *amoebas*, the *sporozoa*, and the *ciliates*.

The Flagellates

The *flagellates* classified as protozoa are divided into two groups: the plantlike forms (phytoflagellates) and the animal-like forms (zooflagellates). Their flagella differentiate them from most other major groups of protozoa.

Some of the phytoflagellates have already been discussed with the algae (e.g., *Euglena* and *Chlamydomonas*). All of them typically have chloroplasts and are mainly free-living. Only the zooflagellates will be discussed in this section.

The zooflagellates have no chlorophyll and must obtain their food heterotrophically. All members of this group have one or more flagella; some members are capable of forming pseudopodia. The cells are ovoid to elongated and characteristically reproduce asexually by longitudinal binary fission. A form of multiple fission takes place in some species. Sexual reproduction is rare. Encystment is a common form of survival.

Some zooflagellates are free-living, while others are parasitic and may cause disease in humans. *Giardia lamblia* [FIGURE 10.26] is associated with diarrhea in children and, infrequently, in adults. Its feeding, or vegetative, form (trophozoite) has eight flagella and a ventral sucker with which it attaches to the intestinal mucosa. It is passed out of the intestine and survives in a cyst form until ingested by the next host. Diagnosis of the disease, called *giardiasis*, is based on identification of the cyst in feces.

Trichomonas hominis and *T. vaginalis* are two other parasitic zooflagellates found in humans. *Trichomonas hominis* causes diarrhea, whereas *T. vaginalis*

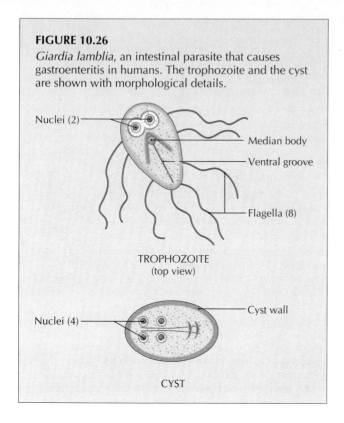

FIGURE 10.26

Giardia lamblia, an intestinal parasite that causes gastroenteritis in humans. The trophozoite and the cyst are shown with morphological details.

Nuclei (2)

Median body

Ventral groove

Flagella (8)

TROPHOZOITE
(top view)

Cyst wall

Nuclei (4)

CYST

is one of the world's most common causes of sexually transmitted infections. The latter is found in the urogenital tract, where it may cause inflammation and a purulent discharge. It is transmitted not only by sexual intercourse but also by contaminated toilet facilities and toweling. Each year, an estimated 2.5 to 3 million American women contract *trichomoniasis* (*Trichomonas* infection). In females, *T. vaginalis* causes vaginitis, a chronic and irritating inflammation of the vagina. Males may have the organism in their urinary tract, but are usually asymptomatic. Diagnosis of the disease is by microscopic detection of the trophozoite stage in vaginal or urethral discharges. *Trichomonas vaginalis* does not have a cyst stage and cannot survive outside the host.

Another group of zooflagellates are parasites of the bloodstream and hence are called *hemo*flagellates. These are trypanosomes that are responsible for some human diseases. Trypanosomes are characterized by a leaf-shaped body and a flagellum that is attached to the cell by an undulating membrane and extends along and beyond the cell body [see FIGURE 4.33c]. They have a single nucleus and reproduce asexually. Some species pass through a complex life cycle, part of which is spent in a bloodsucking insect. The insect transmits the parasite to humans and other vertebrate animals. Important species of this group include *Trypanosoma gambiense* and *T. rhodesiense*, which are transmitted by the tsetse fly and cause African sleeping sickness. Studies of this disease helped early microbiologists understand interactions between microorganisms and insects. *Trypanosoma*

cruzi, the agent of Chagas' disease, is carried to humans by biting insects, such as *Triatoma*, or the kissing bug (so named because it is attracted to lips). After entering an insect, a trypanosome rapidly multiplies by fission. If the insect then defecates while biting a person, the trypanosomes pass into the bite wound and enter the host's bloodstream. From the bloodstream, the microorganisms localize in the heart and central nervous system, often causing fatal damage.

Another zooflagellate genus, *Leishmania*, includes species with both nonmotile and motile stages in their life cycles. Bloodsucking insects transmit the motile form to humans; then nonmotile (nonflagellated) forms are produced inside the cells of the spleen and other organs of the body and sometimes inside white blood cells. *Kala-azar* is a tropical disease caused by *L. donovani*; a skin disease known as *oriental sore* is caused by *L. tropica*. *Leishmania brasiliensis*, common in South America, causes a disease characterized by ulcers in the mouth and nose.

The Amoebas

Amoebas get their name from the Greek word *amoibe* (meaning "change"), because their shapes are constantly changing. An amoeba cell is composed of a protoplasm differentiated into a cytoplasmic membrane, cytoplasm, and a nucleus [see FIGURE 4.44]. The cytoplasm contains granules, as well as vacuoles filled with food, wastes, water, and possibly gases. The cytoplasmic membrane is selective, permitting the passage of certain soluble nutrients into the cell and waste material out of the cell. These microorganisms are almost constantly in motion. They move by sending out portions of their bodies in one direction so that the whole cell moves into the location of the projection, called the *pseudopodium*. Several *pseudopodia* may be sent out at one time from a single cell. These pseudopodia are also used to capture food; they surround the food particles, which become enclosed in vacuoles inside the cytoplasm. Enzymes secreted into these vacuoles digest the food, which is then used by the cell for metabolism.

Reproduction in amoebas is by binary fission. For protection during periods unfavorable for normal growth, some amoebas can form cysts. The cyst often undergoes nuclear multiplication without cell division, resulting in several nuclei within a single cyst. The number of nuclei is often characteristic of a species and is used to distinguish harmless intestinal protozoa such as *Entamoeba coli* from *E. histolytica*, the cause of amoebic dysentery (amoebiasis) in humans.

The trophozoite of *E. histolytica* [FIGURE 10.27] is capable of invading tissues. The posterior end of the parasite is known as the *uroid*; it is a small, rounded structure, occasionally with long mucoid extensions. In acute

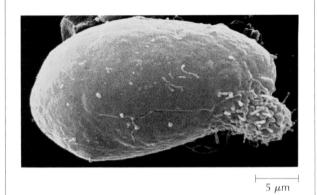

FIGURE 10.27

Scanning electron micrograph of an *Entamoeba histolytica* trophozoite. The knoblike structure called the *uroid* is the posterior end of the amoeba. Crystal-like structures seen are starch granules.

5 μm

amoebic dysentery, large numbers of red blood cells appear in the feces as a result of ulceration and bleeding from the mucous membrane lining the intestine. Red blood cells released by the bleeding are ingested by the parasite.

Other interesting amoebas include the free-living foraminiferans, many of which produce a chalky calcium shell with numerous chambers. Radiolarians, like foraminiferans, are marine forms, but most of them construct shells of silica. These microorganisms obtain their food by pseudopodia that extend through pores in the shells. The famous white cliffs of Dover in England are the skeletal remains of foraminiferans that settled to the ocean floor over millions of years and were later uplifted by geological activity.

The Sporozoa

All sporozoa are parasitic for one or more animal species. Adult forms have no organs of motility, but immature forms and gametes occasionally move by means of flagella, flexion of the body, or gliding. Sporozoa cannot engulf solid particles, and so they feed on dissolved nutrients in the body fluids of their hosts. Many have complex life cycles with alternating sexual and asexual stages that often occur in different hosts. The *intermediate host* usually harbors the asexual (immature) forms and the *definitive host* the sexual forms (adult parasites mature and reproduce sexually in the definitive hohost). Sometimes humans serve as hosts to both forms, depending on the species of sporozoa.

Toxoplasmosis and malaria are the principal human diseases caused by sporozoa. *Toxoplasma gondii* is the etiologic agent of toxoplasmosis; symptoms vary greatly depending on the location of the parasites in the body. They can mimic the symptoms of meningitis and hepatitis, for example. *Toxoplasma gondii* is the most widespread of the parasites that infect vertebrates. More than 50 percent of adults in the United States have been infected at some time, but the disease is usually mild and asymptomatic. Spontaneous recovery usually follows infection. However, transplacental infection (infection of the human embryo from the mother) may have serious consequences. The result may be a stillborn child or a child with mental retardation and other disorders. The disease can also cause fatal illness in people with impaired immune systems, such as those with AIDS or those undergoing radiation therapy. *Toxoplasma gondii* develops asexually in humans and other animals and in this form can cause disease; but it undergoes sexual reproduction only in the intestinal cells of members of the cat family, which act as carriers of the parasite.

Although toxoplasmosis can be serious, in terms of human suffering the most important sporozoa to affect humans are those that cause malaria. Malaria is a mosquito-borne disease of humans caused by members of the genus *Plasmodium*. These microorganisms invade the liver and the red blood cells. The definitive host is the female anopheline mosquito, in which sexual reproduction takes place. The infective form of the parasite is the *sporozoite*, which is inoculated into the host by the infected mosquito during a bite. The sporozoite forms inside the *oocyst*, a circular body attached to the mosquito midgut [FIGURE 10.28]. Asexual reproduction takes place in the human host's cells. Malaria has been one of the greatest killers of humans through the ages. It has been conservatively estimated that, at any given time, 300 million people in the world have malaria and that about 3 million of those will die from the disease.

FIGURE 10.28

Midgut of a mosquito (*Aedes aegypti*) infected with *Plasmodium gallinacium*. The oocysts appear as round bodies attached to the gut epithelium.

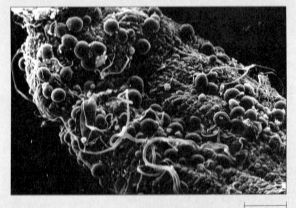

10 μm

FIGURE 10.29

Ventral surface of a *Euplotes* cell. **[A]** Scanning electron micrograph of *E. aediculatus*. Cirri (A). Each cirrus is composed of 80 to 100 individual cilia that are not fused but beat as a functional unit in locomotion. Cilia (B). Two to three long rows of cilia function in locomotion as well as in food collection. Buccal cavity (C). Cytostome (cell "mouth") (D). **[B]** Diagrammatic representation of a *Euplotes* cell.

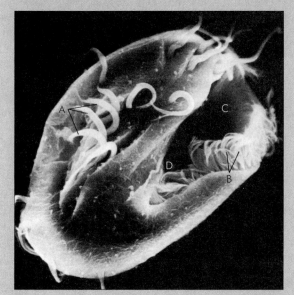

[A]   20 μm

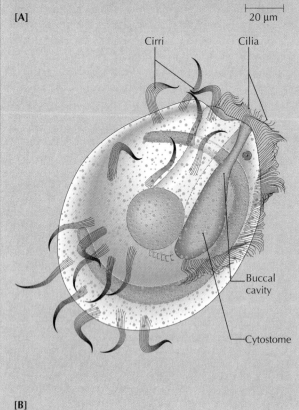

[B]

The Ciliates

The largest of the principal protozoan groups, the ciliates, includes some 7200 species, many of which are still not well known. These microorganisms are mainly unicellular, and they have cilia on their surface. Often the entire cell is covered with hundreds of cilia, which beat in a coordinated fashion to move the cell and also to direct food into the *cytostome* [FIGURE 10.29]. Food vacuoles, formed at the base of the cytostome, enclose the food particles. Then they circulate around the cell until the food materials are digested. Undigested particles are eliminated from the cell through the *cytoproct*. Within the cell is the contractile vacuole, which maintains the water balance of the cell. In some species, cilia are restricted to certain areas or are fused together to form tufts called *cirri* (tufts of hair) as shown in FIGURE 10.29. These structures can function as "legs" that the cell uses to creep along surfaces.

Besides their ciliated morphology, the ciliates are also unique among protozoa for their two types of nuclei. The *macronucleus* directs cell growth and asexual reproduction by transverse binary fission. The *micronucleus* plays an essential role in sexual reproduction; it contains the genetic information that is exchanged during *conjugation*, a temporary union of cells with exchange of nuclear material. The ciliates are the only protozoa in which sexual reproduction is by conjugation.

A common example of the ciliated protozoa is *Paramecium*. It lives in freshwater ponds and lakes where sufficient food is available. Conjugation may occur when two mating strains of paramecia happen to touch each other. The two individuals come together and unite along their oral grooves; their nuclei undergo division and the cells exchange haploid nuclei derived from their micronuclei. In each conjugant, the two haploid nuclei fuse to form a diploid nucleus. The cells then separate, and nuclear divisions and fissions result in the asexual form. The only ciliate that is a human parasite is *Balantidium coli*, a cause of dysentery.

ASK YOURSELF

1 What animal-like characteristics do protozoa have?

2 Why are some protozoa claimed by phycologists for their study? Which protozoa are studied both by mycologists and protozoologists?

3 List and outline the differences among the four major groups of protozoa that are of interest to microbiologists.

SUMMARY

1 Classification of the fungi is based primarily on characteristics of the sexual spores and fruiting bodies, the nature of the life cycle, and the morphology of vegetative mycelia.

2 The three major groups of fungi are the slime molds, the flagellated lower fungi, and the terrestrial fungi. Each of these groups has distinguishing features, such as the protozoanlike vegetative stage and the funguslike fruiting stage of the slime molds.

3 Among the fungi are those that are parasitic or saprophytic. Some cause plant and animal diseases. Fungi have perfect and imperfect life cycles. Their organs of reproduction can be quite elaborate in structure. Most familiar of these are the caps of edible mushrooms.

4 The algae are photosynthetic microorganisms without a vascular system. All algae possess chlorophyll a as their primary photosynthetic pigment, and accessory carotenoid pigments. Some algae can also be heterotrophic.

5 The microscopic algae may be divided into the green algae, the euglenoids, the chrysophytes (diatoms and golden-brown algae), and the pyrrophytes (dinoflagellates). The last three groups are almost entirely unicellular.

6 Protozoa are microorganisms with animal-like characteristics. Their classification is based on modes of locomotion as well as on structural details revealed by electron microscopy. They can be divided into the flagellates, the amoebas, the sporozoa, and the ciliates.

7 Among the zooflagellates are the etiologic agents of trichomoniasis, African sleeping sickness, and gastroenteritis.

8 Amoebas change their shapes constantly and use pseudopodia to move and to capture food.

9 All sporozoa are parasitic for animals; they include the etiologic agents for toxoplasmosis and malaria.

10 Ciliates have cilia on their surfaces. There are many species, but only one species is a human parasite.

KEY TERMS

acellular slime molds
algae
asci (singular, ascus)
ascocarps
Ascomycetes
ascospores
auxospore
basidiocarp
Basidiomycetes
basidiospores
basidium (plural, basidia)
cellular slime molds
Chytridiomycetes
definitive host
Deuteromycetes
diatoms
dinoflagellates
ergot
euglenoids
flagellates
frustule
fungi
hyperplasia
hypertrophy
Hyphochytridiomycetes
imperfect fungi
intermediate host
mycorrhizal
myxamoebas
oocyst
Oomycetes
perfect fungi
Plasmodiophoromycetes
plasmodium (plural, plasmodia)
protozoa
pseudoplasmodia
pseudopodium (plural, pseudopodia)
rhizomycelium
sporozoite
swarm cells
valves
Zygomycetes
zygospore

CLASSIFICATION OF
THE FUNGI

1 Fungi with known sexual stages are called _____ fungi.

2 The slime molds are like fungi in one stage of their growth cycle because they produce _____ and sporangia.

3 The plasmodium of acellular slime molds is not _____.

4 The flagellated lower fungi typically produce _____ cells at some stage during the life cycle.

5 *Saprolegnia ferax* has been implicated in diseases of

_____.

6 Fungi that cause hypertrophy and hyperplasia in host tissues are in the class

_____.

7 Sexual spores produced by the terrestrial fungi are zygospores,

_____, and _____.

8 Which of the following is not characteristic of fungi? **(a)** filamentous shape; **(b)** eucaryotic structure; **(c)** nutrition by absorption; **(d)** chlorophyll; **(e)** cell walls.

9 Which of the following is an ascocarp? **(a)** pycnidium; **(b)** perithecium; **(c)** sporangium; **(d)** ascus; **(e)** antheridium.

10 Beadle and Tatum received the Nobel Prize for their work on **(a)** *Saccharomyces;* **(b)** *Saprolegnia;* **(c)** *Penicillium;* **(d)** *Agaricus;* **(e)** *Neurospora.*

11 Each cell of a dikaryotic hypha contains **(a)** two paired nuclei; **(b)** one nucleus; **(c)** no nucleus; **(d)** three nuclei; **(e)** none of the above.

In items 12–14, indicate whether the statement is true **(T)** *or false* **(F).** *If the statement is false, rewrite it as true.*

CLASSIFICATION OF
THE ALGAE

12 The three algal groups euglenoids, chrysophytes, and pyrrophytes are composed almost entirely of unicellular organisms. _____

_____

_____

13 The distinctive characteristic of green algae is the possession of chlorophylls similar to those in vascular green plants. _____

_____

_____

14 *Chlamydomonas* is like *Chlorella* because both are motile algae. _____

_____

_____

15 *Chlorella* is a unicellular _____ green alga.

16 The diatoms have cell walls impregnated with _____.

17 *Ochromonas* is very versatile in its nutrition; it can grow heterotrophically, photoautotrophically, and _____.

18 The frustule of a diatom cell consists of two overlapping halves called

_____ .

19 *Noctiluca miliaris* exhibits the characteristic property of

_____ .

20 Red tides, or blooms, are caused by **(a)** diatoms; **(b)** euglenas; **(c)** chlorellas; **(d)** dinoflagellates; **(e)** red algae.

21 Which one of the following characteristics is not used for the classification of algae? **(a)** nature and properties of pigments; **(b)** life cycle and reproductive nature; **(c)** nature of reserve and storage products; **(d)** morphology and characteristics of cells and thalli; **(e)** host range of parasitism.

CLASSIFICATION OF THE PROTOZOA

22 Match each disease on the right with the correct agent on the left.

_____ *Giardia intestinalis*

_____ *Trichomonas vaginalis*

_____ *Leishmania tropica*

_____ *Trypanosoma gambiense*

_____ *Trypanosoma cruzi*

_____ *Leishmania donovani*

(a) Venereal infection
(b) Diarrhea
(c) African sleeping sickness
(d) Oriental sore
(e) Kala-azar
(f) Chagas' disease

23 Amoebic dysentery in humans is caused by _____ .

24 The white cliffs of Dover are formed from the protozoan skeletons of

_____ and _____ .

25 *Toxoplasma gondii* is the etiologic agent of _____ .

26 The female anopheline mosquito is the _____ host for the plasmodia that cause malaria.

27 The only human ciliate parasite is _____ .

REVIEW QUESTIONS

1 Write a statement on the pigmentation of the green algae.

2 What are *imperfect fungi?*

3 Why are the acellular slime molds termed *acellular?*

4 Name the four classes of the lower flagellated fungi and give the characteristics that distinguish them.

5 Describe the process of zygospore formation in a typical zygomycete.

6 Explain with examples what is meant by sexual and asexual fruiting bodies or structures.

7 Draw the life cycle of *Saccharomyces cerevisiae.*

8 What is a dikaryotic mycelium?

9 Explain why some genera of molds, such as *Penicillium* and *Aspergillus*, contain some species that are designated as ascomycetes and other species as deuteromycetes.

DISCUSSION QUESTIONS

1 Why is *Candida albicans* called an *opportunistic* pathogen?

2 What is the significance of a report that species of the chrysophycean alga *Dinobryon* can phagotrophically ingest bacteria?

3 Why do mycologists have a taxonomic group called Deuteromycetes?

4 Explain why the slime molds are favorite subjects for the study of *morphogenesis.*

5 Compare the overall morphological properties of procaryotes with those of the eucaryotes, and comment on the contribution of morphology to their respective classification schemes.

6 In comparing the classification schemes of the three groups of eucaryotic microorganisms (the fungi, the algae, and the protozoa), which scheme would you consider to have most reliance on ultrastructural data from electron microscopy?

7 Discuss the role of locomotion in the classification of the protozoa.

8 Explain why George Beadle and Edward Tatum chose the ascomycete *Neurospora* to do their Nobel Prize work in genetics.

9 What is the contribution of *phylogeny* to each of the three classification schemes of the eucaryotic microorganisms?

10 Some cynics compare shellfish aficionados to people playing Russian roulette. Is there any truth to this comparison?

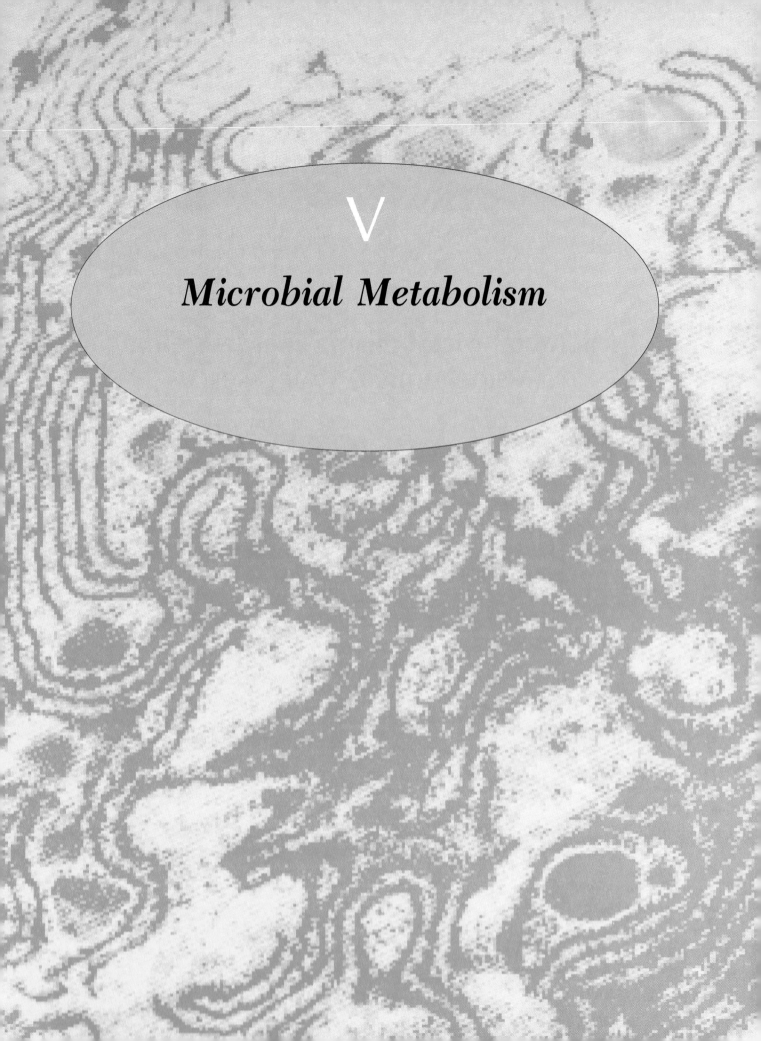

V

Microbial Metabolism

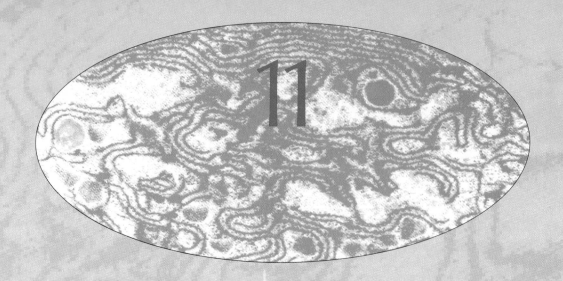

Microbial Metabolism: Energy-Yielding Biochemical Processes

OBJECTIVES

After reading this chapter you should be able to

1 Differentiate exergonic (energy-releasing) reactions from endergonic (energy-requiring) reactions, and explain how cells can couple the two kinds of reactions.

2 Name the most important high-energy-transfer compound in a cell.

3 Differentiate between substrate-level phosphorylation, oxidative phosphorylation, and photophosphorylation.

4 Diagram the sequence of events in an electron-transport system.

5 Explain the nature and importance of the proton-motive force.

6 Describe how phototrophic organisms convert light energy to chemical energy.

7 Explain how microorganisms break down complex nutrients to simple compounds.

8 Describe the major features of the dissimilatory pathway called *glycolysis*.

9 Explain how yeasts ferment glucose to ethanol.

10 Differentiate between respiration and fermentation.

OVERVIEW

Living organisms are, in a sense, chemical machines—their structure and functions can be traced directly or indirectly to chemical reactions. The term *metabolism* denotes all the chemical activities performed by an organism. These activities are of two general types: those involved in liberating energy and those involved in utilizing energy. Energy is the ability to do work, and a living cell must perform many different types of work, such as making enzymes, synthesizing a cell wall and cytoplasmic membrane, and repairing damage. To do this work, a cell needs a vast amount of energy. The source of this energy for some organisms is the nutrient molecules (chemicals) that are taken in by the cell. When the chemical bonds in these nutrients are broken, energy is liberated in the form of chemical energy, which the cell can trap and subsequently use to carry out work. For other organisms, the source of energy is light; when exposed to light, they convert the energy of light into chemical energy used for metabolism. This chapter discusses some basic principles of energy-yielding biochemical reactions and describes how microorganisms trap the energy released from these reactions. It is important to realize that many of these microbial metabolic mechanisms are also used by higher organisms (including humans) to obtain energy.

ENERGY REQUIREMENTS OF MICROBIAL CELLS

A living cell requires energy to perform many different kinds of work, including:

1 Construction of the structural parts of the cell such as wall, membrane, or external appendages
2 Synthesis of enzymes, nucleic acids, polysaccharides, phospholipids, and other chemical components of the cell
3 Repair of damage and maintenance of the cell in good condition
4 Growth and multiplication
5 Accumulation of nutrients and excretion of waste products
6 Motility

Although some microorganisms can use light as an energy source, most microorganisms obtain energy by *dissimilation*, the breakdown of nutrients or chemical substances. During dissimilation, energy is released from the nutrient molecules and is stored temporarily in an *energy-trapping system* until needed. The energy-trapping system also serves as an *energy-transfer system* that supplies energy when it is needed for synthesis of cell constituents. Dissimilation of nutrient molecules also provides the building blocks from which cell constituents can be synthesized.

Although the processes of dissimilation and synthesis are opposite to one another, they are interrelated and proceed concurrently in a microbial cell [FIGURE 11.1].

ASK YOURSELF

1 What different kinds of work does a living cell need to perform?

2 What is dissimilation?

3 How does an energy-trapping/energy-transfer system link the processes of dissimilation and synthesis?

FIGURE 11.1

Relationships between the processes of dissimilation and synthesis in microbial cells. An energy trapping and transfer (coupling) system carries usable energy between the two processes.

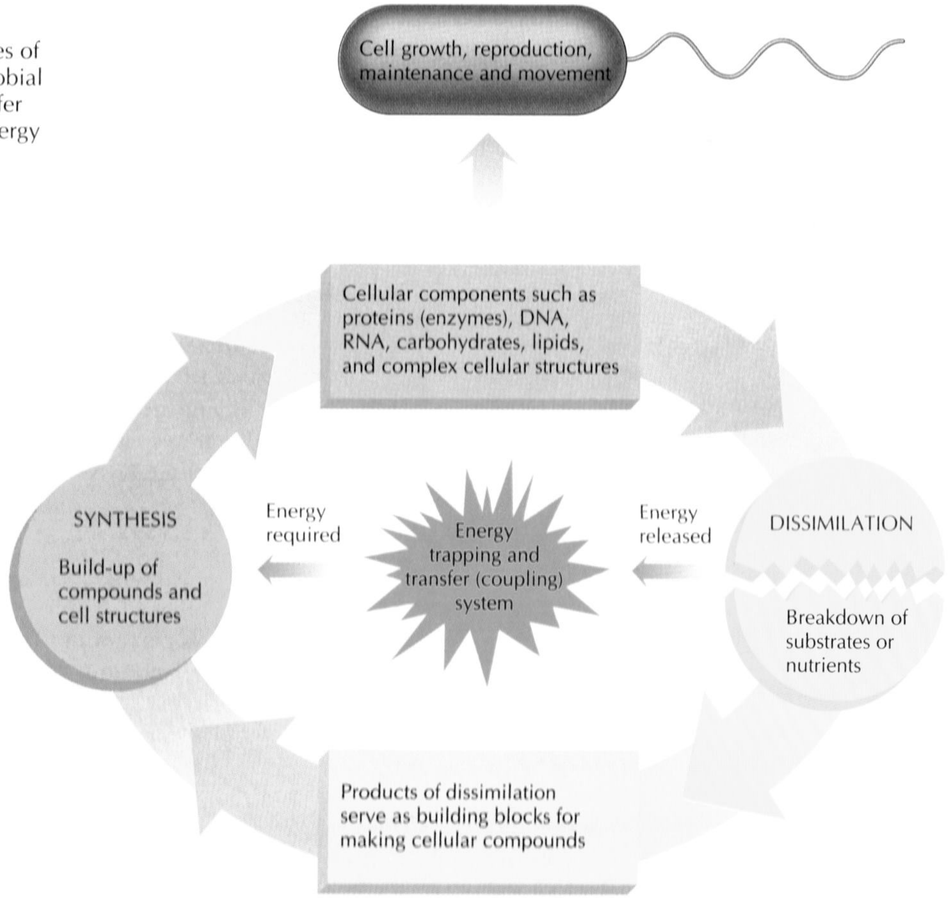

MAJOR ENERGY-YIELDING SOURCES FOR MICROORGANISMS

Chemotrophic microorganisms obtain energy by dissimilating nutrients, or chemical substrates. During dissimilation, energy is released and trapped, and end products accumulate. *Chemoheterotrophic* microorganisms are chemotrophs that dissimilate *organic* compounds to obtain energy. For example:

Streptococcus lactis + glucose →
Chemoheterotroph   Organic substrate

energy + lactic acid
End product

On the other hand, *chemoautotrophic* microorganisms dissimilate *inorganic* compounds to obtain energy. For example:

Nitrosomonas europaea + ammonia →
Chemoautotroph   Inorganic substrate

energy + nitrite
End product

There are some microorganisms that do not obtain energy by dissimilating chemical substrates. Instead, these microorganisms use light as their energy source and are called *phototrophs*. Phototrophic microorganisms contain special pigments that absorb the light and trap its energy. For example:

Anabaena cylindrica + light →
Phototroph

absorption of light by cell pigment → energy

ASK YOURSELF

1 What kind of nutrients do chemoheterotrophic microorganisms dissimilate to obtain energy?

2 What kind of nutrients do chemoautotrophic microorganisms dissimilate to obtain energy?

3 What is the source of energy for phototrophic microorganisms?

CHEMICAL ENERGY AND ENERGY TRANSFER

Although energy can exist in various forms, *chemical energy* is used universally by living organisms. Chemical energy is the energy contained in the chemical bonds within special nutrient molecules. When these bonds are broken during dissimilation of a nutrient or chemical substrate, chemical energy is released. Under certain optimal conditions, bacterial cells can dissimilate an amount of nutrient equivalent to their own weight *every few seconds*.

Radiant energy (the energy of light) can be used by some microorganisms, but these microorganisms must convert the light energy into *chemical energy* in order to have the energy in a form useful for cell functions.

Heat energy (the energy associated with the random motions of molecules or atoms) is a form of energy that *cannot* be used by living organisms. However, a certain amount of heat is necessary in order for chemical reactions, even when catalyzed by enzymes, to proceed at rates fast enough to sustain life. For instance, the rate of most enzyme-catalyzed reactions increases by a factor of about 2 for each 10°C increase in temperature, up to the temperature at which the particular enzyme begins to deteriorate.

Energy Transfer Between Exergonic and Endergonic Chemical Reactions

The dissimilation of nutrients and the synthesis of cell constituents are not single-step processes. Instead, they involve numerous chemical reactions, each catalyzed by a specific enzyme. In the course of any chemical reaction, chemical energy is either released or absorbed. A chemical reaction that liberates energy is called an *exergonic* reaction, whereas a chemical reaction that takes up energy is called an *endergonic* reaction. An endergonic reaction will not proceed unless energy is supplied. Exergonic reactions are associated with the dissimilation of a nutrient or chemical substrate, while endergonic reactions are associated with *synthesis* of cell constituents. *In a living organism, the exergonic reactions provide the energy to fuel the endergonic reactions.* In order to link these reactions, organisms have developed a process called *energy coupling:*

Exergonic reaction liberates energy.
↓
A portion of the energy is trapped into an
energy-transfer (coupling) compound.
↓
The energy-transfer compound then donates the
trapped energy to an endergonic reaction.

The energy-transfer compounds that are of most use to a cell are those capable of transferring large amounts of energy *(high-energy-transfer compounds)*. Several kinds of high-energy-transfer compounds occur in cells, but one is by far the most important: *adenosine triphosphate (ATP)*. ATP is composed of one molecule of the purine base adenine, one molecule of the pentose sugar ribose, and three phosphate groups [FIGURE 11.2]. It is formed by adding a phosphate group to *adenosine diphosphate (ADP)*, which has only two phosphate groups:

$$\text{ADP} + \text{phosphate} \xrightarrow{\text{Energy}} \text{ATP} + \text{water}$$

A large amount of energy is needed to form the chemical bond linking the third phosphate group to ADP; for this reason, this bond is called a *high-energy phosphate bond.* The energy trapped in the high-energy phosphate bond of ATP can be liberated if the bond is later broken:

$$\text{ATP} + \text{water} \xrightarrow[\text{Energy}]{} \text{ADP} + \text{phosphate}$$

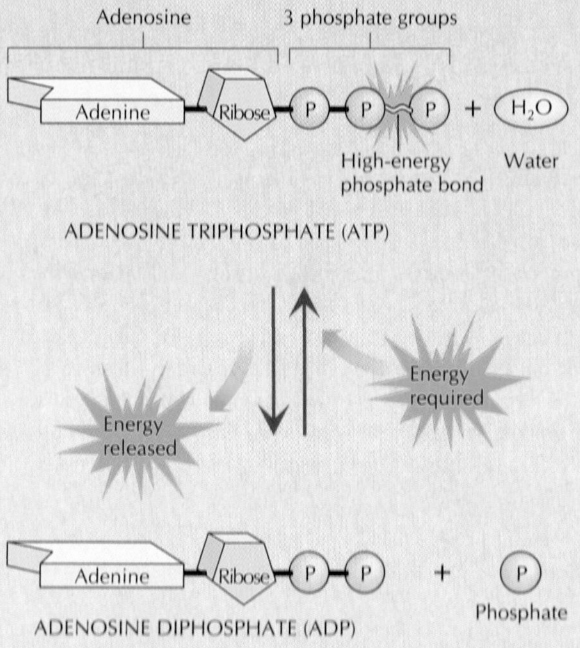

FIGURE 11.3
The flow of chemical energy from dissimilation of nutrient molecules to ATP, and then from ATP to the energy-requiring (endergonic) reactions of a microbial cell. Some energy is always lost in the form of heat.

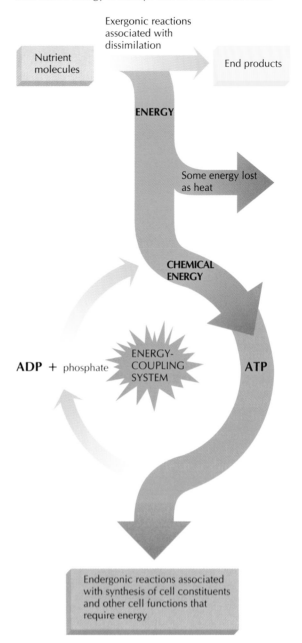

The general role of ATP in energy coupling is illustrated in FIGURE 11.3. Just as money constitutes a common medium for buying and selling of items in a society, so ATP constitutes the "energy currency" of a cell during the exchange of chemical energy between many different kinds of exergonic and endergonic chemical reactions.

FIGURE 11.2
ATP is composed of the purine base adenine, the sugar ribose, and three phosphate groups. The third phosphate is linked to the molecule by a high-energy phosphate bond. Breakdown of ATP to ADP releases chemical energy, whereas synthesis of ATP from ADP requires energy.

Adenosine   3 phosphate groups

Adenine — Ribose — P — P — P   +   H₂O

High-energy   Water
phosphate bond

ADENOSINE TRIPHOSPHATE (ATP)

Energy
required

Energy
released

Adenine — Ribose — P — P   +   P

Phosphate

ADENOSINE DIPHOSPHATE (ADP)

GENERATION OF ATP BY MICROORGANISMS

Phosphorylation is the addition of a phosphate group to a compound. ATP is formed by phosphorylation of ADP, with energy for the addition provided by an exergonic reaction. There are three general ways in which this phosphorylation of ADP can occur:

1 *Substrate-level phosphorylation,* a process in which the phosphate group of a chemical compound is removed and directly added to ADP

2 *Oxidative phosphorylation,* a process by which the energy liberated by chemical oxidations of nutrient chemical compounds is used for the synthesis of ATP from ADP

3 *Photophosphorylation,* a process in which the energy of light is used for the synthesis of ATP from ADP

Substrate-Level Phosphorylation

In many instances, the rearrangement of atoms within chemical compounds may result in a new compound that contains a high-energy phosphate bond. Such rearrangements occur when cells break down nutrients into chemical compounds. The phosphate group involved in this bond can then be transferred directly to ADP, forming ATP, which now contains the high-energy phosphate bond.

For example, if a cell uses the sugar glucose as a nutrient, one of the compounds that may result from glucose breakdown is *2-phosphoglyceric acid.* (The

phospho- in the name of this compound indicates that a phosphate group is present.) The cell then rearranges the atoms in the 2-phosphoglyceric acid by removing a molecule of water, thus forming a new compound, *phosphoenolpyruvic acid.* However, unlike 2-phosphoglyceric acid, phosphoenolpyruvic acid contains a *high-energy phosphate bond.* In fact, the bond has sufficient energy to allow the phosphate group on phosphoenolpyruvic acid to be transferred directly to ADP, forming ATP [FIGURE 11.4].

Oxidative Phosphorylation

All oxidation reactions liberate energy, and many organisms have developed ways to use the energy from chemical oxidations for ATP synthesis. The overall process of using the energy from oxidation reactions to make ATP from ADP is called *oxidative phosphorylation.* The sequence of events in this process can be summarized as follows:

Energy is liberated by an integrated series of sequential chemical oxidation reactions called an *electron-transport system.*

↓

The energy is stored temporarily in the form of a *protonmotive force.*

↓

The protonmotive force powers the synthesis of ATP from ADP.

To understand the process of oxidative phosphorylation more fully, you first need to understand the nature of oxidation reactions and electron-transport systems.

Oxidation Reactions. *Oxidation* is the loss of one or more electrons from an atom or a molecule, with the electrons being transferred immediately to a recipient atom or molecule. In biology, many oxidations involve the loss of a hydrogen atom from a molecule; since a hydrogen atom contains an electron in addition to its proton, a molecule that loses a hydrogen atom has automatically lost an electron. The opposite of oxidation is **reduction,** or the gain of electrons (or hydrogen atoms). The following are examples of oxidation reactions:

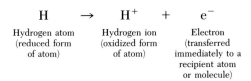

H	→	H$^+$	+	e$^-$
Hydrogen atom (reduced form of atom)		Hydrogen ion (oxidized form of atom)		Electron (transferred immediately to a recipient atom or molecule)

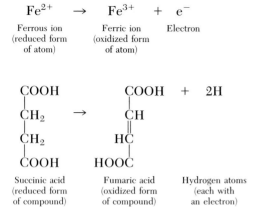

$$Fe^{2+} \rightarrow Fe^{3+} + e^-$$

| Ferrous ion (reduced form of atom) | Ferric ion (oxidized form of atom) | Electron |

Succinic acid (reduced form of compound) / Fumaric acid (oxidized form of compound) + 2H Hydrogen atoms (each with an electron)

Unlike oxidation reactions, reduction reactions do not liberate energy but instead *require* energy in order to proceed. An example of a reduction reaction is:

$$Fe^{3+} + e^- \rightarrow Fe^{2+}$$

Ferric ion (oxidized form of atom) / Ferrous ion (reduced form of atom)

From this example it is clear that *the reverse of any oxidation is a reduction and the reverse of any reduction is an oxidation*. In each reaction, a *pair* of substances is involved—one is the oxidized form, the other the reduced form (e.g., Fe^{3+} and Fe^{2+}, H^+ and H, fumaric acid and succinic acid). Each pair of such substances is called an **oxidation-reduction (O/R) system.**

Electron-Transport Systems. Cells that use the energy of oxidation reactions for ATP synthesis do not rely on a single oxidation reaction that liberates a large burst of energy. Instead, a cell uses an *integrated series of sequential oxidation reactions* called an **electron-transport system,** which liberates the energy in several smaller increments. This allows the cell to obtain energy in a more efficient manner. An electron-transport system is composed of a series of O/R systems in which each successive O/R system has a greater ability to gain electrons (a greater oxidizing ability) than the one preceding it. An electron-transport system can be described in general terms as follows:

ELECTRON-TRANSPORT SYSTEM

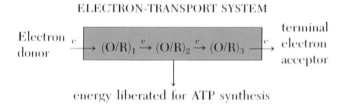

Electron donor $\xrightarrow{e}$ (O/R)$_1$ $\xrightarrow{e}$ (O/R)$_2$ $\xrightarrow{e}$ (O/R)$_3$ $\xrightarrow{e}$ terminal electron acceptor

energy liberated for ATP synthesis

FIGURE 11.4

An example of substrate-level phosphorylation. Many microbial cells can break down glucose to 2-phosphoglyceric acid, and, when an enzyme subsequently removes a molecule of water from 2-phosphoglyceric acid, a molecule of phosphoenolpyruvic acid is formed. The phosphoenolpyruvic acid contains a high-energy phosphate bond, and the energy of this bond can be used to transfer the phosphate group directly to ADP to make ATP.

Glucose

Intermediate reactions

2-Phosphoglyceric acid — Phosphate group

Removal of water molecule / H_2O

The removal of the molecule of water results in formation of a high-energy phosphate bond.

Phosphoenolpyruvic acid

Adenine — Ribose — P — P

ADP

Substrate-level phosphorylation

Adenine — Ribose — P — P — P

ATP

Pyruvic acid

FIGURE 11.5

Schematic illustration of an electron-transport system. An electron donor ($X_{(red)}$), which may be any of a variety of reduced compounds, initially supplies electrons to the electron-transport system and becomes oxidized ($X_{(ox)}$). The electrons are passed along a series of intermediary O/R systems ($A_{(ox)}/A_{(red)}, B_{(ox)}/B_{(red)}, C_{(ox)}/C_{(red)}, D_{(ox)}/D_{(red)}$), each having greater oxidizing power than the one that precedes it. The electrons eventually reach the terminal electron acceptor, $Y_{(ox)}$, which is an oxidized compound such as oxygen (O_2), potassium nitrate (KNO_3), or potassium sulfate (K_2SO_4). This compound takes up the electrons and becomes reduced ($Y_{(red)}$). Energy is released at each oxidation step along the electron-transport system, and at some steps the amount of energy released is great enough to allow the synthesis of ATP from ADP.

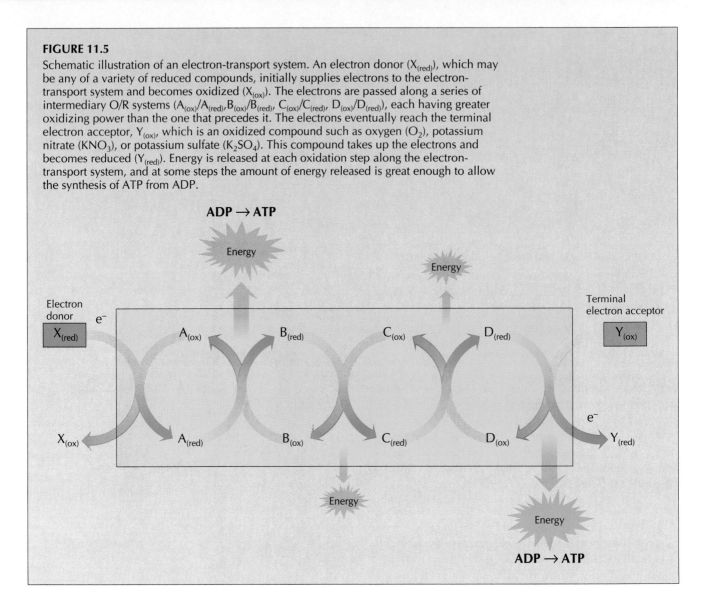

The system begins with an *electron donor,* a reduced compound which provides the electrons. This reduced compound is either a nutrient that has been taken in by the cell or a compound resulting from the breakdown of a nutrient. For instance, some microorganisms use lactic acid as an electron donor:

Lactic acid → pyruvic acid + $2H^+ + 2e^-$

The electrons from the electron donor are removed by an initial O/R system. This O/R system is in turn oxidized by the next O/R system, that O/R system is oxidized by the next O/R system, and so forth. Finally the electrons are taken up by a *terminal electron acceptor,* an oxidized compound obtained from the cell's environment. For instance, aerobic organisms use oxygen as the terminal electron acceptor; after accepting the electrons from the last O/R system, the oxygen becomes reduced to water:

$\frac{1}{2}O_2 + 2e^- + 2H^+ \rightarrow H_2O$

Anaerobic organisms that have an electron-transport system do not use oxygen as a terminal electron acceptor; instead, they use a chemical such as nitrate, sulfate, or fumaric acid.

The importance of an electron-transport system lies in the fact that *energy is liberated at each step in the sequential series of oxidations.* At some steps, the amount of energy liberated is so great that it can allow ATP to be made [FIGURE 11.5]. However, as indicated earlier, this energy must first be stored in the form of a protonmotive force (described in the following paragraphs) before it can be used to make ATP.

Where is the electron-transport system located in a cell? In a bacterium, it is located in the cytoplasmic membrane, whereas in a eucaryotic cell it is in the inner membrane of the mitochondria.

The Protonmotive Force. In 1978, the biochemist Peter Mitchell received a Nobel Prize for discovering the way by which energy liberated by an electron-transport system is used for the synthesis of ATP. He showed that the energy is used *to pump protons* (hydrogen ions, or H^+) *across the membrane* where the electron transport is located. Some of these protons are derived from the hydrogen atoms of the electron donor; others are the hydrogen ions that occur in water. After the protons are pumped across the membrane they cannot easily return, because the membrane is not permeable to protons. Therefore, *the continued operation of an electron-transport system results in accumulation of protons on one side of the membrane (outside the bacterial cell) and a deficit of protons on the opposite side (inside the bacterial cell).* The result is that one side of the membrane becomes much more positively charged and acidic than the other side:

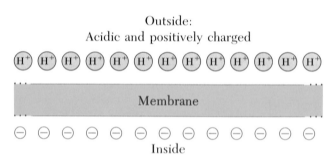

Outside:
Acidic and positively charged

Inside

In fact, the concentration of protons may be 100 times greater on one side of the membrane than the other. This unequal distribution of protons and electric charges across the membrane represents an important form of potential energy called the ***protonmotive force,*** which is used to synthesize ATP.

The protonmotive force represents potential energy in much the same way that a body of water held back by a dam represents potential energy. If a gate in the dam were opened, the water would flow down from the higher elevation toward a lower level; this water flow can operate a turbine and generate hydroelectric power. The membrane of a cell is like a dam—it separates protons at a high concentration on one side from a lower proton concentration on the other side. If a channel specific for protons is present in the membrane, the protons will flow "downhill" to the side where they are less concentrated. This proton flow can be used by a cell to perform work.

Indeed, certain specific channels do exist in the cytoplasmic membranes that allow passage of protons back to the other side of the membrane. The proton flow through these channels is harnessed by the cell to do the work of phosphorylating ADP to ATP. These channels occur within the molecules of an enzyme called ***adenosine triphosphatase (ATPase),*** which spans the membrane. The proton flow forces this enzyme to phosphorylate ADP, thereby forming ATP. The principle is illustrated in terms of a simple mechanical model in FIGURE 11.6. However, the actual mechanism is biochemical, as illustrated for a bacterial cell in FIGURE 11.7. In fact, certain kinds of poisons can prevent the synthesis of ATP by "short-circuiting" the protonmotive force [DISCOVER 11.1].

Photophosphorylation

Photophosphorylation is the overall process in which light is used as a source of energy for ATP synthesis. The general way in which photophosphorylation occurs is as follows:

1 Light is used to generate a protonmotive force.
2 The protonmotive force then powers ATP synthesis.

The most important example of photophosphorylation is the type carried out by cyanobacteria, algae, and green plants. The photophosphorylation system in these organisms occurs within the cells in special flattened membranous sacs called *thylakoids*. In cyanobacteria, the thylakoids occur directly within the cytoplasm [FIGURE 11.8]. But in the cells of algae and green plants, they are contained within the grana of chloroplasts. Thylakoid membranes contain **chlorophyll (Chl)**, a light-absorbing green pigment that plays a major role in the photophosphorylation process.

In addition to their ability to carry out photophosphorylation, cyanobacteria, algae, and green plants are also able to use carbon dioxide (CO_2) as their sole source of carbon; that is, they are *autotrophic* organisms. They reduce the CO_2 to carbohydrate $(CH_2O)_x$ by a process called **CO_2 fixation.** This process requires two components: (1) ATP, which serves as an energy source and is made by photophosphorylation; and (2) $NADPH_2$, the reduced form of a coenzyme called ***nicotinamide adenine dinucleotide phosphate (NADP).*** The $NADPH_2$ is used as an electron donor for reduction of CO_2.

The generation of ATP and $NADPH_2$ depends on the activity of two different kinds of chlorophyll-containing reaction centers, called *photosystem I (PS I)* and *photosystem II (PS II),* which are located in thylakoid membranes. The two photosystems work together in tandem as illustrated in FIGURE 11.9. Three main steps are involved:

1 When light is absorbed by the chlorophyll molecules in PS I, the energy of the light raises the molecules to an excited state, causing an electron to be

FIGURE 11.6

Schematic drawing illustrating the concept of the protonmotive force by means of a mechanical model. Energy liberated by the oxidation reactions of an electron-transport system is used to pump protons to the outside of the bacterial cytoplasmic membrane. The protons reenter the cell via an enzyme called ATPase, which in turn catalyzes the synthesis of ATP. No mechanical devices like those depicted here are actually present in cell membranes.

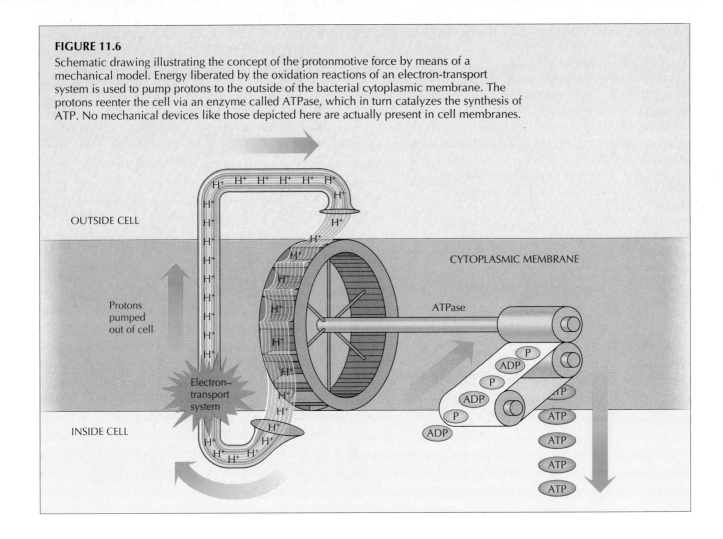

FIGURE 11.7

Schematic representation of an electron-transport system in a bacterial cytoplasmic membrane. Electrons from an electron donor pass along an electron-transport system and eventually reach a terminal electron acceptor (in this case O_2, which becomes reduced to water). The energy liberated by the electron-transport system is used to pump protons (hydrogen ions, H^+) across the membrane to the outside of the cell, generating a protonmotive force. The protons can return to the inside only by passing through a channel in the enzyme ATPase, which causes the enzyme to synthesize ATP from ADP.

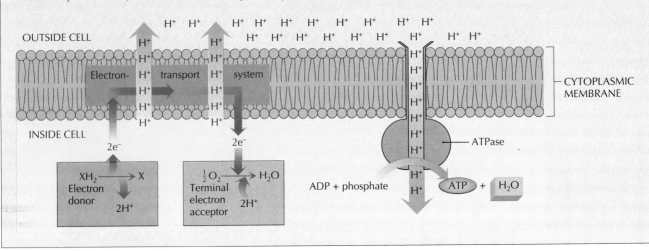

11.1 UNCOUPLING AGENTS: A GROUP OF UNUSUAL CELL POISONS

In oxidative phosphorylation, the energy liberated by an electron-transport system is coupled to the energy-requiring process of making ATP. The coupling mechanism is analogous to the clutch on an automobile: when the clutch is engaged, it allows the power from the engine to be transmitted to the wheels. When the clutch is not engaged, the power from the engine is not transmitted to the wheels, even though the engine continues to run.

Certain chemicals called *uncoupling agents* have long been known to poison cells by disengaging a "biochemical clutch" during oxidative phosphorylation. In other words, these chemicals do not stop an electron-transport system from operating, but they do prevent the energy released by the electron-transport system from being used to make ATP. The exact way in which this uncoupling occurs remained a mystery until the 1970s, when the British biochemist Peter Mitchell found the Nobel Prize–winning answer: uncoupling agents destroy the protonmotive force that is generated by an electron-transport system.

In a bacterial cell, an electron-transport system generates a protonmotive force by pumping protons across the cytoplasmic membrane to the outside of the cell. The protons that accumulate outside can return only by flowing through a specific channel in the enzyme ATPase, which spans the membrane. This proton flow forces the enzyme to make ATP. Mitchell discovered that uncoupling agents are able to destroy the protonmotive force by acting as *proton conductors*. They can carry protons freely back across the membrane, bypassing the ATPase. Consequently, while the electron-transport system is busily pumping protons to the outside of a bacterial cell, the uncoupling agent is carrying them right back in again. Hence there is no accumulation of protons outside the cell, and there is no protonmotive force to power ATP synthesis.

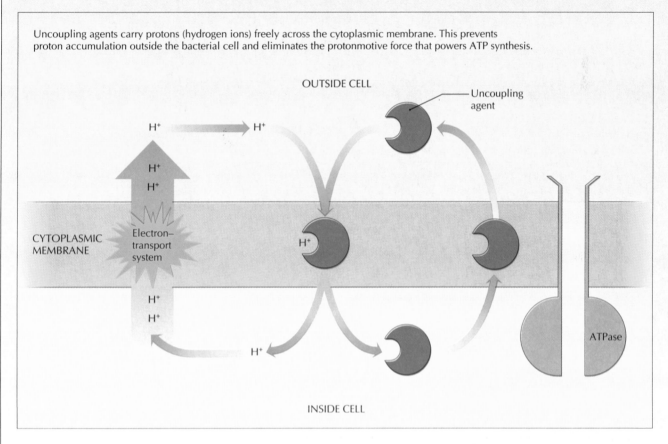

Uncoupling agents carry protons (hydrogen ions) freely across the cytoplasmic membrane. This prevents proton accumulation outside the bacterial cell and eliminates the protonmotive force that powers ATP synthesis.

FIGURE 11.8

Electron micrograph of a thin section through the cyanobacterium, *Anabaena azollae*, showing the thylakoids — the sites of photophosphorylation. Most of the thylakoids are near the periphery of the cell, but some extend into the midportions of the cell. The structures called *polyhedral bodies* are found in many autotrophic bacteria. These bodies contain an enzyme system that allows the bacteria to use carbon dioxide as their sole or major carbon source.

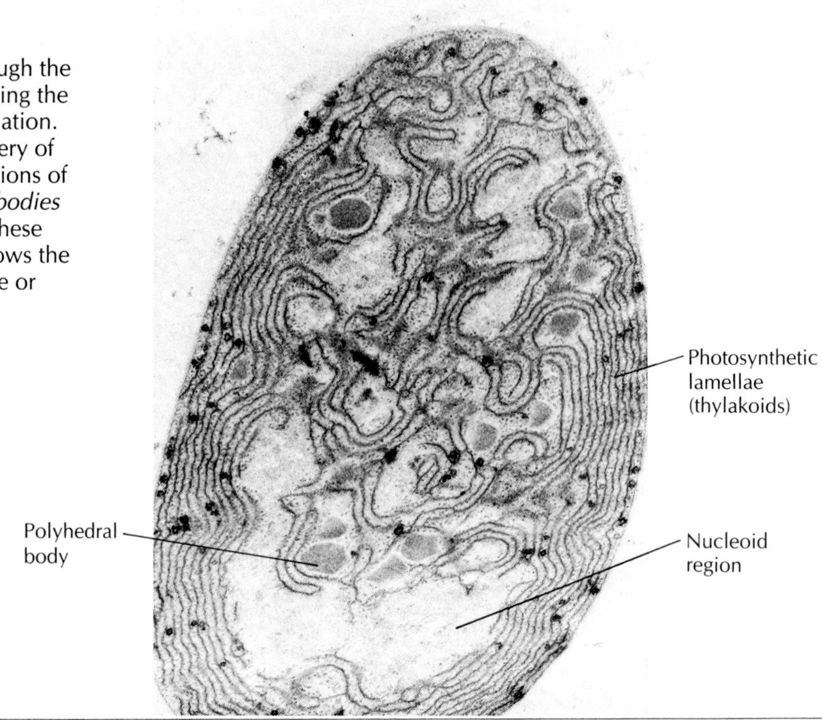

Photosynthetic lamellae (thylakoids)

Polyhedral body

Nucleoid region

FIGURE 11.9

Schematic diagram showing how light energy is used by cyanobacteria for the production of ATP and $NADPH_2$. In the presence of light, electrons are ejected from photosystem I (PS I) and photosystem II (PS II), leaving both photosystems electron-deficient. The electrons ejected from PS I are used to reduce NADP to $NADPH_2$, while those ejected from PS II pass along an electron-transport system and reach PS I. The electron-transport system generates a protonmotive force that causes ATPase to synthesize ATP. The electron-deficient PS II obtains electrons from water (H_2O) molecules, and this oxidation of water results in the production of oxygen gas (O_2).

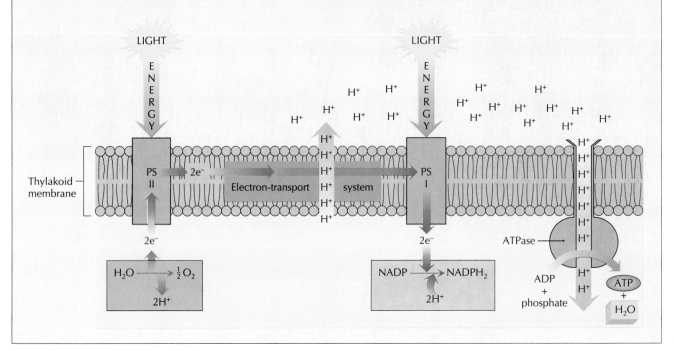

ejected from each. These ejected electrons are used to reduce NADP to $NADPH_2$:

$$2Chl_{(PS\,I)} \longrightarrow 2e^- \longrightarrow NADP + 2H^+$$
$$2Chl_{(PS\,I)}^+ \qquad\qquad NADPH_2$$

This leaves the chlorophyll of PS I temporarily deficient in electrons, giving it a positive charge.
2 Similarly, light is absorbed by the chlorophyll of PS II and causes electrons to be ejected by this photosystem. These electrons pass along an electron-transport system and reach the electron-deficient Chl^+ of PS I:

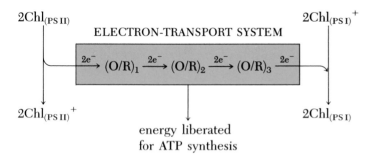

$$2Chl_{(PS\,II)} \qquad\qquad\qquad\qquad 2Chl_{(PS\,I)}^+$$

ELECTRON-TRANSPORT SYSTEM

$$\xrightarrow{2e^-} (O/R)_1 \xrightarrow{2e^-} (O/R)_2 \xrightarrow{2e^-} (O/R)_3 \xrightarrow{2e^-}$$

$$2Chl_{(PS\,II)}^+ \qquad\qquad\qquad\qquad 2Chl_{(PS\,I)}$$

energy liberated
for ATP synthesis

This electron-transport system is much like the electron-transport system described previously for oxidative phosphorylation. However, it differs in that the electron donor $Chl_{(PS\,II)}$ and the terminal electron acceptor $Chl_{(PS\,I)}^+$ *are supplied by the cell itself*, rather than being obtained from the environment. Nevertheless, *the result is the same as with oxidative phosphorylation—a protonmotive force is generated across the membrane and is used to power ATP synthesis.*
3 At this point, $Chl_{(PS\,II)}^+$ is still deficient in electrons. However, $Chl_{(PS\,II)}^+$ is a very strong oxidizing agent—so strong that *it can regain electrons by removing them from molecules of water*. This oxidation of water results in the formation of gaseous oxygen:

$$H_2O \longrightarrow 2e^- \longrightarrow 2Chl_{(PS\,II)}^+$$
$$\tfrac{1}{2}O_2 + 2H^+ \qquad\qquad 2Chl_{(PS\,II)}$$

Thus cyanobacteria, algae, and green plants are *oxygen-generating* organisms that are responsible for producing *almost all the oxygen in the earth's atmosphere.* Geologists estimate that the atmosphere of the primitive earth was essentially devoid of oxygen until sometime between 1 and 3 billion years ago, when cyanobacteria first evolved. Only after appreciable levels of O_2 accumulated was it possible for *aerobic* organisms to evolve; these organisms used the O_2 as a terminal electron acceptor for oxidative phosphorylation.

ASK YOURSELF

1 What are the major differences between substrate-level phosphorylation, oxidative phosphorylation, and photophosphorylation?

2 How does oxidation differ from reduction?

3 What is an electron-transport system, and how does it function in oxidative phosphorylation?

4 What is the protonmotive force, and how is it related to ATP synthesis?

5 How do phototrophic organisms convert the energy of light into the chemical energy of ATP?

6 What similarities are there between photophosphorylation and oxidative phosphorylation? What differences are there?

PATHWAYS FOR DISSIMILATION OF NUTRIENTS

As mentioned earlier, chemotrophic organisms use chemical compounds rather than light as an energy source. Those that derive energy from organic nutrients usually must first break down those nutrients into compounds that can be used for ATP generation. They accomplish this by a series of consecutive enzyme-catalyzed chemical reactions called a ***dissimilatory pathway.*** Dissimilatory pathways serve not only to liberate energy from nutrients but also to supply many of the building blocks from which a cell can construct its proteins, lipids, polysaccharides, and nucleic acids. FIGURE 11.10 shows general pathways that many organisms use for the dissimilation of nutrients.

Dissimilation of Complex Nutrients

Microorganisms can use a wide variety of compounds as energy sources. Sometimes these compounds are large, complex molecules such as proteins, lipids, or polysaccharides, which must first be broken down to smaller molecules before they can be used to supply energy. Microorganisms use enzymes to catalyze the dissimilation of proteins to amino acids, fats to glycerol and fatty acids, and polysaccharides to monosaccharides. These products can then be converted to other compounds that can enter the main dissimilatory pathways of a cell, such as glycolysis.

FIGURE 11.10
Overall general scheme showing some of the dissimilatory pathways used by organisms for the breakdown of complex nutrients. These pathways are detailed more fully in FIGURES 11.11 through 11.12.

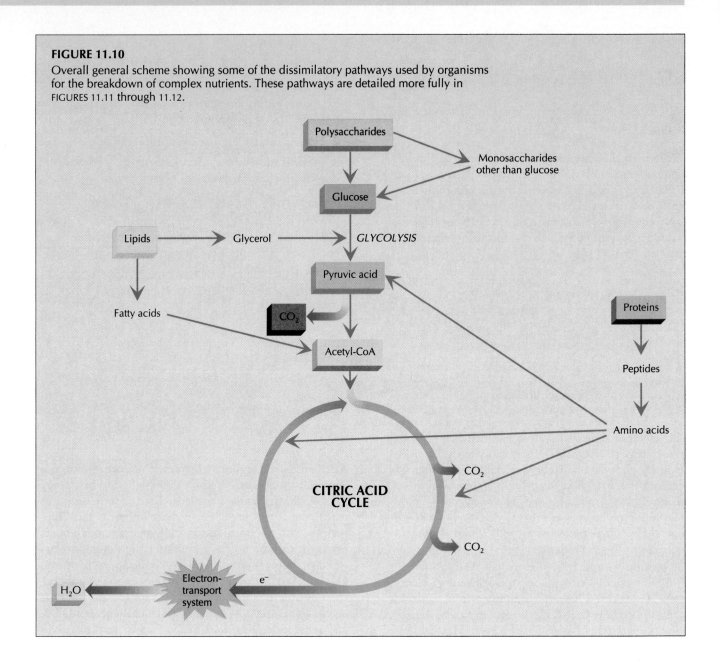

Glycolysis

Many chemoheterotrophs can dissimilate monosaccharides, especially the six-carbon sugar glucose. Although different kinds of pathways for glucose dissimilation may occur, the most common pathway is **glycolysis.** This pathway is found in many microorganisms as well as in animals and plants. The steps in the pathway are indicated in FIGURE 11.11. The most important features of glycolysis are:

1 *Two molecules of ATP are used* for the conversion of glucose to fructose-1,6-diphosphate.

2 *A total of four molecules of ATP are produced* by substrate-level phosphorylation. Two ATP molecules are produced during conversion of two molecules of 1,3-diphosphoglyceric acid to two molecules of 3-phosphoglyceric acid. The other two ATP molecules are produced during conversion of two molecules of phosphoenolpyruvic acid to two molecules of pyruvic acid [see FIGURE 11.4].

3 Although four molecules of ATP are made, two molecules are used; therefore, *the net yield of ATP per molecule of glucose is two molecules of ATP.*

4 In the overall process of glycolysis, one molecule of glucose, which has six carbon atoms, is eventually

FIGURE 11.11

Glycolysis. A molecule of glucose is broken down to two molecules of pyruvic acid. Two ATP molecules are used up in the process; however, four ATP molecules are produced by substrate-level phosphorylation. Thus there is a net gain of two ATP molecules. Two molecules of $NADH_2$ are also produced, and these must be oxidized back to NAD so that glycolysis can continue to break down more glucose molecules.

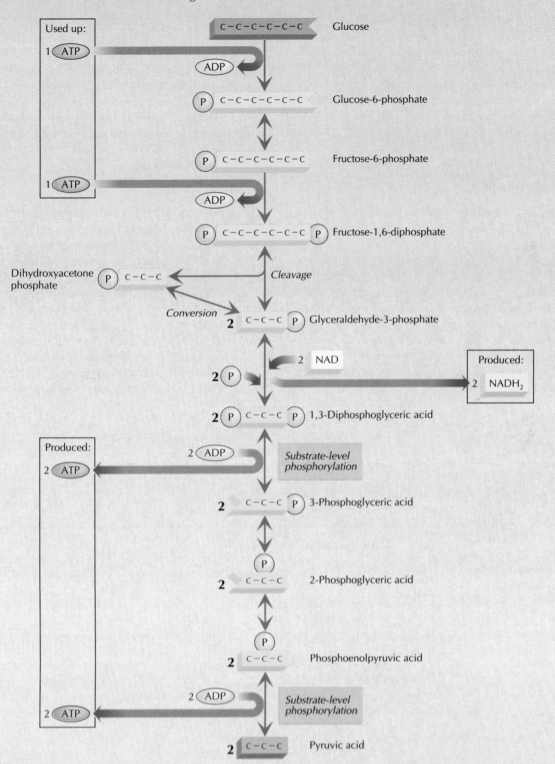

cleaved into two molecules of pyruvic acid, each having three carbon atoms.

5 One molecule of a coenzyme called *nicotinamide adenine dinucleotide (NAD)* is used to oxidize each molecule of glyceraldehyde-3-phosphate to a molecule of 1,3-diphosphoglyceric acid. (NAD is similar to the coenzyme NADP mentioned earlier in this chapter, except that NAD lacks an extra phosphate group.) Since two molecules of glyceraldehyde-3-phosphate are oxidized, *two molecules of NADH$_2$ are formed*.

The last feature is a very important aspect of glycolysis because a cell contains a very limited amount of NAD. A means of continuously regenerating NAD from NADH$_2$ must exist in order for glycolysis to continue.

Regeneration of NAD

Living organisms use one of two methods to regenerate NAD from NADH$_2$—namely, *fermentation* and *respiration*.

Fermentation is an oxygen-independent process in which the NADH$_2$ that is produced during glycolysis or another dissimilatory pathway is used to reduce an organic electron acceptor made by the cell itself. For instance, when yeast cells are grown with glucose under anaerobic conditions, they carry out an *alcoholic fermentation* [FIGURE 11.12]. After making pyruvic acid by glycolysis, they remove a molecule of CO_2 from the pyruvic acid to form acetaldehyde:

$$2 \text{ pyruvic acid} \rightarrow 2 \text{ acetaldehyde} + 2CO_2$$

Then the yeast cells use the acetaldehyde as an acceptor for the electrons of the NADH$_2$ that was produced during glycolysis. The acetaldehyde oxidizes the NADH$_2$ from glycolysis and becomes reduced to ethanol (ethyl alcohol), thus regenerating NAD [FIGURE 11.12A]:

$$2 \text{ acetaldehyde} + 2NADH_2 \rightarrow 2 \text{ ethanol} + 2NAD$$

The ability of yeasts to carry out alcoholic fermentation is the basis for the alcoholic beverage industry.

Other microorganisms use different fermentations to regenerate NAD. For instance, *Streptococcus lactis* carries out a *lactic acid fermentation* by using pyruvic acid itself as the electron acceptor:

$$2 \text{ pyruvic acid} + 2NADH_2 \rightarrow 2 \text{ lactic acid} + 2NAD$$

The ability of *S. lactis* to produce lactic acid as a fermentation product is of great importance in the dairy industry. Many other types of fermentations may be carried out by bacteria that lead to various end products [TABLE 11.1]. Knowledge of the kinds and amounts of products made by a particular bacterium is often helpful in identifying that bacterium. Moreover, some fermentation products (such as acetone, isopropanol, butanol, propionic acid, and butyric acid) are useful in industry. However, fermentation products are toxic waste substances as far as the cells that produce them are concerned. For instance, the ethanol content of natural wine seldom

---

TABLE 11.1

Major Products of the Breakdown of Glucose by Some Bacterial Species

Species	Major fermentation products
Acetivibrio cellulolyticus	Acetic acid
Actinomyces bovis	Formic acid, acetic acid, lactic acid, and succinic acid
Clostridium acetobutylicum	Acetone, acetyl methyl carbinol, butanol, ethanol, butyric acid, acetic acid, carbon dioxide, and hydrogen
Enterobacter aerogenes	Butylene glycol, acetyl methyl carbinol, ethanol, formic acid, carbon dioxide, and hydrogen
Escherichia coli	Ethanol, succinic acid, lactic acid, acetic acid, formic acid, carbon dioxide, and hydrogen
Lactobacillus brevis	Lactic acid, acetic acid, ethanol, glycerol, and carbon dioxide
Propionibacterium acidipropionici	Propionic acid, succinic acid, acetic acid, and carbon dioxide
Streptococcus lactis	Lactic acid
Succinimonas amylolytica	Succinic acid and acetic acid

FIGURE 11.12

Methods used by yeast cells to regenerate NAD from the $NADH_2$ produced in glycolysis.
[A] In alcoholic fermentation the $NADH_2$ reduces acetaldehyde to ethanol. **[B]** In aerobic
respiration the $NADH_2$ serves as the electron donor for an electron-transport system, which
in turn generates a protonmotive force that drives the synthesis of ATP.

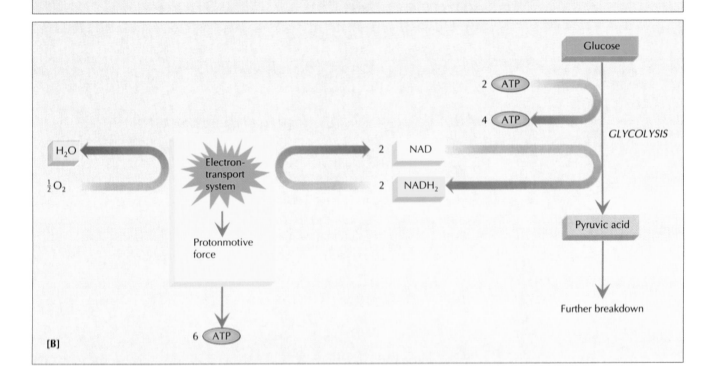

FIGURE 11.13

The citric acid cycle. Initially, pyruvic acid from glycolysis is oxidized to acetyl-CoA, which then undergoes a condensation with oxaloacetic acid to form citric acid. This condensation is the first reaction in a cyclic series of reactions that regenerates oxaloacetic acid. $NADH_2$ and $FADH_2$ molecules are produced at various steps and can serve as electron donors for an electron-transport system that generates a protonmotive force. GTP is generated by substrate-level phosphorylation; energetically, it is equivalent to ATP.

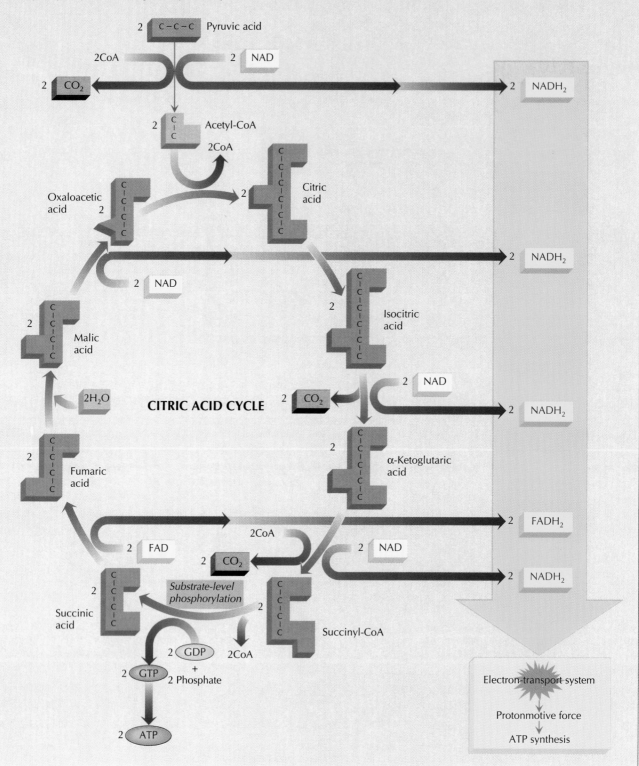

exceeds 12%, because this level of ethanol poisons the yeast cells and prevents them from making any additional alcohol.

Fermentation is a very inefficient process for extracting energy, because the end products still contain a great deal of chemical energy. An example is the ethanol produced by yeasts—proof of its high energy content is the fact that ethanol is an excellent fuel and liberates a great deal of heat when burned. As you will see, another process, called *respiration*, is much more efficient than fermentation for yielding energy.

Respiration is the process of regenerating NAD by using $NADH_2$ as the electron donor for an electron-transport system. If oxygen is the terminal electron acceptor for the electron-transport system, the process is called *aerobic respiration*. However, many bacteria can carry out respiration under anaerobic conditions by using a terminal electron acceptor other than oxygen, such as nitrate or sulfate. This process is termed *anaerobic respiration*. Respiration has a great advantage over fermentation: *not only is NAD regenerated, but the electron-transport system generates a protonmotive force that can be used to drive synthesis of additional ATP molecules.* If yeast cells are grown aerobically with glucose, the $NADH_2$ molecules produced during glycolysis can donate their electrons to an electron-transport system that has oxygen as the terminal electron acceptor. This results not only in regeneration of NAD but also in the generation of a protonmotive force, which can drive the synthesis of an additional six molecules of ATP [FIGURE 11.12B].

The dissimilation of glucose by aerobic organisms does not normally stop with the production of pyruvic acid. Further breakdown begins with the oxidation of the pyruvic acid by NAD to *acetyl-CoA* (a two-carbon acid, acetic acid, linked to coenzyme A). Each of the two resulting molecules of $NADH_2$ can serve as the electron donor for an electron-transport system, with consequent ATP synthesis [FIGURE 11.13].

Each of the two acetyl-CoA molecules is in turn condensed with a four-carbon acid, *oxaloacetic acid*, to form a six-carbon acid, *citric acid* [FIGURE 11.14]. This is the first step in a cyclic sequence of reactions known as the **citric acid cycle.** For every two acetyl-CoA molecules entering the cycle, the following events happen:

1 *Six molecules of $NADH_2$ are generated*, each of which can serve as the electron donor for an electron-transport system, with subsequent ATP synthesis.
2 *Two molecules of guanosine triphosphate (GTP) are generated* by substrate-level phosphorylation. The two GTPs are energetically equivalent to two ATPs:

$$2GTP + 2ADP \rightarrow 2GDP + 2ATP$$

3 *Two molecules of the reduced form of a coenzyme called flavin adenine dinucleotide (FAD) are generated*. Each $FADH_2$ can serve as the electron donor for an electron-transport system, with subsequent synthesis of two ATPs.

In the case of yeast cells respiring aerobically with glucose, the net yield of ATP from complete breakdown of one glucose molecule is 38 ATP molecules. Thirty-four of these are formed when $NADH_2$ and $FADH_2$ serve as electron donors for the yeast cell's electron-transport system [FIGURE 11.14]. The remainder are formed via substrate-level phosphorylation during glycolysis and the citric acid cycle.

In sharp contrast to aerobic respiration is the yield of ATP from fermentation when yeast cells are grown anaerobically, where the yield is only two ATPs per molecule of glucose. From this you can see that aerobic respiration is far more efficient than fermentation in extracting the chemical energy of glucose.

Fermentation and Respiration As Related to Habitat

Fermentative organisms usually occur naturally in environments that provide a continual source of fermentable nutrients, such as the intestinal tract of humans and animals. The large intestine of humans contains an extraordinarily high number of bacteria—up to 10^{11} (100,000,000,000) per gram of feces. If fermentation is an inefficient process, how can so many bacteria be present? The reason is that even an inefficient process can yield large amounts of ATP if unlimited amounts of fermentable nutrients are available.

On the other hand, if only low nutrient levels occur, as in the surface waters of unpolluted lakes, then heterotrophic microorganisms must use a more efficient process (respiration) to obtain energy. A remarkable example is that of certain aerobic heterotrophs, such as *Aquaspirillum* and *Caulobacter*, that are often found growing in bottles of stored distilled water in laboratories! One might think distilled water would be devoid of any organic nutrients, and this is true in freshly distilled water. However, during prolonged storage tiny amounts of gaseous organic nutrients from the air can dissolve in the water. The bacteria that derive energy from these minute amounts of nutrients are able to do so because of the high efficiency of their respiratory processes.

FIGURE 11.14
Summary of ATP production by yeast cells grown aerobically with glucose. The complete breakdown of glucose to six molecules of CO_2 results in a net yield of 38 ATP molecules.

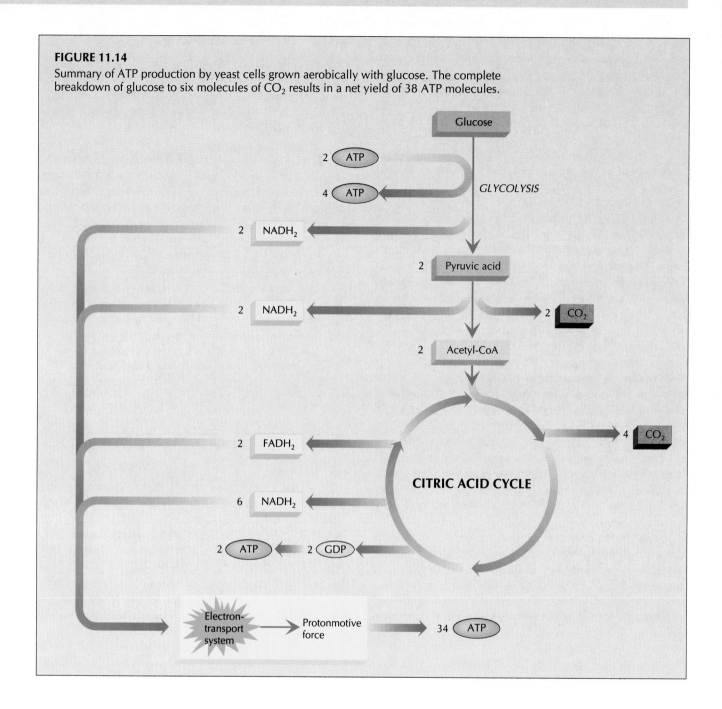

ASK YOURSELF

1 How do microorganisms break down complex nutrients to simple compounds?

2 What accounts for the net gain of two ATP molecules for each glucose molecule consumed during glycolysis? How many $NADPH_2$ molecules are formed?

3 How does a cell use fermentation to regenerate NAD?

4 How does a cell use respiration to regenerate NAD?

5 Why is respiration more efficient than fermentation in extracting the chemical energy of glucose?

SUMMARY

1 Some biochemical activities of living organisms lead to energy release, whereas others require energy. The kind of energy used universally by living organisms is chemical energy. The energy of light can be used by some microorganisms, but it must be converted into chemical energy to be useful for cell functions.

2 Chemical reactions that yield energy are exergonic; those that require energy are endergonic. In order for an organism to live, it must be able to use the energy from exergonic reactions to drive endergonic reactions. This coupling is done by means of energy-transfer compounds. ATP is the most important high-energy-transfer compound in a cell.

3 ATP can be generated by three mechanisms: **(a)** substrate-level phosphorylation, in which the phosphate group is removed from a substrate and directly added to ADP; **(b)** oxidative phosphorylation, in which electrons from an electron donor pass along an electron transport system to a terminal electron acceptor, releasing energy that pumps protons across the membrane and thus generates a protonmotive force used to make ATP; and **(c)** photophosphorylation, in which light is used as a source of energy for ATP synthesis, through generation of a protonmotive force. $NADPH_2$ is also generated for CO_2 fixation.

4 Cells derive energy from the dissimilation of nutrients by dissimilatory pathways. The most common dissimilatory pathway for glucose breakdown is glycolysis, in which each glucose molecule is broken down into two molecules of pyruvic acid, with net production of two ATP molecules and two $NADH_2$ molecules.

5 In order for glycolysis to continue, NAD must be regenerated through fermentation or respiration. Respiration is a much more efficient process than fermentation for obtaining energy from nutrients.

KEY TERMS

adenosine diphosphate (ADP)
adenosine triphosphatase (ATPase)
adenosine triphosphate (ATP)
chlorophyll (Chl)
citric acid cycle
CO_2 fixation
dissimilation
dissimilatory pathway
electron-transport system
endergonic
exergonic
glycolysis
high-energy phosphate bond
metabolism
nicotinamide adenine dinucleotide (NAD)
nicotinamide adenine dinucleotide phosphate (NADP)
oxidation
oxidation-reduction (O/R) system
oxidative phosphorylation
phosphorylation
photophosphorylation
protonmotive force
reduction
respiration
substrate-level phosphorylation

REVIEW GUIDE

ENERGY REQUIREMENTS OF MICROBIAL CELLS

1 Dissimilation is the _____ of nutrients, and during this process _____ is released from the nutrient molecules.

2 Which of the following statements is correct?

(a) The energy liberated by dissimilation is used directly for synthesis of cell constituents, with no intervening energy-trapping system.

(b) Dissimilation of nutrients provides the building blocks for synthesis of cell constituents.

(c) Energy is not required for repair of damage and maintenance of a cell in good condition.

(d) Synthesis of cell constituents is an energy-liberating process.

(e) Dissimilation is an energy-requiring process.

MAJOR ENERGY-YIELDING SOURCES FOR MICROORGANISMS

3 A chemoheterotroph is an organism that: **(a)** dissimilates inorganic nutrients to obtain energy; **(b)** uses light as its source of energy; **(c)** dissimilates organic substrates to obtain energy; **(d)** is exemplified by *Nitrosomonas europaea*; **(e)** is exemplified by *Anabaena cylindrica*.

CHEMICAL ENERGY AND ENERGY TRANSFER

4 The form of energy that is used universally by living organisms is _____ energy.

5 By what factor does the rate of most enzyme-catalyzed reactions increase for each 10°C increase in temperature up to the temperature at which the enzyme begins to be damaged? **(a)** 0.5; **(b)** 2; **(c)** 4; **(d)** 10; **(e)** 100.

6 Match the description on the right with the correct item on the left.

_____ heat
_____ energy-transfer
_____ endergonic
_____ exergonic

(a) Chemical reactions that liberate energy
(b) Type of compound that permits the coupling of energy-liberating reactions with energy-requiring reactions
(c) Chemical reactions that require energy
(d) Type of energy that cannot be used for energy-requiring cell functions

7 A molecule of ATP consists of the purine base called _____, the pentose sugar called _____, and three _____ groups.

GENERATION OF ATP BY MICROORGANISMS

8 The addition of a phosphate group to a compound is called _____.

9 Match the description on the right with the correct item on the left.

_____ O/R system
_____ substrate-level phosphorylation
_____ photophosphorylation
_____ oxidation
_____ oxidative phosphorylation
_____ reduction

(a) Process in which the phosphate group of a compound is removed and directly added to ADP
(b) Process in which the energy liberated by chemical oxidations is used for the synthesis of ATP
(c) Process in which the energy of light is used for the synthesis of ATP
(d) The loss of electrons from an atom or a molecule
(e) The gain of electrons by an atom or a molecule
(f) A pair of related substances, one in the oxidized form and the other in the reduced form

10 A molecule that loses a hydrogen atom is said to have been oxidized, because a hydrogen atom contains **(a)** an electron; **(b)** a proton; **(c)** a neutron; **(d)** an ion; **(e)** a nucleus.

11 A ferric ion (Fe^{3+}) can take up an electron and become reduced to a(n) _____ ion; a hydrogen ion (H^+) can take up an electron and become reduced to a(n) _____.

12 The compound that supplies electrons for an electron-transport system is called the _____, whereas the compound that ultimately accepts the electrons is called the _____.

13 During the operation of an electron-transport system, _____ ions are pumped across the membrane and accumulate on one side. The resulting unequal distribution of these ions represents a storage form of energy called the _____ force, which can be used to synthesize _____.

14 Which one of the following is an enzyme that contains a channel which allows protons expelled from a bacterial cell to flow back across the cytoplasmic membrane? **(a)** proteinase; **(b)** fumarase; **(c)** ATPase; **(d)** hydrogenase; **(e)** dehydrogenase.

15 What two compounds are required for CO_2 fixation? **(a)** hydrogen sulfide and oxygen; **(b)** fumaric acid and ATP; **(c)** thylakoids and iron-sulfur proteins; **(d)** cytochrome and ATP; **(e)** $NADPH_2$ and ATP.

16 In cyanobacteria, algae, and green plants, the thylakoid membranes contain two kinds of chlorophyll-containing reaction centers called _____ and _____. Of these, it is _____ that is responsible for oxidizing water to O_2.

17 In the thylakoid membranes of cyanobacteria, algae, and green plants, electrons ejected from photosystem _____ pass along an electron-transport system and reach the electron-deficient Chl^+ of photosystem _____. This electron-transport system generates a(n) _____ force that is used for the synthesis of _____.

PATHWAYS FOR DISSIMILATION OF NUTRIENTS

18 Complex nutrients must first be broken down to simpler molecules before they can be used for energy generation. Proteins are broken down to _____ acids, polysaccharides to _____, and fats to _____ and _____ acids.

19 Glycolysis is a dissimilatory pathway that results in breakdown of a molecule of glucose to two molecules of _____.

20 In glycolysis, for each glucose molecule that is broken down there is a net gain of **(a)** 1 ATP molecule; **(b)** 2 ATP molecules; **(c)** 3 ATP molecules; **(d)** 4 ATP molecules; **(e)** 6 ATP molecules.

21 During glycolysis, what type of phosphorylation generates ATP? **(a)** photophosphorylation; **(b)** oxidative phosphorylation; **(c)** substrate-level phosphorylation; **(d)** cyclic phosphorylation; **(e)** transphosphorylation.

22 In glycolysis, in addition to pyruvic acid and ATP two molecules of

_____ are made per molecule of glucose; these must be

reoxidized to _____ if the process of glycolysis is to continue.

23 In alcoholic fermentation by yeasts, the $NADH_2$ produced during glycolysis is used to reduce **(a)** acetaldehyde to ethanol; **(b)** NADP to $NADPH_2$; **(c)** fumaric acid to succinic acid; **(d)** pyruvic acid to lactic acid; **(e)** lactic acid to pyruvic acid.

24 *Streptococcus lactis* uses the $NADH_2$ produced during glycolysis to reduce **(a)** acetaldehyde to ethanol; **(b)** NADP to $NADPH_2$; **(c)** fumaric acid to succinic acid; **(d)** pyruvic acid to lactic acid; **(e)** lactic acid to pyruvic acid.

25 Match the description on the right with the correct item on the left.

_____ fermentation

_____ citric acid cycle

_____ respiration

(a) The method of regenerating NAD from $NADH_2$ by using the $NADH_2$ as the electron donor for an electron-transport system

(b) The series of reactions that begins when acetyl-CoA reacts with oxaloacetic acid

(c) The method for regenerating NAD from $NADH_2$ by using the $NADH_2$ to reduce an organic electron acceptor supplied by the cell itself

26 In comparing the efficiency of fermentation versus respiration with regard to ATP

yield, _____ is the more efficient process.

27 Even though most intestinal bacteria are fermentative, their growth is not limited by the low efficiency of fermentation, because they have

_____ .

REVIEW QUESTIONS

1 What is energy coupling, and why is it important to the life of a cell?

2 What role does ATP play in energy trapping and energy transfer in cells?

3 What are the main differences between substrate-level phosphorylation, oxidative phosphorylation, and photo-phosphorylation?

4 In oxidative phosphorylation, how is the energy derived from an electron-transport system used for ATP synthesis?

5 Explain why fermentation is a less efficient process for obtaining energy than respiration.

6 In cyanobacteria, algae, and green plants, what differences occur between the functions of photosystem I and photosystem II?

7 The citric acid cycle *directly* generates only two molecules of ATP (derived from GTP) for every two molecules of acetyl-CoA that enter the cycle. Nevertheless, the cycle can lead *indirectly* to the generation of many more ATP molecules. Explain how these additional ATP molecules are made.

8 For what contribution to biochemistry was Peter Mitchell awarded the Nobel Prize?

9 Why would you expect that most of the bacteria that inhabit the surface waters of unpolluted lakes obtain energy by respiration rather than by fermentation?

DISCUSSION QUESTIONS

1 Suppose that you have a suspension of *E. coli* cells that have been starved in a nonnutrient buffer solution for a long time. Their ATP level is extremely low, but the cells cannot make any ATP by either respiration or fermentation, since no nutrients are present. The pH inside the cells and in the buffer solution is 8. Suppose that you add some hydrochloric acid (HCl) to the suspension, so that the pH of the medium suddenly drops from 8 to 3. What would happen to the ATP level in the cells? How could you account for this? Why would the effect be only a temporary one?

2 Bacteria of the genus *Halobacterium* normally generate ATP by aerobic respiration. Some halobacteria have a purple pigment called *bacteriorhodopsin* in their cytoplasmic membrane. When this pigment is exposed to light it bleaches, causing hydrogen ions to be ejected from the cell. These are immediately replaced by other hydrogen ions from the cell's cytoplasm, thus restoring the purple color of the pigment. This cycle of bleaching and restoration of color can be repeated over and over.

On the basis of this information, how would you account for the ability of halobacteria to generate ATP under *anaerobic conditions* when exposed to light? How do these organisms differ from phototrophic microorganisms that contain chlorophyll?

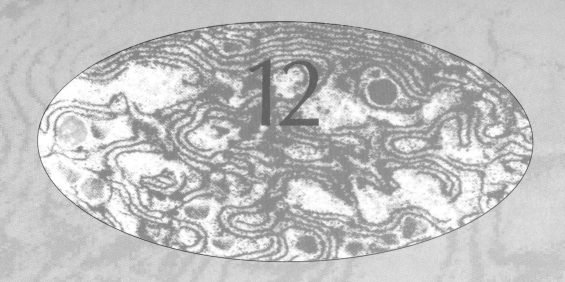

Microbial Metabolism: Energy-Requiring Biochemical Processes

OBJECTIVES

After reading this chapter you should be able to

1 Outline the general way in which the complex chemical constituents of the cell are synthesized.

2 Describe the role of feedback inhibition in regulating the synthesis of biochemical building blocks.

3 Name the energized biochemical building blocks from which polysaccharides, lipids, proteins, and nucleic acids are synthesized.

4 List the steps involved in the biosynthesis of bacterial cell-wall peptidoglycan.

5 Explain how long-chain fatty acids are synthesized and how they are used to construct phospholipids.

6 Indicate the key reactions of the Calvin cycle and their significance for autotrophic microorganisms.

7 Differentiate between simple diffusion, facilitated diffusion, and active transport.

8 Explain how a microorganism can accumulate a nutrient at a greater concentration inside the cell than exists outside the cell.

9 Identify the energy source that causes bacterial flagella to rotate.

OVERVIEW

Just as an electric generator provides power to machinery, the exergonic reactions described in Chapter 11 provide energy for cellular activities. These activities, or biochemical processes, are endergonic (energy-requiring). The energy they use is supplied by adenosine triphosphate (ATP), or by some other energy source such as guanosine triphosphate (GTP), uridine triphosphate (UTP), or a protonmotive force. Organisms use this energy to fuel the many endergonic reactions required for the life of the cell. For instance, ATP is needed for biosynthesis of the various chemical components of the cell—deoxyribonucleic acid (DNA), ribonucleic acid (RNA), enzymes, cell-wall peptidoglycan, and the phospholipids of the cell membrane. ATP can energize amino acids, nucleotides, monosaccharides, and fatty acid precursors, which then enter their respective pathways as building blocks of proteins, carbohydrates, and lipids. Besides biosynthesis, a cell also needs ATP or other forms of energy for processes such as motility and the active transport of nutrients across the cell membrane.

ENERGY UTILIZATION FOR BIOSYNTHETIC PROCESSES

In Chapter 11 you learned the various ways in which a cell obtains energy. The next step is learning how this energy is used to fuel the various endergonic processes essential to the life of a cell. Some of these energy-requiring processes are *biosynthetic* processes, by which the complex chemical constituents of a cell are constructed. The cell is a marvelous chemical engineer, busily engaged in assembling the intricate molecules of life. Indeed, many of the chemical substances made easily by living cells are so complex that they cannot yet be artificially synthesized by chemists in the laboratory.

As previously noted, microorganisms show great diversity in their nutritional requirements. These differences are a reflection of their varying biosynthetic abilities. For instance, some microorganisms can synthesize all their cellular constituents from simple inorganic compounds. Others with less biosynthetic ability must be provided with sugars, amino acids, and vitamins. An example of a microorganism that has relatively simple nutritional requirements is the bacterium *Escherichia coli*. This bacterium can grow in a medium containing only glucose and a few inorganic compounds, including a source of nitrogen such as ammonium sulfate [$(NH_4)_2SO_4$]. From these nutrients it can synthesize (1) nitrogenous substances, including proteins (such as enzymes) and nucleic acids (DNA and RNA); (2) carbohydrates, including complex polysaccharides such as the carbohydrate part of the peptidoglycan; and (3) phospholipids, which are important components in the cytoplasmic membrane.

How does *E. coli* make all these substances? FIGURE 12.1 illustrates the overall scheme; the details of the various biosynthetic pathways are described later in this chapter. However, some generalizations can be made about these pathways, because all of them share fundamental features:

FIGURE 12.1

Schematic illustration of how the bacterium *Escherichia coli*, when grown in a medium containing glucose plus ammonium sulfate and other inorganic salts, can synthesize the biochemical building blocks for construction of proteins, polysaccharides, lipids, and nucleic acids, as well as all cell structures. Some structural and functional parts of the cell are indicated by the colored boxes.

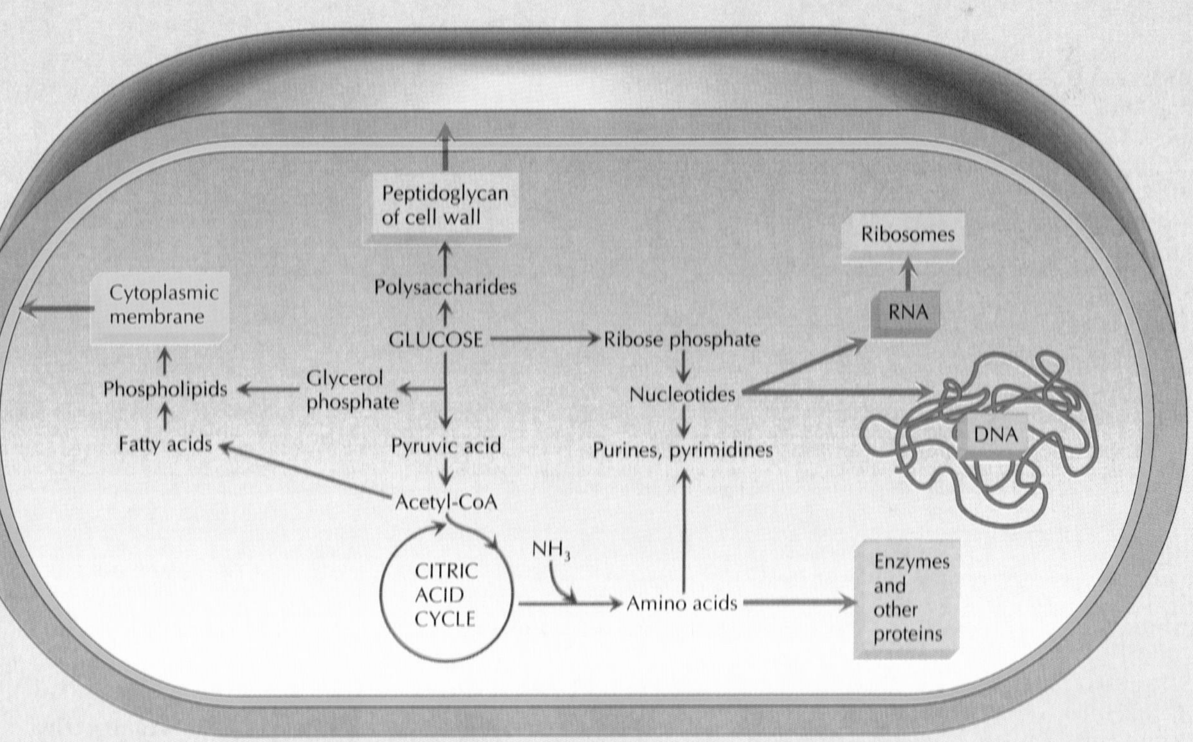

1 A biosynthetic pathway begins with the synthesis of the biochemical building blocks needed to make more complex substances.

2 The building blocks are then energized, usually with the energy of ATP molecules. This energy is needed to establish the covalent bonds that subsequently will link the building blocks.

3 The energized building blocks are linked together to form complex substances that become structural or functional parts of the cell.

ASK YOURSELF

1 Do biosynthetic processes require energy?

2 Which of the following has the least biosynthetic ability, and which has the greatest biosynthetic ability: **(a)** an autotrophic microorganism; **(b)** an organism that requires glucose and a few inorganic compounds; or **(c)** an organism that requires glucose, several amino acids, and several vitamins?

3 What are the three fundamental features of all biosynthetic pathways?

BIOSYNTHESIS OF NITROGENOUS COMPOUNDS

Microorganisms show great diversity in the starting materials from which they synthesize nitrogenous substances, as shown in the following generalized sequence of reactions:

Nitrogen gas (from the atmosphere) **or** Other forms of inorganic nitrogen (such as ammonia)

↓

Amino acid

↓

An array of amino acids

↓

Proteins (e.g., enzymes)   Purines and pyrimidines

↓

Nucleotides

↓

Nucleic acids (DNA, RNA)

This sequence begins with nitrogen gas (N_2), which accounts for 78 percent of the earth's atmosphere. N_2 cannot be used as a nitrogen source by most living organisms. However, some bacteria such as *Azotobacter chroococcum* are able to use the gas for synthesis of nitrogenous compounds [DISCOVER 12.1]. These bacteria take N_2 from the atmosphere and reduce it with electrons to form ammonia (NH_3). The process is called *nitrogen fixation*, and it requires considerable energy in the form of ATP:

$$N_2 + 6e^- + 6H^+ + 16ATP \rightarrow$$
$$2NH_3 + 16ADP + 16 \text{ phosphate}$$

After ammonia has been formed, the bacteria combine the ammonia with a carbon compound to make an amino acid. From this initial amino acid, *A. chroococcum* can synthesize all the other amino acids required for growth.

Other microorganisms such as *Escherichia coli* cannot use atmospheric nitrogen, but they can use other inorganic forms of nitrogen—such as the nitrogen in ammonium sulfate—to make amino acids. Some microbial species cannot use inorganic forms of nitrogen and must be provided with one or more organic forms of nitrogen, such as amino acids. For example, *Leuconostoc mesenteroides* requires 19 amino acids in its culture medium because it cannot synthesize these amino acids.

After amino acids are synthesized (or provided in the culture medium), microorganisms assemble the amino acids into proteins. Most of the proteins of a cell are enzymes, which the cell needs to catalyze biochemical reactions. Microorganisms also use some amino acids for the synthesis of purines and pyrimidines, which are then used to make nucleotides and eventually nucleic acids.

Biosynthesis of Amino Acids and Proteins

One of the most important amino acids a microorganism needs to make is glutamic acid. *Escherichia coli* can make glutamic acid by combining ammonia (from the ammonium sulfate in the culture medium) and α-ketoglutaric acid (from the citric acid cycle; refer to FIGURE 11.13) in the following reaction:

$$\alpha\text{-Ketoglutaric acid} + NADPH_2 + NH_3 \rightarrow$$
$$\text{glutamic acid} + NADP + H_2O$$

This reaction, called **reductive amination,** is a very important reaction, because the amino group ($-NH_2$) on glutamic acid can be *traded* for an oxygen atom on various organic acids to convert them to amino acids. This trading process is called **transamination.** For instance, the amino acid alanine is made from pyruvic acid by transamination:

12.1 193,000,000 TONS!

Although nitrogen gas (N_2) accounts for 78 percent of the earth's atmosphere, it is not in an industrially or biologically useful form. It must first be "fixed," that is, reduced to ammonia (NH_3). However, nitrogen fixation is not an easy process. For instance, in the industrial production of ammonia, hydrogen gas (H_2) and nitrogen gas (N_2) are reacted together:

$$N_2 + 3H_2 \rightarrow 2NH_3$$

Although this reaction seems simple, the hydrogen gas is very expensive; moreover, the two gases must be mixed under high pressure at a very high temperature (400 to 600°C) in the presence of an inorganic catalyst. Nevertheless, nearly 44 million tons of N_2 is fixed each year by this industrial process, and much of it is used to make fertilizer to improve soil fertility in agriculture. Unfortunately, many underdeveloped countries lack the equipment and money for the industrial manufacture of fertilizer.

Most living organisms are unable to fix N_2, but some bacteria do have this ability. Amazingly, these bacteria fix nitrogen under quite ordinary conditions, without using high temperatures or pressures. However, they do require a considerable amount of chemical energy in the form of ATP. To fix one molecule of N_2 requires sixteen ATP molecules. Therefore, just as the chemical industry finds it expensive to fix nitrogen, so do nitrogen-fixing bacteria, in terms of the ATP required. Nevertheless, it has been estimated that nitrogen-fixing bacteria fix *193,000,000 tons of N_2 globally each year*—far more than is fixed industrially! Indeed, all life on earth depends, directly or indirectly, on bacterial nitrogen fixation, because the ammonia that is produced is needed by living organisms for biosynthesis of amino acids, nucleotides, and other nitrogen-containing biochemical compounds.

$$\underset{\text{Glutamic acid}}{\text{HOOCCH}_2\text{CH}_2\overset{\overset{\text{H}}{|}}{\underset{\underset{\text{NH}_2}{|}}{\text{C}}}\text{COOH}} + \underset{\substack{\text{Pyruvic acid}\\\text{(from glycolysis)}}}{\text{CH}_3\overset{\overset{\text{O}}{\|}}{\text{C}}\text{COOH}} \rightarrow \underset{\alpha\text{-Ketoglutaric acid}}{\text{HOOCCH}_2\text{CH}_2\overset{\overset{\text{O}}{\|}}{\text{C}}\text{COOH}} + \underset{\text{Alanine}}{\text{CH}_3\overset{\overset{\text{H}}{|}}{\underset{\underset{\text{NH}_2}{|}}{\text{C}}}\text{COOH}}$$

Another way in which glutamic acid can be used to make other amino acids is by altering its molecular structure. For example, proline is made in this manner [FIGURE 12.2]. Such structural changes require energy in the form of ATP.

How does a cell control its production of an amino acid such as proline? A cell needs to make many kinds of amino acids besides proline in order to synthesize proteins, and it would waste energy by overproducing any single amino acid. Moreover, if an amino acid is provided in the culture medium, it would be wasteful for the cell to expend energy in making more of that amino acid. One type of control mechanism used by cells is called *feedback inhibition,* in which a biosynthetic pathway becomes self-regulating. This is illustrated by the proline pathway, in which proline is not only the end product of the pathway, but also *an inhibitor of the first enzyme in the pathway* [FIGURE 12.2]. Besides its active site, this first enzyme has a binding site for proline; this allows the proline to act as an allosteric inhibitor (see Chapter 1). The more proline the cell produces, the greater the degree of inhibition of the first enzyme and the slower the rate of synthesis of more proline. In fact, if a high level of proline is provided in the culture medium, the microorganism will not synthesize proline at all.

Energization of Amino Acids. As indicated earlier in this chapter, biochemical building blocks must be energized before they can be used to make complex substances. Accordingly, amino acids need to be energized before they can be linked together to make proteins. Cells energize amino acids by using the energy of ATP, as follows:

$$\text{Amino acid} + \text{ATP} \rightarrow \underset{\substack{\text{Energized amino}\\\text{acid}}}{\text{amino acid-AMP}} + \underset{\substack{\text{Two phosphate}\\\text{groups linked}\\\text{together}}}{\text{pyrophosphate}}$$

The AMP linked to the amino acid is *adenosine monophosphate,* which is formed by removal of two phosphate groups from ATP.

Protein Synthesis. A microorganism synthesizes hundreds of different proteins, each protein having its own unique sequence of amino acids. The blueprint for making proteins is contained in the nucleotide sequence of the DNA of the cell. This blueprint must first be transcribed into RNA molecules before proteins can be made. Thus RNA synthesis is prerequisite to protein synthesis. Chapter 13 includes a discussion of how cells synthesize RNA and proteins under the direction of DNA.

FIGURE 12.2

The biosynthesis of the amino acid proline from glutamic acid in *E. coli*. Note the utilization of metabolic energy in the form of ATP. Overproduction of proline is prevented by feedback inhibition, in which increasing levels of proline inhibit the activity of enzyme 1.

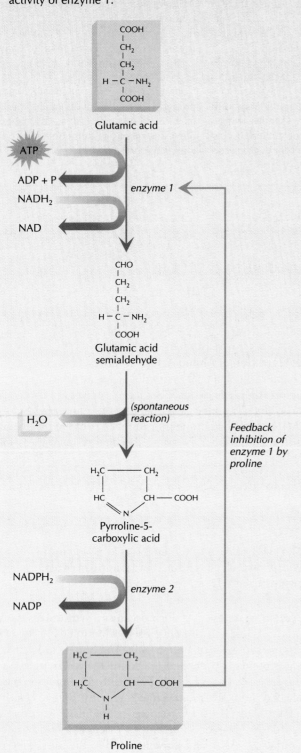

Biosynthesis of Nucleotides and Nucleic Acids

Amino acids are not only used by a cell to synthesize proteins; they are also used to synthesize nucleotides, the building blocks of RNA and DNA:

Nucleotides → DNA and RNA

In the first chapter of this book you learned that a nucleotide is constructed as follows:

Nucleotide = nitrogenous base-pentose-phosphate

Nucleotides that contain the sugar *ribose* as the pentose are called **ribonucleotides** and are used for biosynthesis of RNA. Nucleotides having the sugar *deoxyribose* as the pentose are called **deoxyribonucleotides** and are used for biosynthesis of DNA:

Ribonucleotides → RNA

Deoxyribonucleotides → DNA

Ribonucleotides and deoxyribonucleotides that have *adenine* or *guanine* as the nitrogenous base are *purine nucleotides*, whereas those having either *cytosine*, *thymine*, or *uracil* as the nitrogenous base are *pyrimidine nucleotides*. TABLE 12.1 lists the purine and pyrimidine nucleotide building blocks of DNA and RNA.

The sequence of reactions, or biosynthetic pathway, used by a cell to make purine nucleotides is shown in FIGURE 12.3. Notice that the amino acids glycine, aspartic acid, and glutamine are required in the pathway. Energy in the form of ATP and GTP (guanosine triphosphate, equivalent in energy to ATP) is also required. The ribose phosphate at the beginning of the pathway is made from glucose (see the section of this chapter on carbohydrate biosynthesis).

FIGURE 12.4 illustrates the biosynthetic pathway for pyrimidine nucleotides. Notice that the amino acids glutamine and aspartic acid are required in the pathway, and that energy in the form of ATP is also required.

Energization of Nucleotides. After a nucleotide has been synthesized, it becomes energized by ATP. In this process the nucleotide, which already has one phosphate group, acquires two more phosphate groups. For instance, guanosine monophosphate (GMP) is converted to its energized form, guanosine triphosphate (GTP):

GMP + 2ATP → GTP + 2ADP

It is interesting that ATP itself is the energized form of a nucleotide, adenosine monophosphate (AMP). Thus ATP is not only the major "energy currency" of a cell; it is also an important energized building block for the synthesis of nucleic acids.

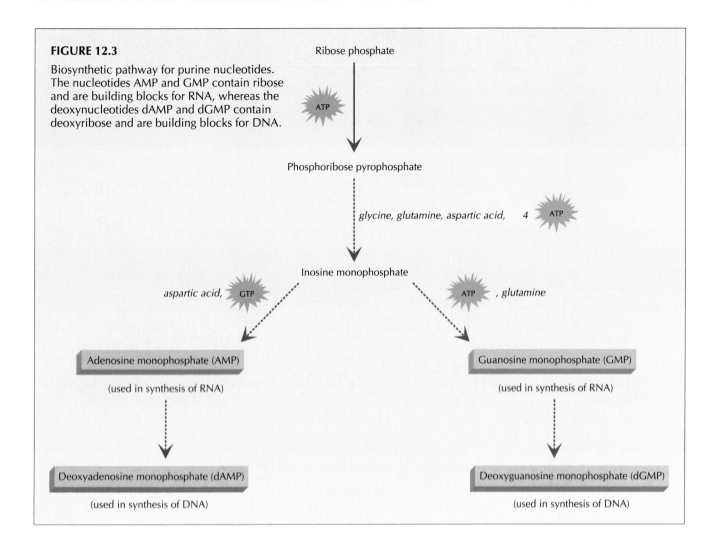

FIGURE 12.3

Biosynthetic pathway for purine nucleotides. The nucleotides AMP and GMP contain ribose and are building blocks for RNA, whereas the deoxynucleotides dAMP and dGMP contain deoxyribose and are building blocks for DNA.

TABLE 12.1

Purine and Pyrimidine Building Blocks of DNA and RNA

Nucleotide	Abbreviation	Composed of
USED FOR SYNTHESIS OF RNA		
Purine ribonucleotides:		
Adenosine monophosphate	AMP	Adenine-ribose-phosphate
Guanosine monophosphate	GMP	Guanine-ribose-phosphate
Pyrimidine ribonucleotides:		
Cytidine monophosphate	CMP	Cytosine-ribose-phosphate
Uridine monophosphate	UMP	Uracil-ribose-phosphate
USED FOR SYNTHESIS OF DNA		
Purine deoxyribonucleotides:		
Deoxyadenosine monophosphate	dAMP	Adenine-deoxyribose-phosphate
Deoxyguanosine monophosphate	dGMP	Guanine-deoxyribose-phosphate
Pyrimidine deoxyribonucleotides:		
Deoxycytidine monophosphate	dCMP	Cytosine-deoxyribose-phosphate
Deoxythymidine monophosphate	dTMP	Thymine-deoxyribose-phosphate

FIGURE 12.4

Biosynthetic pathway for pyrimidine nucleotides. The nucleotides UMP and CMP are building blocks for RNA, whereas the deoxynucleotides dTMP and dCMP are building blocks for DNA.

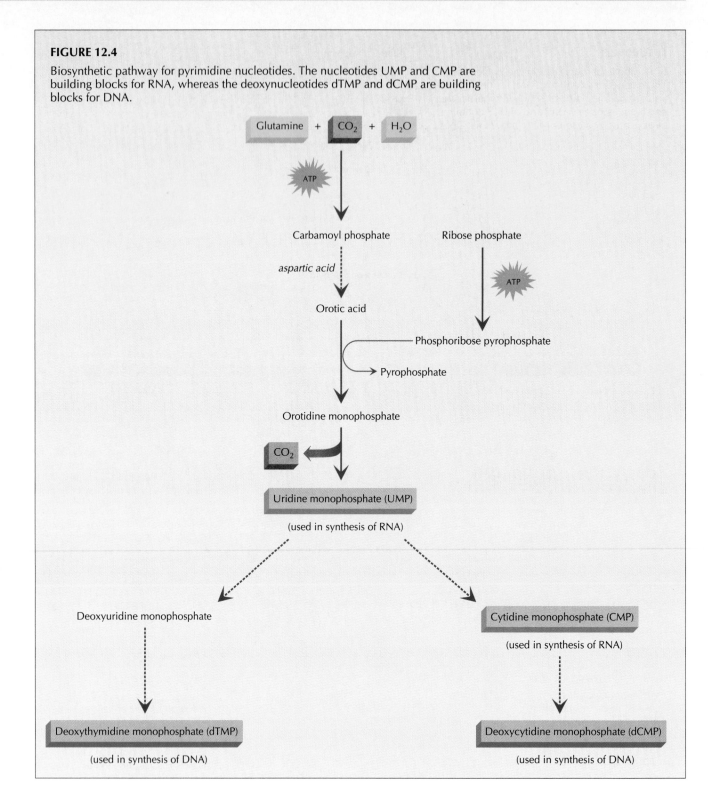

Nucleic Acid Biosynthesis. DNA and RNA are synthesized from energized nucleotides. The sequence of deoxynucleotides in DNA represents the hereditary information of an organism. During the synthesis of new DNA by an organism, that sequence is copied very accurately. Moreover, the biosynthesis of RNA and proteins is dependent upon the nucleotide sequence of DNA. Later you will learn the mechanisms by which cells make DNA and RNA.

ASK YOURSELF

1 What is nitrogen fixation?

2 By what process is glutamic acid made from α-ketoglutaric acid? By what process is alanine made from pyruvic acid?

3 What role does feedback inhibition play in the pathway for synthesis of proline made from glutamic acid?

4 How are amino acids energized?

5 What are the four ribonucleotide building blocks of RNA? What are the four deoxyribonucleotide building blocks of DNA?

6 How are nucleotides energized? Is ATP an energized nucleotide?

BIOSYNTHESIS OF CARBOHYDRATES

Microorganisms synthesize carbohydrates through diverse mechanisms, as shown by the following generalized sequence of reactions:

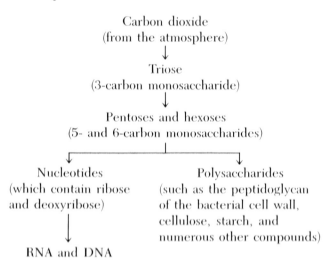

Some microorganisms, the *autotrophs*, are capable of using carbon dioxide (CO_2) from the atmosphere and converting it into organic compounds. This process is called CO_2 fixation. Autotrophs use ATP as the energy source for CO_2 fixation. *Photoautotrophs* such as cyanobacteria make ATP by using the energy of light, whereas *chemoautotrophs* (e.g., *Nitrosomonas* and *Thiobacillus*) make ATP by using the chemical energy liberated during the oxidation of inorganic compounds. Compounds oxidized by chemoautotrophs include hydrogen gas, ammonia, nitrites, and reduced sulfur compounds such as hydrogen sulfide and thiosulfate.

In addition to ATP, an autotroph must provide $NADPH_2$ (or, in some organisms, $NADH_2$) as an electron donor to reduce CO_2 and convert it to organic cell material. In Chapter 11 you learned how photoautotrophs such as cyanobacteria obtain $NADPH_2$ by using electrons that are ejected from chlorophyll in the presence of light. Chemoautotrophs obtain $NADPH_2$ by using electrons that are removed during the oxidation of inorganic compounds.

The principal method of carbon dioxide fixation in autotrophic organisms is the **Calvin cycle** [FIGURE 12.5]. This cycle is named after Melvin Calvin, who, with his colleagues at the University of California, discovered during the 1940s the specific reactions in this process. In the initial reaction of the Calvin cycle, CO_2 is added to a five-carbon sugar compound called *ribulose bisphosphate*. This results in the formation of two molecules of a three-carbon compound, *phosphoglyceric acid*:

$$CO_2 + \text{ribulose bisphosphate} \rightarrow 2 \text{ phosphoglyceric acid}$$

(1 carbon atom)　　　(5 carbon atoms)　　　(3 carbon atoms each)

Then $NADPH_2$ or $NADH_2$ provides electrons to reduce the phosphoglyceric acid to glyceraldehyde-3-phosphate (*triose phosphate*). ATP provides the necessary energy for this step. All of the organic carbon compounds needed by the cell are then synthesized from the phosphoglyceric acid and the triose phosphate.

However, CO_2 fixation is dependent on a continual supply of ribulose bisphosphate, and so most of the triose phosphate produced must be used to regenerate ribulose bisphosphate [FIGURE 12.5]. Thus the process of CO_2 fixation is cyclic. Each turn of the cycle results in the fixation of one molecule of CO_2. After six turns of the cycle, six molecules of CO_2 are fixed. This provides enough carbon atoms to allow the cell to make one molecule of glucose according to the following overall reaction:

$$6CO_2 + 12NADH_2 + 18ATP + 12H_2O \rightarrow$$

$$C_6H_{12}O_6 + 12NAD + 18ADP + 18 \text{ phosphate}$$

Glucose

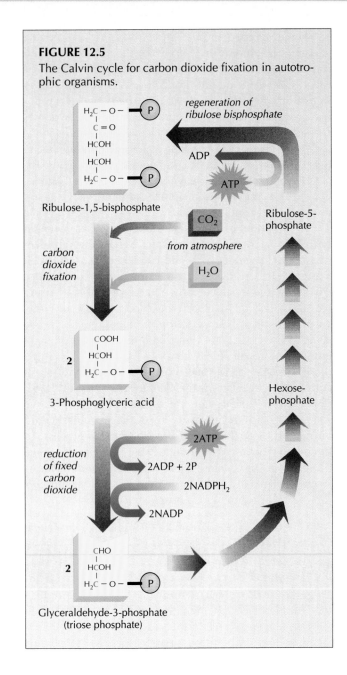

FIGURE 12.5

The Calvin cycle for carbon dioxide fixation in autotrophic organisms.

Note the high requirement for reducing power (in the form of $NADH_2$) and for energy (in the form of ATP) in order to make glucose from CO_2.

Heterotrophic organisms such as *E. coli* must be provided with an organic compound such as glucose as their major source of carbon. *Escherichia coli* can convert the glucose in the culture medium to various other monosaccharides. For instance, *E. coli* makes ribose phosphate—which is needed to synthesize nucleotides—from glucose by the following overall reaction:

Glucose + ATP + 2NADP →

 ribose-5-phosphate + CO_2 + ADP + $2NADPH_2$

Energization of Monosaccharides

Just as amino acids and nucleotides must be energized in order to be assembled into proteins and nucleic acids, monosaccharides must also be energized in order to be assembled into polysaccharides. For example, the energized form of glucose is *uridine diphosphate glucose (UDP-glucose)*. The energy sources used to make UDP-glucose are ATP and uridine triphosphate (UTP), the energized form of uridine monophosphate (UMP):

Glucose + ATP + UTP →

 UDP-glucose + ADP + pyrophosphate

Not all energized monosaccharides are UDP sugars. For example, the energized form of ribose phosphate is *phosphoribose pyrophosphate*, which is formed by the reaction

Ribose phosphate + ATP →

 phosphoribose pyrophosphate + AMP

This energized compound is not used for the synthesis of polysaccharides, but instead for the synthesis of purine and pyrimidine nucleotides [see FIGURES 12.3 and 12.4].

Biosynthesis of Cell-Wall Peptidoglycan

Bacterial polysaccharide synthesis can be illustrated by the biosynthesis of peptidoglycan, the substance that gives strength and rigidity to bacterial cell walls. Although peptidoglycan is located in the cell wall, most of the chemical energy needed for its synthesis is expended inside the cell.

The steps involved in synthesis of a peptidoglycan building unit are shown in FIGURE 12.6 and summarized as follows:

1 The energy of ATP and other high-energy-transfer compounds is used to convert glucose to an energized building block called *N-acetylglucosamine-UDP (NAG-UDP)* by a series of enzyme-catalyzed reactions.
2 A second energized building block, *N-acetylmuramic acid-UDP (NAM-UDP)*, is made from some of the NAG-UDP molecules. Energy in the form of phosphoenolpyruvic acid (from glycolysis) is required for this step.
3 Five amino acid molecules are added to each molecule of NAM-UDP to form a *pentapeptide chain*, a chain of five amino acids. The addition of each amino acid requires ATP as an energy source. Some of these amino acids are D-amino acids, the optical isomer of amino acids that is normally rare in nature.

FIGURE 12.6
Biosynthesis of a peptidoglycan building unit. The six steps refer to those described in the text. Note the expenditure of energy in the form of the high-energy transfer compounds ATP, acetyl-CoA, UTP, and phosphoenolpyruvic acid. The lipid carrier enables the unit to pass from the inside of the cell across the cytoplasmic membrane to the cell wall.

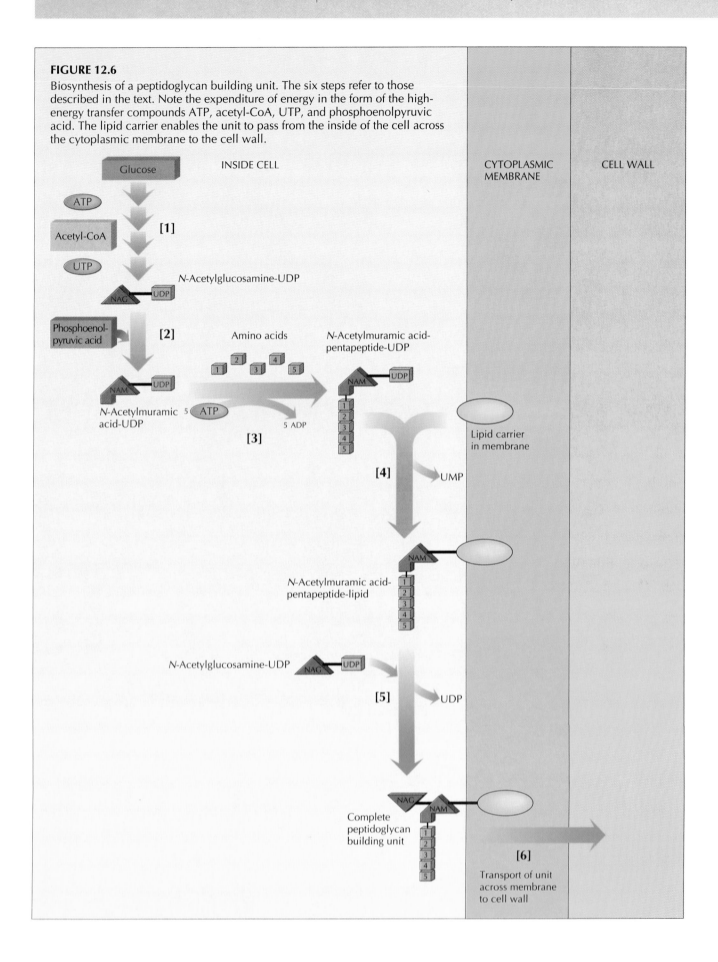

FIGURE 12.7

Having crossed the cytoplasmic membrane, the peptidoglycan unit is added to an existing peptidoglycan strand. Eventually the various peptidoglycan strands are cross-linked. The chemical bond between amino acids 4 and 5 on each pentapeptide chain is broken by the enzyme transpeptidase, and the energy that is liberated is used to establish cross-links as shown.

CYTOPLASMIC
MEMBRANE

SECTION THROUGH CELL WALL

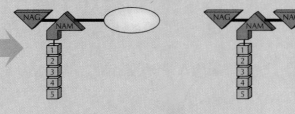

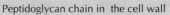

Peptidoglycan chain in the cell wall

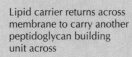

Lipid carrier returns across membrane to carry another peptidoglycan building unit across

Addition of unit to peptidoglycan chain

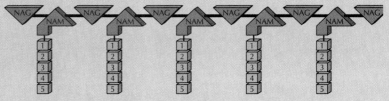

Cross-linking between peptidoglycan chains to form rigid framework (cell-wall structure)

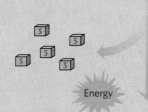

Energy

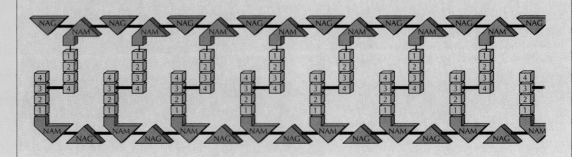

4 The UDP group on the NAM-pentapeptide-UDP is now replaced with a large molecule of lipid, called a *lipid carrier.* (The term *carrier* refers to the ability of this lipid group to carry a completed peptidoglycan building unit across the lipid-rich cytoplasmic membrane to the cell wall. The peptidoglycan building unit has many polar groups and cannot pass across the hydrophobic membrane without the help of the lipid carrier.)

5 A molecule of NAG-UDP is now added to the NAM-pentapeptide-lipid carrier to form a complete energized building unit for peptidoglycan.

6 With the aid of the lipid carrier, the energized unit is now transported across the cytoplasmic membrane to be integrated into the cell-wall structure.

After an energized peptidoglycan building unit passes across the cytoplasmic membrane, an enzyme catalyzes the addition of the unit onto an already existing peptidoglycan strand, thereby elongating the strand [FIGURE 12.7]. More units are added until the peptidoglycan strands become very long. It is now necessary that these chains be *cross-linked* in order for the peptidoglycan to become a strong, rigid framework surrounding the cell—rather than just an assemblage of loose strands. In a sense, the strands are like the steel girders used during construction of a new office building. To be functional, the girders must be riveted together to form a rigid framework.

The process of cross-linking peptidoglycan strands is particularly interesting because of the way energy is provided for this process. It comes directly from the penta-peptides attached to the peptidoglycan strands. An enzyme called *transpeptidase* breaks the linkage between the fourth and fifth amino acids on each of the pentapeptide chains, thereby converting the pentapeptides to *tetrapeptides*. The breakage of these linkages liberates energy, which the transpeptidase enzyme then uses to establish new linkages. This time, however, the new linkages are established between the tetrapeptides on one peptidoglycan chain and those on another chain [FIGURE 12.7]. The result is a rigid cross-linked material that can maintain the shape of the bacterial cell [FIGURE 12.8].

ASK YOURSELF

1 What is CO_2 fixation? What is required for CO_2 fixation by the Calvin cycle? What are the initial reactions in the cycle?

2 What is the energized form of glucose? Of ribose?

3 Of what is the complete energized building unit for peptidoglycan composed? What function does the lipid-carrier portion of this building block serve?

4 Where does the energy come from for the cross-linking of peptidoglycan chains? What function does this cross-linking serve?

FIGURE 12.8
Three-dimensional arrangement of the completed peptidoglycan structure of the bacterial cell wall. Note that not all the tetrapeptides are cross-linked.

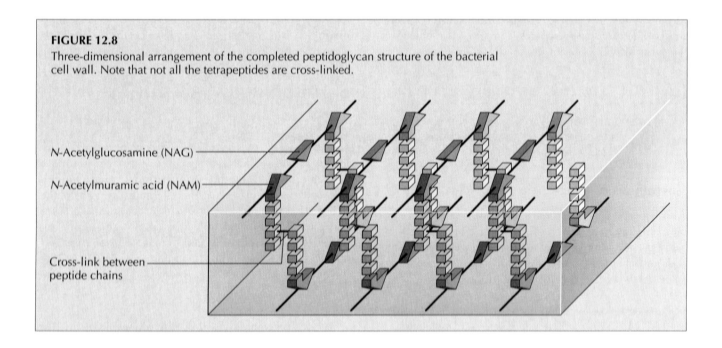

N-Acetylglucosamine (NAG)

N-Acetylmuramic acid (NAM)

Cross-link between peptide chains

BIOSYNTHESIS OF LIPIDS

The major lipids of bacterial cells are the phospholipids that, together with proteins, form the structure of the cytoplasmic membrane. The general way in which microorganisms make phospholipids can be summarized as follows:

$$
\begin{array}{c}
\text{Glucose} \\
\downarrow \text{Glycolysis} \\
\text{Pyruvic acid} \\
\downarrow \\
\text{Acetyl-coenzyme A and malonyl-coenzyme A} \\
\downarrow \\
\text{Long-chain fatty acids} \\
\downarrow \text{————— Glycerol phosphate} \\
\text{Phospholipids}
\end{array}
$$

Notice that two important building blocks for long-chain fatty acids are *acetyl-coenzyme A (acetyl-CoA)* and *malonyl-coenzyme A (malonyl-CoA)*. Acetyl-CoA is the energized form of acetic acid (CH_3COOH) and is usually made by the oxidation of pyruvic acid [see FIGURE 11.14]. However, some bacteria can make acetyl-CoA directly from acetic acid. In this case the energy of ATP is required:

Acetic acid + ATP + coenzyme A →

   acetyl-CoA + AMP + pyrophosphate

Malonyl-CoA is an energized building block made from acetyl-CoA. Unlike an acetyl group, which contains two carbon atoms, a malonyl group contains three carbon atoms. The extra carbon comes from CO_2, and energy in the form of ATP is required for this addition:

$$
\underbrace{\text{Acetyl-CoA}}_{\text{(2 carbon atoms)}} + \underbrace{CO_2}_{\text{(1 carbon atom)}} \xrightarrow{\text{ATP}} \underbrace{\text{Malonyl-CoA}}_{\text{(3 carbon atoms)}}
$$

Biosynthesis of Long-Chain Fatty Acids

Before a cell can make a phospholipid, it must first synthesize long-chain fatty acids, which are fatty acids with many carbon atoms. Fatty acids are made from acetyl-CoA and malonyl-CoA by the following sequence of enzyme-catalyzed steps [FIGURE 12.9]:

1 The coenzyme A group on both malonyl-CoA and acetyl-CoA is replaced by a large protein molecule that serves to anchor the compounds so that appropriate enzymes can act upon them.

2 A malonyl-protein complex reacts with an acetyl-protein complex. In this reaction, two of the three carbon atoms of the malonyl group are added to the acetyl group to make a four-carbon *butyryl* group; the third carbon atom of the malonyl group is liberated as CO_2:

$$
\underbrace{\text{Acetyl-protein}}_{\text{(2 carbon atoms)}} + \underbrace{\text{Malonyl-protein}}_{\text{(3 carbon atoms)}} \rightarrow
$$

$$
\underbrace{\text{Butyryl-protein}}_{\text{(4 carbon atoms)}} + \underbrace{CO_2}_{\text{(1 carbon atom)}}
$$

3 If the butyryl group were to be released from the protein, it would become *butyric acid*, a four-carbon fatty acid. However, a four-carbon fatty acid is not long enough for lipid synthesis. The cell reacts the butyryl-protein complex with another malonyl-protein complex to add another two-carbon unit, resulting in a six-carbon fatty acid–protein complex. This process of adding two carbons at a time to elongate the fatty acid chain can be continued until a fatty acid of the desired length is obtained (usually 16 or 18 carbon atoms long).

Biosynthesis of Phospholipids

After the fatty acids are long enough, the cell uses them to construct phospholipids. In addition to the fatty acids, *glycerol phosphate* is needed for the synthesis of phospholipids. It is made from *dihydroxyacetone phosphate*, a compound formed during glycolysis [see FIGURE 11.11]:

Dihydroxyacetone phosphate + $NADH_2$ →

   glycerol phosphate + NAD

As shown in FIGURE 12.10, two fatty acid molecules are linked to one molecule of glycerol phosphate to form a molecule of *phosphatidic acid*, a simple phospholipid. The cell may then link other chemical groups to the phosphate group of the phosphatidic acid to make other phospholipids. For example, the amino acid serine can be added to phosphatidic acid to make *phosphatidylserine*. Energy in the form of cytidine triphosphate (CTP, the energized form of CMP) is required for this reaction:

Phosphatidic acid + CTP + serine →

   phosphatidylserine + pyrophosphate + CMP

FIGURE 12.9

The biosynthesis of fatty acids proceeds by the sequential addition of two-carbon units until a long-chain fatty acid group is formed, usually having 16 or 18 carbon atoms.

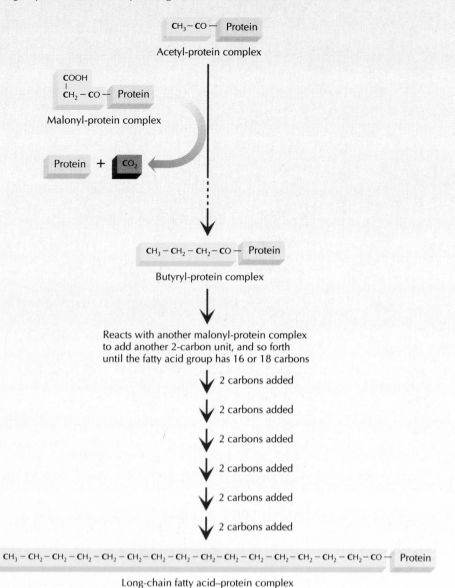

FIGURE 12.10

Biosynthesis of phosphatidic acid, a simple phospholipid.

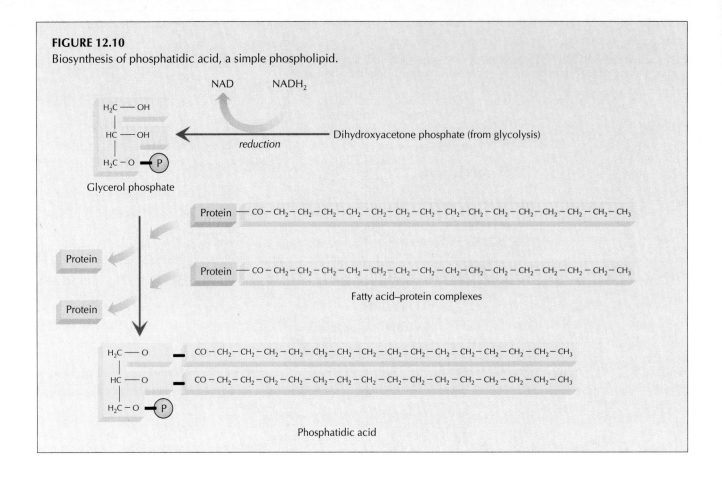

Phosphatidic acid

ENERGY UTILIZATION FOR PROCESSES OTHER THAN BIOSYNTHESIS

Some of the energy-requiring processes carried out by a cell serve functions other than the synthesis of complex chemical constituents. For example, a bacterial cell uses energy to operate the transport mechanisms that carry nutrients from the environment into the cell. The functioning of flagella for cell motility is another energy-requiring process that does not involve biosynthesis.

Transport of Nutrients into Cells

Because it encloses the protoplasm of a cell, the cytoplasmic membrane controls the passage of nutrients into a cell. It constitutes a barrier that is difficult for most nutrients to penetrate. For this reason, most nutrients are transported across the cytoplasmic membrane by special proteins called *carrier proteins.* However, water molecules and some lipid-soluble nutrients can pass freely across the membrane by a process called *simple diffusion* [FIGURE 12.11A]. In simple diffusion, molecules can pass across the membrane in either direction; however, if the concentration is greater outside the cell than inside, then there will be a net movement of molecules inward across the membrane until the concentration is equal on both sides. *Simple diffusion does not require the input of metabolic energy, nor does it result in a higher concentration of nutrient molecules inside the cell than outside.*

FIGURE 12.11

In simple diffusion [A], nutrient molecules pass freely across a cell membrane, whereas in facilitated diffusion [B] they bind to a specific site on a carrier protein and are transported across the membrane. In either case, when the concentration inside the cell becomes equal to that outside, molecules will leave the cell at the same rate they enter the cell.

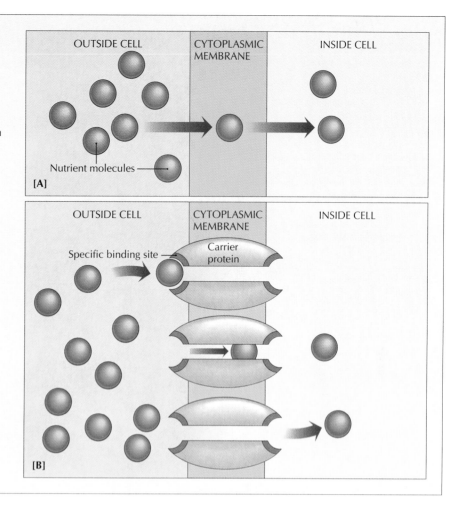

Most nutrients do not enter a cell by simple diffusion, but are transported across the cytoplasmic membrane by carrier proteins. There is a specific carrier protein for each type of nutrient. There are two major categories of carrier-mediated transport, namely, *facilitated diffusion* and *active transport*.

Facilitated Diffusion. The process of facilitated diffusion differs from simple diffusion in that the nutrient molecule must first bind to a carrier protein in order to be transported across the membrane [FIGURE 12.11B]. However, facilitated diffusion does have certain features in common with simple diffusion: metabolic energy is not required, and there is a net movement of molecules from a higher to a lower concentration until the concentration is equal inside and outside the cell.

Active Transport. Most nutrients are transported into a cell by active transport. This process allows the cell to concentrate nutrients to high levels that are suitable for metabolic activities—levels that may be hundreds of times greater inside the cell than those outside the cell.

This transport of nutrients "uphill" from a lower to a higher concentration *requires the input of metabolic energy* [FIGURE 12.12].

Motility

Motile bacteria propel themselves through water by rotating their corkscrew-shaped flagella. The motor apparatus that causes a flagellum to rotate is associated with the disks found in the basal body of the flagellum [see FIGURE 4.8]. It is composed of proteins instead of wires and armatures like an electric motor, and microbiologists do not fully understand how it works. However, they do know that it is driven directly by the *protonmotive force* generated across the bacterial cytoplasmic membrane. Thus a flagellar motor is a *proton motor*, driven by a flow of protons [FIGURE 12.13].

Unlike bacterial flagella, the cilia and flagella of eucaryotic cells do not rotate but merely bend in a complex manner. This bending requires the energy of ATP.

FIGURE 12.12
Active transport of nutrient molecules across the cell membrane results in a higher concentration inside the cell than outside. **[A]** In one type of active transport, the energy of ATP or the protonmotive force distorts the binding site of the carrier, making it difficult for a molecule to leave the cell once it has entered. **[B]** In a second type of active transport, the carrier is an enzyme that adds a phosphate group from phosphoenolpyruvic acid to the nutrient molecules during transport. The altered nutrient molecules no longer fit the binding site on the carrier and accumulate within the cell.

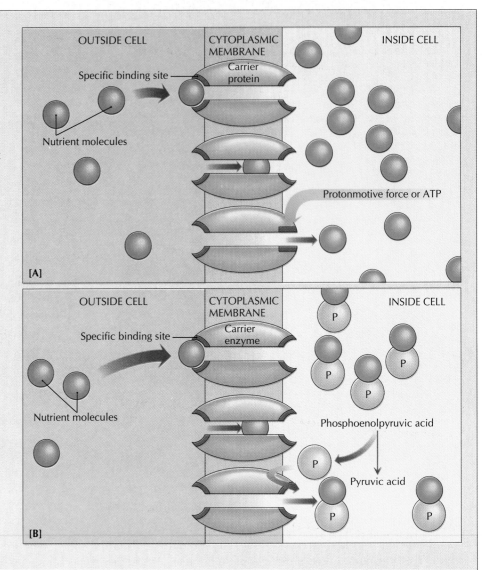

FIGURE 12.13
The rotary motor that drives a bacterial flagellum is associated with the disks of the basal portion of the flagellum and is powered by the protonmotive force.

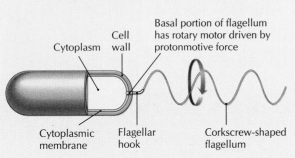

ASK YOURSELF

1 What are two energy-requiring processes that do not involve biosynthesis?

2 What are the differences between simple diffusion, facilitated diffusion, and active transport?

3 What drives the rotary motor at the base of a bacterial flagellum?

4 How do the flagella and cilia of eucaryotic cells differ from the flagella of bacterial cells with respect to their type of movement and energy source?

SUMMARY

1 Most energy-requiring processes carried out by a living cell are biosynthetic processes. In these processes, biochemical building blocks are made, energized, and then linked together to form complex cell constituents. Biosynthetic pathways may be self-regulating, such as the pathway for proline synthesis, in which feedback inhibition occurs.

2 In order to make nitrogenous compounds, some bacteria can fix nitrogen from the atmosphere by reducing it to ammonia. Other organisms use inorganic nitrogen compounds such as ammonia, and still others require organic forms of nitrogen such as amino acids.

3 The amino acid glutamic acid can be made from α-ketoglutaric acid by reductive amination; many other amino acids can subsequently be made from glutamic acid by transamination or structural conversion. Amino acids are energized by ATP to form amino acid-AMP molecules, which are used by the cell to synthesize hundreds of different proteins.

4 Amino acids are used in the biosynthesis of purine and pyrimidine nucleotides, which are the building blocks of RNA and DNA. Energy for this process is supplied by ATP and other high-energy-transfer compounds. The assembly of energized deoxyribonucleotides into DNA requires that the deoxyribonucleotides be linked together in a specific sequence. There is a different sequence for each species of organism. The biosynthesis of RNA and proteins depends upon the nucleotide sequence of DNA.

5 Chemoautotrophic and photoautotrophic microorganisms can fix atmospheric carbon dioxide into organic compounds—principally through the Calvin cycle. Operation of this cycle requires ATP energy and $NADPH_2$ as an electron donor. Heterotrophic organisms must be provided with organic compounds such as glucose as their source of carbon.

6 The biosynthesis of peptidoglycan involves the formation of the UDP derivatives of N-acetylglucosamine (NAG) and N-acetylmuramic acid (NAM). Amino acids, NAG, and NAM are joined together; the building unit is then transported by a lipid carrier across the cytoplasmic membrane to the cell wall. A transpeptidase cross-links the units to form a rigid structure.

7 Long-chain fatty acids (built of acetyl-CoA and malonyl-CoA) are needed in order to synthesize cell phospholipids. During fatty acid synthesis, the carbon chain is lengthened by two carbon atoms at a time until the fatty acid is of suitable length. Then the fatty acids are combined with glycerol phosphate to form a phospholipid.

8 Some energy-requiring processes carried out by a living cell are for functions other than biosynthesis. Examples include nutrient transport and cell motility.

9 Some nutrients may pass into a cell by simple diffusion, but most need to be transported across the cytoplasmic membrane by specific proteins called *carriers*. Facilitated diffusion is carrier-mediated, but, like simple diffusion, it does not require the input of energy and does not result in a higher concentration of nutrient molecules inside the cell than exists outside. However, active transport does allow nutrient accumulation at higher concentrations within the cell, and it requires a source of energy such as the protonmotive force, ATP, or phosphoenolpyruvic acid.

10 The rotation of bacterial flagella is driven directly by the energy of the protonmotive force. Eucaryotic cilia and flagella do not rotate but merely bend in a complex manner, which requires ATP.

KEY TERMS

active transport
Calvin cycle
carrier proteins
deoxyribonucleotides
facilitated diffusion
feedback inhibition
lipid carrier
reductive amination
ribonucleotides
transamination
transpeptidase

ENERGY UTILIZATION FOR BIOSYNTHETIC PROCESSES

1 An organism that has simple nutritional requirements has _____ _____ biosynthetic ability than one that has complex nutritional requirements.

2 In general, biosynthetic processes occur as follows: (1) synthesis of the biochemical building blocks needed to make complex substances, (2) _____ _____ of the building blocks, and (3) assembly of the building blocks into complex substances.

BIOSYNTHESIS OF NITROGENOUS COMPOUNDS

3 In nitrogen fixation, N_2 from the atmosphere is combined with _____ atoms to form _____.

4 Glutamic acid can be made from α-ketoglutaric acid and ammonia by a process called _____.

5 The trading of the amino group on glutamic acid for an oxygen atom on pyruvic acid to form the amino acid alanine is an example of the process called **(a)** oxidative deamination; **(b)** destructive amination; **(c)** transformation; **(d)** transamination; **(e)** transoxygenation.

6 In feedback inhibition, the product of a biosynthetic pathway inhibits the _____ _____ enzyme in the pathway.

7 Which of the following is an example of an energized amino acid? **(a)** adenosine monophosphate; **(b)** glutamic acid; **(c)** alanine-AMP; **(d)** AMP; **(e)** glutamic acid-pyrophosphate.

8 The blueprint for making proteins is contained in the nucleotide sequence of a cell's _____.

9 A deoxyribonucleotide is a nucleotide that contains the sugar _____ _____.

10 Pyrimidine nucleotides are nucleotides that **(a)** contain adenine and guanine; **(b)** contain ribose instead of deoxyribose; **(c)** contain uracil, cytosine, or thymine; **(d)** contain deoxyribose instead of ribose; **(e)** are building blocks for RNA but not DNA.

11 The two purine nucleotides that are building blocks for RNA are (give only abbreviations) _____ and _____, whereas the two that are building blocks for DNA are _____ and _____.

12 The two pyrimidine nucleotides that are building blocks for RNA are (give only abbreviations) _____ and _____, whereas the two that are building blocks for DNA are _____ and _____.

13 Which of the following is an example of an energized nucleotide? **(a)** GMP; **(b)** dCMP; **(c)** UMP; **(d)** dCTP; **(e)** dAMP.

14 The biosynthesis of both RNA and proteins is dependent upon the nucleotide sequence of _____.

BIOSYNTHESIS OF CARBOHYDRATES

15 CO_2 fixation by the Calvin cycle requires _____ as an energy source. It also requires $NADPH_2$ or $NADH_2$ as a(n) _____ donor.

16 In the initial reaction of the Calvin cycle, a 5-carbon compound and a 1-carbon compound react to form **(a)** one 4-carbon compound and one 2-carbon compound; **(b)** one 5-carbon compound and a 1-carbon compound; **(c)** three 2-carbon compounds; **(d)** one 6-carbon compound; **(e)** two 3-carbon compounds.

17 UDP-glucose is the energized form of glucose that is needed for polysaccharide synthesis. Which of the following is the energized form of ribose that is needed for nucleotide synthesis? **(a)** ribose phosphate; **(b)** ribulose phosphate; **(c)** phosphoribose pyrophosphate; **(d)** polyribose; **(e)** UDP-ribose.

18 *Before* it is transported out of the bacterial cell by the lipid carrier, the energized building unit for peptidoglycan has a peptide chain consisting of how many amino acids? **(a)** 2; **(b)** 3; **(c)** 4; **(d)** 5; **(e)** 6.

19 Transpeptidase is an enzyme that catalyzes the: **(a)** transport of peptidoglycan building blocks across the cytoplasmic membrane; **(b)** formation of cross-linkages between the tetrapeptide chains of peptidoglycan; **(c)** synthesis of *N*-acetylmuramic acid-pentapeptide; **(d)** addition of amino acids to *N*-acetylmuramic acid to form a pentapeptide chain; **(e)** transport of peptidoglycan into the cell.

BIOSYNTHESIS OF LIPIDS

20 Which of the following are building blocks for long-chain fatty acids? **(a)** amino acids; **(b)** acetyl-CoA and glycerol phosphate; **(c)** malonyl-CoA and acetyl-CoA; **(d)** ribose and glucose; **(e)** proline and pyruvic acid.

21 Microorganisms usually make acetyl-CoA by oxidizing **(a)** pyruvic acid; **(b)** acetic acid; **(c)** α-ketoglutaric acid; **(d)** fumaric acid; **(e)** glutamic acid.

22 The acetyl portion of acetyl-CoA has two carbon atoms, whereas the malonyl portion of malonyl-CoA has three carbon atoms. This is because malonyl-CoA is formed by the reaction of acetyl-CoA with: **(a)** glucose; **(b)** ATP; **(c)** CO_2; **(d)** a long-chain fatty acid; **(e)** glutamic acid.

23 During the biosynthesis of a fatty acid molecule, how many carbon atoms are added at each stage until the fatty acid is sufficiently long to be used for phospholipid synthesis? **(a)** 1; **(b)** 2; **(c)** 3; **(d)** 10; **(e)** 20.

24 Long-chain fatty acids are linked to what compound to form a phospholipid? **(a)** glucose phosphate; **(b)** ribose phosphate; **(c)** serine; **(d)** ATP; **(e)** glycerol phosphate.

ENERGY UTILIZATION FOR PROCESSES OTHER THAN BIOSYNTHESIS

25 If nutrients pass into a cell by either _____ diffusion or _____ diffusion, they cannot accumulate to a higher concentration inside the cell than exists outside the cell.

26 Which one of the following processes does not involve carrier-mediated transport? **(a)** active transport; **(b)** facilitated diffusion; **(c)** simple diffusion; **(d)** transport that involves adding a phosphate group to a nutrient; **(e)** transport that is powered by the protonmotive force.

27 The energy source that directly causes bacterial flagella to rotate is called

_____ .

28 The flagella of eucaryotic cells do not rotate like bacterial flagella; instead, they merely bend in a complex manner. This bending requires energy in the form of

_____ .

1 Give the general steps that occur in any biosynthetic process, and give a specific example for each step.

2 Explain how cross-linking of peptidoglycan strands in the cell wall can occur in the absence of ATP or other high-energy-transfer compounds.

3 Starch is a polysaccharide that consists of a long chain of glucose molecules. Why would a cell need to use UDP-glucose rather than just glucose to make a starch molecule?

4 How do the nucleotide building blocks for DNA differ from those for RNA?

5 What special problems complicate the biosynthesis of DNA or proteins compared with, say, the biosynthesis of peptidoglycan or phospholipids?

6 What advantage would an active transport system have for a microorganism living in an environment that has a low concentration of nutrients, such as a nonpolluted lake?

1 In the initial reaction of the Calvin cycle, two molecules of a three-carbon compound (phosphoglyceric acid) are produced. Why does an autotrophic organism have to wait for six turns of the Calvin cycle to make a six-carbon hexose instead of immediately using the two three-carbon compounds?

2 Some catabolic pathways such as glycolysis and the citric acid cycle function not only to yield energy but also to provide building blocks for biosynthetic pathways. How many examples of this can you cite?

3 Many cyanobacteria are both autotrophs and nitrogen fixers. A great deal of ATP is required for CO_2 fixation and nitrogen fixation; yet cyanobacteria do not seem to have much difficulty surviving, considering their widespread distribution in nature. What might account for this?

4 Some long-chain fatty acids have an odd number of carbon atoms instead of an even number. How might a cell synthesize such fatty acids? *(Check your answer by referring to a biochemistry textbook.)*

5 Whereas many other antibiotics such as tetracycline and streptomycin are bacteriostatic antibiotics, penicillin is a *bactericidal* antibiotic. Why?

VI

Microbial Genetics

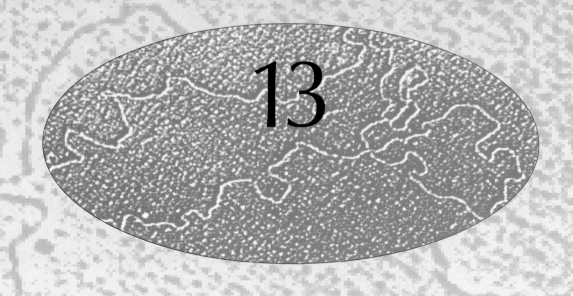

Inheritance and Variability

OVERVIEW

If you use isolation techniques to obtain a pure culture of a particular microorganism such as a yeast or bacterium, a colony of that organism growing on a Petri dish of agar medium will consist of a community of like individuals descended from the parent cell. These offspring are nearly identical to the parent and to each other, sharing many characteristics such as size, shape, or the ability to ferment sugars. But variants may arise spontaneously or as the result of the action of various chemical or physical agents, such as nitrosoguanidine or ultraviolet light. Consequently, some offspring may show traits different from those of the parent.

Genetics is the study of such similarities and differences, referred to by scientists as inheritance and variability, respectively. The concept of inheritance, then, refers to those processes responsible for the high degree of "likeness" between parent and offspring. The hereditary information of a microbial cell, like that of plant and animal cells, is found in the specific arrangement of molecules that form its own DNA code, or "blueprint." A cell can replicate, or copy, its DNA with great accuracy and transmit this information to the next generation.

Although genetics is frequently thought of as the study of the similarity between parent and progeny, some degree of variability also exists and is a necessary feature of living organisms.

An ability to change as the environment changes improves a species' chance for survival. Inability to adapt to slight increases in water temperature, for example, could well result in elimination of an aquatic microbial species. But if one organism in that species contains an altered form of the DNA blueprint that allows tolerance of the higher temperatures, that organism may be able to multiply and continue the species line.

CHROMOSOMES OF PROCARYOTIC AND EUCARYOTIC CELLS

Like a neatly tied bundle sent by parcel post, a *chromosome* is a dense structure inside cells that physically carries hereditary information from one generation to the next. Each bacterial cell contains only one chromosome, consisting of a single molecule of double-stranded deoxyribonucleic acid (DNA) in the form of a closed circle. Recent studies have shown that the DNA is associated with "histonelike" proteins, which resemble the arginine- and lysine-rich proteins called histones that occur in combination with the DNA of eucaryotic cells (Chapter 4). The procaryotic chromosome is naked, lacking the nuclear membrane found in eucaryotic cells. Because its length is about 1200 times that of the entire cell, the *bacterial chromosome* is twisted, coiled, and packaged into a highly compact form [FIGURE 13.1].

In addition to its chromosome, a bacterial cell may contain one or more interesting DNA structures called *plasmids* [FIGURE 13.1]. Plasmids are double-stranded DNA molecules that are much smaller than the chromosome and can replicate independently of the chromosome. Most are circular DNA molecules, but linear plasmids have been found in a few bacteria, such as the spirochete that causes Lyme disease. Plasmids have been used extensively in genetic engineering techniques, and their properties are discussed later in this chapter.

The chromosomes of eucaryotic microorganisms—fungi, algae, and protozoa—appear in their most extended state (i.e., during interphase) like a long string of beads when viewed with the electron microscope. Each chromosome consists of a single long, double-stranded DNA molecule which, at regular intervals, is tightly wound around an aggregate of histone proteins, thus forming the "beads" on the string. During mitosis, eucaryotic chromosomes become tightly folded into a condensed form that can be seen with an ordinary light microscope (Chapter 6). Eucaryotic chromosomes differ from bacterial chromosomes in several respects: (1) each chromosome is *linear* rather than circular; (2) the DNA molecules are at least 10 times longer than those in bacteria; and (3) there is usually more than one chromosome per cell. A cell that contains only one of each kind of chromosome is a *haploid* organism. Since bacteria have a single chromosome, they are necessarily haploid. On the other hand, most eucaryotic cells are *diploid*, because they have two of each kind of chromosome.

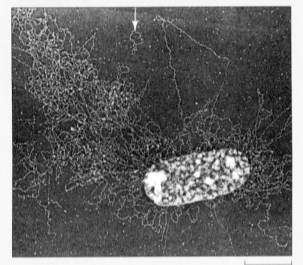

FIGURE 13.1

A disrupted *E. coli* cell showing the ropelike DNA that has spilled out. Note the plasmid (arrow), a circular piece of DNA which is not part of the *E. coli* chromosome and which replicates separately from it.

1.0 μm

ASK YOURSELF

1 What is a bacterial chromosome?

2 What is a plasmid?

3 In what three ways do eucaryotic chromosomes differ from bacterial chromosomes?

REPLICATION OF DNA

As mentioned in Chapter 1, the sequence, or ordered arrangement, of purine and pyrimidine nucleotides in DNA constitutes the hereditary information of a cell. *DNA replication* is the process that copies the nucleotide sequence of a double-stranded parent DNA molecule into two double-stranded daughter DNA molecules—each of which will end up in a daughter cell. This process is called **semiconservative replication**, because each daughter molecule contains one strand from the parental molecule (i.e., one old, or *conserved*, strand) and one newly synthesized strand.

FIGURE 13.2

[A] Early stage in DNA replication. A localized unwinding of the two strands results in two replication forks. At each fork individual energized nucleotides are assembled into new complementary DNA strands by the enzyme DNA polymerase, using the old strands as templates. Note that where there is a G in the old DNA strand, a C is inserted in the new strand, and where there is an A in the old strand, a T is inserted in the new strand. A, adenine; T, thymine; C, cystosine; G, guanine. **[B]** Polarity of a nucleotide of DNA. Each nucleotide in DNA has a 3' (deoxyribose) end and a 5' (phosphate) end.

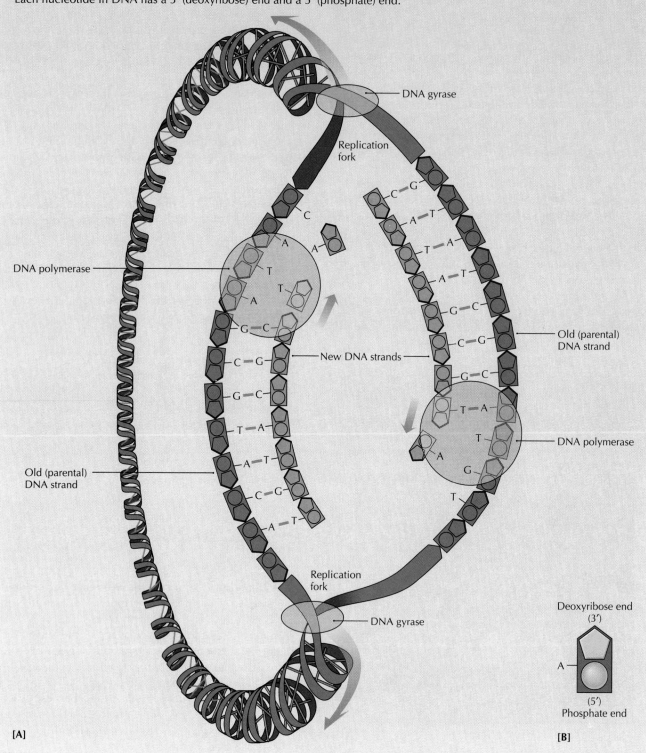

DNA gyrase

Replication fork

DNA polymerase

New DNA strands

Old (parental) DNA strand

Old (parental) DNA strand

DNA polymerase

Replication fork

DNA gyrase

Deoxyribose end (3')

A

(5')
Phosphate end

[A]   **[B]**

Replication of bacterial DNA begins when two parental strands are unwound by an enzyme called *DNA gyrase* at a specific site on the DNA molecule, forming two replication forks [FIGURE 13.2A]. The forks move in opposite directions around the circular molecule until they eventually meet. As the two parental strands separate, each strand serves as a template, or pattern, for the construction of a new strand, one that is *complementary* to the parental strand. Complementarity always exists between the purine and the pyrimidine bases of a double-stranded DNA molecule: *adenine* (A) on one strand pairs with *thymine* (T) on the other strand, and *guanine* (G) on one strand pairs with *cytosine* (C) on the other strand. This arrangement is maintained throughout the synthesis of a new DNA strand.

An enzyme called **DNA polymerase** ensures complementarity by adding nucleotides to the new strand in such a way that each new nucleotide is complementary to the corresponding base on the parental strand. For instance, if the nucleotide on the parental strand contains the base adenine, DNA polymerase will add a thymine-containing nucleotide to the corresponding site on the new strand.

Each nucleotide on the newly synthesized daughter strand also has a *polarity* that is opposite to that of the complementary nucleotide on the parental strand. Polarity refers to the direction in which the nucleotide molecule faces as it rests in the DNA strand. Each nucleotide molecule has two ends: the *deoxyribose end* (called the 3' end) and the *phosphate end* (called the 5' end) as shown in FIGURE 13.2B. If the nucleotides on the parental strand are arranged in the 5' → 3' direction, those on the new complementary strand will be arranged in the 3' → 5' direction. If the nucleotides on the parental strand are arranged in the 3' → 5' direction, those on the new strand will be arranged in the 5' → 3' direction. Thus, the old parental strand and the newly synthesized strand will have opposite polarity [FIGURE 13.2A].

As the old circular DNA unwinds, the two new strands continue to grow at both replication forks. Each new strand grows in two directions, from both the 3' end and the 5' end of the strand [FIGURE 13.3]. This bidirectional growth presents a problem for the cell, because DNA polymerase can add nucleotides one at a time only to the 3' *end* of a growing strand. Then how does the 5' end grow? It grows because a number of short segments of DNA are synthesized by the DNA polymerase and then linked together to form a continuous strand. This happens in the following way. Near the replication fork a short complementary molecule of ribonucleic acid (RNA), called an *RNA primer*, is made by a special enzyme. Then DNA polymerase extends the primer by adding deoxyribonucleotides to its 3' end to form a short strand of DNA. The elongation stops when the 3' end of the DNA strand reaches the RNA primer of a previously synthesized strand. DNA polymerase removes the

FIGURE 13.3
Schematic illustration of the overall replication of bacterial DNA. As shown, there are two directions of replication from the origin; i.e., there are two growing points (replication forks). In *E. coli* the average rate at which these two growing points move during replication is about 45,000 bases per minute per fork at 37°C, and the rate of unwinding of the parental double helix at each fork is about 4,500 turns per minute.

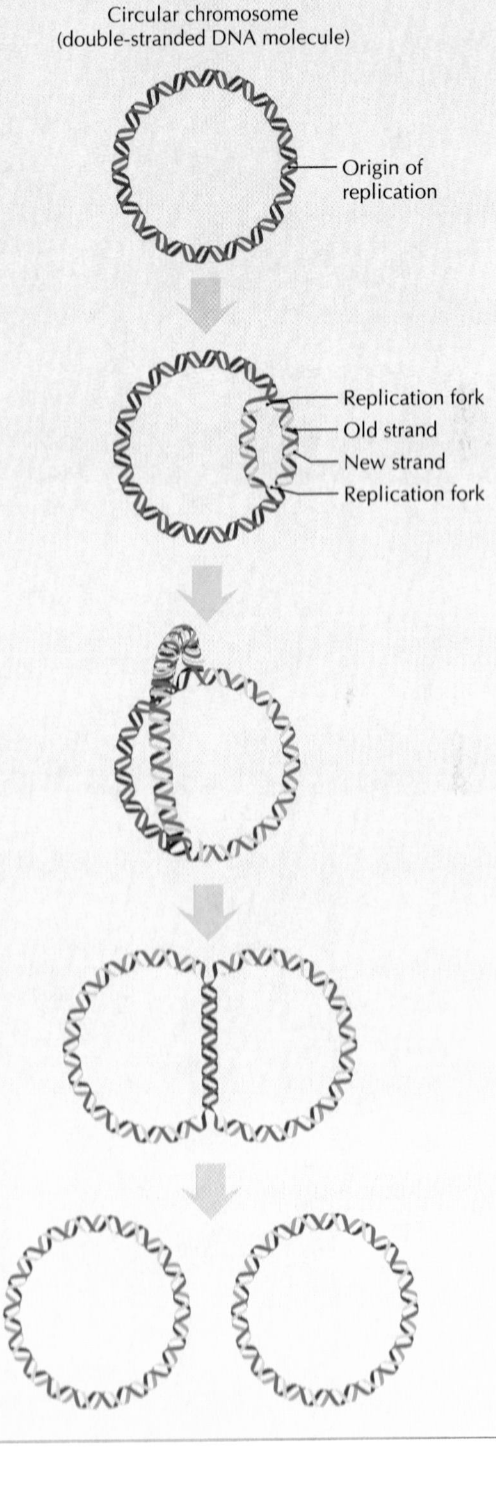

Circular chromosome
(double-stranded DNA molecule)

Origin of replication

Replication fork
Old strand
New strand
Replication fork

FIGURE 13.4
Replication fork, showing DNA synthesis at the ends of new complementary strands of DNA. The 3' end of a new strand is elongated by DNA polymerase in a continuous manner, with deoxynucleotides being added one by one. However, the 5' end of a new strand is elongated in a discontinuous manner. A short segment of RNA called a *primer* is synthesized near the

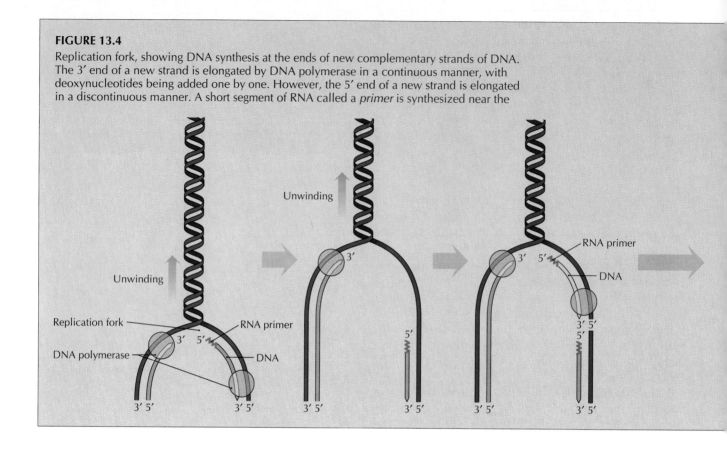

FIGURE 13.5
The mode of DNA replication of linear eucaryotic DNA involves the formation of multiple replication "bubbles." (The double-helical form of DNA strands is not shown, for the sake of simplicity.)

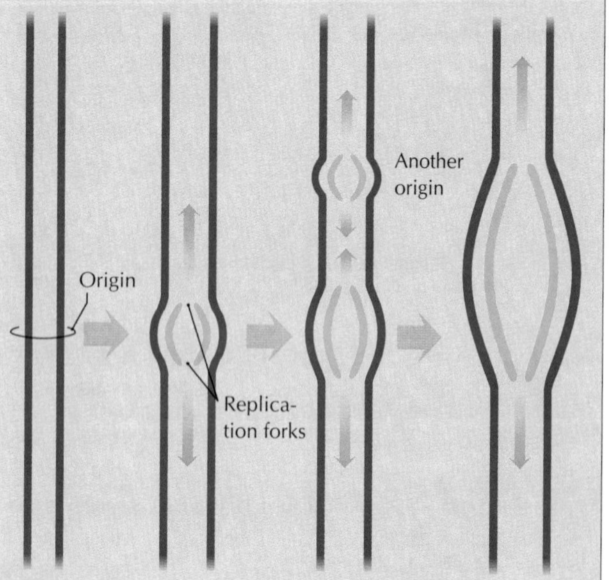

primer, and an enzyme called **DNA ligase** joins the DNA segments [FIGURE 13.4].

In eucaryotic organisms, which have linear DNA molecules, replication of DNA starts at many sites on the molecule (sometimes hundreds of them) with the formation of replication "bubbles" [FIGURE 13.5]. A replication bubble grows in size as DNA replication proceeds in opposite directions from the point of initiation. Adjacent bubbles fuse to form larger ones until, finally, two linear double-stranded molecules are formed.

ASK YOURSELF

1 What is meant by *semiconservative replication?*

2 What enzyme synthesizes new complementary strands of DNA?

3 What accounts for the great accuracy with which DNA is replicated?

4 Does a newly synthesized strand of DNA have the same polarity as the parental strand, or does it have opposite polarity?

5 What is the function of DNA ligase in DNA replication?

replication fork. DNA polymerase extends the primer by adding deoxyribonucleotides to form a short 5' → 3'strand of DNA. After the parental DNA is unwound further, another RNA primer is made, another short DNA strand is synthesized by DNA polymerase, and so forth. The short DNA strands are then connected by DNA ligase to form a long continuous strand.

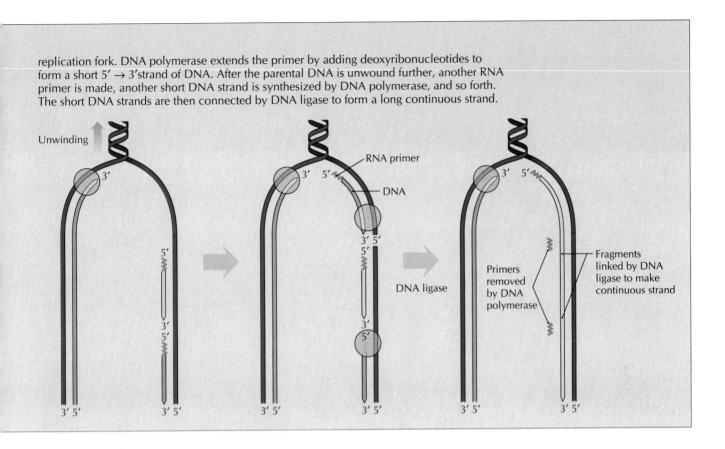

TRANSCRIPTION AND TRANSLATION OF GENETIC INFORMATION

Dictated by specific nucleotide sequences in the DNA, genetic messages direct the manufacture of RNA and proteins, which are essential components of all living cells. A segment of DNA that contains the nucleotide sequence for making a particular protein is called a *gene*. Since a cell makes thousands of proteins, a DNA molecule contains thousands of genes, one for each protein. The way in which a cell uses the information in a gene to make a particular protein can be summarized as follows:

1 The information in the gene (DNA) is copied to a molecule of *messenger ribonucleic acid (mRNA)* by a process called *transcription.*
2 The *mRNA* carries the transcribed information from the nuclear region of the cell to the ribosomes in the cytoplasm.
3 The ribosomes then carry out *translation,* a process in which the information in the *mRNA* is used to synthesize the corresponding protein from amino acids.

Transcription

Transcription of a particular gene involves only one of the two DNA strands of double-stranded DNA. An enzyme called **DNA-dependent RNA polymerase** is responsible for transcribing the gene to *mRNA*. This enzyme first binds to a special sequence of DNA nucleotides called the *promoter* region, whereupon the two DNA strands then separate and the polymerase begins to move forward and synthesize a strand of *mRNA* that is complementary to one of the DNA strands [FIGURE 13.6]. For example, if a deoxynucleotide on the DNA strand contains *guanine*, the corresponding ribonucleotide on the RNA strand will contain *cytosine*, and if a deoxynucleotide on the DNA strand contains *adenine*, the corresponding ribonucleotide on the RNA strand will contain *uracil* (see FIGURE 1.25; recall from Chapter 1 that RNA contains uracil instead of thymine). Ribonucleotides are added to the growing *mRNA* strand at the 3' end, so that the strand grows in the 5' → 3' direction [FIGURE 13.6]. As the ribonucleotides are added, the DNA double helix continually opens ahead of the growing point and then closes behind it to preserve the double-stranded configuration of the DNA. The polymerase stops when it reaches the end of the genetic message, which is indicated by a particular nucleotide sequence on the gene called the *termination sequence*.

FIGURE 13.6

Transcription of DNA. DNA-dependent RNA polymerase binds to the promoter sequence and then adds energized nucleotides to build a strand of *m*RNA complementary to the DNA message. Note that where there is a G in DNA, a C is inserted in *m*RNA, and where there is an A in DNA, a U is inserted in *m*RNA. Synthesis of *m*RNA ends when the polymerase encounters a termination sequence. The *m*RNA will serve later as a template for protein synthesis. A, adenine; T, thymine; C, cytosine; G, guanine; U, uracil.

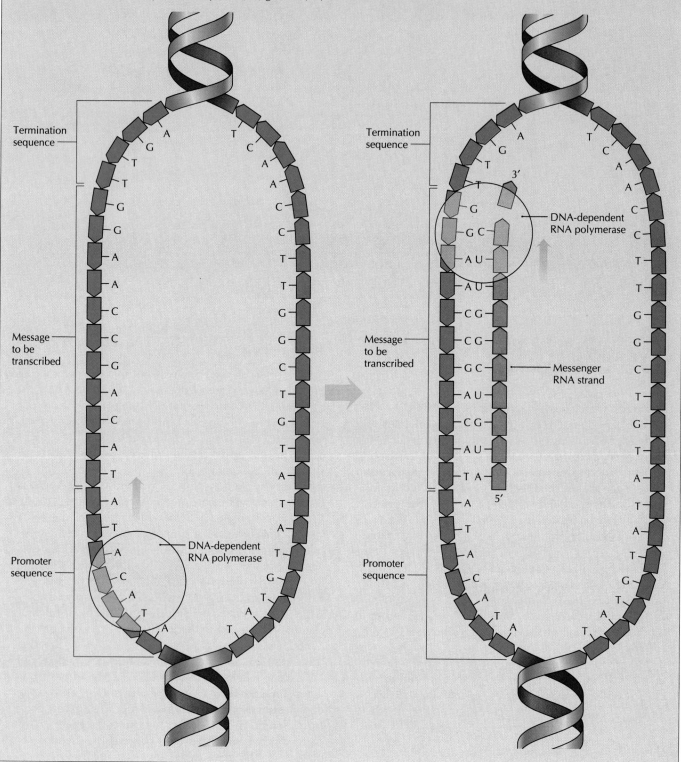

13.1 PCR—THE MARVELOUS TOOL

Can a suspect be convicted or cleared of a crime on the basis of a single hair found at the scene? Can clinicians detect the AIDS virus in an infected person's blood even when all attempts to isolate the virus fail? The answer is yes to these and similar questions, thanks to one of the most significant developments in molecular biology—the laboratory procedure called *polymerase chain reaction*, or *PCR*. This technique makes it possible to produce an enormous number of copies of one or more genes from very tiny initial quantities of DNA—quantities so small that they are impossible to detect by routine methods. Large amounts of DNA can be produced from minute amounts present in substances such as water, food, blood, hairs, and clinical samples taken from patients. This "amplification" of DNA has many applications in microbiology, including clinical diagnosis, forensic (legal) medicine, and basic research. For instance, if only a few AIDS virus genes are present in a sample of an infected person's cells, these genes can be amplified in number to give quantities of DNA large enough for the genes to be identified. This has enabled clinicians to detect infection by the AIDS virus when other methods have failed. PCR has also become a powerful tool for diagnosing various genetic diseases—such as sickle cell anemia—in a fetus still in its mother's womb. This is possible because the technique can amplify the genetic information provided by just a few fetal cells, which can be obtained without harming the fetus. There are also exciting uses for PCR in the field of legal medicine. Trace amounts of DNA in fluids such as blood or semen, or in tissues such as hair found at the scene of a crime, can be amplified by PCR and then analyzed to see whether the DNA is identical to that of a person suspected of committing the crime. Courts are beginning to accept such evidence, which will help solve otherwise unsolvable crimes.

The starting material for a PCR is a segment of double-stranded DNA containing the *target sequence*, a nucleotide sequence containing the gene of interest. In the first cycle (see the accompanying figure) the DNA is heated to separate the two strands. Then two kinds of *primers*—short synthetic pieces of DNA—are added. Each primer has a nucleotide sequence that is complementary to a particular region at the end of the gene to be amplified. When the mixture of primers and DNA is cooled, the primers bind to the gene. The enzyme *DNA polymerase* then adds energized nucleotides one at a time to one end of each primer and synthesizes a long strand of complementary DNA. At the end of the cycle two copies of the gene are formed from each initial copy.

Subsequent cycles are done in a similar manner. The value of the PCR technique lies in the fact that the number of copies of the target gene increases exponentially with each cycle: 2, 4, 8, 16, 32, and so on. By the twenty-fifth cycle, there are millions of copies of the target sequence—enough to be easily analyzed by routine laboratory procedures.

The PCR technique is still too new to be used routinely in all laboratories, but it is so powerful as a detection tool that its use is likely to expand rapidly.

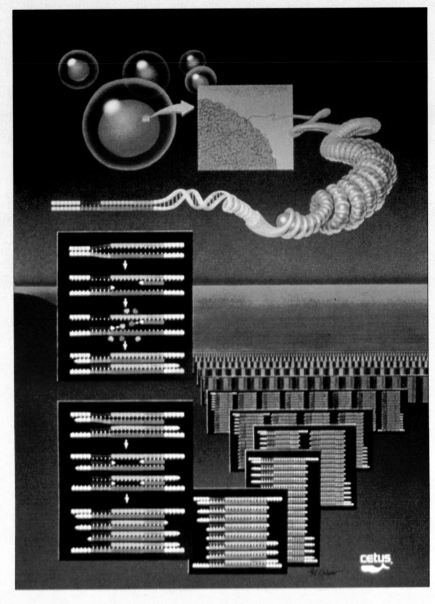

mRNA and the Genetic Code. The "words" of the genetic message carried by mRNA (and initially encoded in the DNA segment from which it was transcribed) are written in a chemical language called the **genetic code.** This code is based upon units called mRNA *codons,* each of which consists of *three* of the four bases of mRNA [adenine (A), guanine (G), cytosine (C), and uracil (U)]. During translation, each mRNA codon tells a ribosome which of the 20 different amino acids is to be added to a growing protein chain. The codon UGG (uracil-guanine-guanine), for example, signals the addition of the amino acid tryptophan. TABLE 13.1 lists the complete codon–amino acid dictionary of the genetic code. This dictionary, which is nearly universal for all species, has three particularly interesting features:

1 The codon AUG, which codes for the amino acid methionine, is also a *start codon* and always appears at the beginning of the genetic message. It acts as a signal to tell the cell where the gene to be translated begins. Methionine will always be the initial amino acid as synthesis of a new protein molecule begins. However, this initial methionine is often removed later, leaving the next amino acid as the first in the final protein chain. For example, the amino acid lysine becomes the first amino acid in the enzyme ribonuclease [see FIGURE 1.19].

2 Three codons (UAA, UAG, and UGA) are *nonsense codons,* for which there are no corresponding amino acids. *These codons cause termination of translation and stop synthesis of the protein being translated.*

3 Since there are four different bases, there can be 4^3, or 64, kinds of codons. However, there are only 20 amino acids to be coded. *Consequently, some amino acids are coded for by more than one codon.* For example, leucine is coded for by any of six codons: UUA, UUG, CUU, CUC, CUA, and CUG [TABLE 13.1].

An example will show how the genetic code operates. Suppose the base sequence on mRNA is

AUG-AGA-AAA-UUU-AGU-GGG-ACU-UCU-UAA

From TABLE 13.1, the translation of this code into a chain of amino acids by a ribosome would be

Met-Arg-Lys-Phe-Ser-Gly-Thr-Ser-STOP

TABLE 13.1

The Genetic Code for the Base Triplets of mRNA and the Amino Acids for Which They Code

First base	Second base U	C	A	G	Third base
U	UUU UUC Phe / UUA UUG Leu	UCU UCC UCA UCG Ser	UAU UAC Tyr / UAA STOP* / UAG STOP*	UGU UGC Cys / UGA STOP* / UGG Trp	U C A G
C	CUU CUC CUA CUG Leu	CCU CCC CCA CCG Pro	CAU CAC His / CAA CAG Gln	CGU CGC CGA CGG Arg	U C A G
A	AUU AUC AUA Ile / AUG Met†	ACU ACC ACA ACG Thr	AAU AAC Asn / AAA AAG Lys	AGU AGC Ser / AGA AGG Arg	U C A G
G	GUU GUC GUA GUG Val	GCU GCC GCA GCG Ala	GAU GAC Asp / GAA GAG Glu	GGU GGC GGA GGG Gly	U C A G

*Codons UAA, UAG, and UGA cause termination of synthesis of a protein chain.
†The codon AUG, which specifies methionine, is the initial triplet of the mRNA; thus methionine is always the first amino acid as synthesis of a new protein molecule begins (although it is usually removed later).

If the methionine is later removed, the final sequence would be

Arg-Lys-Phe-Ser-Gly-Thr-Ser-STOP

Translation

Ribosomes, which are composed of proteins and ribosomal RNA (*r*RNA), translate the coded information in *m*RNA to make a particular protein from amino acids. As you learned in Chapter 4, a bacterial ribosome is composed of a 50-S subunit and a 30-S subunit, which combine during protein synthesis to form a complete 70-S ribosome. A eucaryotic ribosome, on the other hand, is composed of a 60-S subunit and a 40-S subunit, which combine to form a complete 80-S ribosome.

Before a ribosome can construct a protein from amino acids, the amino acids must first be *energized* (activated) with the energy of ATP, a compound discussed in Chapter 11. The energized amino acids are then linked to the end of special RNA molecules called **transfer RNA (*tRNA*)**, which carry the amino acids to the ribosomes [FIGURE 13.7]. Transfer RNA molecules are much shorter in length than *m*RNA molecules and are folded back on themselves by pairing between complementary bases (adenine with uracil, guanine with cytosine). This folding and pairing gives each *t*RNA molecule a "cloverleaf" configuration [FIGURE 13.7].

There is a specific *t*RNA for each of the 20 amino acids. In each *t*RNA molecule, three of the unpaired bases constitute an *anticodon* [FIGURE 13.7], which can recognize a complementary codon in *m*RNA. For example, the *t*RNA to which only leucine is linked (called *t*RNA^Leu) has the anticodon AAC, which is complementary to the *m*RNA codon UUG for leucine.

After *t*RNA molecules carry energized amino acids to a ribosome [FIGURE 13.8A], the ribosome links the amino acids together to form a protein. A ribosome is analogous to a videotape-playing machine: just as the machine will produce any kind of image, depending on the videotape played, the ribosome will manufacture any kind of protein, depending on the kind of *m*RNA supplied. FIGURE 13.8B illustrates the steps involved in translating the coded instructions contained in an *m*RNA molecule into a specific protein. Notice that it is the specific alignment of the *t*RNA anticodons with their complementary *m*RNA codons that allows amino acids to be assembled in correct sequence.

As shown in FIGURE 13.9, several ribosomes can be actively engaged in translating a single *m*RNA molecule at the same time. Elongation of a protein chain stops when the ribosome finally reaches a nonsense codon (UAA, UAG, or UGA).

FIGURE 13.7

Energized amino acids can bind to transfer RNA (*t*RNA). The *t*RNA has a cloverleaf structure because of complementary base pairing between portions of the molecule; of the remaining unpaired bases, three constitute the anticodon. In the *t*RNA illustrated here, the anticodon is AAC; the corresponding *m*RNA codon is UUG, the codon for leucine. Thus this transfer RNA is called *t*RNA^Leu, and a molecule of energized leucine can bind to it. There is a specific transfer RNA for each kind of amino acid.

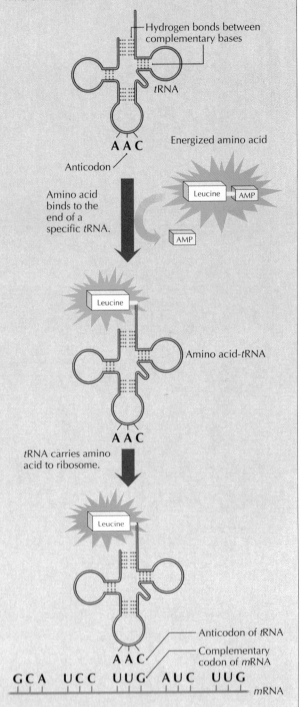

FIGURE 13.8

[A] Model of a bacterial ribosome showing the smaller subunit (blue) and the larger subunit (red). [B] Synthesis of a protein chain on a bacterial ribosome. The cloverleaf structures represent *t*RNA molecules. The initial amino acid is always methionine, but this is usually removed later. Elongation of the chain stops when the ribosome comes to a "nonsense" codon (UAA, UAG, or UGA) on the *m*RNA; the protein chain is then released and the ribosome dissociates back into 50-S and 30-S subunits.

[A]

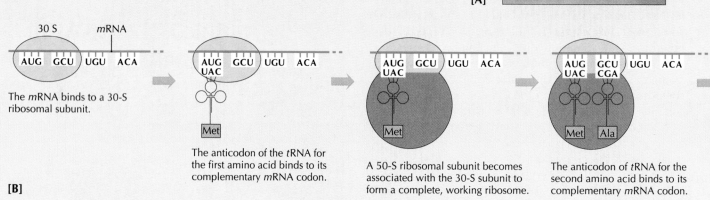

The *m*RNA binds to a 30-S ribosomal subunit.

The anticodon of the *t*RNA for the first amino acid binds to its complementary *m*RNA codon.

A 50-S ribosomal subunit becomes associated with the 30-S subunit to form a complete, working ribosome.

The anticodon of *t*RNA for the second amino acid binds to its complementary *m*RNA codon.

[B]

FIGURE 13.9

Schematic drawing of several ribosomes reading a single molecule of *m*RNA simultaneously. Solid cubes are amino acids.

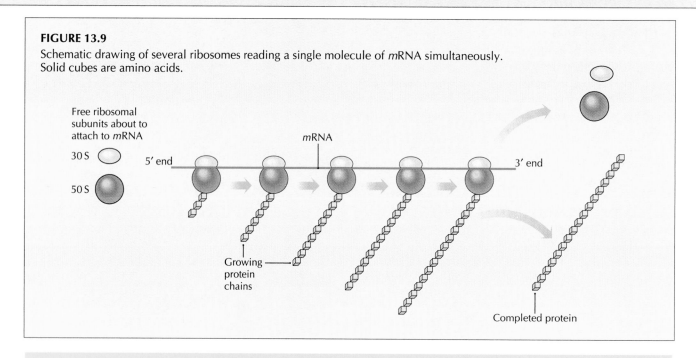

ASK YOURSELF

1 What is the difference between the transcription and the translation of a genetic message?

2 What enzyme synthesizes messenger RNA? What governs where the enzyme starts and stops?

3 What is the basis of the genetic code?

4 What roles do ribosomes, transfer RNA, and messenger RNA play in translation?

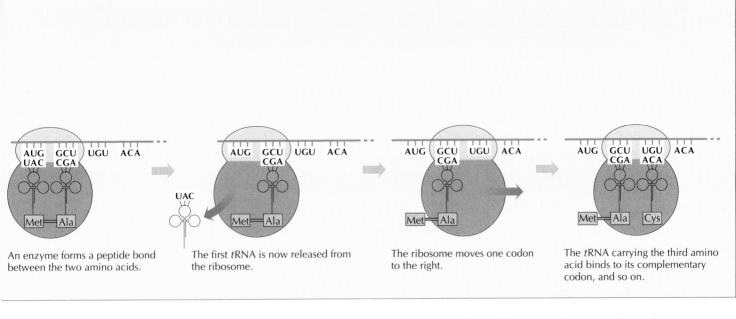

An enzyme forms a peptide bond between the two amino acids.

The first *t*RNA is now released from the ribosome.

The ribosome moves one codon to the right.

The *t*RNA carrying the third amino acid binds to its complementary codon, and so on.

VARIABILITY IN MICROORGANISMS

To this point you have been learning the mechanism by which genetic information can be transmitted from parent to progeny with great accuracy, carrying specific traits from generation to generation. However, genetic variability is as necessary to a biological species as constancy. Living organisms need to maintain a proper balance between these two characteristics. Consequently, you also must understand the mechanisms that result in variability.

Variability is associated with two fundamental properties of an organism, its **genotype** and its **phenotype.** Genotype refers to the entire genetic capability of an organism as found in its DNA. In a bacterial cell, this includes the chromosomal DNA plus any plasmid DNA that may be present; in a eucaryotic cell, it includes the chromosomal DNA plus the DNA of the mitochondria and, in an algal or plant cell, the DNA of the chloroplasts as well. Cells obviously carry much more genetic information than is used or expressed at any one time. Thus the genotype represents the *inheritable total potential* of a cell. In contrast, the phenotype represents the portion of the genetic potential that is *actually expressed by the cell under a given set of conditions.* This may be a particular color or size of bacterial colony, or the utilization by yeast of specific chemicals as energy sources. Another example is the presence of bacterial capsules, which may

or may not be formed by certain bacteria, depending on their environment. It is important to note that a single genotype may result in many phenotypes.

Phenotypic Changes

Both the genotype and the environment influence the phenotype of an organism. For instance, bacteria of the genus *Azomonas* form large, gummy colonies when grown with the sugar sucrose, and smaller, nongummy colonies in the absence of this sugar [FIGURE 13.10]. Although the bacterium is always potentially capable of making the gummy material, it is the presence or absence of the sucrose that determines whether this trait is expressed. In other words, some phenotypic changes may be caused by changes in the environment rather than by changes in the genetic information of a cell, and a return to the original phenotype will occur if the original environmental conditions are restored.

Genotypic Changes

Although some phenotypic changes are the result of environmental influences, others are the result of changes in the DNA. These can occur as the result of (1) *mutation,* a change in the nucleotide sequence of a gene, or (2) *recombination,* a process that leads to new combinations of genes on a chromosome.

FIGURE 13.10
Appearance of colonies of *Azomonas* sp. grown on agar media. **[A]** Small, nongummy colonies growing on trypticase soy agar medium lacking sucrose. **[B]** Large, gummy colonies growing on trypticase soy agar medium containing sucrose. In many instances, the borders of individual colonies have fused, giving confluent growth.

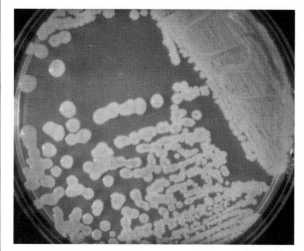

[A]

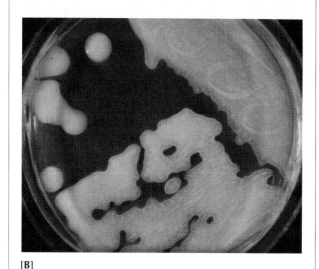

[B]

Mutation. Any gene can undergo mutation. Because a mutated gene has an altered nucleotide sequence, the protein for which it codes may have an altered amino acid sequence. A cell or an organism carrying a mutated gene is called a *mutant*, whereas the parent organism with a normal (nonmutated) gene is called the *wild type*. By studying mutations, scientists can learn more about such things as cell biochemistry, genetic disorders such as Huntington's chorea and achondroplasia, and development of drug resistance in microbial pathogens.

Mutations can occur in all living organisms. Now and then an albino cat appears in a black litter, or a yellow pea grows among many green peas. The same phenomenon can occur among microorganisms. In nature, however, mutations are relatively rare events that can occur at random without any apparent cause. In bacteria, such spontaneous mutations usually occur at rates of only one mutation in a population of several million bacterial cells. Therefore, isolating a mutant cell from a bacterial culture is like looking for the proverbial needle in a haystack.

Microbiologists have developed some helpful techniques to find, or select, these rare mutants. For example, an antibiotic can be added to a growth medium to select for mutants that are antibiotic-resistant. Under these conditions, the wild-type cells will be killed and only the mutant cells will survive and multiply. Similarly, a virus that attacks bacteria can be introduced into a growing bacterial culture to find bacterial mutants that are resistant to the virus. *It is important to realize that such mutations have occurred before exposure to the antibiotic or the virus, not as a result of such exposure.* The antibiotic or virus merely *selects* for a mutant that is already present.

Some mutants require more complicated selection methods. For instance, a mutant cell of *Escherichia coli* may be unable to make an essential amino acid or vitamin normally made by the wild type. An ingenious procedure is used to increase the proportion of such mutants in a population, greatly enhancing their isolation:

1 A culture of *E. coli* containing the wild-type cells and a few mutant cells is inoculated into a medium lacking the nutrient that the mutant cannot make (e.g., the amino acid tryptophan). The wild-type cells can reproduce but the mutant cells cannot.
2 Penicillin is added to the culture. This antibiotic kills only cells that are reproducing. Thus the wild-type cells are killed, whereas *the mutant cells are not killed, because they are not reproducing.*
3 The enzyme penicillinase is added to destroy the penicillin, or the cells can simply be centrifuged out of the penicillin-containing medium.
4 The cells are plated onto an agar medium containing tryptophan. The mutant cells (and any remaining viable wild-type cells) multiply and form colonies.

The *replica plating technique*, a selective isolation procedure developed in 1952, can now be used to identify which of the colonies on the agar plate are mutants [FIGURE 13.11]. This procedure uses a *velvet disk replicator*, a cylinder covered with sterile velveteen cloth. When the cloth-covered end of the replicator is pressed onto the agar plate, the velveteen fibers pick up bacteria

FIGURE 13.11

Replica plating is used for isolating nutritional mutants of *E. coli*. In this illustration it is used to isolate a mutant that has lost the ability to synthesize the amino acid tryptophan. The key step is the use of velveteen cloth to inoculate the bacteria in the same pattern as the colonies on the original plate. Although the plate illustrated here has only six colonies for simplicity, plates having 100 or more colonies can be analyzed.

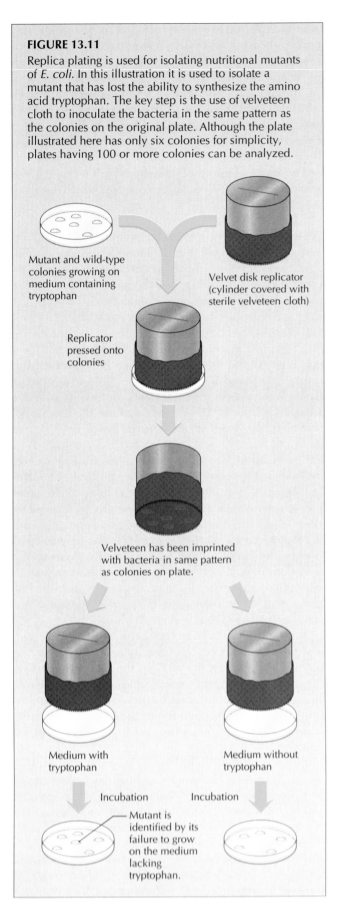

Mutant and wild-type colonies growing on medium containing tryptophan

Velvet disk replicator (cylinder covered with sterile velveteen cloth)

Replicator pressed onto colonies

Velveteen has been imprinted with bacteria in same pattern as colonies on plate.

Medium with tryptophan

Medium without tryptophan

Incubation

Incubation

Mutant is identified by its failure to grow on the medium lacking tryptophan.

from the colonies. The pattern of imprinting corresponds to the arrangement of the colonies on the plate. The replicator is then pressed onto two sterile agar plates, one containing tryptophan and the other without tryptophan. The fibers inoculate bacteria onto these new plates in the same pattern as that of the colonies on the original plate. Mutant bacteria will be able to grow only on the tryptophan-containing medium, whereas wild-type bacteria will grow on both media. By comparing the two plates after incubation, you can identify the mutants.

Other techniques for selecting specific mutants include the use of filtration systems and the use of viruses that infect specific bacteria. Many of the techniques traditionally used by microbiologists for mutant induction and selection have been adapted to the study of animal and plant cells grown in laboratory cultures. Automated techniques have been developed for the detection and isolation of mutant cells.

Mutations can be classified into various types based upon the kinds of changes they produce in a gene. Two common types are *point mutations* and *frameshift mutations*. A point mutation is one that results from the *substitution of one nucleotide for another* in a gene. In one form of point mutation, called *neutral mutation*, the altered codon continues to code for the same amino acid as before and thus the same protein is synthesized. For example, if the *m*RNA codon AA<u>U</u> became AA<u>C</u>, it would still code for the amino acid asparagine because more than one codon codes for this amino acid [TABLE 13.1]. In another form of point mutation, called *missense mutation*, the altered codon codes for a different amino acid. For example, if the codon AA<u>U</u> became AA<u>G</u>, it would code for lysine instead of asparagine. This might alter the properties of the protein, or even make it nonfunctional.

A good example of a missense mutation in humans is the disease sickle cell anemia. A single base substitution in the codon for the sixth amino acid of normal hemoglobin A changes this amino acid from glutamic acid (codon = G<u>A</u>G) to valine (codon = G<u>U</u>G). (Hemoglobin is the protein in red blood cells that carries oxygen.) The result is the abnormal hemoglobin, hemoglobin S, that characterizes sickle cell anemia. At low oxygen concentrations in the blood, the hemoglobin S molecules become stacked into crystals, distorting red blood cells into sickle shapes. These abnormally shaped cells cause a variety of health problems.

In a third type of point mutation, called *nonsense mutation*, the nucleotide substitution produces a chain-terminating codon (for example, a change of UA<u>U</u> to UA<u>A</u>). This results in premature halting of protein synthesis during translation. The product is an incomplete protein that is probably nonfunctional.

Frameshift mutations occur with either the *addition* or the *loss* of one or more nucleotides in a gene and are termed *insertion mutations* or *deletion mutations*, respectively. Since *m*RNA is read in consecutive blocks of three bases (codons), a frameshift mutation causes a shift of what is called the *reading frame* of the gene. This usually leads to the formation of a nonfunctional protein, a situation analogous to adding or deleting one or more letters in a sentence. For instance, if a sentence began

See the cat and the rat ___ ___ ___

and you added an extra letter, *d*, but continued to keep the letters grouped in triplets, the sentence would become

See th<u>d</u> eca tan dth era t___ ___ ___

which makes no sense. Similarly, if you deleted a letter in the original sentence, the result would make no sense.

Mutations may occur spontaneously, without any apparent cause, or they may result from exposure to a *mutagen.* A mutagen is any physical or chemical agent that causes the *mutation rate* (number of mutations per gene per generation) to exceed the normal spontaneous rate. Examples of mutagenic physical agents are ultraviolet (UV) light and x-rays. Chemical mutagens include nitrous acid, acridine orange dye, 5-bromouracil, ethyl methane sulfonate, and nitrosoguanidine. Overexposure to sunlight, which contains UV light, and to chemicals in cigarette smoke is considered a health risk because of these agents' potential to cause mutations.

Mutagens act by altering the structure of DNA or its components. For example, as x-rays pass through a cell they can remove electrons from atoms and molecules, leaving a trail of ions. These ions can directly or indirectly cause alterations in the structure of purine and pyrimidine bases. Ultraviolet light causes the formation of *thymine dimers*, in which two adjacent pyrimidines on a DNA strand become bonded together; this bonding distorts the normal conformation of the DNA. Nitrous acid can cause normal purine or pyrimidine bases of DNA to be converted into abnormal bases such as uracil and hypoxanthine. Molecules of acridine orange dye can wedge themselves between the two strands of double-stranded DNA, thereby causing deformations in the DNA helix and frameshift mutations. Ethyl methane sulfonate produces a high proportion of point mutations. These and other alterations in DNA often cause errors in nucleotide sequences during DNA replication.

Many mutagens are also *carcinogens* (cancer-inducing agents), thus supporting the idea that genetic influences are somehow tied to cancer. Scientists now know that human cells contain a number of special genes, called *protooncogenes*, that have the potential to cause cancer. Under normal conditions, protooncogenes probably code for proteins essential for cell growth at specific stages of development of the organism. But if these genes are altered or are expressed at an abnormal stage, perhaps because of the action of mutagens or certain viruses, they apparently can contribute to the development of cancer and are called **oncogenes**.

In the early 1970s, researchers discovered a surprising new group of mutagens that are composed of DNA itself. These small, mobile pieces of DNA, called *transposons,* contain genetic information that allows them to insert themselves into chromosomes at numerous locations. They cause mutations by interrupting the nucleotide sequence of the genes into which they are inserted.

It is important to recognize that the mutations caused by mutagens differ from spontaneous mutations *only in frequency, not in kind.* For example, exposure to an ultraviolet lamp in the laboratory causes a greatly increased rate of mutation, but the kinds of mutation are similar to those that occur spontaneously. Ultraviolet light is frequently used in the laboratory to create mutants for research.

Fortunately, cells contain specific enzymes that repair much of the DNA damage done by mutagens. Because of these repair enzymes, some cells can escape the damaging effects of mutations and continue to function normally. Types of DNA repair include the removal of damaged base pairs or of mispaired bases.

Recombination. Recombination is a process that leads to a new genotype through the exchange of genetic material between two homologous chromosomes. Homologous chromosomes have similar genes at corresponding sites. However, the genes, although similar, may not necessarily be *identical.* For example, the gene at a particular site on one chromosome may have undergone a mutation. If so, it will not be identical to the corresponding gene on the other chromosome. Such corresponding genes that differ from each other in their mutational state are called *alleles.*

In eucaryotic microorganisms such as fungi, algae, and protozoa, genetic recombination may occur during meiosis [see FIGURE 6.9]. When the homologous chromosomes pair they may cross, break, and then rejoin in such a way that a piece of each chromosome is exchanged [FIGURE 13.12]. The point where the chromosomes cross is the *chiasma*, and the entire exchange process is called *crossing-over.*

In a procaryotic cell there is only a single chromosome. Therefore, before recombination can occur, a homologous chromosome (usually only a piece of it) must first be *transferred* from a donor bacterium to the recipient bacterium. Since the donor's chromosome must be homologous with the recipient's chromosome, the donor and the recipient bacteria usually belong to the same species or to closely related species. After chromosomal transfer is accomplished, recombination may occur in

FIGURE 13.12

Schematic drawing showing crossing-over between homologous eucaryotic chromosomes during meiosis. Capital letters and corresponding lowercase letters (A and a, B and b, etc.) represent alleles (corresponding genes that differ in their mutational states).

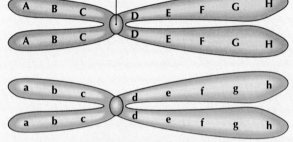

Two pairs of homologous chromosomes carrying different alleles

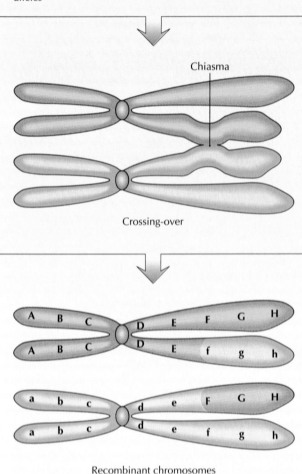

Crossing-over

Recombinant chromosomes

either of two ways, depending upon whether the donor DNA is double- or single-stranded [FIGURE 13.13].

In bacteria, gene transfer that can lead to recombination may occur in any of three different ways: *transformation, transduction,* and *conjugation.* Each of these gene transfer processes has unique, interesting features.

Transformation is the simplest type of gene transfer: a recipient cell acquires genes from "free-floating" DNA molecules in the surrounding medium. In nature, the DNA may come from dead cells that lyse and release their DNA. In the laboratory, however, the DNA is extracted by chemical methods from a suspension of donor bacteria and then added to a culture of recipient bacteria. In nature or in the laboratory, a recipient bacterium may be able to absorb a small fragment of the donor DNA, and incorporate it into its own chromosome by recombination [FIGURE 13.14]. Thus a recipient bacterium can acquire one or more inheritable characteristics from a donor bacterium and become what is called *transformed*. Only certain species of bacteria are known to undergo transformation, and even these must be in a state of growth receptive to the incorporation of donor DNA; that is, they must be *competent*. This condition usually occurs only when the recipient bacteria are in the late logarithmic phase of their growth. Competent bacterial cells produce a special protein that binds donor DNA fragments at specific sites on the cell surface.

Although chromosomal DNA can be readily transferred to competent recipient bacteria, plasmid DNA is *not* easily transferred by ordinary transformation procedures that simply add DNA to recipient cells. However, special procedures widely used in genetic engineering can be used to accomplish transformation with plasmid DNA. Plasmids are discussed in more detail later in this chapter; some practical uses for them in genetic engineering are illustrated in the next chapter.

Transduction is gene transfer in which a *virus* serves as the vehicle for carrying DNA from a donor bacterium to a recipient bacterium. Viruses that attack bacteria are called *bacteriophages,* or simply *phages* (described in Chapter 15). A phage consists of a nucleic acid, usually DNA, surrounded by a protein coat to form a head. A tail-like appendage serves to attach the phage to the surface of a susceptible host bacterium. After the phage injects its DNA into the host cell, the phage DNA is replicated rapidly while the bacterial DNA is degraded. The phage DNA then directs the synthesis of new phage proteins by the host cell. Within 10 to 20 minutes the new phage DNA molecules combine with the new phage proteins to form numerous whole phages, which are released as the host cell disintegrates [FIGURE 13.15].

During assembly of the phage progeny within the infected host cell, any fragment of the host bacterium's DNA that is approximately the same size as the phage DNA may be accidentally incorporated into a new phage

FIGURE 13.13

In bacterial recombination, a fragment of DNA from a donor cell replaces a corresponding segment of DNA in a recipient cell. **[A]** Method of recombination when the donor DNA fragment is double-stranded. **[B]** Method when the donor DNA fragment is single-stranded. Genes D and d, and E and e, are alleles.

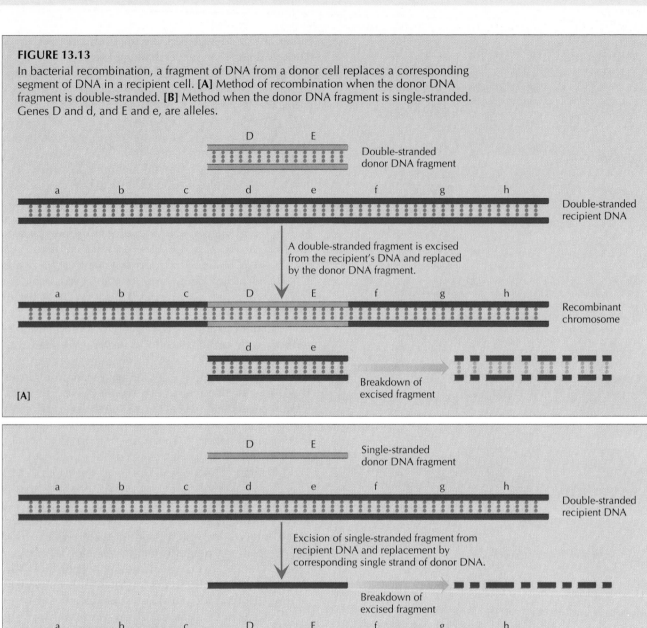

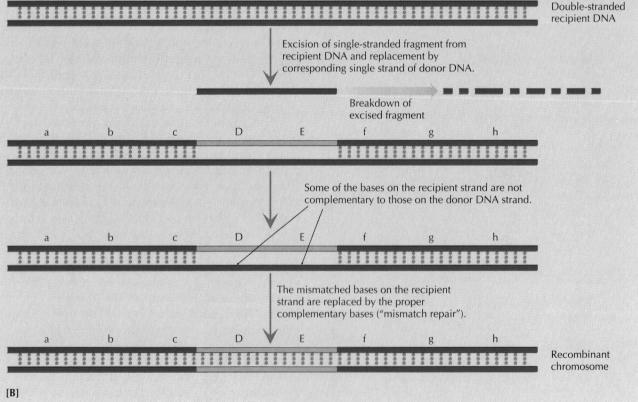

FIGURE 13.14

Bacterial transformation. Addition of DNA extracted from a donor bacterium to a closely related bacterium may result in the recipient's taking up the DNA and, by recombination, acquiring one or more inheritable characteristics from the donor. In the system depicted here, the recombination step occurs by the method shown in FIGURE 13.13A. In some transformation systems, one strand of the double-stranded donor DNA may be degraded after passing into the recipient cell; the remaining single strand recombines with the recipient's chromosome by the method shown in FIGURE 13.13B.

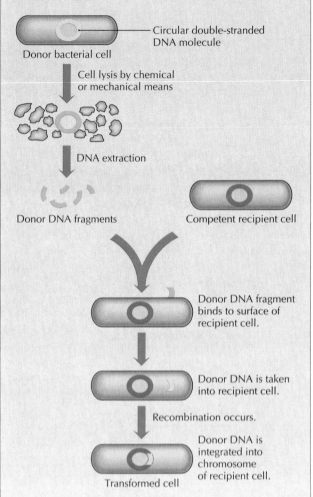

FIGURE 13.15

Transduction. After a phage injects its DNA into a host bacterium, the host's chromosome is degraded into small fragments. During maturation of the phage progeny, a phage head may envelop fragments of bacterial DNA instead of phage DNA. When this bacterial DNA is introduced into a new host cell, it can become integrated into the recipient's chromosome by genetic recombination.

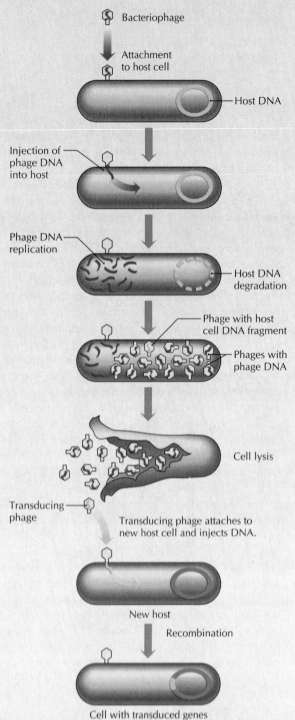

head *instead of the phage DNA*. A phage carrying such a fragment is called a *transducing phage*, because, if it infects another bacterium, it injects the bacterial DNA fragment into the new host. (Because the transducing phages do not contain all the viral DNA, they do not kill the new host cell.) The fragment can then undergo recombination with the corresponding part of the new host's chromosome and become a permanent part of that chromosome [FIGURE 13.15]. Thus the second bacterial host acquires one or more genes from the first host. Besides chromosomal genes, plasmids can also be transferred to recipient cells via phages.

Conjugation *is a process of gene transfer that requires cell-to-cell contact*, and thus differs from transformation and transduction. As a result of conjugation, DNA may be transferred directly from one bacterium to another. This may be regarded as a primitive means of sexual reproduction. However, bacterial conjugation differs from sexual mating in eucaryotes in that it does not involve the fusion of two gametes to form a single cell.

In some types of conjugation, only a plasmid may be transferred from the donor bacterium to the recipient bacterium. In other types, large segments of the donor cell's chromosome, or even the entire chromosome, may be transferred to a recipient cell. This differs from transformation and transduction, in which only relatively small chromosomal fragments can be transferred.

Studies of conjugation in *E. coli* have revealed that this bacterium has two different mating types: a donor and a recipient. The "donor" cells contain a plasmid called the **F plasmid** ("F" stands for "fertility"). Like most plasmids, the F plasmid is a small, circular piece of double-stranded DNA that is not part of the bacterial chromosome and can replicate independently. It contains about 40 genes that control the plasmid's replication and the synthesis by the host cell of a filamentous appendage called the *sex pilus* [see FIGURE 4.13]. Cells containing the F plasmid are referred to as F⁺ cells and are donors in mating. Recipient cells lack the F plasmid and are called F⁻ cells.

When F⁺ and F⁻ cells are mixed together (in what is termed an F⁺ × F⁻ cross), the end of the F⁺ sex pilus binds to a nearby F⁻ cell and then retracts, pulling the F⁻ and F⁺ cells into close contact [FIGURE 13.16]. A channel is formed between the two cells, through which is transferred one DNA strand from the donor's F plasmid to the F⁻ cell. Once inside the recipient cell, the DNA strand acts as a template for the synthesis of a second, complementary DNA strand. The ends of the double-stranded DNA molecule then join to form a circular F plasmid, and the recipient cell has become an F⁺ cell capable of donating DNA. In this way, the conjugation process can continue until all the F⁻ cells in the culture are converted.

In an F⁺ × F⁻ cross, it is usually only the donor's F

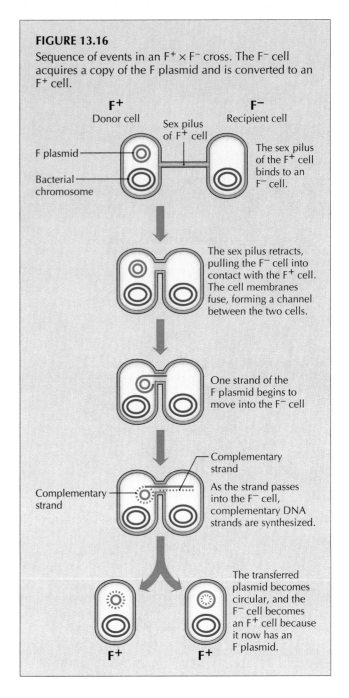

FIGURE 13.16
Sequence of events in an F⁺ × F⁻ cross. The F⁻ cell acquires a copy of the F plasmid and is converted to an F⁺ cell.

F⁺
Donor cell

Sex pilus of F⁺ cell

F⁻
Recipient cell

F plasmid

Bacterial chromosome

The sex pilus of the F⁺ cell binds to an F⁻ cell.

The sex pilus retracts, pulling the F⁻ cell into contact with the F⁺ cell. The cell membranes fuse, forming a channel between the two cells.

One strand of the F plasmid begins to move into the F⁻ cell

Complementary strand

As the strand passes into the F⁻ cell, complementary DNA strands are synthesized.

Complementary strand

The transferred plasmid becomes circular, and the F⁻ cell becomes an F⁺ cell because it now has an F plasmid.

F⁺

F⁺

plasmid that moves to the F⁻ cell. Chromosomal genes can be transferred along with the F plasmid, but this is a rare event, occurring in only 1 in 10 million matings.

However, there are exceptions. Researchers have isolated certain F⁺ cells that can transfer chromosomal genes to F⁻ cells at rates at least 1000 times greater than those achieved by ordinary F⁺ cells. These special donor cells are called *high-frequency recombination* (Hfr) cells. *They are F⁺ cells in which the F plasmid has become integrated into the bacterial chromosome* [FIGURE 13.17]. In other words, the F plasmid no longer replicates independently of the bacterial chromosome. More-

FIGURE 13.17
An Hfr cell arises from an F⁺ cell when the F plasmid becomes integrated into the bacterial chromosome. The process is reversible, and an F plasmid that has been integrated can become extrachromosomal again.

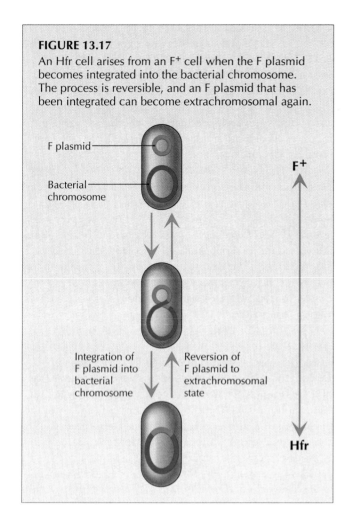

F plasmid

Bacterial chromosome

F⁺

Integration of F plasmid into bacterial chromosome

Reversion of F plasmid to extrachromosomal state

Hfr

FIGURE 13.18
Sequence of events in an Hfr × F⁻ cross. The longer conjugation remains uninterrupted, the more chromosomal genes will be transferred to the F⁻ cell. In such matings, the F⁻ cell almost always remains F⁻, because the Hfr cell rarely transfers the entire DNA strand; thus the recipient cell usually does not acquire a complete F plasmid.

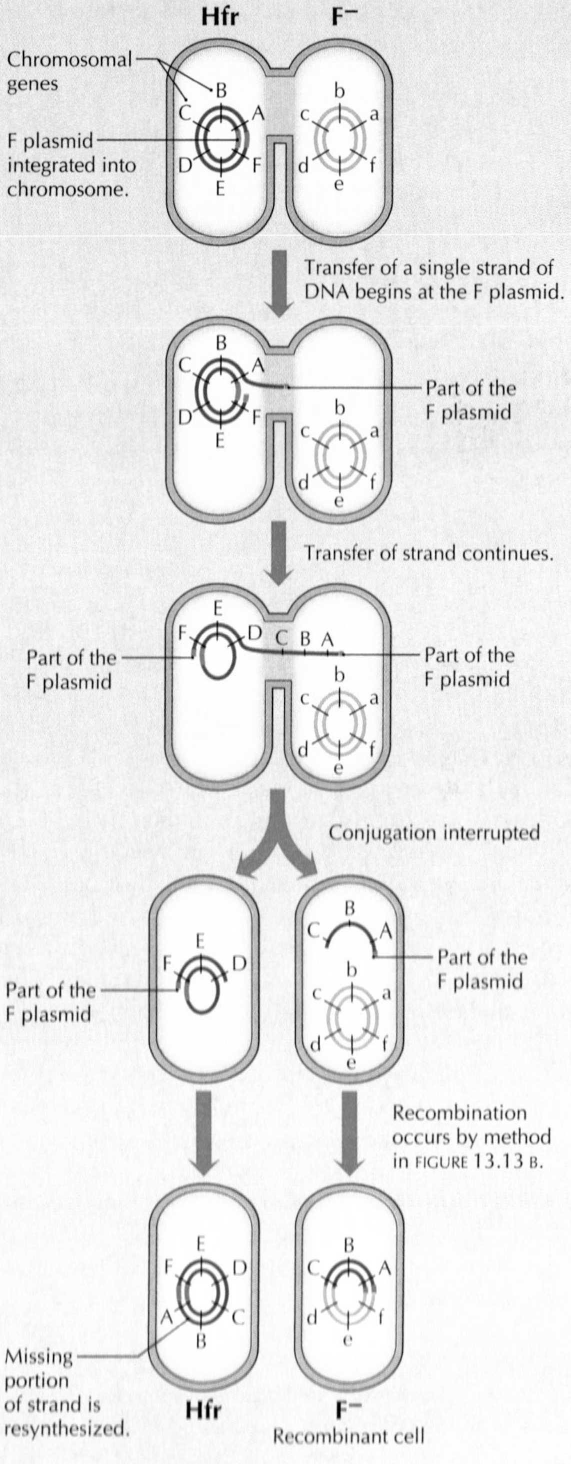

Hfr   F⁻

Chromosomal genes

F plasmid integrated into chromosome.

Transfer of a single strand of DNA begins at the F plasmid.

Part of the F plasmid

Transfer of strand continues.

Part of the F plasmid

Part of the F plasmid

Conjugation interrupted

Part of the F plasmid

Part of the F plasmid

Recombination occurs by method in FIGURE 13.13 B.

Missing portion of strand is resynthesized.

Hfr   F⁻
Recombinant cell

over, Hfr cells differ from F⁺ cells in that the F plasmid itself is rarely transferred during conjugation. Thus, in an Hfr × F⁻ cross, the frequency of gene recombination is high, but the transfer of the F plasmid itself is low. This is just the opposite of what happens in F⁺ × F⁻ crosses. In an Hfr × F⁻ cross, the following events occur [FIGURE 13.18]:

1 A single strand of Hfr chromosome is transferred to the recipient cell in a linear fashion, beginning with a small piece of the F plasmid. The genes enter the F⁻ cell sequentially like beads on a string, beginning with the one that was nearest the F plasmid and—if conjugation goes uninterrupted—ending with the remainder of the F plasmid.
2 It takes about 100 min for complete strand transfer. However, conjugation is almost always interrupted by accident before transfer is complete.
3 The portion of donor strand transferred to the recipient cell becomes incorporated into the recipient's chromosome by recombination (FIGURE 13.13B).

Since the entire donor strand would have to be transferred in order for the recipient to acquire a complete F plasmid, *most recipient cells remain F⁻ cells after conjugation with Hfr cells.*

ASK YOURSELF

1 What is the difference between the genotype and the phenotype of an organism?

2 What are mutagens, and how do they act?

3 What are the differences between neutral mutations, missense mutations, nonsense mutations, and frameshift mutations?

4 What is genetic recombination?

5 What are the major differences between the three ways in which genetic material can be transferred from one bacterial cell to another?

6 What is the role of the F plasmid in the transfer of genetic material from one *E. coli* cell to another? How do F⁺, F⁻, and Hfr cells of *E. coli* differ?

PLASMIDS

Although they are rare in eucaryotic cells (other than some yeasts), plasmids are quite common inside bacteria. Usually unnecessary for host survival, these DNA molecules nonetheless can enable their host bacteria to kill other bacteria, resist the effects of antibiotics, or serve as tiny industrial workhorses in waste management. There are many different kinds of plasmids, which can be categorized according to their function.

Conjugative plasmids can be transmitted by conjugation from one bacterium to another, such as the *E. coli* F plasmid described in the preceding section. *Nonconjugative plasmids* are not transmitted by conjugation, but can be transferred by transduction or, with special procedures, by transformation. Nonconjugative plasmids can also be transmitted to a recipient cell by the cooperative action of conjugative plasmids that may coexist with them in the same cell.

Bacteriocinogenic plasmids contain a gene that directs the host bacterium to synthesize a *bacteriocin*. A bacteriocin is a protein that kills bacteria belonging to the same or closely related species and lacking the plasmid. Interestingly, a bacterium that makes a particular bacteriocin is not killed by that bacteriocin, although it may be killed by other bacteriocins. There are many different bacteriocins, including those produced by bacteria normally found in the intestine. They are used in medical bacteriology to help identify the different subgroups of bacteria such as *E. coli* and *Pseudomonas* species. Such tests help determine whether several outbreaks of an infectious disease are due to one or more particular strains of bacteria.

Other plasmids carry genes for resistance to antibiotics. Each antibiotic-resistance gene in these *R plasmids* codes for an enzyme that destroys or inactivates a particular antibiotic [FIGURE 13.19]. For example, most strains of *Staphylococcus aureus* isolated in hospitals today contain an R plasmid with a gene that codes for β-lactamase, an enzyme which inactivates many penicillins. Some R plasmids are conjugative plasmids, readily transferring antibiotic-resistance genes to other bacterial cells by conjugation.

The ability of a conjugative R plasmid to confer upon recipient bacteria a simultaneous resistance to several antibiotics can frustrate medical treatment. In many instances, the plasmid-mediated resistance of various bacteria to frequently used antibiotics such as ampicillin, chloramphenicol, tetracycline, kanamycin, and streptomycin makes it difficult to treat infections successfully. Indiscriminate use of antibiotics to treat patients can increase the incidence of antibiotic-resistant bacteria.

Plasmids that code for important degradative enzymes are called *dissimilation plasmids*. This plasmid type is responsible for the ability of certain *Pseudomonas* species to break down difficult-to-degrade industrial solvents such as toluene and xylene. A combination of several plasmids, when transferred to *Pseudomonas* bacteria, allows the bacteria to break down complex hydrocarbons and other compounds present in crude oil.

FIGURE 13.19
Bacterial plasmid shown as a molecule of looped DNA. The drug-resistant plasmid shown is called R28K, carries ampicillin resistance, and has a length of 21 μm.

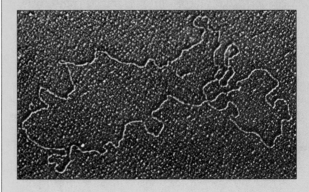

13.2 OIL-EATING BACTERIA AWAIT CALL TO DUTY

When the first patent application was filed for a genetically engineered organism, the "new" bacterium attracted attention because it loves to eat crude oil. But, despite its potential as an "oil spill scavenger," it still sits on a laboratory shelf. Twenty years later, the story illustrates the problems and promises of using microbial genetics to produce new organisms with a practical use.

In 1971, the microbiologist Ananda Chakrabarty filed for an unusual United States patent, the first for a genetically engineered organism. The organism was a strain of *Pseudomonas* bacteria into which Chakrabarty had placed different plasmids. Each plasmid had the genetic instructions for degrading one of the various constituents of crude oil. Bacteria containing only one plasmid were unable to break down crude oil, but Chakrabarty's organism *thrived* on crude oil and degraded it efficiently. This was because Chakrabarty had placed the various plasmids into *the same bacterial cell*. Theoretically, if a culture of this multi-plasmid-containing organism were sprayed onto environments contaminated by oil spills, it would be highly effective in eliminating the oil.

In 1980 the Supreme Court ruled that Chakrabarty's genetically engineered organism could be patented, and a patent was issued by the U.S. Patent Office in March 1981, a decade after the application had been filed. Amazingly, however, the organism has yet to be used to treat large oil spills. Even after the disastrous oil spill from the tanker *Exxon Valdez* in Prince William Sound, Alaska, in 1989, the oil-eating organism remained confined to its test tube.

Why wasn't it used to combat the worst oil spill in U.S. history? Basically, because there were legitimate concerns about releasing genetically engineered organisms into the environment (see Chapter 14).

So far, no commercial organization has been willing to take over development of the organism, and Chakrabarty's oil-eating bacterium remains patiently on the shelf, waiting for a chance to show what it can do.

These bacteria have potential use for treatment of environments contaminated by oil spills [DISCOVER 13.2].

Some plasmids can replicate only in a few species of closely related bacteria, while others have a much broader host range. An example of the latter are conjugative plasmids called *IncP plasmids*, which can be transmitted to and replicated in nearly all species of Gram-negative bacteria. There also are some plasmids that are very selective about their neighbors; they cannot coexist in the same cell with certain other plasmids. On the basis of this, plasmids have been classified into various *incompatibility groups*, where those in one group cannot coexist with those in other groups.

Treating bacterial cells with certain chemical agents, such as certain dyes, or with high temperatures can sometimes free them of plasmids. Cells thus treated are said to be "cured." For example, *E. coli* can be "cured" by using the dye acridine orange.

ASK YOURSELF

1 What are conjugative plasmids? Bacteriocinogenic plasmids? R plasmids? Dissimilation plasmids?

2 How are plasmids related to a bacterium's ability to resist several antibiotics simultaneously?

3 What are plasmid incompatibility groups?

4 How can a cell be "cured" of its plasmids?

REGULATION OF GENE EXPRESSION

A living cell contains more than 1000 different enzymes, each an effective catalyst for some chemical reaction. These enzymes must act together in a coordinated effort so that all the chemical activities in a cell are smoothly integrated with one another. One consequence of this enzyme coordination is the synthesis and dissimilation of materials as required for normal growth and metabolism.

Proper control of cellular metabolism is ultimately accomplished by the regulation of enzymes. Microorganisms have evolved a variety of enzyme regulatory mechanisms to accommodate the changing needs of the microbial cell in a changing environment. These regulatory mechanisms fall into two general categories: (1) those that regulate the *activity* of enzymes, and (2) those that regulate the *synthesis* of enzymes.

In the previous chapter you learned of one mechanism that can regulate enzyme activity: *feedback inhibition*. Here the end product of a biosynthetic pathway inhibits the activity of the first enzyme in the pathway [see FIGURE 12.2]. But cells also manipulate events that occur during gene transcription in order to control enzyme synthesis. As mentioned earlier, cells carry far more genetic information than is utilized or expressed under any one set of environmental conditions. Thus each cell has regulatory mechanisms that, depending upon the current environment, allow some genes to be transcribed, while preventing transcription of others.

In bacteria, the genes that code for the enzymes of a metabolic pathway are usually arranged in a consecutive manner to form a functional unit called an **operon.** A commonly used and well-studied example is the three genes that form the *lac* operon, needed for the transport and metabolism of the sugar lactose [FIGURE 13.20]. These three genes are transcribed into a single *mRNA* molecule, so that control of the transcription process affects the entire operon. Most transcriptional control mechanisms for operons involve either *enzyme induction* or *end-product repression.*

Enzyme Induction

An enzyme or a nutrient-transporting carrier protein is *constitutive* if it is always produced by a cell, whether or not the substrate for the enzyme or carrier protein is present. This means that the gene for that protein is always transcribed, as in the case of the genes for the glycolysis enzymes. An *inducible* protein, on the other hand, is made by a cell only when needed and *only in the presence of a particular substrate.* This form of control of gene transcription, with the gene transcribed only when an appropriate substrate for the protein is present, is called **induction.** Induction is used mainly to control the synthesis of proteins that are used to transport and break down nutrients. It is useful because it prevents a cell from wasting energy synthesizing large amounts of a protein to catabolize a nutrient that is not available.

The *lac* operon in *E. coli* provides a good example of how induction works. In this bacterium the proteins needed for lactose transport and breakdown are inducible; that is, they are synthesized *only if lactose (or some very similar compound) is present.* As shown in FIGURE 13.20A the *lac* operon consists of a promoter region (promoters were discussed earlier in this chapter; see FIGURE 13.6) and an operator region followed by three genes that code for the lactose-metabolizing proteins. In order to transcribe these three genes into *mRNA,* the enzyme RNA polymerase must first bind to the promoter. But before the polymerase can bind to this region, it may have to clear one more regulatory hurdle: *lac* transcription is under the control of a *regulator gene,* which codes for an *active repressor protein* [FIGURE 13.20B]. In the absence of lactose, this protein binds to the DNA of the operator region, thereby preventing RNA polymerase from binding to the promoter region [FIGURE 13.20C]. But if lactose is present, the repressor protein is inactivated by the binding of lactose, and the

RNA polymerase is free to bind to the promoter and transcribe the operon into *mRNA* [FIGURE 13.20D].

End-Product Repression

In contrast to pathways responsible for breaking down materials such as lactose, transcription of an operon for a synthetic pathway is often regulated *by its end product,* and not by the initial substrate of the pathway. This type of control of gene transcription is called **end-product repression.** For instance, if a high level of the amino acid tryptophan is present in the culture medium, the microorganism will not waste energy synthesizing enzymes for tryptophan synthesis. This is because end-product repression prevents any of the genes in the operon that codes for these enzymes from being transcribed into *mRNA.*

In *E. coli,* a promoter, an operator, and five genes that code for tryptophan-synthesizing enzymes form the *trp* operon [FIGURE 13.21A]. A *trp* regulator gene directs the synthesis of an *inactive repressor protein* [FIGURE 13.21B]. Unlike the mechanism described earlier for the active repressor protein, this repressor cannot bind to the *trp* operator if tryptophan is in short supply [FIGURE 13.21C]. Thus the RNA polymerase can transcribe the *trp* operon, and enzyme synthesis occurs. However, if tryptophan is present and no more is needed, the repressor protein binds tryptophan and is converted to an active form, which now binds to the operator and prevents operon transcription and subsequent enzyme synthesis [FIGURE 13.21D].

ASK YOURSELF

1 How do constitutive enzymes differ from inducible enzymes?

2 What are the functions of the promoter region, operator region, and repressor protein in induction?

3 How does the role of the repressor in end-product repression differ from that of the repressor in induction?

4 How does end-product repression differ from feedback inhibition?

FIGURE 13.20

Enzyme induction. **[A]** The *lac* operon consists of a promoter region, an operator region, and three genes involved in lactose transport and breakdown. **[B]** The *lac* regulator gene codes for an active repressor. **[C]** The active repressor binds to the *lac* operator, preventing the attachment of RNA polymerase to the promoter. This prevents transcription of the operon into *m*RNA. **[D]** In the presence of lactose the repressor is inactivated and RNA polymerase is free to bind to the operator and transcribe the operon.

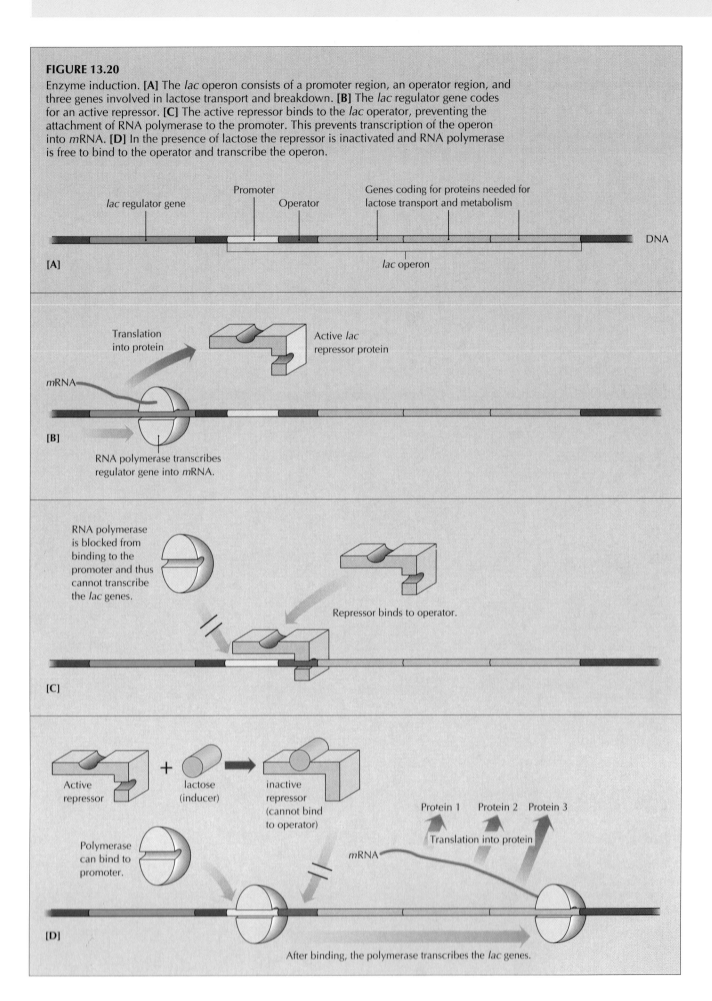

FIGURE 13.21

End-product repression. **[A]** The *trp* operon consists of a promoter region, an operator region, and five genes involved in biosynthesis of tryptophan. **[B]** The *trp* regulator gene codes for an inactive repressor protein. **[C]** The inactive repressor cannot bind to the operator and thus does not prevent attachment of RNA polymerase to the promoter. The RNA polymerase transcribes the operon into *m*RNA. **[D]** In the presence of tryptophan the repressor becomes active and can bind to the operator. This blocks attachment of RNA polymerase to the promoter and prevents transcription of the operon.

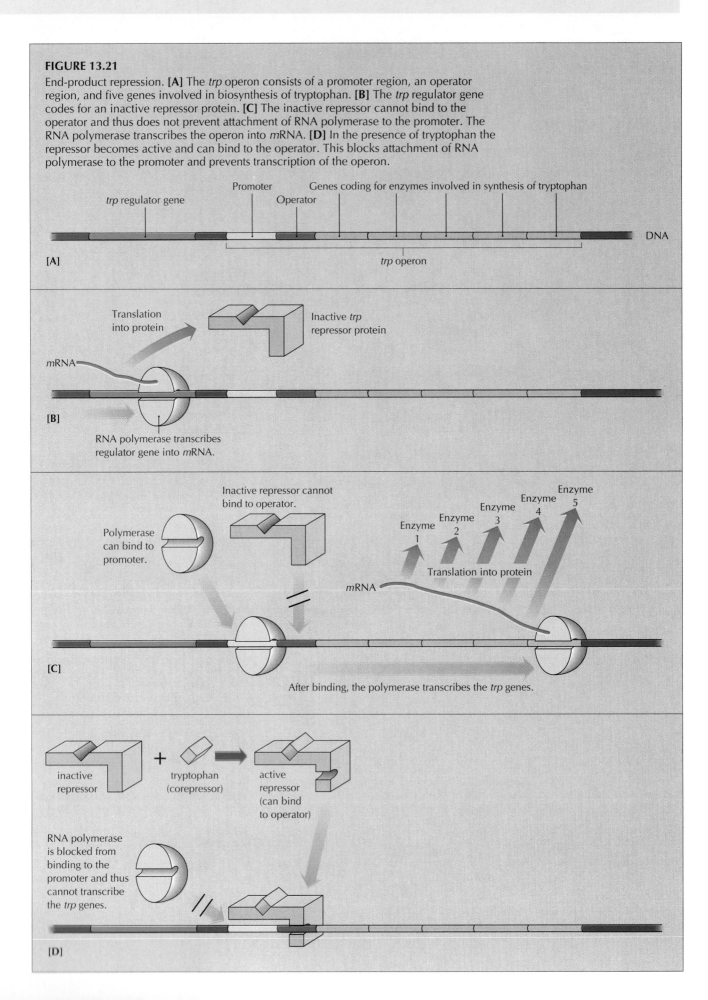

SUMMARY

1 A procaryotic (bacterial) cell has one chromosome, in the form of a single, circular DNA molecule. A eucaryotic cell (such as an algal or a yeast cell) usually has more than one linear chromosome.

2 The genetic information of a cell is represented by the nucleotide sequence of its DNA. This genetic information is accurately passed from generation to generation during the semiconservative replication of DNA.

3 Genetic information in DNA directs the synthesis of proteins, most of which are enzymes essential for cellular metabolism. A gene is a segment of DNA that contains the nucleotide sequence for making a particular protein. Protein synthesis involves two stages, transcription and translation. Transcription is the process of copying the information in a gene to *m*RNA. Nucleotide sequences in *m*RNA are based upon the genetic code; each triplet of nucleotides specifies a particular amino acid. During translation, ribosomes use the coded information in *m*RNA to take the amino acids brought by *t*RNA and assemble them into proteins.

4 In addition to the inheritance of characteristics from parental cells, microorganisms also exhibit variability in their genotype and phenotype. The genotype is the genetic constitution of an organism as contained in its DNA. The phenotype is the portion of the genetic potential that is actually expressed by the cell under a given set of conditions. Phenotypic changes may be noninheritable, caused by changes in the environment, or they may be inheritable, due to changes in the genotype. Genotypic changes can occur as a result of mutation or recombination.

5 Two common types of mutations are point mutations (which include neutral, missense, and nonsense mutations) and frameshift mutations (which include insertion and deletion mutations).

6 Recombination leads to new combinations of genes on chromosomes. In bacteria, this process can occur following transfer of chromosomal genes from one cell to another. There are three main types of bacterial gene transfer: transformation, transduction, and conjugation. In transformation, a recipient cell acquires genes from free DNA molecules in the surrounding medium. In transduction, DNA from a donor cell is carried by a virus (bacteriophage) to a recipient cell. Conjugation is dependent on cell-to-cell contact; it may involve transfer of a plasmid, such as the F plasmid in *E. coli*.

7 A plasmid is a small, usually circular DNA molecule that is not part of the bacterial chromosome and can replicate independently. In addition to conjugative plasmids such as the F plasmid, there are nonconjugative plasmids that can be transmitted only by transduction or transformation, or by cooperative action with a conjugative plasmid. Some plasmids are bacteriocinogenic plasmids; others carry genes for antibiotic resistance or for enzymes that break down complex chemicals.

8 Regulation of gene expression in bacteria is carried out by processes called *induction* and *end-product repression*. In enzyme induction, a repressor protein that normally binds to the operator region of an operon is rendered inactive in the presence of an inducer such as lactose; this allows RNA polymerase to bind to the promoter and transcribe the operon. In end-product repression, the repressor is normally inactive and does not prevent transcription of the operon; however, if the end product of the particular synthetic pathway is present, the repressor is activated, binds to the operator region, and prevents transcription of the operon.

KEY TERMS

conjugation
DNA-dependent RNA polymerase
DNA ligase
DNA polymerase
end-product repression
F plasmid
gene
genetic code
genetics
genotype
induction
messenger RNA (*m*RNA)
mutation
oncogenes
operon
phenotype
plasmids
recombination
semiconservative replication
transcription
transduction
transfer RNA (*t*RNA)
transformation
translation
transposons

CHROMOSOMES OF PROCARYOTIC AND EUCARYOTIC CELLS

1 The bacterial chromosome occurs as **(a)** a single linear molecule; **(b)** a pair of linear molecules; **(c)** a single cylindrical molecule; **(d)** an aggregate of several chromosomes; **(e)** a single circular molecule.

2 In addition to its chromosome, a bacterial cell may contain small circular molecules of DNA called **(a)** RNA polymerases; **(b)** plasmids; **(c)** ribosomes; **(d)** diploid molecules; **(e)** diploid chromosomes.

3 Unlike a bacterial chromosome, a eucaryotic chromosome is

_____ in form and is at least

_____ times longer.

REPLICATION OF DNA

4 In DNA replication, each daughter DNA molecule contains one parental strand and one newly synthesized strand. This is called **(a)** conservative replication; **(b)** repetitive replication; **(c)** semiconservative replication; **(d)** ultraconservative replication; **(e)** restricted replication.

5 During DNA synthesis, DNA polymerase can add nucleotides one by one to which end(s) of a growing DNA strand? **(a)** the phosphate end; **(b)** the 5′ end; **(c)** the 4′ end; **(d)** the 3′ end; **(e)** both ends.

6 During DNA synthesis, elongation at the 5′ end of a growing DNA strand occurs by the synthesis of a series of short 5′ → 3′ segments which are then linked together and added to the end of the strand by an enzyme called DNA **(a)** polymerase; **(b)** kinase; **(c)** dismutase; **(d)** ligase; **(e)** hydrolase.

7 Replication of eucaryotic DNA is initiated at many sites by the formation of replication **(a)** "splits"; **(b)** "bubbles"; **(c)** "circles"; **(d)** "strands"; **(e)** "supercoils."

TRANSCRIPTION AND TRANSLATION OF GENETIC INFORMATION

8 Match the description on the right with the correct item on the left.

_____ codon

_____ DNA-dependent RNA polymerase

_____ tRNA

_____ anticodon

_____ promoter

_____ ribosomes

_____ methionine

_____ nonsense codon

_____ mRNA

(a) The substance into which the coded information in DNA is transcribed

(b) The enzyme that synthesizes mRNA

(c) Small particles in the cytoplasm that carry out the process of translation

(d) The special DNA nucleotide sequence to which RNA polymerase must bind before transcription can begin

(e) A base triplet on mRNA that codes for an amino acid

(f) The amino acid for which the "start" codon always codes

(g) A base triplet on mRNA that causes the termination of translation

(h) The substance that carries energized amino acids to the ribosomes

(i) The base triplet on tRNA that is complementary to an mRNA codon

9 In a molecule of transfer RNA (tRNA), three of the unpaired bases constitute: **(a)** a codon; **(b)** a cloverleaf configuration; **(c)** a promoter region; **(d)** an anticodon; **(e)** a termination region.

VARIABILITY IN MICROORGANISMS

10 The genetic constitution of an organism as represented by its DNA is: **(a)** the phenotype; **(b)** that portion of the genetic potential that is actually expressed by the cell under a given set of conditions; **(c)** the codon; **(d)** indicated by the formation of large, gummy colonies; **(e)** the genotype.

11 The extent to which the genetic potential of a cell is actually expressed under a given set of conditions is called the **(a)** codon; **(b)** genotype; **(c)** translation element; **(d)** phenotype; **(e)** variability.

12 Phenotypic changes caused by changes in the _____ rather than by changes in genotype are not inheritable and usually involve most or all the cells in a culture.

13 A cell or an organism carrying a mutated gene is called a(n)

_____, whereas the nonmutated organism is called the

_____.

14 Match the description on the right with the correct item on the left.

      (a) A point mutation that results in no difference in the protein coded by a gene

_____ nonsense

_____ neutral

_____ missense

_____ frameshift

      (b) A point mutation that results in a protein containing a different amino acid

      (c) A point mutation that results in premature termination of the synthesis of a protein

      (d) The type of mutation caused by the insertion or deletion of one or more nucleotides in a gene

15 A(n) _____ is any physical or chemical agent that increases the mutation rate in an organism.

16 Small pieces of DNA that can insert themselves into chromosomes at numerous locations and cause mutations are called **(a)** carcinogens; **(b)** wild-type genes; **(c)** transposons; **(d)** replica genes; **(e)** frameshift genes.

17 In the chromosomes of human cells, special genes exist which have the potential to cause cancer; these genes are called _____.

18 Match the description on the right with the correct item on the left.

      (a) The type of gene transfer in which a recipient cell acquires genes from free DNA molecules in the surrounding medium

_____ transformation

_____ transduction

_____ conjugation

_____ Hfr

_____ alleles

      (b) The type of gene transfer in which a bacteriophage serves as the vehicle for carrying DNA from one bacterium to another

      (c) The type of gene transfer that depends on cell-to-cell contact

      (d) Genes which occur at corresponding sites on homologous chromosomes but which differ in their mutational state

      (e) An F^+ cell in which the F plasmid has become integrated into the host-cell chromosome

19 In an $F^+ \times F^-$ cross: **(a)** the F^+ cell becomes an Hfr cell; **(b)** the F^- cell becomes an Hfr cell; **(c)** the F^+ cell becomes an F^- cell; **(d)** the F^- cell becomes an F^+ cell; **(e)** the chromosomal genes of the F^+ cell are often transferred to the F^- cell.

20 Recombination in eucaryotic cells can occur during meiosis by an exchange process called _____.

PLASMIDS

21 A plasmid may cause a bacterium to produce a protein that kills other bacteria of the same or closely related species. Such a protein is called a(n) **(a)** bacteriophage; **(b)** bacteriocin; **(c)** carcinogen; **(d)** histone; **(e)** F plasmid.

22 The plasmids associated with resistance to antibiotics are: **(a)** R plasmids; **(b)** Hfr plasmids; **(c)** D plasmids; **(d)** F⁻ plasmids; **(e)** all plasmids.

23 Plasmids have been classified into various _____ groups on the basis of their ability to coexist in the same cell with other plasmids.

24 A bacterial cell treated so that it is freed of plasmids is said to be

_____.

REGULATION OF GENE EXPRESSION

25 In bacteria, the genes that code for the enzymes of a metabolic pathway are usually arranged consecutively to form a functional unit called a(n) **(a)** induction system; **(b)** end-product repression system; **(c)** constitutive enzyme system; **(d)** operon; **(e)** chromosome.

26 A(n) _____ enzyme is synthesized only in response to the presence of a particular substrate, whereas a(n) _____ enzyme is synthesized regardless of whether a particular substrate is present or not.

27 In the presence of lactose, the *lac* repressor (can, cannot) _____ bind to the _____ region of the *lac* operon and thus (can, cannot) _____ prevent transcription of the *lac* operon by RNA polymerase.

28 End-product repression differs from feedback inhibition by regulating **(a)** enzyme activity; **(b)** enzyme synthesis; **(c)** enzyme stability; **(d)** an enzyme's structure; **(e)** an enzyme's catalytic ability.

29 With regard to the *trp* operon, in the presence of tryptophan the *trp* repressor protein (can, cannot) _____ bind to the _____ region and thus (can, cannot) _____ prevent transcription by RNA polymerase.

REVIEW QUESTIONS

1 Describe the process of DNA replication and indicate how it promotes constancy in the characteristics of progeny and parent.

2 What differences in function are there between *m*RNA and *t*RNA?

3 What differences exist between the processes of translation, transformation, and transduction?

4 In what ways might a change occur in the phenotype of bacterial cells?

5 Why do frameshift mutations usually result in the synthesis of nonfunctional proteins?

6 Describe the events that take place during conjugation of an Hfr and an F⁻ cell of *E. coli.*

7 Outline the ways by which DNA can be transferred from a donor bacterium to a recipient bacterium.

8 Describe the different types of plasmids that occur in bacteria.

9 How can induction and end-product repression benefit a microorganism?

DISCUSSION QUESTIONS

1 Suppose bacterium X is susceptible to ampicillin, tetracycline, kanamycin, and streptomycin, whereas bacterium Y, which is unrelated to X, is resistant to these antibiotics. After adding some cells of Y to a culture of X and incubating this mixture of cells, you find that nearly every X cell has become resistant to all four antibiotics. When the X cells are subsequently treated with acridine orange, many lose their newly acquired antibiotic resistance. What might account for these findings?

2 Suppose that you have the following two strains of *E. coli:* (1) an Hfr strain that is susceptible to streptomycin and has genes *leu⁺*, *lac⁺*, and *gal⁺* and (2) an F⁻ strain that is resistant to streptomycin and has the allelic genes *leu⁻*, *lac⁻*, and *gal⁻*. The superscript plus sign means that the genes are functional; thus the Hfr strain can make leucine and can grow on lactose or galactose as a carbon source. The superscript minus sign means that the genes have undergone mutation and are not functional; thus the F⁻ strain requires leucine for growth and cannot use lactose or galactose as a carbon source for growth.

Describe an experiment that would enable you to determine the locations of *leu, lac,* and *gal* on the *E. coli* chromosome. That is, how could you "map" these genes? (*Hint:* Bacterial conjugation can be deliberately interrupted at various times by removing a sample from the culture and agitating it in a kitchen blender. This breaks apart the paired bacteria.)

3 Human immunodeficiency virus (HIV), which causes AIDS, does not contain DNA as its genetic material. Instead it contains only single-stranded RNA. Yet in order to be replicated inside a human host cell, this virus must make DNA.

HIV contains an enzyme called *reverse transcriptase.* From its name, what do you suppose this enzyme does? How would you contrast the function of this enzyme with that of the DNA-dependent RNA polymerase of the host cell? How do you suppose HIV progeny are produced that contain only single-stranded RNA?

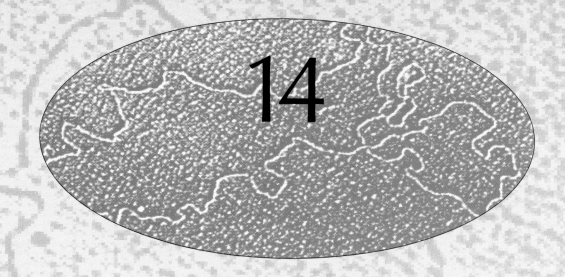

14

Microbes and Genetic Engineering

OBJECTIVES

After reading this chapter you should be able to

1 Give the advantages of the production of human insulin from genetically engineered bacteria, comparing it with the extraction of insulin from the pancreatic tissues of cattle.

2 Describe the normal function of restriction endonucleases in bacteria.

3 Explain how restriction endonucleases and DNA ligase can be used to construct a recombinant plasmid.

4 Discuss the importance of cDNA for the cloning of eucaryotic genes into procaryotic cells.

5 Explain how the technique of calcium chloride transformation has contributed to genetic engineering.

6 Give a method for identifying the bacteria that are making the product of a particular cloned gene.

7 List five problems associated with gene cloning and the production of cloned gene products.

8 Suggest three new potential applications of genetic engineering that could benefit society.

9 Discuss how rigorous the regulation of genetic engineering should be in order to minimize potential hazards.

OVERVIEW

Present knowledge makes it possible to deliberately change the genetic makeup of living cells in order that those cells can produce new substances. This process is called *genetic engineering,* or recombinant DNA technology. Research scientists can combine novel and unique characteristics from different cells—even those as widely separated as bacteria and human cells. With these techniques, microorganisms have been engineered to commercially produce such substances as the hormone insulin, the virus-fighting compound interferon, and a new vaccine against foot-and-mouth disease. The scientific advances that have made genetic engineering possible have exciting, broad implications for future scientists and consumers. By introducing foreign genes into microorganisms, it is possible to develop strains of microbes that offer new solutions for such diverse problems as pollution, food and energy shortages, and the control of diseases. Because scientists can now patent unique, novel, and useful microorganisms, an entire industry has developed based on genetic engineering.

INTRODUCTION TO GENETIC ENGINEERING

Since the discovery of recombinant DNA technology in 1973, scientists have developed techniques making it possible to move genes from one cell type to another (for example, from plants and mammals to bacteria). The future of genetic engineering is considered almost unlimited in its commercial applications; it already has solved some major research problems. For instance, rather than rely on extraction of limited quantities of a valuable compound from normal plant and animal tissue, a gene that codes for production of the compound can be taken from a plant or animal cell and placed into a bacterial cell. The bacterial cell may then synthesize unlimited quantities of the gene product. As a specific example, if you place copies of the human gene coding for the hormone insulin into a cell of the bacterium *Escherichia coli*, the bacterium and its progeny can make the gene product, human insulin [FIGURE 14.1]. The insulin is then extracted from the bacterial cultures. This industrial process produces the human form of insulin—of particular importance because a certain proportion of human diabetics must use human insulin, rather than the commonly available bovine insulin, because their immune systems react against the "foreign" bovine insulin.

Why Microorganisms Are Useful in Genetic Engineering

Animal and plant cells usually cannot be cultured for the production of medicinally useful compounds such as insulin. For instance, the tissue cells that make insulin in normal humans lose their ability to produce this hormone when they are isolated and grown in the laboratory. Moreover, the cultivation of tissue cells in the laboratory is expensive and requires highly enriched complex media.

The use of microorganisms to produce medicinally important compounds avoids many of the problems associated with obtaining them from higher organisms. Bacteria carrying the human insulin gene can be grown indefinitely and thus will produce human insulin indefinitely.

From the Laboratory to Industrial Application

In 1974 scientists predicted that it would take from 5 to 10 years to place the human gene for insulin into a bacterium. However, it was done successfully within 1 year,

FIGURE 14.1
[A] Transmission electron micrograph of genetically engineered *E. coli* containing insulin protein. Arrows indicate concentrations of this protein in the cells. [B] The first crystals ever obtained of human insulin made by genetic engineering.

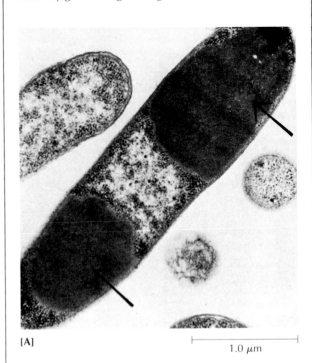

[A]   1.0 μm

[B]   250 μm

and similar success with the gene for interferon was attained within 2 years. Today, the microbial production of human insulin, as well as human and bovine growth hormones, vaccines against hepatitis and foot-and-mouth disease, and certain amino acids, has moved from research-and-development laboratories through pilot plants to industrial production. In 1982 the Eli Lilly Company announced that it had approval from the governments of Great Britain and the United States for the sale of human insulin produced by genetic engineering. (The genetically engineered microorganism that produced the human insulin was developed by Genentech, Inc., a San Francisco based biotechnology firm.) Thus molecular biology moved from the discovery of a promising research method to the marketing of an important health care product in less than a decade. It is important to recognize, however, that not all bioengineered products move this quickly from research to application. Requirements by various governmental agencies must first be met, and this can take considerable time and can cost millions of dollars.

ASK YOURSELF

1 What advantage does the production of human insulin from genetically engineered bacteria have over the extraction of insulin from the pancreatic tissues of cattle?

2 What are the limitations of using cultures of animal and plant cells for production of medicinally useful compounds such as insulin?

3 How long did it take molecular biology to move from the discovery of a promising research method to the marketing of genetically engineered human insulin?

PRODUCING A GENETICALLY ENGINEERED BACTERIUM

Different methods are used to combine genetic material from two different cell types, but the general procedures resemble one another. The following basic steps are used to produce a genetically engineered bacterium [FIGURE 14.2]:

1 DNA containing the particular gene to be transplanted is obtained from a donor organism, or, in some instances, it can be synthesized by laboratory procedures from nucleotides.

2 Plasmid DNA (cyclic DNA found outside the bacterial chromosome) is isolated to serve as the carrier for the particular gene.

3 Both the donor DNA and the plasmid DNA are treated with the same enzyme, a *restriction endonuclease*, that cleaves or cuts the DNA in such a way as to form complementary single-stranded ends ("sticky ends"). These ends are capable of joining to other fragments of DNA having the same complementary single-stranded ends.

4 The sticky ends of a fragment of the donor DNA then join with the sticky ends of the plasmid DNA, thus forming a modified plasmid which now carries the donor DNA fragment.

5 The plasmid is then added to a suspension of recipient bacteria, which take up the plasmid by the process of transformation described in Chapter 13. These plasmid-containing bacteria are identified and isolated.

6 Colonies of plasmid-containing bacteria that either have the gene or can make the product of the transplanted gene are then identified.

7 The genetically engineered bacteria are propagated in large quantities, and the product (protein) coded for by the transplanted gene is recovered from the cultures and purified.

Subsequent sections of this chapter will discuss various aspects of these general steps.

Isolating Plasmid DNA

In the 1960s scientists developed techniques for isolating plasmid DNA from bacteria, which meant separating it from cells and chromosomal DNA. One procedure is illustrated in FIGURE 14.3. A key step in this procedure is the use of **density gradient centrifugation.** During this technique, a tube containing a solution of cesium chloride and ethidium bromide is spun at high speed in a centrifuge. This distributes the cesium chloride in a continuous *concentration gradient*, with the top segment containing the least concentration of cesium chloride (i.e., the lowest density) and the bottom the highest concentration (highest density). If DNA is present in the tube, it will form a band that "floats" at the depth where its buoyant density exactly matches that of the cesium chloride solution. Because plasmid DNA and chromosomal DNA have different buoyant densities in the cesium chloride–ethidium bromide solution, each DNA will form a separate band [FIGURE 14.3]. The band containing the plasmid DNA can then be collected and used for genetic engineering experiments. Derivatives of natural plasmids suitable for use in cloning have been isolated and are called *plasmid cloning vectors*.

FIGURE 14.2
General scheme for producing a genetically engineered bacterium.

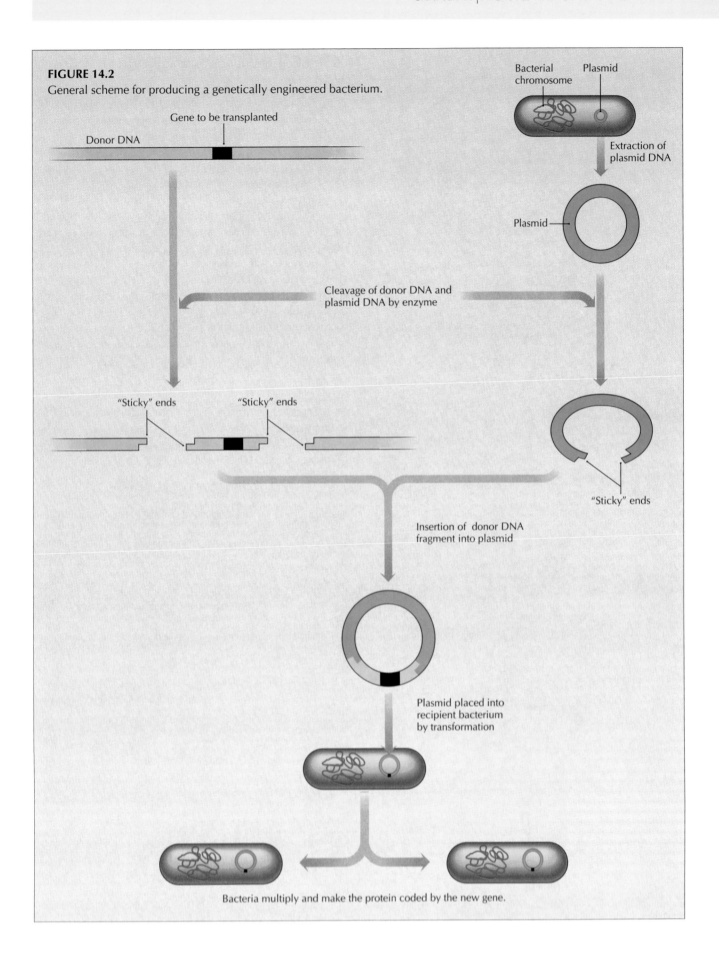

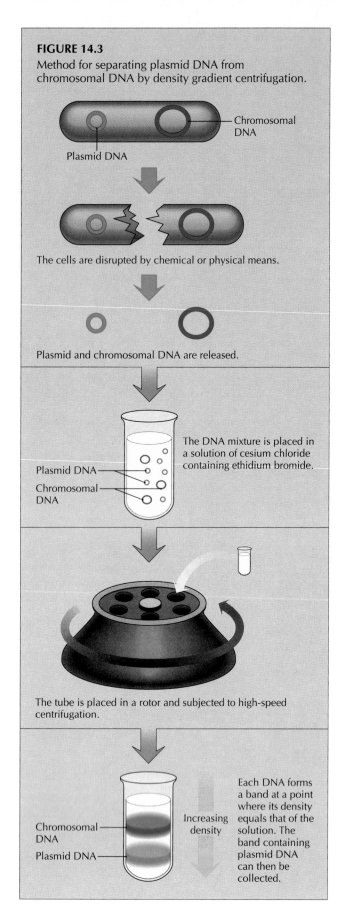

FIGURE 14.3
Method for separating plasmid DNA from chromosomal DNA by density gradient centrifugation.

Chromosomal DNA

Plasmid DNA

The cells are disrupted by chemical or physical means.

Plasmid and chromosomal DNA are released.

The DNA mixture is placed in a solution of cesium chloride containing ethidium bromide.

Plasmid DNA

Chromosomal DNA

The tube is placed in a rotor and subjected to high-speed centrifugation.

Chromosomal DNA

Plasmid DNA

Increasing density

Each DNA forms a band at a point where its density equals that of the solution. The band containing plasmid DNA can then be collected.

Restriction Endonucleases and Sticky-Ended DNA

Both the donor DNA and plasmid DNA must be cleaved in such a way that sticky-ended fragments are formed. Enzymes called *restriction endonucleases* are used to accomplish this special type of DNA cleavage. It is because of the resulting sticky ends that a donor DNA fragment can be inserted into the plasmid.

Restriction endonucleases are present in nearly all microorganisms. Their normal function is to identify and destroy "foreign DNA" that might enter a cell [FIGURE 14.4]. They do this by recognizing certain sites (short, specific nucleotide sequences of four to six base pairs) in double-stranded DNA molecules and then making a cut in the deoxyribose-phosphate backbones of both DNA strands, like a pair of scissors cutting a piece of tape. This destroys the biological activity of the foreign DNA.

It would be disastrous if a cell used its restriction endonucleases to destroy its own DNA ("self DNA").

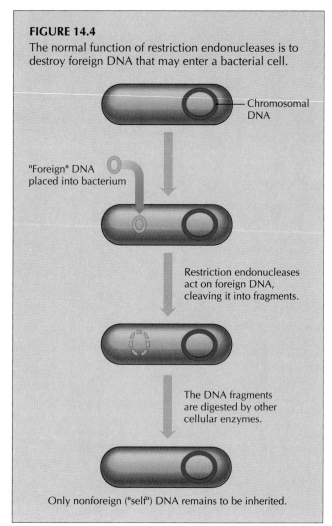

FIGURE 14.4
The normal function of restriction endonucleases is to destroy foreign DNA that may enter a bacterial cell.

Chromosomal DNA

"Foreign" DNA placed into bacterium

Restriction endonucleases act on foreign DNA, cleaving it into fragments.

The DNA fragments are digested by other cellular enzymes.

Only nonforeign ("self") DNA remains to be inherited.

Consequently a cell provides identification marks for its own DNA in the form of methyl (—CH₃) groups, which are added to certain nucleotides within the specific sequences. This process of adding methyl groups is called **DNA modification.** If the specific DNA sequences have been modified by methylation, then the DNA chain cannot be cleaved by the cell's own restriction endonucleases [FIGURE 14.5]. Thus a cell can distinguish foreign, unmodified DNA from its own modified DNA.

Although some restriction endonucleases cut both DNA strands at the same position within the specific sequence and thus produce DNA fragments with *blunt ends* (nonsticky ends), the ones that are most useful in genetic engineering are able to make the cut in each strand at a different position. Therefore, the cuts are staggered so that the cleaved DNA molecule has *two single-stranded ends* [FIGURES 14.5 and 14.6]. Such DNA is called *sticky-ended DNA* because, after cutting, the complementary single-stranded ends can join by hydrogen bonds (the same kind of bonds which normally hold the two strands of double-stranded DNA together).

Although the sticky ends of a DNA molecule can join, the structure is fragile because the breaks in the sugar-phosphate backbone still remain. Another enzyme, called **DNA ligase,** together with ATP as an energy source, can be used to connect, or ligate, these broken sugar-phosphate linkages [FIGURE 14.6].

Constructing Recombinant Plasmids

Discovery of restriction endonucleases led to the realization that, if two different kinds of DNA are treated with the same restriction endonuclease, then each DNA will have similar sticky ends. As a result, the two DNAs can be joined to form a single DNA molecule. In 1973, Stanley Cohen and Annie Chang of the Stanford University School of Medicine, and Herbert Boyer and Robert Helling of the University of California, San Francisco, were the first to demonstrate that plasmids containing two different kinds of DNA (*recombinant plasmids*) could be constructed [FIGURE 14.7]. These scientists isolated two different types of circular plasmid DNA—one having a gene for resistance to one antibiotic, the other having a gene for resistance to a different antibiotic—and cleaved them with a particular restriction endonuclease, allowed them to rejoin, and then ligated (firmly linked by covalent bonding) the resulting circular molecules. In addition to the re-formation of the two parental strands back into the original plasmids, the researchers obtained a recombinant plasmid that contained DNA from both plasmid types: one having a gene for resistance to one antibiotic, the other having a gene for resistance to the other antibiotic. Existence of this recombinant plasmid could be confirmed only after the new

FIGURE 14.5

A cell distinguishes its own DNA from foreign DNA by adding methyl groups to its own DNA, thus protecting it from being destroyed by restriction endonucleases such as *Eco*R I. The latter enzyme recognizes the nucleotide sequence G-A-A-T-T-C and cleaves the DNA at this point unless the sequence has been modified by methylation. G, guanine; A, adenine; T, thymine; C, cytosine.

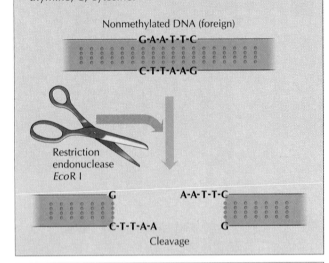

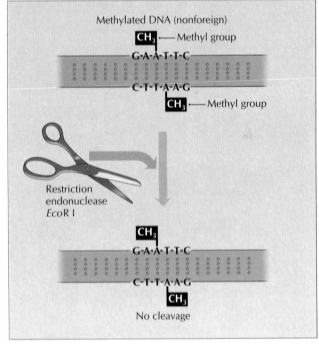

plasmid was introduced into a recipient bacterial cell so that it could be propagated and studied. The methods for doing this are discussed later in this chapter.

It is important to understand that a recombinant plasmid can be formed because the cleavage products made by restriction endonuclease can join, regardless of

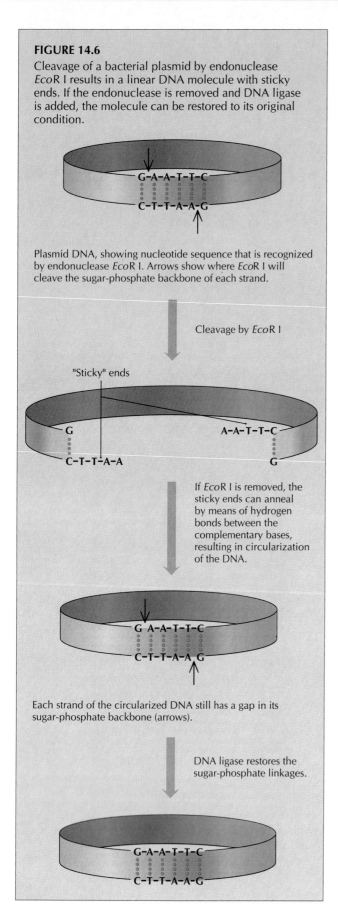

FIGURE 14.6
Cleavage of a bacterial plasmid by endonuclease *Eco*R I results in a linear DNA molecule with sticky ends. If the endonuclease is removed and DNA ligase is added, the molecule can be restored to its original condition.

Plasmid DNA, showing nucleotide sequence that is recognized by endonuclease *Eco*R I. Arrows show where *Eco*R I will cleave the sugar-phosphate backbone of each strand.

Cleavage by *Eco*R I

"Sticky" ends

If *Eco*R I is removed, the sticky ends can anneal by means of hydrogen bonds between the complementary bases, resulting in circularization of the DNA.

Each strand of the circularized DNA still has a gap in its sugar-phosphate backbone (arrows).

DNA ligase restores the sugar-phosphate linkages.

whether or not they are from the same plasmid. This is because the pieces of DNA have similar sticky ends, allowing complementary base pairs to be matched as two DNA segments join together.

Recombinant Plasmids Containing Eucaryotic DNA.
Theoretically, this use of restriction endonucleases could result in the joining of any kind of DNA molecule to any other kind of DNA molecule, and possibly in the expression of the new sequence. This was initially proved by the demonstration that the DNA coding for ribosomal RNA (*r*RNA) from the South African frog *Xenopus laevis* could be incorporated into bacterial plasmid DNA, and that the resulting recombinant plasmid was inherited in the recipient bacteria and the cells produced *Xenopus* *r*RNA [FIGURE 14.8].

Although a gene from a eucaryote such as a frog may be inserted into a plasmid, the gene may not necessarily be expressed. This means that the bacteria that eventually receive the plasmid may not be able to make the specific gene product coded for by the eucaryotic gene, as illustrated in the following:

1 The DNA sequences in eucaryotic cells that start and stop gene expression do not function the same way in bacterial cells. To solve this problem, it is necessary to insert eucaryotic genes in the plasmid in such a manner that their expression can be governed by DNA sequences that are appropriate for bacterial gene expression.
2 Eucaryotic genes, unlike bacterial genes, usually contain *introns* (regions that do not code for proteins) in addition to *exons* (regions that code for proteins). After eucaryotic cells transcribe such intron-containing genes into *m*RNA, they process the *m*RNA so that the introns are removed. The exons that are left are spliced together to make a proper messenger RNA that can be translated into the correct protein [FIGURE 14.9]. Unfortunately, bacteria do not carry out this *m*RNA processing. This means that merely placing a recombinant plasmid containing a eucaryotic gene into a bacterial cell will probably not result in transcription of the gene into the proper messenger RNA. The solution is to isolate the *messenger RNA* instead of the DNA from the eucaryotic cells. This messenger RNA is then used in the laboratory as a template for construction of a corresponding DNA molecule that can be inserted into a plasmid. Construction of the DNA molecule is accomplished by means of an enzyme called *reverse transcriptase* (RNA-directed DNA polymerase). Thus it is the artificially produced *complementary DNA*, or *cDNA*, rather than DNA obtained directly from the eucaryotic cells, that is inserted into a plasmid and eventually incorporated into a bacterial cell.

FIGURE 14.7

Two different, initially circular plasmids are cleaved when treated with a restriction endonuclease such as *Eco*R I. The sticky ends can anneal (form hydrogen bonds) and be joined through the action of DNA ligase, giving rise to a recombinant plasmid.

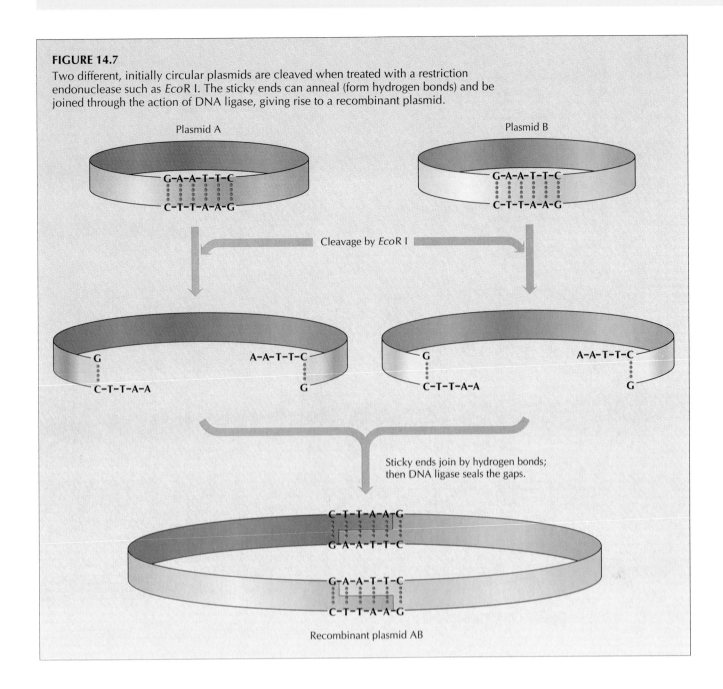

Recombinant plasmid AB

Placing Recombinant Plasmids into Recipient Bacteria

Not all the plasmids resulting from a plasmid construction experiment may be suitable for genetic engineering. Many may not be recombinant plasmids at all but have merely rejoined their own sticky ends. In other instances, the endonuclease may have made a cut within the desired donor gene itself and thus the recombinant plasmid will contain only a piece of the desired gene. Microbiologists do not know whether they have constructed a satisfactory recombinant plasmid until they propagate the plasmids in suitable recipient bacteria.

But before plasmids can be propagated, they first must be inserted into the recipient cells.

The usual method for inserting plasmids into recipient bacteria is transformation, a process described in Chapter 13. Unfortunately, most bacteria do not readily take up plasmid DNA. However, a method called the *calcium chloride (CaCl₂) transformation procedure* has proved effective. It involves treating the recipient cells with CaCl₂ under cold temperatures (0 to 4°C for *E. coli*), adding DNA from the plasmid construction experiment, and then warming the recipient cells (to 42°C for *E. coli*) in order to heat-shock them [FIGURE 14.10]. This alters bacterial permeability, allowing the DNA to

FIGURE 14.8

The major steps in producing genetically engineered bacteria containing genes from a frog. In this particular instance, the genes to be cloned are those that code for frog ribosomal RNA. The plasmid contains a gene for resistance to a particular antibiotic. A recombinant plasmid is constructed which contains the antibiotic-resistance gene and also the genes for frog ribosomal RNA. When the recombinant plasmid is introduced into recipient bacteria by transformation, the recipient bacteria become resistant to the antibiotic. Unlike bacteria that have not received the plasmid, the recipient bacteria are capable of growing on media containing the antibiotic. This allows easy selection of those bacteria that have received the plasmid.

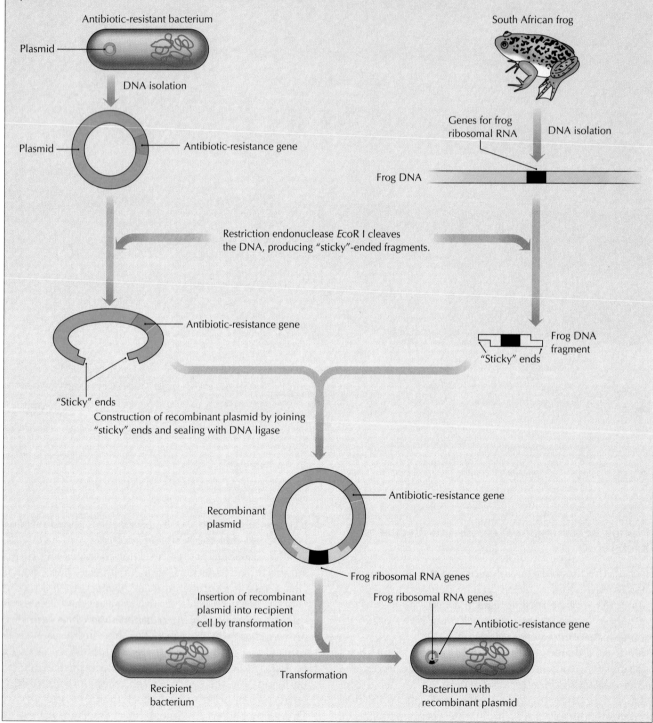

FIGURE 14.9

Some eucaryotic genes contain intron-intervening regions that do not code for protein. These genes cannot be used directly for genetic engineering. Instead, the messenger RNA, which has had the introns removed and the exons spliced together, is obtained from the cells and used as a template to construct cDNA, that is, DNA that does not contain the introns. The cDNA is used for genetic engineering purposes.

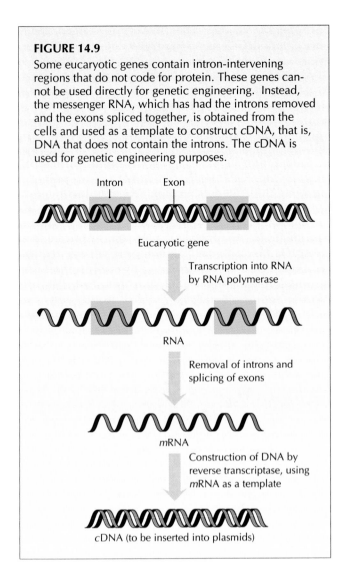

Intron   Exon

Eucaryotic gene

Transcription into RNA
by RNA polymerase

RNA

Removal of introns and
splicing of exons

mRNA

Construction of DNA by
reverse transcriptase, using
mRNA as a template

cDNA (to be inserted into plasmids)

FIGURE 14.10

The CaCl$_2$ transformation procedure for inserting plasmids into bacterial cells.

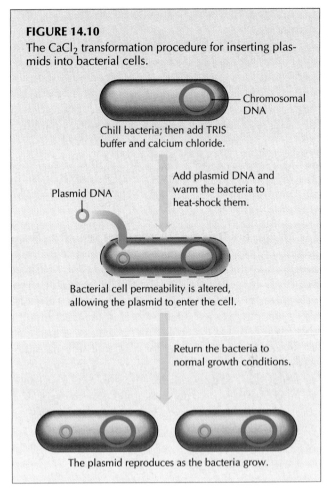

Chromosomal
DNA

Chill bacteria; then add TRIS
buffer and calcium chloride.

Plasmid DNA

Add plasmid DNA and
warm the bacteria to
heat-shock them.

Bacterial cell permeability is altered,
allowing the plasmid to enter the cell.

Return the bacteria to
normal growth conditions.

The plasmid reproduces as the bacteria grow.

enter the cells. Recently it has been shown that plasmid DNA can be taken up by the cells following an electric shock treatment (*electroporation*). It is thought that the short electric pulse results in the formation of pores through which the plasmid may diffuse into the recipient cell.

Identifying the Bacteria That Have Acquired the Plasmid. Even with the CaCl$_2$ transformation procedure, only a small proportion of the cells in the recipient population actually acquire the new plasmid. Thus the initial goal is to select those few that have the new plasmid, since only those cells will have a chance of containing the new gene.

One method to identify the plasmid-containing transformed cells is the use of antibiotics. For instance, genes for resistance to antibiotics such as tetracycline and ampicillin are often present in a plasmid. If the recipient bacteria are initially susceptible to these antibiot-

ics, then only those cells that have incorporated the plasmid DNA will become antibiotic-resistant [see FIGURE 14.8]. When the mixture of plasmid-containing and plasmid-lacking bacteria is spread onto agar media containing the antibiotics, only the bacteria that contain the plasmid will be able to form colonies.

Propagating Recombinant Plasmids

Once a recombinant plasmid is successfully placed into a bacterial cell, that cell can proliferate to produce a large population of identical cells—called a *clone*—in which the new gene is present in every cell. Thus the new gene is inherited and is said to be a *cloned gene.* Since a plasmid was the vehicle by which the new gene was placed into the bacterial cell, the plasmid is said to be a *cloning vector.* Plasmids are the major kind of cloning vector because they are inherited without having to be integrated into the bacterial chromosome. Sometimes certain bacteriophages are used as vectors, but their DNA must be integrated into the bacterial chromosome in order to be inherited by the bacterial progeny, unless the phage DNA has been altered to behave like a plasmid.

For certain plasmids, exposure to low levels of the antibiotic chloramphenicol results in uncontrolled plasmid replication such that nearly 100 copies of the plasmid (and any new gene it may carry) can be made per bacterial cell. Such abnormal, enhanced replication of plasmids is called *amplification.* The result of amplification is that larger amounts of the product of a cloned gene can be made per bacterial cell (after the chloramphenicol has been removed) than will be produced by bacteria having only one or a few copies of the recombinant plasmid.

Identifying the Bacteria That Express the New Gene.

After $CaCl_2$ transformation and subsequent selection of recipient bacteria that contain a plasmid, you still need to identify which of the bacteria, if any, contain a properly constructed recombinant plasmid, one that contains the gene to be cloned. One way to do this is to identify those bacteria that can make the cloned gene's product. This is often like searching for a needle in a haystack. Even if the recombinant plasmid were properly constructed, there are several reasons why recipient bacteria might not express the new gene (see the next section). The problem of identifying bacteria that make a particular gene product can be especially formidable if the entire DNA of a donor cell has been used as a source of the new gene. A donor cell may contain 100,000 to 1 million genes, and the exact location of a specific gene may be unknown. Therefore, scientists may need to use the entire array of genes in order to obtain that gene. This is appropriately called *shotgun cloning.* Treatment of the total cellular DNA with an endonuclease results in many random fragments, each having a chance of being inserted into a plasmid. Consequently, many different recombinant plasmids will result—but only a few will have the fragment that contains the desired gene.

Screening the colonies derived from thousands of different transformed bacteria to see which one makes a particular gene product can be very time-consuming. Nevertheless, several methods have been devised that can expedite the search. For example, if the gene of interest is the one for human insulin, you can inject a small amount of insulin (derived from human tissue) into a rabbit. The rabbit responds by producing antibodies (specific proteins) in its blood serum that can bind only to human insulin. These antibodies can be purified from the rabbit's serum and labeled with a radioactive element. They can then be used to identify the colonies of bacteria in which the insulin gene may have been placed because they attach to insulin produced by the bacteria and can be detected by an instrument that measures radioactivity [FIGURE 14.11].

Many of the difficulties involved in shotgun cloning can be avoided if only a particular donor gene is used. One way to do this is to use *c*DNA derived from the appropriate messenger RNA. The *m*RNA can be recovered from the cells producing large amounts of that protein (e.g., the islet cells of the pancreas, which produce insulin). Still another approach is to make an *artificial gene* constructed in the laboratory, and then insert it into the plasmid vector. With special equipment, laboratory construction of genes has become feasible, particularly when the gene is a relatively short one that codes for a small protein, such as the gene for insulin. The amino acid sequence of insulin had already been determined by chemical analysis of insulin extracted from human tissue. Knowing the amino acid sequence of insulin made it possible to deduce the DNA base sequence of the corresponding gene and then to construct this sequence in the laboratory from individual nucleotides. An artificial insulin gene was made in this manner, inserted into a plasmid vector, and successfully cloned into the bacterium *E. coli.*

ASK YOURSELF

1 What basic steps are used to produce a genetically engineered bacterium?

2 How is plasmid DNA isolated?

3 What is the normal function of restriction endonucleases in bacteria? How does a bacterial cell protect its own DNA from its own restriction endonucleases? How are restriction endonucleases used to construct a recombinant plasmid?

4 What is the importance of using cDNA for the cloning of eucaryotic genes into procaryotic cells? How is cDNA obtained?

5 How has the technique of calcium chloride transformation contributed to genetic engineering?

6 How can the bacteria that make the product of a particular cloned gene be identified?

PROBLEMS INVOLVED IN GENE CLONING

Given the complexities of living cells and the complicated nature of genetic processes, there can be numerous difficulties in cloning genes and producing the cloned gene product. These may be summarized as follows:

FIGURE 14.11
Specific antibodies labeled with a radioactive element can be used to identify those genetically engineered bacteria that can make the product of a particular cloned human gene.

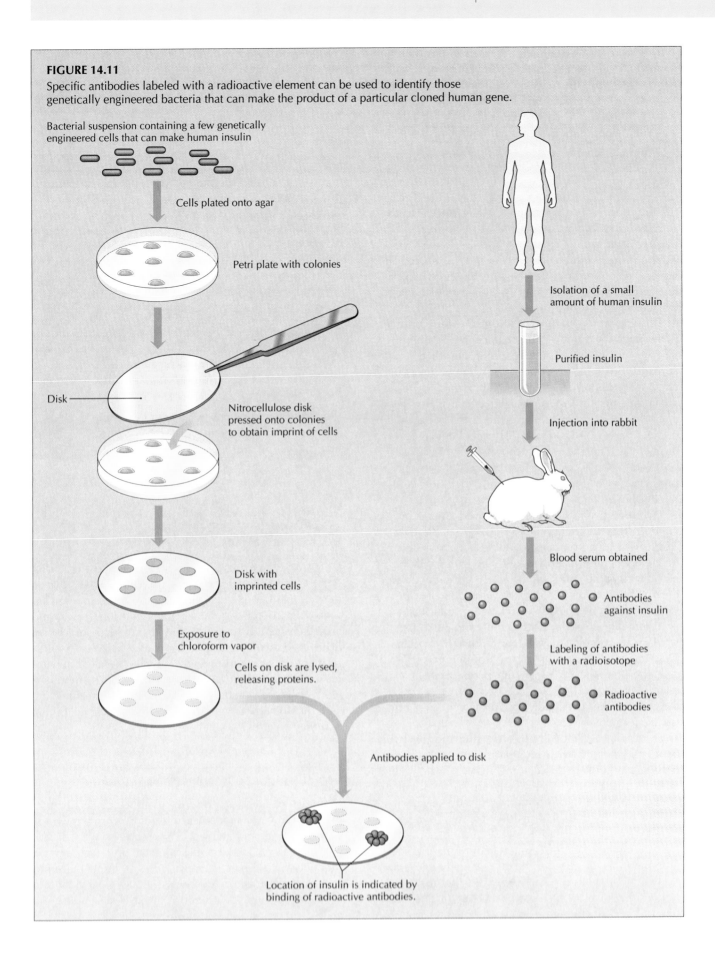

Bacterial suspension containing a few genetically engineered cells that can make human insulin

Cells plated onto agar

Petri plate with colonies

Disk

Nitrocellulose disk pressed onto colonies to obtain imprint of cells

Disk with imprinted cells

Exposure to chloroform vapor

Cells on disk are lysed, releasing proteins.

Isolation of a small amount of human insulin

Purified insulin

Injection into rabbit

Blood serum obtained

Antibodies against insulin

Labeling of antibodies with a radioisotope

Radioactive antibodies

Antibodies applied to disk

Location of insulin is indicated by binding of radioactive antibodies.

1 The restriction endonucleases used to cut the donor DNA into small sticky-ended fragments might cut and destroy the gene to be cloned. Another possibility is that more than one gene might be involved in expression of a particular characteristic, and the additional gene may not be identified or inserted into a vector.

2 The donor gene may be incorrectly inserted into the plasmid vector. This could result in the failure of the bacterium to express the gene (make the desired protein) because the bacterium cannot recognize the start and stop punctuation signals that are part of the eucaryotic gene.

3 The protein product may occur within the cell in large, insoluble aggregates. Sometimes this aggregation is irreversible, and thus isolation of the protein will not yield a useful product.

4 There may be overproduction of the gene product. Sometimes the synthesis of a cloned gene product may be lethal to the bacterial cell if too much product is made. For instance, when genes for the unregulated synthesis of phenylalanine (an amino acid used in the manufacture of aspartame, an artificial sweetener) were cloned in bacteria, the bacteria died because they produced very high intracellular levels of phenylalanine. Lowering the number of copies of the cloned genes resulted in a bacterial strain that produced lower (but still reasonably high) levels of phenylalanine and continued to grow.

5 The gene product may be destroyed after it is made. Although bacteria are relatively simple compared with higher organisms, they do have systems for detecting and destroying foreign proteins if they occur within the cell (just as restriction endonucleases destroy foreign DNA). A variety of mammalian proteins whose genes have been cloned into bacteria are preferentially degraded within the recipient cells.

6 Plasmid instability may occur. Although foreign DNA may be successfully inserted into a bacterial cell, the plasmid vector may not be inherited by every daughter cell during cell division. As a result, the culture may eventually contain many cells without the cloned gene.

7 There may be difficulty in extracting and purifying the gene product because of natural products or structures made by the recipient cells. Gram-negative bacteria such as *E. coli* are normally used as recipients of foreign genes, but such bacteria typically do not secrete proteins into their culture medium, where the proteins could be easily recovered. This is because the outer membrane of Gram-negative bacteria keeps proteins from leaving the cell. It is usually necessary to disrupt the cells in order to extract the desired protein. Gram-positive bacteria such as *Bacillus subtilis* lack an outer membrane and do secrete proteins; thus they can be more useful as producers of gene products. However, they often make proteolytic enzymes that destroy the product. Since yeasts lack an outer membrane and usually do not make proteolytic enzymes, they might prove very useful for expression of foreign genes. Recently, the gene for a bacterial cellulase (an enzyme that degrades cellulose) was cloned in yeast cells. The gene was provided with an auxiliary DNA sequence that enabled these eucaryotic yeast cells to secrete the bacterial enzyme into the culture medium.

ASK YOURSELF

1 What problems in gene cloning might be attributable to the type of restriction endonuclease used?

2 Assuming that a gene has been properly cloned into a plasmid vector and that the vector has been inserted successfully into a bacterial cell, what might account for failure to obtain a useful product from the bacteria?

3 What might be the advantages of cloning genes into yeast cells instead of bacterial cells?

BENEFITS AND POTENTIAL HAZARDS OF GENETIC ENGINEERING

Genetic engineering provides almost limitless possibilities for the benefit of society, from innovative vaccine development to plants that naturally resist harmful insects. On the other hand, giving new properties to microorganisms also poses potential problems for human health and the environment. As a citizen of society and a resident of the environment, you may be called upon to make decisions about genetic engineering. You most certainly will be affected by the products of this technology, and should understand some of its basic benefits and potential hazards.

Benefits of Genetic Engineering

Genetic technologies, present and future, can contribute to the improvement of our health, our environment, our supply of food, and many other aspects of our lives. The pharmaceutical industry has already produced several products for human therapy, such as human insulin, human growth factor, tissue plasminogen activator and urokinase (for the treatment of blood clots), interferon, and somatostatin (a brain hormone).

New techniques for vaccine development have

14.1 ENGINEERING A VACCINE AGAINST HEPATITIS TYPE B

Viral hepatitis type B (serum hepatitis) is an infection of humans that primarily damages the liver. The causative agent is a virus called HBV, which is transmitted in much the same way as the AIDS virus is transmitted. In fact, some of the early work done on AIDS involved information gathered about hepatitis type B infection. Approximately 200,000 persons are infected by HBV each year in the United States. Of these, more than 10,000 require hospitalization and 250 die of the infection. Worldwide, hepatitis B affects millions. Infection may cause a relatively mild disease or cause more serious problems such as liver cancer.

If HBV could be cultivated in the laboratory in unlimited amounts, it could be chemically inactivated and then injected into humans as a vaccine to stimulate immunity against hepatitis type B. Unfortunately, it is not yet possible to grow HBV in laboratory culture. The virus can be obtained only from the blood of humans and experimentally infected chimpanzees or other primates. But these sources do not supply enough HBV to develop a commercial vaccine.

However, the blood of chronically infected persons contains numerous particles of a harmless protein component of the virus. This protein, called HBsAg, can be extracted from the blood, purified, and treated chemically to destroy any live virus that might also be present. When the HBsAg particles are injected into humans, they stimulate immunity against the complete infectious virus. On this basis an effective vaccine was licensed in 1981. However, HBsAg particles were expensive to produce and in short supply because they were obtained only from infected persons.

In 1982 a new source of HBsAg par-

ticles became available, thanks to genetic engineering. Using DNA from HBV, researchers found a way to clone the gene for HBsAg into cells of the common bread yeast *Saccharomyces cerevisiae*. The yeast expressed the gene and made HBsAg particles that could be extracted after the cells were broken. Since yeast cells are easy to propagate, it was now possible to obtain unlimited quantities of HBsAg particles. In 1986 the Food and Drug Administration approved the use of a new vaccine containing yeast-made HBsAg.

This was the first vaccine against a human disease produced with genetic engineering methods. Its success suggests that similar vaccines might be developed against other diseases caused by infectious agents that cannot be readily cultivated in the laboratory, such as the causative agents of malaria, schistosomiasis, and syphilis.

---

emerged from genetic engineering. For example, the gene for a harmless protein from the coat of the foot-and-mouth disease virus was inserted into an *E. coli* plasmid, and bacteria containing this plasmid then produced the viral protein [FIGURE 14.12]. When the protein was extracted from the bacteria and injected into cattle, it stimulated the production of antibodies in the animals against the protein. These antibodies were able to protect the animals against live foot-and-mouth disease virus. This method of vaccine development completely avoided the dangers and difficulties associated with the usual method of making foot-and-mouth disease vaccine, in which the infectious virus must be grown in the laboratory and subsequently treated with agents to destroy its infectivity but not its antigenicity (ability to cause antibody formation). Another vaccine, against the hepatitis type B virus, was recently developed by genetic engineering techniques [DISCOVER 14.1].

A similar strategy may be used eventually to produce a vaccine against the deadly human disease AIDS (acquired immune deficiency syndrome). The surface of the AIDS virus contains two proteins that arise from the splitting of a large protein called gp160. The viral gene that codes for gp160 was cloned by researchers at the National Institute of Allergy and Infectious Diseases in Bethesda, Maryland. Subsequently, scientists at MicroGeneSys, a pharmaceutical firm in Connecticut, were able to insert the gene into the DNA of a baculovirus, a virus that attacks insects. When cultures

of insect tissue cells were infected with the recombinant baculovirus, the gp160 gene was expressed and the cultures produced protein gp160. This protein is being tested at present in humans to see whether it can induce an effective immunity against AIDS.

Genetic engineering has also been used to improve the industrial production of important chemical substances. Vitamin C (ascorbic acid) is one example. Worldwide production of ascorbic acid amounts to 40 million pounds per year, with annual sales of approximately $400 million. One potential new method for industrial production involves making ascorbic acid by the following sequence of reactions:

$$\text{Glucose} \xrightarrow{\text{enzyme A}} \underset{\text{(Diketogluconate)}}{\text{KGLC}} \xrightarrow{\text{enzyme B}} \underset{\text{(Ketogulonate)}}{\text{KGUL}} \xrightarrow[\text{treatment}]{\text{acid}} \underset{\text{acid}}{\text{ascorbic}}$$

It was hoped that a microorganism might be used to carry out the first two steps, but unfortunately, no microorganism was known to possess both enzyme A and enzyme B. Some bacteria made A but not B; others made B but not A. However, when the gene for B was cloned into a bacterium that could make A, the resulting genetically engineered bacterium could convert glucose completely to KGUL, thus providing unlimited quantities of KGUL for conversion to ascorbic acid.

Genetic engineering may also provide benefits for agriculture. One agricultural application being developed involves the use of genetically altered strains of

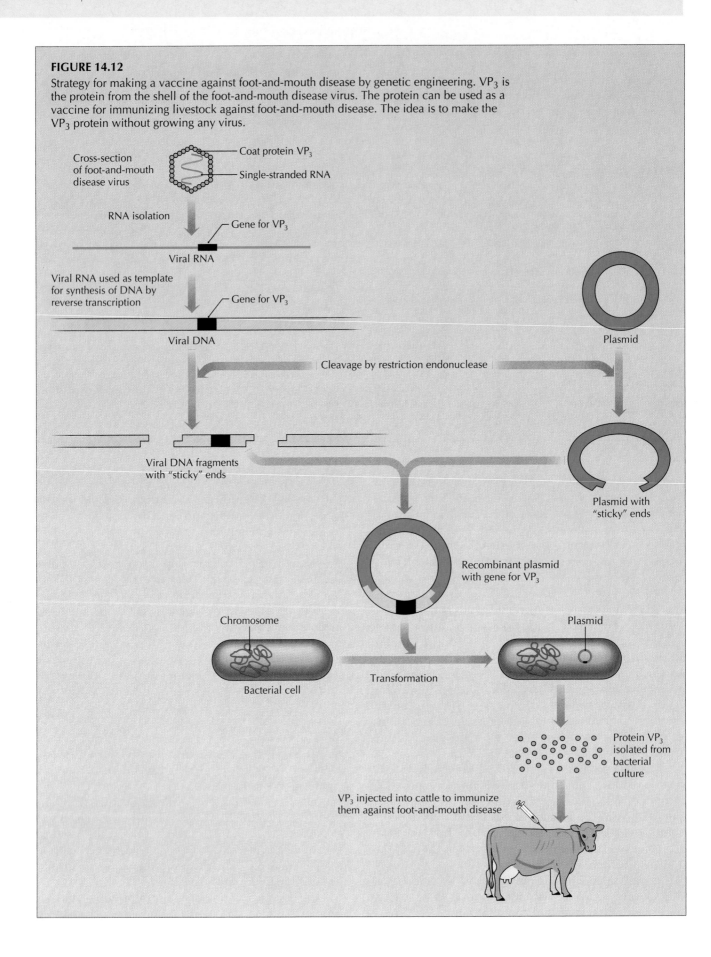

FIGURE 14.12
Strategy for making a vaccine against foot-and-mouth disease by genetic engineering. VP$_3$ is the protein from the shell of the foot-and-mouth disease virus. The protein can be used as a vaccine for immunizing livestock against foot-and-mouth disease. The idea is to make the VP$_3$ protein without growing any virus.

Pseudomonas syringae and *Pseudomonas fluorescens* to protect fruit against frost damage. Normal strains of these plant-associated bacteria secrete a protein that allows the cells to act as nuclei in ice crystal formation (i.e., to act as centers for initiation of the process of crystallization), which damages the plants. By recombinant DNA techniques, a portion of the gene that codes for the nucleation protein was deleted. It is thought that the altered bacterial strains, when used to inoculate fruit trees, may replace the normal strains and thus protect the fruit from ice crystal damage. Other potential agricultural applications of genetic engineering might result in enhanced temperature tolerance and drought resistance in plant crops, leading to a vastly expanded range of food production on a global scale. Similarly the development of plants with resistance to insects and microbial agents of disease would greatly enhance crop productivity. Endowing nitrogen-fixing bacteria with the capability of growing symbiotically with cereal grain crops would greatly increase agricultural production, particularly in those parts of the world that experience shortages of commercial fertilizer.

Genetic engineering may also provide new ways to protect the environment. For instance, microorganisms have been genetically engineered to decompose oil in oil spills. Other commercial applications are likely to be made in pollution-control industries as well as in mining and oil recovery.

During the past several years, hundreds of companies have been built upon the new *recombinant DNA technology*. A large sector of the industry is actively pursuing potential products suggested by genetic engineering studies of microorganisms and other cells. Most state governments, aware of what the new technology promises, have placed a high priority on establishing biotechnology centers where universities and industry can collaborate.

Potential Hazards of Genetic Engineering

The ability to move genes across species lines, such as from animals to bacteria, to create new, redesigned organisms has raised questions of the risks involved.

There is concern that production of recombinant DNA molecules that are functional in vivo could prove biologically hazardous. If they are carried in a microbe such as *E. coli*, which is a normal inhabitant of the human intestine and can exchange genetic information with other types of bacteria, they might possibly become widely disseminated among human, bacterial, plant, or animal populations, with unpredictable results.

Of special concern is construction of new bacterial plasmids that could, if not carefully controlled, introduce antibiotic resistance or toxin formation into bacterial strains that do not at present have such capability. Experiments to link all or part of the DNA from tumor-

producing viruses or other viruses to autonomously replicating DNA elements (such as bacterial plasmids or other viral DNAs) also pose threats.

Regulation of Genetic Engineering

Because of the concerns associated with genetic engineering, the National Institutes of Health has established guidelines for research involving recombinant DNA molecules. Under these guidelines, the National Institutes of Health oversees research by sponsoring risk-assessment programs, certifying new host-vector systems, serving as an information clearinghouse, and coordinating federal and local activities. This monitoring function is being expanded through the U.S. Department of Agriculture and the Environmental Protection Agency to cover the use of genetically engineered organisms in the environment.

How rigorous should regulation of genetic engineering be? Most scientists think that the present guidelines and safeguards are adequate and that the risks involved in the new technology are small compared with the vast potential benefits. The genetic engineering efforts that have been accomplished so far have resulted in no demonstrable hazards, but some element of risk will always exist when anyone deliberately manipulates the genetic makeup of organisms. On the other hand, there can be no progress if absolute safety against all imagined future hazards becomes the goal. Indeed, excessive restrictions on genetic engineering present another kind of risk—that of effectively halting progress in both the research laboratory and industrial development. A good compromise would be the use of sensible precautions in genetic engineering, rather than the imposition of severely repressive constraints.

ASK YOURSELF

1 How were the genetically engineered vaccines against foot-and-mouth disease and hepatitis B developed?

2 How was genetic engineering used to improve the industrial production of ascorbic acid?

3 How might genetically altered strains of bacteria be used to protect fruit against frost damage?

4 What are some of the potential hazards of genetic engineering?

5 How rigorous should the regulation of genetic engineering be? Should absolute safety against all imagined future hazards become the goal of such regulation?

SUMMARY

1 Genetic engineering is the in vitro transfer of segments of genetic material from one cell to another using a gene carrier called a *vector*. Bacteria are the usual recipients of the transplanted genetic material, because they can be grown indefinitely on simple and inexpensive media, thus producing unlimited amounts of a gene product. Plasmids have usually been used as vectors because they are easily isolated and manipulated, and do not have to be integrated into the bacterial chromosome in order to be replicated by the recipient cells.

2 The steps in constructing a genetically engineered bacterium are as follows:
(a) DNA containing the desired gene can either be isolated from donor cells or synthesized by laboratory procedures. In the case of eucaryotic genes, which contain introns, cDNA derived from messenger RNA by the action of reverse transcriptase is usually used as the donor DNA.
(b) The plasmid vector is obtained from the bacterial species into which the donor gene is to be placed.
(c) Both the donor DNA and the plasmid DNA are then treated with the same restriction endonuclease. The sticky ends of a donor DNA fragment form hydrogen bonds with the complementary sticky ends of the plasmid DNA, and DNA ligase is used to repair the break in the sugar-phosphate backbone.
(d) The resulting recombinant plasmid is then incorporated into a recipient bacterium by means of a technique such as $CaCl_2$ transformation or electroporation.
(e) Colonies of those bacteria that can express the new gene are then propagated and the gene product is extracted from the cultures.
The gene must be expressed at high levels in order for pilot plant and commercial manufacture of the gene product to be feasible. A high level of expression can occur if multiple copies of the plasmid develop in each bacterial cell and the proper genetic signals for gene expression are present.

3 The impact of the new technology has already been significant in many areas and, in time, will affect the health and welfare of people globally. Agriculture and food production, waste management and environmental quality, raw material for the chemical industry, new pharmaceutical products, and disease control are some of the areas where benefits will occur. However, genetic engineering poses some potential risks that require careful assessment of consequences.

KEY TERMS

amplification
calcium chloride ($CaCl_2$)
  transformation procedure
clone
cloned gene
cloning vector
complementary DNA (cDNA)
density gradient centrifugation
DNA ligase
DNA modification
exons
genetic engineering
introns
recombinant plasmids
restriction endonucleases
reverse transcriptase
shotgun cloning
sticky-ended DNA

INTRODUCTION TO
GENETIC
ENGINEERING

1 Instead of relying on extraction of limited amounts of a medicinally valuable substance from humans, animals, or plants, we can place the

_____ that codes for the substance into a microbial cell and then let this cell and its progeny produce the substance in unlimited quantities.

2 Which one of the following statements is correct? **(a)** Since all diabetic patients can use the commonly available bovine insulin, there is no need to produce human insulin. **(b)** Bacterial cells are more expensive to cultivate in the laboratory than human tissue cells. **(c)** Human insulin is the only genetically engineered product that is commercially available at the present time. **(d)** Once isolated, the insulin gene can be grown indefinitely in the absence of any living organisms. **(e)** Modern technology makes it possible to move a gene from a plant or animal cell into a bacterial cell.

3 It took less than a decade for the production of human insulin by genetically engineered bacteria to move from a potential research-and-development method through

_____ plants and finally to _____ production.

PRODUCING A
GENETICALLY
ENGINEERED
BACTERIUM

4 Although DNA to be used for genetic engineering procedures can sometimes be made by laboratory methods from nucleotides, it is usually obtained by extracting it

from a(n) _____ .

5 The carrier for a particular gene to be placed into a recipient cell is usually a(n) **(a)** chromosome; **(b)** allele; **(c)** plasmid; **(d)** transposon; **(e)** strand of *m*RNA.

6 Both donor DNA and the plasmid DNA are cleaved by the same enzyme to form DNA fragments with complementary single-stranded ends, called **(a)** replication bubbles; **(b)** blunt ends; **(c)** fragmented ends; **(d)** circular ends; **(e)** sticky ends.

7 The enzyme in question 6 is called a(n) **(a)** nucleotide transferase; **(b)** RNA-dependent RNA polymerase; **(c)** restriction endonuclease; **(d)** RNA-dependent DNA polymerase; **(e)** DNA ligase.

8 The modified plasmid can be placed into a recipient bacterium by a process called **(a)** transduction; **(b)** conjugation; **(c)** differentiation; **(d)** transformation; **(e)** transpeptidation.

9 A key step in the separation of plasmid DNA from chromosomal DNA is the use of a technique called **(a)** transformation; **(b)** transduction; **(c)** density gradient centrifugation; **(d)** conjugation; **(e)** the Svedberg procedure.

10 In the technique indicated in question 9, DNA is added to a tube containing a solution of ethidium bromide and **(a)** calcium chloride; **(b)** rubidium chloride; **(c)** sodium phosphate; **(d)** potassium phosphate; **(e)** cesium chloride.

11 Match the description on the right with the correct item on the left.

_____ restriction endonuclease

_____ DNA modification

_____ foreign DNA

_____ DNA ligase

_____ hydrogen bonds

(a) Substance that, upon entering a cell, is destroyed by the cell's restriction endonucleases
(b) Process that allows a cell to distinguish its "self DNA" from "foreign DNA"
(c) Substance that is exemplified by *Eco*R I
(d) Responsible for the initial joining of two DNA fragments that have similar sticky ends
(e) Responsible for permanently joining two DNA fragments by repairing the breaks in their sugar-phosphate backbones

12 The separation of plasmid DNA from chromosomal DNA by the technique indicated in question 9 depends on the difference in _____ of the two kinds of DNA.

13 A cell protects its own DNA from attack by its own restriction endonucleases by adding _____ to certain nucleotides at the sites that are recognized by the endonucleases.

14 The idea that any kind of DNA could be joined to any other kind of DNA was first proved when DNA that coded for the _____ of a frog was incorporated into a bacterial plasmid.

15 Whether a recombinant plasmid has been successfully constructed can be determined only after the plasmid has been introduced into a(n)

_____ so that it can be propagated and studied.

16 Match the description on the right with the correct item on the left.

	(a) Plasmid containing two different kinds of DNA
_____ intron	**(b)** A region in eucaryotic DNA that codes for protein
_____ recombinant plasmid	**(c)** A region in eucaryotic DNA that does not code for protein
_____ reverse transcriptase	
_____ exon	**(d)** Substance used to prepare cDNA from eucaryotic messenger RNA

17 One reason why a eucaryotic gene may not be expressed in a recipient bacterium is that the DNA sequences that _____ and

_____ gene expression in eucaryotic cells are not operational in bacterial cells.

18 An effective method for placing plasmid DNA into recipient bacteria is called the **(a)** insertion mutation procedure; **(b)** buoyant density transformation procedure; **(c)** calcium chloride transformation procedure; **(d)** cesium chloride density gradient procedure; **(e)** plasmid translation procedure.

19 In the method indicated in question 18, after treating potential recipient cells with $CaCl_2$ in the cold, the plasmid is added and then the cells are

_____ .

20 Recipient cells that have taken up the plasmid can be easily selected if the plasmid has a gene for resistance to **(a)** restriction endonucleases; **(b)** an antibiotic; **(c)** $CaCl_2$; **(d)** potassium phosphate; **(e)** cDNA.

21 If a gene has been transplanted into a recipient bacterial cell and the bacterial cell has proliferated to produce a large number of identical progeny, the gene is said to have been **(a)** cloned; **(b)** transformed; **(c)** partitioned; **(d)** conjugated; **(e)** centrifuged.

22 An advantage of using plasmids as cloning vectors is that they can replicate

_____ of the chromosome.

23 Amplification is desirable in genetic engineering because it results in larger amounts of _____ .

24 Match the description on the right with the correct item on the left.

(a) A large population of identical cells

(b) Abnormal, enhanced replication of a plasmid to produce many copies of the plasmid in each cell

_____ radioactive antibody

_____ artificial gene

_____ amplification

_____ clone

_____ shotgun cloning

(c) The use of the entire array of genes of an organism in order to obtain the particular gene one wishes to clone

(d) Substance that can be used to identify colonies of genetically engineered bacteria that make a particular gene product

(e) Substance that can be constructed in the laboratory if its base sequence can be deduced from the amino acid sequence of the protein it codes for

PROBLEMS INVOLVED IN GENE CLONING

25 It will not be possible to clone a gene if the restriction endonuclease that is used makes a cut within _____.

26 If a eucaryotic gene is incorrectly inserted into a plasmid vector, the recipient bacterium may fail to express the gene because it cannot recognize the eucaryotic (a) DNA-dependent RNA polymerase; (b) introns; (c) $mRNA$ codons; (d) $tRNA$ anticodons; (e) start and stop punctuation signals.

27 Isolation of a gene product from bacteria may not be possible if the protein is formed but is later _____ by the bacterium, or if the protein forms large intracellular _____ that cannot be solubilized.

28 Lowering the number of copies of a cloned gene per cell may prevent undesirable (a) instability of the plasmid; (b) overproduction of the gene product; (c) cleavage of the gene product; (d) production of harmful by-products; (e) tangling of the genes.

29 Extraction and purification of the product of a cloned gene could be greatly expedited if the protein could be _____ by the bacteria into the medium; this is more likely to occur with Gram-_____ bacteria than with Gram-_____ bacteria.

BENEFITS AND POTENTIAL HAZARDS OF GENETIC ENGINEERING

30 An advantage of the foot-and-mouth disease vaccine that was developed through genetic engineering is that it is not necessary to prepare the vaccine from (a) the VP_3 protein; (b) interferon; (c) tissue plasminogen activator; (d) live infectious virus; (e) antibodies against the virus.

31 Since the foot-and-mouth disease virus contains single-stranded RNA as its genetic material, which of the following had to be used before researchers could begin to construct a recombinant plasmid containing the gene for VP_3? (a) cellulase; (b) DNA-directed RNA polymerase; (c) a restriction endonuclease; (d) reverse transcriptase; (e) tissue plasminogen activator.

32 Genetically engineered strains of *Pseudomonas syringae* that fail to secrete a nucleation protein may replace normal strains and protect fruit against damage caused by (a) radioactive fallout; (b) insect pests; (c) ice crystal formation; (d) bacterial infection; (e) foot-and-mouth disease virus.

33 A goal of absolute safety against the risks posed by genetic engineering might prevent potential biological hazards but would also effectively prevent

_____ .

REVIEW QUESTIONS

1 In what way did the development of genetic engineering depend on basic research on plasmids and restriction endonucleases?

2 How does a bacterial cell protect its own DNA from attack by its own restriction endonucleases?

3 Why do plasmids make good cloning vectors?

4 How can plasmid DNA be separated from chromosomal DNA?

5 What is the function of DNA ligase in the construction of a recombinant plasmid?

6 What is meant by an ''artificial gene''? What use can be made of such a gene?

7 In genetic engineering, what is meant by *amplification,* and what value might amplification have?

8 What special problems must be considered if you wish to clone eucaryotic genes into procaryotic cells, i.e., problems that do not exist when you clone procaryotic genes into procaryotic cells? How could you overcome these difficulties?

DISCUSSION QUESTIONS

1 Suppose that you wish to alter *E. coli* by genetic engineering so that it will be able to make an enzyme that now occurs only in *Corynebacterium roseum*. One problem is that, after transformation of *E. coli* with a plasmid vector that you think carries the *C. roseum* gene, only a few *E. coli* cells will have acquired the plasmid. It would be desirable to allow only the plasmid-containing cells to grow. How might you accomplish this?

2 With reference to question 1, after you select the transformed bacteria and grow them, suppose that none of the transformed bacteria express the acquired gene (i.e., the *E. coli* cells fail to make the *C. roseum* enzyme). What might account for this?

3 A hypothetical protein X, made in the body in tiny amounts by X cells, is found to cure certain cancers. The X gene contains several introns. Although bacterial cells will not excise introns from *m*RNA, how might this human gene be usefully cloned into a bacterial cell?

4 Suppose that you successfully clone gene X into a bacterial cell. The progeny of that cell express the gene and produce protein X, but only a low amount of the protein is produced. How might you be able to increase the amount of protein produced per cell? What problems might arise if you increase the production per cell to a high level?

5 Give three future potential applications of genetic engineering that are not mentioned in this chapter.

VII

Viruses

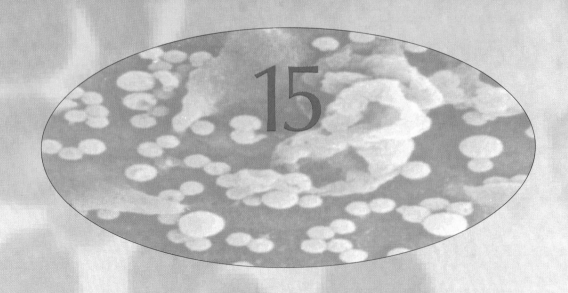

15

Viruses:
Morphology, Classification, Replication

OBJECTIVES

After reading this chapter you should be able to

1 Define a virus and discuss the notion of whether it is living or nonliving, as well as list the general characteristics of viruses.

2 Give the chemical composition of the different structures of a virus particle.

3 Give an account of the discovery of bacteriophages.

4 Draw and label the structure of a typical bacterial virus.

5 Classify bacteriophages into families according to particle morphology and nucleic acid composition.

6 Describe the lytic cycle of a bacteriophage.

7 Explain the meaning of lysogeny in a bacterium and the molecular regulation that determines its occurrence.

8 Compare the morphology of some representative viruses that infect animals, plants, and bacteria.

9 Describe the classification schemes for plant and animal viruses.

10 Cite the main features that differentiate bacteriophage replication from plant or animal virus replication, and plant virus replication from animal virus replication.

OVERVIEW

Early microbiologists were sometimes unable to isolate any pathogenic microorganism from the tissues of diseased plants and animals. As described in the Prologue of this book, such observations eventually led to the discovery of *viruses*. The term *virus* is a Latin word for "poison" or "venom," an appropriate name, given the problems viruses can cause. Viruses are minute infectious agents that can be seen only with aid of the electron microscope. They are 10 to 100 times smaller than most bacterial cells, with an approximate size range of 20 to 300 nm (0.02 to 0.3 μm). Because they pass through filters that prevent the passage of bacteria, they were once called "filterable viruses."

Viruses do not have the complex organization of cells and are structurally quite simple. They consist of either DNA or RNA wrapped in a protein coat. Incapable of independent growth in artificial media, they can replicate only in animal, plant, or microbial cells. Viruses therefore are referred to as obligate intracellular parasites and represent the ultimate sophistication in parasitism. They can actually "take over" the genetic machinery of the host cell.

Given these characteristics, a virus can be defined as concisely as possible in the following way: *Viruses are noncellular infectious entities whose genomes are either DNA or RNA. They replicate only in living cells, using the cell's energy-producing and biosynthetic machinery to synthesize copies of themselves for transfer of their own genomes to other cells.* **Although a virus contains a nucleic acid as its hereditary material and is capable of reproducing itself, it has none of the other attributes of a living organism. Thus viruses are viewed as existing at the borderline between living and nonliving. For this reason it is preferable to use terms such as "functionally active" or "inactive," rather than "alive" or "dead," when referring to viruses.**

This chapter describes some basic characteristics of viruses, including structure, chemical composition, replication, and ways in which viruses are classified into taxonomic groups. Chapter 16 discusses more applied aspects of *virology* (the study of viruses), such as the ability of viruses to cause disease and methods used to study viruses in the laboratory.

GENERAL CHARACTERISTICS OF VIRUSES

Viruses are widely distributed in nature—there are viruses that infect animal or plant cells, and others that infect microorganisms. Whatever type of host cell they invade, all viruses are *obligate parasites*. That is, they can reproduce only within a metabolizing host cell, using the protein-synthesizing and energy-generating systems of the cell. However, viruses differ in their degree of dependence on the host cell for *replication*, which is the production of new viruses inside the host cell. For instance, some viruses that infect bacteria—called *bacteriophages*, or *phages*—have fewer than 10 genes and depend almost entirely on bacterial cell functions for replication. Others have 30 to 100 genes and are more independent of host-cell functions.

Replication is not the only viral process that must involve the host cell. Viruses lack metabolic machinery of their own to generate energy or to synthesize proteins, and so they depend on host cells to carry out these vital functions. Once inside a cell, viruses have genes for usurping the host cell's energy-generating and protein-synthesizing systems. In addition to their intracellular form, viruses have an extracellular form that carries the viral nucleic acid from one host cell to another. In this *infectious* form, viruses are simply small packets of genes wrapped in a protein coat. The coat protects the genes outside the host cell; it also serves as a vehicle for entry into another host cell because it binds to receptors on cell surfaces. The structurally mature, infectious viral particle is called a *virion.*

Outside the host cell, in the extracellular form, the virion is inert; that is, it is not metabolizing or replicating. Thus viruses have been considered nonliving entities. However, once inside a host cell, the nucleic acid becomes active and the virus "comes to life." A host organism needs no convincing that the virus is an active entity—just ask anyone afflicted with the miseries of the common cold virus! Thus, during replication in the host cells, viruses may cause disease just as bacterial, fungal, and protozoan pathogens do.

Basic Morphology of Viruses

With the electron microscope, it is possible to determine the morphological characteristics of viruses. The virions range in size from 20 to 300 nm (1 nm = 1/1000 μm). They thus represent the smallest and simplest of infectious agents. Since most viruses measure less than 150 nm, they are beyond the limit of resolution of the light microscope and are visible only by use of the electron microscope. By using materials of known size for comparison, microscopists can use electron microscopes to determine the size and structure of individual virions.

Viruses are composed of a central core of nucleic acid surrounded by a protein coat called a *capsid* [FIGURE 15.1]. The viral proteins self-assemble to give the capsid its characteristic symmetry—usually either *icosahedral* or *helical* [FIGURE 15.2]. The nucleic acid and capsid together constitute the *nucleocapsid* of the virion.

Most viruses that appear polyhedral or spherical have a capsid whose basic framework is that of an *icosahedron*, which means that its surface is made of 20 triangular facets and 12 vertices. Each triangular facet is an equilateral triangle; these facets come together to form the 12 vertices [see FIGURE 15.2A]. In viral capsids, the viral proteins (*protomers)* form the clusters known as *capsomeres*, which are visible by electron microscopy [FIGURE 15.3]. In the larger and more complex polyhedral capsids, the triangular facets of the basic icosahedron are subdivided into a progressively larger number of equilateral triangles. Thus a capsid may be composed of hundreds of capsomeres, but it is still based on the simple icosahedron model. The total number of capsomeres forming the capsid is characteristic of each virus group. The polyhedral heads of some phages are greater in length than in width, resulting in a distorted icosahedral shape, and may have tails attached [FIGURE 15.4].

In the icosahedral head, the nucleic acid molecule is highly compacted and folded, because the length of the molecule is far greater than any dimension of the head.

FIGURE 15.1

General structure of a virion. Drawings show all the major components that may be part of a virion. A virion has a nucleic acid core enclosed by a protein capsid; this combination is called a *nucleocapsid*. A virion may have a membranous (lipoprotein) envelope surrounding the nucleocapsid. The envelope may have surface projections called *spikes*.

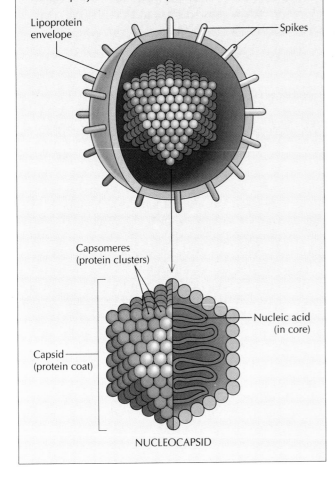

FIGURE 15.2

[A] Diagram of the simplest icosahedral capsid. The colored triangular outlines delineate the icosahedron. The circle and ovoids represent capsomeres. The nucleic acid core is enclosed within the capsid. [B] Diagram of part of a rod-shaped virus with helical symmetry. The capsomeres are arranged helically around a hollow core containing a spiral coil of nucleic acid.

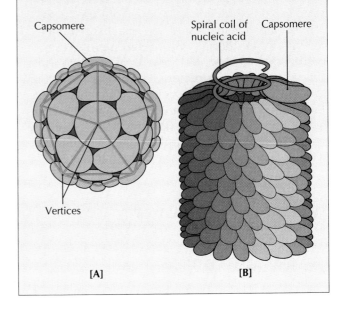

either there is no discrete structure enclosing it (as in the arenaviruses) or it is surrounded by multiple unique membranes (as in the poxviruses; FIGURE 15.7).

A schematic representation of the morphology of several viruses is shown in FIGURE 15.8.

Nucleic Acids

Our understanding of genetics was broadened by the discovery that DNA is not the only possible constituent of viral genes: some viral genes may consist of RNA instead. Viruses contain either DNA or RNA, but never both in the same virion. This, of course, is in contrast to all *cellular* forms of life, which without exception contain *both* types of nucleic acids in each cell. Furthermore, the genome of higher organisms such as animals and plants consists of double-stranded DNA (dsDNA). But the genome of a virion can consist of DNA or RNA that is either double-stranded or single-stranded. All four types of genomes have been found among the bacterial, animal, and plant viruses—double-stranded DNA (dsDNA), single-stranded DNA (ssDNA), double-stranded RNA (dsRNA), and single-stranded RNA (ssRNA).

Viruses with helical symmetry have a capsid whose capsomeres are packed around the nucleic acid in the form of a helix [see FIGURE 15.2B]. Plant viruses with helical symmetry are typically rod-shaped [FIGURE 15.5]. One of the first viruses studied by electron microscopy is the now well-known tobacco mosaic virus, which is a helical virus. Animal viruses with helical capsids include the causative agents of measles, mumps, influenza, and rabies. In these viruses, the capsid is enclosed by a lipoprotein envelope with radially projecting spikes [FIGURE 15.6].

There are animal viruses with complex or uncertain symmetries. For example, the arenaviruses and the poxviruses have no recognizable capsid symmetry. Although these viruses have nucleic acid within the virion core,

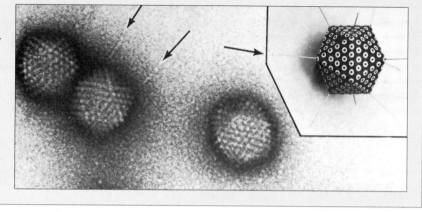

FIGURE 15.3
Electron micrograph of the simian adenovirus SV 15 showing the distinctive capsomeres. Arrows point to fibers that extend from the virion pentamers. Such fibers are only rarely seen in negatively stained specimens. Model of an icosahedral particle is shown in inset.

0.1 μm

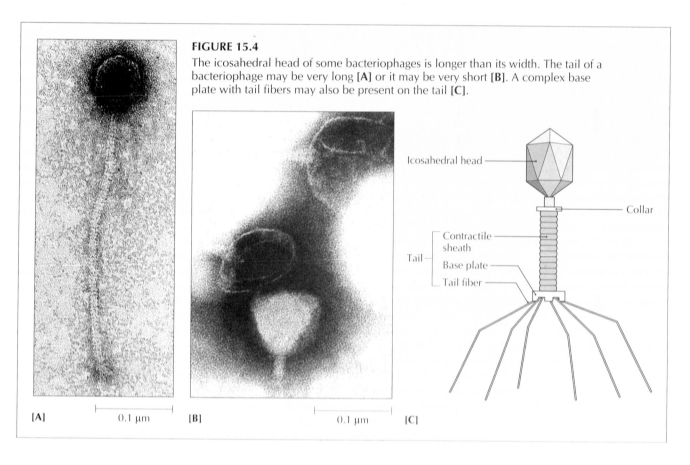

FIGURE 15.4
The icosahedral head of some bacteriophages is longer than its width. The tail of a bacteriophage may be very long [A] or it may be very short [B]. A complex base plate with tail fibers may also be present on the tail [C].

Icosahedral head
Collar
Contractile sheath
Tail
Base plate
Tail fiber

[A] 0.1 μm [B] 0.1 μm [C]

The amount of nucleic acid present may vary in different groups of viruses. Small viruses such as parvoviruses and picornaviruses each contain about three or four genes, while large viruses such as the herpesviruses and poxviruses have several hundred genes per virion.

In addition, the structure of double-stranded or single-stranded DNA in the virion may be either *linear* or *circular*. For example, simian vacuolating virus 40 (SV 40), found in monkey kidney cells, has circular dsDNA, while herpesvirus has linear dsDNA. In contrast, the RNA in animal viruses exists only as *linear* double-stranded or single-stranded molecules. However, some plant viruses appear to have a genome of circular dsRNA.

Unlike viral DNA, the RNA within a virion may also exist as a *segmented* genome (in several separate molecules). For instance, the genome of most influenza viruses consists of eight separate segments of ssRNA; reoviruses contain 10 different segments of dsRNA; retroviruses contain two identical single-stranded genomes. Such a complicated organization of genetic material requires unique mechanisms for ensuring its proper distri-

FIGURE 15.5
Electron micrograph of tobacco mosaic virus. The virus particles are rod-shaped.

0.5 μm

FIGURE 15.7
Vaccinia virus, a poxvirus with complex morphology. **[A]** Virion showing surface tubules. **[B]** Immature virion obtained from an infected cell showing the viral membrane with subunit projections.

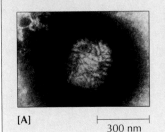 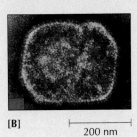

[A]   300 nm   [B]   200 nm

bution during replication. But it also provides the viruses with unique opportunities to vary their genomes.

Those viruses containing single-stranded RNA that acts directly as messenger RNA (*m*RNA) have been designated as plus-strand, or (+) strand, viruses; such ssRNA molecules are known as plus, or (+), strands. Those viruses that must first replicate their RNA to form a complementary strand (which acts as the *m*RNA) are designated as minus-strand, or (−) strand, viruses, and their RNA molecules (which serve as templates) are known as minus, or (−), strands. Replication of the minus RNA strand is always catalyzed by an RNA polymerase carried within the virion.

FIGURE 15.6
Influenza virus. Note the fringe of spikes on the surface of the virions.

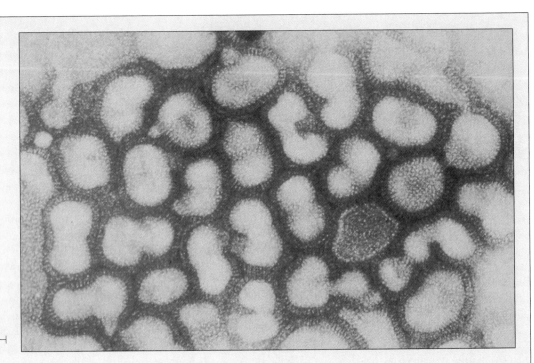

100 nm

FIGURE 15.8

Morphology of some well-known viruses. Icosahedral symmetry: **[A]** polio, wart, adeno, rota; **[B]** herpes. Helical symmetry: **[C]** tobacco mosaic; **[D]** influenza; **[E]** measles, mumps, parainfluenza; **[F]** rabies. Uncertain or complex symmetry: **[G]** poxvirus; **[H]** T-even phages.

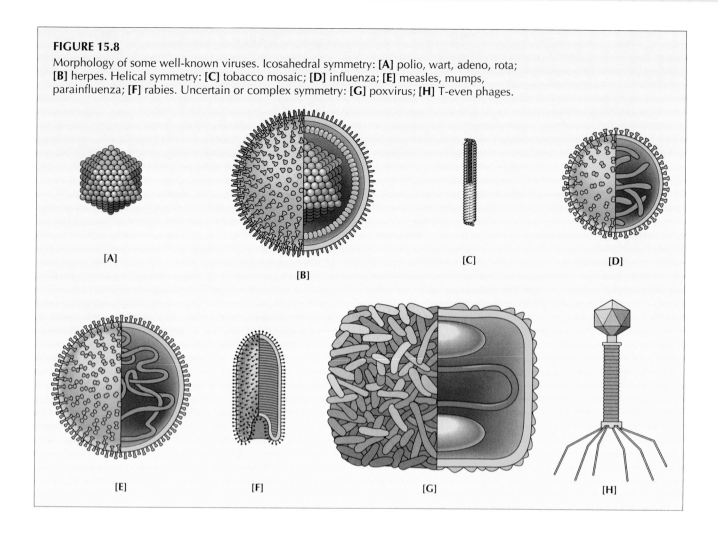

Viral DNA can also exist as plus or minus ssDNA. But ssDNA must be converted to dsDNA in order to be transcribed by RNA polymerase to form *m*RNA. During transcription of dsDNA, generally only one strand is read and it is considered the plus strand; its complementary strand is considered the minus strand.

Other Chemical Components

Besides nucleic acids, the major chemical component of the virion is protein. In addition to their protein coat, many viruses contain within their capsid one or more enzymes that are released after the virus is uncoated in the host cell. These enzymes function in the replication of the nucleic acid of the virus. The most common viral enzymes are polymerases. Except for the RNA viruses carrying the single (+) strand of *m*RNA, all RNA

viruses contain RNA polymerase. The (+) strand RNA viruses code for their own RNA polymerase, which is synthesized by the host cell during translation of the viral *m*RNA. Without a viral polymerase, viral RNA could not be transcribed and the virus could not replicate. The retroviruses contain an enzyme (RNA-dependent DNA polymerase, or *reverse transcriptase*) that synthesizes a DNA strand, using the viral RNA genome as a template. (Remember that in Chapter 14 you learned that this enzyme was very useful in genetic engineering when you need to make *c*DNA from eucaryotic *m*RNA.) The term *retrovirus* is derived from the first two letters of *reverse transcriptase*.

A wide variety of lipid compounds have also been found in viruses. These include phospholipids, glycolipids, neutral fats, fatty acids, fatty aldehydes, and cholesterol. Phospholipids, found in the viral envelope discussed later in this chapter, are the predominant lipid substances in viruses.

All viruses contain carbohydrate, since the nucleic acid itself contains ribose or deoxyribose. Some enveloped animal viruses, such as the influenza virus, have spikes made of glycoprotein on the envelope.

Replication

Virus particles outside a host cell have no independent metabolic activity and are incapable of reproduction by processes characteristic of other microorganisms (for example, binary fission in bacteria). Reproduction of viruses takes place by *replication*, in which the viral protein and nucleic acid components are reproduced within susceptible host cells. The viruses effectively redirect the metabolic processes of many host cells to produce new virions rather than new host-cell material.

Most virus-specific enzymes, which are those encoded by viral genes, are usually not part of the virion itself. This includes those necessary for replication. The smallest naked virions (without an envelope) do not contain any preformed enzymes. Larger virions may contain one or a few enzymes, which usually function in aiding the virus to penetrate the host cell or to replicate its own nucleic acid. Those enzymes that are lacking may be synthesized only when the virion is within the host cell, which spends part of its energy making viral enzymes rather than cellular components.

The entire process of cell infection by viruses may be generalized as follows. The virion attaches to a susceptible host cell at a specific site. Either the whole virus or its viral nucleic acid penetrates the cell interior. If a whole virus has entered the cell, uncoating of the virus must take place to release the viral nucleic acid, which is then free to convert the cell into a factory for the production of viral progeny. The specific intracellular site of progeny assembly and maturation is characteristic for each group of viruses. Once assembled and mature, the virions are released from the host cell.

Despite these basic similarities, there are several distinctive differences between bacteriophage replication and plant and animal virus replication. Plant and animal viruses differ from phages in their mechanisms of entry into the host cell. Once inside the host cell, plant and animal viruses also differ from phages in the synthesis and assembly of the new viral components, partly because of the differences between the bacterial *procaryotic* cell and the plant or animal *eucaryotic* cell. Finally, the mechanisms of maturation and release, and the effects on the host cell, differ between plant and animal viruses and those of phages. These differences will become evident as you learn about viral replication in greater detail later in this chapter.

ASK YOURSELF

1 Why are viruses obligate parasites?

2 Why have viruses been considered nonliving entities?

3 Explain why all viruses do not have the same dependence on host-cell functions to replicate.

4 What are enveloped viruses?

5 How does the genetic system of viruses differ from all cellular forms of life?

6 Other than nucleic acids, what chemical substances are found in virions?

THE DISCOVERY OF BACTERIOPHAGES

Viruses that infect bacteria were discovered independently by Frederick W. Twort in England in 1915 and by Félix d'Hérelle at the Pasteur Institute in Paris in 1917. Twort observed that bacterial colonies sometimes dissolved and disappeared because their component cells *lysed*, or burst. More interesting was his observation that this lytic effect could be transmitted from colony to colony. Even highly diluted material from a lysed colony that had been passed through a bacterial filter could lyse other bacteria. However, heating this filtrate destroyed its lytic property. From these observations Twort cautiously suggested that the lytic agent might be a filterable infectious agent.

When d'Hérelle discovered this phenomenon (hence the term *Twort-d'Hérelle phenomenon*), he coined the word *bacteriophage*, which means "bacteria eater." He concluded that the filterable agent was an invisible entity—a virus—that was parasitic toward bacteria.

ASK YOURSELF

1 Why did Frederick W. Twort think that his lytic agent might be a filterable infectious agent?

2 What is the Twort-d'Hérelle phenomenon?

3 Who coined the word *bacteriophage*, and what does it mean?

15.1 BACTERIOPHAGES AS THERAPEUTIC AGENTS

When Frederick W. Twort and Félix d'Hérelle separately discovered bacteriophages in the early 1900s, they had a particular vision. They wanted to use the "bacteria eaters" to devour bacterial pathogens in the human body! However, experimental results obtained by them and others who shared their vision were not promising. While the phages easily destroyed the bacteria in the laboratory, they often failed to heal patients infected with bacteria—even though such patients swallowed copious volumes of phages. When both Twort and d'Hérelle died in the middle of the twentieth century, the idea of using phages as therapeutic agents died with them.

Recently, visionary microbiologists have been taking a second look at the dismal results obtained by early investigators who used phages to treat cholera and dysentery in humans. They realize that the Tworts and d'Hérelles of a past era did not have today's understanding of viruses, such as the *specificity* of phage-host interaction. Undaunted by past failures in the medical literature, Williams Smith and Michael Huggins of Houghton College in New York State are working with phages to treat infected animals. In one experiment, they injected a specific highly virulent phage into mice suffering from an infection caused by the host bacterium. They found that the phage not only cured the infection but was more effective than 4 out of 5 antibiotics used for comparison. Furthermore, the few bacterial mutants resistant to the phage that did develop were almost nonvirulent. Such success spurred Smith and Huggins on to greater efforts, including the use of such animals as calves and piglets as subjects, and of mixtures of phages to combat naturally occurring phage mutants. In all experiments, successful results were obtained.

This visitation back to a historical failure has rebounded with a promise for the future. It is now clear that phage therapy may work. Early failures could be attributed to improper controls, crude preparation of phages, poor discrimination in the selection of test phages, and bad choice of animal models. In some ways phage therapy has advantages over antibiotic therapy because: (1) phages can be given in just a single dose, since the phages can replicate themselves and are not diluted out by body fluids; (2) phage-resistant bacterial mutants that develop are much less virulent than the parental wild types; (3) phages can target bacterial pathogens much like a heat-sensing missile; and (4) in cases of intestinal infection, phages eliminated along with fecal material will help thwart the spread of infection if the fecal material contaminates food or water.

Who knows? Perhaps this rediscovery could be as significant as the milestones of sulfa drugs and antibiotic discoveries!

MORPHOLOGY AND CHEMICAL COMPOSITION OF BACTERIOPHAGES

Microbiologists have been able to separate bacteriophage structures and determine their chemical content. Like other viruses, all phages have a nucleic acid core covered by the protein-containing capsid, which protects the core from nucleases and other harmful substances. The phage core usually consists of a single nucleic acid molecule, which may be single- or double-stranded linear or circular DNA, or single-stranded linear RNA. (The one known exception is phage $\phi6$, which has three linear double-stranded RNA molecules whose base sequences differ from one another.) FIGURE 15.9 shows the threadlike appearance of a DNA molecule extruded from a T2 phage.

There are three basic morphological forms of bacteriophages: icosahedral head with no tail, icosahedral head with a tail, and filamentous [FIGURE 15.10]. As indicated earlier, the icosahedral heads of some phages have lengths longer than their widths. In a filamentous phage, the nucleic acid is in an extended helical form along the length of the protein coat. The phage tail may be very short or up to 4 times the length of the head, and it may be flexible or rigid. A complex *base plate* may also be present on the tail; it typically has from one to six tail fibers [see FIGURES 15.4 and 15.11].

ASK YOURSELF

1 Comment on the nucleic acid molecule of the phage core.

2 What are the three basic morphological forms of bacteriophages?

3 What is the base plate in a tailed phage?

FIGURE 15.9
The DNA of a T2 phage, released from the virion by gentle disruption, appears as a single, tangled thread in this electron micrograph. Measurements of the DNA thread indicate a length of about 49 μm. The phage "ghost" is the flask-shaped object in the center.

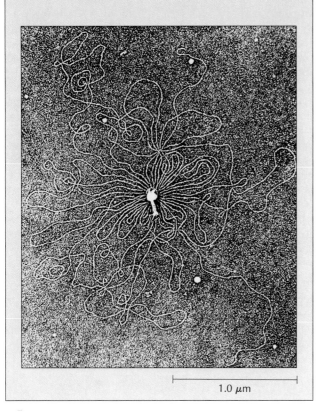

1.0 μm

FIGURE 15.11
Phage of the bacterium *Aeromonas salmonicida* showing six tail fibers projecting from the baseplate.

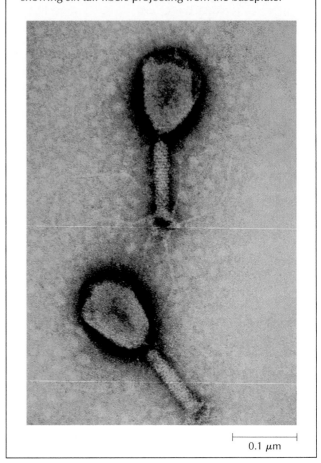

0.1 μm

FIGURE 15.10
The three basic morphological forms of bacteriophages. **[A]** Icosahedral head with no tail: phage MS2. **[B]** Icosahedral head with contractile tail. Virus shown is the T4 bacteriophage of *Escherichia coli*. **[C]** Filamentous phage If1 of *Escherichia coli*.

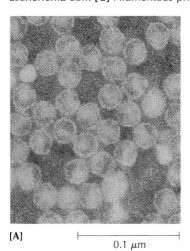

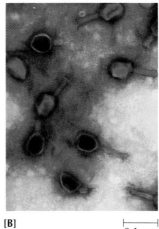

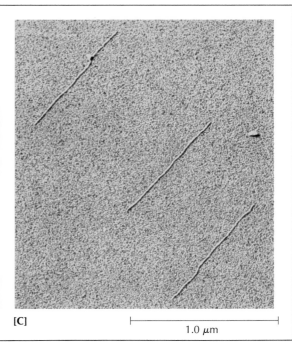

[A]   0.1 μm   [B]   0.1 μm   [C]   1.0 μm

CLASSIFICATION AND NOMENCLATURE OF BACTERIOPHAGES

The common names of bacteriophages do not follow particular guidelines. They are simply designations or code symbols assigned by investigators. Although serving the practical needs of the laboratories, this is a haphazard way of naming a group of infectious entities.

Consequently, the International Committee for Taxonomy of Viruses (ICTV) has a Bacterial Virus Subcommittee working on the classification and nomenclature of bacteriophages. The families of bacterial viruses (names ending in -*viridae*) approved by the ICTV are shown in FIGURE 15.12. They are grouped on the basis of clear-cut differences in morphology and chemical composition. (Virus examples are named in parentheses in the figure.) It may be pointed out that the family Cystoviridae includes only one virus, whereas the largest family, Siphoviridae, has over 1200 members. More than 95 percent of the known viruses infecting eubacteria belong

to one of the three families of long-tailed phages [FIGURE 15.12]. The morphology of most of the families of bacteriophages is depicted in FIGURE 15.13.

System of Classification Based on Differences in Transcriptional Processes

In 1971, David Baltimore (a Nobel laureate for his work on tumor viruses) proposed a classification of viruses, with a unifying concept based on how the viral genome is replicated and expressed. All viruses were placed into one of six classes according to the particular pathway of *m*RNA synthesis involved [FIGURE 15.14]. A central role is assigned to *m*RNA, since protein synthesis takes place by the same mechanism in all cells. Although this scheme groups together viruses with similar replicative steps, it also groups very different virions together in the same class (for example, bacteriophages and animal viruses). It also does not take into account other properties of viruses. Such a scheme finds favor with molecular bi-

FIGURE 15.12
Schematic representation of the families of bacterial viruses. Note that all the diagrams have been drawn to the same scale and provide a good indication of the shapes and relative sizes of the virions. To aid recognition, the name of a well-known, representative member of the family is given in parentheses, but the dimensions and shapes used for the drawing may not be exactly those of the representative virus. Note: ds, double-stranded; ss, single-stranded.

THE FAMILIES OF BACTERIAL VIRUSES

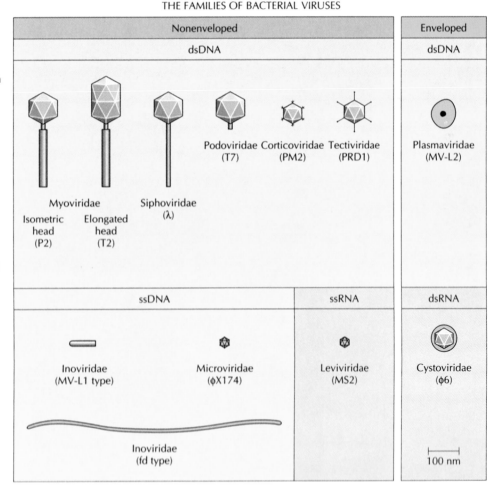

FIGURE 15.13

Morphology of the families of bacteriophages.
[A] Family Myoviridae. The smallest phage with a
contractile tail; phage of *Aeromonas salmonicida*.
[B] Family Siphoviridae. The largest siphovirus; phage
of *Streptococcus lactis*. [C] Family Podoviridae. One of
the largest podoviruses; phage of *Escherichia coli*.
[D] Family Tectiviridae. *Bacillus megaterium* phage
Bam 35. Note the double capsid of the empty particle
as well as apical spikes. [E] Family Corticoviridae.
Phage PM2 of *Alteromonas espejiana*. [F] Family
Inoviridae. Coliphage X, filamentous and characterized
by extreme flexibility; no envelope. Coliphage X
belongs to the genus *Inovirus*; the genus *Plectrovirus*
consists of phages that are short rods. [G] Family
Microviridae. Coliphage ΦX174. [H] Family
Leviviridae. Coliphages MS2 (free) and R17 (adsorbed
on an F pilus). [I] Family Cystoviridae. Phage Φ6 of
Pseudomonas phaseolicola. Phage has a lipid-containing
envelope surrounding a dodecahedral capsid
(solid with 12 faces; all other cubic phages are icosahedral).

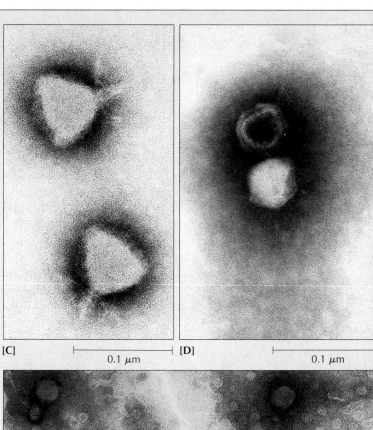

[C]   0.1 μm   [D]   0.1 μm

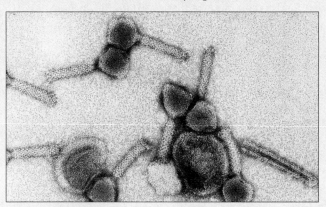

[A]   0.1 μm

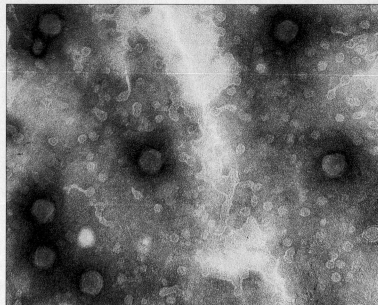

0.1 μm

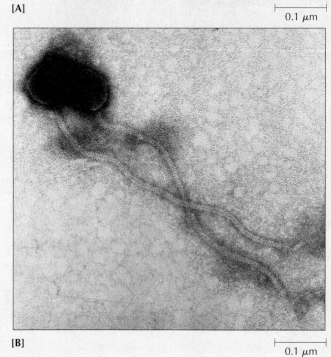

[B]   0.1 μm

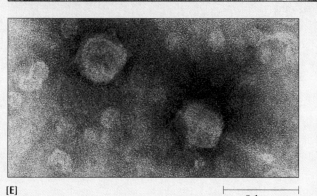

[E]   0.1 μm

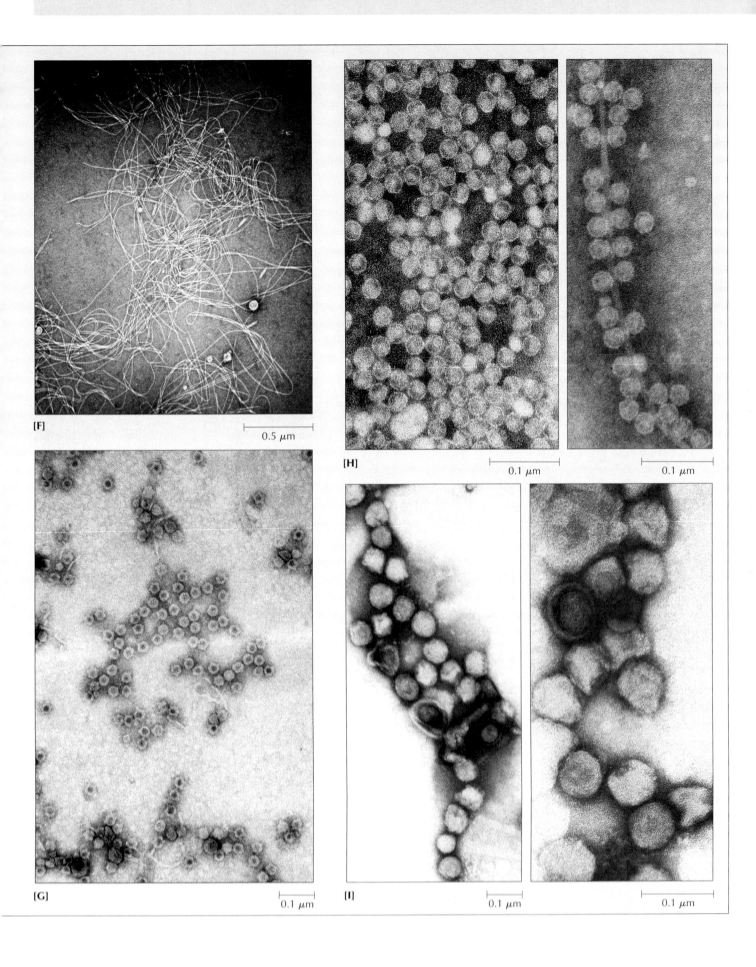

[F]

0.5 μm

[H]

0.1 μm

0.1 μm

[G]

0.1 μm

[I]

0.1 μm

0.1 μm

FIGURE 15.14

Types of transcriptional processes in viruses. Transcription of the viral nucleic acid into viral messenger RNA (*m*RNA) is the key event in viral infection. The *m*RNA is used for synthesis of viral proteins that bring cellular functions to a halt and carry out replication of the viral nucleic acid.

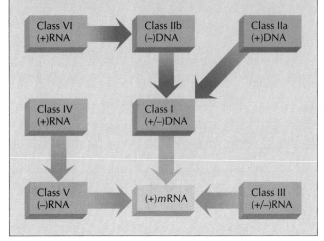

TABLE 15.1

Classification of Viruses Based on Differences in Transcriptional Processes (after Baltimore)

Class	Characteristics
I	Viruses have a double-stranded DNA genome. In this class the designation of (+) and (−) is not meaningful, since different *m*RNA species may be synthesized from either strand.
IIa	Viruses have a single-stranded DNA genome of the same sequence as *m*RNA.
IIb	Viruses have DNA complementary to *m*RNA. Before the synthesis of *m*RNA can proceed, the DNA must be converted to a double-stranded form.
III	Viruses have a double-stranded RNA genome. All known viruses of this type have segmented genomes, but *m*RNA is synthesized on only one strand of each segment.
IV	Viruses have a single-stranded RNA genome of the same sequence as *m*RNA. Synthesis of a complementary strand precedes synthesis of *m*RNA.
V	Viruses have a single-stranded RNA genome which is complementary in base sequence to the *m*RNA.
VI	Viruses have a single-stranded RNA genome and have a DNA intermediate during replication.

ologists who study viruses. But biology-minded virologists prefer a more general approach modeled after Linnaeus' classification scheme, using nomenclature for families, genera, and species. TABLE 15.1 summarizes the Baltimore scheme of classification of viruses based on differences in transcriptional processes.

Bacteriophages of *Escherichia coli*

The most extensively studied group of bacteriophages are the *coliphages,* a name that refers to phages that infect the bacterium *Escherichia coli.* One group of coliphages that infect *E. coli* is designated T1 to T7 ("T" refers to "type"). All the viruses in this group are composed almost exclusively of DNA and protein in approximately equal amounts. Except for T3 and T7, all have tadpole shapes, with polyhedral heads and long tails; the tails of T3 and T7 are very short [see FIGURE 15.12]. The T phages range from about 65 to 200 nm in length and 50 to 80 nm in width. The looped molecule of double-stranded DNA (about 50 *μ*m long, or about 1000 times as long as the phage itself) is tightly packed in the protein head.

Other coliphages have morphology and chemical composition very different from those of the T phages. For example, the f2 phage ("f" for filamentous) is much smaller than the T phages, has a single-stranded linear molecule of RNA rather than DNA, and lacks a tail.

There are also coliphages that possess single-stranded DNA. Morphologically they can be either icosahedral or filamentous. An icosahedral phage with circular single-stranded DNA is *ϕ*X174.

ASK YOURSELF

1 How are common names given to bacteriophages? Are there any guidelines to follow in giving such names?

2 What are the two main criteria used by the ICTV for grouping bacterial viruses into families?

3 Which family includes only one virus?

4 Why did Baltimore propose a scheme of classification based on differences in transcriptional processes?

5 What are the limitations of Baltimore's scheme?

6 Describe the specific pathway of *m*RNA synthesis for each of the six classes of viruses in the Baltimore scheme of viral classification.

7 Describe the T group of coliphages.

BACTERIOPHAGE LIFE CYCLES

There are two main types of bacteriophages: *lytic* (or *virulent*) and *temperate* (or *avirulent*). Lytic phages destroy their host bacterial cells. In the lytic infective process, after replication of the virion, the host cell bursts, or lyses, releasing new progeny phages to infect other host cells. This is called a *lytic cycle.*

Temperate phages do not destroy their host cells. Instead, in the temperate type of infection, the viral nucleic acid is integrated into the host-cell genome and replicated in the host bacterial cells from one generation to another without any cell lysis. This process is called *lysogeny* and is carried out only by phages containing double-stranded DNA. However, under the right circumstances, temperate phages may occasionally become spontaneously lytic in some subsequent generation and lyse the host cells.

The Lytic Life Cycle—Virulent Phages

The basic lytic cycle is shown in FIGURE 15.15, using the T-even coliphages (types with even-numbered names) with double-stranded DNA as a model. It consists of the following six steps:

I. Adsorption (Attachment). The first step in infection of a host bacterial cell by a phage is attachment of the phage to one specific type of bacterial cell [FIGURE 15.15]. The tip of the phage tail becomes adsorbed on the cell at specific receptor sites on the bacterial cell surface. This attachment can take place only when the phage tail and the bacterial receptors have molecular configurations that are complementary to each other, like the key that fits a specific lock. FIGURE 15.16 shows the adsorption of phage T4 on its host by means of its tail. Infection of a host bacterial cell cannot occur without adsorption. Some bacterial mutants, having lost the ability to synthesize specific receptors, become resistant to infection by specific phages.

Initial adsorption of the phage on the receptor is reversible when only the tail fibers are attached to the cell surface. Adsorption soon becomes irreversible when the tail pins attach; this is shown in FIGURE 15.17.

Most filamentous phages (with single-stranded DNA) are adsorbed on the tip of special hollow pili known as the F pili (described in Chapters 4 and 13). Exactly how they enter the cell is still unknown, but it may be that the entire virion is pulled into the cytoplasm via the F pili.

FIGURE 15.15
Typical life cycle of a virulent DNA phage.

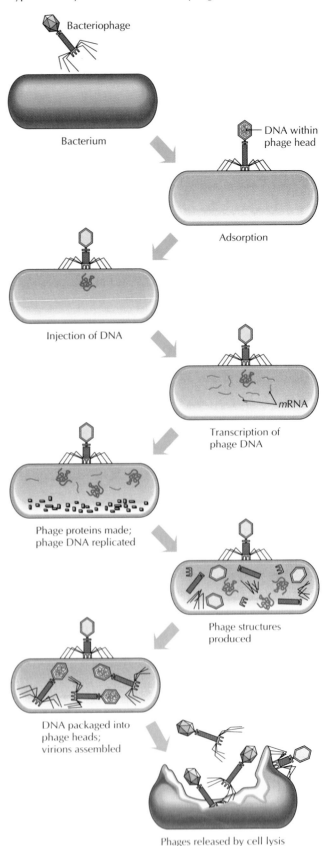

FIGURE 15.16

Phage T4 adsorption and DNA injection into *Escherichia coli* spheroplasts. The phage particles were incubated with the spheroplasts at 37°C for 10 min, negatively stained, and examined under an electron microscope.

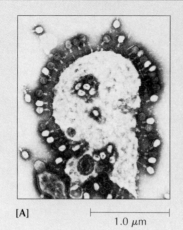

[A]

1.0 μm

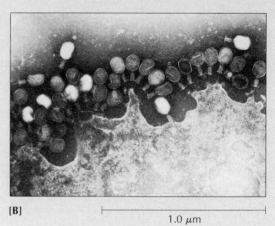

[B]

1.0 μm

FIGURE 15.17

Injection sequence of a tailed phage. In the injection stage, the tail sheath contracts and drives a core protein tube through the cell wall like a hypodermic syringe.

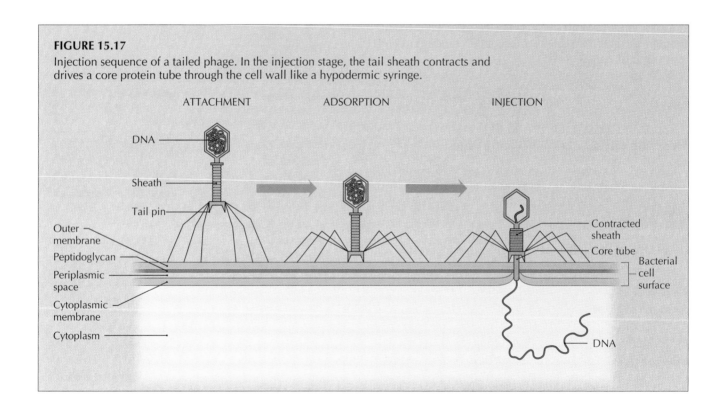

II. Phage Genome Enters Cell. After the phage has attached to the host cell, the DNA in the phage head passes through the cell wall and into the cytoplasm of the bacterium [FIGURE 15.17]. This is accomplished in one of several ways, depending on the phage. In the T-even phages, passage takes place through the following steps:

1 The phage sheath contracts, forcing the tail core tube into the cell through the cell wall and membrane.
2 The DNA in the phage head passes through the tube and into the cytoplasm of the bacterial host cell.

The protein coat, which forms the phage head, and the tail structure remain outside the cell [FIGURE 15.18]. In this process, the nucleic acid injected into the cell is never exposed to the medium outside the host cell.

Phages such as T1 and T5 that do not have a contractile sheath also inject their nucleic acid through the cell envelope, possibly at adhesion sites between the inner and outer membranes. Thus sheath contraction is not a prerequisite for phage infection. With tailless phages, the protein coat may break open and first release its nucleic acid onto the cell wall before the nucleic acid enters the cell.

FIGURE 15.18

Transmission electron micrograph of a cross section of an *Escherichia coli* cell. Phage particles are adsorbed to the cell wall and new T2 phage heads are already synthesized within the cell.

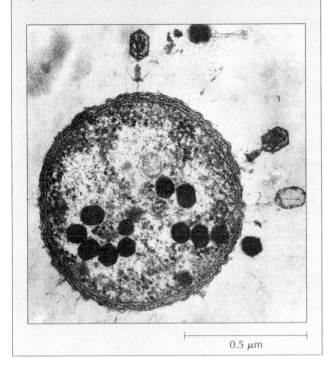

0.5 μm

The filamentous rod-shaped single-stranded DNA phages (such as fd and M13) enter the bacterial cell as discrete virions, without leaving part of their structure outside the cell. As the DNA penetrates into the cell, the capsid protein becomes incorporated into the cell's cytoplasmic membrane and is later reutilized during virus release.

III. Conversion of Host Cell to Phage-Producing Cell.

The synthesis of viral components inside the host cell can be divided into *early* and *late functions*. Early functions are those events that involve the takeover of the host cell and the synthesis of early viral *mRNA* (as discussed in this section). Late functions include the subsequent synthesis of other proteins and assembly of the nucleocapsid. Enzymes made early in the life cycle (such as nucleases and DNA-dependent RNA polymerase) are called *early proteins*. The proteins made late in the life cycle (the *late proteins*) are different from the early proteins and include both enzymes and structural proteins (such as those in phage heads, tails, and tail fibers). The early proteins are encoded in early *mRNA*, and the structural proteins are encoded in late *mRNA*.

Within a few minutes of entry of phage DNA, the bacterial host loses the ability either to replicate or to transcribe its own DNA; sometimes it loses both abilities. This shutdown of bacterial DNA or RNA synthesis is carried out in different ways, depending on the phage species. For example, host DNA may be quickly degraded to small fragments, dispersing and thus becoming inactivated.

The phage directs the bacterial synthesis of copies of phage nucleic acid, using several mechanisms and the bacterium's replication proteins. Transcription of phage *mRNA* from the phage DNA is almost always initiated by the host-cell RNA polymerase, which recognizes the viral promoter that governs the transcription of the genes coding for viral protein synthesis. For the most part, the phage *mRNA* codes for nucleases that break down host DNA. This makes the nucleotides of the host DNA available for phage DNA synthesis. After the first phage *mRNA* is made, either the host-cell polymerase is modified to recognize the other viral promoters, or a special phage-specific RNA polymerase is synthesized.

In the filamentous phages, the entering single-stranded DNA (the *plus* DNA strand) serves as a template for synthesis of its complementary strand (the *minus* DNA strand). The cell's DNA polymerase is used, since this process takes place before transcription of *mRNA* begins. The resulting double-stranded DNA is the replicative form from which multiple copies of the plus strand are synthesized, using the minus strand as a template.

RNA-containing phages differ from DNA-containing phages with respect to use of host replication enzymes. RNA phages must code their own replication enzymes, because the host cell does not have enzymes that replicate RNA. A phage that contains single-stranded RNA uses the RNA as a plus strand (as *mRNA* for the synthesis of RNA polymerase and other proteins). The RNA polymerase makes a *minus* RNA strand (replicative strand) using the viral genome (the *plus* RNA strand) as a template. The replicative strand (the *minus* RNA strand) is used as a template to make numerous viral plus RNA strands, which combine with coat protein to form many infectious virions [FIGURE 15.19].

Thus viral transcription, which produces viral *mRNA* from viral nucleic acid, represents the key event in viral infection—when control of biochemical synthesis by cellular genes is switched to control by viral genes.

IV. Production of Phage Nucleic Acid and Proteins.

Nucleic acid replication, which follows early protein synthesis, serves as the demarcation line between early and late functions in the viral replication process. Since late *mRNA* is not synthesized until after viral nucleic acid replication has begun, it is transcribed from viral progeny genomes. This means that late protein synthesis takes place after nucleic acid replication. Translation of *mRNA* into proteins takes place in the host-cell cyto-

FIGURE 15.19
Life cycle of a single-stranded plus RNA phage.

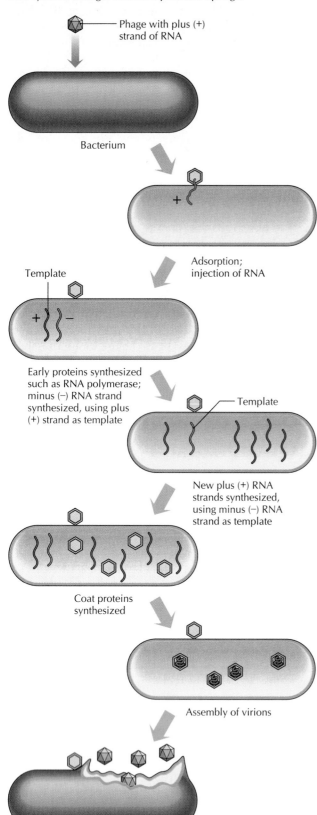

Phage with plus (+) strand of RNA

Bacterium

Adsorption;
injection of RNA

Template

Early proteins synthesized such as RNA polymerase; minus (−) RNA strand synthesized, using plus (+) strand as template

Template

New plus (+) RNA strands synthesized, using minus (−) RNA strand as template

Coat proteins synthesized

Assembly of virions

Release of virions by cell lysis

plasm and uses ribosomes, transfer RNAs, and enzymes found in the cytoplasm. (If the *m*RNA is synthesized in the nucleus of the host cell, it first passes to the cell cytoplasm before translation.)

Toward the end of the replication cycle, the phages synthesize late proteins, including the structural proteins necessary for virion self-assembly, enzymes involved in the maturation process, and enzymes used in the release of phages from the bacterial cell [see FIGURE 15.15].

V. Assembly of Phage Particles. Two kinds of late proteins are required for phage assembly: *structural* proteins of the phage particle and *enzymes* that catalyze reactions of the assembly process but do not become integral parts of the bacteriophage. Assembly of icosahedral phages takes place in several steps [see FIGURE 15.15]:

1 Aggregation of phage structural proteins to form a head and a tail (if needed). At this time, the tail is not attached to the head.
2 Condensation of the nucleic acid and entry into a preformed head.
3 Attachment of the tail to a packed head.

About 25 min after initial infection of a host cell, usually 50 to 1000 phage particles have been assembled [FIGURE 15.20], the number depending on the particular species and the growth conditions of the culture.

VI. Release of Assembled Phages. One of the late proteins synthesized in the lytic cycle of infection is an enzyme called an **endolysin**. This enzyme lyses the bacterial cell and releases the mature phages.

Host cells infected with filamentous phages generally do not release assembled phages by lysis; instead, they release phage particles continuously by outfolding of the cell wall. As the viral DNA is extended through the membrane, it picks up protein molecules (newly synthesized as well as those derived initially from the infecting virions). Such an extrusion process does not cause damage to the cell, which can continue to produce bacteriophages for a long time.

The Lysogenic Life Cycle—Temperate Phages

Lysogeny is an alternative life cycle exhibited by some bacteriophages. A good part of our knowledge on lysogeny comes from studies of *Escherichia coli* phage lambda (λ). Phage λ is one of a class of phages that can utilize either a lytic or a lysogenic life cycle. Each virion of phage λ consists of a straight molecule of double-stranded DNA packed in a polyhedral capsid with a tail through which the DNA enters the host bacterium.

FIGURE 15.20
The intracellular location of assembled phages is seen in this electron micrograph of a thin section of an *Escherichia coli* cell just prior to cell lysis. Note the hexagonal shape of the phage particles in the middle of the cell.

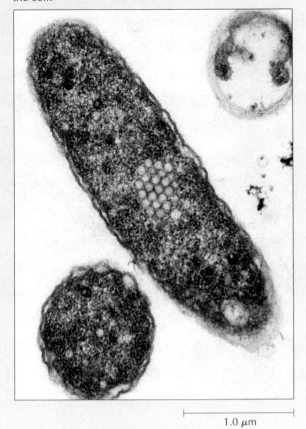

1.0 μm

III. Integration of Viral DNA. The phage DNA joins with the DNA in the bacterial chromosome and is inserted into it by the action of a phage-coded DNA-insertion enzyme (coded by the *int* gene). Integrated in this way, the viral genome is now called a ***prophage.***

Phage DNA is inserted at a certain position in the *E. coli* chromosome, between the *gal* (galactose) and *bio* (biotin) genes. During this insertion, the phage DNA forms a circle, followed by physical breakage and rejoining of phage and host DNA. This mechanism is shown schematically in FIGURE 15.22.

Other temperate phages have their own sites of integration on the bacterial chromosome. However, some temperate phages, such as phage Mu, have no specific site for insertion and may be able to insert multiple copies of their DNA at various sites in a single bacterial chromosome. Wherever insertion occurs, inactivation of the specific bacterial gene at that location gives rise to a *mu*tant host cell; hence, the phage name Mu.

IV. Attainment of Lysogeny. The bacterial host cell remains alive and continues to grow and multiply, despite having a prophage integrated among its own genes. The phage genes replicate as part of the bacterial chromosome.

Continued production of the repressor maintains the integrated prophage condition in the lysogenic cells. If at any time the repressor is inactivated (e.g., by a protease enzyme induced by exposure to ultraviolet light), the phage operons become derepressed and start functioning, and the phage enters the lytic cycle and destroys its host cell. Thus a single repressor gene decides the fate of both the bacterial cell and the phage.

The lysogenic cycle of phage λ is shown in FIGURE 15.21 and consists of the following four steps:

I. Entry of Phage Genome into Cell. The DNA molecule from the phage passes into the bacterial host cell via the same process described for lytic bacteria and becomes a closed circle.

II. Synthesis of Early Protein. A brief period of *m*RNA synthesis by the host cell is necessary in order to synthesize a repressor protein coded by the phage DNA. This protein inhibits the synthesis of the specific *m*RNA that encodes the lytic functions. The crucial regulatory test here is how fast a critical level of the specific repressor can be synthesized. The outcome determines whether the phage will undergo a lytic or a lysogenic cycle. If sufficient repressor is present, it blocks the transcription of all other phage genes. As a consequence, none of the virion proteins is made, and the cell does not lyse.

Nonintegrative Lysogeny

Most temperate phages enter the lysogenic cycle in the way just described for phage λ—namely, insertion of a prophage at a unique site on the bacterial host chromosome. There is another, less common type of lysogeny in which there is no DNA-insertion system and the phage DNA becomes a *plasmid*, or independently replicating circular DNA molecule, rather than part of the host chromosome. *Escherichia coli* phage P1 typically carries out this type of lysogenic life cycle. Following infection, the DNA of P1 circularizes and is repressed, but unlike the DNA of phage λ, it remains as a free DNA molecule in the cytoplasm. During the bacterial life cycle the P1 DNA replicates once, at a time that coincides with the bacterium's chromosomal replication (the coupling of the two events is controlled by a phage gene). When the bacterial cell divides, each daughter cell receives a P1 plasmid. How this orderly assortment is accomplished is still not known.

FIGURE 15.21
The lysogenic and lytic life cycles of bacteriophage λ.
The frequency of spontaneous induction is about 1 in 10⁵.

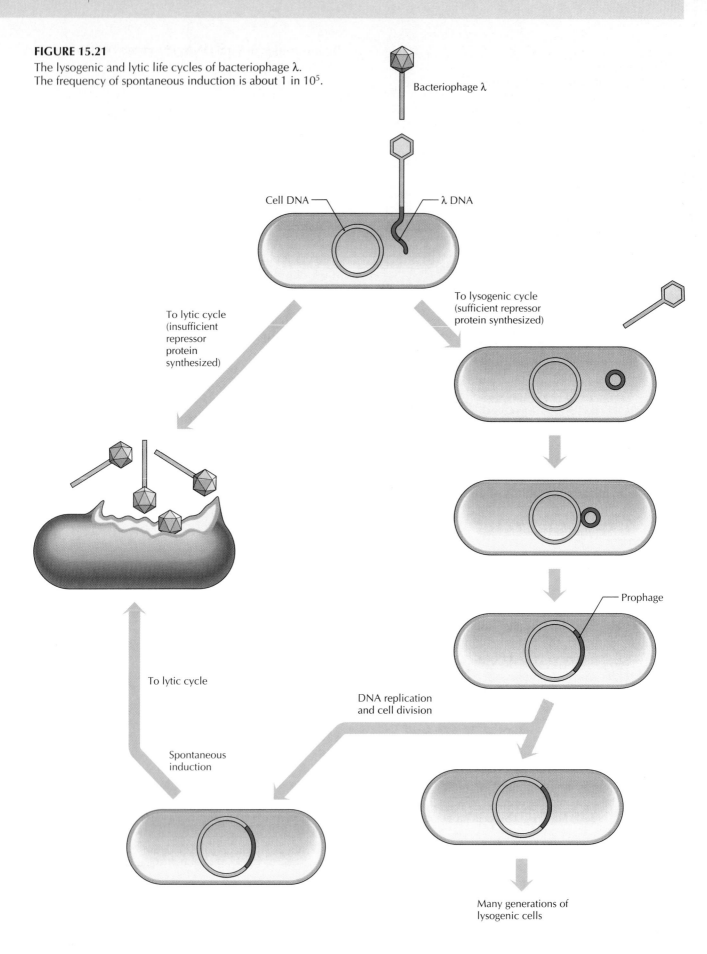

Bacteriophage λ

Cell DNA

λ DNA

To lytic cycle
(insufficient
repressor
protein
synthesized)

To lysogenic cycle
(sufficient repressor
protein synthesized)

Prophage

DNA replication
and cell division

To lytic cycle

Spontaneous
induction

Many generations of
lysogenic cells

FIGURE 15.22

The mechanism of insertion of phage λ DNA into the host *Escherichia coli* chromosome. The linear phage DNA (*A* and *R* represent the ends of the linear molecule) is first converted into a covalently closed ring before insertion. The phage attachment site has been denoted *POP'*; the bacterial attachment site is *BOB'*. After insertion the prophage is flanked by two new attachment sites labeled *BOP'* and *POB'*. (Excision results in a replicative form of phage λ.)

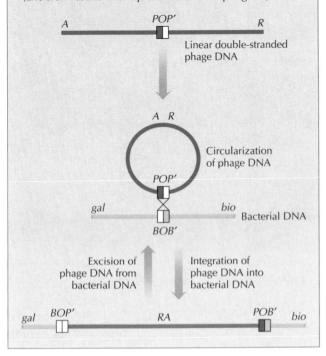

ASK YOURSELF

1 What are the two main types of bacteriophages?

2 Does infection with a temperate phage mean that the host cell is forever safe from lysis?

3 Distinguish between early functions and late functions in the infection of a host cell by a virion.

4 What process serves as the demarcation line between early and late functions in the viral replication process?

5 What regulatory process determines whether a phage undergoes a lytic or a lysogenic cycle?

6 When is the phage genome considered a prophage?

MORPHOLOGY AND CHEMICAL COMPOSITION OF ANIMAL AND PLANT VIRUSES

Plant and animal viruses do not have the familiar tadpole shape of *some* bacteriophages. Instead, they vary greatly in size [see FIGURE 15.8] and shape [FIGURES 15.23 and 15.24]. In fact, size and morphology are characteristic properties of each kind of virus.

FIGURE 15.23

Electron micrographs of some plant viruses. **[A]** Potato virus X particles appear as flexuous rods. Also shown are two latex spheres used in electron microscopy to show relative sizes. **[B]** Tomato ringspot virus is icosahedral in morphology. **[C, D]** Tobacco rattle virus particles appear as both long and short rods. Particles of both lengths are necessary to establish infection.

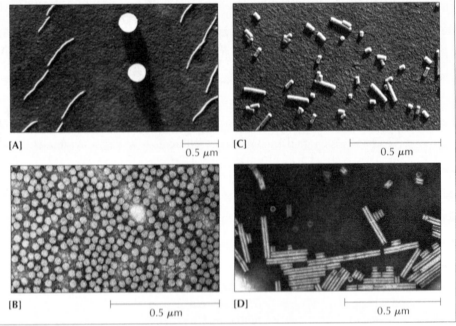

FIGURE 15.24
Electron micrographs of some animal viruses. [A] An adenovirus with icosahedral morphology. [B] An enveloped icosahedral herpesvirus. [C] Ebola viruses (which cause hemorrhagic fever) are pleomorphic, filamentous virions that exhibit a variety of bizarre cylindrical and fishhooklike forms. Their length varies considerably from 130 nm to up to 14,000 nm. Prominent cross striations are also seen.

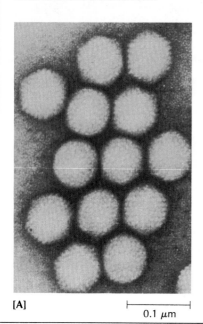
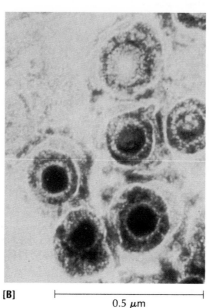
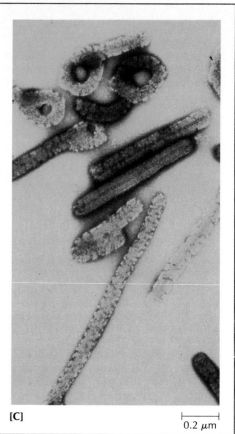

[A] |—— 0.1 μm ——| [B] |———— 0.5 μm ————| [C] |—— 0.2 μm ——|

Morphology

Animal and plant viruses that appear polyhedral or spherical have *icosahedral* symmetry, with a basic framework that is an icosahedron, as described previously. Viruses with *helical* symmetry have a capsid whose capsomeres are packed as a spiral around the nucleic acid to form a helix [see FIGURE 15.2B]. Plant viruses with helical symmetry appear as rods [see FIGURE 15.5]. The causative agents of measles, mumps, influenza, and rabies have helical symmetry.

In addition to those with helical or icosahedral symmetry, there also are plant and animal viruses with complex or uncertain symmetries. These viruses have nucleic acid within the virion core; either there is no discrete structure enclosing the nucleic acid or the nucleic acid is surrounded by multiple unique membranes.

Chemical Composition

In addition to a nucleic acid core, the majority of animal viruses and many plant viruses have a protein capsid enclosed by an envelope made of lipids, proteins, and carbohydrates [see FIGURE 15.1]. (Only a few phage groups have a lipid-containing envelope.) The envelope has surface projections, or spikes, made of glycoprotein [see FIGURE 15.6]. These projections may be important in viral attachment to host cells, and are studied as possible components of viral vaccines. Virions that have envelopes can be destroyed by lipid solvents such as ether and chloroform. The infectivity of these viruses is thus inactivated by these chemical solvents. Nonenveloped virions are referred to as *naked* virions; their capacity to infect cells is not affected by lipid solvents.

Whether or not they have an envelope, most viruses have symmetrical shapes [see FIGURE 15.8].

ASK YOURSELF

1 What are the basic shapes of plant and animal viruses?

2 When are animal viruses considered "naked"?

3 What are capsomeres?

TABLE 15.2
Properties Used for Classification of Viruses

Primary characteristics	Secondary characteristics
Chemical nature of nucleic acid: RNA or DNA; single- or double-stranded; single or segmented genome; (+) or (−) strand; molecular weight	Host range: Host species; specific host tissues or cell types
Structure of virion: Helical, icosahedral, or complex; naked or enveloped; complexity; number of capsomeres for icosahedral virions; diameter of nucleocapsids for helical viruses	Mode of transmission: e.g., feces
Site of replication: Nucleus or cytoplasm	Specific surface structures: e.g., antigenic properties

CLASSIFICATION AND NOMENCLATURE OF ANIMAL AND PLANT VIRUSES

There have been many classification schemes for animal and plant viruses used through the years. One of the earliest methods, still in limited use, based classification on the kind of host the viruses normally infect (e.g., hog cholera virus, swine influenza virus, fowl plague virus, cucumber mosaic virus, tobacco mosaic virus). Another early scheme relied on the tissue affinities of the virus; for example, viruses that attached to nerve cells were called *neurotropic* viruses and those specific for skin were called *dermatotropic* viruses. This method was useful for physicians, epidemiologists, and some allied health investigators. However, as knowledge of the physical, chemical, and biological characteristics of viruses has accumulated, classification schemes based on more fundamental biological properties have been formulated. Such properties are summarized in TABLE 15.2.

System of Classification Based on Physical, Chemical, and Biological Characteristics

Physical, chemical, and biological characteristics of viruses have been used by the International Committee on Taxonomy of Viruses (ICTV) to classify viruses. Like the bacterial virologists, animal virologists have subscribed to a nomenclature for various taxa. Family names agreed upon end in *-viridae*, subfamily names in *-virinae*, and genera, like species, in *-virus*. Prefixes to the family endings connote descriptions of the family characteristics. For example, Picornaviridae means small (*pico*) RNA viruses; Hepadnaviridae means "causing liver disease" (*hepa*) DNA viruses. Other family names refer to historical origins.

However, the plant virologists have not classified their viruses in a similar manner. They use *groups* of viruses (instead of families and genera) that share similar properties. Names for these groups are usually derived from the name of the prototype, or most representative member, of the group. For example, the name of the group of viruses related to tobacco mosaic virus is the *tobamo* group or *tobamoviruses*.

TABLE 15.3 shows the classification of viruses that infect animals arranged according to symmetry and in descending order of size. FIGURES 15.25 and 15.26 are line drawings showing how basic morphology is used to classify animal and plant viruses. An alternative system of classification, the Baltimore scheme summarized in TABLE 15.1, has already been described.

ASK YOURSELF

1 What characteristics are used to classify animal and plant viruses in the classification schemes of the ICTV?

2 How is the nomenclature of plant viruses different from that of bacterial and animal viruses?

3 Name a well-known member in each of the families or groups of animal and plant viruses.

TABLE 15.3
Classification of Viruses Infecting Humans and Other Animals

Capsid symmetry	Envelope (genome)	Virion diameter (nm)	Family	Typical genera or subfamilies	Typical viruses	Assembly site (envelopment site)
Icosahedral	No (dsDNA)	70–90	Adenoviridae	*Mastadenovirus*	Human adeno 2	Nucleus
Icosahedral	No (dsRNA)	65–75	Reoviridae	*Reovirus* *Rotavirus*	Reovirus Rotavirus	Cytoplasm
Icosahedral	No (dsDNA)	45–55	Papovaviridae	*Polyomavirus* *Papillomavirus*	SV 40 Wart viruses	Nucleus
Icosahedral	No (ssRNA)	30–37	Caliciviridae	*Calicivirus*	Calicivirus	Cytoplasm
Icosahedral	No (ssRNA)	24–30	Picornaviridae	*Enterovirus* *Rhinovirus*	Polio Coxsackievirus Common cold	Cytoplasm
Icosahedral	No (ssDNA)	18–26	Parvoviridae	*Parvovirus*	Kilham rat	Nucleus
Icosahedral	Yes (dsDNA)	120–200	Herpesviridae	Alphaherpesvirinae	Herpes simplex	Nucleus (nuclear membrane and/or cytoplasm)
Icosahedral	Yes (ssRNA)	80–140	Retroviridae	Oncovirinae	RNA tumor	Cytoplasm (plasma membrane and/or cytoplasm)
Icosahedral	Yes (ssRNA)	40–70	Togaviridae	*Rubivirus*	Rubella	Cytoplasm (plasma membrane or cytoplasm)
Icosahedral	Yes (dsDNA)	42	Hepadnaviridae		Hepatitis B	Nucleus (cytoplasm)
Helical	Yes (ssRNA)	130–300 × 50–100	Rhabdoviridae	*Vesiculovirus* *Lyssavirus*	Vesicular stomatitis Rabies	Cytoplasm (cytoplasm and/or plasma membrane)
Helical	Yes (ssRNA)	100–150	Paramyxoviridae	*Paramyxovirus*	Mumps	Cytoplasm (plasma membrane)
Helical	Yes (ssRNA)	80–120	Orthomyxoviridae	*Influenzavirus*	Influenza	Cytoplasm (plasma membrane)
Helical	Yes (ssRNA)	75–160	Coronaviridae	*Coronavirus*	Coronavirus	Cytoplasm (cytoplasm)
Helical	Yes (ssRNA)	90–120	Bunyaviridae	*Bunyavirus*	Bunyamwera	Cytoplasm (cytoplasm)
Complex or uncertain	Yes (dsDNA)	200–350 × 115–260	Poxviridae	*Orthopoxvirus*	Variola	Cytoplasm (cytoplasm)
Complex or uncertain	Yes (ssRNA)	50–300	Arenaviridae	*Arenavirus*	Lassa	Cytoplasm (plasma membrane and/or cytoplasm)

REPLICATION OF ANIMAL AND PLANT VIRUSES

Basic differences between replication of bacteriophages and replication of animal and plant viruses were pointed out earlier in this chapter. The following sections discuss the replication of animal viruses in more detail and point out how this process differs from plant virus replication.

Attachment (Adsorption)

A prerequisite step in the viral infective process of animal and bacterial cells is *attachment*, or adsorption, of the virion on specific receptor sites on the surface of a susceptible cell. A cell lacking a receptor for a specific virus is not infected by that virus.

For naked virions, the surface capsid proteins are probably responsible for binding to a specific cell recep-

FIGURE 15.25

Line drawings of the families of viruses infecting vertebrates. All diagrams have been drawn to the same scale. For each drawing the family name is given together with a well-known member of it (but the dimensions and shape used for the drawing may not be exactly those of the virus named).

THE FAMILIES OF VIRUSES INFECTING VERTEBRATES

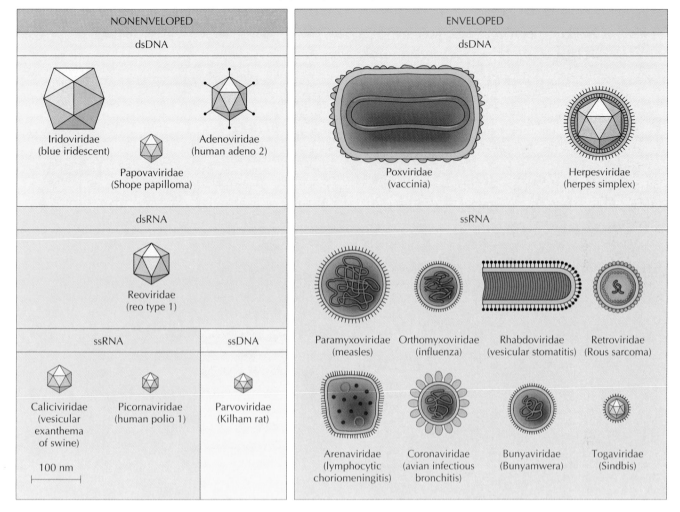

tor. For enveloped virions, the surface glycoproteins of the envelope membrane (the spikes) are responsible for recognition of a cell surface receptor, which is followed by attachment.

This specific virion-cell interaction explains why certain virions infect only particular types of cells. For example, the influenza virus infects epithelial cells of the upper respiratory tract, and the human immunodeficiency virus (HIV) invades specific cells in the body, including white blood cells called CD4 lymphocytes. In contrast to specific adsorption of animal and bacterial viruses on certain cell types, plant viruses do not appear to require specific receptor sites to attach to cells.

Penetration

The second step in the viral infective process is *penetration* of the virion into the host cell. The virions of a few viruses such as poliovirus undergo a structural change so that their free nucleic acid is released directly into the cytoplasm. But most enveloped viruses enter the host cell by fusion of the host-cell membrane and the viral envelope [FIGURE 15.27]. This releases the naked nucleocapsid into the cell cytoplasm. Some enveloped and most nonenveloped virions are engulfed within the host cell in a membrane-bounded vacuole. Then these nucle-

FIGURE 15.26
Line drawings of the families and groups of viruses infecting plants. All diagrams have been drawn to the same scale. For each drawing the group name is given together with a well-known member of it (but the dimensions and shape used for the drawing may not be exactly those of the virus named).

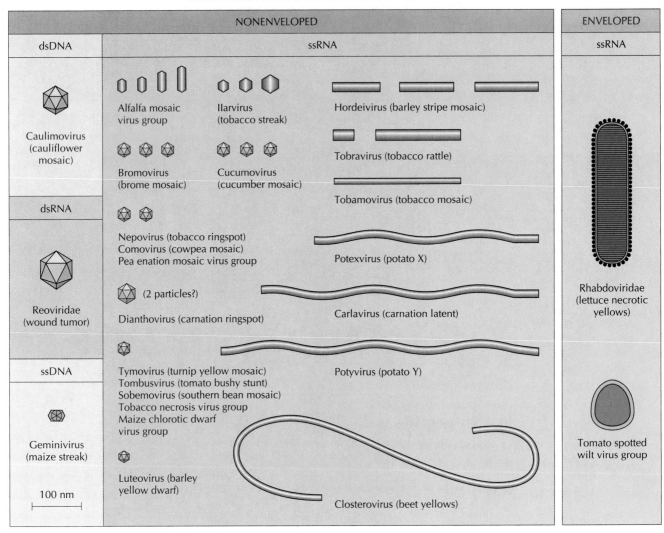

ocapsids are released into the cytoplasm by one of the mechanisms illustrated in FIGURE 15.28.

The viral nucleic acid must then be released from the capsid so that it becomes available for transcription, translation, and replication. To release the nucleic acid, some viruses are uncoated in the phagocytic vacuoles in the host cell by the action of host-cell enzymes. These enzymes digest the capsid, freeing the viral nucleic acid. Depending on the virus, uncoating occurs within the vacuoles, in the cytoplasm, or in the nucleus. In most cases, the uncoating process is poorly understood.

Penetration of plant cells is complicated by the presence of the thick wall surrounding the cell. Probably the most important way in which plant viruses penetrate this wall is by insects. Insects that have the viruses on their mouth parts or that harbor them within their tissues can inoculate these viruses directly into plant cells during feeding. Plant viruses may also penetrate plant cell walls by means of the scattered pores that extend through the wall. These pores normally allow water and nutrients to pass into the cell; they are also used by the cell to excrete substances such as waxes.

FIGURE 15.27
Penetration of virion into host cell by fusion of viral envelope and cell membrane. The nucleocapsid is released directly into the cell cytoplasm.

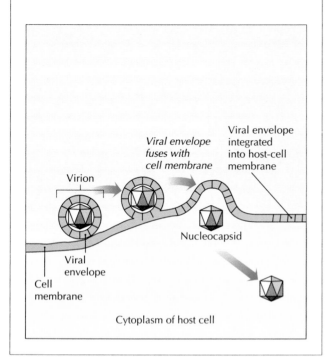

FIGURE 15.28
Penetration of a virion into a host cell by vacuolar ingestion. **[A]** With an enveloped virus, the virus envelope adsorbs on the cell membrane and the entire virion is engulfed in a vacuole, which then fuses with a lysosome to form a vesicle. The viral envelope then fuses with the vesicle membrane, releasing the nucleocapsid into the cell cytoplasm. **[B]** With a nonenveloped virus, the naked virion is engulfed in a temporary vacuole. The vacuole membrane fuses with an internal membrane system (Golgi complex or endoplasmic reticulum), releasing the free nucleocapsid.

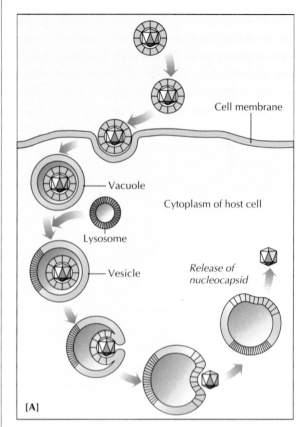

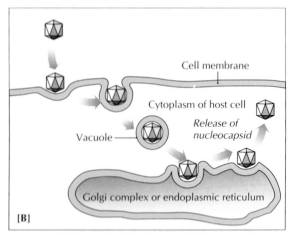

Biosynthesis of Virus Components

As is the case for bacteriophages, the biosynthesis of animal and plant viruses within the host cell can be divided into *early* and *late functions*. You will recall that early functions are those biochemical events that take over the host cell and synthesize early viral *m*RNA. Late functions are those that later synthesize other proteins and assemble the nucleocapsid.

Maturation and Assembly

When a critical number of the various viral components have been synthesized, they are assembled into mature virus particles in the nucleus and/or cytoplasm of the infected cell. The time period from the uncoating until the assembly of new, mature virions is referred to as the *eclipse* period, because if the host cell is broken open during this period no infectious virus is found. The same is true in the bacteriophage life cycles. However, unlike that of bacteriophages, the process of *assembly* does not appear to involve special biosynthetic enzymes, but

FIGURE 15.29

Replication of herpes simplex virus. Specific glycoproteins in the viral envelope are essential for optimal adsorption on host cell receptors in the cytoplasmic membrane. The viral envelope and cell membrane fuse, and the nucleocapsid of the virion is released into the cytoplasm. The virion is uncoated and the freed viral DNA is transported to the nucleus. Early transcription and *m*RNA processing are apparently catalyzed by host-cell enzymes. The resulting enzymes (early proteins) are used in viral DNA replication. Nuclear RNA transcripts synthesized after DNA replication are responsible for the synthesis of structural proteins that go to form the capsid and envelope as well as the glycoproteins in the nuclear membrane. The structural proteins enter the nucleus to participate in the assembly of the virions. The nucleocapsids are enveloped by budding through the nuclear membrane. The virus is released from the cell by unknown mechanisms.

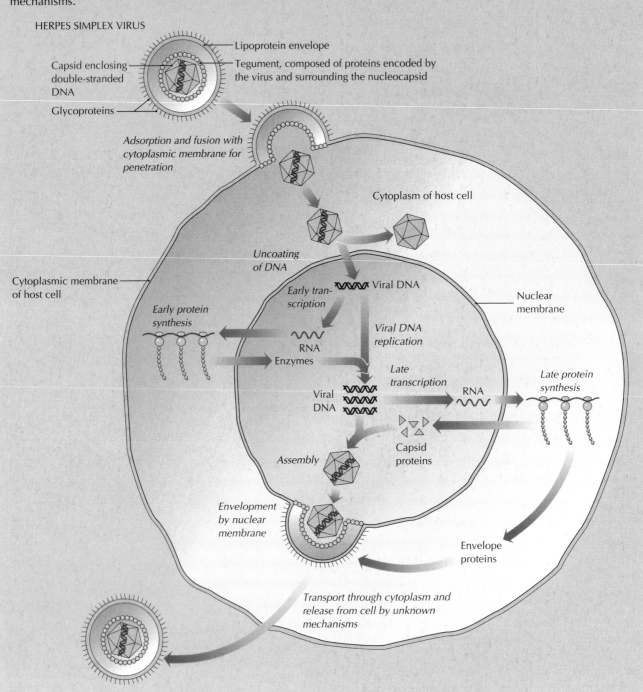

rather occurs spontaneously as a result of the highly specific molecular interaction of capsid macromolecules with the viral nucleic acid. Thus *maturation* may be defined as that phase of viral infection during which structural components of the virion are produced and assembled together with the newly replicated viral nucleic acid to form the nucleocapsid structure.

Release

Release of the mature virions from the host cell is the final step in viral multiplication. The mechanism of release varies with the type of virus. In some animal virus infections, the host cells disintegrate, releasing the virions. Naked virions are generally released in a burstlike fashion (all at once) as the cells disintegrate, or lyse. Alternatively, they may be extruded from the cell over a period of time by *exocytosis*, a process that is essentially the reverse of the penetration process shown in FIGURE 15.28B. With a few naked animal and plant viruses, the host cells are not destroyed. The virions leave the cells by special channels (tubules) over an extended period of time.

Enveloped animal viruses (and presumably enveloped plant viruses) are released by *budding* through special areas of the host-cell membrane coded for by the virus. In this process the virions acquire a portion of the host membrane. Budding may take place along the cytoplasmic membrane, the nuclear membrane, or even other intracytoplasmic membranes. It involves a protrusion outward, or *bud*, by a membrane that is associated with a nucleocapsid. This protrusion soon pinches off to form a closed sac that completely surrounds the nucleocapsid. Then the bud is excised by the action of special enzymes on the envelope surface. For example, the spikes that project from the envelope of influenza viruses are composed of a releasing enzyme called *neuraminidase* [see FIGURE 15.6]. If a virion becomes enveloped by budding at the cytoplasmic membrane, it is automatically released from the cell at the same time. If the envelope comes from internal membranes, the mature virus is usually released by exocytosis or through special channels. Poxviruses appear to acquire their envelope *de novo* by biosynthesis within the cytoplasm.

The yield of virus particles per cell varies with the virus, the type of cell, and the growth conditions. The average yield of plant and animal virions ranges from several thousand to about 1 million per cell, compared with a yield of only several hundred phages from a bacterial cell.

As an example of the viral replicative process in the eucaryotic cell, FIGURE 15.29 illustrates the replication of the herpes simplex virus, which is the cause of "fever blisters" ("cold sores") and genital herpes. As you can see in the figure, the events related to biosynthesis occur in both the nucleus and the cytoplasm, with assembly of the virion initiated in the nucleus. The nucleocapsids of these viruses then migrate to the cytoplasmic membrane (after envelopment by budding through the nuclear membrane). There the mature enveloped viruses apparently reach the surface of the cell through cytoplasmic channels.

ASK YOURSELF

1 Describe the adsorption or attachment of animal viruses to host cells.

2 Describe the process by which most enveloped animal viruses enter the host cell.

3 How do plant viruses penetrate into host cells?

4 What is meant by the maturation phase of viral infection?

5 How does the yield of virus particles per cell compare between bacteriophages and animal and plant viruses?

6 Describe the replication cycle of the herpes simplex virus.

430

SUMMARY

1 Viruses are noncellular infectious entities whose genomes are either DNA or RNA. They replicate only in living cells, using the cell's own biosynthetic machinery to make more viruses, which then infect other cells. Viruses consist of a nucleic acid core surrounded by a protein coat, or capsid.

2 Twort and d'Hérelle discovered bacterial viruses in 1915 and 1917, respectively. The word *bacteriophage,* coined by d'Hérelle, means "bacteria eater." The three basic morphological forms of phages are: icosahedral with no tail, icosahedral with tail, and filamentous.

3 The common names of phages are code symbols. Scientific names are given to families of phages grouped together on the basis of particle morphology and chemical composition.

4 There are two main types of phages: lytic and temperate. The lytic life cycle goes through the following stages: adsorption, genome entry, conversion of host cell into a phage-producing "factory," production of phage nucleic acid and proteins, assembly of phage particles, and release of mature phages.

5 Temperate phages may undergo either a lytic cycle or a lysogenic cycle. The lysogenic life cycle goes through these stages: adsorption, genome entry, phage *m*RNA synthesis to form a repressor protein, insertion of phage DNA into the bacterial chromosome, and prophage replication as part of the bacterial chromosome. In another type of lysogeny, the phage DNA remains as a plasmid in the host cytoplasm.

6 Capsids of plant and animal viruses are usually icosahedral or helical, although there are some with more complex or uncertain symmetry. The majority of animal viruses and many plant viruses is enclosed by an envelope made of lipids, proteins, and carbohydrates.

7 Animal and plant viral replication takes place in the following steps: attachment, penetration, biosynthesis of viral components, maturation and assembly, and release.

8 In addition to the phage classification system mentioned previously, viruses may be classified on the basis of physical, chemical, and biological characteristics, a system established by the International Committee on Taxonomy of Viruses. Alternatively, viruses may be grouped into six classes based on differences in transcriptional processes (the Baltimore scheme).

KEY TERMS

avirulent
bacteriophages (phages)
capsid
capsomeres
coliphages
early functions
early proteins
endolysin
late functions
late proteins
lysed
lysogeny
lytic
lytic cycle
nucleocapsid
prophage
protomers
replication
temperate
virion
virology
virulent
viruses (singular, virus)

GENERAL CHARACTERISTICS OF VIRUSES

1 Viruses can replicate only within a metabolizing host cell, using the

_____-synthesizing and _____

-generating systems of the cell.

2 Viruses that infect bacteria are called _____, or

_____.

3 The protein coat of viruses also serves as a vehicle for entry into another host cell

because it binds to _____ on cell surfaces.

4 Virions range in size from _____ to

_____ nm.

5 Viruses are composed of a central core of _____ sur-

rounded by a protein coat called a(n) _____.

6 The two symmetries of viral capsids are _____ and

_____.

7 In viral capsids, the viral proteins called _____ form the

clusters known as _____, which are visible by electron
microscopy.

8 Unlike that in plant and animal cells, the nucleic acid of a virion can only be

_____ or _____.

9 Which of the following features are true of the SV 40 genome? **(a)** linear nucleic
acid strands; **(b)** circular nucleic acid strands; **(c)** dsDNA; **(d)** ssDNA; **(e)** ssRNA.

10 Plus-strand RNA can serve directly as _____.

11 The retroviruses contain an enzyme called _____ that
synthesizes a DNA strand, using the viral RNA genome as a template.

THE DISCOVERY OF BACTERIOPHAGES

12 The phenomenon of bacterial lysis by a filtrate is called the

_____ phenomenon, in honor of the discoverers.

13 The word *bacteriophage* means _____.

MORPHOLOGY AND CHEMICAL COMPOSITION OF BACTERIOPHAGES

14 All phages have a(n) _____ core covered by a(n)

_____ capsid.

15 The genetic material of phages may consist of either DNA or

_____.

16 The three basic morphological forms of bacteriophages are (1) icosahedral head

with a tail, (2) icosahedral head with no tail, and (3) _____.

CLASSIFICATION AND NOMENCLATURE OF BACTERIOPHAGES

17 Match each description on the right with the correct phage family on the left.

_____ Siphoviridae

_____ Cystoviridae

_____ Myoviridae

_____ Inoviridae

_____ Microviridae

(a) Has one virus member
(b) Has over 1200 virus members
(c) ϕX174 is a member
(d) Long-tailed phages
(e) Filamentous phages

In items 18 through 20, indicate whether the statement is true (**T**) *or false* (**F**). *If the statement is false, rewrite it as true.*

18 The common names of bacteriophages follow the rules of viral nomenclature and are binomial. _____

_____

_____

19 Fewer than 20 percent of the known viruses infecting eubacteria belong to one of the four families of long-tailed phages. _____

_____

_____

20 The T3 and T7 phages are tadpole-shaped and have very short tails. _____

_____

_____

21 Which one of the following criteria is *not* used by the International Committee on Taxonomy of Viruses to classify viruses? **(a)** biological characteristics; **(b)** chemical characteristics; **(c)** physical characteristics; **(d)** differences in transcriptional processes; **(e)** none of the above.

22 A system of classification based on how the viral genome is replicated and expressed was proposed by a Nobel laureate named _____.

23 Which class of viruses (Baltimore scheme) has an ssRNA genome and a DNA intermediate during replication? **(a)** class I; **(b)** class IV; **(c)** class V; **(d)** class VI.

BACTERIOPHAGE LIFE CYCLES

24 Which term is *not* descriptive of bacteriophage types? **(a)** lytic; **(b)** temperate; **(c)** avirulent; **(d)** lysogenic; **(e)** virulent.

25 When a virulent phage infects cells, which of the following does *not* occur? **(a)** Infected cells produce large numbers of virions. **(b)** The host cells burst, or lyse. **(c)** New phages are released to infect other cells. **(d)** The phage DNA integrates with the host chromosomes. **(e)** Phage particles are assembled within the host cells.

26 The process of lysogeny is carried out only by phages containing _____ DNA.

27 During adsorption, the tip of the virus tail becomes attached to the cell surface at specific _____.

28 The tail tube within the sheath of a phage is called the _____ _____.

29 During infection of a bacterial cell, the phage sheath _____ _____.

30 Within minutes of entry of phage DNA into a bacterium, the host cell loses its ability either to _____ or to _____ _____ its DNA.

31 Match each item on the left with the most appropriate description on the right:

_____ early proteins

_____ lysed host cell suspension

_____ structural proteins

_____ extrusion

_____ endolysin

(a) Coded in late *m*RNA

(b) Coded in early *m*RNA

(c) Lyses bacterial cell

(d) Suspension of newly released phages

(e) Release of progeny phages continuously by outfolding of the cell wall

In items 32 through 34, indicate whether the statement is true **(T)** *or false* **(F)**. *If the statement is false, rewrite it as true.*

32 A temperate phage produces a specific repressor that blocks transcription of phage genes. _____

_____

_____

33 In the usual type of lysogeny, the prophage remains free in the cytoplasm as a plasmid. _____

_____

_____

34 Although phage Mu has no site specificity for insertion, it is able to insert only one copy of its DNA into a host chromosome. _____

_____

_____

MORPHOLOGY AND CHEMICAL COMPOSITION OF ANIMAL AND PLANT VIRUSES

35 Animal and plant viruses do not have the familiar _____

_____ shape of some bacteriophages.

36 Animal and plant viruses are composed of a central core of

_____ surrounded by a protein coat called a(n)

_____ .

37 Some animal viruses have a(n) _____ , which has

surface projections called _____ .

38 Nonenveloped viruses are called _____ virions.

39 Whether or not they have envelopes, most viruses have _____

_____ shapes.

CLASSIFICATION AND NOMENCLATURE OF ANIMAL AND PLANT VIRUSES

40 Family names of viruses have which suffix? **(a)** *-virinae;* **(b)** *-viridae;* **(c)** *-virus.*

41 Match each virus family on the left with the most appropriate description on the right.

_____ Herpesviridae

_____ Reoviridae

_____ Parvoviridae

_____ Retroviridae

(a) dsRNA

(b) dsDNA (enveloped)

(c) ssRNA (enveloped)

(d) ssDNA

REPLICATION OF
ANIMAL AND PLANT
VIRUSES

42 The letters on the right represent sequential steps of animal or plant viral replication. Match them with the appropriate events on the left to indicate the correct sequence of viral replication.

_____ Genome enters cell

_____ Release

_____ Attachment to specific cell

_____ Amplification of genome

_____ Synthesis of early *m*RNA

_____ Synthesis of late proteins with maturation and assembly

(a) a
(b) b
(c) c
(d) d
(e) e
(f) f

43 A cell lacking a(n) _____ for a specific virus is resistant to infection by that virus.

44 In enveloped virions, the envelope membrane surface glycoproteins called

_____ are responsible for recognition of a cell surface receptor to bring about adsorption.

45 Most enveloped viruses enter the host cell by _____ of the host cell membrane and the viral envelope.

46 _____ is probably the most important means of plant viral transfer in nature.

47 _____ serves as the demarcation line between early and late functions in the viral replication process.

In items 48 and 49, indicate whether the statement is true (**T**) *or false* (**F**). *If the statement is false, rewrite it as true.*

48 The process of viral assembly involves special biosynthetic enzymes. _____

_____

_____

49 The average yield of plant and animal virions per cell is comparable with the yield of phages from a bacterial cell. _____

_____

_____

REVIEW QUESTIONS

1 Explain why viruses are called *obligate intracellular parasites*.

2 Give a concise definition of a virus.

3 What is the nucleocapsid of a virion?

4 Discuss the relationships of capsid symmetries to protomers and capsomeres.

5 Compare the genomes found in viruses with those found in plant and animal cells.

6 Give a brief, generalized description of the entire process of cell infection by viruses.

7 What is meant by the Twort-d'Hérelle phenomenon?

8 Describe the T phages.

9 Describe the lytic cycle of bacteriophages as exemplified by the T-even phages of *Escherichia coli*.

10 Outline the lysogenic cycle of bacteriophages using phage λ.

11 What are the chemical composition and function of the envelope on the animal virion?

12 In what way is the nomenclature of plant viruses different from the nomenclature of animal viruses and bacteriophages in the ICTV system of viral classification?

13 List the five essential steps in the process of viral replication.

DISCUSSION QUESTIONS

1 What are some of the contributions of the study of bacterial viruses that led to the development of animal and plant virology?

2 Give reasons why the bacteriophage is considered a good model for the study of virology in general.

3 What is the molecular basis for the regulation of lysogeny in phage λ?

4 Félix d'Hérelle envisioned using bacteriophages for the treatment of patients infected with bacteria. Why has this not occurred?

5 State the case for and against the consideration of viruses as living entities.

6 Discuss the advantages or disadvantages to the virion of carrying out integrative or nonintegrative lysogeny.

7 Give the advantages and disadvantages of the ICTV classification of viruses versus the Baltimore classification.

8 Why do you think there are no effective antibiotics for the treatment of viral infections?

9 What is the most rapid way to diagnose viral infections? Use hepatitis B infection as one example.

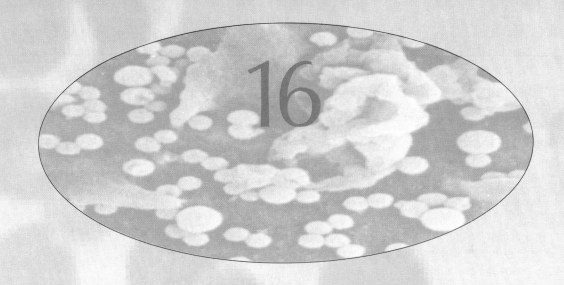

Viruses:
Cultivation Methods, Pathogenicity

OBJECTIVES

After reading this chapter you should be able to

1 Discuss methods used to cultivate bacterial viruses.

2 Explain what is meant by the one-step growth curve.

3 Compare the various methods used to cultivate animal viruses.

4 Describe how plant viruses are cultivated.

5 Explain the meaning of prions and viroids.

6 Present evidence implicating viruses as a cause of cancer.

7 Relate the significance of oncogenes to cancer.

OVERVIEW

In Chapter 15 you studied viruses that infect bacterial cells, plant cells, or animal cells. Viruses also infect other living cells, such as cells of fungi, algae, and protozoa. In fact, it is probable that there are few cells, procaryotic or eucaryotic, that cannot be infected by a virus. Viral infections of many kinds of organisms may go unnoticed if they cause only mild effects in the host, or they may cause devastating results.

In phage-infected bacteria, the visible outcome is death of the host bacterium by lysis, if the phage is virulent for the bacterium. In multicellular animals and plants, the cells infected with viruses usually either die or continue to function as abnormal cells. But such multicellular organisms may also have uninfected cells. Consequently, the obvious effects on the whole animal or plant could be death of the organism, or the appearance of nonfatal symptoms that depend on the virus causing the infection. For example, in humans infected with viruses that cause polio, permanent disability or death may result because of the destruction of nerve cells. But other viruses, such as the wart viruses, may cause a relatively harmless growth of infected cells.

Still other viruses may cause changes that transform normal cells into cancer cells, resulting in uncontrolled tumor growth in the host. There are also viruses that attack only certain types of cells, such as the virus that causes acquired immune deficiency syndrome (AIDS). The target cells of human immunodeficiency virus (HIV) are principally the immune system cells called CD4 lymphocytes, along with cells called macrophages and monocytes (the immune system is described in Chapter 19). AIDS and other viral diseases of humans are discussed in greater detail later in this book (Part IX).

When cells of plants are infected, the most common visible effect is the necrotic lesion, an area of dead tissue at the site of infection. Even if necrotic lesions are not visible, the plant may develop a variety of symptoms related to coloration or structural defects. These include chlorosis (yellowing of green parts) and mosaic (patchy variation of the normal green color). In addition, some plant viruses cause diseases characterized by unusual growth. For instance, wound tumor virus produces multiple tumors that grow at sites where the plants have been wounded.

Much of the knowledge about viral diseases is made possible by being able to cultivate, or grow, viruses in the laboratory. This chapter discusses various isolation and cultivation techniques, as well as some of the discoveries made during virological research. Among these were the discovery of "virus-like" infectious particles called *viroids* and *prions,* as well as the intriguing connection between viruses and cancer. Viruses, especially phages, have also provided the microbiologist with a convenient and important model system for the fundamental study of genetics at the molecular level.

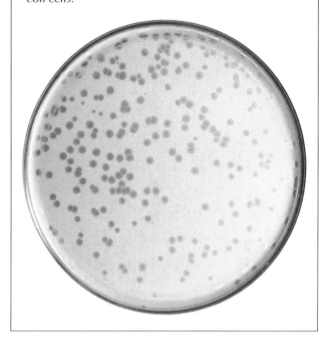

FIGURE 16.1
Plaques (clear zones) are formed when localized areas of bacterial cells in a confluent, turbid layer (lawn) are lysed by bacteriophages. The plaques shown were caused by bacteriophage T4 on a lawn of *Escherichia coli* cells.

CULTIVATION OF BACTERIOPHAGES

In order to isolate and cultivate viruses in the laboratory, living host cells must be provided. Bacterial viruses are easily isolated and cultivated on young, actively growing cultures of bacteria in broth or on agar medium. An important requirement for isolation and cultivation of phages is that optimal conditions for growth of the host organisms be provided. In fluid cultures, lysing of the bacteria will cause a turbid culture to become clear. In agar-plate cultures, bacterial lysis results in clear zones, or *plaques,* in a confluent, turbid layer of bacteria called a *lawn* [FIGURE 16.1].

The formation of plaques comes about in the following manner. When a phage is present in a layer of susceptible bacteria on a nutrient medium, it will be adsorbed on one of the bacterial cells on the agar medium. Soon after, the infected bacterium will lyse and release

about 100 phages, each of which will be adsorbed on adjacent bacteria. These bacteria in turn will lyse and release phages that infect other bacteria in the vicinity. These multiple cycles of infection continue until, after several hours, the phages will have lysed all the bacteria in a localized area. The result is a plaque (clear zone) on the surface of the agar-plate medium. Since one plaque forms from the action of one initial phage particle, the number of plaques on a lawn of bacteria gives an estimate of the number of phage particles (also called *plaque-forming units,* or pfu) introduced on the plate. Such a quantitative procedure is called a *plaque assay.*

The best and most useful way to isolate bacteriophages is from the habitat of the particular host bacterium. For example, coliphages or other phages pathogenic for bacteria found in the intestinal tract can best be isolated from sewage or manure. This is done by centrifuging or filtering the source material to remove large particles and debris and then adding chloroform to kill any bacterial cells. A small amount (such as 0.1 ml) of this preparation is mixed with the host organism and spread on an agar medium. Growth of phage is indicated by the appearance of plaques.

ASK YOURSELF

1 How can it be determined that a culture of bacteria has been attacked by virulent bacteriophages?

2 Explain how a phage can form a plaque on a lawn of bacterial cells.

3 Why can the formation of plaques be used in a plaque assay?

4 Describe how to go about isolating phages from a natural habitat.

THE ONE-STEP GROWTH CURVE

The sequence of events initiated by the passage of the phage nucleic acid into the host cell and culminating in the release of newly synthesized virions can be studied in a classic experiment called the *one-step growth curve.* The cells in a culture are infected simultaneously with a low number of phages so that no cell can be infected with more than one phage. At various time intervals, samples are removed for a plaque assay. This assay is a quantitative determination of the number of phages present in the medium. The results are plotted as in FIGURE 16.2. This graph describes the production of progeny virions by cells as a function of time after infection. In other words, it represents the production of bacteriophages in a culture of host cells, all of which were infected simultaneously at time zero.

During the first 10 min or so after injection of phage nucleic acid, the number of plaques is constant [FIGURE 16.2]. The plaques are formed only by infected cells, with each infected cell producing one plaque. During this period, called the *eclipse period,* no phage can be recovered from infected cells by *disrupting* them, which means that no mature virus progeny have been produced. At the end of the eclipse period, however, mature phages begin to accumulate intracellularly [see FIGURES 15.18 and 15.20] until they are released by cell lysis. The time from infection until lysis begins is the *latent period.* The number of free phages in the medium (released by cell lysis) increases until it reaches a constant number at the end of the replication cycle; this time interval is termed the *rise period.* The difference between the initial and the final number of plaques (phages) is called the *burst size* [FIGURE 16.2].

FIGURE 16.2

One-step growth curve of plaque-forming units. In a one-step growth experiment, after adsorption of the virus on the host, antiserum is added to inactivate unadsorbed phage, and then the culture is highly diluted (1000-fold) so that virions released after the first round of replication cannot attach to uninfected cells; thus only one round of replication can occur. Each plaque-forming unit in a plaque assay is equal to one phage particle in the original suspension. "Intracellular virus" represents the production of phages within the cell as observed by the plaque assay following the artificial lysis of culture samples at timed intervals.

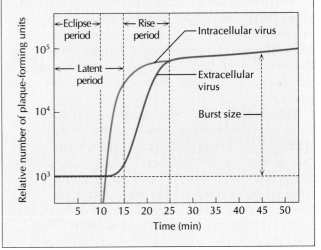

ASK YOURSELF

1 What is the purpose of carrying out an experiment called the *one-step growth curve?*

2 List the types of data one can get from such an experiment.

3 Why do we start the experiment with a low number of phages?

4 Why is antiserum added to the culture after adsorption of the phages on the host cells?

5 How many rounds of phage replication can occur in a one-step growth curve experiment?

6 How are the numbers of intracellular phages determined?

CULTIVATION OF ANIMAL VIRUSES

Microbiologists cultivate viruses in order to isolate and produce them in quantity for study or for the production of vaccines. In general, there are three main ways of cultivating animal viruses: in living animals, in embryonated chicken (or duck) eggs, and in cell cultures.

Living Animals

Using animals for the cultivation of viruses is not the method of choice, for the following reasons: it is expensive, it is labor-intensive, and it may add other factors, such as contaminating bacteria, into a study. But some animal viruses, such as the hepatitis B virus, can be cultured only in living animals. Studies of host immune responses to a viral infection also demand the use of living animals. In the laboratory, mice, rabbits, guinea pigs, and nonhuman primates are usually used. Animal inoculation is also a good diagnostic tool to determine whether a virus will cause infection; the animal will exhibit typical disease symptoms, and sections of infected tissue can be examined microscopically for evidence of infection.

Embryonated Chicken Eggs

One of the most economical and convenient methods for cultivating a wide variety of animal viruses is the use of the fertilized, embryonated chicken egg [FIGURE 16.3]. The discovery that viruses could be cultivated by this simple technique was made in 1931. Embryonated chicken eggs can be inoculated aseptically with virus, using a needle and syringe, through a hole drilled in the shell. The opening is sealed with paraffin and the eggs are incubated at 36°C for 2 to 3 days to allow the viruses to multiply.

Chick embryos contain several kinds of cells and tissues [FIGURE 16.4] in which various viruses will replicate. By using embryos of different ages and using different methods of inoculation, it is possible to cultivate the type of virus desired. Different tissues within the egg are inoculated, depending on the type of virus used. For example, the chorioallantoic membrane will support the growth of the herpesvirus, smallpox virus (variola), Rous sarcoma virus, and eastern equine encephalitis virus; the amniotic cavity will permit growth of the influenza and mumps viruses. The influenza virus also has an affinity for the allantoic cavity. As a matter of fact, the embryonated chicken egg is used routinely for the production of influenza vaccines, as well as for vaccines against smallpox, yellow fever, and other diseases. Furthermore, if a virus, such as the vaccinia virus, multiplies on one of the embryonic membranes, it produces a very distinct type of lesion called a *pock*. The yolk sac and the embryo itself can also be used to grow viruses (rabies virus and yellow fever virus in the yolk sac; eastern equine encephalitis virus in the embryo).

Tissue Cultures

The most widely used method for the cultivation of animal viruses is *cell culture*, or *tissue culture*, a single layer (monolayer) of cells growing in liquid medium in a flat-bottomed container. Once a cell culture has been grown, it is possible to use it as an in vitro host for a virus (*in vitro* means "in glass"). Viruses invade the cells, usually causing some type of visible change in the growth of the monolayer tissue cells near the site of initial infection. This localized change, called the **cytopathic effect (CPE),** is a deterioration of the tissue culture cells caused by the virus. The CPE may have different appearances, depending on the particular virus and the type of cells in the culture. FIGURE 16.5 shows a typical CPE in cell culture.

FIGURE 16.3

An embryonated hen's egg is used for the cultivation of many mammalian viruses.

FIGURE 16.4

Diagrammatic representation of a section through an embryonated hen's egg 10 to 12 days old. The hypodermic needles show the routes of inoculation of the yolk sac, allantoic cavity, and embryo (head).

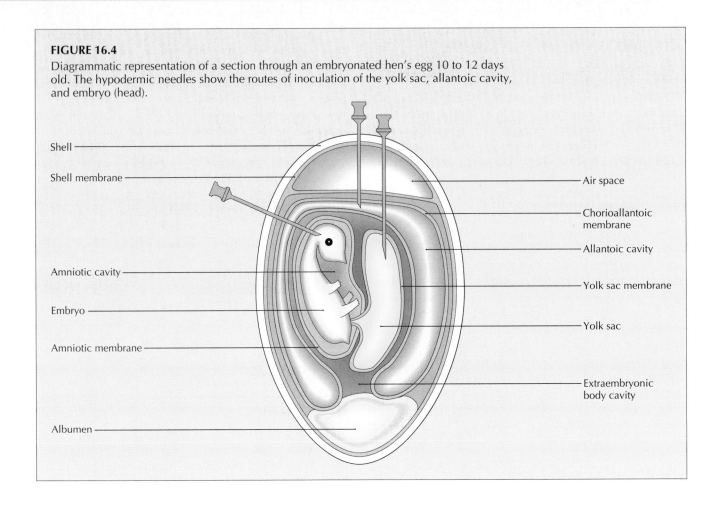

FIGURE 16.5

Light-microscopic view of tissue culture used for the cultivation of viruses. **[A]** Normal human lung fibroblast cell culture. **[B]** Human lung fibroblast cell culture infected with adenovirus type 3. Note the characteristic cytopathic effect (CPE): rounded and enlarged cells.

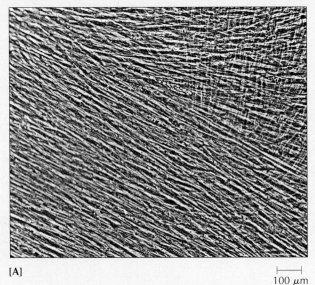

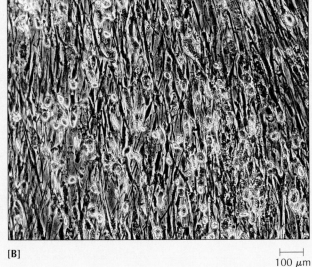

[A] 100 μm

[B] 100 μm

FIGURE 16.6

Inclusion bodies produced by viruses in certain host tissues. **[A]** Guarnieri body of variola (smallpox) virus in the cytoplasm of a rabbit corneal cell. **[B]** Negri bodies in the cytoplasm of a Purkinje cell (nerve cells of the brain) infected with rabies virus. **[C]** Bollinger bodies in the cytoplasm of a cell infected with fowl pox virus. **[D]** In herpesvirus infections, cells called *giant cells* occur which contain a conglomeration of several nuclei. Each nucleus contains a large inclusion body surrounded by a clear "halo."

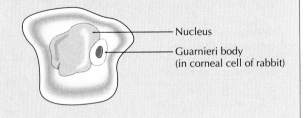

Nucleus

Guarnieri body
(in corneal cell of rabbit)

[A]

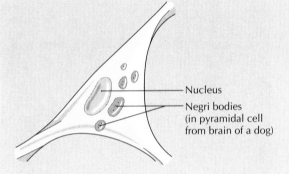

Nucleus

Negri bodies
(in pyramidal cell
from brain of a dog)

[B]

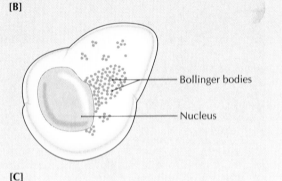

Bollinger bodies

Nucleus

[C]

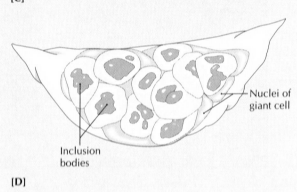

Nuclei of
giant cell

Inclusion
bodies

[D]

One type of CPE is an ***inclusion body,*** which is an abnormal intracellular structure. Inclusion bodies are important because their presence can help identify the virus causing an infection [FIGURE 16.6]. For instance, small particles called *Guarnieri bodies* can be seen in the cytoplasm of cells infected with the smallpox virus. These are aggregates of virions that have developed in the cytoplasm. *Negri bodies* occur in the cytoplasm of nerve cells from the brains of animals with rabies, and their presence is important for the diagnosis of this disease. Intracytoplasmic inclusion bodies also occur in several other diseases such as sheep pox, fowl pox, and molluscum contagiosum. Intranuclear inclusions are found in cells infected with viruses of chicken pox and herpes.

In cell culture, groups of lysed cells (plaques) have been used in the assay of virus concentration—the number of plaques is proportional to the number of infectious virus particles present in a sample. Each animal virion causes formation of a single plaque on a monolayer of susceptible animal cells [FIGURE 16.7], just as a bacteriophage forms a plaque on a lawn of susceptible bacterial host cells.

FIGURE 16.7

Virus particles in a suspension may be enumerated by means of a plaque assay. Shown are plaques of polyoma virus on monolayers of mouse kidney cells in tissue-culture dishes. Note that as the dilution of the viral suspension increases, the number of plaques in the dishes decreases.

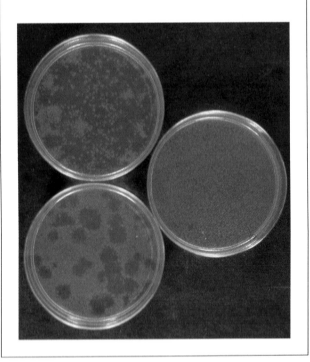

ASK YOURSELF

1 What are the three main ways for the cultivation of viruses?

2 Give the pros and cons for using living animals for cultivating viruses.

3 List some advantages in the use of embryonated chicken eggs for cultivating viruses.

4 What are CPEs? Inclusion bodies?

CULTIVATION OF PLANT VIRUSES

Plant viruses cause many diseases of economically important crops, such as tomatoes (tomato spotted wilt virus), corn and sugarcane (wound tumor virus), potatoes (potato yellow dwarf virus), and lettuce (lettuce necrotic yellows). The effects of viral infection on some plants are shown in FIGURE 16.8. As with bacterial and animal viruses, it is important for microbiologists to be able to cultivate and study plant viruses in a controlled laboratory setting.

Plant viruses can be cultivated by inoculating a plant with a virus suspension through a hypodermic needle or by scratching plant leaves with virus material. Scratching is aided with an abrasive such as carborundum. This can lead to formation of local lesions as well as general infection. Some plant viruses can replicate to large numbers in infected plants. For example, a single hair cell of an infected tobacco plant may contain over 10^7 (10 million) tobacco mosaic virions. Indeed, as much as 10 percent of the dry weight of infected leaves may be tobacco mosaic virus.

Transfer of infection from cell to cell occurs by passage of virions through bridges that connect the cells of plant tissue. Also, in most plant diseases, infected cells can continue to manufacture virus without either disintegrating or dying. Diseased plant material can be crushed to release plant juices containing the virions, which can then be purified, sometimes to crystals. Using this method in the 1930s, Wendell M. Stanley obtained purified tobacco mosaic virus in crystal form, the first crystallization of any virus. He was awarded the 1946 Nobel Prize in chemistry for this research.

In recent years some progress has been made in the preparation of plant cells which have had their walls removed. Such wall-less cells are bounded only by the cytoplasmic membrane and are called *protoplasts*. For instance, protoplasts made from specific tobacco plant

FIGURE 16.8

Illustrations of plant infections caused by viruses. **[A]** Leaf of *Grammatophyllum scriptum* (orchid) exhibiting necrotic ringspots caused by bacilliform particles (virions). **[B]** *Cattleya* flower exhibiting necrosis resulting from infection by cymbidium mosaic virus. **[C]** *Nicotiana tabacum* (tobacco) leaf exhibiting necrotic ringspot resulting from infection by tomato ringspot virus. **[D]** Leaf of *N. tabacum* (tobacco) exhibiting mosaic symptoms resulting from infection by cucumber mosaic virus. **[E]** Leaf of *N. glutinosa* (tobacco) exhibiting local lesions resulting from mechanical inoculation with tobacco mosaic virus (similar to a phage plaque assay described earlier in this chapter). The number of local lesions are proportional to virus concentration and are seen approximately 48 h after inoculation.

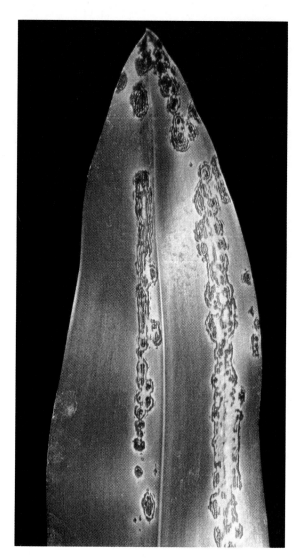

[A]

[B]

[D]

[C]

[E]

cells can be infected directly with tobacco mosaic virus. Progress has also been made in the development of monolayer cultures of susceptible cells from the insects that transmit some viral plant diseases. For example, rhabdovirus has been cultivated in leafhopper cell culture, with a yield of over 10,000 virions per cell.

ASK YOURSELF

1 Describe some symptoms expressed by plants when infected with viruses.

2 How does one infect a plant artificially? How are plants infected with viruses in nature?

3 Give an example describing the yield of virus from infected plants.

4 Who first crystallized viruses? What virus was used for this?

5 Are tissue cultures used for the cultivation of plant viruses?

"VIRUSLIKE" INFECTIOUS AGENTS

While studying plant and animal diseases, virologists have discovered some unusual infectious agents called *viroids* and *prions* that have some attributes of viruses. However, the structure of these particles differs drastically from that of viruses.

Viroids

Viroids are the smallest known infectious agents. Shown to occur only in plants, they cause several important diseases of cultivated plants, including potato spindle tuber, citrus exocortis, chrysanthemum stunt, and cucumber pale fruit. Unlike viruses, *viroids do not possess a protein coat*. Some viroids are made up of circular single-stranded RNA; others are linear single-stranded RNA molecules. Each contains between 270 and 380 nucleotides. In spite of their small size, viroids replicate in cells of susceptible plant species, but so far they have not been shown capable of coding for any proteins of their own. They appear to be totally dependent on their hosts' metabolic machinery for replication.

It is not known how viroids cause disease. Their location in the nucleus, along with their inability to act as *m*RNA, suggests that they cause host symptoms by direct interference with host gene regulation.

Comparison of nucleic acid sequences has shown that viroids share many detailed structural similarities with a certain region of small nuclear RNAs which are involved in the splicing of introns in animal cells (Chapter 14). This finding suggests that viroids originated from introns; their pathogenicity might be due to interference with the normal splicing of introns in the cell.

Prions

Several transmissible diseases have a slow, progressive course, usually with a fatal outcome. They are characterized as chronic central nervous system diseases. Incubation periods, from infection to appearance of symptoms, are measured in years, rather than hours or days! They are caused by peculiar transmissible agents whose properties and behavior suggest an *unconventional* virus. An example of their unusual properties is a high resistance to ultraviolet radiation and heat. These agents are called *prions* (proteinaceous infectious particles), because they appear to have no nucleic acids at all, with protein their only detectable component. However, like viruses, they reproduce inside cells. It may be possible that prion proteins are coded for by a gene found in normal host DNA.

There are several classic diseases caused by prions, all of them neurological diseases. These include kuru and Creutzfeldt-Jakob disease of humans, and scrapie, a disease of sheep. It has been suggested by some researchers that Alzheimer's disease, the most common type of senile dementia and a leading cause of death among the elderly, might also be caused by prions.

ASK YOURSELF

1 What are the unique attributes of viroids?

2 Describe the genome of viroids.

3 How do viroids cause disease?

4 What is the speculation about the origin of viroids?

5 Describe the characteristic features of diseases caused by prions.

6 What are some specific diseases ascribed to prions?

VIRUSES AND CANCER

Cancer is the collective name for a number of dreaded diseases characterized by uncontrolled growth of cells in

16.1 ONCOGENES AND CANCER

Oncogenes are genes that, when activated in cells, can transform normal cells to cancerous cells. All nucleated cells possess oncogenes, including normal human cells. Such genes are very similar to, and in some cases may even be the same as, normal genes. Genes that function normally but have the *potential* of becoming oncogenes are referred to as *protooncogenes*. Under normal conditions these genes probably code for proteins that are necessary for cell growth, but mutations can alter them into genes that cause cancerous transformations of cells. Thus cancer may be viewed as a disease of genes, arising from genetic damage of protooncogenes. Such damage can change either the expression or the biochemical function of genes.

The participation of viruses in oncogenesis is easier to understand when you realize that oncogenes may be carried into normal cells by infecting retroviruses. Genes carried into cells in this fashion were the first oncogenes identified. So far 19 distinct transforming genes have been isolated from the genomes of retroviruses. They are called viral oncogenes, or v-*onc* genes. Oncogenes are given three-letter code names. Thus the first of the v-*onc* genes to be discovered—from the Rous chicken sarcoma virus—is called the v-*src* gene. Other examples include the v-*ras* gene in the Harvey rat sarcoma virus and the v-*sis* gene in the simian sarcoma virus. The *src* oncogene and many of the other retroviral oncogenes code for the synthesis of protein kinase enzymes, which phosphorylate amino acids of proteins such as tyrosine. Just how this phosphorylation leads to cancer is not yet known. One hypothesis is that the protein kinases might alter key proteins in the cell's internal cytoskeleton, resulting in major abnormalities in cellular structure and function.

In other cases the oncogene is already present in the normal human cell, and it needs only a mutation or another activating event to change it from a harmless, and possibly even essential, gene into an actively oncogenic gene. Activation can be by a variety of agents, including mutagenic chemicals, high-energy radiation, and oncogenic viruses. At present some 30 oncogenes have been identified in humans, and the number is expected to exceed 100. Some of these protooncogenes have DNA sequences homologous to the v-*onc* genes and are called c-*onc* genes. This means that most of the oncogenes found in viruses and cancer cells have counterparts in normal human cells. It has been postulated that the cellular counterparts (the c-*onc* genes) are progenitors of the v-*onc* genes!

the body. These *malignant* cells arise from several types of normal tissue cells. The human body contains more than 100 different kinds of cells, each of which can malfunction in its own distinctive way to cause cancer. More than 100 clinically distinct types of cancer are recognized, each with a unique set of symptoms. Most of them can be grouped into four major categories [see DISCOVER 16.1]:

1 *Leukemias:* conditions in which abnormal numbers of white cells (leucocytes) are produced by the bone marrow.
2 *Lymphomas:* conditions in which abnormal numbers of lymphocytes (a type of leucocyte) are produced by the spleen and lymph nodes.
3 *Sarcomas:* solid tumors that grow from connective tissue, cartilage, bone, muscle, and fat.
4 *Carcinomas:* solid tumors that grow from epithelial tissues and are the most common form of cancer. Epithelial tissues are the internal and external body surface coverings and their derivatives, and thus include skin, glands, nerves, breasts, and the linings of the respiratory, gastrointestinal, urinary, and genital systems.

Not all tumors are cancerous; noncancerous tumors are called **benign tumors.** Cancerous tumors are known as **malignant tumors.** As indicated in the preceding list, tumors are generally named by attachment of the suffix *-oma* to the name of the tissue from which the tumor arises. Cancer cells are not sensitive to the signals that inhibit excessive reproduction of normal cells; they grow in an uncontrolled way, often rapidly. Most persons who die from cancer are not killed by the primary tumor that develops, but by the spread of the cancer to other parts of the body. The cancerous cells take over or displace healthy tissues, preventing normal body processes. Thus cancer has three major characteristics:

1 *Hyperplasia:* uncontrolled proliferation of cells.
2 *Anaplasia:* structural abnormality of cells; cells so affected have loss of or reduction in their functions.
3 *Metastasis:* ability of a malignant cell to detach itself from a tumor and establish a new tumor at another site within the host.

For a long time, microbiologists have entertained the idea that at least some types of cancer might be caused by viruses. The first evidence came in 1908, when it was shown that certain chicken leukemias could be transferred to healthy chickens by blood serum. Three years later it was shown that chicken sarcoma could be transmitted by bacteria-free filtrates of tumor extracts. Virus-induced carcinomas in mice were discovered in 1936, and it was clearly demonstrated that an agent causing mouse mammary tumors could be transmitted from mother to offspring through the mother's milk. Many viruses have since been found capable of inducing cancer in animals. But for many years these discoveries were not considered relevant to the cause of human cancer. Furthermore, human cancer did not appear to be infectious, and there were no confirmed isolations of a virus from human cancer cells. Hence the idea that viruses are a cause of human cancer became less attractive.

In recent years, however, even stronger evidence has linked viruses to animal cancers. These more recent findings revived the idea that human cancers might also be caused by viruses. Both RNA and DNA viruses have been found capable of inducing cancer in animals. For instance, in 1980 a retrovirus called *human T-cell lymphotrophic virus type I* (HTLV-I) was identified as the probable cause of a rare, malignant cancer of humans called *adult T-cell leukemia*. This leukemia occurs in Japan, Africa, and the Caribbean. In 1982, a related virus, HTLV-II, was identified as the likely cause of some cases of a human leukemia called *hairy-cell leukemia*. (Interestingly, HTLV-I and HTLV-II are similar in many ways to HIV, the virus that causes AIDS, although HIV is not a cancer virus.) Even before the discovery of HTLV-I and HTLV-II, several other viruses had been implicated in human cancer; for example, hepatitis B virus was associated with a form of liver carcinoma, and Epstein-Barr virus was associated with a form of lymphoma. Although there is strong circumstantial evidence that such viruses can cause human cancers, it is quite a different matter to prove this unequivocally. Such proof would require either (1) experiments involving inoculation of human subjects with the viruses, which is out of the question for ethical reasons, or (2) demonstration that the cancer can be prevented by immunization of human subjects with the appropriate viral vaccine. Although the latter approach is possible, the viral vaccines have not been developed and, even if they were, it would require years to obtain a definitive answer about their effectiveness.

The induction of cancer is termed **oncogenesis** (from the Greek word *onkos*, meaning "mass"); viruses that cause cancer are said to be *oncogenic*. In animals with cancer caused by oncogenic viruses, the affected cells are *transformed*, resulting in the formation of tumors. Transformed cells acquire morphological, biochemical, and other properties distinctly different from uninfected cells or infected cells in which tumors are not produced. One outstanding characteristic of transformed cells is the loss of *contact inhibition*, a property of normal cells. Normal cells recognize cellular boundaries and limit their cell populations through the process of contact inhibition, which means they are inhibited from growing when they touch other cells. This is why, when normal cells are propagated in tissue culture, they form a monolayer. Transformed cells in cell culture reproduce indefinitely and pile on top of one another. Other properties of transformed cells include invasiveness (they produce tumors when injected into animals), chromosomal abnormalities (unusual numbers of and/or breaks in chromosomes), and an increased rate of sugar transport across the cytoplasmic membrane.

Among the RNA viruses, only members of the family Retroviridae (more commonly known as the *RNA tumor viruses*) cause cancer in animals. They replicate through a DNA intermediate. None of the other RNA viruses, all of which replicate through an RNA intermediate, are known to cause cancer. In contrast, among the DNA viruses, members of at least three families (Herpesviridae, Adenoviridae, and Papovaviridae) can cause cancer in animals.

A common characteristic of all oncogenic viruses is that the viral genome in some way becomes integrated into the host cell's DNA and replicates along with the host cell's chromosomes. The host cell does not lyse—a situation similar to the phenomenon of lysogeny in bacteria infected with temperate phages, as mentioned in the previous chapter. If the viral genome is RNA, it serves as a template for the synthesis of a DNA molecule complementary to it; the enzyme *reverse transcriptase* is responsible for this synthesis, giving rise to a DNA-RNA hybrid. Then a second strand of DNA is synthesized complementary to the first strand. This results in a double-stranded DNA molecule synthesized from the viral RNA, which can now be integrated into the host DNA as a *provirus*. In this way transformation and oncogenesis are induced in host cells [DISCOVER 16.2].

Oncogenic DNA Viruses

Oncogenic viruses are found within several groups of DNA-containing viruses. As mentioned previously, these groups include the papovaviruses, the herpesviruses, and the adenoviruses.

Papovaviruses include the papillomaviruses that cause benign warts in humans and other animals and have been implicated in cervical cancer [DISCOVER 16.3]; polyoma viruses that cause several kinds of tumors when injected into newborn mice; and simian virus 40 (SV 40), originally isolated from cell cultures used for the cultivation of polioviruses for polio vaccines. SV 40 cannot induce tumors in the monkey, its natural host, but can do so in rodents in the laboratory; this is why it was not detected when monkey cells (which showed no cytopathic effect even though SV 40 was present) were used initially for the cultivation of viruses for polio vaccine production.

16.2   THE AIDS VIRUS HAS RNA AS ITS HEREDITARY MATERIAL

DNA is the hereditary material in all cellular organisms, but a virus is not a cellular organism, and some viruses have RNA as their hereditary material instead of DNA. The AIDS virus is one example of an RNA-containing virus, and it replicates its RNA in an interesting manner.

After penetrating a human host cell, the AIDS virus makes a strand of DNA that is complementary to the RNA, thus forming an *RNA-DNA hybrid* (see the accompanying illustration). In other words, the AIDS virus acts in a manner just opposite to that of cellular organisms: *instead of using DNA as a template to make RNA, it uses RNA as a template to make DNA.* It can do this because the virus has a special enzyme called *reverse transcriptase.* After the RNA-DNA hybrid has been made, a second DNA strand is synthesized complementary to the first DNA strand, resulting in a molecule of *double-stranded DNA.* This double-stranded viral DNA becomes integrated into the DNA of the human host cell, and thus it becomes hereditary in that cell. In the host cell, the viral DNA can be transcribed into molecules of single-stranded viral RNA, which can be used to make AIDS virus progeny.

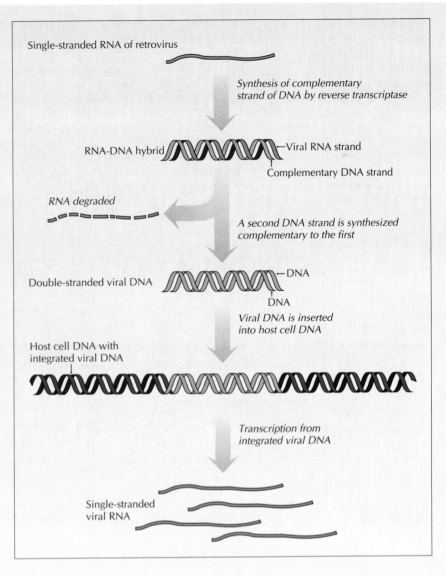

Among the herpesviruses that affect humans are the herpes simplex viruses and the Epstein-Barr virus (EBV). The latter is the probable cause of Burkitt's lymphoma, a cancer of the lymphoid system. EBV has an affinity for blood cells called *lymphocytes* and has the potential for transforming them into rapidly proliferating cells. EBV has also been implicated in Hodgkin's disease (another form of lymphoma) and in nasopharyngeal carcinoma (a cancer of the nose and throat). This virus is also the cause of infectious mononucleosis (regarded by some authorities as a self-limiting leukemia). Herpes simplex virus type 1 (HSV 1) is the cause of cold sores, but it has been implicated in lip cancers. Herpes simplex virus type 2 (HSV 2), which causes more than 80 percent of genital herpes infections, has been associated with cervical cancer.

Oncogenic RNA Viruses

Among the RNA-containing viruses, only the retroviruses are oncogenic. They include the lymphoma, leukemia, and sarcoma viruses of cats, chickens, and mice, as well as the mammary tumor viruses of mice. Thus many different types of cells can be transformed by these viruses. Some examples of oncogenic retroviruses are shown in TABLE 16.1.

16.3 WHAT? THE WART VIRUS IS DEADLY?

Papillomaviruses, members of the family Papovaviridae, have long been thought to cause only common benign warts, despite the fact that other papovaviruses have been shown to be oncogenic. However, it now appears that papillomaviruses that cause sexually transmitted disease may also cause several kinds of cancer.

More than 50 types of papillomavirus are known. While many types seem to cause no serious disease, a large number have been linked to cervical cancers and a few other malignancies. Circumstantial evidence suggests strongly that these viruses are factors in the cause and growth of cancers.

Less serious but more widespread, genital warts caused by papillomaviruses are causing increasing health care problems. It has been suggested that at least 10 percent of American adults are infected with papillomaviruses of the genital tract and that there may be a million new infections each year. Most such infections appear to have no serious consequences; they are self-limiting and eventually subside. Whether the virus is completely eradicated or enters a latent, inactive state is unknown.

But some infections apparently lead to cancer of the cervix. Genetic material of the virus has been found integrated into cancer cells of patients. Papillomavirus has also been found in cancers of the vulva and vagina and in cancers of the penis and rectum.

Epidemiologists at the Centers for Disease Control in Atlanta say that reported cases of genital infections with papillomaviruses have become increasingly common. It is now recognized that even if papillomaviruses are not directly the cause of genital cancers, they are at least important contributors to the progression of such cancers. Thus some papillomaviruses, long thought to cause nothing more serious than common warts, are shedding their guise of innocence and now constitute a major sexually transmitted threat that carries the risk of several kinds of cancer.

TABLE 16.1
Examples of Oncogenic Retroviruses

Host	Virus	Cancer type
Human	HTLV-I	Adult T-cell leukemia
	HTLV-II	Hairy-cell leukemia
Monkey	Woolly monkey sarcoma virus	Sarcoma
	Gibbon ape leukemia virus	Leukemia
Chicken	Avian erythroblastosis virus	Erythroleukemia; sarcoma
	Avian leukosis virus	B-cell lymphoma
	Avian myeloblastosis virus	Myeloblastic leukemia
	Rous sarcoma virus	Sarcoma
Cattle	Bovine leukemia virus	Leukemia
Mouse	Bittner mammary tumor virus	Mammary carcinoma
	Gross murine leukemia virus	Leukemia
	Moloney murine leukemia virus	Leukemia
	Harvey murine sarcoma virus	Sarcoma
Cat	Feline leukemia virus	Leukemia

The ability of these viruses to be oncogenic is related to their capacity to become proviruses, which are the double-stranded DNA molecules synthesized from the viral RNA that become integrated into the host cell's DNA. The principal reason why retroviruses can cause cancer is that they introduce new genetic material into the host's DNA and cause transformation.

ASK YOURSELF

1 What are the four major categories of cancer?

2 Describe the three major characteristics of cancer.

3 When was the first evidence found linking viruses to cancer, and what was it?

4 What recent findings have revived the idea that human cancers might be caused by viruses?

5 What is unique about *reverse transcriptase?*

6 Name the oncogenic DNA viruses and the cancers they cause.

7 What are the animal diseases caused by oncogenic RNA viruses?

SUMMARY

1 In fluid cultures, the lysis of bacteria by phages clears the turbid growth of bacterial cells. In agar-plate cultures, bacterial lysis results in the formation of plaques on a lawn of bacteria.

2 The habitat of the bacterial host is the best source for isolating bacteriophages. Optimum conditions for growth of the host cells are also best for the isolation and cultivation of specific phages.

3 Study of the viral replication cycle provides information on stages involved in the multiplication of phages. The data obtained for the viral replication cycle may be plotted as a one-step growth curve.

4 Animal viruses may be cultivated in animals, embryonated chicken (or duck) eggs, or cell cultures. For economic and other reasons, cell cultures are the method of choice. Plants or plant cell protoplasts may be used for the cultivation of plant viruses.

5 Viroids are the smallest known infectious agents; they are composed of RNA only and lack protein and other components found in viruses. They may have arisen from untranslated segments of eucaryotic RNA called *introns*.

6 Prions are transmissible infectious agents that are composed only of proteins.

7 Cancer is actually a number of diseases characterized by uncontrolled growth of cells in the body. There is evidence that viruses play a role in the development of some cancers. These so-called oncogenic viruses include both RNA and DNA viruses.

KEY TERMS

anaplasia
benign tumors
burst size
carcinomas
cytopathic effect (CPE)
eclipse period
hyperplasia
inclusion body
latent period
lawn
leukemias
lymphomas
malignant tumors
metastasis
oncogenes
oncogenesis
one-step growth curve
plaques
prions
rise period
sarcomas
viroids

CULTIVATION OF BACTERIOPHAGES

1 Lysis of a bacterial culture by specific bacteriophages will *not* result in the following: **(a)** loss of turbidity; **(b)** increase in turbidity; **(c)** formation of plaques; **(d)** clear zones; **(e)** phage release.

2 The best and most useful source for isolation of bacteriophages is the host's

_____ .

3 Chloroform is used in a phage suspension to kill _____.

THE ONE-STEP GROWTH CURVE

4 Conditions for a one-step growth curve do *not* include which one of the following? **(a)** The cells in a culture are infected simultaneously. **(b)** A cell is infected with no more than one phage. **(c)** Each cell is infected by several phages. **(d)** Specific phage antiserum is added to inactivate unadsorbed phages. **(e)** Infected cells are highly diluted to prevent a second round of phage infection and replication.

5 The time from phage infection until the beginning of cell lysis is termed **(a)** the rise period; **(b)** the eclipse period; **(c)** the latent period; **(d)** the burst period.

CULTIVATION OF ANIMAL VIRUSES

6 The three main ways of cultivating animal viruses are in living animals, in cell cultures, and in _____ .

7 In the embryonated egg, the _____ membrane will support the growth of the herpesvirus, smallpox virus, Rous sarcoma virus, and eastern equine encephalitis virus, while the _____ cavity will permit growth of the influenza and mumps viruses.

8 The localized change or deterioration in the tissue culture monolayer as the virus multiplies is called the _____ .

9 Inclusion bodies diagnostic of rabies are called **(a)** elementary bodies; **(b)** Paschen bodies; **(c)** Negri bodies; **(d)** Guarnieri bodies.

CULTIVATION OF PLANT VIRUSES

10 As much as _____ percent of the dry weight of infected tobacco leaves may be tobacco mosaic virus.

11 Plant cell _____ have been used for the cultivation of plant viruses.

12 The first crystallization of any virus was made with _____ _____ virus by Wendell M. Stanley in the 1930s.

"VIRUSLIKE" INFECTIOUS AGENTS

13 Viroids, the smallest known infectious agents, have which of the following characteristics? **(a)** infect only animals; **(b)** infect only plants; **(c)** possess a protein coat; **(d)** are made up of single-stranded circular or linear RNA; **(e)** are capable of coding for their own proteins.

14 Introns are _____ sequences within genes of eucaryotic cells.

15 Viroids do not have a _____ .

16 The incubation periods of so-called slow virus diseases are measured in **(a)** weeks; **(b)** months; **(c)** days; **(d)** years.

17 The only detectable chemical component of prions is _____ _____ .

18 Classical diseases caused by prions may be described as _____ _____ diseases.

VIRUSES AND
CANCER

19 Match each type of cancer in the left column with its correct definition in the right column.

____ lymphomas

____ leukemias

____ carcinomas

____ sarcomas

(a) Solid tumors growing from connective tissue, cartilage, bone, muscle, and fat
(b) Abnormal numbers of lymphocytes produced by the spleen and lymph nodes
(c) Abnormal numbers of leucocytes produced by the bone marrow
(d) Solid tumors growing from epithelial tissues

20 The ability of a malignant cell to detach itself from a tumor and establish a new tumor at another site within the host is called **(a)** anaplasia; **(b)** metastasis; **(c)** hyperplasia; **(d)** metaplasia.

21 The first demonstration that certain chicken leukemias could be transferred to healthy chickens by blood serum was made in **(a)** 1808; **(b)** 1875; **(c)** 1908; **(d)** 1938; **(e)** 1987.

22 Which one of the following characteristics is *not* a characteristic of transformed cells? **(a)** contact inhibition; **(b)** loss of contact inhibition; **(c)** invasiveness; **(d)** chromosomal abnormalities; **(e)** increased rate of sugar transport across cytoplasmic membrane.

In items 23 through 28, indicate whether the statement is true **(T)** *or false* **(F).**

23 Among the viruses that contain RNA, only members of the Retroviridae can cause cancer in animals. ____

24 The retroviruses replicate through a DNA intermediate. ____

25 The retrovirus provirus is a DNA-RNA hybrid. ____

26 SV 40 induces tumors in monkeys and laboratory rodents. ____

27 HSV 2 has been associated with more than 80 percent of genital herpes infections and is implicated in cervical cancer. ____

28 The human immunodeficiency virus isolated from humans with AIDS is a retrovirus. ____

REVIEW QUESTIONS

1 Describe a brief procedure for the isolation of coliphages.

2 Explain what a plaque assay is.

3 Draw a one-step growth curve and explain the different stages of phage replication.

4 What are some advantages in using live animals for cultivating animal viruses?

5 Describe how embryonated chicken eggs are used for the cultivation of animal viruses.

6 How are plants usually infected with viruses?

7 In what ways are prions different from typical virions?

8 What is the hypothesis for the origin of viroids?

9 Describe the three major characteristics of cancer.

10 How are transformed cells different from normal cells?

11 Why is a retrovirus so called?

DISCUSSION QUESTIONS

1 Lysogeny exists in temperate phage-infected cells. Explain whether such a state exists in animal cells.

2 What happens to a multicellular organism when infected with a virus?

3 Clearing of a turbid culture of bacteria may be due to lytic enzymes or to lysis by virulent bacteriophages. How do we determine which is the agent of lysis— enzyme or phage?

4 Explain the significance of the one-step growth curve experiment.

5 Why do you think the technology of plant tissue cultures has not advanced as much as that of animal tissue cultures?

6 In what ways are prions different from viroids?

7 Even though the first evidence for linking viruses to human cancer was presented in 1908, why was this possibility not taken seriously by medical researchers?

8 Present recent evidence that implicates a role for viruses in human cancer.

9 Why is it difficult to prove unequivocally that viruses do cause cancer in humans?

10 What ability do viruses possess that enables them to become oncogenic?

11 Explain how retroviruses can contribute to oncogenesis.

12 How was it possible that SV 40 was injected into thousands of people without their knowledge?

VIII

Microorganisms and Disease: Resistance to Infection

Normal Flora of the Human Body

OBJECTIVES

After reading this chapter you should be able to

1 Differentiate between resident flora and transient flora.

2 Identify those areas of the human body that are normally inhabited by microorganisms.

3 Explain when and how the normal flora microbes are acquired by a human.

4 Describe how germfree animals are obtained and how these animals can be used to identify the beneficial effects of the normal flora.

5 List the factors that influence the microbial population of the conjunctiva, skin, nasopharynx, mouth, intestinal tract, and genitourinary tract.

6 Identify the areas of the body where the highest numbers of the normal flora are located.

OVERVIEW

There are countless microorganisms in the environment. Within this environment, humans encounter these microorganisms continuously. But our most intimate contact is with the large numbers of microorganisms that actually live in and on our bodies. It is estimated that the adult human body is host to at least 100 trillion microbial cells at any time. These indigenous microorganisms, most of which are bacteria, are called the *normal flora* of the human body. (Intracellular viruses are not considered part of the normal human flora.) They inhabit the skin and some of the inner surfaces of the body. The species and numbers of the flora vary according to particular sites (such as the skin, mouth, nasopharynx, ears, intestinal tract, and lower urogenital tract), and sometimes at particular ages of the host. Sex of the host may also influence the composition of the normal microbial flora. Most members of the normal flora are highly adapted to survival and growth in these areas, which may contain physical and chemical conditions that discourage other kinds of microorganisms.

However, many organs and sites in the healthy human host are free of microorganisms. These include the cerebrospinal fluid, blood, urinary bladder, uterus, fallopian tubes, middle ear, paranasal sinuses, and kidneys.

Members of the normal flora may also be thought of as the *resident flora,* those microbes regularly found in a given site at a particular host age. There are other microbes that are simply harbored for a short time by the human body; these are microorganisms from the environment that have taken up temporary abode in the host. They may be present only for several hours, days, or weeks, and then disappear. This group constitutes the *transient flora*. The transient flora has little significance so long as the resident flora remains intact. But if members of the latter group are diminished, transient microbes may then colonize, reproduce, and cause disease.

NORMAL FLORA OF THE HEALTHY HUMAN HOST

The human body is inhabited by a large number of microorganisms, which together are called the body's *normal flora*. Most members of the normal flora are bacteria, but fungi and protozoa inhabit the body as well. Some of the microbes occur on the skin, but most live on the inner surfaces of the body. These surfaces include the mucous membranes that line the nose, mouth, upper respiratory tract, intestinal tract, and genitourinary tract. It is important to recognize that the internal organs and tissues of the healthy human body are usually free of microorganisms. Indeed, finding microorganisms in the internal regions of the body—for instance, in the bloodstream—usually means that the person is infected and ill.

The term *normal flora* implies that such microbial inhabitants are harmless; for the most part, normal flora microorganisms do not cause disease. They are *residents* of the healthy human body, and are permanent occupants. In contrast, those that are *transients* of the healthy human body may establish themselves briefly, but tend to be excluded by competition from residents or by the host's immune defense mechanisms. Transients are not considered part of the normal flora.

Most normal flora microbes are *commensals*: they benefit from the association with the host, but the host is not adversely affected. Others have a *mutualistic* association with the host—they benefit the host in some fashion while thriving in the host's body (i.e., both benefit from the association).

Some normal flora organisms can be *opportunistic pathogens*, which cause infections if tissue injury occurs at specific body sites, or if the resistance of the body to infection is decreased. These organisms have become especially important in recent years because there has been a rising incidence of infections from them, due to the prolonged use of antibiotics and the use of immunosuppressive chemicals for treatment.

Microbiologists study the human normal flora because it is important to know what kinds of microorganisms are harbored by the healthy body. This knowledge

FIGURE 17.1

Candida albicans, an opportunistic yeast that is a member of the normal human flora. This is a 48-h slide culture of the organism which produces chlamydospores on a medium containing 1% sodium taurocholate.

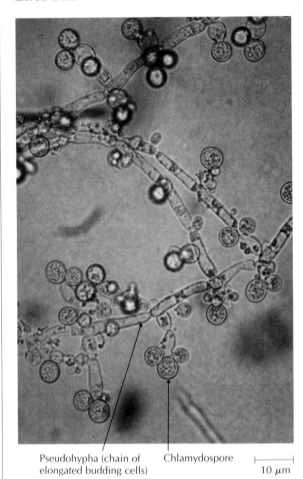

Pseudohypha (chain of elongated budding cells)   Chlamydospore   10 μm

gives insight into the kinds of infections that might occur following tissue trauma at various sites. For instance, the cause of heart valve infection may be traced to a tooth extraction. This enables the physician to evaluate the nature of the infection and treat it more effectively. Knowledge of the normal flora also leads to an understanding of overgrowth of normally absent microorganisms that may take place at a particular site. An example is the heavy growth of a yeast such as *Candida albicans* [FIGURE 17.1] in the oral cavity as a consequence of intensive, broad-spectrum antibacterial drug therapy or profound suppression of the immune system. It also gives us a better appreciation of the role played by the normal flora in preventing exogenous microbes from successfully colonizing our bodies.

ASK YOURSELF

1 Where on the human body do we find members of the normal flora?

2 What areas of the human host are free of microorganisms?

3 What is the difference between the *transient* flora and the *resident* flora?

4 How can a normal flora microorganism become an opportunistic pathogen?

5 What are the advantages of knowing the normal flora of the human body?

6 Differentiate between mutualism and commensalism.

ORIGIN OF THE NORMAL FLORA

Before birth a healthy human fetus is free of microorganisms. Under natural circumstances, the newborn infant first encounters microorganisms while passing down the mother's birth canal, especially the vagina. It acquires them by surface contact, swallowing, or inhaling. These microbes are soon joined by others from sources in the newborn's immediate surroundings, including the skin (such as that of the hands and breasts) and respiratory tract of those caring for the infant. During the first few days of life, the flora often includes microorganisms that can grow on particular sites in the *absence* of competitors. Soon, as the infant is exposed to the full range of microorganisms in the immediate environment, those microbes that compete best with others in particular sites become predominant. Such microbes form a stable normal flora.

Each part of the human body, with its special environmental conditions, has its own particular mixture of microorganisms. For example, the oral cavity acquires a different natural microbial population from that of the intestines. In a short time, the child will have the same general kind of normal flora as an adult person in the same environment; the nature of that flora depends on such factors as the frequency of washing, diet, hygienic practices, and living conditions.

ASK YOURSELF

1 Is a human fetus free of microorganisms?

2 How does a human acquire a stable normal flora?

3 Does each part of the human body have the same kinds of microorganisms? What example might illustrate the answer?

EFFECT OF THE NORMAL FLORA ON THE HUMAN HOST

What effect does the establishment of the normal flora have on the body? Three approaches have been used to answer this question:

1 Use of germfree animals. If the colonization of experimental animals by microorganisms can be prevented, one can compare the properties of such germfree animals with those of normal animals. The results can be helpful in understanding the functions of the normal flora of humans.
2 Use of antimicrobial agents. If the balance that occurs between the normal flora and the human host is altered by use of antimicrobial agents, the effects are useful in understanding the role of the normal flora.
3 Knowledge of certain characteristics of the normal flora that inhibit the growth of other microbes. These characteristics suggest that normal flora organisms may help to discourage the growth of microorganisms that are not part of the indigenous flora.

Germfree Life

Louis Pasteur did not believe that animals could live in the absence of microorganisms. In 1897, following his suggestion, scientists made an unsuccessful attempt to raise germfree chickens. In Germany between 1899 and 1908, bacteria-free chickens were raised for the first time, but they failed to develop normally and died in about a month. This supported the notion that intestinal bacteria were essential in the nutrition of vertebrates. However, in 1912, 17 germfree chickens were raised at the Pasteur Institute in France, showing that vertebrate life was in fact possible in the absence of microorganisms.

FIGURE 17.2

Germfree equipment. **[A]** Schematic diagram of a germfree isolator unit. The interior can be sterilized prior to an experiment and maintained in that condition. **[B]** Germfree facility in a biotechnology company.

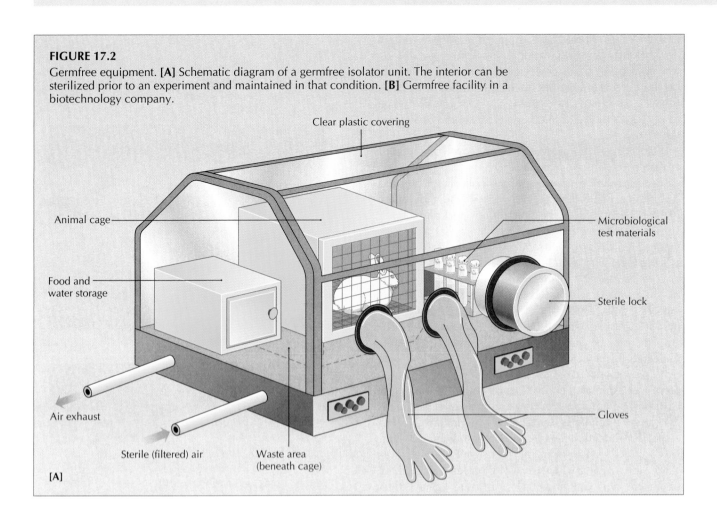

In 1928, James A. Reyniers at the University of Notre Dame in the United States began his work on germfree animals. He and his associates developed equipment and techniques for rearing several generations of chickens, rats, mice, and other animals in the absence of microorganisms. They compiled anatomical and physiological descriptions of these animals, including comparisons with conventional nongermfree animals of the same species. As a result of these studies, germfree animals no longer belong to the realm of biological curiosities. Instead, they are practical tools for solving problems of importance in biology and medicine. Germfree laboratory units have been designed to raise such animals [FIGURE 17.2]. Such units made it possible to study the effects of microorganisms added to germfree animals. Animals that are raised in an environment with one or more *known* microorganisms are said to be **gnotobiotic**.

The first germfree animals raised by Reyniers were chickens obtained by sterilizing the shells of 20-day-old embryonated eggs with a germicide and then placing them in sterile containers such as glass jars or steel,

tanklike cages. Sterile air was passed into these containers and waste gases removed. Sterile food and water also were placed in the cages prior to adding the ready-to-hatch chicks. Periodic microbiological monitoring of the exhaust air, feathers, excreta, and body orifices confirmed the absence of microorganisms in the cages or on the birds.

Germfree laboratory units are now commercially available. Germfree mammals such as rats, mice, and guinea pigs can be obtained by *cesarean section,* a surgical incision made through the walls of the abdomen to deliver the offspring. This operation is performed under sterile conditions in a special chamber that allows the young animals to be introduced directly into a sterile rearing cage. These babies must be hand-fed hourly for 2 or 3 weeks, using a formula containing, as nearly as can be determined, all of the components of the natural mother's milk (which is avoided because it may contain microorganisms). Once established, a colony of germfree animals can be maintained by natural reproduction under germfree conditions.

Germfree Animals versus Normal Animals. Compared with normal animals, germfree animals have an underdeveloped immune system, making them unusually susceptible to infection if exposed to microorganisms. They lack *antibodies* to normal flora *antigens*, which often share similarity to the antigens of disease-causing microorganisms and confer partial protection against these pathogens. Germfree animals are vulnerable not only to pathogenic bacteria but also to many nonpathogenic bacteria. This is because immunologic priming (a buildup of resistance to antigens) has not occurred under the protection of maternal antibodies soon after birth.

Germfree animals require higher levels of B vitamins in their diet than do normal animals; they also require vitamin K, which normal animals do not require in their diet. These findings indicate that the normal flora makes a significant contribution to satisfying the vitamin requirements of the host.

Other Uses for Germfree Animals. Germfree animals have been used gnotobiotically to assess the effect of particular species of microorganisms on a host. The animal is reared in the presence of one or more *known* microbial species, in order to determine the effect of those species on growth and development of the animal or on various physiological processes. Similarly, one can inoculate a germfree animal with one or several known species of microorganisms to determine the microorganisms' ability to produce disease or cause pathological or immunological changes in the animal. For example, gnotobiotic techniques have helped us to understand the role of bacteria in causing dental caries [FIGURE 17.3].

FIGURE 17.3
Bacteria have been shown to play a role in causing dental caries. [A] Healthy teeth of a rat. [B] Carious rat teeth due to bacterial growth in dental plaque.

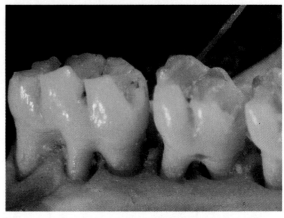

[A]

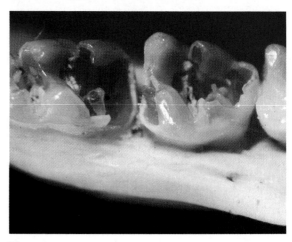

[B]

Effect of Antimicrobial Agents on the Normal Flora

Experiments designed to suppress the normal flora with antibiotics or other antimicrobial agents indicate that these microorganisms defend the host against potential pathogens. For instance, treating the skin of humans with antibacterial agents, such as hexachlorophene, suppresses colonization by the normal Gram-positive microbes and promotes growth and clinical infection by Gram-negative rods and other microorganisms that are not normally able to cause infection. Such opportunistic microorganisms generally are relatively resistant to the antimicrobial agent used. In another example, hospital patients receiving antibiotics may lose much of the nor-

17.1 ANTIBIOTIC-ASSOCIATED COLITIS

Some hospital patients taking antibiotics may develop a severe inflammation of the colon called *pseudomembranous colitis* (PMC), characterized by high fever, severe abdominal pain, and diarrhea.

PMC is caused by *Clostridium difficile,* a bacterium that normally occurs only in very low numbers in the colon because it competes poorly with the normal flora bacteria. However, antibiotics that inhibit the normal flora may allow *C. difficile* to multiply to large numbers and produce two toxins (poisons), A and B. Toxin A causes the diarrhea, which washes many of the residual normal-flora bacteria out of the intestine. Both toxins kill the epithelial cells that line the colon wall, causing blood plasma to leak into the colon and clot. The clots consist of fibrin, dead epithelial cells, and white blood cells; they appear as tough, whitish-yellow plaques of pseudomembrane (false membrane) on the colon wall.

The death rate in severe, untreated cases is 10 to 20 percent. Fortunately, PMC can be effectively treated by using vancomycin or metronidazole to stop the growth of *C. difficile.*

mal flora of the large bowel, leading to pseudomembranous colitis—a severe disease caused by excessive growth of toxin-producing strains of an anaerobic spore-forming bacterium, *Clostridium difficile,* which normally is absent or is only a minor component of the normal flora. In humans not receiving antibiotic therapy, such microorganisms are held in check by the normal flora [DISCOVER 17.1]. The yeast *Candida albicans* [see FIGURE 17.1], a minor component of the normal flora, may multiply dramatically following antibiotic therapy (since it is a eucaryote, it is resistant to antibacterial antibiotics). *Candida albicans* can cause diarrhea and superficial fungal infections in the mouth, vagina, or anal area.

Thus the normal flora can prevent the establishment of pathogens by various means, including successful competition for available nutrients or formation of inhibitory metabolic products. This protective role of the normal flora is well illustrated by the beneficial effect of breast-feeding infants. The bacteria acquired from the mother's milk in the colon of the breast-fed infant create an environment antagonistic to enteric pathogens. This protective effect is augmented by ingested maternal antibodies against those pathogens.

Characteristics of Normal Flora Organisms

Certain properties of the normal flora have given them a selective advantage over other bacteria, allowing them to become residents of the body. These properties may include physical characteristics such as the ability to adhere to body surfaces, or metabolic characteristics such as the production of antimicrobial substances.

Adherence to Host Cells. Many species of the normal flora can adhere to the surface of host epithelial cells, the tissue cells that cover body surfaces. Thus these species have a selective advantage over nonadhering microorganisms in colonizing the host. Adherence is the result of an interaction between the microbial cell surface and a chemical receptor on the body cell. Proteins or polysaccharides on the surface of the microbial cells, as well as *pili* which extend out from the microbial cell, have been implicated in adherence. The particular means of adherence varies with the species. Adherence allows the bacteria to multiply while they avoid removal by the flushing effects of surface fluids and *peristalsis,* a progressive wave of contraction that forces contents toward an opening. Microorganisms may often adhere specifically to one body site. For example, *Streptococcus salivarius* adheres mainly to the surface of the tongue, whereas *Streptococcus mutans* selectively binds to the smooth enamel surface of the teeth.

A phenomenon that affects microbial adherence is *desquamation,* the detachment of host epithelial cells from body surfaces and replacement of the lost cells by new cells. In some body sites like the intestinal tract, the rate of desquamation may be very high. One result of desquamation is the elimination of microorganisms that are not part of the normal flora (are transients) and that are only weakly attached to the epithelial cells. Normal flora microorganisms, however, have the ability to reattach firmly to the fresh epithelial layer and thus persist at these body sites.

Production of Antimicrobial Substances. Some resident microorganisms produce metabolic products that can inhibit other microbes. For example, in the large bowel certain anaerobic bacteria produce organic acids such as acetic, lactic, or butyric acid as metabolic waste products; these can inhibit the growth of other bacteria. Some strains of skin staphylococci produce antibiotics that inhibit a wide variety of other bacteria.

ASK YOURSELF

1 What three approaches have been used to study the effect of the normal flora on the human body?

2 Explain why a *gnotobiotic* animal is not a *germfree* animal.

3 How are germfree animals obtained?

4 What characteristics differ between germfree animals and normal animals?

5 How have germfree animals been used in microbiology?

6 Give some examples of how the use of antimicrobial agents reveals the protective effects of the normal flora against pathogens.

7 What are some characteristics of the normal flora that enable them to become residents of the human body?

DISTRIBUTION AND OCCURRENCE OF THE NORMAL FLORA

Because bacteria account for most of the normal flora of the human body, this chapter deals mainly with the distribution and occurrence of various bacterial genera and species. Some fungi (mainly yeasts) and protozoa may also inhabit the human body, but their numbers are usually very low compared with the bacterial flora. Intracellular parasites such as viruses do not belong to the normal flora of the body. However, some viruses can replicate themselves in tissues for long periods without causing any apparent disease symptoms. For instance, certain human intestinal viruses were discovered only by noting their destructive effects on nonhuman animal cells in laboratory tissue cultures; thus they were termed *echoviruses* (enteric *c*ytopathogenic *h*uman *o*rphans). Similarly, *coxsackieviruses*, which also occur in the gastrointestinal tract of human hosts, were initially discovered only because of their pathogenicity for suckling mice in the laboratory; they apparently were not associated with human disease. Many echoviruses and coxsackieviruses have since been found to cause a number of diseases in humans—such as diseases of the respiratory tract, intestinal tract, and central nervous system. However, it must be recognized that not all of these viruses have been shown to have disease-causing ability, even though they are obligate intracellular parasites.

In another example, chronic adenovirus infections are known to occur without causing disease symptoms. The presence of certain adenoviruses in the lymphoid tissue of normal individuals may become evident only after the tissue cells have been cultured in vitro in the laboratory. These studies suggest that some viruses apparently cause chronic asymptomatic infections.

FIGURE 17.4 illustrates some predominant microorganisms of the normal flora. TABLE 17.1 summarizes the predominant normal flora found in body sites. The normal flora of the body comprises many distinct species of microorganisms that are harmless—and may even be beneficial in their usual locations in the human body. However, if they are introduced into other locations of the body, they may produce disease, especially if predisposing factors are present. (The transient bacteremia discussed in the next paragraph is a good example.) For this reason, members of the normal flora may be described as opportunistic microorganisms when they cause disease.

Blood, Body Fluids, and Tissues

In a healthy individual, the blood, cerebrospinal fluid, other body fluids, and tissues are normally free of microorganisms. Occasional microbes may cross protective epithelial barriers as a result of trauma, such as tooth extraction or childbirth. For a very brief time, such microbes may be found in the bloodstream before they are filtered out in the pulmonary capillaries or removed by cells of the immune system. Such *transient bacteremia* may cause infection of damaged or abnormal heart valves, leading to subacute bacterial *endocarditis* (inflammation of the membrane lining the heart and its valves).

Skin

The *epidermis,* or outer surface layer of the skin, covers a connective tissue layer, called the *dermis* [FIGURE 17.5]. Together they form an effective barrier against most microorganisms, which is why the skin is frequently called the "first line of defense." For instance, the outermost layer of the epidermis is a layer of dead, nonnucleated horny cells that is constantly in contact with microorganisms from the surrounding environment. Although cuts, abrasions, or burns can allow microbes to penetrate this layer, it is normally impermeable to microorganisms. The skin varies widely in structure (for example, thickness of the epidermis) and function, depending on its location on the body. These differences determine the types and numbers of microorganisms that occur on each skin site. FIGURE 17.5 shows the locations of common microorganisms that either grow on or contaminate the skin.

TABLE 17.1

Summary of Predominant Normal Flora Found According to Body Site

Body site	Microorganisms	Body site	Microorganisms

Skin	*Staphylococcus epidermidis,*
	    S. aureus
	Propionibacterium acnes
	Diphtheroids
	Candida spp.
	Pityrosporum spp.
		Gastrointestinal tract
		    Stomach
			Lactobacillus spp.
			Yeasts (*Candida* spp.)

Eye	*Staphylococcus epidermidis,* *S. aureus* *Corynebacterium* spp. *Streptococcus pneumoniae* *Neisseria* spp. *Moraxella* spp. *Haemophilus parainfluenzae*	Small intestine	Enterococci Lactobacilli Corynebacteria *Candida albicans* *Bacteroides* spp. *Escherichia coli*

Upper respiratory
    tract
	Staphylococcus epidermidis,
	    S. aureus
	Streptococcus pneumoniae
	Corynebacterium spp.
	Neisseria spp.
	Branhamella spp.
	Haemophilus spp.
	Micrococcus spp.
		Large intestine	>300 bacterial species found,
			    including:
			Escherichia coli
			Proteus spp.
			Klebsiella spp.
			Enterobacter spp.
			Bacteroides fragilis,
			    B. melaninogenicus,
			    B. oralis
			Fusobacterium spp.
			Bifidobacterium spp.
			Eubacterium spp.
			Lactobacillus spp.
			Clostridium perfringens
			Trichomonas hominis
			Entamoeba, Endolimax, and
			    Iodamoeba spp.

Tongue and buccal
    mucosa
	Streptococcus salivarius,
	    Streptococcus spp.
	Neisseria spp.
	Veillonella spp.
	Actinomyces spp.
	Lactobacillus spp.
	Yeasts (*Candida* spp.)
		Genitourinary tract	*Staphylococcus epidermidis*
			Streptococcus faecalis
			Corynebacteria
			Neisseria spp.
			E. coli
			Lactobacilli
			Enterococci
			Candida albicans
			Clostridium spp.
			Peptostreptococci
			Trichomonas vaginalis

Teeth and gingival
    crevices
	Bacteroides spp.
	Fusobacterium spp.
	Streptococcus mutans,
	    Streptococcus spp.
	Actinomyces spp.
	Lactobacillus spp.
	Porphyromonas gingivalis
	Prevotella spp.
	Spirochetes (*Treponema*
	    denticola)
	Wolinella spp.
	Selenomonas spp.
	Trichomonas tenax		

Constant exposure to the environment means the skin harbors many transient microbes. However, the skin surface is hostile to the survival and growth of many nonresident bacteria. For instance, *Streptococcus pyogenes* does not survive for more than a few hours on the skin, whereas it may survive for weeks in room dust. Several factors are responsible for discouraging microbial growth on the skin:

1 *Dryness.* The relatively dry surface of the skin is inhibitory to microbial growth. When allowed to dry, many bacteria enter a dormant condition; some species die in a matter of hours. Some sites of the skin are more moist than others, including the armpit region, the skin between the toes, and the skin at the lower end of the trunk between the thighs. These regions have higher numbers of normal flora organ-

FIGURE 17.4

The morphology and principal characteristics of the predominant microbial species comprising the normal flora of the human body.

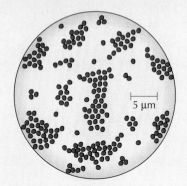

Staphylococcus aureus

Gram-positive cocci
  arranged in grapelike
  clusters
Nonmotile
Facultative
Coagulase produced
Found in nasal membranes,
  skin, hair follicles

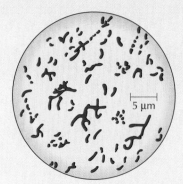

Propionibacterium acnes

Gram-positive
  pleomorphic rods
  arranged in short
  chains or clumps
  with V and Y forms
Nonmotile
Anaerobic
Propionic acid produced
Found on the skin

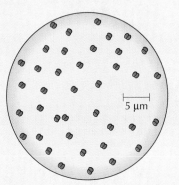

Branhamella catarrhalis

Gram-negative cocci
  arranged in pairs with
  adjacent sides flattened
Nonmotile
Aerobic
Oxidase test positive
Found in mucous
  membranes

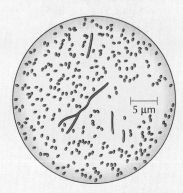

Haemophilus influenzae

Gram-negative rods
  exhibiting filaments
  and pleomorphism
Nonmotile
Aerobic
Normally found in the
  nasopharynx

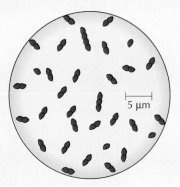

Streptococcus pneumoniae

Gram-positive oval or
  spherical cells; typically
  in pairs or short chains;
  distal ends of cells pointed
Nonmotile
Facultative
Bile-soluble
Found in the upper respiratory
  tract

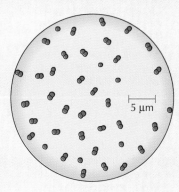

Neisseria meningitidis

Gram-negative cocci
  typically arranged in
  pairs with adjacent
  sides flattened
Nonmotile
Aerobic
Oxidase test positive
Found in the nasopharynx

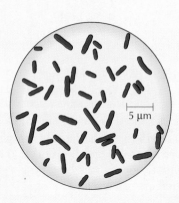

Lactobacillus sp.

Gram-positive straight
  or curved rods
Nonmotile
Facultative or anaerobic
Complex nutritional
  requirements
Found in the mouth, vagina,
  and intestinal tract

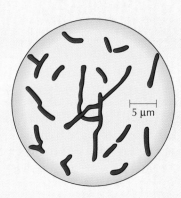

Actinomyces israelii

Gram-positive rods
  which may show
  true branching
Nonmotile
Anaerobic
Normally found in
  the oral cavity

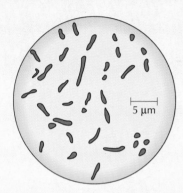

Bacteroides fragilis

Gram-negative uniform
 or pleomorphic rods
Nonmotile
Anaerobic
Found in the lower intestinal
 tract and mouth

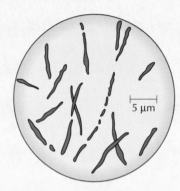

Fusobacterium nucleatum

Gram-negative rods
 with pointed ends
Nonmotile
Anaerobic
Found in the mouth

Clostridium perfringens

Gram-positive rods
Oval subterminal
 endospores
Nonmotile
Anaerobic
Found in feces

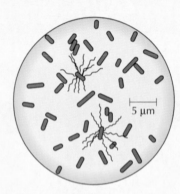

Escherichia coli

Gram-negative rods
Motile
Facultative
Produces gas and acid
 in lactose broth
Found in the lower part
 of the intestine

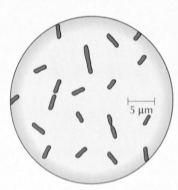

Klebsiella sp.

Gram-negative rods;
 capsulated
Nonmotile
Facultative
Found in the intestine

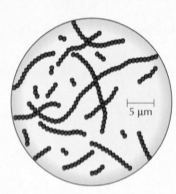

Peptostreptococcus sp.

Gram-positive cocci
 arranged in chains
Nonmotile
Anaerobic
Found in the colon and
 the vagina

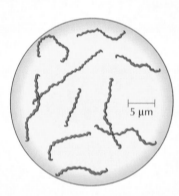

Treponema denticola

Gram-negative slender
 helical cells; ends of
 cells are pointed and
 slightly bent
Motile with jerky motion
Anaerobic
Found in the oral cavity

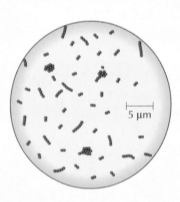

Veillonella alcalescens

Gram-negative small
 cocci arranged in small
 masses, pairs, or short
 chains
Nonmotile
Anaerobic
Complex nutritional
 requirements
Found in the mouth and
 in the intestinal and
 respiratory tracts

FIGURE 17.5
The major microbial symbionts found on or in the skin of humans.

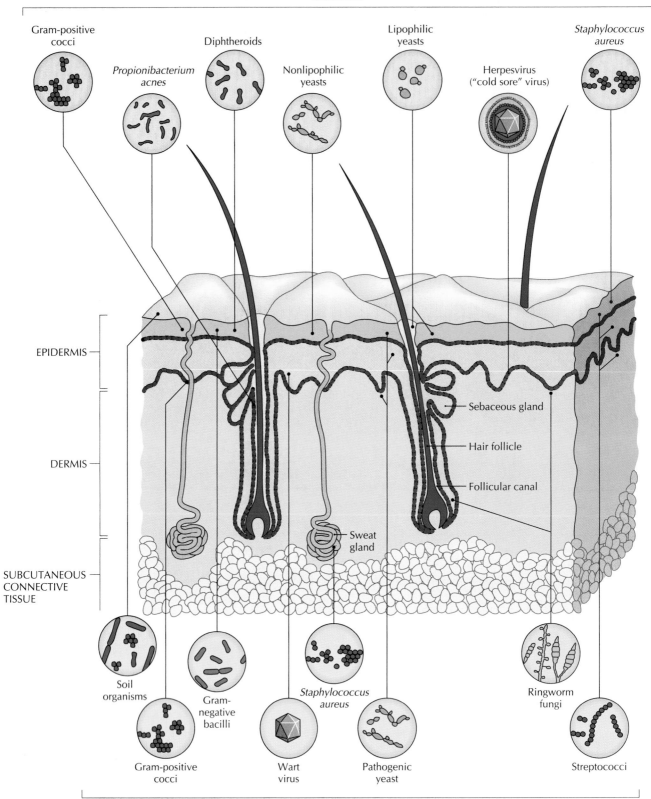

isms (about 10^6 bacteria per square centimeter) than do the drier areas of skin (about 10^2 to 10^4 bacteria per square centimeter). When the skin in moist areas becomes damp and soft, certain fungi easily produce skin infections. An example is the fungus that causes athlete's foot.

2 *Low pH.* Skin has a normal pH between 3 and 5 (higher in moist regions), due in part to organic acids such as lactic acid produced by normal skin microorganisms. This low pH can inhibit the growth of many kinds of microorganisms.

3 *Inhibitory substances.* Several bactericidal or bacteriostatic compounds occur on the skin. For example, sweat glands [FIGURE 17.5] secrete lysozyme, an enzyme that destroys the peptidoglycan of bacterial cell walls. Sebaceous glands [FIGURE 17.5] secrete complex lipids, which may be partially degraded by bacteria such as *Propionibacterium acnes* to produce long-chain fatty acids, such as oleic acid, that are highly inhibitory to other bacteria.

Despite these formidable antimicrobial factors, some bacteria not only survive on the skin but even grow, forming the normal flora. The secretions of the sweat glands and sebaceous glands provide water, amino acids, urea, salts, and fatty acids, which can serve as nutrients for these microorganisms. Most of these bacteria are species of *Staphylococcus*—mainly, *S. epidermidis*—but *Micrococcus*, *Corynebacterium*, and *Propionibacterium* also occur. Fungi (e.g., *Candida* spp. and *Pityrosporum* spp.) are often present in skin folds. Acid-fast nonpathogenic mycobacteria occur in areas rich in sebaceous secretions, such as in the genitalia and external ear. In the deep sebaceous glands, anaerobic bacteria such as *Propionibacterium acnes* thrive on the lipids present in the gland secretions. Part of the normal flora, *P. acnes* is usually harmless; however, it has been associated with *acne vulgaris*, a disease of the sebaceous glands of the skin. Because of their deep location, the numbers of these propionibacteria are little affected by washing or by disinfecting solutions.

Eye

Lining the eyelids and covering the eyeball is a delicate membrane called the **conjunctiva**. It is a continuation of the skin at the margin of the eyelids and is a mucous membrane that is continually washed by a flow of tears, which tends to remove microorganisms. Moreover, lysozyme, an antimicrobial substance, is secreted in tears. Consequently, the conjunctival flora is sparse. The main organisms found are *Staphylococcus epidermidis*, *Staphylococcus aureus*, *Corynebacterium* spp., *Streptococcus*

pneumoniae, *Neisseria* spp., *Moraxella* spp., and *Haemophilus parainfluenzae*; other microorganisms may be isolated occasionally.

Respiratory Tract

The respiratory tract includes the mouth, tonsils, nasopharynx, throat, trachea (windpipe), tracheal branches (bronchi), and lungs [FIGURE 17.6]. Although these moist areas might appear to be prime sites for microorganisms, they actually are rather difficult to colonize.

Upper Respiratory Tract. The upper respiratory tract is that portion above the larynx, the organ of the voice situated between the trachea and the base of the tongue. The mucous membranes of the upper respiratory tract are more moist than skin; nevertheless, they can create problems for microorganisms. As you breathe, the air containing microorganisms passes along the tortuous nasal passages and then into the nasopharynx (that part of the pharynx that lies above the level of the soft palate), and many microorganisms will stick to the thin, moist layer of highly viscous mucus that overlies the epithelial surfaces. Because of the rhythmic beating of cilia on the surface of the epithelial cells lining the nasopharynx, the mucus layer continuously flows downward toward the oropharynx. The trapped bacteria are eventually swallowed and may be destroyed by hydrochloric acid in the stomach. In addition to this mechanical removal of bacteria, the enzyme lysozyme in nasal mucus kills bacteria.

Despite these factors, the nose and nasopharynx are inhabited by numerous microorganisms as part of their normal flora. This is possible because of the microbial ability to adhere to the epithelial cell layer of the mucous membranes, thereby avoiding being swept away by the flow of mucus. The bacteria most frequently and most consistently found in the nose are *Staphylococcus epidermidis* and *Staphylococcus aureus*; in the nasopharynx avirulent strains of *Streptococcus pneumoniae* and other α-hemolytic streptococci predominate. But species of the genera *Corynebacterium*, *Neisseria*, *Branhamella*, *Haemophilus*, and *Micrococcus* are also common [see FIGURE 17.4].

Lower Respiratory Tract. The mucous membrane surfaces of the trachea and the bronchi do not have a normal flora, because of the efficient mechanical removal of microorganisms by an upward, cilia-driven flow of mucus. The few bacteria that do manage to traverse the air passages all the way to the air sacs of the lungs are usually engulfed and destroyed by phagocytic body cells called *macrophages.*

FIGURE 17.6
Distribution of some members of the normal flora of the human body.

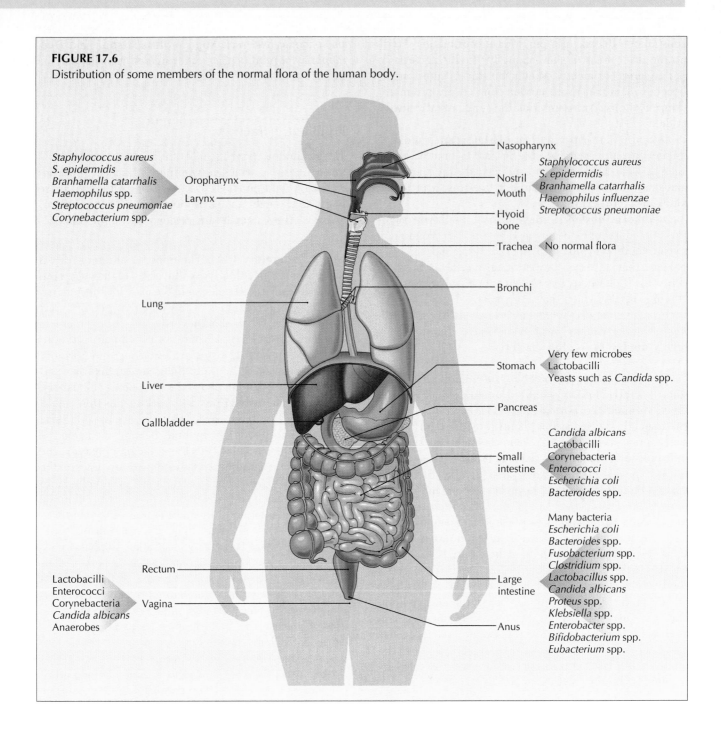

Staphylococcus aureus
S. epidermidis
Branhamella catarrhalis
Haemophilus spp.
Streptococcus pneumoniae
Corynebacterium spp.

Oropharynx
Larynx

Lung

Liver

Gallbladder

Rectum

Lactobacilli
Enterococci
Corynebacteria
Candida albicans
Anaerobes

Vagina

Nasopharynx

Nostril
Mouth

Hyoid
bone

Trachea — No normal flora

Bronchi

Staphylococcus aureus
S. epidermidis
Branhamella catarrhalis
Haemophilus influenzae
Streptococcus pneumoniae

Stomach

Very few microbes
Lactobacilli
Yeasts such as *Candida* spp.

Pancreas

Small
intestine

Candida albicans
Lactobacilli
Corynebacteria
Enterococci
Escherichia coli
Bacteroides spp.

Large
intestine

Many bacteria
Escherichia coli
Bacteroides spp.
Fusobacterium spp.
Clostridium spp.
Lactobacillus spp.
Candida albicans
Proteus spp.
Klebsiella spp.
Enterobacter spp.
Bifidobacterium spp.
Eubacterium spp.

Anus

Mouth

The abundant moisture and constant presence of dissolved food and small food particles would seem to make the mouth an ideal environment for bacterial growth. However, the continuous flow of saliva through the mouth causes a mechanical flushing action that removes many microorganisms, which are swallowed and destroyed by the hydrochloric acid of the stomach. Desquamation of epithelial cells is a second mechanical fac-

tor that removes microorganisms from the oral cavity. Consequently, it is not surprising that many of the microbes that constitute the normal flora of the mouth resist such mechanical removal by being able to adhere firmly to various surfaces of the oral cavity.

Acquisition of Mouth Flora. At birth the oral cavity is essentially a sterile, warm, and moist cavity containing a variety of nutritional substances. The saliva is composed of water, amino acids, proteins, lipids, carbohydrates, and inorganic compounds. Together they provide a rich environment for microbial growth. (Saliva itself generally contains transient microbes from other sites of the oral cavity, particularly from the upper surface of the tongue; it usually has a microbial population of about 10^8 bacteria per milliliter.)

The normal flora of a newborn is established within a few days after birth. The predominant bacterial species belong to the genera *Streptococcus, Neisseria, Veillonella, Actinomyces,* and *Lactobacillus;* yeasts are also present. The numbers and kinds of microbial species found are related to the infant's diet and to associations with other people and objects such as towels and feeding bottles. The only species consistently recovered from the oral cavity, starting on the second day after birth, is *Streptococcus salivarius.* This species has an affinity for epithelial tissues and appears in large numbers on the upper surface of the tongue.

Normal Microbial Flora of the Teeth. Until eruption of the teeth, most microorganisms in the mouth are aerobes and facultative anaerobes. As the first teeth appear, the tissue surrounding the teeth now provide an anaerobic environment, and species of Gram-positive anaerobic bacteria become more evident.

The teeth themselves can become areas for microbial adherence. *Streptococcus mutans* is associated with the tooth surface and appears to be the major causative agent of dental caries, or tooth decay. *Streptococcus mutans* produces glucan, a sticky polymer of glucose that acts like a cement and binds the bacterial cells together and to the tooth surface. This glucan is formed only in the presence of the disaccharide *sucrose* (the type of sugar found in confections), through a process catalyzed by an enzyme located on the surface of the cocci. The enzyme splits the sucrose molecules into their component monosaccharides, *glucose* and *fructose.* The enzyme then links the glucose molecules together to form the glucan, while the fructose molecules are fermented by the streptococci into lactic acid. Lactic acid can etch the surface of the teeth, enhancing microbial adherence. Although *S. mutans* initiates dental caries, other bacteria such as *Lactobacillus* and *Actinomyces* species can contribute to caries as secondary invaders. The aggregation of bacteria and organic matter on the surface of the teeth is termed **dental plaque** [FIGURE 17.7]. Dental plaque contains a very high number of bacteria, about 10^8 cells per milligram.

The normal flora of the healthy human *gingiva* (gum) consists mainly of Gram-positive bacteria such as *Streptococcus sanguis,* a facultative organism, and species of *Actinomyces,* an anaerobic genus. In diseased gums, there is a shift in the type of flora. Gum diseases range from *gingivitis,* an inflammation that results in redness and sometimes bleeding of the gums, to *periodontitis,*

inflammation in which the cement between the gum and enamel of the teeth comes apart, resulting in pockets that become filled with anaerobic bacteria. In these diseases, the bacterial flora is predominantly Gram-negative and consists mainly of species of *Porphyromonas, Prevotella, Bacteroides,* and *Fusobacterium,* which are nonmotile, and of motile bacteria such as *Treponema denticola* [FIGURE 17.8], and *Wolinella* and *Selenomonas* species. Some Gram-positive anaerobes such as *Eubacterium* are also present. One organism that is suspected as a cause of periodontitis is *Porphyromonas gingivalis;* however, periodontitis is probably not caused by a single organism but rather by the combined action of a group of organisms.

In addition to bacteria, certain commensalistic protozoa may inhabit the oral cavity. For instance, the flagellated *Trichomonas tenax* may occur in gum margins and in the plaque and cavities of the teeth. Its presence is usually associated with poor oral hygiene.

FIGURE 17.7

Scanning electron micrograph of bacteria in dental plaque adhering to the surface of teeth. Cocci may be seen coating some filamentous bacteria resulting in "corncob" arrangements.

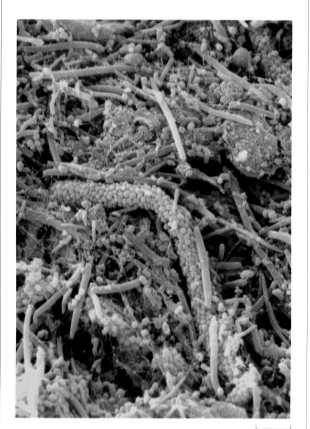

5 μm

FIGURE 17.8
Scanning electron micrograph of *Treponema denticola*, an anaerobic spirochete found in gingival crevices.

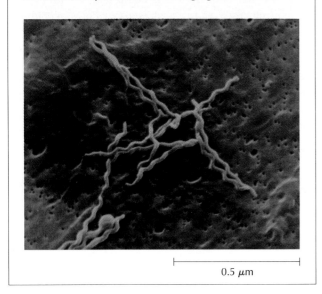

0.5 μm

Gastrointestinal Tract

Some of the highest concentrations of normal flora are found in the human gastrointestinal tract [see FIGURE 17.6], which includes the esophagus, stomach, small intestine, and large intestine (colon).

Stomach. Although the stomach constantly receives numerous transient bacteria from the oral cavity, the fluid contents of a healthy stomach generally contain fewer than 10 bacteria per milliliter. This scarcity is due to the bactericidal effect of the stomach's hydrochloric acid and digestive enzymes. The few organisms found are mainly lactobacilli and yeasts such as *Candida* species. Following the ingestion of food the number of bacteria in the stomach increases (10^3 to 10^6 organisms per gram of contents), but it soon falls as gastric juice is secreted and the pH of the stomach drops.

Small Intestine. The upper portion of the small intestine is called the *duodenum*. Few bacteria (usually $<10^3$ per milliliter of fluid) survive in the duodenum, because of the combined influence of a strongly acidic environment in the stomach and the inhibitory action of bile from the gallbladder. Of those present, the majority are Gram-positive cocci and bacilli. The second part of the small intestine is the *jejunum;* here species of enterococci, lactobacilli, and corynebacteria occasionally occur. The yeast *Candida albicans* may also be found in this part of the small intestine [DISCOVER 17.2]. The third and last portion of the small intestine is the *ileum,* where the flora begins to resemble that of the heavily populated large intestine. In the ileum, anaerobic bacteria such as *Bacteroides* species and facultative anaerobes such as *Escherichia coli* grow in large numbers.

Large Intestine. In the human body, the colon, or large intestine, has the largest microbial population. It has been estimated that the number of microorganisms in stool specimens is about 10^{11} organisms per gram wet weight, which means that about 25 percent of feces is made up of microorganisms. Over 300 different bacterial species have been isolated from human feces. It has been calculated that an adult excretes 3×10^{13} (30 trillion) bacterial cells daily through defecation.

Various factors tend to remove microorganisms from the large intestine. One factor is the continual movement of intestinal contents through the channel of the intestine, due to peristalsis of the intestine. Desquamation of surface epithelial cells to which bacteria are attached is another factor. Mucus is a third factor—just as this substance is important in the mechanical removal of microorganisms from the respiratory tract, it also plays a similar role in the intestine. However, the mucus in the intestine forms a discontinuous, meshlike layer rather than a continuous layer. Movement of intestinal contents causes adherence of microorganisms to the mucus, which subsequently rolls up into small masses that are eliminated in the feces, along with the attached microorganisms.

There are about 300 times as many anaerobic bacteria as facultatively anaerobic bacteria (the latter include *Escherichia coli*) in the large intestine. The anaerobic Gram-negative bacilli principally include species of *Bacteroides* (*B. fragilis, B. melaninogenicus, B. oralis*) and *Fusobacterium.* The Gram-positive bacilli are mainly species of *Bifidobacterium, Eubacterium,* and *Lactobacillus; Clostridium perfringens,* a major causative agent of gas gangrene, is invariably present.

The facultatively anaerobic species found in the large intestine, which account for less than 1 percent of the total flora, belong to the genera *Escherichia, Proteus, Klebsiella,* and *Enterobacter.* Anaerobic streptococci are also common, and the yeast *Candida albicans* is present.

Some protozoa may also occur as harmless commensals in the large intestine, where they grow anaerobically by ingesting the bacteria that are present. For instance, a flagellated protozoan, *Trichomonas hominis* [FIGURE 17.9], inhabits the cecum (the dilated pouch at the beginning of the large intestine). In another example, amoebas belonging to the genera *Entamoeba, Endolimax,* and *Iodamoeba* are commensals of the colon. One species, *Entamoeba histolytica* [FIGURE 17.10], can live as a commensal but can also be pathogenic, causing amoebiasis.

17.2 *CANDIDA ALBICANS*, A TREACHEROUS GUEST!

In FIGURE 17.1, you see a photomicrograph of an interesting microorganism—the yeast *Candida albicans*. This microbe is an indigenous member of the normal microbial flora of the human body. It is harbored as a guest in many intimate places of the body—it is fed and sheltered in the gastrointestinal tract, in the upper respiratory tract, in the buccal cavity, and in the vaginal tract. When we are healthy, *C. albicans* does not cause any disease symptoms; it lives happily with us in perfect harmony. However, *C. albicans* is a fairweather friend. The moment our resistance to disease is down, this treacherous guest turns on us and multiplies unchecked into large numbers.

In the healthy body, *C. albicans* is suppressed by the growth of other members of the normal flora. However, if anything interferes with the growth of the other members of the normal flora, *C. albicans* multiplies rapidly and produces disease. Thus we can expect this yeast to flourish when we undergo antibiotic therapy that suppresses growth of procaryotic cells or immunosuppressive drug treatment, decreasing our normal resistance to infection. It is not surprising that people with AIDS (acquired immune deficiency syndrome), in whom there is suppression of cell-mediated immunity, often develop *C. albicans* infections. In fact, the yeast often is one of the first opportunistic pathogens to appear (it causes *thrush*, or oral candidiasis).

Candida albicans is usually seen as a yeast form (unicellular) when it causes infection in tissues, but sometimes the mycelial structures may appear. In laboratory media it produces mycelial structures regularly, and the formation of chlamydospores is used to help identify the yeast.

It is doubtful whether any other microorganism produces as diverse a spectrum of disease in humans as does *C. albicans*! Because of its ubiquity as a normal resident of the human body, all tissues and organs are susceptible to invasion by this traitorous parasite. It causes not only infectious disease throughout the body, but also allergic disorders such as asthma and eczema. Indeed, *C. albicans* is no mutualistic house guest, but an opportunistic foe waiting for our guard to drop before striking.

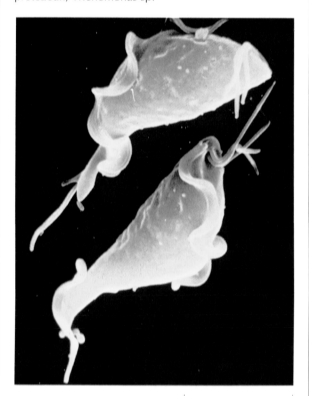

FIGURE 17.9

Scanning electron micrograph of the flagellated protozoan, *Trichomonas* sp.

5 μm

Newborns lack an intestinal normal flora, but very soon after birth the infant's intestine becomes colonized by microorganisms. It is interesting that the intestinal normal flora of the young breast-fed infant consists mainly of bifidobacteria, which are Gram-positive anaerobic rods, whereas bottle-fed infants have lactobacilli, which are Gram-positive microaerophilic to anaerobic rods. With eventual substitution of solid food and an adult-type diet, a Gram-negative normal flora consisting mainly of *Bacteroides* species will predominate. This is probably because without the high lactose content of milk for fermentation by the bifidobacteria and the lactobacilli to form organic acids, the stool becomes less acidic and favors the growth of the Gram-negative microorganisms.

Factors Influencing the Normal Flora of the Intestine. The composition of the normal flora of the intestine can be influenced by various factors, such as strong emotional stress and starvation. It should be noted that, in the progress of intestinal infections caused by pathogenic microorganisms, the intestinal flora undergoes considerable change. Alteration of the flora also occurs in persons receiving antibiotic treatment; here, microorganisms susceptible to the antibiotic being administered may be overgrown by antibiotic-resistant strains. Other factors that may affect or regulate the normal flora are diet, the bile acids secreted into the duodenum from the gallbladder, and the presence of antibodies secreted into the intestine.

FIGURE 17.10
Entamoeba histolytica, a commensal amoeba in the human colon, can be the cause of amoebiasis (amoebic dysentery) under certain conditions.

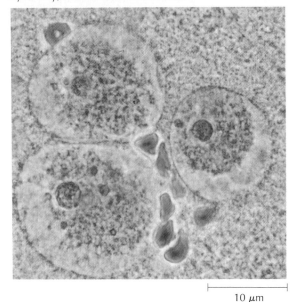

10 μm

Implantation of Lactobacilli. As indicated in the preceding paragraph, prolonged therapy with certain antibiotics may eliminate many normal intestinal microorganisms, permitting antibiotic-resistant species to thrive. This, in turn, may cause gastrointestinal disturbance such as constipation or diarrhea. The oral administration of the harmless Gram-positive bacterium *Lactobacillus acidophilus* will alleviate the intestinal disorder in some instances. The principle is that ingestion of large numbers of the lactobacilli may result in replacement of undesirable intestinal organisms by harmless or beneficial organisms, a concept first proposed by the Russian bacteriologist Elie Metchnikoff in the early days of bacteriology. The implantation of the lactobacilli seems to depend on ingestion of a large number of the organisms and on supplying a suitable carbohydrate such as lactose that is not readily absorbed by the body but can be used easily by the organisms. Several commercial products containing lactobacilli are available for therapeutic use.

Genitourinary Tract

In a healthy person, the kidney, ureters, and urinary bladder are free of microorganisms. The upper portion of the urethra, the canal that carries the urine to the outside of the body, is also bacteria-free; thus, in health the urine within the bladder is sterile. However, bacteria are commonly found in the *lower* portion of the urethra in both males and females. Gram-positive bacteria (*Staphylococcus epidermidis, Streptococcus faecalis,* and corynebacteria) are found frequently; Gram-negative cocci (*Neisseria* spp.) and Gram-negative facultatively anaerobic rods such as *E. coli* are occasionally present. The upper portion of the urethra, near the bladder, has no microorganisms, apparently because of some antibacterial effect exerted by the urethral mucous membranes and because of the mechanical removal of microorganisms by the frequent flushing of the urethral epithelium by urine. Urine acquires microorganisms as it passes from the bladder to the outside of the body through the lower portion of the urethra.

The adult female genital tract has a very complex normal flora. The character of this population changes with the menstrual cycle. The main residents of the adult vagina during the years of ovarian activity are the acid-tolerant lactobacilli; these break down glycogen produced by the vaginal epithelium, forming lactic acid in the process. As a result, the pH in the vagina is maintained at about 4.4 to 4.6. Microorganisms capable of multiplying at this low pH are found in the vagina and include enterococci, corynebacteria, the yeast *Candida albicans,* and large numbers of anaerobic bacteria. The accumulation of glycogen in the vaginal wall is due to the activity of the ovaries, the female reproductive organs that produce eggs and sex hormones. Thus glycogen is not present before puberty or after menopause. In its absence the vaginal secretions are mildly alkaline and contain normal skin and colon microorganisms.

ASK YOURSELF

1 What sites in the body are free of microorganisms?

2 What factors make the skin hostile to the survival and growth of nonresident bacteria?

3 How does the upper respiratory tract mechanically remove bacteria?

4 Why is there not a normal flora in the lower respiratory tract?

5 Why is adherence an important characteristic of members of the normal flora in the oral cavity?

6 What is dental plaque?

7 Why are there very few bacteria in the stomach?

SUMMARY

1 The human body is inhabited by about 10^{14} microorganisms, mainly bacteria, which comprise the *resident* flora found on the mucous membranes of inner surfaces of the body and on the skin. *Transient* microorganisms are found on or in the body, but only for short periods of time.

2 A healthy human fetus is microbiologically sterile, but it acquires microorganisms during and after birth. Eventually the child will have the same kind of normal flora as an adult in the same environment.

3 Studies comparing germfree animals with normal animals have shown that the normal flora stimulates development of the immune system and resistance to infection in the host, and that it also contributes vitamins to an animal's nutrition.

4 Antimicrobial agents can suppress the normal flora and produce undesirable effects in the host, because, for example, the natural flora serves as a defense against infection by potential pathogens.

5 Resident microorganisms adhere to host epithelial cells by means of surface proteins or polysaccharides, or by pili. The normal flora may also produce antimicrobial substances that inhibit other microbes.

6 In a healthy individual, different sites on the body have characteristic normal flora, or perhaps no normal flora. For example, the blood, body fluids, and tissues are free of microorganisms.

7 The skin is a hostile environment for many microbes because of its dryness, its low pH, and the presence of inhibitory substances such as fatty acids. However, normal skin resident microbes can survive and thrive.

8 The normal flora of the conjunctiva is sparse because of the flushing action of tears and lytic action of lysozyme.

9 The mucus layer covering the epithelial cells of the upper respiratory tract traps many microbes. Cilia cause the mucus to flow downward and to be swallowed, and trapped microbes are destroyed by hydrochloric acid of the stomach. However, resident microbes adhere to the epithelial cells and are not removed. The lower respiratory tract does not have a normal flora.

10 The mouth is a hostile environment for many microbes because of the flushing action of saliva; however, normal flora microbes adhere firmly to the mouth surfaces. Dental plaque contains a very high number of bacteria. *Streptococcus mutans* initiates dental caries. *Treponema denticola, Porphyromonas gingivalis,* and other anaerobic bacteria are probably the cause of gum disease.

11 In the stomach, the normal flora are sparse because hydrochloric acid destroys many bacteria. Relatively few bacteria occur in the duodenum and jejunum, but the numbers increase markedly in the ileum.

12 The large intestine has the highest number of microbes, despite the continual movement of material through its channel, desquamation of epithelial cells, and the trapping action of mucus.

13 In the genitourinary tract, the kidney, ureters, bladder, and upper portion of the urethra are normally free of bacteria. However, bacteria normally occur in the lower portion of the urethra. The adult female genital tract has a complex normal flora. Its composition changes with variation in the menstrual cycle.

KEY TERMS

cesarean section
conjunctiva
dental plaque
dermis
desquamation
endocarditis
epidermis
gnotobiotic
normal flora
opportunistic pathogens
peristalsis
resident flora
transient flora

NORMAL FLORA OF THE HEALTHY HUMAN HOST

1 The normal flora of the human body is composed mainly of: **(a)** fungi; **(b)** protozoa; **(c)** bacteria; **(d)** viruses; **(e)** algae.

2 The microbes that compose the normal flora of the body reside mainly: **(a)** in the blood; **(b)** in the internal organs; **(c)** on the skin and mucous membranes; **(d)** in the tissues; **(e)** throughout the body.

3 A microorganism that is normally harmless but can cause disease if the defense mechanisms of the body against infection are weakened is called a(n) _____ _____ .

4 The normal flora may be considered the _____ flora. Microorganisms that disappear after a brief period constitute the _____ flora.

ORIGIN OF THE NORMAL FLORA

5 Which *two* of the following statements are correct? **(a)** Before birth a healthy human fetus has already acquired a normal flora. **(b)** Under natural circumstances, the fetus first acquires microorganisms while passing down the birth canal. **(c)** A normal, healthy human fetus is microbiologically sterile before birth. **(d)** A child will eventually have a very different kind of normal flora from that of an adult person in the same environment. **(e)** The normal flora of the skin on a child would have the same mixture of microbial species as the normal flora of the large intestine.

EFFECT OF THE NORMAL FLORA ON THE HUMAN HOST

6 Match the term on the left with the appropriate description on the right.

_____lactic acid

_____cesarean section

_____pili

_____S. salivarius

_____desquamation

_____C. difficile

(a) Detachment of epithelial cells from body surfaces
(b) Responsible for attachment of some bacteria to host cells
(c) A fermentation product that may inhibit some bacteria
(d) The means of initially obtaining germfree animals
(e) Adheres preferentially to the surface of the tongue
(f) Causes pseudomembranous colitis

7 Microbial adherence occurs as a result of a molecular interaction between the microbial cell surface and a chemical _____ on the body cell.

8 Germfree animals require vitamin _____, which normal animals do not require from an exogenous source.

9 Treatment of the skin of humans with antibacterial agents results in suppression of the normal Gram-_____ flora and promotes growth of Gram-_____ bacilli.

DISTRIBUTION AND OCCURRENCE OF THE NORMAL FLORA

10 Most viruses are not considered a part of the normal flora, because if they are present they usually _____ .

11 The enteric cytopathogenic human orphan viruses, commonly referred to as _____ , were termed orphans because they were not associated with any _____ .

12 The skin surface is a hostile environment for many bacteria because of three of the following factors: **(a)** dryness; **(b)** high pH; **(c)** high acidity; **(d)** lysozyme in sweat gland secretions; **(e)** high moisture content.

13 Some skin regions, such as the skin between the toes, have a higher population of bacteria than other skin areas because they are more _____.

14 A common anaerobic bacterium that lives in the fluid of sebaceous glands is:
(a) *Streptococcus salivarius;* **(b)** *Staphylococcus epidermidis;* **(c)** *Clostridium difficile;*
(d) *Propionibacterium acnes;* **(e)** *Escherichia coli.*

15 Match the item on the left with the appropriate statement on the right.

_____ conjunctiva

_____ hydrochloric acid

_____ lysozyme

_____ macrophages

_____ cilia

(a) Have a beating action that causes the mucus layer to flow along

(b) Antimicrobial agent found in tears

(c) Delicate membrane lining the eyelids and covering the eyeball

(d) Antimicrobial agent secreted by the stomach

(e) Body cells that can engulf and destroy bacteria

16 As inspired air passes along the air passages of the nose and nasopharynx, microbes can be trapped by the _____ that overlies the epithelial surfaces.

17 Two factors that tend to remove microorganisms from the mouth are (1) desquamation and (2) _____.

18 *Streptococcus mutans* produces a glucan that enables the cells to adhere firmly to the surface of the _____. The glucan is formed by the action of an enzyme on the disaccharide _____.

19 In adults, the gingival crevices in the mouth become colonized by: **(a)** yeasts;
(b) anaerobic bacteria; **(c)** *Streptococcus mutans;* **(d)** *Trichomonas hominis;*
(e) aerobic bacteria.

20 The fluid contents of the stomach generally contain fewer than _____ bacteria per milliliter.

21 The numbers of bacteria are generally low in the small intestine, except for an increase in the third or last portion, called the _____.

22 The percent of the wet weight of feces that is represented by bacteria and other microorganisms is: **(a)** 1; **(b)** 25; **(c)** 40 to 50; **(d)** 75; **(e)** 95.

23 The two major genera of Gram-negative anaerobic bacilli in the colon are:
(a) *Streptococcus* and *Lactobacillus;* **(b)** *Escherichia* and *Proteus;* **(c)** *Bacteroides* and *Fusobacterium;* **(d)** *Bifidobacterium* and *Eubacterium;* **(e)** *Klebsiella* and *Candida.*

24 A species of protozoa which can live as a commensal in the intestine but can also be pathogenic, causing amoebiasis, is _____.

25 The main bacterial inhabitants of the adult vagina during the years of ovarian activity are lactobacilli, which form lactic acid by breaking down: **(a)** proteins;
(b) sucrose; **(c)** fatty acids; **(d)** glycogen; **(e)** amino acids.

26 The acid-tolerant flora of the adult vagina during the years of ovarian activity includes enterococci, corynebacteria, anaerobic bacteria, and the yeast _____.

REVIEW QUESTIONS

1 How are germfree animals obtained and reared?

2 Differentiate between *resident* and *transient* microorganisms found on the human body.

3 Give the practical reasons for knowing about the normal human flora.

4 Explain how a healthy human fetus acquires a normal flora.

5 What benefits might a human host derive from the normal flora?

6 Discuss the factors that make the following environments difficult to colonize: **(a)** skin; **(b)** upper portion of the urethra; **(c)** trachea; **(d)** stomach; **(e)** conjunctiva.

7 What role does microbial adherence play in establishment of the normal flora? Give an example.

8 What role does mucus play in preventing microorganisms of inhaled air from reaching the air sacs of the lung?

9 Describe the microorganisms that are found in the acidic environments of the human body.

10 Discuss the implications of germfree life on animals.

DISCUSSION QUESTIONS

1 Why should there be a characteristic flora at each body site of the human host that harbors microorganisms?

2 Why are viruses not generally considered part of the normal flora? Does the requirement for viral replication support this concept?

3 Why is it inadvisable to change the ecology of the normal flora on the human host?

4 What can we learn about the normal flora from the use of germfree animals in research?

5 Discuss the characteristics of members of the normal flora that enable them to have selective advantages over other microorganisms.

6 When members of the normal flora of a particular site are moved to another location of the human body, do they remain as commensals?

7 What are some host factors that work to keep transient microorganisms from colonizing the respiratory tract?

8 Why can we say that proper maintenance of the normal flora is important in keeping the mouth healthy?

Host-Parasite Interactions: Nonspecific Host Resistance

OBJECTIVES

After reading this chapter you should be able to

1 Appreciate that good health is the best protection against infections by invading microorganisms.

2 Differentiate between a primary pathogen and an opportunistic pathogen.

3 Define terms used in describing the pathogenicity of microorganisms.

4 Describe several microbial virulence factors.

5 Describe some predisposing factors of host resistance at the species, racial, and individual level.

6 Explain the significance of inflammation and fever in the host-parasite relationship.

7 Identify the components of the body's vanguard of defense against invading microorganisms.

8 Discuss the roles played by the different soluble mediators in the internal defense mechanisms of the host.

9 Describe the two kinds of nonspecific cellular mediators in host defense against tumors or invading microorganisms.

OVERVIEW

Our entire life is spent in contact with microorganisms. In Chapter 17 you learned that many kinds of microbes normally inhabit the human body as harmless commensals. However, if the defense mechanisms of the body are weakened, some of these commensals may become opportunistic pathogens and cause disease. Other pathogenic microorganisms (considered as parasites) may also invade the human body and cause disease. Whether a disease condition occurs depends on the outcome of the interaction between the parasitic microbe and its host.

The interactions that form the host-parasite relationship are complex. When a parasite tries to establish infection, the host responds by mobilizing an array of defense mechanisms. The ability to ward off disease through defense mechanisms is termed *resistance*. Lack of resistance is termed *susceptibility*.

Host resistance to parasite invasion may be divided into two types: *nonspecific resistance* and *specific resistance*. Nonspecific, or natural, resistance includes those natural defense mechanisms that protect the host from any kind of parasite regardless of whether or not the body has encountered that type of parasite previously; it is discussed in this chapter. Specific resistance, or *immunity,* concerns those defense mechanisms that have developed in response to a particular, or specific, parasite. Such specific immune defense mechanisms—the subject of the next chapter—are acquired by the host as a result of exposure to the parasite.

In the world of organisms, nonspecific resistance is the most common and basic means of warding off disease. Plants and most animals survive a hostile world of potential pathogens with only nonspecific resistance as their defense. Only vertebrate animals are capable of specific resistance, or acquiring a specific immune response. Thus they are more efficient in combating infection. First they use nonspecific resistance mechanisms, which are immediately available, against invading parasites; later on, they rely on the mechanisms of specific immunity as reinforcement or, in the case of a persistent infection, as the ultimate means of resistance. If the combined effects of both natural resistance and acquired immunity are unable to halt the spread of infection, the death of the host is invariably the final result.

To help the host, antimicrobial therapy, such as the use of antibiotics, is administered. This treatment does not always completely destroy the parasites. In most instances it only "buys time" to give the host an opportunity to eliminate the parasite by whatever defense mechanisms the host can bring to bear on the parasite.

THE MICROORGANISM AS A PATHOGEN

The capability of a microorganism to cause disease is called **pathogenicity.** When a microbe invades a host (i.e., when it enters the body tissues and multiplies), it establishes an *infection.* If the host is susceptible to the infection and its functions are impaired, this is called *disease.* Thus a *pathogen* is any microorganism or larger organism capable of causing disease. An example of a larger pathogen is the *Trichinella* worm that causes trichinosis, a parasitic disease affecting muscle tissue.

The ability of a pathogenic microorganism to cause disease (its *pathogenicity*) is influenced not only by the properties inherent in the microbe, but also by the ability of the host to resist infection. In recent years, increasing numbers of infections have been caused by microorganisms previously considered nonpathogens; most are members of the normal flora described in Chapter 17. These infections develop in people whose resistance factors are compromised by another disease or by prolonged antibiotic and immunosuppressive therapy. Such microorganisms are called *opportunistic pathogens;* they are distinguished from *primary pathogens,* which can initiate disease in *healthy* individuals.

The *degree* of the ability of a pathogen, opportunistic or primary, to cause disease is termed **virulence.** Thus microbial properties that enhance a microorganism's pathogenicity are called *virulence factors.* If one

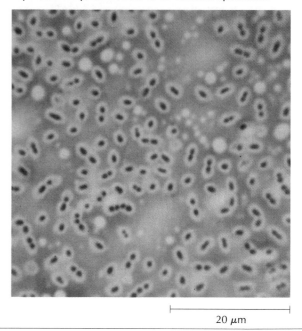

FIGURE 18.1

Large capsules, made up of polysaccharides, are produced by *Streptococcus pneumoniae*. The presence of capsules in pneumococci confers virulence upon the bacterium, as it does in other bacteria. Shown is capsulated *S. pneumoniae* in an exudate specimen.

20 μm

microbe is more capable of producing a disease, it is said to be more virulent than another. The virulence factors of some pathogens are easily identified. For example, cells of *Streptococcus pneumoniae* that have capsules are virulent and can cause pneumonia, whereas those without capsules are avirulent [FIGURE 18.1]; virulent strains of *Corynebacterium diphtheriae* produce a toxin that causes diphtheria. For most pathogens, however, the virulence factors are not so obvious.

In order to cause infectious disease, a pathogen *must* accomplish the following complex steps:

1 It must infect the host (a primary pathogen must enter the host).
2 It must metabolize and multiply in the host tissue.
3 It must resist host defenses, for a time.
4 It must damage the host.

Microbial Virulence Factors

Some bacteria secrete substances that contribute to their virulence, while others have special structures. Unfortunately, in many microorganisms, the properties conferring virulence are either unclear or unknown. Several well-known microbial virulence factors are considered here.

Toxins. Some microorganisms produce poisonous substances known as *toxins.* The capability of a microorganism to produce a toxin—a substance that has a damaging effect on cells and tissues in a host—and the potency of the toxin are important factors in the ability of the microorganism to cause disease. The toxins produced by microorganisms may be *exotoxins,* toxins excreted into the surrounding medium; or *endotoxins,* toxins retained within the cell as part of the cell.

Exotoxins are excreted from the microbial cells into a culture medium or into the circulatory system and tissues of a host. The medium might be an improperly processed can of vegetables contaminated with *Clostridium botulinum,* for example; ingestion of the vegetables containing botulinum toxin results in food poisoning called *botulism.* In botulism food poisoning, the exotoxin that is ingested by an individual causes paralysis by affecting the person's nervous system; thus the toxin is called a *neurotoxin.* Infection of the host by the bacterium is not necessary for the disease to occur. Therefore, strictly speaking, botulism is not an infectious disease, but a *toxemia* caused by a bacterial toxin produced outside of the host. When the bacillus *Corynebacterium diphtheriae* grows in the human throat and secretes its exotoxin, the toxin is absorbed into the bloodstream and causes the disease diphtheria. When the tetanus bacillus *Clostridium tetani* is introduced into a wound, it may grow and form tetanus exotoxin (which is also a neurotoxin). Thus, unlike botulism, tetanus and diphtheria are caused by organisms that produce their toxins *while growing within the host.*

Exotoxins are proteins; they can be produced by either Gram-negative or Gram-positive bacteria. Their effects on human tissues are usually highly specific. For example, the toxins of botulism and tetanus are neurotoxins. The cholera vibrio secretes an exotoxin called an *enterotoxin* which decreases the retention of fluid by the intestine, thereby causing diarrhea. Thus exotoxins usually have an affinity for a particular tissue to which they can cause damage. Exotoxins lose their toxicity when they are heated or treated chemically. Phenol, formaldehyde, β-propiolactone, and various acids can modify exotoxins chemically so that they lose their toxicity. They are then called *toxoids.*

Both toxins and toxoids have the ability to stimulate the production of **antitoxins,** antibodies which neutralize the toxicity of toxins in the body of the host. This ability is important in the protection of susceptible hosts from diseases caused by bacterial toxins. Antitoxins can be produced commercially as well. TABLE 18.1 shows some of the well-known diseases caused by exotoxin-producing bacteria.

Many microorganisms, particularly the Gram-negative bacteria, do not secrete a soluble toxin, but make an endotoxin that is liberated only when the cells disintegrate. The endotoxins of Gram-negative bacteria are structural components of the outer membrane of Gram-negative bacterial cell walls. These components are lipopolysaccharides (specifically, the lipid A portion). Endotoxins are effective poisons both in the bound state (when still part of the intact cell wall) and when released as lytic products upon cell disintegration. Compared with exotoxins, endotoxins are highly heat-stable, do not form toxoids, and are less toxic. Endotoxins are responsible for many disease symptoms such as fever and shock. The general characteristics of exotoxins and endotoxins are summarized in TABLE 18.2.

The detection of endotoxin in various body fluids is helpful in the laboratory diagnosis of infections caused by Gram-negative bacteria. A laboratory method called the *Limulus amebocyte lysate* (LAL) assay can detect tiny amounts of endotoxin. *Limulus polyphemus* is the Atlantic coast horseshoe crab, and the hemolymph (blood) of this crab contains a single type of white cells

TABLE 18.1
Some Well-Known Diseases Caused by Bacteria That Produce Exotoxins

Disease	Bacterial species	Toxin activity in vivo
Botulism	*Clostridium botulinum*	Neurotoxin, muscle paralysis
Cholera	*Vibrio cholerae*	Loss of fluid from small intestine; vomiting
Staphylococcal food poisoning	*Staphylococcus aureus*	Nausea; vomiting; diarrhea
Diphtheria	*Corynebacterium diphtheriae*	Nerve paralysis; heart damage
Bacillary dysentery	*Shigella dysenteriae*	Neurological disturbances; diarrhea
Tetanus	*Clostridium tetani*	Neurotoxin, spasmodic muscle contraction
Scarlet fever	*Streptococcus pyogenes*	Rash
Whooping cough	*Bordetella pertussis*	Paroxysmal coughing; vomiting

TABLE 18.2
Some Distinguishing Characteristics of Exotoxins and Endotoxins

Property	Exotoxin	Endotoxin
Bacterial source	Excreted by certain Gram-positive and Gram-negative bacteria	Released from cell walls of lysed Gram-negative bacteria
Chemical nature	Proteins	Lipopolysaccharide
Heat tolerance	Labile	Stable
Immunology	Convertible to toxoids	Cannot form toxoids
Biological effect	Specific for a particular type of cell function	Generalized effect such as shock and fever
Lethal dose	Minute amounts (high toxicity)	Much larger amounts (low toxicity)

TABLE 18.3
Some Extracellular Enzymes That Contribute to Microbial Virulence

Enzyme	Action	Example of enzyme-producing bacteria
Hyaluronidase	Hydrolyzes hyaluronic acid in tissue; invasive factor	Staphylococci, streptococci, clostridia
Coagulase	Clots plasma; useful in identification	*Staphylococcus aureus*
Lecithinase	Hydrolyzes membrane lipids	*Clostridium perfringens*
Collagenase	Hydrolyzes collagen in tissue; invasive factor	*Clostridium perfringens*
Leucocidin	Kills leucocytes	*Staphylococcus aureus*
Hemolysin	Lyses red blood cells; invasive factor	Staphylococci, streptococci, clostridia

called *amebocytes*. Each amebocyte is packed with proteins responsible for clotting. When the crab blood contacts endotoxin in a purified form or as a component of Gram-negative bacteria, the clotting proteins of the amebocytes are released and the blood forms a gel or clot. This clotting reaction is supposed to be advantageous to the crab because it localizes an infection in a walled-off area and prevents blood loss.

Extracellular Enzymes. The virulence of some microorganisms is partly due to the production of extracellular enzymes. Although no single extracellular enzyme has been proved to be the sole factor responsible for virulence, there is no doubt that such enzymes do play some role in the pathogenic process. The ability of pathogenic bacteria to penetrate tissues, or *invasiveness*, is due to some of these enzymes. TABLE 18.3 lists some extracellular bacterial enzymes that contribute to the disease process. The most common of these are discussed in the paragraphs that follow; some of these can be used to help identify the pathogen causing disease.

Hyaluronidase may help the pathogen to penetrate the tissues of the host by hydrolyzing hyaluronic acid, an essential "tissue cement" that helps hold living cells together. Because of this, the enzyme is referred to as the "spreading factor." *Staphylococcus aureus*, *Streptococcus pyogenes*, and *Clostridium perfringens* produce hyaluronidase. *Lecithinase* is an enzyme that lyses various tissue cells, especially red blood cells, by hydrolyzing membrane lipids. For example, the virulence of *Clostridium perfringens* (cause of gas gangrene) is due, at least in part, to the production of lecithinase. *Collagenase*, also produced by *Clostridium perfringens*, destroys collagen, a tissue fiber found in muscle, bone, and cartilage. Collagen provides the meshwork within which the tissue cells lie. Without it, tissue is more susceptible to invasion by a pathogen.

Some virulent staphylococci produce the enzyme called *coagulase*. It acts with a substance in the plasma to transform fibrinogen to fibrin. This causes the deposition of fibrin around the bacterial cells, thus protecting them from the action of host phagocytes (cells that eat foreign

FIGURE 18.2

[A] α Hemolysis. Enzymes produced by some bacteria only partially hemolyze red blood cells of certain species of animals. Colonies on blood-agar plates are surrounded by a greenish-colored zone which is due to the reduction of hemoglobin in the red blood cells to methemoglobin. [B] β Hemolysis. Enzymes produced by other bacteria completely hemolyze red blood cells of certain species of animals. Colonies on blood-agar plates are surrounded by a clear, colorless zone.

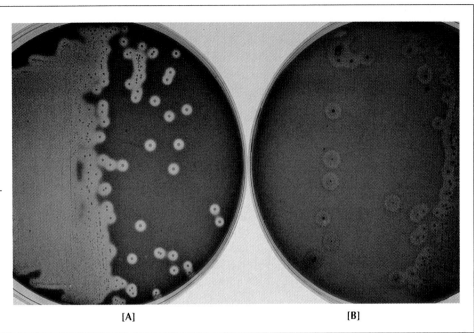

[A]   [B]

objects). There is some evidence that coagulase is also involved in the *walling-off* process (formation of peripheral insoluble protein) in boils caused by staphylococci.

Hemolysins are substances that lyse red blood cells, releasing their hemoglobin. Generally speaking, hemolytic strains of pathogenic bacteria are more virulent than nonhemolytic strains of the same species. Bacterial hemolysins from various species differ in their chemical nature and mode of action. Some hemolysins produce visible changes on blood-agar plates [FIGURE 18.2]. On these plates, colonies of certain hemolytic bacteria are surrounded by a clear, colorless zone where the red blood cells have been lysed completely. This is called **β hemolysis.** Other types of bacteria can reduce the hemoglobin in red cells to methemoglobin, which results in a greenish zone around the colonies. This is called **α hemolysis.** Hemolytic reactions are used frequently in the clinical laboratory to help identify a pathogen; for example, group A streptococci, a cause of strep throat, produce β hemolysis on blood-agar plates.

Cellular Factors. The virulence of bacteria is influenced, in many cases, by the presence or absence of *capsules.* When pathogens lose their capsules, such as by mutation, they lose their ability to cause disease. Pneumococci are virulent when capsulated [see FIGURE 18.1] but avirulent when not capsulated. The increased virulence of capsulated strains is due to the ability of the capsular polysaccharide to prevent **phagocytosis**, or engulfment, by host phagocytes. This ability is probably due to surface properties of the capsule, which prevent the phagocyte from forming a close enough contact with the bacterium to engulf it.

Another cellular factor that may enhance the virulence of some pathogens is the *pilus.* Pili help an organism adhere better to the surface of host cells, tissues, and mucous membranes. For example, virulent strains of *Neisseria gonorrhoeae* (which causes gonorrhea) and *Escherichia coli* (which can cause urinary tract infection) possess pili.

ASK YOURSELF

1 What is the difference between a *primary* pathogen and an *opportunistic* pathogen?

2 Distinguish between the *pathogenicity* of a microbe and the *virulence* of a pathogenic microorganism.

3 What steps must a pathogen accomplish before it can cause disease?

4 In what respects are exotoxins different from endotoxins?

5 What virulence factors other than toxins do microorganisms use in causing disease?

PREDISPOSING FACTORS OF HOST RESISTANCE

There are predisposing factors of disease **resistance** (ability to ward off disease) that are inherent in each host and in the host's environment. These mechanisms of protection are not directed at any one specific pathogen and thus are *nonspecific* resistance factors. Some of these factors are difficult to evaluate in a quantitative sense. If a host develops defense mechanisms in response to a *specific* pathogen, or specific resistance, that host has *immunity* against that pathogen.

Environmental Resistance Factors

Naturally resistant hosts either do not provide some of the essential nutritional factors required by the microorganism for growth, or they have other defense mechanisms to resist infection by the microbe. Certain environmental factors of the human host may also play a role in giving the host either resistance or *susceptibility* (lack of resistance) to infection. These include physical and emotional stresses on the host, and the host's age, general health and state of nutrition, social and economic conditions, occupational hazards, and personal hygiene. These factors are so intertwined that it is difficult to evaluate their individual contributions to the disease process. Overall, whenever susceptibility factors exceed resistance factors in the delicate balance between disease and health, disease develops [FIGURE 18.3].

Severe physical and emotional stresses—such as sleep deprivation, fatigue, anxiety, and depression—make a person more vulnerable to disease. In the stressed condition, there is enhanced production of epinephrine (adrenaline) accompanied by altered levels of adrenal corticoid hormones; this suppresses the function of many groups of defensive cells and depresses a wide range of defense mechanisms used by the body. For example, people who undergo prolonged sleep deprivation are predisposed to infections.

Age of the host also plays a role in disease susceptibility, with the very young and the very old having the highest risk of infection. In a young child the immune system is less developed or experienced, while in an elderly person it is no longer as efficient. Thus young people are susceptible to "children's diseases" such as measles and chicken pox. The aged are susceptible to diseases such as pneumococcal pneumonia.

Many other environmental factors of the human host are quite obvious. Poor nutrition and substandard housing contribute to greater disease incidence. For instance, a diet containing the required amounts of proteins and vitamins is directly related to protection from microbial disease. Dietary proteins are used to make healthy tissues and serum proteins, while vitamins promote efficient metabolism and maintain integrity of skin and membrane surfaces. People working at certain jobs have a greater-than-average risk of certain infections. For example, dental health care personnel have a greater risk of being infected with the hepatitis B virus, carried in aerosols of saliva and blood from their patients. Fortunately, health care personnel have been educated on how to protect themselves, as well as how to prevent spreading the disease to others.

Species, Racial, and Individual Resistance

Resistance to infection varies with the species of animal or plant. For example, *Yersinia pestis* may be carried by ground squirrels, in which it causes no obvious disease. But when the bacterium is transmitted by fleas from the squirrels to humans, it causes the fatal disease called *plague*. Dogs do not become infected with measles, and humans do not contract dog distemper. The reason resistance varies from one species to another is usually unknown. However, basic physiological and anatomical characteristics of a species can determine whether a microorganism can be pathogenic for that species. For example, because of differences in normal body tempera-

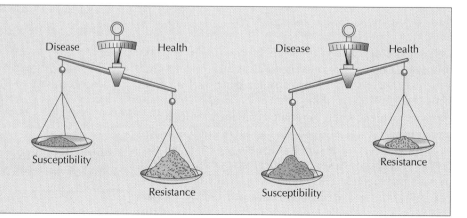

FIGURE 18.3

Host-parasite relationship in health and disease: the balance between resistance and susceptibility. Excess of resistance factors over susceptibility factors means good health; excess of susceptibility factors over resistance factors means disease.

ture, many diseases of mammals do not affect fish or reptiles, and vice versa. Herbivorous animals are usually resistant to enteric diseases of carnivores—probably because herbivores have multiple stomachs and different intestinal microbial flora and digestive juices. Diseases of the skin, to which humans are quite susceptible, are often resisted by other animals because they have more hair and thicker hides. Species resistance is an obstacle in biomedical research, because it is more difficult to study diseases that cannot be reproduced in laboratory animals used as disease models. Two such diseases are syphilis and cholera, which have no animal models for use in laboratory experiments.

In some cases, there may be genetic factors that make certain races of people more susceptible (or more resistant) than other races to a particular infection. For instance, resistance to malarial infection is found in almost all African blacks. This is attributed to the absence of a specific component on their red blood cell membranes to which the malarial parasite *Plasmodium vivax* must bind in order to invade and multiply. The Plains Indians of North America lost two-thirds of their population to smallpox and tuberculosis because their resistance to these diseases was very low. They had not been exposed to these diseases previously, unlike the European settlers who survived because their ancestors were genetically more resistant as a result of selection due to prior exposure.

Some people appear to experience fewer or less severe infections than others, even though they apparently have the same racial background and opportunity for exposure. Such individual resistance is probably due to a combination of nonspecific and specific resistance factors inherited from their parents. Thus some people have many more colds during the winter than do others.

ASK YOURSELF

1 What is meant by predisposing factors of host resistance?

2 Why are such host resistance factors *nonspecific*?

3 What are some environmental resistance factors of the human host?

4 What explanations are offered to explain species resistance to disease?

EXTERNAL DEFENSE MECHANISMS

External defense mechanisms are another factor in nonspecific host resistance. These are largely mechanical, but chemical barriers are also involved. Mechanical barriers created by the skin and mucous membranes, together with host secretions, are usually regarded as the body's vanguard of defense against invading microorganisms [DISCOVER 18.1].

Skin and Mucous Membranes

As mentioned in Chapter 17, the unbroken skin and mucous membranes are effective mechanical barriers to infectious agents [FIGURE 18.4]. The surface of the skin is also inhibitory to the growth of most microorganisms because of low moisture, low pH, and the presence of secreted inhibitory substances. However, it is possible for some microorganisms to enter the skin through hair follicles, sebaceous glands, sweat glands, or abrasions.

Similar to the skin, mucous membranes consist of an epithelial layer and an underlying connective tissue layer. They line the entire digestive, respiratory, urinary, and reproductive tracts [FIGURE 18.4]. The epithelial layer of a mucous membrane secretes *mucus*, a viscous fluid that prevents the tracts from drying out and aids in the removal of any microorganisms present. Mucous secretions collect and hold many microorganisms until they can be disposed of or have lost their infectivity.

Chemical Secretions

In addition to the mechanical barriers such as skin and mucous membranes, secreted chemical substances with antimicrobial action are an important component of external defense. (Some of these were also mentioned in Chapter 17.) For instance, the mucous membranes secrete many substances, including enzymes, which can impair microbial infectivity. More specifically, *lysozyme* is an enzyme found in many body fluids and secretions such as tears; it can break down the cell walls of Gram-positive bacteria and a few Gram-negative bacteria by hydrolyzing peptidoglycan. An oily substance called *sebum* is produced by the sebaceous glands of the skin; it prevents hair from drying and becoming brittle and forms a covering over the skin surface. Sebum contains unsaturated fatty acids, which inhibit the growth of certain microorganisms. Gastric juice is produced by the glands of the stomach. It is a mixture of hydrochloric

FIGURE 18.4

The skin and mucous membranes are effective mechanical barriers between the environment and the internal parts of the human body. Areas of the human body lined by skin or mucous membranes are indicated.

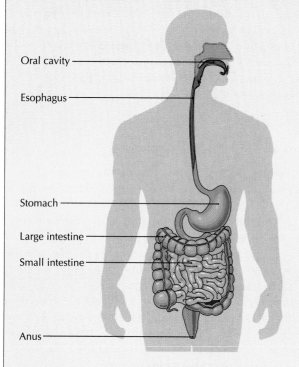

Oral cavity

Esophagus

Stomach

Large intestine

Small intestine

Anus

ALIMENTARY TRACT

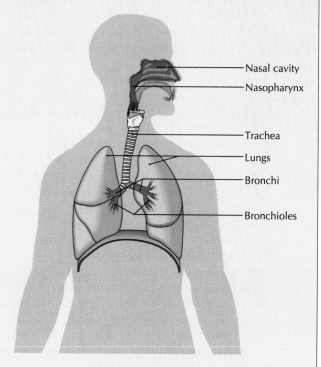

Nasal cavity

Nasopharynx

Trachea

Lungs

Bronchi

Bronchioles

RESPIRATORY TRACT

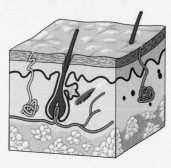

SKIN

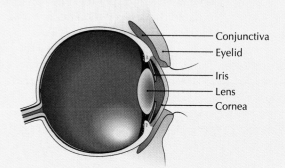

Conjunctiva

Eyelid

Iris

Lens

Cornea

CONJUNCTIVA OF THE EYE

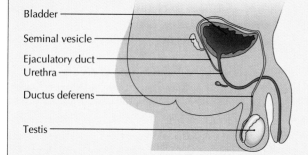

Bladder

Seminal vesicle

Ejaculatory duct

Urethra

Ductus deferens

Testis

MALE GENITOURINARY TRACT
(SAGITTAL SECTION)

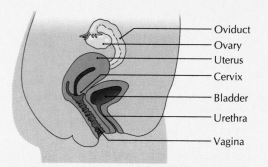

Oviduct

Ovary

Uterus

Cervix

Bladder

Urethra

Vagina

FEMALE GENITOURINARY TRACT
(SAGITTAL SECTION)

18.1 WHY NOT IMMUNIZATION OF GREEN PLANTS?

Devastating animal diseases such as smallpox and distemper have been eliminated or at least controlled by immunization. But the diseases of plants can be devastating as well, destroying the economics of a region and causing food shortages. Despite the importance of plant diseases, the primary defense for green plants against plant disease is the development of resistant plants through breeding. At present, breeding provides the only mechanism for resistance to viral diseases and the only economically sound mechanism for resistance to bacterial diseases. This differs from animals, in which immunization is the basis for preventive medicine. But plants are also attacked by microorganisms that travel from host to host. So, why not immunization for green plants?

Although there have been sporadic reports of plant immunization from as long ago as 1933, only recently has research clearly established the validity of plant immunization.

Most of the recent work has been done by Joseph Kuc of the Department of Plant Pathology, University of Kentucky in Lexington. He and others have shown that plants can be systemically immunized against microbial diseases by using a restricted infection with fungi, bacteria, or viruses. For example, Kuc showed that controlled infection with the fungus *Collectatrichum lagenarium* or with tobacco necrosis virus protected cucumber, watermelon, and muskmelon against a broad range of pathogens. This "controlled infection" might be inoculation of just one leaf.

The pathogens stopped by this method included fungi, local lesion and systemic viruses, and fungi and bacteria that cause wilts or lesions on foliage and fruit. Immunization was systemic and required a lag period between induction (primary infection) and challenge (introduction of other pathogens). Furthermore, immunization could be enhanced by a booster inoculation. Tangible evidence for successful immunization was an approximately threefold increase in peroxidase activity brought about by a chemical signal which came from the site of induction.

Perhaps we can soon do away with noxious pesticides and increase our green produce by this new promise of disease control in plants!

---

acid, enzymes, and mucus. The high acidity of gastric juice (pH 1.2 to 3) is sufficient to kill most microorganisms. The extreme acidity or alkalinity of body fluids has a detrimental effect on many microorganisms and helps to prevent potential pathogens from entering the deeper tissues of the body. For example, the high acidity of the adult human vagina during the years of ovarian activity protects its membranous surfaces against colonization by many types of pathogenic microbes.

Another protein with known antimicrobial activity is *lactoferrin*. It is an orange-red, iron-containing protein found in milk as well as in most of the secretions that bathe human mucosal surfaces (including bronchial mucus, saliva, nasal discharges, tears, hepatic bile, pancreatic juice, seminal fluid, and urine). It is also an important component of the granules of phagocytic cells. Its serum counterpart is *transferrin*, which is also orange-red when saturated with iron. These proteins tie up, or chelate, available iron in the environment, thus limiting the availability of this essential mineral nutrient to invading microorganisms.

Naturally Occurring Microbial Flora

The important role played by the normal microbial flora in protecting the human host from infection was considered in the preceding chapter. It is therefore sufficient here to emphasize the great importance of the normal flora in competing with pathogenic intruders for particular ecologic niches in the human body.

ASK YOURSELF

1 What factors are usually considered to be the body's vanguard of defense against invading microorganisms?

2 How do the skin and the mucous membrane form effective barriers to infectious agents?

3 What are the specific chemical substances secreted by the human body that are unfavorable for microbial growth or even kill invading microorganisms?

INTERNAL DEFENSE MECHANISMS

When microorganisms breach the external defense mechanisms of the host, they still have to contend with internal defense mechanisms. Components of internal defense mechanisms constitute formidable barriers to infection. They include the cellular mediators of the immune system (natural killer cells and phagocytic cells) and a wide variety of soluble factors that mediate how these cells respond. They also include the complex physiological responses that lead to inflammation and fever.

Inflammation

The *inflammatory response* is the vascular and cellular reaction to the presence of invading microorganisms, injury, or nonliving irritants such as splinters. *Inflammation* is one of the most effective defense mechanisms in animals. Evidence of the inflammatory response can be observed during the body's reaction to a simple thing like a thorn in the flesh. After a few hours the area becomes red, then swollen and painful. The affected area is perceptibly warmer than the surrounding tissue. The redness and heat are caused by an increase in blood flow; blood vessels that carry blood to the area enlarge (the enlargement is called *vasodilation*), while those that carry blood away from the area constrict. Capillary permeability increases, permitting influx of fluids and blood cells into the site; this causes swelling and pain (a result of increased pressure). Vasodilation and increased permeability are triggered by toxic chemicals (such as histamine) released from damaged cells at the site of injury.

If the cause of inflammation is due to invasive microorganisms, then the most important thing that occurs in the inflammatory response is the migration of phagocytic cells from the capillaries to the site of infection. Phagocytic cells engulf and destroy microbes. Thus the inflammatory response brings scavenger cells to the site of infection. (The phagocytic process will be described in more detail later in this chapter.)

In addition to destroying and removing an injurious agent (such as a microbe) or its products, the inflammatory response also limits the effects of the agent (or its products) by confining it or walling it off from the surrounding tissues. This is possible because blood clots around the site prevent the microbe or its noxious byproducts from spreading to other parts of the body. As a consequence, there is a localized collection of *pus* in a cavity caused by the breakdown of body tissues, forming an *abscess*. Pus consists of dead inflammatory cells and tissue cells, as well as dead and living microorganisms.

The final stage of inflammation is *tissue repair*, when all harmful agents or substances have been removed or neutralized at the injury site. The ability of a tissue to repair itself depends in part on the tissue involved. Skin, being a relatively simple tissue, has a high capacity for regeneration. But nerve tissue in the brain, which is highly specialized and complex, appears not to regenerate.

The process of inflammation is summarized in FIGURE 18.5.

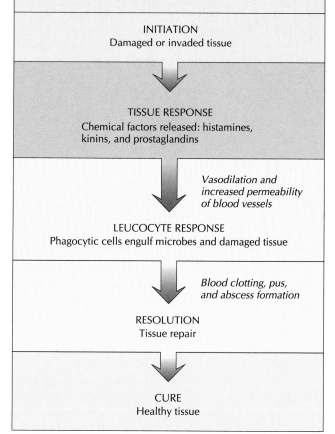

FIGURE 18.5

The process of inflammation may be divided into the following stages: initiation, tissue response, leucocyte response, resolution, and cure. The characteristics of inflammation include redness, swelling, tenderness, and an increase in temperature of the affected area. These symptoms reflect the cellular events that take place. The redness is due to an accumulation of red blood cells in the area. The swelling is due to fluid (plasma) and phagocyte accumulation.

INITIATION
Damaged or invaded tissue

TISSUE RESPONSE
Chemical factors released: histamines, kinins, and prostaglandins

Vasodilation and increased permeability of blood vessels

LEUCOCYTE RESPONSE
Phagocytic cells engulf microbes and damaged tissue

Blood clotting, pus, and abscess formation

RESOLUTION
Tissue repair

CURE
Healthy tissue

Fever

One of the most important *systemic* responses (responses of the body as a whole) to microbial invasion is *fever,* an abnormally high temperature of the body. The most frequent cause of fever is infection by bacteria or viruses. It may actually be a result of products produced by either the microbe or the host cells as a result of infection. During fever there is a loss of appetite; there also is a headache resulting from dilation of blood vessels in the brain. The temperature rise is due largely to an increase in metabolic heat production. There is also a raised metabolic rate which, together with reduced food intake, results in a high excretion of nitrogen in the urine. If the fever is prolonged, there is a rapid wasting of body fat and muscle.

In humans, the mean daily temperature of the body is 37°C. This constant body temperature is controlled by a "body thermostat" in a part of the brain called the *hypothalamus;* this thermostat is normally set at the body temperature of 37°C. During infections, certain substances affect the hypothalamus, "resetting" the thermostat at a higher temperature. Among these substances are the endotoxins from Gram-negative bacteria; for example, as little as 2 ng per kilogram of body weight of endotoxin from *Salmonella typhi* (the causative agent of typhoid fever) can result in a fever of 43°C. Another fever-inducing substance is *endogenous pyrogen,* produced by the body's phagocytic cells and present in inflammatory exudates and in plasma during disease. (A pyrogen is any fever-inducing substance.) The fever is maintained until the endotoxin or the endogenous pyrogen is eliminated; at this point the thermostat is "reset" at 37°C. The immune response of the body to an infection can also cause a fever. As infections subside, heat-reducing mechanisms such as vasodilation and sweating swing into operation.

Fever is popularly thought to be beneficial to the host, since it increases both the activity of phagocytic cells and the rate of induction of inflammatory and immune responses that have antimicrobial effects. The high temperatures reached during fevers are said to inhibit or destroy infecting microorganisms. However, only the microbes causing two bacterial infections, gonorrhea and syphilis, are actually killed by fever temperatures. In most clinical cases, the high temperatures needed to kill microbes are rarely reached. Indeed, people become disoriented or irrational at 43.3°C, and above this temperature they usually become comatose. Death often results if body temperatures rise to 45°C or brain temperature reaches 40.5°C. This means that there is very little evidence that fever actually kills microorganisms.

Natural Killer Cells

Natural killer cells (NK cells) are large (12 to 15 μm in diameter) lymphocytes whose function is to kill undesirable cells such as tumor cells and virus-infected cells. Lymphocytes are a type of white blood cell, as indicated in TABLE 18.4. They are not phagocytic and do not have the conventional surface markers of other lymphoid cells of the specific immune system. There is also some evidence linking NK cells to nonspecific defense against intracellular protozoan and fungal parasites. NK cell activity is nonspecific and is functional without any specific antigenic stimulation (prior exposure or immunization to antigens of the target cells).

Natural killer cells kill by binding to target cells and

T A B L E 18.4
The White Blood Cells (Leucocytes) in Circulating Blood

Type of leucocyte	Percentages in a normal leucocyte differential count	Function
Granulocytes		
Neutrophils (PMNs)	60–70	Phagocytosis
Basophils	0.5–1	Production of heparin and histamine
Eosinophils	2–4	Phagocytosis
Agranulocytes		
Monocytes	3–8	Phagocytosis
Lymphocytes	20–25	Specific immunity

NOTE: Other formed elements in blood are red blood cells, or erythrocytes (transport of oxygen and carbon dioxide); and platelets, or thrombocytes (blood clotting).

FIGURE 18.6

[A] Natural killer cells shown attacking a target melanoma cell, a type of malignant tumor cell. Two natural killer cells are seen conjugated with a melanoma target.
[B] At higher resolution, the natural killer cell at the bottom of part [A] is seen to have cell projections (arrows) pushed deeply into invaginations of the target melanoma cell.

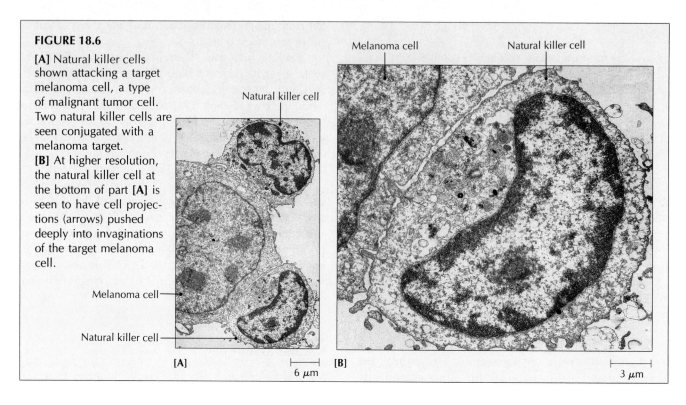

Natural killer cell

Melanoma cell

Natural killer cell

Melanoma cell

Natural killer cell

[A]   6 μm   [B]   3 μm

FIGURE 18.7

A natural killer (NK) cell is able to destroy other cells, such as a tumor cell. Cellular contact is necessary for this to occur. An outstanding feature of NK cells is the presence of prominent cytoplasmic granules which interface with the target cell. The granules are released into the intercellular space at the contact point. A lytic molecule, perforin, creates pores in the target-cell membrane.

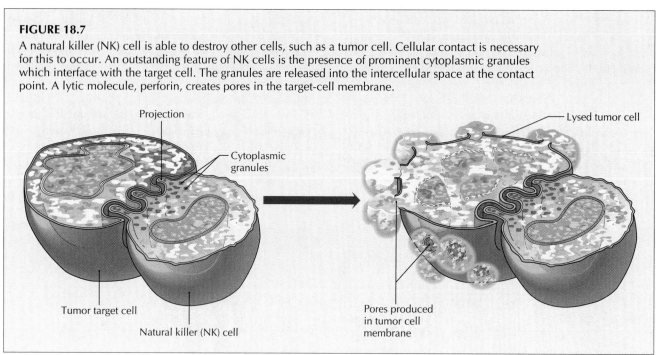

Projection

Cytoplasmic granules

Lysed tumor cell

Tumor target cell

Natural killer (NK) cell

Pores produced in tumor cell membrane

releasing membrane-destroying protease and phospholipase enzymes. However, it is not clear how they recognize their targets. Cell contact is necessary; electron micrographs have shown that projections of the NK cells push deeply into the target cells [FIGURE 18.6]. The killer cells then lyse the target cells by releasing lethal proteins that punch holes in the target cytoplasmic membranes, much like those caused by the ***complement*** system. This system, which is discussed in a later section of this chapter, consists of a group of serum proteins that participate in immune reactions. Ordinarily, each NK cell is able to lyse only a few target cells. Lysis of a tumor cell is shown diagrammatically in FIGURE 18.7. However, the maturation of NK cells is hastened and their natural killing activity is enhanced by **interferon,** a group of proteins that helps the body protect itself against viral infection. (Interferon is discussed later in this chapter.) Interferon-exposed NK cells are able to lyse many target cells. Some of the beneficial effects attributed to interferon in tumor therapy are due to interferon enhancement of NK cell activity.

NK cells are considered very important because of their role in controlling tumors through surveillance. That is, NK cells seek, recognize, and destroy tumor cells as soon as they appear—even before there are sufficient numbers of tumor cells to stimulate a specific immune response. In this way, NK cells serve as the first line of defense against cancer.

Phagocytic Cells

The importance of *phagocytosis* as a general defense mechanism to protect the body from infection was first recognized by the Russian zoologist Elie Metchnikoff (1845–1916). He called human amoeboid, particulate-eating cells *phagocytes* (from the Greek words *phagein*, "to eat," and *kytos*, "cell"). Phagocytosis was described in Chapter 4 as a method certain protozoa have of capturing food. However, phagocytosis is also the means by which cells in the human body resist infection by pathogenic microorganisms. Human cells that participate in this activity also are called *phagocytes*. All of them are types of white blood cells (called *leucocytes*) or derivatives of white blood cells [TABLE 18.4]. Leucocytes are grouped into two types, *granulocytes* and *agranulocytes* [FIGURE 18.8]. Granulocytes are so named because of the presence of granules in their cytoplasm. They, in turn, are differentiated into three types based on the staining reactions of the granules [FIGURE 18.8]:

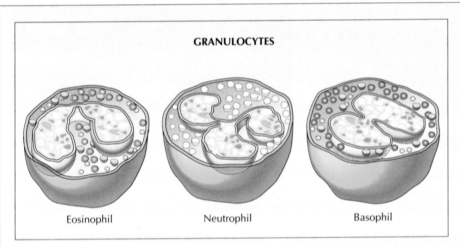

GRANULOCYTES

Eosinophil   Neutrophil   Basophil

FIGURE 18.8
Principal kinds of leucocytes. Neutrophils and macrophages are the major types of phagocytes. Arrow means that macrophages develop from monocytes when they migrate to an infected area.

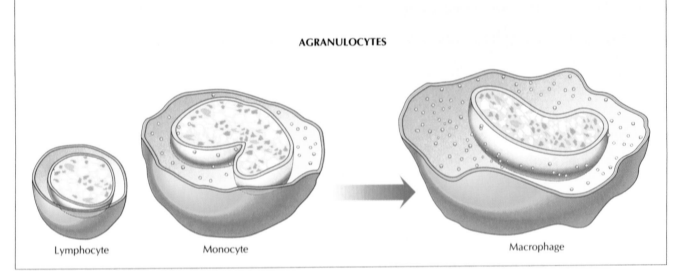

AGRANULOCYTES

Lymphocyte   Monocyte   Macrophage

1 *Neutrophils:* The granules of neutrophils stain light-blue with a mixture of acidic and basic dyes.
2 *Eosinophils:* The granules of eosinophils stain red with the acidic dye eosin.
3 *Basophils:* The granules of basophils stain dark blue with the basic dye methylene blue.

Neutrophils are also called *polymorphonuclear leucocytes (PMNs)* and are highly phagocytic. They can leave the blood and enter infected tissue, where they phagocytose foreign matter. Basophils are not phagocytic cells. They release substances such as heparin, serotonin, and histamine into the blood, and are transformed into *mast cells* when they enter tissues outside the bloodstream. Heparin is a blood anticoagulant, while histamine is responsible for allergic manifestations and some inflammation reactions. Serotonin acts as a nervous system moderator. Eosinophils are weakly phagocytic and can leave the blood to enter tissues.

Agranulocytes, as their name implies, lack granules in their cytoplasm. The two kinds of agranulocytes are *lymphocytes* and *monocytes* [FIGURE 18.8]. Lymphocytes play a key role in *specific* immune responses of the body. Lymphocytes circulate in the blood and occur in lymphoid tissues (tonsils, lymph nodes, spleen, thymus, bone marrow, appendix, and Peyer's patches of the small intestine). Monocytes are not very phagocytic until they are stimulated by *lymphokines*, another type of protein discussed later in this chapter that influences how the immune system responds. Monocytes develop into actively phagocytic *macrophages* (literally, "big eaters").

Types of Phagocytic Cells. From the preceding discussion it is apparent that there are two *major* types of phagocytes: *neutrophils* (PMNs or polymorphs) and *macrophages.* Both originate in the bone marrow; when infection occurs, both migrate to the infected area. After the PMNs enter the tissues from the blood they do their work for a few hours and then die, to be replaced by the continuous discharge of vast numbers of PMNs into the blood from the bone marrow. At any given time, about half of the PMNs are adherent to or moving slowly along the walls of capillaries and small veins.

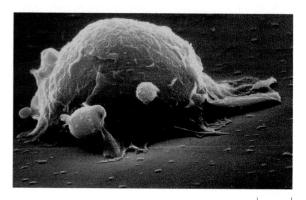

FIGURE 18.9
Scanning electron micrograph of a pulmonary alveolar macrophage (taken on a glass slide) which is phagocytosing glass spheres of fly ash.

1.0 µm

TABLE 18.5
Locations of Various Phagocytic Cells

Phagocytic cell type	Where found	Final location
Circulating monocytes and PMNs	In blood	Enter tissue on maturation (monocytes) and during inflammation (monocytes, PMNs)
Wandering macrophages	In tissue and body cavities	Skin Peritoneal cavity Uterus Bladder Thoracic cavity
Fixed macrophages (histiocytes)	Attached to tissues of the liver, lymph nodes, bone marrow, and glands, and along lymph and blood vessels	Thymus Spleen Lymph nodes (dendritic macrophages) Bone marrow Brain (microglia) Liver (Kupffer cells) Adrenal gland Pituitary gland Lungs (alveolar macrophages)

The circulating monocytes enlarge and develop into highly phagocytic macrophages as soon as they leave the blood at the site of infection and enter the tissues. Phagocytosis by a macrophage is shown in FIGURE 18.9. When macrophages leave the blood and migrate through tissue to infected areas, they are called *tissue macrophages*. Tissue macrophages also migrate to the lungs, spleen, and other sites where microbes are likely to be encountered. Some *fixed macrophages* (called *histiocytes*) enter certain tissues and organs and remain there. Fixed macrophages are found in the liver (these are called *Kupffer cells*), lungs (*alveolar macrophages*), nervous system (*microglial cells*), bronchial tissue, lymph nodes (*dendritic macrophages*), spleen, peritoneal cavity, and bone marrow. The locations of the various phagocytic cells are shown in TABLE 18.5.

Macrophages may survive for many weeks after leaving the circulating blood. The monocytes and macrophages constitute the functional network of cells generally called the *mononuclear phagocyte system*. The neutrophils and macrophages not only carry out phagocytosis; they are also equipped with a potent arsenal of antimicrobial substances (discussed in the paragraphs that follow).

Mechanism of Phagocytosis in PMNs. The process of phagocytosis first requires adherence of the microbe to the phagocytic cell. Electrostatic forces are involved in initial attachment, since divalent cations such as Ca^{2+} and Mg^{2+} are required. Firm attachment and ingestion are facilitated by serum substances called **opsonins.** Opsonins include acquired or naturally occurring antibodies and a component of the complement system (discussed later in this chapter). PMNs have specific receptors on their surfaces for such antibodies, as well as for the C3b complement fragments. The opsonins first become attached to the surface of microbes, thus making them more "attractive" to phagocytes [FIGURE 18.10].

After the phagocyte attaches a microbe to its surface, it sends out projections called *pseudopodia* that surround the microbe during ingestion [FIGURE 18.11]. These pseudopodia fuse and form a phagocytic vacuole called a **phagosome** that contains the microbe. The phagosome then pinches off from the membrane and enters the cytoplasm. Subsequent events depend on the activity of cytoplasmic granules called **lysosomes,** which contain digestive enzymes and microbicidal substances. The lysosomes move toward the phagosome, fuse with its membrane, and form a digestive vacuole called a **phagolysosome.** The lysosomes discharge their toxic contents into the phagolysosome, thus initiating the intracellular killing and digestion of the microorganism.

Within the phagolysosome, the pH becomes acidic (pH 3.5 to 4.0), killing many bacteria. The lysosomal enzymes emptied into the digestive vacuole include ly-

FIGURE 18.10

Mechanisms of microbial opsonization. Adherence of microbes to phagocytes is enhanced by receptors on the phagocyte surface. Receptors are specific for both antibodies and complement fragments on the microbes.

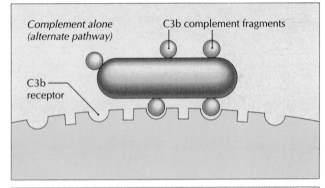

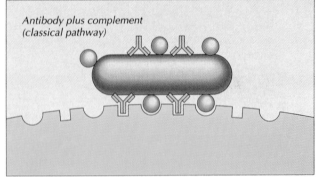

sozyme (which hydrolyzes peptidoglycan in bacterial cell walls) and a variety of other hydrolytic enzymes that break down the macromolecular components of microorganisms. Over 60 different enzymes have been found within lysosomes! The major microbicidal mechanism is produced by the "respiratory burst": the activated phagocytic cell increases its oxygen consumption to support the increased metabolic activity of phagocytosis. Highly toxic oxygen metabolites are generated, including singlet oxygen, superoxide, hydrogen peroxide, hydroxyl radicals, and hypochlorite. Within the phagolysosome, most microbes are killed by enzymes, low pH, or oxygen

FIGURE 18.11
[A] Phagocytosis of a microbial cell by a phagocyte. Scheme from left to right shows: adherence; ingestion; formation of the phagosome; fusion of the phagosome with a lysosome to form a phagolysosome; destruction of the ingested microbe; release of microbial debris.
[B] Electron micrograph of white blood cells ingesting bacteria (arrows indicate some bacterial cells).

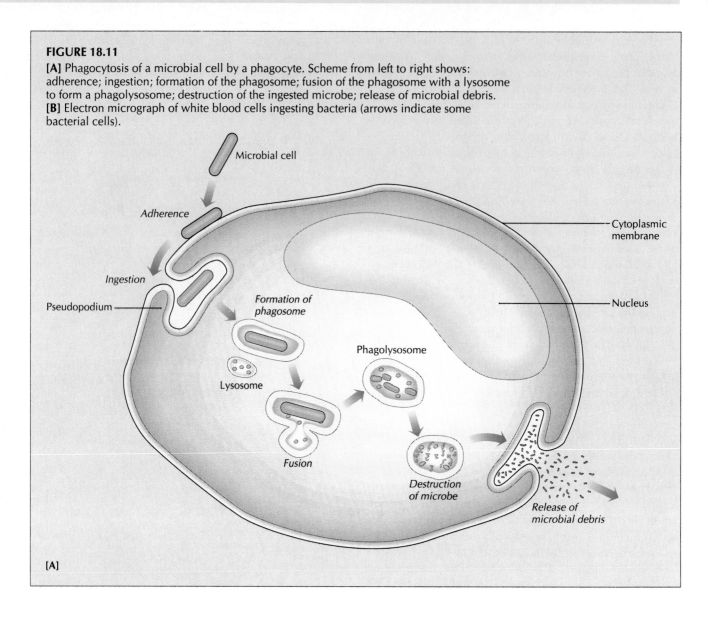

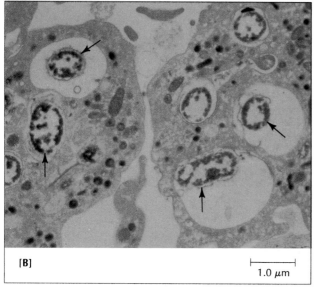

metabolites within 10 to 30 min, although the complete destruction may take a few hours.

The combined actions of the lysosomal enzymes and toxic oxygen metabolites are usually sufficient to destroy all invading microorganisms. However, microbes vary in their response to phagocytic activity. Gram-positive bacteria are rapidly destroyed. Gram-negative bacteria are somewhat more persistent because their cell wall is relatively resistant to digestion. But some bacteria, such as *Mycobacterium tuberculosis* and *Listeria monocytogenes*, as well as some fungi and parasites, are so resistant to phagocytic action that they may literally multiply within the phagocytes.

Mechanism of Phagocytosis in Macrophages. The processes of adherence, ingestion, and digestion of microbes in macrophages are generally similar to those in PMNs, although there are some important differences.

Macrophages have the ability to change their surface shape (forming ruffles) and to differentiate. They also secrete at least 32 different metabolic products, ranging from lysozyme to collagenase, which contribute to antimicrobial defense. They do not move in response to the same chemicals as the PMNs. The lysosomal enzymes of macrophages also differ from those of the PMNs. Macrophages do not have the same cationic proteins found in polymorph granules; nor do they produce highly toxic oxygen metabolites as efficiently. These differences are reflected in their ability to deal with ingested microorganisms. For example, macrophages are much less effective than PMNs in killing the yeast *Candida albicans* or the bacterium *Mycobacterium tuberculosis.* However, macrophages that have been activated by interferon (becoming "angry" macrophages) can kill these microorganisms.

Soluble Mediators: Complement, Lymphokines, Interferon

Besides the cellular mediators of the body's internal defense, there are soluble mediators that contribute to host resistance.

Complement. The serum of higher animals contains a group of about 20 interacting proteins referred to collectively as complement, so named because their action complements that of certain *antibody*-mediated reactions. (An *antibody* is a globular serum protein produced by the immune system which can specifically combine with a substance called an *antigen;* see Chapter 19.) Complement plays an important role in resistance against infection; it is the principal soluble mediator of the inflammatory response. The individual component proteins of complement are identified by a numbering system. Once activated by an invading microorganism or by antibody binding, these components of the complement system react sequentially in a cascade fashion, or like a row of falling dominoes. Some complement proteins act as protease enzymes, cleaving and activating the next protein in the sequence. Others act on surrounding inflammatory cells.

The key step in the activation of the complement system is the cleavage of the component called C3 into two fragments, C3a and C3b. The critical C3 cleavage step may be initiated in two distinctly different ways: the *classical pathway,* or the *alternate pathway* [FIGURE 18.12]. C3a promotes inflammatory changes, while C3b accumulates on microorganisms, causing them to be bound by the receptors for C3b on phagocytic macrophages and neutrophils in a process called **opsonization.** (Antibodies also opsonize microorganisms, enhancing phagocytosis because macrophages and neutrophils also express surface receptors for antibodies.) The deposition of C3b on a cell or microbial surface can lead to complement fixation resulting in cell lysis. The *classical pathway* of complement fixation must be triggered by a *specific* antibody binding to the antigen, a substance such as a microorganism which, when introduced into an animal body, stimulates the production of antibodies. As each complement component in the cascade is activated, it in turn activates the next component in the pathway [FIGURE 18.13].

The *alternate pathway* is the *nonspecific* activation of the complement cascade when sufficient quantities of specific antibody are not available for activation of the classical pathway. It is triggered by microbial polysaccharides or endotoxin contained in the cell membranes of Gram-negative bacteria, protozoa, or yeasts. This can occur in body fluids rather than on a cell surface and does not require the presence of the antigen-antibody complex or the C1 recognition unit.

Eventually the classical and alternate pathways follow a common pathway to form the **membrane attack unit,** which in turn generates the *lytic complex* [FIGURE 18.12]. The lytic complex forms a channel across the cytoplasmic membrane of the cell. This channel allows potassium ions to leave the cell and water and sodium to enter; the cell swells and lyses. Such cell damage is dramatically shown in FIGURE 18.14. The complement proteins thus participate in both *nonspecific* resistance and *specific* immune resistance.

There are three general ways in which the complement system is protective:

1 Its early steps stimulate the inflammatory response.
2 Its intermediate steps release substances that attract phagocytic cells and render them highly active.
3 Once activated, the complement system results in the assembly of lytic complexes that cause lysis of invading microorganisms.

Lymphokines. *Lymphokines* are soluble proteins produced and secreted by sensitized *T lymphocytes* (or *T cells,* described in Chapter 19), which are a type of leucocyte [see TABLE 18.4]. These cells are described as "sensitized" because they have mounted a prior response to a specific antigen. Sensitized T lymphocytes that produce lymphokines are also known as **delayed hypersensitivity lymphocytes (DHLs)** because of the skin reactions they can produce. They are also called "helper" T lymphocytes, because they help other cells to amplify their response to antigen. Lymphokines display a wide variety of biological activities toward various target cells. Indeed, approximately 100 different biological activities have been ascribed to lymphokines. For example, lymphokines can attract macrophages. They can also inhibit macrophage migration, activate macrophages,

FIGURE 18.12

An overall view of the complement events leading to cell lysis by the classical and by the alternate pathways. Each protein component of complement has been assigned a number in the order of its discovery, and that number is preceded by the capital letter "C" for complement. Unfortunately, the first four components do not interact in the order of their discovery, but rather in the sequence C1, C4, C2, and C3. However, the remaining components do react in the appropriate numerical sequence C5, C6, C7, C8, and C9. There are also B and D factors and several regulatory proteins involved in the alternate pathway.

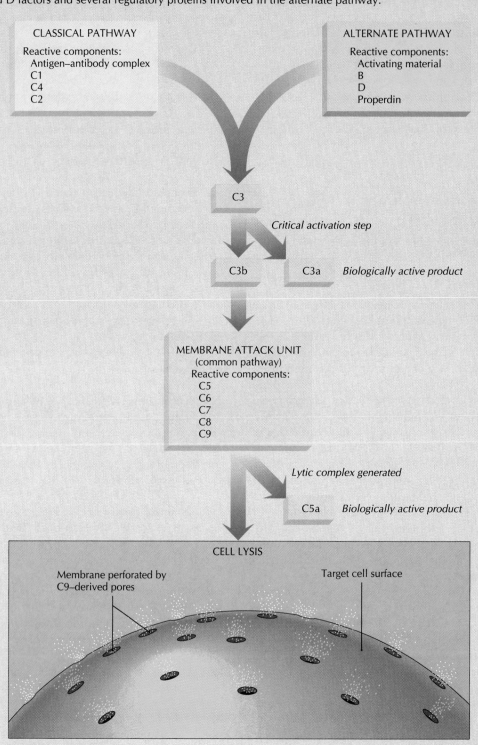

FIGURE 18.13

Model of complement component assembly on the membrane of a bacterial cell which occurs during the sequence of events in the complement cascade by the *classical* pathway leading to cell lysis. C1 has three subcomponents, C1q, C1r, and C1s. Fragments of components resulting from cleavage by other components acting as enzymes are assigned lowercase letters a, b, c, d, or e; for example, C3a and C3b. The antigen-antibody combination forms a complex first with C1q, C1r, and C1s, resulting in the formation of an activated C1. C1q binds to the antibody molecule, leading to the activation of C1r, which then cleaves C1s, generating an activated C1s. C1s cleaves low–molecular weight peptides from C4 and C2 and exposes their active forms, C4b and C2a, which then fuse. The C4bC2a complex acts as an enzyme whose substrate is C3. C3 splits into two fragments, C3a and C3b. C3b associates with the C4bC2a complex to form C4bC2aC3b, an enzyme that reacts with the next component, C5. Thus this enzyme complex is called C5 convertase. (C3a interacts with tissue leucocytes called *mast cells* which release mediators of the inflammatory response.) The result is the cleavage of C5. C5a is the chemotactic factor that attracts phagocytes. C5b is equally important; it initiates another stage of complement function: formation of a large functional cluster of complement proteins. The C5b fragment, the components C6, C7, and C8, and sixteen molecules of C9 bind sequentially on the surface of a target cell to form a lytic complex. In the *alternate pathway* (shown in FIGURE 18.12), the microbial substances cause C3 to react with a serum component called factor B to produce a C3B complex, which reacts with another C3 molecule, a reaction leading to the generation of C3b by cleaving the second C3 into C3a and C3b. In other words, C3B acts as an enzyme on the substrate C3. C3B can also react with another serum component, factor D, resulting in the formation of the C3bBb complex. The C3bBb complex is unstable unless it reacts with properdin, another serum factor, to form a C3bPBb complex. When a second C3b molecule is added to the C3bPBb complex, a conformational change occurs that makes it into an enzyme (C5 convertase) that reacts with C5 to form C5b. At this step, the alternate and classical pathways follow a common pathway to form the membrane attack unit, which results in lysis of the target cell.

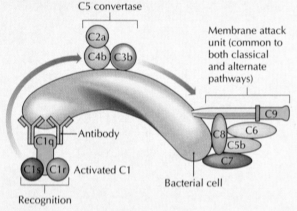

FIGURE 18.14

Nonimmune catfish (those lacking a specific antibody) possess an alternate complement pathway which can act as an immediate defense mechanism against bacterial invasion. **[A]** Scanning electron micrograph of *Pseudomonas fluorescens* exposed to phosphate-buffered saline, pH 7.4. Cells do not exhibit shape changes. **[B]** Scanning electron micrograph of *P. fluorescens* exposed to plasma of normal channel catfish, *Ictalurus punctatus*. Cell damage includes shape changes, holes, and membrane damage with accompanying ionic changes, swelling and cell lysis.

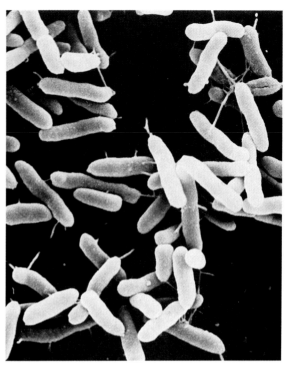

[A]   1.0 μm

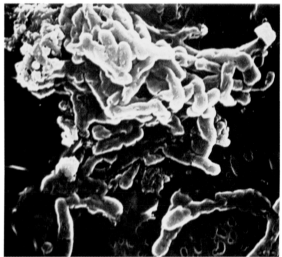

[B]   1.0 μm

and poison foreign cells or virus-infected cells, and they may account for much of the cell damage and destruction seen in some inflammatory reactions. Thus a variety of cells can be affected by lymphokines, including neutrophils, other lymphocytes, endothelial cells that line heart cavities and blood vessels, and fibroblasts. In a general way, lymphokines may be considered substances that signal other cells to increase or decrease a specific activity; they serve as intercellular communication signals.

Although lymphocytes can be stimulated by *specific antigens* to produce lymphokines, lymphokine production is essentially nonspecific. For instance, *mitogens* (substances that induce cells to enter mitosis) such as phytohemagglutinin (a glycoprotein extract from red kidney beans) or concanavalin A (a glycoprotein extract from jack beans) can stimulate lymphocytes to produce lymphokines.

The wide-ranging effects of lymphokines produced by DHLs suggest a complex lymphokine network. One of the major players is called *interleukin-2 (IL-2)*, because it acts as a signal between leucocytes. Another lymphokine is interferon, which helps halt viral infection not only by triggering the production of antiviral proteins in adjacent cells but also by increasing the cytotoxicity of T cells. Macrophages may also produce lymphokines that influence both lymphocytes and other body cells. For example, macrophage lymphokines help stim-

ulate DHLs to produce interleukin-2 and some body cells to make various proteolytic enzymes. Such lymphokines are named *interleukin-1 (IL-1)*. Interleukin-1 is also known as *endogenous pyrogen*, since it is responsible for the alterations of the hypothalamic center resulting in fever during infections. Thus IL-1 is produced by macrophages and IL-2 is produced by T cells.

Therefore, it is apparent that the overall effect of lymphokines is enhanced activity of nonspecific protective mechanisms against infection.

Interferon. In 1957 Alick Isaacs and Jean Lindenmann of the National Institute for Medical Research in London found an interesting substance in the supernatant fluid from cultures of cells that had been infected with virus. This substance, which they called *interferon*, protected other cells from infection with the same or unrelated viruses. Interferon is still virtually the only natural substance with the distinctive ability to inhibit intracellular viral replication.

There are several kinds of interferon, each made by a different cell type. Interferon-α (IFN-α) is produced by leucocytes; interferon-β (IFN-β) is produced by fibroblasts (a type of cell in tissues); and interferon-γ (IFN-γ), which is also called *immune interferon*, is produced by sensitized T cells.

Interferons are small proteins produced by eucaryotic cells in response to viral infection or foreign double-

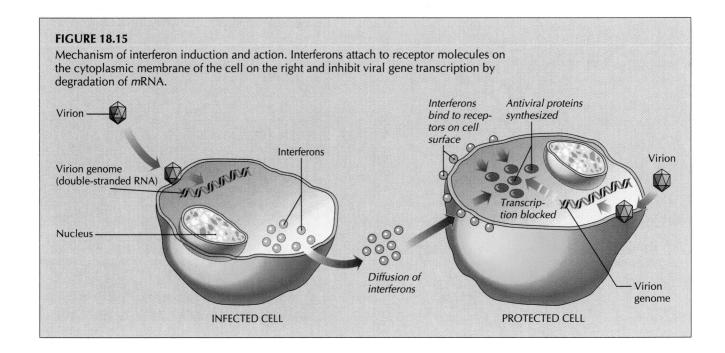

FIGURE 18.15

Mechanism of interferon induction and action. Interferons attach to receptor molecules on the cytoplasmic membrane of the cell on the right and inhibit viral gene transcription by degradation of *mRNA*.

stranded RNAs (viral or synthetic). The infected cell produces interferon for a few hours, even for a day. Interferon is excreted and used by other cells. When these cells become infected with virus, the interferon causes the cells to produce molecules that prevent replication of the infecting virus [FIGURE 18.15]. The current understanding of the events occurring in cells that react with interferon is as follows.

Interferon acts on an uninfected cell by binding to a receptor on the cell surface, causing the cell to synthesize another protein that remains in the cell and protects it from infection by all other viruses. The overall effect is the inhibition of viral gene transcription by degradation of mRNA. In this way, the cycle of virus replication is interfered with, and either the infection is halted or the process is slowed down sufficiently to enable the specific immune response to eliminate the infecting virus. Specifically, interferon first induces the production of a molecule called *2,5-oligoadenylate synthetase*. If a cell that has interacted with interferon, and is producing 2,5-oligoadenylate synthetase, becomes infected with virus, the virus activates the enzyme to produce 2,5-linked oligoriboadenylate. The presence of this compound in turn activates a preexisting, inactive molecule called *ribonuclease L* that degrades mRNA.

Interferons lack virus specificity because they do not react directly with the virion but instead induce a general antiviral state in host cells. Conversely, interferons were found to be species-specific with respect to the species of cells that produced them; in other words, they induce little or no resistance in cells from other species. Thus human interferon is most effective in protecting human cells and poorly protective for mouse or chicken cells. Similarly, mouse interferon has no action on chicken or human cells.

Interferon would seem to be the ideal chemotherapeutic antiviral agent for use in humans, since it is produced naturally by human cells, has only mild side effects, and is active against a broad spectrum of viruses. However, although purified interferons are stable at low pH and fairly heat-resistant, they are relatively unstable at the physiological pH in tissue fluids. Interferon also is secreted by cells only in minute amounts and is extremely difficult to purify. Furthermore, clinical results in human patients have not been dramatic except on surface lesions, like those caused by herpesvirus. At present, more than 30 years after its discovery, interferon is still not of great practical importance in medicine. But this situation may soon change because recent advances in genetic engineering have permitted the production and synthesis of interferons in large quantities for experimental and clinical use.

Interferon is also capable of promoting the natural cytotoxic activity of *natural killer cells* (discussed earlier in this chapter), and so it may have a role in immunologic surveillance against malignancies. However, the primary protective role of interferons is against naturally acquired viral infections, because interferons are produced locally and more promptly than specific antibodies.

ASK YOURSELF

1 Why is inflammation considered one of the most effective defense mechanisms in animals?

2 What is the function of natural killer cells? Why are they important?

3 What is the mechanism of phagocytosis in polymorphonuclear leucocytes? In macrophages?

4 What are the protein components of complement?

5 Describe the key step in the activation of the complement system.

6 What are the two pathways of complement activation?

7 What are the three general ways in which the complement system is protective?

SUMMARY

1 The pathogenicity of a microbe is determined by its virulence as well as by host resistance factors. There are both opportunistic pathogens and primary pathogens. Only some microbial virulence factors are well understood.

2 Predisposing factors of host resistance are those of the environment, as well as those inherent in the individual, race, or species. Environmental factors that influence host resistance and susceptibility include physical and emotional stresses, as well as age of the host.

3 The unbroken skin and mucous membranes are important mechanical barriers to invasion by external microorganisms. The human body also produces many antimicrobial chemical secretions.

4 Inflammation and fever are complex responses by a host against microbial infection. (Both may result from other causes as well.)

5 The two cellular mediators of nonspecific internal defense are natural killer cells and phagocytic cells. Natural killer cells have an important role in controlling tumors by surveillance. Neutrophils and macrophages are the two major types of human phagocytic cells that destroy invading microorganisms. The process of phagocytosis involves adherence, ingestion, and destruction of the unwanted microbe.

6 Soluble mediators that play important roles in the internal defense mechanisms of the human host include complement, interferon, and lymphokines.

7 Complement plays an important role in resistance against infection and is the principal soluble mediator of the inflammatory response. Its individual component proteins are numbered by a complicated system. The two pathways of complement activation are the classical pathway and the alternate pathway.

8 Lymphokines are soluble proteins produced and secreted by sensitized cells. For example, lymphocytes and macrophages secrete lymphokines called interleukin-2 and interleukin-1, respectively. Lymphokines display a wide variety of biological activities toward target cells.

9 Interferons are small proteins that inhibit intracellular viral replication. Their primary role is to protect against naturally acquired viral infections.

KEY TERMS

alternate pathway
antitoxins
classical pathway
complement
delayed hypersensitivity lymphocytes (DHLs)
hemolysis, α and β
immunity
inflammation
interferon
interleukin-1 (IL-1)
interleukin-2 (IL-2)
lymphokines
lysosomes
macrophages
membrane attack unit
mitogens
natural killer cells (NK cells)
opsonins
opsonization
pathogenicity
phagocytosis
phagolysosome
phagosome
resistance (specific and nonspecific)
susceptibility
toxins
toxoids
virulence

REVIEW GUIDE

THE
MICROORGANISM AS
A PATHOGEN

1 Match the description on the right with the appropriate item on the left:

_____ virulence

_____ disease

_____ pathogenicity

_____ primary pathogen

(a) Capability of a microbe to cause disease

(b) Microbe that can initiate disease in a healthy host

(c) Degree of ability of a pathogen to cause disease

(d) Impairment of body function due to infection

2 A toxin retained within the cell as part of the cell is a(n) _____.

3 The toxin that causes botulism is a(n) _____.

4 Toxins and toxoids have the ability to stimulate the production of

_____.

5 Compared with exotoxins, endotoxins are relatively _____,

do not form _____ when treated with formaldehyde, and

are _____ toxic.

6 *Limulus polyphemus* contains a single type of white blood cell called

_____.

7 Colonies of hemolytic bacteria on a blood-agar plate surrounded by a clear, color-

less zone exhibit _____ hemolysis.

PREDISPOSING
FACTORS OF HOST
RESISTANCE

8 Which of the following diseases are considered to be children's diseases:
(a) measles; **(b)** chicken pox; **(c)** pneumonia; **(d)** plague; **(e)** hepatitis.

9 Many diseases of mammals do not affect fish or reptiles, or vice versa, because of

the following most probable reason: _____.

10 Resistance to malarial infection in African blacks is due to: **(a)** morphology of red
blood cells; **(b)** genetic disposition; **(c)** malnutrition; **(d)** greater exposure to the
vector; **(e)** lack of specific receptor for the protozoan on the erythrocyte membrane.

EXTERNAL DEFENSE
MECHANISMS

11 Match the item on the left with the appropriate description on the right:

_____ lysozyme

_____ gastric juice

_____ sebum

_____ lactoferrin

(a) Prevents hair from drying and becoming brittle

(b) Chelates available iron in environment

(c) Mixture of hydrochloric acid, enzymes, and mucus

(d) Hydrolysis of peptidoglycan

12 Microorganisms can sometimes enter the unbroken skin through hair

_____, _____ glands, and

_____ glands.

INTERNAL DEFENSE
MECHANISMS

13 The inflammatory response serves to _____ or

_____ an injurious agent (microbe) or its products and to

_____ the effects of the agent by walling it off.

14 Natural killer cells cannot do which *two* of the following? **(a)** phagocytose bacterial cells; **(b)** kill tumor cells; **(c)** destroy virus-infected cells; **(d)** react with specific
antibodies; **(e)** control tumors by surveillance of body cells.

15 Leucocytes are grouped into two types: _____ and

_____ .

16 The two major types of phagocytes are _____ and

_____ .

17 Neutrophils are also called which *two* of the following? **(a)** agranulocytes; **(b)** lymphocytes; **(c)** monocytes; **(d)** polymorphs; **(e)** PMNs.

18 Indicate whether these statements are true **(T)** or false **(F):**

(a) The mononuclear phagocyte system is a functional network of cells consisting of macrophages and monocytes. _____

(b) Macrophages are short-lived after leaving the circulating blood. _____

(c) Opsonins include acquired or naturally occurring antibodies as well as a component of the complement system. _____

19 Macrophages are much _____ effective than PMNs in the killing of *Candida albicans*.

20 Which *three* of the following are soluble mediators in the internal defense of the human host? **(a)** natural killer cells; **(b)** interferons; **(c)** complement; **(d)** lymphokines; **(e)** PMNs.

21 Indicate whether each of the following statements is true **(T)** or false **(F)**. Restate it as a true statement if false.

(a) The first four components of the complement cascade interact in the sequence C1, C4, C2, and C3. _____

_____

_____

(b) The early steps of the complement cascade depress the inflammatory response. _____

_____

_____

22 The key step in the complement system is the cleavage of the C3 component into

the two fragments _____ and _____ .

23 The _____ complement pathway is triggered by specific antibody binding to antigen.

24 Immune interferon is **(a)** INF-α; **(b)** INF-β; **(c)** INF-γ.

25 Indicate whether the following statements are true **(T)** or false **(F):**

(a) Interferons lack virus specificity. _____

(b) Interferons are species-specific with respect to the species of cells that produce them. _____

(c) Interferon is exported from virally infected cells and is used by other cells. _____

(d) Interferon can promote the natural cytotoxicity of natural killer cells. _____

26 Which *three* substances are lymphokines? **(a)** mitogen; **(b)** concanavalin A; **(c)** interleukin-1; **(d)** interleukin-2; **(e)** immune interferon.

REVIEW QUESTIONS

1 What is the difference between a primary pathogen and an opportunistic pathogen?

2 Compare and contrast endotoxins and exotoxins.

3 Discuss some well-known extracellular enzymes that are known virulence factors.

4 Why do some bacteria exhibit hemolysis on blood-agar plates?

5 List and comment on some environmental factors that affect host resistance to disease.

6 Give some specific examples of how species and race can affect host resistance to disease.

7 Give reasons for the symptoms manifested by the inflammatory response.

8 Is fever beneficial to a host? Explain.

9 Explain how some important chemical secretions of the host exert their antimicrobial activity.

10 What major role do natural killer cells play? In what way is this role related to interferon tumor therapy?

11 Explain how the granulocytes are differentiated into three types.

12 Explain why *opsonins* are important in the process of phagocytosis.

13 Describe the mechanism of phagocytosis in PMNs.

14 Describe three general ways in which the complement system is protective for the host.

15 List the three types of interferon and indicate the cell types that produce them.

16 Describe the molecular events occurring in cells that react with interferon to protect them from infection by viruses.

17 Although 90 different biological activities have been ascribed to lymphokines, can you make a *general* statement about the activity of lymphokines?

DISCUSSION QUESTIONS

1 On what basis can we say that vertebrate animals are more efficient in combating infections than plants and other animals?

2 Why is the presence of β-hemolytic colonies of streptococci from a throat swab in a case of sore throat very alarming?

3 What role does inflammation play in defense of the animal host?

4 What is immune surveillance, and how does it contribute to our health?

5 Compare and contrast the location, properties, and modes of action of neutrophils and macrophages.

6 Compare the classical pathway with the alternate pathway of complement activation.

7 Can you explain why interferon has been used clinically to treat cancer?

The Immune Response: Specific Host Resistance

OBJECTIVES

After reading this chapter you should be able to

1 Describe the effectors of humoral and cellular immunity.

2 Specify the four primary characteristics of the immune response.

3 Distinguish between T cells and B cells and explain how each type develops.

4 Make a drawing to show the cooperation of B cells and T cells in the immune response.

5 Explain the clonal-selection theory.

6 Draw a model of the chain structure of the human IgG monomer.

7 Name the different classes of immunoglobulins and describe their different functions.

8 Differentiate between natural and artificial antigens.

9 Distinguish between thymus-dependent and thymus-independent antigens and the immune responses they induce.

10 Compare the four different types of hypersensitivities.

11 Explain the role of transplantation antigens in grafts.

12 Describe the relative importance of the elements of the immune system in resistance to bacterial or viral disease.

13 Describe some genetic or acquired deficiencies of the immune system and indicate the specific manner in which the immune system is compromised in each type of deficiency.

OVERVIEW

In Chapter 18 you learned that natural resistance produced by macrophages, natural killer cells, and natural substances that inhibit microbial growth is nonspecific and transient. These effectors constitute the nonspecific immune responses, because they nonselectively protect against foreign cells or substances. In contrast, the response of the *immune system* to pathogens is specific and long-lasting; the immune system comprises the specific immune responses of the body. Those cells and organs within a living animal that protect against specific diseases also constitute the immune system.

The field of *immunology* primarily includes the study of the natural resistance to pathogens and of the immune system. The immune system can recognize virtually any foreign material which enters the host organism; it will produce an appropriate response against the foreign substance. Foreign materials which induce a specific immune response are termed *antigens*. An antigen expresses two basic properties: *antigenicity* and *immunogenicity*. The specificity of the immune response is the ability of the factors produced by the immune system to react with only the inducing antigen. The properties that allow an antigen to react with such factors is the antigenicity of an antigen. The immunogenicity of an antigen is a quantitative term indicating the amount of factors that an antigen can induce the immune system to produce. These factors include specific *immune antibodies* and specific *immune cells*.

The immune response has been described as a double-edged sword, because it also causes allergic symptoms and the rejection of tissue and organ transplants. Like all complex systems, the immune system is also subject to a variety of malfunctions. Abnormal activation of the immune system may cause autoimmune disease—such as rheumatoid arthritis—in which the immune system mistakenly reacts against normal body components. A lack of immune responsiveness caused by a genetic or acquired immunodeficiency may result in failure to prevent the growth of bacteria or viruses or even cancer cells, leading to severe disease or death. From birth to old age, a properly functioning immune system protects you from infectious disease and cancer. Total or even partial absence of an immune system at birth is incompatible with survival: the newborn host is soon overwhelmed by infectious microorganisms. In cases where the adult immune system is incapacitated by disease (as in acquired immune deficiency syndrome, or AIDS), the host has a markedly shortened life expectancy. Therefore the intact immune system acts as a security system which constantly surveys the host for foreign intruders. It instantly responds to repel, neutralize, or kill invading microbes, cancerous cells, or other foreign substances.

SPECIFIC IMMUNITY AND THE IMMUNE RESPONSE

The diverse cells of the immune system are found in the blood and in organs and tissues throughout the body. A large number of chemical messengers called *mediators* are another important constituent of the immune system. Nonspecific immune responses were discussed in Chapter 18. This chapter focuses on the specific immune responses of the immune system.

The Dual Nature of Specific Immunity

Immunization occurs when an individual is naturally or artificially exposed to an antigen, and the immune system is activated to produce **humoral immunity** and **cellular immunity**. This means that the effectors of specific immunity are found in both the humoral phase of the body fluids (e.g., blood serum) and among the white blood cells in the blood and lymphoid organs. (Serum is the fluid portion of the blood that remains after the blood has been allowed to clot.) These two effectors of immunity are physically and functionally different; for instance, they resist different types of pathogens. *Antibodies* (soluble mediators in body fluids) are more effective against pathogens found outside cells, and **immune cells** (cellular elements, specifically, T lymphocytes) are more effective against pathogens found inside cells. Thus

humoral immunity defends the body primarily against bacteria, bacterial toxins, and viruses in body fluids. Cellular immunity defends the host from bacteria and viruses located within infected cells or phagocytic cells, as well as from fungi, protozoa, and other parasites, such as helminths. Cellular immunity is also responsible for rejection of transplanted tissues, and is important in defending the body against cancer in a process known as *immune surveillance.*

Characteristics of the Specific Immune Response

The specific immune response has several characteristics that may be described as follows:

1 The specific immune system *discriminates* between "self" (not foreign) and "nonself" (foreign), and responds only to materials foreign to the host. The cells of each individual have a unique array of self-marking membrane molecules called *histocompatibility proteins*. They serve as cellular fingerprints that distinguish self from nonself.
2 The specific immune response is highly *specific* for the antigen to which the antibodies or immune cells will react with greatest strength. This specificity underlies the system's ability to discriminate between self and nonself.
3 The specific immune response is able to produce a greater response more quickly when there is a second exposure to the same foreign antigen. This is called *immunologic memory*, or the **anamnestic response.**
4 Active immune status, or immunity, is transferable only from one *inbred* animal to another, and only by means of living immune lymphocytes and not by antiserum (serum containing antibodies). Transfer of serum antibodies provides only transient immunity, since antibodies are soon lost through natural protein turnover. Immune lymphocytes (lymphocytes that can interact with an antigen) can proliferate and thus regenerate themselves throughout the life of the recipient.

Thus the four primary characteristics of the specific immune response can be summarized in these words: *discrimination, specificity, anamnesis,* and *transferability by living cells.*

The Lymphocytes

The cells capable of responding to antigens are the lymphocytes, which are one of the classes of white blood cells. Lymphocytes are further divided into (1) **thymus-derived lymphocytes**, or **T cells**; (2) **bone marrow-derived lymphocytes**, or **B cells**; and (3) **null cells**.

Though the T and B lymphocytes cannot be distinguished on the basis of morphology, they have distinct membrane glycoproteins, carry out different functions, and respond to different activation stimuli, for example, different *mitogens* (substances that induce cell division, or mitosis).

Null cells are lymphocytes that lack distinguishing surface markers; they include the natural killer (NK) cells and antibody-dependent killer (K) lymphocytes. Otherwise null cells are morphologically similar to T and B lymphocytes. Macrophages, monocytes, and polymorphonuclear leucocytes are also distinguishable by their surface markers and cellular functions.

The Immune System

The lymphatic system consists of an interconnecting network of organs and tissues [FIGURE 19.1A]. A continuous traffic of cells moves along in the flow of blood and lymph that supplies this network. In FIGURE 19.1B, the circulatory and lymphatic systems are diagrammed together to show how a pool of recirculating lymphocytes passes from the blood capillaries into the lymph nodes, spleen, and other tissues. The lymphocytes then circulate back to the blood via the major lymphatic channels such as the thoracic duct. Lymphocytes are the dominant cell type in most of the organs and tissues of the immune system. Thus such tissues and organs are described as *lymphoid.* They include all the body's lymph nodes, the spleen, the adenoids and tonsils, small clusters of lymphoid tissue in the intestinal cell wall called Peyer's patches, and the thymus.

Except for the thymus, the aforementioned tissues and organs make up the *peripheral lymphoid system.* Although the structures of the peripheral lymphoid system are centers of immune reactivity, they are described as peripheral because their development and function are absolutely dependent on cells generated in the thymus and in the bone marrow. For this reason the thymus and the bone marrow are considered the *central lymphoid organs.*

The *hemopoietic,* or hematopoietic (blood-forming), stem cells in the bone marrow are the ultimate origin of the erythrocytes (red cells) and of all leucocytes, including the lymphocytes. Many lymphocytes pass through the thymus and are processed by thymus hormones prior to release. The thymus is an organ whose sole function appears to be the differentiation of lymphocytes into T cells. The majority of the bone marrow–derived lymphocytes do not enter the thymus and are called *B cells.* Studies with chickens have revealed a central lymphoid organ called the *bursa of Fabricius,* which is responsible for inducing mature B-lymphocyte function, just as the thymus induces T-cell function. It is thought that the site in which human B cells mature (that is, the bursal equivalent) may be the fetal liver during embryonic development, followed in later life by the bone marrow. The B cells are destined to synthesize specific humoral antibody, and the T cells become primarily responsible for cellular immunity. The pathways of development of B cells and T cells are shown in FIGURE 19.2A.

How do the antigen-responding cells and the antigens find each other? Lymphocytes have surface receptors specific for different antigens. The function of the macrophages and the lymphatic system is to catch and concentrate antigens and "show" them to the lymphocytes. In the lymph nodes and spleen, macrophages present antigen to the lymphocytes that are constantly circulating both within the organ and from the organ to the circulatory system and back again. Those lymphocytes which have receptors complementary to the specific antigen being presented will be selectively activated and then respond to the antigen. Therefore the antigen can be said to select and activate clones of those lymphocytes with the appropriate receptor. Such lymphocytes are called antigen-binding cells. This is the essential concept of the *clonal-selection theory of immunity.* Selected lymphocytes (whose receptors interact with a specific antigen) respond by undergoing mitosis and developing into a clone of cells expressing the same receptor specificity. Among the progeny of this clone will be plasma cells that secrete and synthesize antibodies specific for the stimulating antigen. Clonal selection also leads to the production of an enlarged pool of lymphocytes (called "memory cells") that are sensitive to the specific antigen.

ASK YOURSELF

1 What constitutes the immune system?

2 Differentiate between *nonspecific* and *specific* immune responses.

3 What are the two components of specific immunity?

4 How are antibodies functionally different from T lymphocytes with respect to infectious agents?

5 Identify four characteristics of the specific immune response.

6 What are the three types of lymphocytes that respond to antigens?

7 What are the central lymphoid organs?

8 Describe the pathways for the development of B cells and T cells.

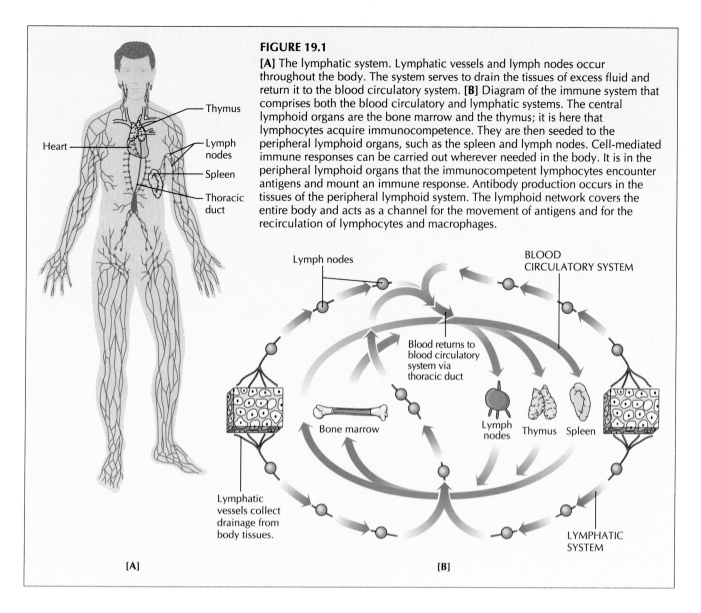

FIGURE 19.1

[A] The lymphatic system. Lymphatic vessels and lymph nodes occur throughout the body. The system serves to drain the tissues of excess fluid and return it to the blood circulatory system. **[B]** Diagram of the immune system that comprises both the blood circulatory and lymphatic systems. The central lymphoid organs are the bone marrow and the thymus; it is here that lymphocytes acquire immunocompetence. They are then seeded to the peripheral lymphoid organs, such as the spleen and lymph nodes. Cell-mediated immune responses can be carried out wherever needed in the body. It is in the peripheral lymphoid organs that the immunocompetent lymphocytes encounter antigens and mount an immune response. Antibody production occurs in the tissues of the peripheral lymphoid system. The lymphoid network covers the entire body and acts as a channel for the movement of antigens and for the recirculation of lymphocytes and macrophages.

HUMORAL IMMUNITY

As indicated before, there are two broad categories of specific immune responses, namely, *humoral* and cell-mediated, or *cellular*, responses. B cells are the effectors of humoral immunity and are responsible for the synthesis of antibodies.

The Antibody Response

During the active immune response (defined in the next paragraph) leading to specific immunity, the T lymphocytes and B lymphocytes, together with a type of macrophage, cooperate to generate the immune response [FIGURE 19.2B]. The macrophage processes and presents antigen in an optimal antigenic form to the T and B lymphocytes. The macrophage in this situation is called an *antigen-presenting cell (APC)*. The T lymphocyte is activated to produce hormonelike factors (lymphokines) called *interleukins*, which promote B-lymphocyte growth and differentiation. B lymphocytes are specifically activated by antigen and the interleukins, producing antibodies as a result. Because the T-cell–derived interleukins are required for B-cell activation, the T cells are often called *helper* T cells (Th cells). Conversely, in some cases immune responses are suppressed by certain T cells called *suppressor* T cells (Ts cells)—which act either by restricting the supply of essential growth factors or by producing molecules that inhibit lymphocyte activation. This suppression gives rise to a state of *immune tolerance* in which the animal fails to respond to the activating antigen.

FIGURE 19.2

[A] Pathways of development of the cells active in the dual immune system: T lymphocytes and B lymphocytes. [B] Specific immunity results from the cooperation of T lymphocytes, B lymphocytes, and a particular type of macrophage called an APC (antigen-presenting cell). Suppression of the immune response can also occur, mediated by certain T lymphocytes called *suppressor T cells*.

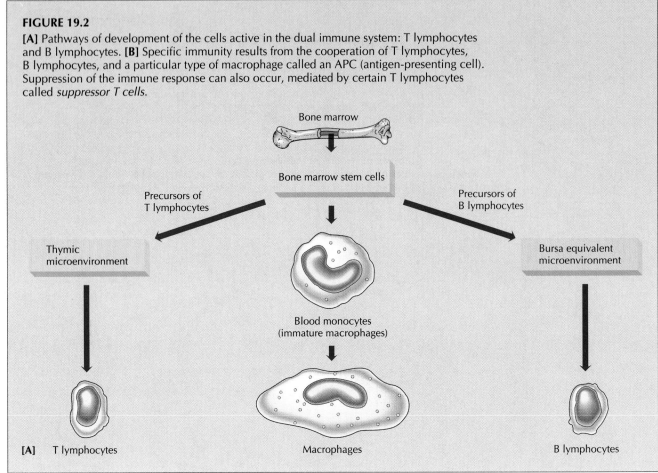

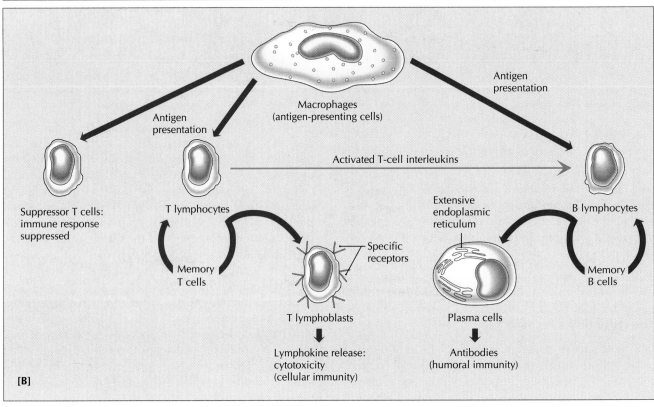

FIGURE 19.3
Relationships of the various types of acquired specific immunity.

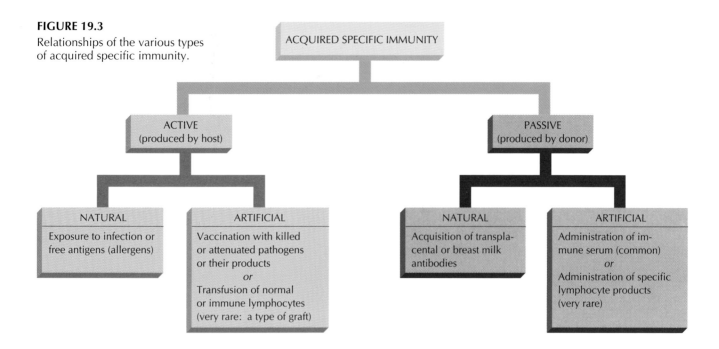

```
                          ACQUIRED SPECIFIC IMMUNITY


         ACTIVE                                        PASSIVE
     (produced by host)                            (produced by donor)


   NATURAL          ARTIFICIAL              NATURAL            ARTIFICIAL
```

NATURAL
Exposure to infection or free antigens (allergens)

ARTIFICIAL
Vaccination with killed or attenuated pathogens or their products
or
Transfusion of normal or immune lymphocytes (very rare: a type of graft)

NATURAL
Acquisition of transplacental or breast milk antibodies

ARTIFICIAL
Administration of immune serum (common)
or
Administration of specific lymphocyte products (very rare)

Mediators of Humoral Immunity

The primary mediator of humoral immunity is the *serum antibody*. The first demonstration of this serum-borne immune factor was made by Emil von Behring in 1890, when he transferred serum from an immune donor animal to a susceptible recipient animal and then challenged the recipient with the virulent pathogen that had made the donor immune. The animal receiving the immune serum resisted the pathogen because the transfer of the preformed antibodies from the donor had conferred *temporary* immunity upon the recipient. Since the recipient did not actively produce the antibodies but just passively received them as a gift from the donor, this type of immunity is called *passive immunity*. This is in contrast to the induction of *active immunity* by exposure of the recipient to either the natural disease or a vaccine that induces the recipient's own immune system to produce the antibodies. Thus specific immunity may be acquired either passively or actively, and by *natural* or *artificial* means, as shown in FIGURE 19.3.

Serum contains about 8% protein, in addition to salts and other components. The antibodies are found among the globular proteins and are often referred to as *immunoglobulins (Ig's)*. A common research method used to study immunoglobulins utilizes an electric field to separate the serum proteins. This method is called *electrophoresis*. All proteins have many positively charged free amino groups ($-NH_3^+$) and negatively charged free carboxyl groups ($-CO_2^-$). But each protein has unique net charge and molecular weight, which determine its relative mobility in an electric field. Positively charged proteins will migrate toward the cathode (negative pole), and negatively charged proteins will travel toward the anode (positive pole). It can be seen in FIGURE 19.4 that the serum is separated into albumin

FIGURE 19.4
Electrophoretic profile of rabbit serum containing antibodies to egg albumin before absorption (——) and after absorption (——) with the same antigen (egg albumin), which removes the specific antibody. Note the decrease in the globulin peaks after absorption, especially that of gamma globulin, demonstrating that the anti-egg albumin antibodies were globulin proteins.

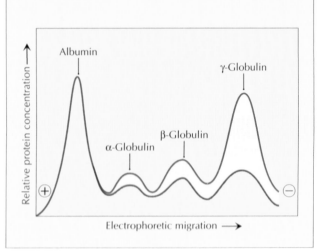

and several groups of globulins labeled *alpha* (α), *beta* (β), and *gamma* (γ). The gamma region contains the most globulins.

The Basic Structure of an Antibody

When the proteins in the gamma region are examined for size and structure, they are mostly of one type. This antibody was called *immunoglobulin gamma*, or *IgG*, by early researchers. A combination of separation techniques, culminating in x-ray crystallography, has revealed the structure of the basic antibody unit. The early research leading to our understanding of the chain structure of the basic IgG monomer earned Nobel Prizes for two important pioneers in this field, R. R. Porter and G. M. Edelman. The antibody unit resembles a small, fat letter Y with three regions corresponding to the arms of the Y; it is constructed from four polypeptide chains [FIGURE 19.5A]. There are two heavy chains with a molecular weight of about 50,000 each, plus two light chains of about 20,000 each—all bound to each other in the intact molecule by disulfide bonds. The light chains are identical and contain 214 amino acid residues each, while the two heavy chains are identical and contain about 446 amino acid residues each. As with many proteins, the IgG molecule is glycosylated (i.e., linked to several complex polysaccharides), thus making it more accurately a globular glycoprotein. The sugar part is not involved in the specific immune nature of the antibody but rather in some of its physical properties.

By electron-microscopic techniques, it was observed that there are two antigen-binding sites on each molecule [FIGURE 19.5A]. This bivalent nature is essential for an antibody to be able to cross-link more than one antigen molecule. This cross-linkage causes aggregation of the antigens, resulting in precipitation, agglutination, and cell activation (described in Chapter 20). A monovalent antibody with a single binding site would be able to neutralize antigens by masking their active sites, but it would not be able to initiate many of the complex reactions possible with bivalent antibodies.

Each antibody has both specific properties and common physical properties, each determined by different parts of the molecule. This can be shown by a combination of biochemical and molecular techniques. If the IgG molecule is partly digested with the enzyme papain (a protease derived from the papaya fruit), the IgG molecule is cleaved at the hinge region, yielding three fragments of about 50,000 daltons each [FIGURE 19.5B]. The two antigen-binding fragments are called *Fab's;* the third fragment is called the *Fc,* because it is crystallizable. The Fc is identical for all antibodies of the same class; it determines many of the physical properties of an antibody molecule. The Fab regions define the specific-ity of the antibodies; only the amino-terminal 107 amino acids of both the heavy and light chains are involved in antigen binding (shaded areas in FIGURE 19.5). Since the Fab amino acid sequence defines the specificity of the binding site, and since antibodies vary in their ability to recognize many antigens, the variable amino acid sequence of the Fab amino-terminal domain is called the *variable region.* In contrast, the remainder of the heavy chain, including the Fc region, is invariant, or conserved; it is called the *heavy-chain constant region* (C_H). The invariant portion of the light chain is called the *light-chain constant region* (C_L).

The antigenic sites recognized by antibodies are very small components of the foreign protein or polysaccharide molecule, and therefore extremely small parts of a whole microbe. Antibody itself usually has relatively little effect on microbial growth and function—unless it happens to react with an active site on an essential component of the microbe or one of its proteins. The major value of antibodies in immune resistance is as a targeting mechanism for other active substances, such as complement.

Antibody Classes and Functions

There are five different classes of immune globulins, and each has a different function in providing humoral immunity to the host [TABLE 19.1]. These include the most common immunoglobulin (IgG); a larger macroglobulin (IgM); a secretory immunoglobulin (IgA); an immunoglobulin involved in allergies (IgE); and immunoglobulin D (IgD), for which no major function has been found. FIGURE 19.6 shows the structure of the different classes of immunoglobulins. Each antibody class is defined by the class of the heavy chain, which is referred to by its Greek letter (IgA = α, IgD = δ, IgE = ϵ, IgG = γ, and IgM = μ) as shown in TABLE 19.1. There are only two types of light chains, kappa (κ) and lambda (λ), and each antibody molecule has either one or the other of these chain types, never a mixture. They are associated indiscriminately with all five classes of heavy chains. A single antibody-forming cell will produce antibodies of only one specificity. Where antibodies form polymers, a joining chain (J chain) is required. The antibody-forming cell also produces this protein in addition to the heavy (H) and light (L) chains. Overall, antibodies account for 15 mg/ml of the total protein in serum (76 mg/ml); but during an active immune response, the total quantity of serum immunoglobulins can more than double.

Immunoglobulin M (IgM). The first class of antibody to be produced in response to an antigen is the IgM antibody. IgM is produced about 4 days after immunization with antigen. It peaks in concentration at day 6 and then

FIGURE 19.5

Model of the chain structure of the human IgG molecule. **[A]** The two light chains are identical, as are the two heavy chains. The chains are held together by disulfide bridges (linking cysteine residues) as well as by the mutual attraction of some of their hydrophobic amino acids. In both light and heavy chains, the sequence of amino acids in the variable regions differs substantially between different kinds of molecules. The constant regions of the chains show far less sequence variability from one kind of molecule to another. (CH_2O = carbohydrate.) **[B]** Two Fab fragments and one Fc fragment result from the cleavage of the IgG molecule by the enzyme papain.

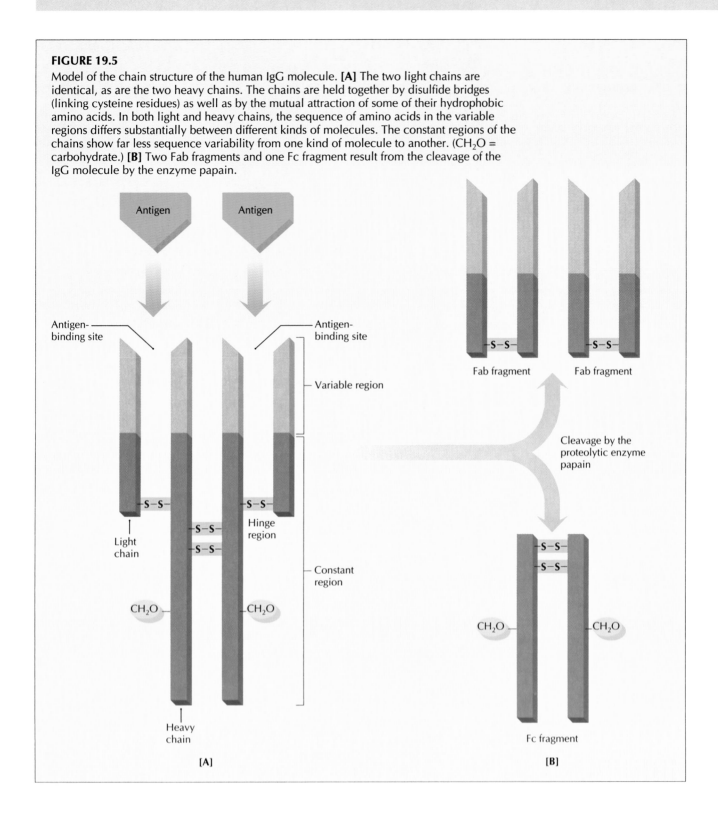

rapidly falls because of its short life span. IgM is the largest antibody, with a molecular weight of 900,000, and it constitutes 1 mg/ml of the total serum immunoglobulins. It is pentameric, which means that it is formed from five basic antibody monomers. IgM antibodies fix complement extremely well (30 times better than IgG) and therefore can effectively cause the lysis of bacteria, enveloped viruses, and infected or aged cells. IgM is too big to pass from a mother to a fetus across the placental barrier, but monomeric IgM (a single unit of 180,000 daltons), coupled to a secretory piece, has been found in mucous secretions. Monomeric IgM is also

FIGURE 19.6

Structures of the different classes of immunoglobulins. IgG, IgD, and IgE each consist of a monomer of two light and two heavy polypeptide chains. The light chain is common to all classes, whereas the heavy chain is structurally distinct for each class. IgM is a large molecule having five monomers in a star formation joined with a J (joining) polypeptide chain. IgA has three forms. When it appears in the serum, it may consist of a monomer or a dimer with a J chain. When it is found in such body fluids as saliva, tears, and nasal secretions, it consists of a dimer joined by a special component known as the *secretory piece* (this dimer also has a J chain). The exact location of the J chain in the IgM and IgA (monomer) molecules is uncertain.

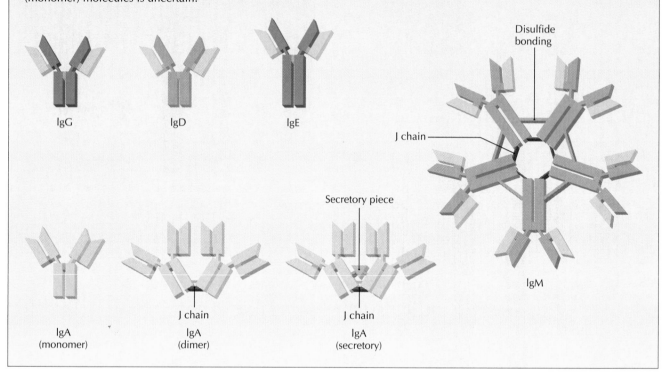

TABLE 19.1

Some Properties of the Different Classes of Human Immunoglobulins

Immunoglobulin	Heavy-chain designation	Number of subclasses	Molecular weight (daltons)	Structure	Other features
IgM	μ (mu)	2	900,000	$(H_2L_2)_5 + J$	First antibodies to appear after immunization
IgD	δ (delta)	1	180,000	H_2L_2	Function uncertain
IgG	γ (gamma)	4	150,000	H_2L_2	Transferred across placenta; major class of antibody
IgA	α (alpha)	2	160,000 390,000 $(160,000)_n$	H_2L_2 $(H_2L_2)_2 + J$ $(H_2L_2)_n + J$	Higher concentrations in mucous secretions
IgE	ϵ (epsilon)	1	185,000	H_2L_2	Binds to basophils and mast cells, sensitizing them for certain allergic reactions

J = joining chain; H = heavy chain; L = light chain.

found in the membranes of unactivated antibody-producing cells, where it acts as a specific primary receptor for antigen.

Immunoglobulin G (IgG). The most common antibody is IgG, which accounts for 80 percent of the immunoglobulins in serum. In general the IgG's are the major humoral line of defense and function to neutralize toxins and viruses and to opsonize bacteria and viruses for phagocytosis. Overall, IgG antibodies fix complement well and therefore can effectively cause the lysis of bacteria, enveloped viruses, and infected or aged cells. Unlike IgM antibodies, IgG antibodies are transferred across the placenta from a mother to her unborn child, providing passive immunity to the child. The production of IgG occurs later in an immune response than the IgM, peaking at day 10 to 14 and then slowly falling, since IgG has a biological half-life of 25 days.

Immunoglobulin A (IgA). IgA is the immunoglobulin which provides humoral immunity in mucous secretions, such as tears, saliva, intestinal mucus, seminal fluid, and *colostrum* (first breast milk). In serum, IgA is present primarily as a monomer at a concentration of 2 mg/ml; but in mucous secretions as a dimer, it can range from 0.2 to 1 mg/ml. The secretory dimer, including the secretory protein and a J chain, is resistant to proteases and appears to be responsible for neutralizing toxins, allergens, bacteria, and viruses before they can enter the body through the mucous membranes. The secretory protein is added by the epithelial cells as the IgA monomers are transported through mucosal tissue. Secretory IgA is a major component of breast milk protein and provides passive immunity against enteric pathogens to the gut of the newborn.

Immunoglobulin D (IgD). IgD is an immunoglobulin without a well-known function. It is primarily seen on unactivated B-cell membranes with IgM and is found in only very small amounts in serum (IgD = 0.03 mg/ml). Other than acting as a primary antibody-producing cell receptor for antigen, IgD has no known specific role in host resistance.

Immunoglobulin E (IgE). IgE is the allergic antibody, responsible for hypersensitive responses to many antigens—from mosquito bites to pollens. These antigens can cause asthma and even fatal allergic attacks. IgE is found in only trace amounts in serum (IgE = 0.00005 mg/ml), but it is found passively attached to the surface membranes of tissue basophils called *mast cells*. Though the serum IgE half-life is very short (2 days), the half-life of mast cell–bound IgE may be much longer. The molecular weight is 190,000. The Fc region of IgE sponta-

neously binds to an IgE-specific Fc receptor on the mast cells without requiring the presence of antigen. When antigen later reaches the mast cell and reacts with the cell-bound antibody, the mast cell is activated and releases the contents of its cytoplasmic basophilic granules. The contents of these granules produce the allergic symptoms, which will be described in a later section of this chapter. The function of IgE is not to cause allergies, but possibly to mount an acute response to parasites entering the host. People in the tropics, where parasites are more common, have elevated levels of IgE.

Maturation of the Immune Response

An active immune response to most antigens involves several sequential changes. One is the sequential production of the immunoglobulin classes from IgM through IgE, although individual cells may not make all of the immunoglobulin classes. This process of producing different classes can be called "class switching" [DISCOVER 19.1]. The immunoglobulins are produced over a period of at least 4 to 14 days after exposure to antigen. A second change is a general increase in the *affinity* of the antibodies. Affinity is a measure of the quality of an antibody in terms of its ability to bind tightly to the specific antigen. Finally, the most important aspect of the maturation of an immune response is the generation of immunologic memory. These changes in the immune response are dependent on the cooperation of T cells and are therefore seen as responses only to antigens that stimulate T cells—the T-cell–dependent antigens (discussed later in the chapter).

Immunologic Memory

As a result of the cell selection and division associated with a specific immune response, the populations of B and T cells that can respond to a specific antigen become enormously enlarged. The B cells will now be readily available for restimulation by antigen, and the host can therefore respond more quickly than before [FIGURE 19.7]. Only T-cell–dependent antigens will induce this immunologic memory. Though the serum will contain antibodies as a result of the primary immune response, their finite half-life will ensure that this type of immunity will be gradually lost. Usually the B cells undergo chronic low-level reactivation as a result of immune responses to other, related antigens. These other antigens cause cross-reactive stimulation so that there are often low levels of antibody to many antigens in the serum at any time. Such antibodies are often called "natural" antibodies, but they probably are the result of this nonspecific reactivation of B cells and merely reflect the cumu-

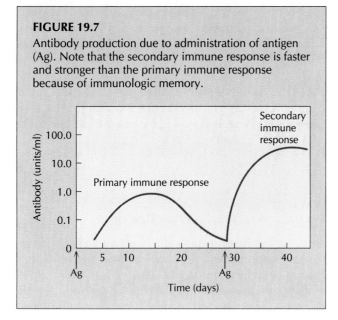

FIGURE 19.7
Antibody production due to administration of antigen (Ag). Note that the secondary immune response is faster and stronger than the primary immune response because of immunologic memory.

lative immunologic memory of the host. The major result of immunologic memory is the anamnestic response, which confers lifelong immunity on the host [FIGURE 19.7].

ASK YOURSELF

1 How are B lymphocytes affected by other cells in order to produce antibodies?

2 What is the difference between *passive* immunity and *active* immunity?

3 What is the chemical nature of antibodies?

4 Describe the unit structure of an antibody with its component parts.

5 What are the five classes of antibodies and their individual functions?

6 What is meant by *class switching*?

7 Why is the anamnestic response beneficial to the host?

ANTIGENS

Antigens are intrinsic to *specific* immune responses of the vertebrate host. They constitute the foreign matter that triggers a specific immune response.

Specificity and Immunogenicity

An *antigen* is any substance that can induce an immune response in a host and react specifically with the mediator cells or molecules that result. The more immunogenic an antigen, the more readily it can induce an immune response. The antibodies produced by the stimulated B lymphocytes will specifically react with only small portions of the antigen called *epitopes.* To be immunogenic an antigen usually has to be larger than 10,000 daltons and has to have several highly charged epitopes that easily provoke antibody production. The epitopes themselves may be less than 1000 daltons in size. Therefore the remainder of the molecule may be referred to as the *carrier* of the epitopes. The carrier determines immunogenicity, while the epitope defines the specificity of the antigen [TABLE 19.2]. During an immune response the T cells recognize the carrier, while B cells produce antibodies to the epitopes.

The complete antigen consists of specific epitopes attached to an antigenic support structure or carrier [FIGURE 19.8]. If the epitopes are removed intact from the carrier molecule, they can still combine with antibody but fail to induce an immune response. Epitopes, when they display specificity but no antigenicity, are called *haptens.* More commonly, *hapten* refers to any small, highly charged compound that becomes antigenic after reacting with proteins. For example, inorganic chemicals such as nickel and organic reagents such as penicillin or insecticides can react spontaneously with

TABLE 19.2
General Properties of a Complete, a Partial, and an Incomplete Antigen

Antigen	Properties
Complete	Has specific foreign epitopes (nonself) Antigenic (stimulatory) Molecular weight large (> 10,000) Stimulates both T cells and B cells Induces both cellular and humoral immunity
Partial	Carrier molecule Molecular weight large (> 10,000) Stimulates T cells when processed by macrophages Determines antigenicity Can induce cell-mediated immunity only
Incomplete	Consists of specific epitopes (haptens) Molecular weight small (< 1000) Fails to stimulate B cells or T cells Reacts specifically with antibodies Induces no immunity

19.1 1987 NOBEL PRIZE IN PHYSIOLOGY OR MEDICINE GOES TO AN IMMUNOLOGIST

For many years, generations of immunologists and microbiologists have been daunted by their failure to understand precisely how the body resists a plethora of infections. More specifically, how do the B cells produce such a staggering variety of antibodies? The antibody-producing genes of each B cell can direct the synthesis of only one specific type of antibody. Yet the number of distinct types of antibodies the body is capable of synthesizing in a lifetime surpasses 1 billion! This astronomical figure far exceeds the number of genes in the human genome, which contains only about 100,000 genes—certainly not enough to code for the diversity of antibodies.

Susumu Tonegawa of the Massachusetts Institute of Technology in Cambridge found the brilliant solution to this enigma—and won the 1987 Nobel Prize in physiology or medicine. He presented the first direct evidence that the genes coding the constant and the variable regions of immunoglobulin molecules could be shuffled. The regions were coded in different parts of the genome and were later joined as development progressed. Essentially, he showed how parts of the genome can be rearranged in B cells to allow synthesis of an infinite number of antibodies to fight off disease.

Tonegawa's convincing and elegant discoveries have contributed much to the current knowledge of antibody diversity. This knowledge may be summarized as follows. Each antibody-forming cell becomes committed during differentiation in the bone marrow to producing antibody with one specificity throughout its life span. However, a cell may produce other classes of immunoglobulins with the same specificity later during the immune response or during subsequent immune responses. The DNA which codes for the heavy chain is formed by the fusion of genes for *specificity* and the genes for antibody *class* (constant region).

This gene rearrangement allows the random linkage of a variable-region gene, taken from a "library" of several hundred variable genes, with the constant-region gene. There is only one copy of each class of constant-region gene, but there are many variable-region genes. In the DNA of the B cell, the constant-region genes are arranged in the sequence M, D, G, E, A. When an antibody-forming cell switches from IgM to IgG production, the intervening IgM and IgD genes are looped out, excised, and lost forever. Therefore, antibody class switching is one-way and irreversible; it is usually in the sequence IgM → IgA during an immune response.

---

protein carriers, thus creating a complete antigen. Antibodies or immune T cells then react with the epitope of the new antigen, often causing allergic reactions.

Natural versus Artificial Antigens

Natural antigens are everywhere. They are in the water you drink, the air you breathe, and the food you eat. Most are harmless and are merely a part of the organic material of which all life is made. But when you are exposed to a significant amount of these antigens in such a way that the immune system is stimulated, then an immune response occurs. The most common source of natural antigens is the microbial world. This is because microbes can actively invade our bodies, grow very rapidly to produce massive amounts of antigen, and express epitopes that are very foreign to the immune system. Therefore most immune responses are generated against microbial antigens as a result of natural exposure during the progress of disease (for example, common colds, measles, or tuberculosis).

In cases where microorganisms are virulent and likely to cause life-threatening disease, it is best to help the host acquire specific immunity before the disease is encountered. Therefore microbiologists have developed cultures of microorganisms as vaccines to deliberately immunize the population, in a sense exposing people to an "artificial antigen." To prevent vaccines from causing disease, the microorganisms are either killed or attenuated (made to have weakened virulence) before injection. Examples include the typhoid vaccine and the Salk and Sabin polio vaccines. In some cases—for example, in immunizing against diphtheria or tetanus—it is sufficient to immunize the host with only a product of the pathogen, such as a *toxin*. The toxin is inactivated before injection (to make a *toxoid*), but the immunity produced also protects the host against the natural toxin.

Soluble versus Cellular Antigens

Antigens may be soluble macromolecules or part of a particle or cell. Most greatly exceed 10 kilodaltons in size. In most cases it is necessary for the antigen to be taken up by a macrophage and partially degraded into immunogenic peptides before presentation to the immune lymphocytes (this has been termed *processing* the antigen). In general, the greater the antigenicity of the antigen, the more easily it can be taken up by the macrophages. Proteins and carbohydrates usually are much more antigenic than nucleic acids and lipids. In the case of immune responses to cellular antigens, there will be antibodies formed to outer-surface epitopes and to

FIGURE 19.8

Anatomy of a complete antigen. It consists of specific epitopes attached to a carrier in order to have specificity and immunogenicity.

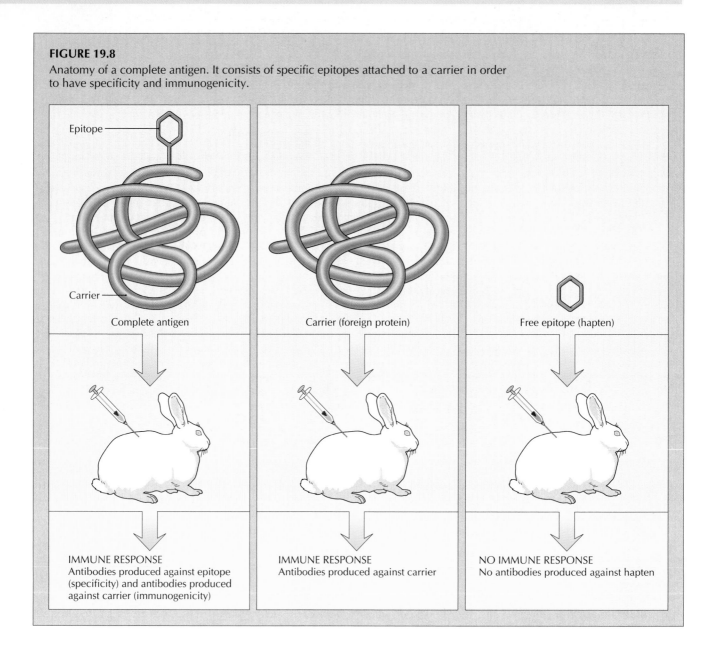

epitopes of cytoplasmic structures such as enzymes and ribosomes. But only the former will be protective, since antibodies do not penetrate living cells. It is important to remember that not all antigens capable of stimulating an immune response are found on pathogens. Immunogenic epitopes are also found on organ transplants, allergenic materials, or body cells and macromolecules.

Thymus-Dependent and Thymus-Independent Antigens

Most antigens are dependent upon T-cell help for their ability to induce an immune response, while others can induce an antibody response without T-cell help [TABLE 19.3]. Most antigens are *thymus-dependent (TD)*, be-

TABLE 19.3

Comparison of Thymus-Dependent and Thymus-Independent Antigens

Parameter compared	Thymus-dependent	Thymus-independent
T-cell help	Required	Not required
B cells	Required	Required
Antibody produced	All classes	IgM only
Antibody class switching	Yes	No
High affinity	Yes	No
Affinity increase	Yes	No
Immune memory	Yes	No

cause B cells cannot respond to them unless they receive "help" from T cells. Thus the response to TD antigens involves the interaction of Th and B cells. Some polymeric antigens, such as bacterial proteins, polysaccharides, or lipopolysaccharides, can directly stimulate B cells to produce antibody without the assistance of Th cells. This is because they have multiple epitopes capable of directly interacting with B-cell receptors, thus activating B-cell growth and differentiation. Such antigens are said to be *thymus-independent (TI)*. They do not cause maturation of the immune response. No antibody class switching occurs, and no immunologic memory is produced [TABLE 19.3].

Adjuvants

Several approaches have been used to increase the immunogenicity of foreign proteins. The incorporation of antigens in a precipitate with alum or as an emulsion in mineral oil prolongs the release of antigen and intensifies the antigenic stimulus [FIGURE 19.9]. Any material used to increase immunogenicity is referred to as an ***adjuvant***. Successful vaccines, such as those against diphtheria and tetanus, often require the addition of adjuvants.

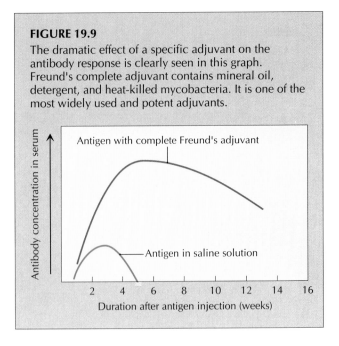

FIGURE 19.9
The dramatic effect of a specific adjuvant on the antibody response is clearly seen in this graph. Freund's complete adjuvant contains mineral oil, detergent, and heat-killed mycobacteria. It is one of the most widely used and potent adjuvants.

sponse to the allergen; different types of immune responses cause different types of allergies. An allergy is the unfortunate side effect of a correctly working immune system. Avoidance of the source of the allergens is the most effective solution for preventing allergies.

HYPERSENSITIVITY

Antibodies do not by themselves do anything unless they react with antigen, and even then they bind only to the epitopes. In the living animal, antigen-antibody reactions activate other host responses intended to protect the host from disease. The physiological response of the immune host may produce symptoms of hypersensitivity to the antigen, a phenomenon commonly called *allergy*. Antigens which can cause allergic symptoms are referred to as *allergens*. The basis for allergies is an immune re-

Immediate-Type, or Anaphylactic, Hypersensitivity (Type I)

The most common and best understood form of allergy is the type which causes hay fever and the acute reactions to insect stings. Type I allergies occur within a few minutes of exposure to a soluble allergen. The acute phase usually ceases within 20 minutes to a few hours, depending on the dose of allergen absorbed. The symptoms vary depending on the tissue site exposed, but the most common symptoms are reddening (erythema) and a soft swelling due to fluid accumulation in the tissues (edema). If the allergen is inhaled and reacts in the lungs, smooth muscles in the bronchioles contract and thus restrict the flow of air, causing the asphyxia seen in severe cases of asthma. This acute type of life-threatening systemic allergy is called ***anaphylaxis.***

The mechanism for immediate-type allergies involves specific IgE antibodies and the mast cells [FIGURE 19.10]. As mentioned earlier, the mast cells have Fc receptors for IgE on their surface membranes, and the IgE spontaneously adheres to these receptors. When the allergen reacts with the IgE antigen-binding sites, the mast cells are activated, releasing the contents of the basophilic granules. These contents include histamine, which causes dilation of the capillaries, increased leak-

FIGURE 19.10

Overall scheme for type I hypersensitivity. An allergen stimulates B cells to produce specific IgE antibodies with the help of T cells. The IgE molecules bind to mast cell Fc receptors, thereby sensitizing these cells. When more allergen subsequently reacts with cell surface–bound IgE, the cell degranulates, releasing mediators that cause the clinical symptoms of type I hypersensitivity.

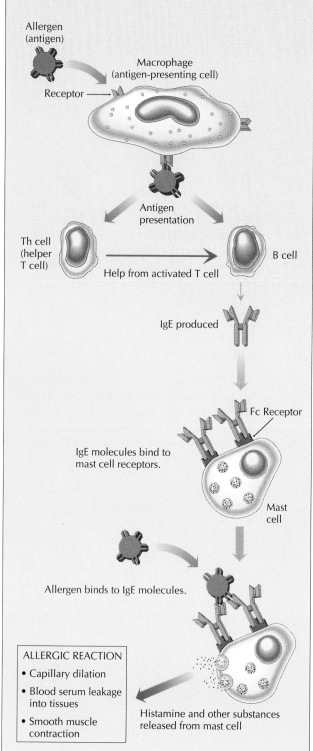

Allergen (antigen)

Macrophage (antigen-presenting cell)

Receptor

Antigen presentation

Th cell (helper T cell)

Help from activated T cell

B cell

IgE produced

Fc Receptor

IgE molecules bind to mast cell receptors.

Mast cell

Allergen binds to IgE molecules.

ALLERGIC REACTION
- Capillary dilation
- Blood serum leakage into tissues
- Smooth muscle contraction

Histamine and other substances released from mast cell

age of serum from the blood vessels into the tissues, and smooth muscle contraction. Dilation of the capillaries leads to reddening of the affected area; leakage of serum is related to edema formation. Other factors released include serotonin and leucotrienes, which cause other symptoms. The area is typically infiltrated with polymorphonuclear leucocytes (PMNs) and eosinophils. This acute form of immune reaction apparently helps prevent invasion by parasites that attempt to burrow through the skin or are injected in insect saliva (e.g., from mosquitoes).

Complement-Mediated, or Cytolytic, Hypersensitivity (Type II)

You learned earlier that IgM or IgG antibodies can activate complement and cause the lysis of some bacteria and viruses. This activity obviously can benefit the host. However, if the antigen is part of red blood cells or is a drug that has become attached to them, the result will be lysis of red blood cells, leading to hemolytic anemia. Type II allergy is primarily directed against cellular targets, requires complement, and occurs over several hours or days. The attached IgG antibody with or without complement can also mark the cellular antigens, and thus cells, for phagocytosis and degradation by macrophages. The acute phase is associated with infiltrates of PMN cells, whereas macrophages are seen during the chronic phase. Therefore, either normal or abnormal immune responses to external cellular antigens or modified cell proteins can result in the activation of complement and the lysis of host cells.

The activation of complement also results in the release of the cleavage products of C3 and C5. C3a and C5a, called *anaphylotoxins* in this case, activate mast cells to release their granules, causing symptoms similar to those described for type I hypersensitivity. The function of such an immune response is to expose and neutralize pathogens or toxins hidden inside cells. But this will work only when some of the antigen is on the surface of the cell. This mechanism may also be responsible for the recognition and removal of worn-out blood cells or the elimination of cancer cells.

Immune-Complex, or Arthus, Hypersensitivity (Type III)

Immune responses to soluble antigens often cause what appears to be a combined response. There is an acute phase similar to immediate-type reactions that starts within a few minutes of antigen exposure, but it lasts much longer (from several hours to days). The antibody involved is usually IgG, though IgM may also be found in affected sites. Complement is also required. The mechanism is almost identical to that of type II hypersensitivity in that complement is activated and anaphylotoxic components (C3a and C5a) cause mast cells to degranulate—resulting in many of the acute symptoms and a PMN cell infiltrate. The chronic-phase symptoms include a macrophage infiltrate, which is a response to accumulations of immune complexes in the host tissues. When this occurs in the skin, a rash typically forms. But the deposition of immune complexes in the kidney may result in renal failure. Again, the primary purpose of the reaction of antibody with soluble antigens is the neutralization and clearance of the antigen.

Delayed, or Cell-Mediated, Hypersensitivity (Type IV)

In some cases the skin reaction elicited by an antigen may be delayed for many hours; once it appears, it gradually becomes bigger over 24 to 48 hours, and then diminishes. The skin reaction is hard and pale in the center with a slight reddening around the periphery. A histological examination of the lesion shows mostly lymphocytes and macrophages. This is an example of a true T-lymphocyte–mediated response and is seen in skin tests (e.g., the Mantoux test for tuberculosis).

After injection of the antigen, it takes many hours for the T cells to gradually infiltrate the site, where they are activated by the antigen [FIGURE 19.11]. The release of lymphokines—including macrophage chemotactic factor, macrophage migration inhibition factor, and macrophage activation factor—results in a massive mononuclear cell infiltrate (as opposed to an infiltrate by polymorphs). A cell-mediated immune response occurs at the site of the lesion, activating cytotoxic T cells and null cells. The function of this response is to kill virus-infected cells or tumor cells, but in the process many normal host cells are killed as innocent bystanders.

ASK YOURSELF

1 What is the immunologic basis for allergies?

2 Name the four different types of hypersensitivities.

3 Why do some people suffer from hay fever?

4 Why do some people die from insect bites?

5 What type of hypersensitivity eliminates cancer cells? What is the mechanism for this?

6 What type of hypersensitivity is involved in the skin test for tuberculosis?

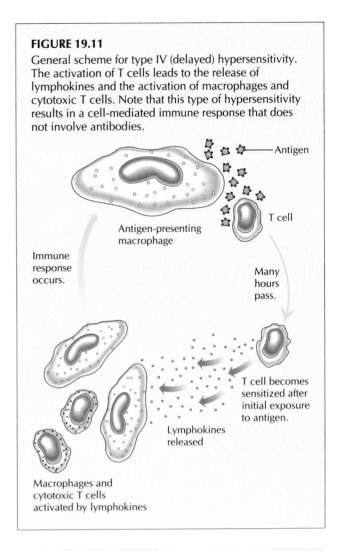

FIGURE 19.11
General scheme for type IV (delayed) hypersensitivity. The activation of T cells leads to the release of lymphokines and the activation of macrophages and cytotoxic T cells. Note that this type of hypersensitivity results in a cell-mediated immune response that does not involve antibodies.

Antigen

T cell

Antigen-presenting macrophage

Immune response occurs.

Many hours pass.

T cell becomes sensitized after initial exposure to antigen.

Lymphokines released

Macrophages and cytotoxic T cells activated by lymphokines

CELLULAR IMMUNITY

Cellular immunity implies T-cell–mediated immunity. Obviously, all immune responses involve cellular activity at some point in their generation and/or reactions. But only T cells can produce true cell-mediated immunity, because they are the primary regulators of the immune response and are capable of reacting to antigens by themselves. Thus all responses that primarily involve T-cell mediators, but do not involve B cells or antibodies, constitute cellular immunity.

Transplantation Immunity

When an organ or tissue is grafted from an unrelated donor to a patient, it is primarily the T-cell–mediated response that rejects the graft. The first cells to recognize the graft as foreign are the helper T cells. They in turn provide the T-cell growth factors to activate the cytolytic T lymphocytes, which kill the graft cells. When the graft is examined microscopically, the prominent mononuclear cell infiltrate seen is very similar to the type IV hypersensitivity infiltrate described previously. A similar cell-mediated response is seen when cancers are regressing as a result of successful immunotherapy.

In general, any graft that is not genetically identical to the recipient's cells will be rejected. Such grafts express an enormous diversity of cell membrane transplantation antigens (histocompatibility proteins). Grafts that are antigenically very dissimilar are usually rejected within 10 to 12 days; they are said to express a major *histocompatibility difference.* Grafts that are more similar (but not wholly genetically identical), such as grafts from relatives or donors who have been tested for their antigenic similarity with the potential recipient, will be accepted for longer periods.

These acceptance periods can last up to several weeks without supportive immunosuppressive drug therapy, but eventually they too will be rejected unless the recipient's immune system is somewhat suppressed by drugs. As shown in FIGURE 19.12, the only grafts which are indefinitely accepted are grafts from "self" (*autografts*) that are genetically identical, or grafts from twin donors (*isografts,* i.e., grafts between genetically identical individuals). Grafts from brothers, sisters, or parents will be similar but not identical and will usually be rejected as quickly as a totally unrelated graft of tissue. A graft from genetically different members of the same species is called an *allograft.* Grafts from different species (*heterografts*) are obviously genetically dissimilar and are rarely used, since they too are quickly rejected [FIGURE 19.12].

Clinically, the rejection response can be temporarily suppressed by treating the recipient with immunosuppressive cytotoxic drugs which control the immune response by impairing the immune system. Since these treatments also severely impair the recipient's ability to fight infections and cancers, their use is quite risky.

In special cases, where the donor tissue may lack major transplant antigens, tissues grafted with only simple matching procedures can be accepted without any major rejection problems. These include transfusions of whole blood. Since red blood cells (RBCs) lack a nucleus and the major transplant antigens, a match (achieved by testing both donor and recipient) of the next most important group of antigens (the A, B, O, and Rh groups) is sufficient to prevent rejection [TABLE 19.4]. Because human serum in a recipient may contain antibodies to the blood group antigens expressed on the donor's red blood cells, the match must be carefully done. The Rh antigen is not as strong as the ABO antigens, but Rh matching is done because recipients often become immunized to the Rh factor when a mismatched transfusion is performed. This can result in problems for pregnant Rh− women who carry Rh+ babies, since the anti-Rh (IgG) antibody can cross the placenta and cause severe hemolytic anemia in their babies before birth.

Cellular Immunity to Viruses

In an individual with viral disease the virus is hidden inside the host cells throughout much of its replication cycle. In addition, viruses can move from cell to cell through intercellular bridges, thus avoiding contact with serum antibodies that could neutralize the virus. The cytolytic T-cell–mediated immune response is effective against infected host cells only if it is directed against viral antigens expressed on the surface of the infected cells. The activity of the cytolytic cells is closely regulated or restricted so that uninfected host cells are not harmed. However, if the virus has selectively infected cells essential to the host, the cytolytic T-cell–mediated immune response will kill these cells in attacking the virus, leaving the host without the normal function of the cells. For example, if the virus has infected insulin-

---

TABLE 19.4
Grafts of Human Blood Between Individuals

BLOOD TYPE			SUCCESSFUL TRANSFUSIONS	
Phenotype	Genotype	Isoantibodies present	Donate to:	Receive from:
A	AA, AO	Anti-B	A, AB	A, O
B	BB, BO	Anti-A	B, AB	B, O
AB	AB	None	AB	A, B, AB, O
O	OO	Anti-A and -B	A, B, AB, O	O
Rh+	D	None	+	+, −
Rh−	d	None	−, +	−

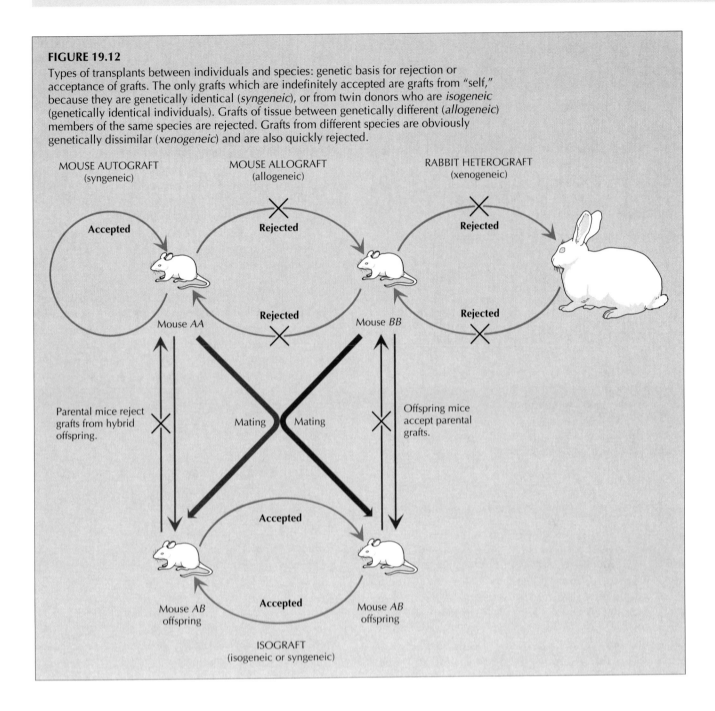

FIGURE 19.12

Types of transplants between individuals and species: genetic basis for rejection or acceptance of grafts. The only grafts which are indefinitely accepted are grafts from "self," because they are genetically identical (*syngeneic*), or from twin donors who are *isogeneic* (genetically identical individuals). Grafts of tissue between genetically different (*allogeneic*) members of the same species are rejected. Grafts from different species are obviously genetically dissimilar (*xenogeneic*) and are also quickly rejected.

MOUSE AUTOGRAFT
(syngeneic)

MOUSE ALLOGRAFT
(allogeneic)

RABBIT HETEROGRAFT
(xenogeneic)

Accepted

Rejected

Rejected

Rejected

Rejected

Mouse *AA*

Mouse *BB*

Parental mice reject grafts from hybrid offspring.

Mating   Mating

Offspring mice accept parental grafts.

Accepted

Mouse *AB* offspring

Accepted

Mouse *AB* offspring

ISOGRAFT
(isogeneic or syngeneic)

producing cells and the immune response kills these cells, the host can develop acute-onset insulin-dependent diabetes. In practice, clinicians must rely on viral vaccines and the few effective antiviral drugs available to treat patients to minimize the cytopathogenic effects of a viral disease in a host.

Implications of the T-Cell Response

It might be possible to improve our ability to manipulate and exploit the immune response if the mechanisms con-

trolling the T-cell response were better understood. The T cell not only helps beneficial immune responses; it may also suppress undesirable immune responses. The interactions of the subclasses of T cells and, in turn, their interactions with the mediator cells of both humoral immune responses and natural resistance mechanisms are extremely complex. At this time, these interactions seem beyond our powers to alter in any sophisticated way. If scientists could learn how to successfully regulate the cell-mediated immune response, then clinicians could specifically suppress the rejection of much-needed organ grafts or increase the immunity to cancers.

ASK YOURSELF

1 What activities do T cells carry out?

2 What is the mechanism for rejection of a transplanted organ?

3 Describe the genetic basis for the acceptance or rejection of grafts between individuals.

4 Do red blood cells have major transplant antigens? If not, what are the most important antigens on RBCs?

5 How do the cytolytic T cells recognize virally infected cells?

ACQUISITION OF SPECIFIC IMMUNITY

Specific immunity includes those immune responses that depend upon *recognition* of the cell or substance to be attacked by the immune system. How the body acquires the ability to respond specifically to such antigens is discussed in this section.

Natural versus Passive Acquisition of Immunity

Specific immunity may be acquired in many ways, both natural and artificial. Acquired active immunity is the result of the recipient's own cells producing antibodies *after* exposure to an antigen (e.g., after vaccination). Passive immunity involves the transfer of *preformed* antibodies to the recipient without induction of an immune response within that recipient [review FIGURE 19.3]. The only *natural* example of the passive acquisition of immunity occurs during fetal and neonatal development in some mammals, particularly humans. During fetal development, antibodies cross the placenta from the mother into the baby's circulation. During the neonatal period (just after birth), the baby acquires additional passive immune antibodies in the early milk called *colostrum*. The passive acquisition of the mother's immunity provides protection to the newborn, whose immature immune system is incapable of resisting all the pathogens encountered during the first few days of life.

Antibody Therapy and Immunotherapy

With the advent of laboratory-produced *monoclonal antibodies*, the use of passive antibodies to provide temporary immunity to hosts may represent an enormous step beyond transfusing antibodies in whole blood. Cell cloning technology, discussed in Chapter 20, makes it possible to produce in the laboratory literally grams of a single antibody. It is hoped that patients who need a therapeutic or diagnostic antibody can obtain it in virtually limitless quantities without the risks associated with transfusing whole blood products. By coupling cytotoxic drugs with monoclonal antibodies reactive to tumor antigens, it is theoretically possible to specifically target tumor cells with the drugs. This has promise as the "magic bullet" envisioned by Paul Ehrlich in 1900!

The subject of immunotherapy, or the treatment of patients by immunological methods, is now taking on a much wider meaning as some of the growth factors of the immune system have been isolated, cloned, and produced in quantity. By administering these growth factors to immunodeficient hosts, some aspects of the immune defense can be restored. Alternatively, host cells can be removed and activated in vitro before they are reintroduced into the host. Both these approaches have been used experimentally to treat some cancer patients.

ASK YOURSELF

1 Describe a *natural* method of passive immunity.

2 Why is the use of monoclonal antibodies promising for antibody therapy?

3 What therapeutic benefit can be derived from knowledge about growth factors of the immune system?

INFECTION, IMMUNITY, AND IMMUNODEFICIENCY

Now that you have examined the components of an immune system, the most important question is, How does it actually work in the human host during the progress of disease, and what components are more important than others? These questions are difficult to answer, since researchers are limited by ethical considerations in what they can do in the way of actual human experimentation. Laboratory animals do not always respond in exactly the same manner as humans. You can observe the natural course of disease in humans, but you must intervene with treatments when this will benefit the patient, altering the true response. The "ideal" experiment would be to obliterate components of the immune system and ob-

FIGURE 19.13

Origins of the cellular components of the hemopoietic (blood-forming) and immune systems.

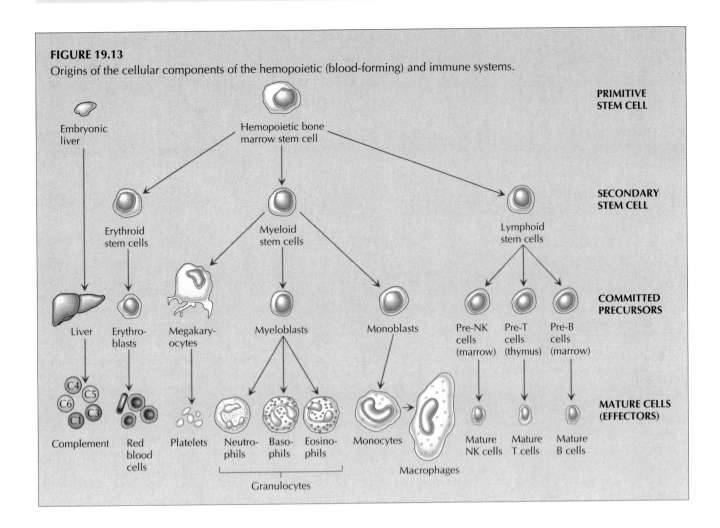

serve the effects on the patient's resistance to disease! Obviously this cannot be done to healthy humans, but there are patients who have genetic or acquired deficiencies of the immune system. Scientists can observe these defects and their effects on the incidence and course of disease.

Immune Defects of T, B, or NK Cells or of Macrophages

Genetic defects of the immune system can appear as defects in either the bone marrow stem cells, from which all white blood cells arise; the microenvironment necessary for the differentiation of some specialized subsets of cells; or the genetic pathway of cellular differentiation. In any event, the production of cells necessary for the optimal functioning of the immune system can fail at any of the steps in the complex pathways of differentiation [FIGURE 19.13]. In most cases this results in a severe impairment of the host's ability to resist disease.

The most important defects affect the generation of the lymphoid elements of the immune system.

DiGeorge's syndrome is associated with a defect in the normal development of the thymus and results in a complete absence of mature T cells and cell-mediated immunity. Various *agammaglobulinemias* (such as Bruton's agammaglobulinemia) result from defects in B-cell development. *Severe combined immunodeficiency* is caused by a defect in the lymphoid stem cells and results in a complete absence of both T cells and B cells. TABLE 19.5 shows the primary features of the major immune deficiencies and their effects on diseases induced by extracellular (e.g., bacterial) and intracellular (e.g., viral) pathogens. Deficiencies of macrophages and complement are also seen, but these are of secondary importance, since they are nonspecific elements of the defense against disease. However, the loss of these cells does exacerbate disease incidence and/or severity.

Effects of Immunodeficiency on Antibacterial Defenses

Since bacteria are attacked primarily by the phagocytic cells, it is expected that increased incidence and severity

TABLE 19.5
Effects of Immunodeficiencies on Host Defenses Against Disease

Immunodeficiency	IMMUNE RESPONSE		DISEASE SEVERITY	
	Cell-mediated (T cell)	Humoral (antibody)	Intracellular*	Extracellular*
T cells (DiGeorge's syndrome)	Absent	IgM normal IgG absent	Increased	Normal
B cells (Bruton's agammaglobulinemia)	Normal	Absent	Normal	Increased
T cells and B cells (severe combined immunodeficiency)	Absent	Absent	Increased	Increased
NK cells (Chédiak-Higashi syndrome)	Normal	Normal	Somewhat increased	Normal
Macrophages (myeloperoxidase defect)	Somewhat decreased	Somewhat decreased	Somewhat increased	Increased
Complement (particularly C3)	Normal	Normal	Normal	Somewhat increased

*Intracellular pathogens include viruses, some bacteria (e.g., mycobacteria), fungal pathogens (e.g., *Microsporum*), and parasites (e.g., malaria). The incidence of cancer is relatively unaffected by deficiencies of T cells or NK cells, but more neoplastic cells survive to produce cancer and cancers grow faster in patients with these deficiencies. Extracellular pathogens are almost exclusively bacteria but may include some yeasts and parasites. Cancers are relatively unaffected by deficiencies of humoral immunity.

of bacterial infections would occur in humans with macrophage deficiency. Because the efficiency of phagocytic cells is greatly increased by the opsonic effect of IgG antibody and/or complement, deficiencies of these components are also associated with a moderate increase in the frequency of severe bacterial infections. A deficiency of T cells does not have a direct effect on antibacterial defenses, but it will indirectly impair T-cell–dependent IgG responses and immunologic memory.

Since many bacterial antigens are thymus-independent, they can directly stimulate B cells to produce IgM antibodies. By doing so, they activate complement, which lyses as well as opsonizes bacterial pathogens. A complete absence of B cells will greatly impair macrophage effectiveness at combating bacterial disease. Remember from Chapter 18 that complement, with or without IgM or IgG antibody, will kill Gram-negative bacteria and is thus an important defense mechanism.

Effects of Immunodeficiency on Antiviral Defenses

During the course of an active viral disease the major mediator of antiviral immunity is the T cell, which can attack infected host cells and eliminate the intracellular reservoir of virus. Therefore deficiencies of T cells result

in a significant increase in the severity of viral disease. Long-term antiviral immunity depends upon the presence of virus-neutralizing IgG antibodies in the host serum and the presence of B cells with immunologic memory for IgG antibody production, which is T-cell–dependent. Therefore both the primary antiviral effector cell and the ability to produce long-term immunity are absent in patients with T-cell deficiencies, in whom viral diseases tend to be more severe, chronic, and recurrent.

The other cellular mediators of resistance to viral disease include the natural killer cells and the macrophages. Macrophages can phagocytose and degrade viruses, and NK cells can kill virally infected cells. A lack of these components increases the severity of disease but does not prevent an eventual cure. The absence of B cells alone has relatively little effect on viral disease other than to permit recurrence of the disease. Complement can lyse enveloped viruses, but complement deficiencies have little or no effect on viral disease.

Effects of Immunodeficiency on Anticancer Defenses

The transformation of a normal cell into a cancer cell results in a situation that is similar immunologically to a cell that has been infected with a virus. The cell no

FIGURE 19.14

[A] Cultured rat pancreatic cells shown growing in an orderly layer in which the proliferation of cells is limited by cell-to-cell contact inhibition. [B] Cells of the same type, when transformed to a cancerous state, lose their contact inhibition and grow over one another in disarrayed clumps.

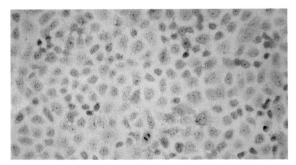

[A]

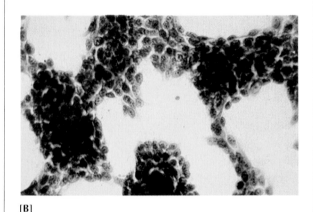

[B]

longer obeys the normal restrictions on cell growth. Cells lose contact inhibition and continue to grow even when they closely touch their nearest neighbors [FIGURE 19.14]. This means that cancer cells pile up and displace normal tissues, disrupting function in complex organs. Cancer cells also invade the surrounding tissues and grow through basement membranes, again disrupting organ function and spreading to adjacent organs, causing adhesions and obstructions. When cancer cells invade blood vessels, they can metastasize throughout the body and subsequently cause organ failure at many sites as a result of cancerous growth. Many cancers can also suppress immune functions and avoid immune rejection.

The immune and natural resistance systems constantly survey the body for newly developing cancer cells. The first cell which has a primary role in immune surveillance to destroy cancer cells is the natural killer (NK) cell. The NK cell can directly recognize the cancer cell as being different from normal cells and can kill it within a few hours before it grows into a primary tumor.

Deficiencies of NK cells or their function are associated with an increased cancer incidence, since more transformed cells will survive to produce primary tumors.

All tumors are clonal in that they arise from a single transformed cell. A basic premise of tumor immunology is that the tumor cell is in some fundamental way antigenically different from normal cells. The tumor may express new tumor-specific antigens. But specific immunity requires a sufficient quantity of antigen and considerable time for the response to be induced. Cancers may take many months or even years to grow to this point. During this time many cancers can evade the immune response and become established as progressive tumors. By definition, any cancer that grows progressively has successfully evaded the immune defenses of the host.

Deficiencies of either B cells or T cells are associated with an increased growth of cancers. Again, T cells are the primary effector of immune rejection of established cancers; the loss of these cells results in a marked acceleration in the growth of tumors. The cellular growth rate does not actually increase, but rather the anticancer defenses are severely diminished—resulting in a reduction in cancer cell loss due to immunity and therefore a faster accumulation of cancer cells in the host. Deficiencies of macrophages, complement, and other factors also have their effects, which are difficult to quantify in a long-term, insidious disease like cancer. There are still many questions to be answered before researchers can use the immune system to effectively eradicate cancer.

ASK YOURSELF

1 What is the defect of the immune system associated with DiGeorge's syndrome? With Bruton's agammaglobulinemia? With severe combined immunodeficiency?

2 What happens in a human host with macrophage deficiency? With a complete absence of B cells?

3 How does a deficiency in T cells affect the human host in combating viral infections? What are the other cellular mediators of resistance to viral disease?

4 What are the distinctive properties of cancer cells?

5 What are the consequences of a deficiency in NK cells?

6 Why are all tumors considered to be clonal? Are tumor cells antigenically different from normal cells?

SUMMARY

1 The specific immune response consists of humoral immunity and cellular immunity.

2 The primary characteristics of the active immune response are discrimination, specificity, anamnesis, and transferability by living cells.

3 Cells that specifically respond to antigens are T cells and B cells, which are distinguished on the basis of distinct surface markers. The thymus and the bone marrow are the central lymphoid organs and are responsible for processing human lymphocytes to form T cells and B cells, respectively.

4 B cells are responsible for humoral immunity, while T cells are responsible for cellular immunity. Cell-mediated immunity refers to cellular reactions directly mediated by T cells or their factors (lymphokines). Humoral immunity is mediated by antibodies, also called *immunoglobulins*.

5 The structure of the basic antibody unit resembles the letter Y and is divided into different regions, which bind antigens and bind to receptors. Five antibody classes exist, each with their separate functions.

6 Immunogenicity and specificity are two characteristics of an antigen. Antigens can be soluble or particulate, natural or artificial, and may or may not be thymus-dependent.

7 There are four types of hypersensitivities, which basically are different types of allergies.

8 Organ and tissue grafts are accepted or rejected on the basis of cellular histocompatibility antigens.

9 The cytolytic T-cell–mediated immune response is effective against virally infected host cells and cancer cells.

10 Immunity may be acquired passively during fetal and neonatal development.

11 There are several naturally occurring defects in humans that affect the generation of the lymphoid elements of the immune system. Immunodeficiencies have a great impact on defenses against bacterial, viral, and parasitic diseases. Immunodeficiencies also affect the growth of cancers.

KEY TERMS

active immunity
adjuvant
allergy
allograft
anamnestic response
anaphylaxis
antibodies
antigenicity
antigens
autografts
bone marrow–derived
  lymphocytes (B cells)
cellular immunity
central lymphoid organs
clonal-selection theory of
  immunity
epitopes
Fab's
Fc
haptens
hemopoietic
heterografts
histocompatibility difference
humoral immunity
immune antibodies
immune cells
immune system
immunogenicity
immunoglobulins (Ig's)
immunology
isografts
null cells
passive immunity
peripheral lymphoid system
thymus-derived lymphocytes
  (T cells)

SPECIFIC IMMUNITY
AND THE IMMUNE
RESPONSE

1 Soluble mediators of humoral immunity are called

_____.

2 Immune cells are the mediators of _____ .

3 The four primary characteristics of the specific immune response are summarized

by these terms: _____ , _____ ,
anamnesis, transferability by living cells.

4 T cells are thymus-derived _____ .

*Indicate whether the statement that follows is true (**T**) or false (**F**). If it is false, restate
it in the correct form.*

5 T and B lymphocytes can be distinguished on the basis of morphology. _____

_____

_____

6 The lymphatic system consists of an interconnecting network of

_____ and _____ .

7 The central lymphoid organs are the _____ and the bone
marrow.

8 The B cells are destined to synthesize specific _____ .

HUMORAL IMMUNITY

9 Match the description on the right with the appropriate item on the left.

_____ null cells

_____ B cells

_____ macrophages

_____ T cells

(a) Cells that process and present antigen in an optimal
immunogenic form to T and B cells
(b) Cells that ultimately produce antibodies
(c) Cells that produce lymphokines
(d) Cells that lack T- and B-cell markers and are
nonphagocytic

10 Indicate whether the following procedures constitute *active* or *passive* immunization:

(a) Vaccination with killed pathogens _____

(b) Vaccination with attenuated pathogens _____

(c) Administration of immune serum _____

(d) Breast milk antibodies _____

11 Indicate whether the following procedures constitute *natural* or *artificial* immunization:

(a) Administration of attenuated pathogens _____

(b) Exposure to allergens _____

(c) Transfusion of immune lymphocytes _____

(d) Recovery from disease _____

12 The basic antibody molecule has _____ polypeptide
chains.

13 An antibody molecule has *two* antigen-binding sites and is said to be

_____ .

14 When an IgG molecule is cleaved by papain, the three resulting fragments are two Fab's and one _____.

15 The first antibody to be produced in response to any antigen is the _____ antibody.

16 The most common antibody is _____.

17 Secretory _____ is a major component of breast milk protein.

18 The allergic antibody is _____.

ANTIGENS

19 An antigen has specificity and _____.

20 A portion of an antigen that reacts with antibodies is called a(n) _____.

21 Haptens display specificity but no _____.

22 An inactivated toxin is called a(n) _____.

23 Can antibodies penetrate living cells? _____

Indicate whether the following statement is true (T) or false (F). If false, rewrite it as a true statement.

24 Thymus-independent antigens do not cause maturation of the immune response. _____

_____

_____

HYPERSENSITIVITY

25 Immediate-type allergy is manifested in which of the following? **(a)** acute reactions to insect stings; **(b)** skin test for tuberculosis; **(c)** anaphylaxis; **(d)** asthma.

26 Type II hypersensitivity is also known as complement-mediated, or _____, hypersensitivity.

27 The deposition of immune complexes in the kidney with resulting renal failure is due to type _____ hypersensitivity.

CELLULAR IMMUNITY

28 The first cells to recognize that a graft is foreign are the _____ cells.

29 The cells that kill foreign graft cells are the _____ T lymphocytes.

30 Grafts that are rejected within 8 to 12 days are said to express a major _____ difference.

31 Which of the following grafts are indefinitely accepted by recipients? **(a)** hetero-grafts; **(b)** homografts; **(c)** autografts; **(d)** isografts.

32 In transfusion of whole blood, the _____ and _____ antigens of the recipient and donor are matched.

ACQUISITION OF SPECIFIC IMMUNITY

33 The cytolytic T-cell–mediated immune response is effective against virally infected host cells only if they express _____ on their surface.

34 The only *natural* example of the passive acquisition of immunity in humans occurs during _____ and _____ development.

35 The isolation, cloning, and production in quantity of growth factors of the immune system and infusing these into immunodeficient patients has given rise to the subject of _____.

36 By coupling cytotoxic drugs with _____ antibodies to tumor antigens, it is possible to specifically target the drug to the tumor cell.

INFECTION, IMMUNITY, AND IMMUNODEFICIENCY

37 DiGeorge's syndrome is associated with a complete absence of mature _____ and _____ immunity.

38 Various agammaglobulinemias result from defects in _____ development.

39 The Chédiak-Higashi syndrome is associated with deficiencies of _____ cells or their function.

40 The _____ is the primary effector of immune rejection of established cancers.

REVIEW QUESTIONS

1 Discuss the four primary characteristics of the immune response.

2 What is the function of the thymus?

3 Explain the clonal-selection theory of immunity.

4 Describe the interaction of B cells, T cells, and macrophages in the antibody response to antigen stimulation.

5 Compare passive immunity with active immunity.

6 Distinguish between natural and artificial immunity.

7 Discuss the class of antibodies that is: (a) produced first in response to any antigen; (b) the most common; (c) present in colostrum; (d) responsible for allergic reactions.

8 What is immunologic memory?

9 What two properties define an antigen?

10 Distinguish between thymus-dependent and thymus-independent antigens.

11 Explain the basis for the acceptance or rejection of organ and tissue grafts by recipients.

12 Discuss the role of cell-mediated immunity in resistance to viral infections.

13 In what way do we indeed have a "magic bullet" like that envisioned by Paul Ehrlich in 1900?

14 Describe the effects of immunodeficiency on bacterial and viral infections.

DISCUSSION QUESTIONS

1 Why has the immune response been described as a double-edged sword?

2 Explain how B cells produce a staggering variety of antibodies in the lifetime of the host body.

3 People in the tropics are said to have elevated levels of IgE. Does this mean that they have fewer parasitic infections than people in temperate climates?

4 Why is AIDS considered an immunodeficiency disease?

5 Do humans have the bursa of Fabricius? If not, what is the bursal equivalent in humans?

6 Because of a genetic defect, an individual fails to develop a thymus. What happens to that person's humoral and cellular immunity?

7 What is the immunologic basis of anaphylaxis, and why is this condition life-threatening?

8 Explain why blood transfusion is successful with matching of only ABO and Rh antigens.

9 Viruses are intracellular parasites; as such, they are protected from the environment. Yet cytolytic T cells can destroy infected host cells. How do the T cells know which cells are virally infected?

10 Discuss three ways by which genetic defects affect the immune system.

11 Why does a deficiency in the immune response result in increased growth of cancer?

12 Do you think the immunotherapeutic hopes for the use of monoclonal antibodies in treatment of patients have been fully realized?

Practical Aspects of Immunity

OBJECTIVES

After reading this chapter you should be able to

1 Explain the mechanism of precipitation for antigen-antibody reactions.

2 Describe several types of qualitative immunodiffusion tests.

3 Describe the radial immunodiffusion technique used as a quantitative immunodiffusion test.

4 Explain what is meant by immunoelectrophoresis.

5 Outline the basic procedures of electroimmunoassay and countercurrent immunoelectrophoresis.

6 Distinguish between direct and indirect agglutination tests.

7 Describe a few well-known bacterial agglutination tests and explain the significance of a rising titer of agglutinating antibodies.

8 Describe the phenomenon of viral hemagglutination and explain the use of the viral hemagglutination inhibition test.

9 Explain the principle of complement-fixation tests, radioimmunoassays, and enzyme-linked immunosorbent assays (ELISAs).

10 Distinguish between the direct and indirect fluorescent antibody techniques.

11 Explain how monoclonal antibodies are produced and the reasons why they are important.

12 List the major skin tests for cell-mediated immunity in humans and the etiologic agents responsible for the diseases that cause positive reactions.

13 Describe several in vitro tests of cell-mediated immune responses.

OVERVIEW

In this chapter you will learn the basic principles of the in vitro tests used to investigate the immune system, especially the host immune response to microbial infection. Immunologic techniques detect, characterize, and quantify antigens, antibodies, immune complexes, and cells involved in the immune response. Such tests, carried out under controlled laboratory conditions, can also provide valuable information for the diagnosis and prevention of disease.

In addition to their practical use in the clinical laboratory, immunologic techniques are used in disciplines far beyond the boundaries of medicine. For instance, they may be used in criminal investigations, such as those in cases of product or package tampering (for example, when horse meat has been substituted for beef). They are also used in fundamental studies of cell biology, such as identifying different protein substances in cell cytoplasm. However, this chapter addresses only those immunologic techniques used by the medical microbiologist, as well as the production of monoclonal antibodies.

MEASUREMENTS OF HUMORAL IMMUNITY (ANTIBODIES)

Many immunologic techniques depend on the fundamental properties of antigen-antibody reactions. You learned in Chapter 19 that antibodies react specifically with the epitopes of the antigen that stimulated their formation. Antibodies are found in blood serum, the fluid left after blood has clotted. Thus the study of in vitro interactions between antigens and antibodies, which uses serum samples, is called *serology.*

Since antibodies cannot be seen with the naked eye, they are detected only when they combine with their specific antigen. Antigen-antibody reactions may be detected by precipitation, agglutination, complement fixation (CF), fluorescence, enzyme activity, and radioisotope binding. Various tests are used to detect the different types of antibody-antigen interactions and are described in this section.

Precipitation Tests

In a precipitation test, a reaction takes place between a soluble antigen and a solution of its homologous antibody. The reaction is indicated by the formation of a visible precipitate when the solutions meet. However, the formation of this precipitate may be inhibited by an excess of either antibody or antigen. This is why the most useful precipitation tests are those that allow slow *diffusion* of antibody and antigen until their optimum concentration for the reaction is reached. The zone of optimum concentration is called the *equivalence zone* and represents the range of concentrations of antigen and antibody for which complete precipitation occurs [FIGURE 20.1]. Since precipitation is the identifiable reaction, the antibodies involved in the formation of precipitates are called *precipitins.* The relative efficiency of IgG, IgM, and IgA in precipitation reactions decreases in that order; IgD and IgE do not mediate precipitation reactions.

Precipitation occurs because all antibodies are at least bivalent, which means that each monomer has at least two identical antigen-binding sites (see Chapter 19). Consequently, any one antibody molecule can bind at least two identical antigen molecules. In other words, antigens can be *bridged* by antibodies. Furthermore, most antigens have several epitopes, so that one antigen molecule may bind more than one antibody molecule. In the first few seconds of a precipitation reaction, there is a rapid reaction between antigen and antibody to form small antigen-antibody complexes. This interaction is followed, within the next few minutes to hours, with antigen-antibody complexes made of large, interlocking aggregates called *lattices*, which precipitate from solution.

As indicated in FIGURE 20.1, lattice formation is governed by the relative concentrations of antigen and specific antibody. If either antigen or antibody is present in much higher concentration than the other, there may be little or no detectable reaction, because a large interlocking lattice will not form. If too much antibody is present, each antigen is able to bind to several antibodies and cross-linkages do not occur. If too little antibody is present, there is not enough to form bridges between antigen molecules. Therefore maximum lattice formation occurs only when neither antigen nor antibody is present in excess. In all serological testing, the proportion of antigen to antibody is critical to the outcome of the test.

Qualitative Immunodiffusion Tests. The simplest precipitation test is performed in the fluid phase, with aqueous solutions of antigen and antibody in a test tube. It is called the *precipitin ring test*, because the precipitate forms a cloudy ring or disk at the interface between the clear solutions of antigen and antibody [FIGURE 20.2A]. This cloudy precipitate occurs where the ratio of antibody and antigen concentrations is optimal—the zone of equivalence.

The precipitin ring test has been used historically to identify pathogenic streptococci in clinical laboratories. Serological groups A, B, C, D, . . . , R of the streptococci are identified on the basis of which polysaccharide antigen (known as C substance) occurs in the streptococcal cell wall. The polysaccharide can be extracted from a suspension of streptococci and added to antibody against group A, antibody against group B, and so forth. The antibody that causes precipitation of the polysaccharide identifies the group to which the streptococci belong. Streptococcus-precipitating antibodies are obtained by immunizing rabbits with heat-killed suspensions or extracts of known *Streptococcus* species. This procedure for typing streptococci is shown in FIGURE 20.3.

Because gelled agar is mostly water, both antibodies and antigens can diffuse through agar if they are soluble in water. For example, the antibody can be contained in an agar gel into which the antigen is allowed to diffuse. This is described as a single-diffusion method; an example is the *method of Oudin*, which directly layers soluble antigen over the antibody-containing agar [FIGURE 20.2B]. Double-diffusion methods (when both antigen and antibody are added) include the *Oakley-Fulthorpe method* and the *Ouchterlony method*. The Oakley-Fulthorpe method separates the antibody and antigen solutions with a layer of clear agar [FIGURE 20.2C]. This

FIGURE 20.1

Precipitation curve corresponding to changing ratio of antibody to antigen. Maximum precipitation is in the zone of equivalence, where there is an optimal ratio of antibody to antigen to allow for lattice formation through linkage of antigen-binding sites on antibodies and antigenic epitopes. In the zone of antibody excess the antigenic epitopes are saturated but not cross-linked by antibody antigen-binding sites. In the zone of antigen excess the antigen-binding sites of antibodies are saturated but not cross-linked with antigenic epitopes.

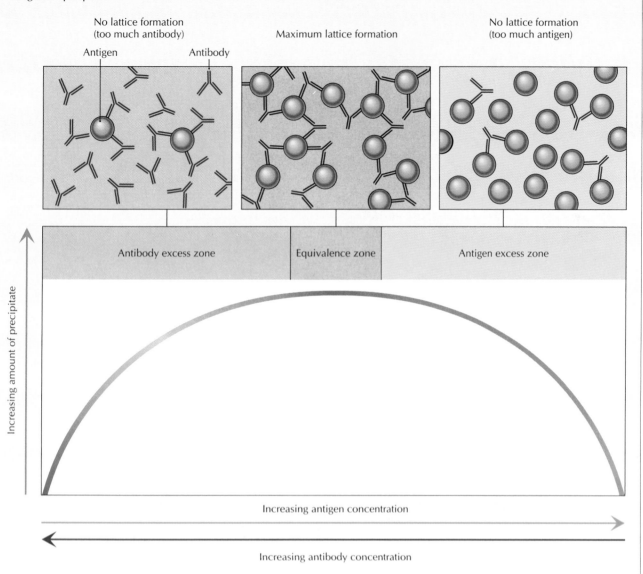

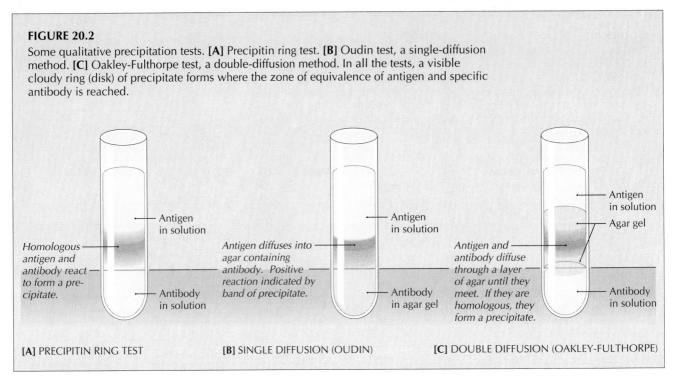

FIGURE 20.2

Some qualitative precipitation tests. **[A]** Precipitin ring test. **[B]** Oudin test, a single-diffusion method. **[C]** Oakley-Fulthorpe test, a double-diffusion method. In all the tests, a visible cloudy ring (disk) of precipitate forms where the zone of equivalence of antigen and specific antibody is reached.

Homologous antigen and antibody react to form a precipitate.

— Antigen in solution

— Antibody in solution

[A] PRECIPITIN RING TEST

— Antigen in solution

Antigen diffuses into agar containing antibody. Positive reaction indicated by band of precipitate.

— Antibody in agar gel

[B] SINGLE DIFFUSION (OUDIN)

— Antigen in solution

— Agar gel

Antigen and antibody diffuse through a layer of agar until they meet. If they are homologous, they form a precipitate.

— Antibody in solution

[C] DOUBLE DIFFUSION (OAKLEY-FULTHORPE)

FIGURE 20.3

Procedure for the typing of streptococci using a precipitin test based on cell wall polysaccharide.

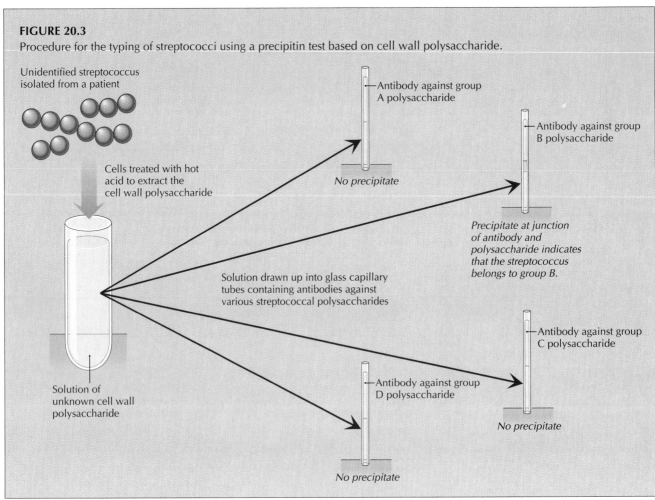

Unidentified streptococcus isolated from a patient

Cells treated with hot acid to extract the cell wall polysaccharide

Solution of unknown cell wall polysaccharide

Solution drawn up into glass capillary tubes containing antibodies against various streptococcal polysaccharides

— Antibody against group A polysaccharide

No precipitate

— Antibody against group B polysaccharide

Precipitate at junction of antibody and polysaccharide indicates that the streptococcus belongs to group B.

— Antibody against group C polysaccharide

No precipitate

— Antibody against group D polysaccharide

No precipitate

FIGURE 20.4

The Ouchterlony test, a precipitation method with double diffusion. Antigen (Ag) and antibody (Ab) are placed in separate wells cut into agar in Petri dishes; each reactant will diffuse out in all directions from its well. A line of precipitate forms where advancing fronts meet and reach equivalence. The subscripts shown refer to the identity of the antigen or antibody. **[A]** The complete fusion of two adjacent precipitin lines is called the *reaction of identity*. Neither antigen nor antibody molecules can diffuse past the line of precipitate; once these meet, they remain fused. **[B]** A projection of precipitate (spur) that forms at the intersection where two lines of precipitate form and fuse gives a reaction of partial identity of the antigens. The spur points toward the well lacking the specific antigen. **[C]** The line of precipitate formed where one antigen-antibody pair crosses another, forming double spurs, indicates a reaction of nonidentity of the antigens.

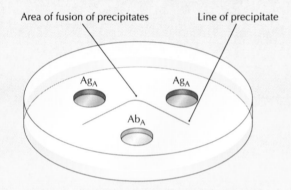

[A] IDENTITY: Precipitate lines fuse.

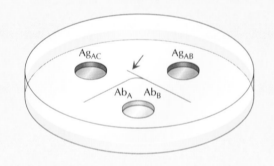

[B] PARTIAL IDENTITY: Spur (at arrow) is due to Ab$_B$.

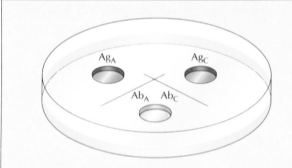

[C] NON-IDENTITY: Precipitate lines cross.

results in the diffusion of both soluble antigen and antibody into the agar and the formation of a precipitin ring.

The Ouchterlony technique is widely used for detecting antigen or antibody. It is used for the comparison of various antigens and antiserums (serums containing antibodies) on one plate of agar [FIGURE 20.4]. By cutting wells in the agar, several antigens can be compared. The antigen and antibody diffuse from the wells to form a precipitate at the equivalence zone. If immune precipitates formed by an antibody preparation with antigens from two separate wells fuse together, there is similarity (identity) between the two antigens [FIGURE 20.4]. On the other hand, crossing of precipitates with no fusion shows a lack of identity. The advantage of the Ouchterlony method over precipitation in liquid is that it makes it easier to distinguish a multicomponent antigen-antibody system, as explained in FIGURE 20.5. Examples of its use include detection of enterotoxin in cases of suspected food poisoning, or of antibodies to specific microbes where infection is present.

Precipitation tests are not limited to the laboratory diagnosis of microbial infections of humans and other animals. They are also useful in many other ways, such as the identification of blood or seminal fluid on clothing, weapons, or other exhibits in criminal investigations.

FIGURE 20.5

Distinguishing a multicomponent antigen-antibody system by the Ouchterlony method. When a rabbit is immunized with human serum, each component of the serum (such as albumin or IgG) will induce formation of antibodies directed against it. When the antiserum containing the antibodies is placed in one well **[1]** and human serum (antigens) in a second well **[2]**, a number of distinct lines of precipitate form between the two wells. The number of lines formed between the two wells indicates the minimum number of different antigens being detected by the antiserum. If a single antigen (in this case, albumin) is placed in a third well **[3]**, fusion of the line formed with one of the multiple lines formed (a reaction of identity) identifies it as one of the components of human serum.

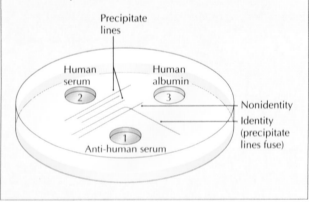

FIGURE 20.6

Single radial immunodiffusion test (Mancini method). The agar gel contains antiserum specific for the standard antigen concentrations (lower row) and the unknown antigen concentrations (upper row). A semilogarithmic plot is made of the diameters of the halos, or rings, formed by the concentrations of standard antigen. From this plot, the unknown concentrations of the test antigen can be determined.

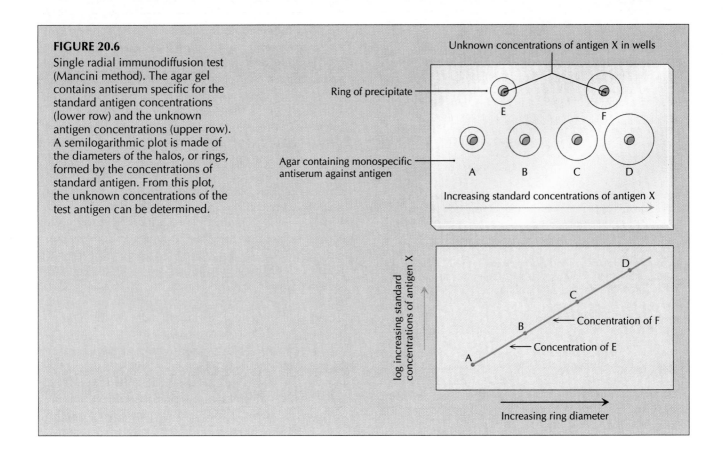

FIGURE 20.7

Separation of charged substances by electrophoresis. Shown here is the separation of the major protein components of whole serum by this electrochemical process. A spot of serum is applied to a matrix that has been soaked in a buffer at a pH of 8.6. At this pH, all the serum proteins carry a net negative charge. A direct electric current is passed through the matrix, causing the protein molecules to move in the electric field and to separate on the basis of their charge. Albumin, being the most negatively charged, migrates most rapidly toward the anode in the electric field. It is followed by alpha globulins and then transferrin (a beta globulin). Last to come are the gamma globulins, the most weakly charged proteins. (Note that the protein bands or spots are seen only after staining.)

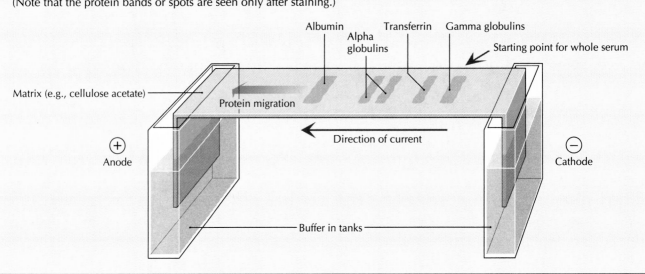

Quantitative Immunodiffusion Test. The *radial immunodiffusion technique* is used to quantify serum proteins, complement factors, antibodies, and many other substances. In the *Mancini method*, antigen is allowed to diffuse from a well into a layer of agar containing specific antibodies. Other wells are filled with various dilutions (concentrations) of a reference standard antigen solution. A ring of precipitate forms around each well, and the diameter of the ring is proportional to the antigen concentration in the well [FIGURE 20.6]. This is a simple but sensitive method for quantifying unknown antigens to concentrations of about 1 μg/ml. The diameters of the rings formed by the standard antigen concentrations are measured and plotted as a function of antigen concentration. Concentration values for the test antigens are then read from the plotted graph.

Immunoelectrophoresis. *Immunoelectrophoresis* combines the techniques of immunodiffusion and electrophoresis. Electrophoresis is an electrochemical process in which substances with a net electric charge migrate under the influence of an electric current [FIGURE 20.7]. This migration occurs in an agar gel or in a liquid-filled buffered matrix such as cellulose acetate. Positively charged substances travel toward the cathode (negative electrode), while negatively charged substances go toward the anode (positive electrode). Different substances move at different rates depending on their charge. This movement is called *electrophoretic mobility*.

Immunoelectrophoresis is performed in two stages. First, a fluid containing protein antigens is placed in a well in the matrix and an electric current is applied. Antigens will be distributed in separate spots along a line passing through the well and parallel to the direction of current flow. These separate spots each represent an individual component of the antigen mixture. When the current is turned off, radial diffusion will begin from each of these spots. A trough running parallel to the direction of the electrophoretic separation is filled with the appropriate antiserum. The antibody molecules in the antiserum diffuse in a straight advancing front toward the antigens. An arc of precipitate, or precipitin band, forms only where each antigen-antibody component meets in its zone of equivalence. This results in a complex pattern of arc-shaped bands of precipitate [FIGURE 20.8].

The great advantage of this technique is its ability to separate the components of complex mixtures. Electrophoresis by itself cannot separate proteins with similar electrophoretic mobility, and other diffusion methods as described so far in this chapter cannot resolve, or distinguish, more than a few lines of precipitation. However, immunoelectrophoresis can resolve as many as 39 individual antigens in a mixture. The technique is used ex-

FIGURE 20.8

Principle of immunoelectrophoresis. **[A]** An antigen (such as serum) is placed in a small well cut in a layer of agar set on a microscope slide. **[B]** A direct current is applied for an hour or so and differential migration of the antigen components (in this case, serum components) takes place. The distances that the antigen components in the well migrate in the electric field are proportional to their electric charge. **[C]** The current is turned off and a trough is cut longitudinally in the agar; an antiserum (here, antibodies to serum components) against the electrophoresed antigen is placed in the trough. **[D]** The antigen components and the specific antibodies diffuse toward each other, and **[E]** precipitin lines form. These lines can be shown more clearly if they are stained by protein stains. Immunoelectrophoresis is a very powerful analytic technique and can show up to about 39 different components in human serum, whereas electrophoresis shows only 4 or 5 different components.

[A] Antigen is added to small well.

[B] Antigen separates into its components.

[C] Antibody added to trough cut in agar.

[D] Antibody and separated antigen components diffuse toward each other.

[E] Precipitate lines form where antibody and antigen components meet at optimal proportions.

tensively to analyze serum samples for their protein components. Abnormalities in immunoglobulins can be detected in this manner.

Electroimmunoassay. *Electroimmunoassay* is a combination of the immunoelectrophoresis assay and the Mancini method (radial immunodiffusion technique). It combines the speed of electrophoresis with the quantification of antigen of the Mancini method. It involves the rapid electrophoretic migration of antigen (standard concentrations and unknowns) from wells into an agar gel containing antiserum, allowing little time for diffusion. When the antigen molecules migrate into the gel, they initially are soluble complexes because they are in the zone of antigen excess. As the antigen molecules migrate in the electric field, their concentration decreases until, at the equivalence point, they form a precipitate with antibodies in the gel. As more antigen arrives, the precipitate at the advancing front dissolves, while the precipitate at the sides remains; this gives a rocketlike configuration. Hence the procedure is commonly called *rocket immunoelectrophoresis.*

The area of each rocket, or, more roughly, its height, is directly proportional to the initial concentration of the antigen placed in the well [FIGURE 20.9].

FIGURE 20.9
Electroimmunoassay. The area enclosed by the precipitin lines in the form of a rocket is directly proportional to the initial concentration of antigen in the well. Each assay includes a set of standard concentrations as well as the unknown concentration(s) of antigen (not shown in drawing).

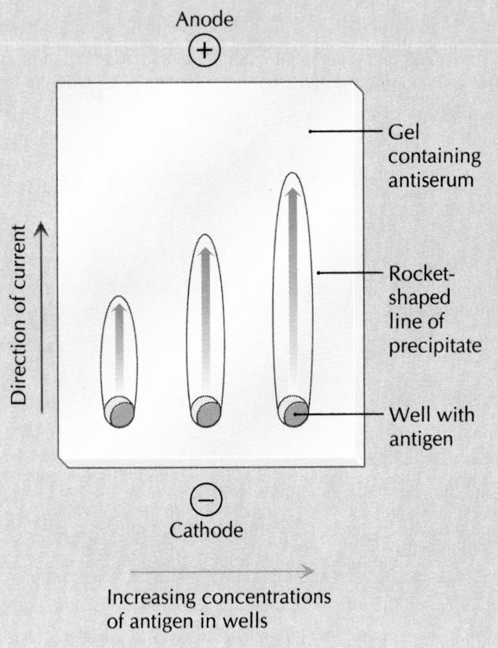

FIGURE 20.10
Technique of countercurrent immunoelectrophoresis. Antigens and antibodies are placed in opposite troughs. The pH of the surrounding medium (agar gel) is adjusted so that the antibody and the antigen have opposite charges. Upon application of an electric current, antibodies and antigens move toward each other and a precipitate line forms where they meet in the equivalence zone.

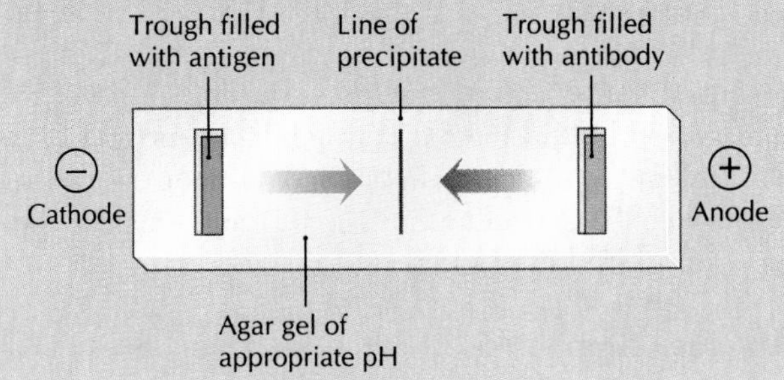

Because of the increased precision afforded by measuring the larger "rocket" height (as opposed to measuring ring diameter in the Mancini method), the sensitivity of this assay allows the measurement of antigens in concentrations as low as 0.5 μg/ml. It is used to quantify several human plasma antigens and even viral antigens.

Countercurrent Immunoelectrophoresis. The technique of *countercurrent immunoelectrophoresis* is used for detecting antigens and antibodies by forcing them to move toward each other in an electric field [FIGURE 20.10]. Antigens and antibodies have opposite charges when they are placed at opposite poles of an electric field in buffers of appropriate ionic strength and pH. When an electric current is turned on, the antigens and antibodies each move toward the respective opposite pole, or toward each other. A line of precipitate forms where specific antigen and antibody meet in equivalent amount. The technique is useful in research laboratories to study immune responses to disease. It can detect minute amounts of microbial or tissue antigens, as well as antibodies in tissue fluids, within one hour. The technique can also be used to identify specific microorganisms in culture media after a brief incubation.

Agglutination Tests

As mentioned earlier, precipitation reactions involve *soluble* antigens. On the other hand, agglutination reactions involve *particulate* antigens (e.g., red blood cells or bacterial cells) in a suspension. Particulate antigens with epitopes on their surfaces may be cross-linked by inert particulate substances such as red blood cells, bentonite particles (a kind of clay), or latex beads. These particles, once coated, react as if they themselves possessed the antigenic specificity of the coating antigen. FIGURE 20.13 shows passive agglutination involving red blood cells, which have been found to be extremely convenient carriers of antigen. When specific antibody is added to antigen-coated red blood cells, antibody bridges are formed between the cells, and large aggregates of the cells are produced. These are easily visible to the naked eye.

As little as 10 ng/ml of specific antibody is detectable by passive agglutination assays, which are used in diagnostic laboratories to detect antitoxins found in such diseases as tetanus and diphtheria and to determine conditions such as pregnancy. For example, in the laboratory test for pregnancy, the first step is to mix the patient's serum or urine with a specific antibody prepared against the hormone chorionic gonadotropin (which is present during pregnancy). After incubation, a red blood cell preparation, to which the hormone has been attached, is added. If the patient's sample contains the hormone, it will have bound the antibody in the first step, and hence agglutination of the red blood cells will not occur—yielding a positive test result. If the hormone is absent from the patient's specimen, the antibody will be free to agglutinate the red blood cells—yielding a negative result.

Bacterial Agglutination. The humoral immune response to bacteria is usually dominated by antibodies specific for epitopes on the surface of the microorganisms. All surface components of the bacterial cell—capsular polysaccharides, cell-wall substances, flagella, outer sheaths—elicit antibody formation. The presence and titer of these antibodies in an antiserum can often be measured by agglutination of bacterial cells added to the antiserum.

Among the bacterial diseases of humans for which the agglutination test is of diagnostic value are typhoid fever, salmonellosis, brucellosis, tularemia, typhus, and Rocky Mountain spotted fever. For example, the **Widal test** was devised specifically to help diagnose typhoid fever. The serum of a patient suspected of having typhoid fever is mixed with a suspension of *Salmonella typhi* bacteria, the causative agent of typhoid. If the bacteria agglutinate, this indicates that the patient's serum contains antibodies against *S. typhi* and the patient has probably been infected with the bacterium. Another agglutinating test used in laboratory diagnosis is the **Weil-Felix reaction.** This test is based on the fact that several of the rickettsias have an antigen in common with certain strains of *Proteus* species. Therefore serums from patients with rickettsial infections agglutinate suspensions of the *Proteus* bacteria. The strains of *Proteus* commonly used are *Proteus* OX-19, OX-2, and OX-K. The

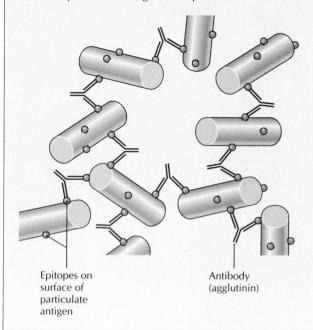

FIGURE 20.11
Mechanism of agglutination. When antibodies react with epitopes on neighboring antigens, the particulate antigens clump into visible aggregates. In direct agglutination (shown in this figure), antibody reacts with free particulate antigen in suspension.

Epitopes on surface of particulate antigen

Antibody (agglutinin)

specific antibodies to form large clumps or aggregates. This process is called *agglutination* [FIGURE 20.11], and antibodies that participate in this process are termed **agglutinins.** More sensitive than precipitation tests, the agglutination test can be used qualitatively to simply indicate the presence or absence of antibodies. It can also be used as a semiquantitative assay of the concentration of agglutinating antibodies in serum specimens.

An agglutination assay is performed by adding a fixed amount of the particulate antigens to a series of tubes containing increasing dilutions (usually *doubling* dilutions) of the antiserum; for example, tube 1 = 1/20, tube 2 = 1/40, tube 3 = 1/80, tube 4 = 1/160, and so on. The reciprocal of the highest dilution in which agglutination occurs becomes the *titer* of the antiserum. Thus if tube 3 contained the highest dilution in which agglutination was observed in an antiserum assay, the titer of that antiserum would be 80 [bottom row, FIGURE 20.12]. This direct agglutination assay is capable of detecting 0.1 μg of antibody per milliliter of serum.

A modification of the direct agglutination test is the *indirect*, or *passive*, *agglutination* test. This modification enables many *soluble* antigens to be detected by agglutination. In passive agglutination, soluble antigens are detected by first being made to adhere to the surfaces of

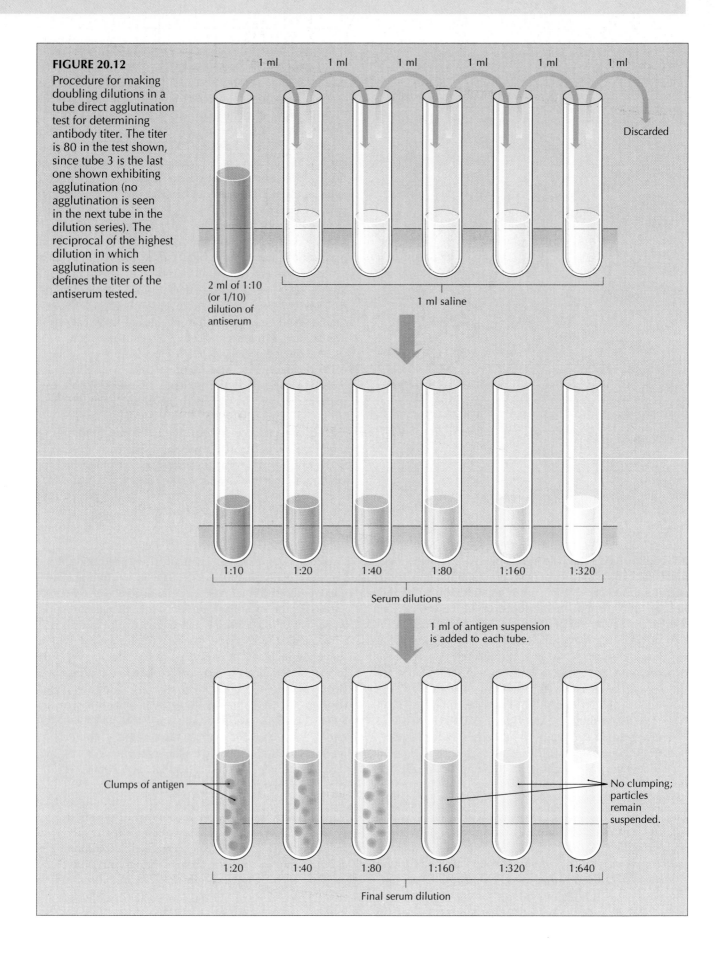

FIGURE 20.12
Procedure for making doubling dilutions in a tube direct agglutination test for determining antibody titer. The titer is 80 in the test shown, since tube 3 is the last one shown exhibiting agglutination (no agglutination is seen in the next tube in the dilution series). The reciprocal of the highest dilution in which agglutination is seen defines the titer of the antiserum tested.

1 ml   1 ml   1 ml   1 ml   1 ml   1 ml

Discarded

2 ml of 1:10 (or 1/10) dilution of antiserum

1 ml saline

1:10   1:20   1:40   1:80   1:160   1:320

Serum dilutions

1 ml of antigen suspension is added to each tube.

Clumps of antigen

No clumping; particles remain suspended.

1:20   1:40   1:80   1:160   1:320   1:640

Final serum dilution

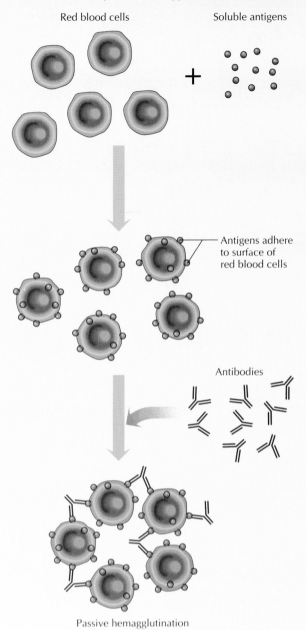

FIGURE 20.13

In passive agglutination, soluble antigens are first made to adhere to particulate carriers before reaction with antibodies. When the carrier is red blood cells, the method is termed *passive hemagglutination.*

Red blood cells   Soluble antigens

Antigens adhere to surface of red blood cells

Antibodies

Passive hemagglutination

good evidence that the disease was present. Also, if it is possible to show that the patient's serum had no antibody titer before the illness but has a significant titer while the disease is progressing, this change is also of diagnostic value.

The most widely used agglutination test is the macroscopic tube agglutination test. Not only does this method reveal the presence of specific agglutinins in the test serum, but their approximate concentration can be determined by this assay. The general procedures for this assay were explained in FIGURE 20.12. A quick and convenient method for determining the presence of agglutinins is by the macroscopic slide agglutination test. A drop of a dense suspension of the bacteria (the antigen) in saline is placed on a clean glass slide. One to three drops of the patient's serum are mixed with the antigen by gentle rotation. Agglutination occurs in a few minutes if antibodies are present in the serum; this can be observed macroscopically. Under the microscope, using the high-dry objective (about 400× magnification), agglutination or nonagglutination appears as shown in FIGURE 20.14.

A modification of direct bacterial agglutination is bacterial coagglutination. In this method, *Staphylococcus aureus* cells are used as carriers of antibodies because a protein on the cell wall reacts with the Fc region of immunoglobulin molecules (antibodies); the method is illustrated in FIGURE 20.15.

Viral Hemagglutination. When agglutination reactions involve the clumping of red blood cells, the reaction is called **hemagglutination.** Hemagglutinating reactions are used widely in blood typing for blood transfusions. Certain viruses, such as those causing mumps, measles, and influenza, have the ability to agglutinate red blood cells from certain species of animals, notably chicken,

Weil-Felix reaction is differential for certain rickettsial diseases because of the selective agglutination of these strains.

For diagnostic purposes, a *rising titer* of antibody is significant; that is, a substantial rise or increase in titer of specific agglutinating antibodies between the time the patient is acutely ill and the time of convalescence is

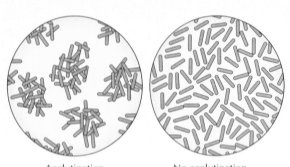

FIGURE 20.14

Results of a slide agglutination test of bacteria as seen under the microscope at about 400x magnification.

Agglutination

No agglutination (antiserum not specific for antigen)

FIGURE 20.15

Bacterial coagglutination test for determining the serological groups of streptococci. Antibodies are bound by their Fc region to protein A on the *Staphylococcus aureus* cell wall. The *S. aureus* cells become carriers of antibodies (to group B streptococci in the case shown). No agglutination occurs with group A streptococci (bottom left). Coagglutination occurs in the presence of group B streptococci (bottom right).

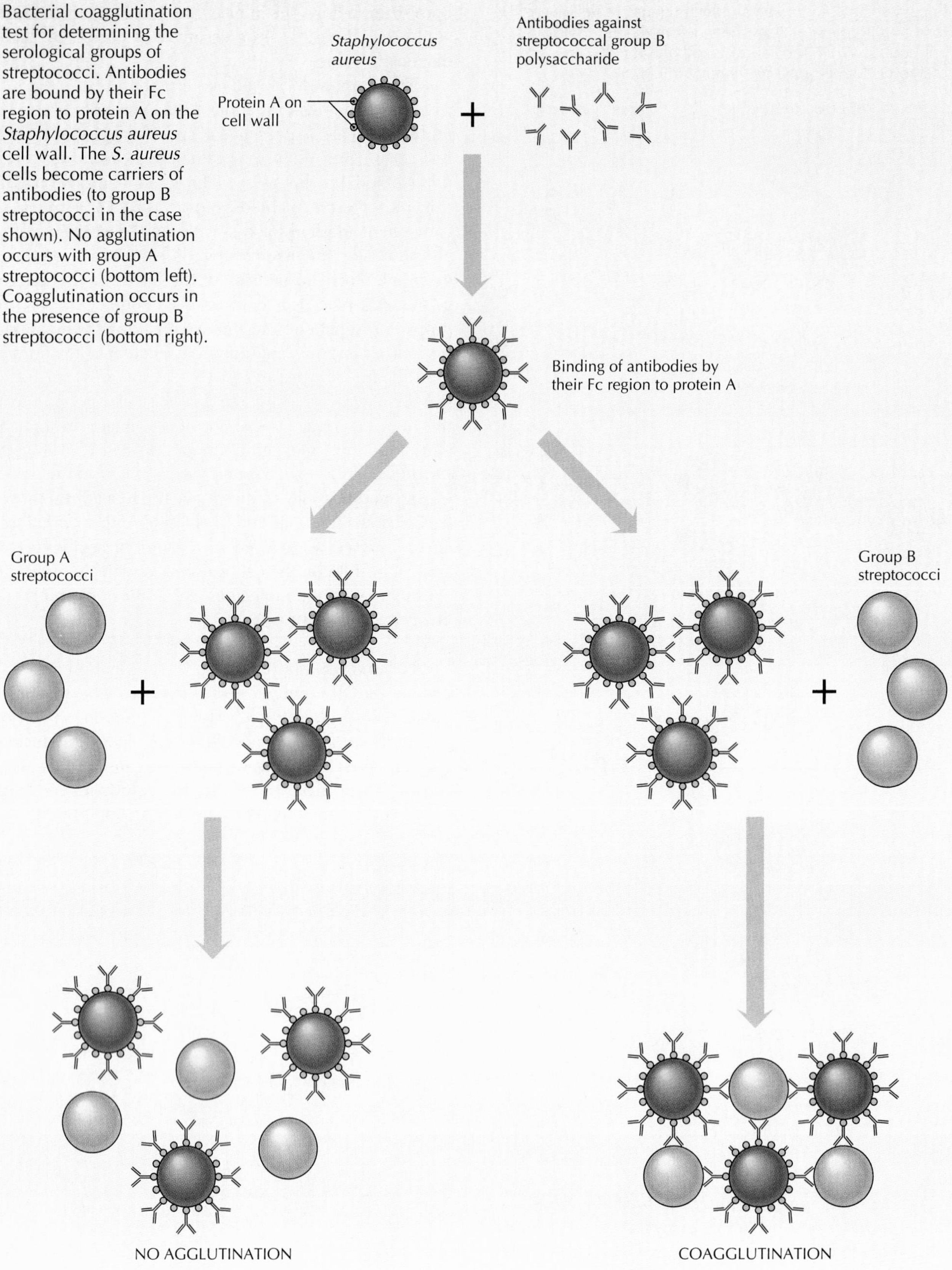

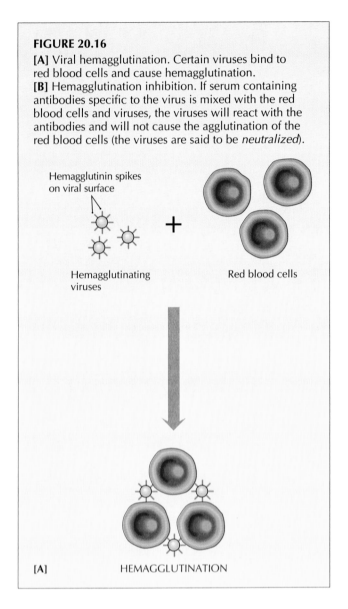

FIGURE 20.16
[A] Viral hemagglutination. Certain viruses bind to red blood cells and cause hemagglutination.
[B] Hemagglutination inhibition. If serum containing antibodies specific to the virus is mixed with the red blood cells and viruses, the viruses will react with the antibodies and will not cause the agglutination of the red blood cells (the viruses are said to be *neutralized*).

Hemagglutinin spikes on viral surface

Hemagglutinating viruses

Red blood cells

[A]   HEMAGGLUTINATION

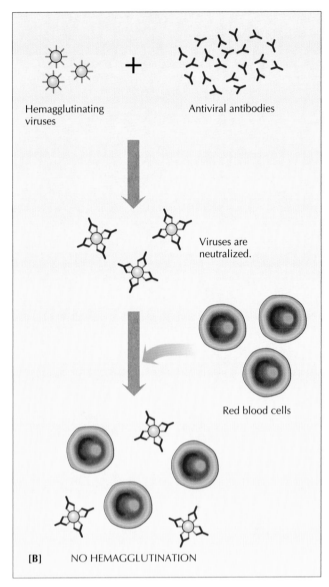

Hemagglutinating viruses

Antiviral antibodies

Viruses are neutralized.

Red blood cells

[B]   NO HEMAGGLUTINATION

guinea pig, or human type O red blood cells. This is due to an interaction in which the virus binds to the red blood cells and then cross-links the red blood cells, much as antibodies do. This process is termed *viral hemagglutination* [FIGURE 20.16A]. Because this aggregation dissociates spontaneously, the test must be read within one hour. The amount of agglutination depends on the concentration of the virus.

If a patient's serum contains antibodies against the viruses that are able to agglutinate red blood cells, these antibodies can bind to the viruses and prevent them from agglutinating the red blood cells. This inhibition phenomenon is termed *viral neutralization*, and the test based on it is called a viral *hemagglutination inhibition test*. For instance, if hemagglutination routinely occurs in a mixture of red blood cells and measles virus, and if hemagglutination does not occur upon addition of the patient's antiserum to the mixture, this inhibition of ag-

glutination indicates the presence of virus-neutralizing measles antibodies in the serum [FIGURE 20.16B]. The hemagglutination inhibition test is used in the diagnosis of viral infections such as influenza and measles.

The procedure for the viral hemagglutination test consists of making serial dilutions of the virus (or of serum from a virus-infected patient), adding the red blood cell suspension to each tube, and incubating the tubes for one hour. Agglutination is indicated by an even coating of red blood cells in the bottom of the tube. In a negative reaction (no agglutination) the red blood cells merely settle to form a compact button in the bottom of the tube. Such hemagglutination reactions can also be performed in plastic trays with numbered wells [FIGURE 20.17]; this is more convenient and uses less glassware. Use of these trays also requires smaller samples. Special equipment can be used to dilute samples quickly and accurately.

FIGURE 20.17
Hemagglutination reactions seen in the wells of a microtiter plate. Top row **[A]**: Complete hemagglutination has occurred in all of the wells. Middle row **[B]**: Only wells 3 through 6 show complete hemagglutination. Bottom row **[C]**: No hemagglutination in any of the wells.

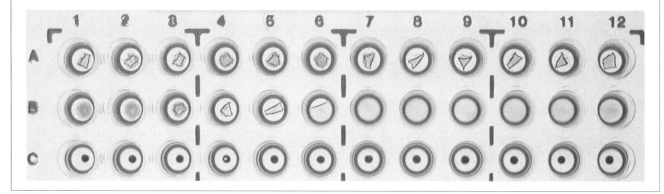

Complement-Fixation Tests

Earlier, in Chapter 18, you learned about a group of serum proteins collectively called *complement.* The complement-fixation test detects the presence of complement-fixing antibodies (IgM and IgG) present in a patient's serum. These antibodies are formed against a soluble antigen, which can be of any origin—tissue, hormonal, enzyme, or microbial. During most antigen-antibody reactions, the complement binds, or is *fixed,* to the antigen-antibody complex. The complement-fixation test can be used to detect amounts of antibody so small (about 1 μg/ml) that they cannot produce a visible reaction such as agglutination or precipitation. Complement-fixation tests are used in the diagnosis of certain viral, fungal, and bacterial diseases; a test of this kind, the Wassermann test, was once used widely in the diagnosis of syphilis.

The complement-fixation test may be carried out in small tubes, in plastic microtitration plates, or even in automated systems. It is performed in two stages, as described in the following and in FIGURE 20.18.

Stage 1: Known antigen + test serum + complement mixture is incubated at 37° for 30 min or longer. The test serum from the patient must first be heated at 56°C for 30 min to inactivate its complement. An antigen-antibody reaction cannot be seen at the end of this stage, since all components are soluble.

Stage 2: Sensitized sheep red blood cells (precoated with anti-sheep red blood cell antibodies) are added. Sensitized sheep red blood cells are extremely sensitive to complement-mediated lysis.

If complement has been fixed in stage 1 because of an antigen-antibody reaction, it is no longer available for lysis of sensitized sheep red blood cells in stage 2. Therefore, the results are read as follows:

No hemolysis = positive result, because the complement-fixing antibodies in the test serum have reacted with antigen in stage 1 and have bound the complement.

Hemolysis = negative result, because complement is available for hemolyzing the sensitized sheep red blood cells in stage 2; therefore no antibodies specific for the known antigen were present in the patient's serum.

Radioimmunoassays

The sensitivity of antigen detection has been greatly increased by the use of radioactively labeled reagents. Immunological assays using radioactive components are called *radioimmunoassays,* or *RIAs.* The technique was introduced in 1960 by Rosalyn Yalow to determine the concentration of insulin in plasma—a discovery for which she won a Nobel Prize in 1977. Today RIAs are available for virtually all the hormones, drugs in body fluids, immunoglobulins, viral antigens such as the hepatitis B virus antigen in donated blood, and other substances.

The assay is based on competition between radioactively labeled antigens (e.g., ^{125}I) and unlabeled antigens to bind to specific antibodies [FIGURE 20.19A and B]. It uses purified radiolabeled antigen of the same kind being tested for, as well as the antigen's specific anti-

FIGURE 20.18
Principle of the complement-fixation test. If complement has been fixed by the antigen-antibody reaction in stage 1, then it is no longer available for hemolysis of the added sensitized sheep red blood cells in stage 2.

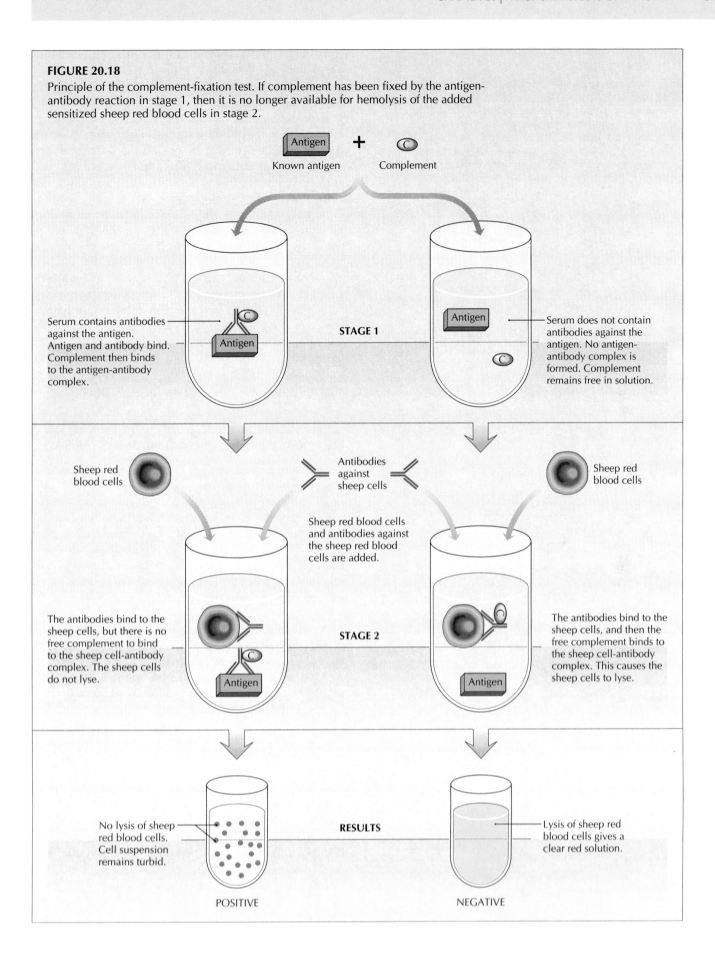

FIGURE 20.19
Radioimmunoassay. **[A]** Radiolabeled antigens bind to specific antibodies. **[B]** Unlabeled antigen (variable amount in test sample) competes with labeled antigen (fixed amount) for antibody-combining sites (fixed amount of antibodies). **[C]** As the amount of unlabeled antigen increases, the ratio of antibody-bound labeled antigen to unbound labeled antigen decreases, as shown in the radioimmunoassay calibration curve.

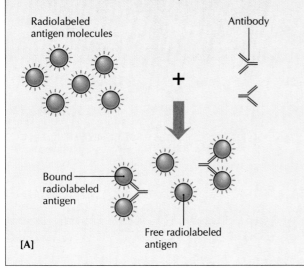

Radiolabeled antigen molecules

Antibody

Bound radiolabeled antigen

Free radiolabeled antigen

[A]

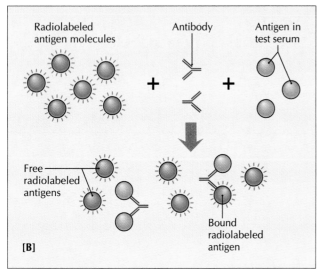

Radiolabeled antigen molecules

Antibody

Antigen in test serum

Free radiolabeled antigens

Bound radiolabeled antigen

[B]

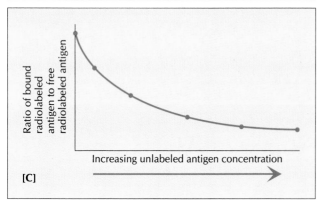

Ratio of bound radiolabeled antigen to free radiolabeled antigen

Increasing unlabeled antigen concentration

[C]

body. Measured quantities of these two are mixed and incubated together, one mixture with and one without an added test sample. If unlabeled antigen is present in the test sample, it competes with the radiolabeled antigen for the binding sites on the antibody molecules. At increasing concentrations of unlabeled antigen, more labeled antigen is displaced, or prevented from binding to the antibody molecules. Then unbound radiolabeled antigen is removed from the mixture, by washing the antigen-antibody precipitate free of unbound antigen. How much of this antigen is displaced, as determined by measuring the radioactivity of the remaining antigen-antibody complexes, is a measure of the amount of unlabeled antigen in the test sample. A standard binding curve can be made [FIGURE 20.19C]. The antigen concentration in the test serum can be read from this curve.

RIAs are popular because of their high sensitivity (a few picograms, where 1 picogram $= 10^{-12}$ g, can be detected), ease of handling of multiple samples, and ability to test samples without purifying them before assay. The limitations are the cost and the potential hazards associated with radioactivity.

Enzyme-Linked Immunosorbent Assays (ELISAs)

Enzyme immunoassay is a technique with the advantages of radioimmunoassay but without the disadvantages. It is as sensitive, capable of detecting antigens at concentrations below 1 picogram per milliliter, and as simple to use. Furthermore, it is less expensive, because it does not require high-cost instrumentation; safer, because no radioactive materials are involved; and just as accurate and reliable. Enzyme immunoassays are based on the following two phenomena:

1 Antibodies and some antigens can *adsorb* to wells of molded polystyrene plates (or other solid supports) and still maintain their full immunologic capabilities.
2 Antigens and antibodies can be *linked* to enzymes, with the resulting complexes still fully functional, both immunologically and enzymatically.

It is apparent why this assay method is more commonly called an **e**nzyme-**l**inked **i**mmuno**s**orbent **a**ssay, or **ELISA.**

Enzyme activity is used to measure the quantity of antigen or antibody present in the test sample. Enzymes used in ELISA include β-galactosidase, glucose oxidase, peroxidase, and alkaline phosphatase. There are two basic ELISA techniques that have clinical value: the *double-antibody-sandwich technique,* for the detection and measurement of antigen; and the *indirect immunosorbent technique,* for the detection and measurement of antibody.

Double-Antibody-Sandwich Technique. In the double-antibody-sandwich technique, antiserum samples are added to the wells in a polystyrene plate, and the antibodies in the antiserum adhere to the inner surface of each well [FIGURE 20.20]. The test antigen is added, and if the antigen is homologous or specific for the antibody, it attaches to the antibody immobilized on the well surface. An antibody-enzyme conjugate is then added; it will bind to the antigen already fixed by the first antibody, creating an antibody (with enzyme)-antigen-antibody "sandwich." Finally, an enzyme substrate is added to react with the enzyme. The rate of enzyme action is directly proportional to the quantity of enzyme-linked antibody present, and that, in turn, is proportional to the amount of test antigen. Enzyme hydrolysis of the substrate causes a color change in the solution, which can be seen visually or measured with a spectrophotometer (an instrument used to analyze color changes in a solution).

Indirect Immunosorbent Technique. As already noted, ELISA is used to assay for antigen. But the method may also be used as a qualitative or quantitative assay for antibodies—e.g., by the indirect immunosorbent technique, which is used to detect, among other things, antibodies against the human immunodeficiency virus, the cause of AIDS [FIGURE 20.21]. The initial step involves coating the well wall with antigen by adsorption. Test antiserum is added and allowed to incubate. If any antibodies in the test antiserum have bound to the immobilized antigen, their presence is detected by adding an enzyme-linked anti-immunoglobulin (anti-antibody, or antibody made against a specific antibody). Enzyme substrate is then added; the rate of its hydrolysis is associated with a color change proportional to the concentration of antibody present in the test sample. This color change can be monitored visually or by a spectrophotometer.

The ELISA has been used for the detection of many infectious viruses, bacteria, fungi, and parasites such as protozoa. For example, one antiserum sample from a pregnant woman can be screened simultaneously for infections caused by rubella virus (the agent for German measles, which can cause congenital malformations or fetal death) and by type 2 herpesvirus (which can cause severe congenital nervous system malformations and smallness of the head in the offspring).

Immunofluorescence

The technique of immunofluorescence uses antibody molecules labeled with a fluorescent dye to detect antigens. For example, it is used as a rapid procedure for the identification of an unknown infectious agent in a clinical specimen, which is likely to contain a mixture of microorganisms. The technique is based on the behavior of

FIGURE 20.20

Double-antibody-sandwich ELISA technique for the detection and measurement of antigen. The detection of staphylococcal enterotoxin in a food extract is illustrated. The presence of as little as 0.4 ng of toxin per milliliter of a food extract can be detected by the ELISA technique. (Note that the necessary washing after each step is not shown.)

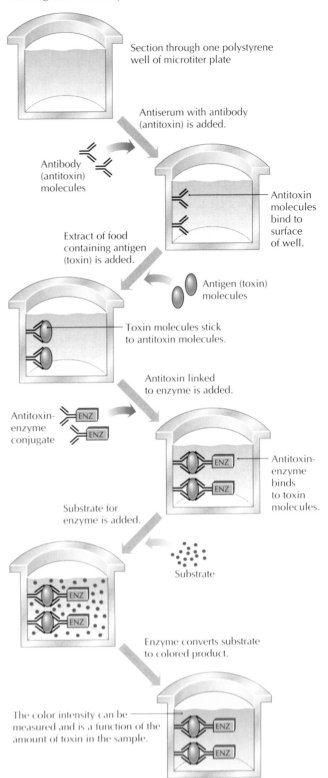

Section through one polystyrene well of microtiter plate

Antiserum with antibody (antitoxin) is added.

Antibody (antitoxin) molecules

Antitoxin molecules bind to surface of well.

Extract of food containing antigen (toxin) is added.

Antigen (toxin) molecules

Toxin molecules stick to antitoxin molecules.

Antitoxin linked to enzyme is added.

Antitoxin-enzyme conjugate

Antitoxin-enzyme binds to toxin molecules.

Substrate for enzyme is added.

Substrate

Enzyme converts substrate to colored product.

The color intensity can be measured and is a function of the amount of toxin in the sample.

FIGURE 20.21

Indirect immunosorbent ELISA technique for the detection and measurement of antibody. The example illustrated here is the detection of antibodies against the AIDS virus (human immunodeficiency virus) in a patient's serum. (Note that the necessary washing after each step is not shown.)

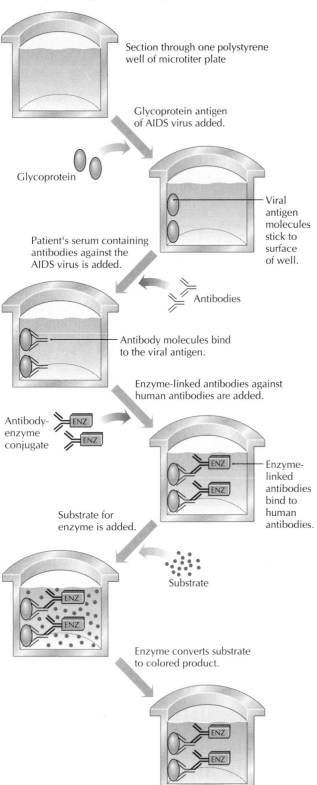

Section through one polystyrene well of microtiter plate

Glycoprotein antigen of AIDS virus added.

Glycoprotein

Viral antigen molecules stick to surface of well.

Patient's serum containing antibodies against the AIDS virus is added.

Antibodies

Antibody molecules bind to the viral antigen.

Enzyme-linked antibodies against human antibodies are added.

Antibody-enzyme conjugate

ENZ

ENZ

Enzyme-linked antibodies bind to human antibodies.

Substrate for enzyme is added.

Substrate

Enzyme converts substrate to colored product.

FIGURE 20.22

Fluorescent antibody technique — direct [A] and indirect [B] methods. The direct method [A] is usually used to identify a particular kind of microorganism in a clinical specimen, e.g., *Streptococcus pyogenes* in a throat swab from a patient. The indirect method [B] is used to detect the presence of antibodies to a specific microorganism in the body fluid of a patient e.g., the presence of IgG antibodies to an oral spirochete in the serum or saliva of a patient with gum disease. The indirect method is more sensitive, since two or more labeled antiglobulin molecules (only one is shown here) can be attached to each antibody bound to its antigen.

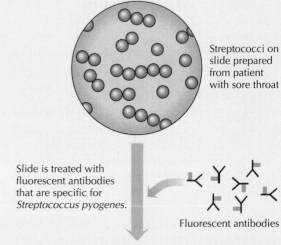

Streptococci on slide prepared from patient with sore throat

Slide is treated with fluorescent antibodies that are specific for *Streptococcus pyogenes*.

Fluorescent antibodies

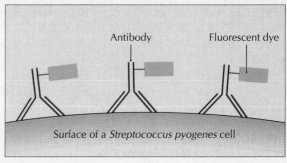

Antibody

Fluorescent dye

Surface of a *Streptococcus pyogenes* cell

Slide is viewed under a fluorescence microscope.

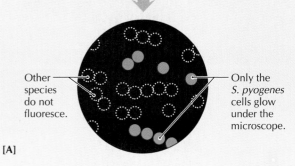

Other species do not fluoresce.

Only the *S. pyogenes* cells glow under the microscope.

[A]

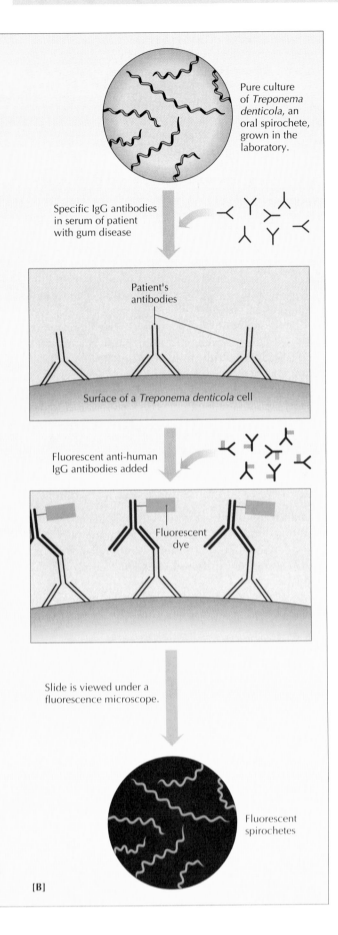

Pure culture of *Treponema denticola*, an oral spirochete, grown in the laboratory.

Specific IgG antibodies in serum of patient with gum disease

Patient's antibodies

Surface of a *Treponema denticola* cell

Fluorescent anti-human IgG antibodies added

Fluorescent dye

Slide is viewed under a fluorescence microscope.

Fluorescent spirochetes

[B]

certain dyes which fluoresce (glow) when exposed to certain wavelengths of light (often ultraviolet light) under the fluorescence microscope. Examples of such dyes are fluorescein and rhodamine. Each dye absorbs light at one wavelength and emits it at another; fluorescein emits a fluorescent yellow-green light, whereas rhodamine emits a fluorescent orange-red light. Antibodies can be attached to these dyes; they are then termed *labeled*, or *fluorescent*, antibodies.

Direct Fluorescent Antibody Technique. In the direct method, the fluorescent dye is directly conjugated with the antibody specific for the antigen. A culture of microorganisms is fixed on a slide (by heat or chemical fixation) and the specimen is flooded with the specific fluorescent antibody to allow binding between the antibody molecules and any cell-bound antigen [FIGURE 20.22A]. After any unbound antibodies are washed off, the smear is examined under the fluorescence microscope. Only those microorganisms that have reacted specifically with the labeled antibodies will be visible. Thus only a few organisms need to be present to be observed.

Indirect Fluorescent Antibody Technique. In the indirect method the antibody initially applied to a fixed smear of microorganisms (antigen) is not labeled. Instead, a second fluorescent-labeled antibody against the immunoglobulin of the animal species used for the preparation of the initial antibody is added in a second step and incubated [FIGURE 20.22B]. This binds the fluorescent label to the specific antibody that has already reacted with antigen in the smear. After any unbound antibody is washed off, the smear is examined under the fluorescence microscope. If the sample fluoresces [FIGURE 20.23], the antibody that matches the second labeled antibody is present. This technique is more sensitive and more widely used than the direct fluorescent antibody technique.

FIGURE 20.23

Spirochetes stained with fluorescent antibody, as seen under a fluorescence microscope.

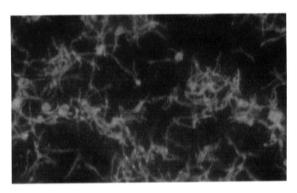

ASK YOURSELF

1 What is *serology* the study of?

2 Why is the equivalence zone important for precipitation to occur?

3 What are the different qualitative immunodiffusion tests?

4 Describe a quantitative immunodiffusion test.

5 Compare electroimmunoassay with countercurrent immunoelectrophoresis.

6 How is agglutination different from precipitation? How is a passive agglutination test different from a direct agglutination test?

7 What is the significance of a *rising antibody titer* in diagnosis of disease?

8 Explain the meaning of *viral neutralization* with respect to viral hemagglutination tests.

9 Describe the procedures for the two types of immunofluorescence technique.

PRODUCTION OF MONOCLONAL ANTIBODIES

When antibody production is triggered in an immune response, each B cell will produce only one type of antibody molecule. However, there are many different clones of B cells in an animal, each capable of producing a different type, or specificity, of antibody. Thus an individual animal, during its lifespan, can produce 1 million or more different types of antibody molecules from 1 million different B-cell clones.

Before the mid-1970s, the only means of producing large quantities of specific antibodies was immunization of animals with as purified an antigen as possible. But such an antigen still contained many epitopes. Consequently, the antibodies in the serums produced by the animals were *polyclonal antibodies,* with a different antibody produced for each epitope. *Highly* specific antibodies could be produced from polyclonal antibodies by meticulous removal of unwanted antibodies. This was done by taking whole antiserum and repeatedly mixing it with antigens containing the unwanted epitopes. However, this very tedious process could not guarantee that all unwanted antibodies were removed.

Now *monoclonal antibodies* are produced by a single clone of genetically identical cells derived from a single stimulated antibody-producing cell. They can be prepared in large quantities by using special cells called *hybridomas* (which will be described in this section). Georges Köhler and Cesar Milstein developed this technique in 1975 at the Medical Research Council laboratories in Cambridge, England. They were awarded a Nobel Prize in 1984 for this research.

B lymphocytes that produce antibodies, like any other cells, can become cancerous. A *myeloma* is a cancer, or unchecked proliferation, of an antibody-producing cell. Because a myeloma begins as a single cell, all of its progeny constitute a clone of identical lymphocytes. The antibody produced by these lymphocytes is homogeneous because it is all derived from the single homogeneous clone of cells. Such an antibody is a monoclonal antibody. Unfortunately, the monoclonal antibody produced by a myeloma tumor is generally specific for an unknown antigen, because the induction of a myeloma is a totally random event.

It had not been possible to induce myelomas specific for a particular antigen until Köhler and Milstein discovered a solution to this problem. They developed a technique for combining the growth characteristics of myeloma cells and the predetermined antibody specificity of normal immune spleen cells. In doing so, they developed a "hybrid" cell which expresses the special properties of both cell types. They did this by fusing a myeloma cell with an antibody-secreting cell from the spleen of an immunized mouse. The result is an artificially created cell called a *hybridoma,* which is essentially a specific antibody-producing factory. In such cells the myeloma portion provides "immortality" (unrestricted rapid proliferation) and thus production of large quantities of monoclonal antibody; the immune lymphocyte portion provides the information for the specificity of the antibody.

The technique for making hybridoma cells and monoclonal antibody is shown in FIGURE 20.24. In this procedure, mice are immunized in the usual manner with a vaccine that contains the particular antigen against which specific antibodies are required. This antigen need *not* be specially purified to contain only the desired epitopes. Each of the epitopes on the antigen stimulates a specific clone of B lymphocytes. Thus a single antigen can stimulate a number of B-cell clones. The mouse spleen is removed and the spleen cell suspension is mixed with a suspension of mouse myeloma cells. Polyethylene glycol is added to the mixture, which causes some of the lymphocytes to fuse with the cancer cells to become hybridomas. Each hybridoma cell proliferates to generate a large clone of cells, each cell producing specific antibody.

Hybridomas are then separated into individual wells of plastic dishes and allowed to grow into clones. Each hybridoma clone may produce monoclonal antibody; the antibodies in each well are screened to see which hy-

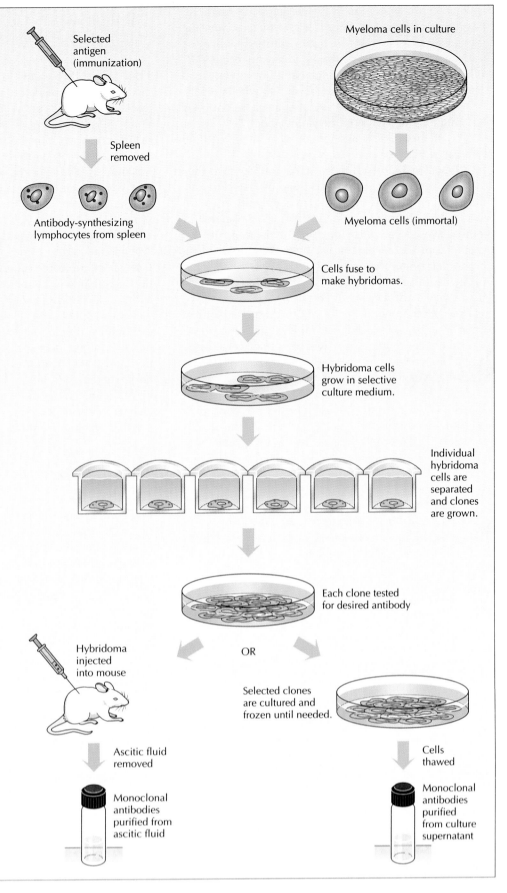

FIGURE 20.24
How monoclonal antibodies are made. The selected antigen is injected into a mouse. A few days later, the spleen is removed from the mouse. The antibody-synthesizing cells from the spleen are then mixed with fast-growing mouse myeloma cells and a chemical "glue," called polyethylene glycol. The resulting hybridomas are separated, cloned, and tested to select those that make the desired monoclonal antibodies. The chosen hybridomas are injected into the peritoneal cavity of mice, where they induce the accumulation of 2 to 20 ml of ascitic fluid containing large amounts of antibody, or the hybridomas may be cultured in the laboratory. (They may be stored frozen until they are needed to generate additional supplies of monoclonal antibody.) The final step is to separate the pure monoclonal antibodies from the hybridomas by differential centrifugation.

Selected antigen (immunization)

Myeloma cells in culture

Spleen removed

Antibody-synthesizing lymphocytes from spleen

Myeloma cells (immortal)

Cells fuse to make hybridomas.

Hybridoma cells grow in selective culture medium.

Individual hybridoma cells are separated and clones are grown.

Each clone tested for desired antibody

Hybridoma injected into mouse

OR

Selected clones are cultured and frozen until needed.

Ascitic fluid removed

Cells thawed

Monoclonal antibodies purified from ascitic fluid

Monoclonal antibodies purified from culture supernatant

bridoma is producing the particular antibody required. (Because screening identifies the specific antibody, the original antigen need not be highly purified.) Once the particular hybridoma is identified, it may be recloned by cell culture or it may be maintained in vivo by injection into the peritoneal (abdominal) cavity of living animals. Cell culture yields about 100 μg of monoclonal antibody per milliliter; in vivo culture yields about 1000 μg or greater of monoclonal antibody per milliliter of fluid from the peritoneal cavity.

Monoclonal antibodies are important because they are homogeneous, highly specific, and produced readily in large quantities. They bind to one and only one antigen, and are therefore monospecific. Monoclonal antibodies have become very important tools in biomedical research; in 1981, for example, they allowed investigators to determine the type of immune system cell that was being destroyed by the AIDS virus. Monoclonal antibodies have also become increasingly important in diagnostic and therapeutic medicine. In a proposed human cancer therapy, monoclonal antibodies are being used experimentally to attack and destroy tumor cells. They can be labeled with radioactive isotopes to locate tumors and to deliver lethal doses of radiation to inaccessible tumors, while leaving normal cells untouched. Monoclonal antibodies can also be used to deliver anticancer drugs to tumor cells in the same manner. Diagnostic kits for many allergies and diseases, using the specificity of monoclonal antibodies for specific antigens, have been produced commercially. Also, monoclonal antibodies have become extremely useful in the differentiation of the myriad strains of microorganisms [DISCOVER 20.1].

Köhler and Milstein never patented their discovery! The market value of commercially produced monoclonal antibodies is now in the millions of dollars annually.

ASK YOURSELF

1 Define *monoclonal* antibodies; hybridomas; myeloma.

2 Why were Köhler and Milstein awarded the Nobel Prize in 1984?

3 Describe the procedure for making hybridoma cells and monoclonal antibodies.

4 What are some of the applied uses of monoclonal antibodies?

MEASUREMENTS OF CELL-MEDIATED IMMUNITY

Prior to the 1960s, only in vivo tests were available for measuring cell-mediated immunity. These were skin tests for delayed-type hypersensitivity (DTH) and allograft rejection (see Chapter 19). The tuberculin, brucellergen, and some other skin tests discussed in this section are based on the detection of a DTH (type IV) response typical of T-cell–mediated immunity. In contact with specific antigen, the T cells release various lymphokines that cause the tissue reaction and may also cause tissue necrosis. DTH reactions are apparent only after about 24 hours and may persist for days. The shaved flank of the guinea pig is usually used for in vivo tests of cell-mediated immunity. DTH reactions can also be studied in mice by injecting the antigen into a footpad and measuring the amount of swelling produced.

It was only in the 1960s that suitable in vitro tests of cell-mediated immune responses were introduced. This heralded an era of accelerated research in cell-mediated immunity, which hitherto had lagged far behind our understanding of humoral immunity. Such tests are highly complex; they are difficult to standardize and may give variable results. However, they provide insight into the fundamental workings of the immune system.

Intradermal Tests for Cell-Mediated Immunity in Humans

In all intradermal tests the antigen is injected into the skin in increasing doses. A positive reaction is seen as a type IV hypersensitive response—a hard, pale swelling with peripheral redness (greater than 5 mm in diameter), appearing 24 to 48 hours after the injection of the test antigen. A positive response indicates that the patient has active T cells that are specifically reacting with the antigen. Some of these tests are shown in TABLE 20.1.

Test for Migration Inhibitory Factor (MIF)

As described in Chapter 18, *migration inhibitory factor (MIF)* is only one of a number of lymphokines released by sensitized T lymphocytes after they encounter the sensitizing antigen. It is a soluble glycoprotein molecule that causes macrophages to remain at the site where they meet the antigen, making the normally motile macrophages nonmotile. The in vitro production of MIF has consistently been shown to correlate with cell-mediated immunity. It is therefore used to assess DTH and to evaluate the status of a patient's cell-mediated immunity to several common viruses, such as influenza virus and

20.1 IMMUNOLOGIC TECHNIQUES PROVIDE NEW WEAPONS IN WAR AGAINST CANCER

At the present time, the only three weapons used routinely against cancer are surgery, chemotherapy, and irradiation. Surgery is effective only when the tumor is wholly accessible and has not spread to unknown or inaccessible parts of the body. Chemotherapy and irradiation are unfortunately not selective in their modes of action. When used by themselves, these therapeutic tools destroy healthy cells as well as malignant ones—with unpleasant side effects.

But the science of immunology has opened up a new front in the battle against cancer with *immune therapy*—the controlled and deliberate mobilization of the immune system to destroy cancer cells.

One of the most promising candidates for such therapy is *interferon*. It is a protein substance produced by eucaryotic cells in response to viral infection and protects healthy cells from viral infection (Chapter 18). With recombinant DNA technology, sufficient interferon is now being produced in bacteria for use in the fight against cancer. Interferons can be used against cancer-inducing viruses as well as to augment immune responses and promote the cytotoxic activity of natural killer (NK) cells (whose function is to kill tumor cells as well as virus-infected cells).

Another promising approach is the use of *interleukin-2 (IL-2)*, a lymphokine produced by sensitized T lymphocytes (Chapter 18). IL-2 hastens the maturation of NK cells and enhances their natural killing activity. IL-2 is being administered to patients with advanced cancer. (Treatment is limited to such patients at the present time because it is expensive and not without side effects of fever, nausea, and vomiting, among others.) One such patient was critically ill early in 1988 with melanoma, a deadly skin cancer. It had spread to her liver, spleen, lungs, and stomach. After about 5 weeks of IL-2 treatment, her tumors had shrunk by 80 percent! The treatment is still regarded as highly experimental. Nonetheless, it has shown promising results in treatment of skin and kidney cancers. Some physicians have observed a synergistic cooperation between interferon and IL-2 in attacking cancer cells. While IL-2 works to make the NK cells more potent, the interferon makes them kill specific cells. Because these therapeutic substances are immunologically active, biomedical scientists are proceeding with caution; they do not know all the consequences yet in manipulating the equilibrium of the immune system.

Another approach against cancer is the use of monoclonal antibodies. As mentioned in this chapter, monoclonal antibodies can be used directly to attack and destroy tumor cells. They can be labeled with radioactive isotopes to locate tumors and deliver lethal doses of radiation. Diagnostically, by using scanning machines along with radiolabeled monoclonal antibodies that are specific

Scanning electron micrograph of a natural killer cell attacking two large tumor cells.

for certain types of cancer, it is possible to determine the exact location of the tumor in the body as well as its size.

Monoclonal antibodies also may be used to bypass the side effects of chemotherapeutic drugs, which destroy both healthy and malignant cells indiscriminately. Monoclonal antibodies would deliver anticancer drugs specifically to cancer cells. To quote Milstein and Köhler, who first developed monoclonal antibodies, such antibodies "might be expected to home in on the cancer cells—only this time they would be dragging along with them a depth charge of monumental proportions."

---

measles virus. The principle, or basis, of the tests for patients' immunity is illustrated by the following example.

1 Capillary tubes are packed with lymphoid cells. A convenient source of cells is the peritoneal exudate of a guinea pig sensitized to the specific antigen by prior inoculation. (The exudate contains mainly lymphocytes and macrophages.)
2 The tubes are placed in small tissue-culture chambers containing culture media with and without the sensitizing antigen. MIF is released by antigen-specific lymphocytes upon contact with the specific antigen.

3 In the culture medium with the specific antigen, the motile macrophages are inhibited from migrating out of the end of the capillary tube by the MIF. In the absence of the sensitizing antigen, the macrophages migrate out from the end of the capillary tube in a fanlike pattern.

A modification of the above experiment resulted in a test for cell-mediated immunity in patients. Lymphocytes from a patient or an animal are first cultured separately with suspected sensitizing antigen for 1 to 2 days. During this time the lymphocytes produce MIF. The lymphocytes are centrifuged out and the supernatant containing MIF is used to test the migration of macro-

TABLE 20.1
Some Intradermal Tests Based on Cell-Mediated Immunity

Test	Etiologic agent	Disease
Tuberculin	Bacterium: *Mycobacterium tuberculosis*	Tuberculosis—pulmonary disease with necrotic tubercles in lungs; may spread to other parts of body
Lepromin	Bacterium: *Mycobacterium leprae*	Leprosy—chronic disease that affects peripheral nerves, as well as face, hands, and feet, to cause disfiguring
Brucellergen	Bacterium: *Brucella* spp.	Brucellosis—undulant (fluctuating) fever in humans
Blastomycin	Fungus: *Blastomyces dermatitidis*	Blastomycosis—lesions develop in lungs, skin, and bones
Histoplasmin	Fungus: *Histoplasma capsulatum*	Histoplasmosis—lesions in lung and lymph nodes, but may spread to other organs, including the liver and spleen
Leishmanin	Protozoan: *Leishmania* spp.	Leishmaniasis—any disease caused by these parasitic flagellates, e.g., kala-azar, a visceral disease with enlarged liver and spleen

phages in a capillary tube [FIGURE 20.25]. Therefore, migration inhibition indicates MIF production, which means the patient has cell-mediated immunity to the sensitizing antigen.

Mixed Lymphocyte Reaction (MLR)

Another cell-mediated response is the *mixed lymphocyte reaction (MLR)*, the in vitro equivalent of a graft rejection reaction. It measures the amount of cell proliferation stimulated by the presence of an antigen. In this reaction lymphocytes from two individuals (or strains of animals) that have different surface antigens are mixed together in a test tube. Each set of cells reacts against the foreign histocompatibility antigens of the other set. They respond by becoming lymphoblasts (primitive lymphoid cells), which begin to synthesize DNA and to multiply by mitosis. This cell proliferation can be quantified by adding radiolabeled DNA precursors (such as tritiated thymidine) to the test mixture. In practice the cells are allowed to interact for 4 or 5 days in culture before addition of tritiated thymidine. After 18 hours of exposure to radioactive thymidine, the radioactive isotope (tritium) is incorporated into the newly synthesized DNA. The DNA is extracted and the amount of radioactivity determined; the amount of radioactivity incorporated is a measure of the degree of cell proliferation.

The assay is most useful when only one set of cells is permitted to respond. The other set, the stimulator

cells, are either irradiated or treated with mitomycin C (an antibiotic) to prevent proliferation; they are still viable but they do not undergo mitosis. In this mode the reaction is called the "one-way" MLR, because the amount of isotope uptake is a measure of the reaction by the responding cells against foreign antigens present on the stimulator cells [FIGURE 20.26].

Cell-Mediated Cytotoxicity (CMC)

If lymphocytes from one individual are cultured with cells bearing foreign epitopes from another individual in a mixed lymphocyte culture, a subset of the first individual's responder T lymphocytes are activated. These activated cells have the capacity to lyse the second individual's stimulating cells and are called cytotoxic T lymphocytes. The cytolytic reaction (called *cell-mediated cytotoxicity*, or *CMC*) is specific, with the sensitized lymphocytes cytotoxic only for target cells bearing the same epitopes as the stimulating cells. The observed phenomenon is an in vitro illustration of the cell-mediated immunity that may be produced during a viral infection. You will recall from Chapter 19 that the cytotoxic T-cell–mediated immune response is effective against infected host cells that express viral antigens on their surfaces.

As usually performed in the laboratory, the assay begins like the one-way MLR previously described. A population of viable lymphocytes is incubated with irra-

FIGURE 20.25

Migration inhibition factor (MIF) test for cell-mediated immunity. Migration of motile macrophages is inhibited by the lymphokine MIF. Macrophages migrate out of the open end of the capillary tube in a fanlike pattern unless inhibited by the presence of MIF.

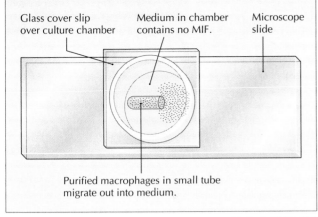

Glass cover slip over culture chamber — Medium in chamber contains no MIF. — Microscope slide

Purified macrophages in small tube migrate out into medium.

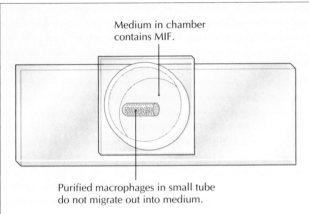

Medium in chamber contains MIF.

Purified macrophages in small tube do not migrate out into medium.

FIGURE 20.26

The one-way mixed lymphocyte reaction (MLR). The assay is termed "one-way" because the stimulator cells from individual A have been irradiated or treated with mitomycin C (an antibiotic) to prevent them from synthesizing DNA, thereby preventing mitotic division. However, they continue to stimulate the responder cells from individual B, which continue to proliferate, i.e., incorporate radioactive thymidine.

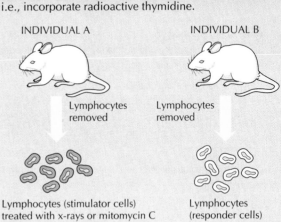

INDIVIDUAL A   INDIVIDUAL B

Lymphocytes removed   Lymphocytes removed

Lymphocytes (stimulator cells) treated with x-rays or mitomycin C to inhibit the cells' ability to undergo mitosis

Lymphocytes (responder cells)

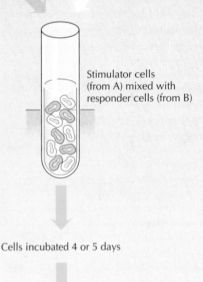

Stimulator cells (from A) mixed with responder cells (from B)

Cells incubated 4 or 5 days

Radiolabeled thymidine is added and cells are incubated for 18 h.

DNA is extracted and the amount of radioactivity incorporated is measured.

diated (or mitomycin C–treated) lymphocytes. After 4 or 5 days, the cells are removed from the culture vessel, washed, and suspended in various degrees of density. Cell suspensions are then mixed with a constant number of target cells whose cytoplasm has been labeled with radioactive chromium. After incubation for 4 hours, the amount of target cell lysis is determined by the amount of radioactive chromium released into the supernatant medium.

ASK YOURSELF

1 What are some current limitations of in vitro tests of cell-mediated immune responses?

2 Describe the MIF, MLR, and CMC tests.

SUMMARY

1 Measurements of humoral immunity are based on antigen-antibody reactions. The study of such reactions is called *serology*, since antibodies are found in serum. In all serological testing, the proportion of antigen to antibody is critical to the test and is optimal in the equivalence zone.

2 Commonly used methods to detect the presence of antibodies take advantage of the precipitation reaction. These tests include the qualitative immunodiffusion tests (the precipitin ring test, and the Oudin, Oakley-Fulthorpe, and Ouchterlony methods) and the quantitative immunodiffusion test called the radial immunodiffusion technique.

3 Immunoelectrophoresis combines the techniques of immunodiffusion and electrophoresis. Electroimmunoassay combines immunoelectrophoresis with radial immunodiffusion.

4 Agglutination tests can be direct or indirect. A rising titer of agglutinating antibodies is good evidence that a patient is infected by a particular pathogen. The well-known bacterial agglutination tests include the Widal test and the Weil-Felix reaction. The hemagglutination inhibition test is used widely in the diagnosis of viral infections.

5 Complement-fixation tests are used in the diagnosis of certain viral, fungal, and bacterial diseases.

6 Radioimmunoassays are immunological assays based on competition between radioactively labeled and unlabeled antigens. Enzyme-linked immunosorbent assays are as sensitive as and simpler to perform than radioimmunoassays. Enzyme activity is a measure of the quantity of antigen or antibody present in a sample.

7 Immunofluorescence can be a direct fluorescent antibody technique or an indirect fluorescent antibody technique.

8 Monoclonal antibodies are produced in large quantities by the use of hybridomas.

9 Measurements of cell-mediated immunity are exemplified by the tests for migration inhibitory factor (MIF), mixed lymphocyte reaction (MLR), and cell-mediated cytotoxicity (CMC).

KEY TERMS

agglutinins
cell-mediated cytotoxicity (CMC)
countercurrent immunoelectrophoresis
electroimmunoassay
ELISA
equivalence zone
hemagglutination
hemagglutination inhibition test
hybridomas
immunoelectrophoresis
migration inhibitory factor (MIF)
mixed lymphocyte reaction
   (MLR)
monoclonal antibodies
myeloma
polyclonal antibodies
precipitins
radioimmunoassays (RIAs)
rocket immunoelectrophoresis
serology
viral hemagglutination
viral neutralization
Weil-Felix reaction
Widal test

REVIEW GUIDE

MEASUREMENTS OF
HUMORAL IMMUNITY
(ANTIBODIES)

1 The study of in vitro interactions between antigens and antibodies is called

_____.

2 The fluid that is left after blood has clotted is called

_____.

3 In the _____ zone, there is optimum concentration of antigen and antibody for complete precipitation to occur.

4 Antigen-antibody complexes that form large interlocking aggregates are called

_____.

5 The simplest precipitation test, the precipitin ring test, is performed in the

_____ phase.

6 The most widely used precipitation test of double diffusion is the: **(a)** method of Oudin; **(b)** Oakley-Fulthorpe method; **(c)** Ouchterlony method; **(d)** Mancini method.

7 Immunoelectrophoresis combines the techniques of immunodiffusion and

_____.

8 Electroimmunoassay is a combination of the Mancini method and the

_____ assay.

9 Precipitins react with _____ antigens; agglutinins react with _____ antigens.

10 The Weil-Felix reaction is differential for certain rickettsial diseases and uses antigens of bacteria belonging to the genus _____.

11 The hemagglutination inhibition test denotes the presence of viral

_____ antibodies.

12 In the complement-fixation test, a negative test (no antibody for a known antigen) is indicated by _____.

13 The principle of radioimmunoassays is based on _____ molecular binding of radioactively labeled and unlabeled antigens to specific antibodies.

14 ELISA is the acronym for _____.

15 One of the following is not an enzyme used in ELISA: **(a)** β-galactosidase; **(b)** glucose oxidase; **(c)** coagulase; **(d)** alkaline phosphatase; **(e)** peroxidase.

16 Two common dyes used in immunofluorescence are: **(a)** congo red; **(b)** fluorescein; **(c)** crystal violet; **(d)** rhodamine; **(e)** nigrosin.

PRODUCTION OF
MONOCLONAL
ANTIBODIES

17 Monoclonal antibodies can be prepared in large quantities by the use of special cells called _____.

18 A cancer of an antibody-producing cell is termed a(n)

_____.

19 The monoclonal antibody technique was developed by: **(a)** Tonegawa; **(b)** Ouchterlony; **(c)** Milstein; **(d)** Köhler; **(e)** Fulthorpe.

In question 20, indicate whether the statement is true (T) or false (F). If the statement is false, restate it in the true form.

20 Each B cell will produce only one type of antibody molecule. _____

_____

_____

21 Match the intradermal test on the right with the corresponding etiologic agent on the left.

_____ *Mycobacterium tuberculosis*
_____ *Blastomyces dermatitidis*
_____ *Brucella* spp.
_____ *Mycobacterium leprae*
_____ *Histoplasma capsulatum*
_____ *Leishmania* spp.

(a) Lepromin
(b) Blastomycin
(c) Leishmanin
(d) Histoplasmin
(e) Tuberculin
(f) Brucellergen

22 The in vitro production of MIF has consistently been shown to correlate with _____ immunity.

23 In the test for MIF, the presence of MIF inhibits the _____ from migrating out of the end of the capillary tube in a fanlike pattern.

24 In the mixed lymphocyte reaction, lymphocytes respond to foreign antigens by becoming _____ and synthesizing _____.

25 Cell proliferation can be quantitated by determining the amount of incorporation of tritiated _____ into DNA.

26 In the cell-mediated cytotoxicity test, a subset of the responder T lymphocytes are activated in the presence of foreign cells that can _____ the stimulating cells.

27 In the CMC test, the amount of cell lysis may be determined by the amount of radioactive _____ released.

REVIEW QUESTIONS

1 Discuss the significance of the equivalence zone in precipitation reactions.

2 Describe the Ouchterlony method of detecting antibody or antigen.

3 Explain why the radial immunodiffusion technique is a *quantitative* immunodiffusion test.

4 What are the purpose and advantage of using immunoelectrophoresis?

5 What is "rocket" immunoelectrophoresis, and why is it called by this name?

6 Distinguish between *direct* and *indirect (passive)* agglutination tests.

7 What is the significance of a rising titer of agglutinating antibodies?

8 Explain the principle of the complement-fixation test.

9 Describe the two basic techniques of the ELISA.

10 Why is the indirect immunofluorescence technique more sensitive than the direct?

11 How are monoclonal antibodies different from polyclonal antibodies?

12 Outline the method for the production of monoclonal antibodies.

13 What are mixed lymphocyte reactions? What happens to stimulator cells when they are irradiated or treated with mitomycin C?

14 How is cell lysis determined in the cell-mediated cytotoxicity test?

DISCUSSION QUESTIONS

1 Explain why diffusion of antigen and antibody is contributory to the success of precipitation tests.

2 How has the precipitation test advanced our knowledge of streptococcal taxonomy?

3 What makes the Ouchterlony method superior to precipitation in liquid?

4 Explain why immunoelectrophoresis is a more sensitive technique than other methods of separation such as precipitation reactions.

5 What do you think is remarkable about the Weil-Felix reaction?

6 Explain why *Staphylococcus aureus* cells can be used as carriers of antibodies.

7 Give some reasons for the popularity of radioimmunoassays.

8 Why do some workers prefer ELISAs over RIAs?

9 Has the promise (hope) in the use of monoclonal antibodies in anticancer therapy been fully realized at the present time?

10 What are some implications of the *positive* tuberculin test?

11 Discuss some clinical applications of in vitro measurements of cell-mediated reactions.

Antibiotics and Other Chemotherapeutic Agents

OBJECTIVES

After reading this chapter, you should be able to

1 Outline the events that led to the modern era of chemotherapy.

2 Distinguish between antibiotics and other types of chemotherapeutic agents.

3 List the properties that would make a compound ideal for use as a chemotherapeutic agent.

4 Understand how antibiotics are classified on the basis of chemical structure and mode of action.

5 Explain how microbial resistance to antibiotics may develop and what importance it has for treatment of diseases.

6 Give specific examples of synthetic chemotherapeutic agents that are useful for treating infections caused by bacteria, fungi, viruses, and protozoa.

7 Describe how a clinical microbiology laboratory could measure the concentration of an antibiotic in a blood sample from a patient undergoing therapy.

8 Explain how you could determine which of several antibiotics are active against a particular bacterium.

9 Describe two nonmedical uses of antibiotics.

OVERVIEW

Chemotherapy is the treatment of diseases with chemical substances. The chemicals used are called *chemotherapeutic agents*. Some of these chemical agents are produced by microorganisms and are called antibiotics. Others are synthesized in laboratories. In this chapter you will learn about the dramatic developments that led to modern chemotherapeutic agents and revolutionized the practice of medicine. Some of these discoveries were accidental, while others were the result of systematic searches for a specific compound. You will see how chemotherapeutic agents differ from one another in their chemical structure and in their mode of action. Sometimes the number of agents available seems bewildering, and some act only against specific microorganisms. But medical laboratories can determine which of the many chemotherapeutic agents is the best one for treating a specific infection. You will also learn that there are several reasons why chemotherapeutic agents must be selected and administered carefully and why improper use of chemicals can result in drug-resistant microorganisms, or a change in the patient's normal flora.

THE DAWN OF CHEMOTHERAPY

Chemotherapy, the treatment of disease by chemical compounds, is not new; it has been practiced for centuries. As early as 1630 Europeans used natural *quinine* from the bark of the cinchona tree to treat malaria, a disease caused by a protozoan. Quinine was used even earlier by South American Indians, who relieved symptoms of malarial fever by chewing the bark of the cinchona tree. As another example, *mercury* was used as early as 1495 to treat syphilis, a sexually transmitted bacterial infection. Despite such early uses of chemicals for treating diseases, it was not until early in the twentieth century that new developments in chemotherapy revolutionized the practice of medicine. The problem with many of the historical chemotherapeutic agents, such as mercury, however, is that they are toxic to human and animal tissue. To be effective in treating an infectious disease, a chemotherapeutic agent not only must kill or inhibit the microbe causing an infection, but must also be relatively harmless for human tissue by exhibiting *selective toxicity*. The beginnings of the modern era of chemotherapy can be traced to discoveries of chemical agents meeting this test by Paul Ehrlich, Gerhard Domagk, and Alexander Fleming.

FIGURE 21.1

Paul Ehrlich in his laboratory. Ehrlich is generally regarded as having established chemotherapy as a science. His research in the early 1900s resulted in the synthesis of an arsenical compound (salvarsan) for the treatment of syphilis. His research methodology represented a major contribution to the systematic search for new chemotherapeutic agents.

Ehrlich and the Discovery of Salvarsan

The first major discovery was made in the early 1900s by Paul Ehrlich, a German physician who had a special talent for chemistry [FIGURE 21.1]. Ehrlich believed that it was possible to make a chemical compound that would specifically cure syphilis without also harming the patient. He knew that arsenic would inhibit the syphilis microbe but that it was also toxic to human tissue. However, Ehrlich believed that arsenic could be incorporated into organic compounds in such a way as to make it nontoxic, while retaining its antimicrobial properties. He was the first person to carry out a deliberate, systematic search for such a compound, and he finally succeeded in finding one that was effective. This substance—Ehrlich's compound no. 606, which was eventually named *salvarsan*—was the first laboratory-synthesized chemical that could cure a disease without poisoning the patient. This discovery earned Ehrlich a Nobel Prize in 1908. Today, however, salvarsan is no longer used in fighting syphilis, having been replaced by a much more effective chemical, the antibiotic penicillin.

Domagk, Tréfouël, and the Discovery of Sulfonamides

Amazingly, no further significant developments in chemotherapy occurred for nearly 30 years following Ehrlich's discovery of salvarsan. Then, in 1935, Gerhard Domagk, working at the Bayer Chemical Company in Germany, made an important discovery. While performing experiments on more than 1000 synthetic dyes to see whether any of them could cure streptococcal infections in mice without poisoning the animals, he discovered that a particular red dye called *Prontosil* was effective, a discovery that won him a Nobel Prize in 1939. Strangely, however, the dye failed to inhibit cultures of bacteria growing on laboratory media; it was effective only on bacteria growing in the animal body.

This apparent contradiction was resolved in the same year by the French chemist Jacques Tréfouël and his colleagues. They discovered that a colorless compound called *sulfanilamide* is liberated in the animal when Prontosil is broken down by body tissues. It was subsequently shown that the sulfanilamide is active not only against bacteria in the body but also against cultures in the laboratory. The discovery of sulfanilamide triggered widespread research on related compounds having therapeutic value, and by 1945 scientists had made several thousand derivatives of sulfanilamide, collectively called *sulfonamides,* or "sulfa drugs." Some of these are much more effective than sulfanilamide itself in inhibiting bacterial growth and are still widely used today for treating some bacterial infections.

Fleming and the Discovery of the Antibiotic Penicillin

Salvarsan and the sulfonamides are examples of *synthetic chemotherapeutic agents* made by chemists in a laboratory. However, a second category of chemotherapeutic agents also exists. These are the *natural chemotherapeutic agents*, more commonly called **antibiotics.** An *antibiotic* is a substance produced by one microorganism which, in very small quantities, is inhibitory to other microorganisms.

These natural substances were known for their curative effects long before they were called antibiotics. For instance, centuries ago the Chinese used moldy soybean curd to treat boils, and controlled foot infections by wearing sandals furry with mold. We now know that these curative properties were probably due to antibiotics produced by the mold. The antibacterial properties of molds were also described in 1881 by the English microbiologist John Tyndall. He observed that culture media which has become cloudy with bacterial growth became clear when mold grew on the surface.

Other early evidence of the existence of antibiotics came from Pasteur and Joubert, who found that, although pure cultures of anthrax bacilli grew well in urine, the bacilli disappeared when certain other microorganisms were present. In 1901 Emmerich and Low discovered that rabbits could be protected against infection by anthrax bacilli if liquid cultures of the bacterium "*Bacillus pyocyaneus*" (now called *Pseudomonas aeruginosa*) were injected into the animals. They thought that the protective substance was an enzyme produced by *B. pyocyaneus*, and accordingly they named the substance *pyocyanase*.

In the early 1920s Gratia and Dath made one of the first systematic searches for antibiotics. This resulted in the discovery of *actinomycetin*, so named because it was produced by certain actinomycete bacteria. Although actinomycetin was never used for the treatment of patients, it was used to dissolve bacterial cells during the production of vaccines.

Despite these discoveries, it was not until 1929 that the modern era of antibiotics began. The microbiologist Alexander Fleming [FIGURE 21.2A] noticed a strange phenomenon on an agar plate he had inoculated with the bacterium *Staphylococcus aureus*. The plate had become contaminated with a mold, and Fleming observed that there was a large clear zone around the mold colony, indicating that the mold had produced a substance which inhibited *S. aureus* [FIGURE 21.2B]. Fleming was inspired to isolate and identify the mold and study its activities. The mold was a *Penicillium* species, and thus Fleming called the antimicrobial substance produced by the mold **penicillin.**

FIGURE 21.2

[A] Sir Alexander Fleming discovered the bacterial inhibitory properties of a metabolic product of *Penicillium notatum*. He called the substance penicillin. This discovery, in 1929, introduced the modern era of chemotherapy. For his discovery Fleming was knighted and shared the Nobel Prize in 1945 with Ernst B. Chain, a chemist, and Sir Howard W. Florey, a physician. [B] Fleming's original Petri dish culture on which he observed inhibition of staphylococcus growth near a large colony of the mold.

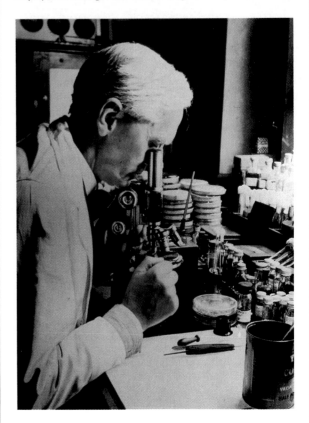

[A]

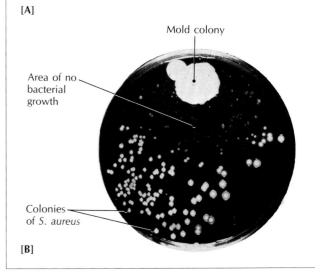

[B]

21.1 PENICILLIN—ITS DISCOVERY AND DEVELOPMENT

Penicillin was discovered in 1927 by Alexander Fleming, a microbiologist working at St. Mary's Hospital in London.

Fleming was conducting experiments in search of new antibacterial agents, particularly ones that would be effective against wound infections. In the course of these experiments, he observed a plate culture of *Staphylococcus aureus* that had been contaminated by a mold. The area around the edges of the mold colony was clear—no bacterial colonies. Apparently, the staphylococcus cells near the mold growth were inhibited or killed by the mold. Further studies of this phenomenon revealed that it was a mold of the genus *Penicillium* that produced a substance which was very potent against staphylococci and hence very attractive as a potential chemotherapeutic agent. Fleming named the substance *penicillin*.

Penicillin was effective against bacteria in laboratory cultures, but was it effective in the human body? This question needed to be answered. Unfortunately, the amount of penicillin produced in the mold cultures was extremely small. In addition, serious problems were encountered in attempts to isolate and purify penicillin.

The first clinical trial with a crude penicillin preparation was conducted on February 12, 1941. The patient, an Oxford policeman, was dying from a staphylococcus infection. The administration of penicillin resulted in an initial dramatic improvement, but five days later, when the supply of penicillin was exhausted, the staphylococci reemerged, the infection spread, and the patient died. This was a tragic end to a trial that did not succeed only because there was not enough penicillin available to treat the patient. The major problem continued to be the failure of large-scale production and recovery of penicillin.

Britain, at this point (1940–1941), was engaged in a grim war. There was little likelihood that a major share of the country's national resources could be diverted to an intensive program for development of penicillin.

Fortunately, the British reports of penicillin attracted the attention of Americans. As a result, the Rockefeller Foundation invited Harold W. Florey, a professor of pathology at Oxford University, who had investigated the development of penicillin as a chemotherapeutic agent, and N. G. Heatley, his colleague, to the United States to explore means of large-scale production of penicillin. They arrived in the United States on July 2, 1941. Meetings were arranged with members of the National Research Council, Charles Thom, a world-class mycologist with the U.S. Department of Agriculture, and others. Work on penicillin production began immediately at the U.S. Department of Agriculture's Northern Regional Research Laboratory in Peoria, Illinois, which had a record of achievements in microbial fermentations.

The U.S. Office of Scientific Research and Development, aware of the tremendous potential of penicillin for treatment of casualties of war, gave this project top priority. Major pharmaceutical companies and universities were called in to cooperate in the research and development of penicillin production. The results proved dramatic. Fleming's original mold cultures produced 2 units/ml; within a matter of months improvements in technology increased the yield to 900 units/ml; today the yield is approximately 50,000 units/ml!

In the autumn of 1941 there was little penicillin available in the United States for treatment of patients. One year later, as a result of the collaborative efforts of governments, universities, and industry, appreciable quantities were available.

Few discoveries have contributed as much as that of penicillin (and the antibiotics that followed) to the health and welfare of people worldwide. The story of penicillin provides an elegant example of the benefits gained from collaboration of scientists from government agencies, industry, and universities.

It was not until World War II, when there was an urgent need to cure Allied soldiers of wound infections, that Fleming's penicillin was appreciated. Through the cooperative efforts of many microbiologists in England and the United States, the inhibitory substance from Fleming's contaminant mold began to be produced in large quantities and became a "miracle drug" that saved countless lives. In 1945 Fleming, Ernest Chain, and Howard W. Florey won a Nobel Prize for their work with penicillin [DISCOVER 21.1].

Other antibiotics were also found during this period. In 1939, René Dubos [FIGURE 21.3] cultured the bacterium *Bacillus brevis* from a sample of New Jersey soil and isolated a substance that killed many Gram-positive bacteria. This substance, produced by *B. brevis*, consisted of two different antibiotics, now called *gramicidin* and *tyrocidine*. Not long after this, the future Nobel Prize winner Selman Waksman and his associates at Rutgers University discovered *streptomycin*, which was produced by the bacterium *Streptomyces griseus*.

Since 1940, many other antibiotics have been isolated and identified, and new antibiotics are still being discovered today. Unfortunately, most of them not only inhibit pathogenic microorganisms but are also toxic to human tissue; thus many are of no practical importance for treatment of disease. However, several dozen relatively nontoxic antibiotics have proved to be invaluable agents for curing microbial infections. Indeed, few other discoveries in science have had such a dramatic effect on the field of medicine as the discovery of antibiotics.

FIGURE 21.3

In 1939, René Dubos isolated two antibiotics, gramicidin and tyrocidine, from the soil bacterium, *Bacillus brevis.*

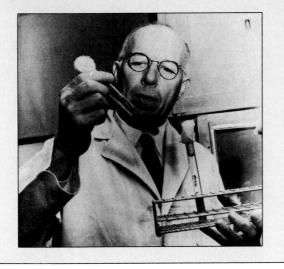

ASK YOURSELF

1 What was Paul Ehrlich's contribution to chemotherapy?

2 What is the relationship of Prontosil to sulfonamides?

3 How did Alexander Fleming come upon the discovery of penicillin?

IDEAL QUALITIES OF A CHEMOTHERAPEUTIC AGENT

For a chemical compound to be an ideal chemotherapeutic agent used for treating microbial infections, it should have the following qualities:

1 It should be able to destroy or inhibit many kinds of pathogenic microorganisms. The larger the number of different microbial species affected, the better. For instance, the most widely used antibiotics are **broad-spectrum antibiotics,** which means antibiotics that are effective against many different species.

2 It should inhibit microorganisms in such a way as to prevent the development of antibiotic-resistant forms of disease-producing microorganisms.

3 It should not produce undesirable side effects in the patient, such as allergic reactions, nerve damage, or irritation of the kidneys or gastrointestinal tract.

4 It should not eliminate the normal microorganisms that inhabit the intestinal tract or other areas of the body. These microorganisms, called the *normal flora,* play an important role in preventing various pathogenic microorganisms from growing and establishing infections. For instance, growth of a pathogenic yeast, such as *Candida albicans,* in the intestine is normally restrained by the normal flora of the intestinal tract. Elimination of the normal flora by a broad-spectrum antibiotic could cause a patient to become susceptible to yeast infections if the yeast is allowed to grow extensively.

5 If the agent is given orally, it should not be inactivated by stomach acids, and it should be absorbed into the body from the intestinal tract. If it is administered by injection, it should not be inactivated by binding to blood proteins.

6 It should be highly soluble in body fluids, since it must be in a solution to be active.

7 It must be able to reach sufficiently high concentration in the tissues or blood of the patient to kill or inhibit disease-causing microorganisms.

It is unlikely that any single chemotherapeutic agent can meet all of these qualifications. Therefore, clinicians must make comparisons among the available agents to select the one best suited for treatment of a specific infection.

ASK YOURSELF

1 What are the characteristics of an "ideal" chemotherapeutic agent?

2 What is the likelihood that a single chemical compound will have all these characteristics?

ISOLATION OF ANTIBIOTIC-PRODUCING MICROORGANISMS FROM NATURE

It was mainly by accident that Fleming discovered that the mold *Penicillium* produces penicillin. Today antibiotic-producing microorganisms are discovered by a deliberate, systematic screening procedure such as the one shown in FIGURE 21.4. The essential steps in searching for a new antibiotic are as follows:

FIGURE 21.4
Schematic illustration of the steps taken in the search for and discovery of new antibiotics.
[A] Isolation of pure cultures. **[B]** Antimicrobial activity testing. **[C]** Production and concentration of antibiotic material. **[D, E]** Further testing and purification of the antibiotic. **[F]** Chemical characterization and clinical evaluation of the antibiotic.

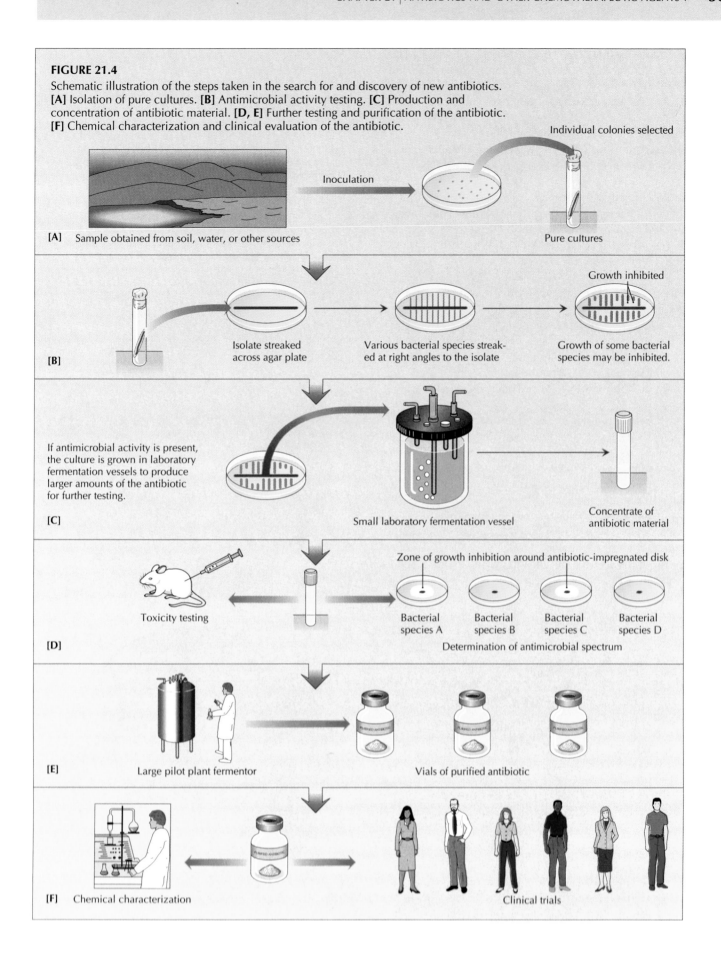

[A] Sample obtained from soil, water, or other sources

Individual colonies selected

Inoculation

Pure cultures

[B] Isolate streaked across agar plate   Various bacterial species streaked at right angles to the isolate   Growth inhibited   Growth of some bacterial species may be inhibited.

[C] If antimicrobial activity is present, the culture is grown in laboratory fermentation vessels to produce larger amounts of the antibiotic for further testing.   Small laboratory fermentation vessel   Concentrate of antibiotic material

[D] Toxicity testing   Zone of growth inhibition around antibiotic-impregnated disk   Bacterial species A   Bacterial species B   Bacterial species C   Bacterial species D   Determination of antimicrobial spectrum

[E] Large pilot plant fermentor   Vials of purified antibiotic

[F] Chemical characterization   Clinical trials

1 Obtain samples of soil, air, plants, vegetables, or water from a variety of environments. Isolate the microorganisms from these samples in pure culture.

2 Test each pure culture against a variety of microorganisms to see whether there is any inhibition or killing of the test organisms.

3 Select any pure cultures that show antimicrobial activity for further study. Grow the culture to produce a larger amount of antibiotic; concentrate the antibiotic material. Perform tests to determine that the antimicrobial activity is due to a new substance, not a previously described antibiotic.

4 Test the material for toxicity and determine its antimicrobial spectrum.

5 If the antibiotic appears to be a new one, grow large cultures, harvest the antibiotic material, and purify the antibiotic.

6 Test further to determine chemical properties and if the antibiotic qualifies as a chemotherapeutic agent by meeting most of the criteria listed in the previous section for an ideal chemotherapeutic agent. The antibiotic must be nontoxic for animals and humans.

Some antibiotics are made by bacteria, with members of the genus *Streptomyces* producing the largest number of useful antibiotics. Species of *Bacillus*, *Micromonospora*, *Nocardia*, and *Micropolyspora* also produce useful antibiotics. Still other antibiotics are produced by fungi, particularly species of *Penicillium*, *Aspergillus*, and *Cephalosporium*. Researchers are searching for new antibiotics produced by aquatic microorganisms as well; for instance, an algicide called *cyanobacterin* is produced by an aquatic cyanobacterium, and a fungicide is produced by *Alteromonas* sp. [FIGURE 21.5].

ASK YOURSELF

1 How would you go about searching for and isolating an antibiotic-producing bacterium from soil?

2 Name some common genera of microorganisms that produce antibiotics.

KINDS OF ANTIBIOTICS BASED UPON THEIR CHEMICAL STRUCTURE

Antibiotics differ widely in their chemical structure. Some idea of the bewildering diversity of these structures can be seen from the examples given in FIGURE 21.6. Antibiotics can be classified into a relatively few major groups based on their chemical structure.

FIGURE 21.5

Antimicrobial activity of *cyanobacterin*, an antibiotic produced by the aquatic bacterium *Scytonema hoffmani*. **[A]** In this experiment, the agar medium was first inoculated with the aquatic bacterium *Lyngbya kuetzingii* and then *Scytonema hoffmani* was streak-inoculated across the middle of the Petri dish. Note the absence of growth of *L. kuetzingii* in the region of *S. hoffmani*. **[B]** The inhibition of the pathogenic marine fungus, *Lagenidium callinectes* (the giant colonies at the top and bottom), by the bacterium *Alteromonas* sp.; the disk in the center is impregnated with an extract of the fermentation broth of an *Alteromonas* sp. culture. Note that the fungus does not grow in the region of the disk. In nature this bacterium grows on the embryos of shrimp and protects them from destruction by the marine fungus. The antifungal substance produced by the bacterium has been identified as 2,3-indolinedione (isatin).

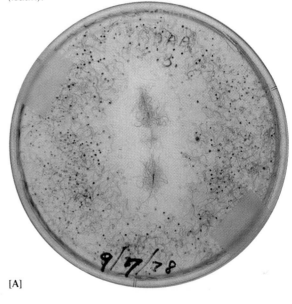

[A]

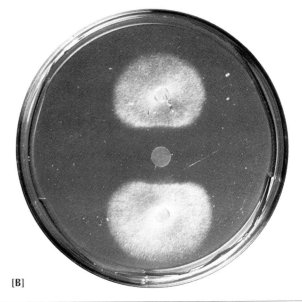

[B]

FIGURE 21.6

The structural formulas of several antibiotics representing different chemical classes. Note the complexity and diversity of these chemical molecules which are synthesized by microorganisms.

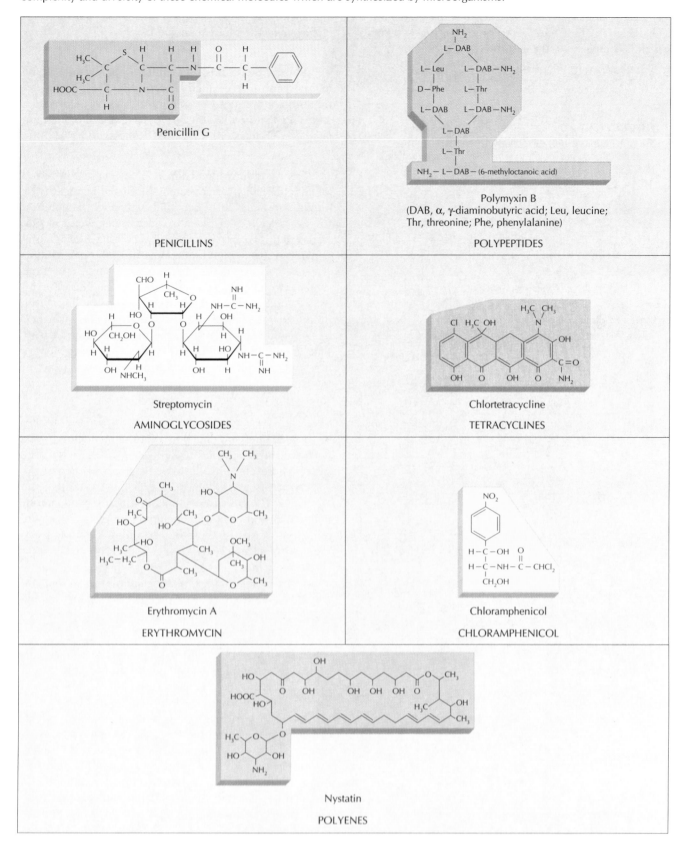

Penicillin G

PENICILLINS

Polymyxin B
(DAB, α, γ-diaminobutyric acid; Leu, leucine; Thr, threonine; Phe, phenylalanine)

POLYPEPTIDES

Streptomycin

AMINOGLYCOSIDES

Chlortetracycline

TETRACYCLINES

Erythromycin A

ERYTHROMYCIN

Chloramphenicol

CHLORAMPHENICOL

Nystatin

POLYENES

The β-Lactam Antibiotics

The β-lactam category includes the penicillins, mono-bactams, cephalosporins, and carbapenems. All contain a characteristic four-membered ring, the *β-lactam ring,* which is composed of three carbon atoms and one nitrogen atom [FIGURE 21.7].

FIGURE 21.7

The β-lactam antibiotics: penicillins, cephalosporins, monobactams, and carbapenems. All are characterized by the β-lactam ring in their structure.

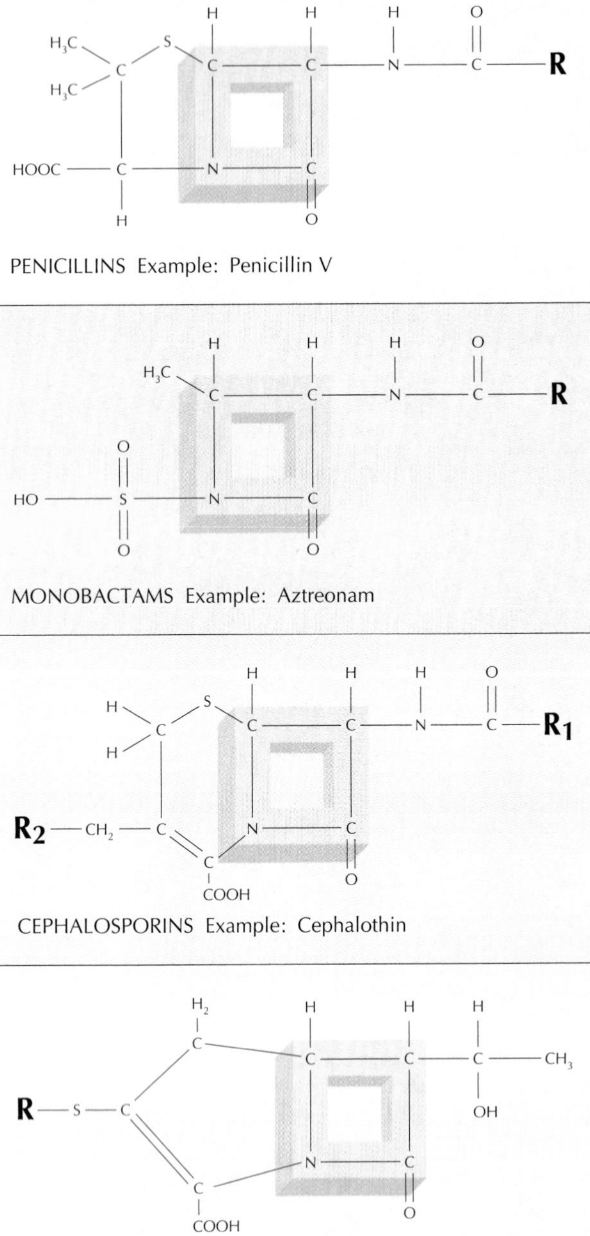

PENICILLINS Example: Penicillin V

MONOBACTAMS Example: Aztreonam

CEPHALOSPORINS Example: Cephalothin

CARBAPENEMS Example: Imipenem

The Penicillins. There are many different penicillins, but all have a core structure called *6-aminopenicillanic acid* [FIGURE 21.8A]. The differences among the various penicillins are due to differences in the side chains (portions of the molecule other than the core).

Natural penicillins. Penicillins that are produced by microorganisms are called *natural penicillins.* These antibiotics are produced by certain species of molds in the genus *Penicillium.* The two most important ones are *penicillin G* and *penicillin V* [FIGURE 21.8B].

Semisynthetic penicillins. The core compound 6-aminopenicillanic acid, can be produced in quantity by molds through fermentation culturing techniques. Chemists have been able to add various chemical side chains to this core compound, thus creating new kinds of penicillins that are not found in nature. These penicillins are called *semisynthetic penicillins* [FIGURE 21.8B], and some have advantages over natural penicillins. For instance, one of the first semisynthetic penicillins to be produced for clinical use was *phenethicillin*, which is more readily absorbed from the intestine into the body than is natural penicillin V. *Pseudomonas aeruginosa*, a frequent cause of wound and burn infections, is resistant to natural penicillins but can be inhibited by several semisynthetic penicillins.

Inactivation of penicillins. Natural penicillins can be destroyed by enzymes called *penicillinases* [FIGURE 21.9]. These enzymes destroy the β-lactam ring in the core structure of penicillins, and for this reason they are also called *β-lactamases*. Penicillinases are produced by many different bacteria, including staphylococci, and infections caused by these bacteria are resistant to treatment with natural penicillins. However, some semisynthetic penicillins have the advantage of being resistant to attack by penicillinases. One example is *methicillin*, which is often used to treat "penicillin-resistant" staphylococcal infections.

Inhibitors of penicillinases. *Clavulanic acid* is a naturally occurring β-lactam compound produced by *Streptomyces clavuligerus*. It has relatively low antibacterial activity, but it is a potent inhibitor of penicillinases, as is *sulbactam*, a semisynthetic compound that has similar characteristics. Currently, there are commercially available products which contain clavulanic acid or sulbactam in combination with the antibiotics ampicillin, amoxicillin, or ticarcillin. These products allow the antibiotics in them to be effective against microorganisms that ordinarily would be resistant because of their ability to make penicillinases.

FIGURE 21.8

[A] The penicillin core (6-aminopenicillanic acid), common to all penicillins. [B] Some natural and semi-synthetic penicillins. Note how the side chains differ in chemical structure.

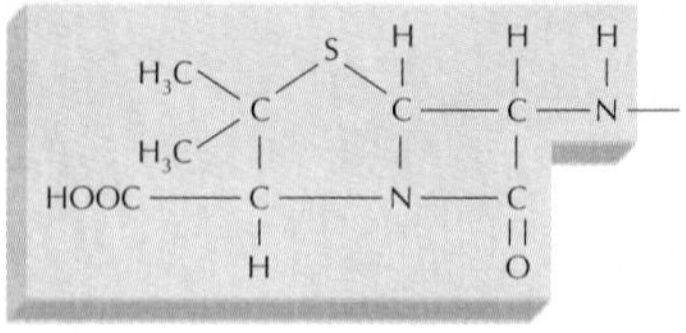

6-Aminopenicillanic acid

[A] THE PENICILLIN CORE

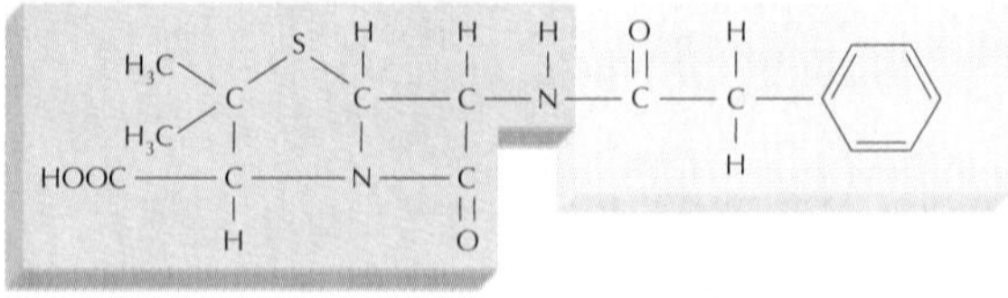

Penicillin G (benzylpenicillin)

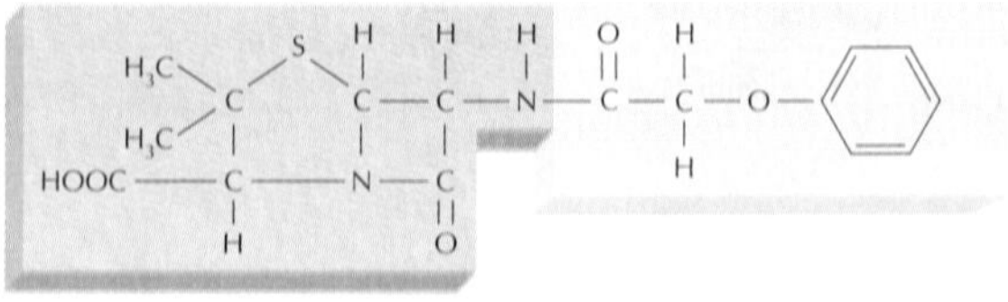

Penicillin V (phenoxymethylpenicillin)

NATURAL PENICILLINS

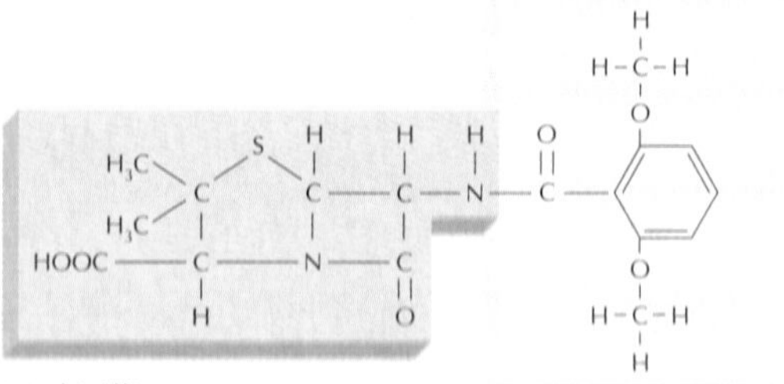

Methicillin

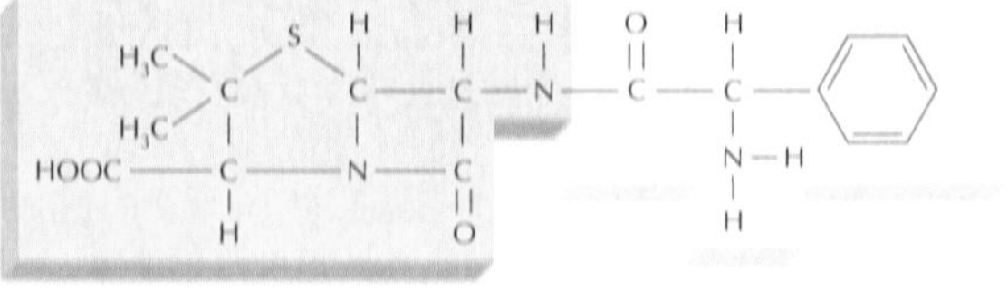

Ampicillin

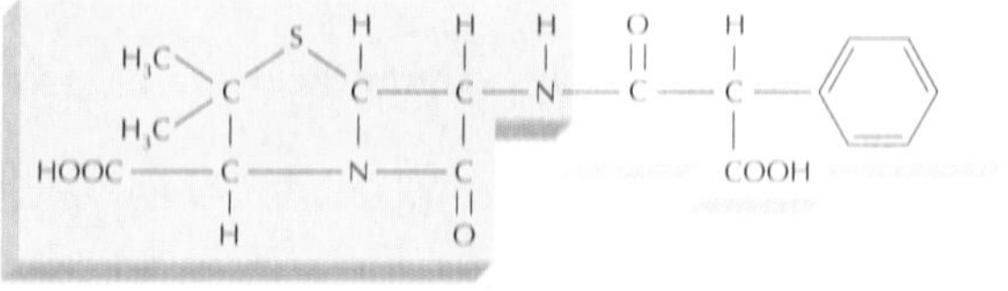

Carbenicillin

[B] SEMISYNTHETIC PENICILLINS

FIGURE 21.9

The inactivation of the penicillins by the enzyme penicillinase results from breaking the β-lactam ring structure.

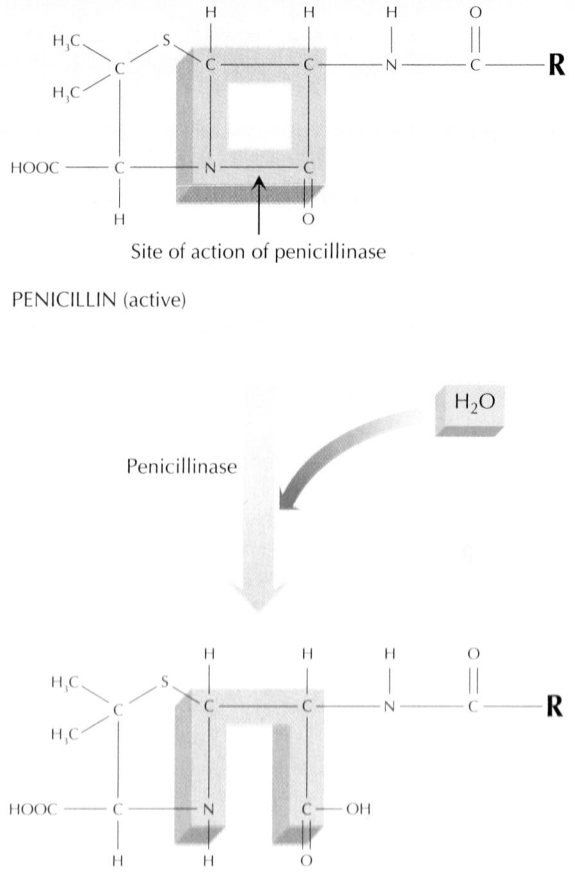

Site of action of penicillinase

PENICILLIN (active)

PENICILLOIC ACID (inactive)

The Monobactams. Another class of β-lactam antibiotics called *monobactams* was originally discovered to be produced by a Gram-negative bacterium, *Chromobacterium violaceum*. One of the monobactams, *aztreonam*, is now made synthetically and is active against a wide variety of aerobic Gram-negative bacteria. Aztreonam has the added advantage of not being inactivated by penicillinases or by other enzymes such as cephalosporinases.

The Cephalosporins. Cephalosporins differ from penicillins in the structure of their core compound, 7-aminocephalosporanic acid [FIGURE 21.7]. They are produced by species of marine fungi belonging to the genus *Cephalosporium* (now reclassified as *Acremonium*). Since the mid-1960s, when this group of antibiotics came into use, pharmaceutical companies have developed many new cephalosporins, each with new and more desirable characteristics for chemotherapy. Cephalosporins are grouped as "first-generation," "second-generation," and "third-generation" products. Second-generation cephalosporins (e.g., cefamandole, cefoxitin, and cefuroxime) and third-generation cephalosporins (e.g., cefotaxime, cefoperazone, ceftriaxone) have greater antimicrobial activity, including a broader spectrum of activity, and are much more resistant to enzymatic inactivation than are the first-generation products.

Carbapenems. Carbapenems, or thienamycins, are produced by *Streptomyces cattleya. Imipenem,* a semisynthetic carbapenem, is produced by chemical modification of thienamycin. Imipenem has a very wide spectrum of antibacterial activity and inhibits most aerobic and anaerobic Gram-positive and Gram-negative bacteria, including those which produce β-lactamases.

The Macrolides

The macrolide category includes the well-known antibiotic *erythromycin,* which consists of a large lactone ring linked with amino sugars as shown in FIGURE 21.6. Erythromycin is produced by a strain of *Streptomyces erythreus,* which was originally isolated from soil collected in the Philippines. This antibiotic is active against many Gram-positive bacteria and also some Gram-negative bacteria, including pathogenic spirochetes. The variety of microbes affected by erythromycin—its *antimicrobial spectrum*—resembles that of the penicillins. However, since erythromycin is not destroyed by penicillinase, it is frequently used as an alternative to penicillin therapy.

The Aminoglycosides

The best-known example of the aminoglycoside antibiotics is *streptomycin* [FIGURE 21.6]. *Neomycin* is also a member of the group. Chemically, aminoglycosides consist of amino sugars and a ring structure called *aminocyclitol.*

Streptomycin is produced by the soil bacterium *Streptomyces griseus.* Its antibiotic activities were first reported in 1944 by Selman Waksman and his colleagues at Rutgers University [FIGURE 21.10]. Streptomycin is a very useful antibiotic because it inhibits many organisms that are resistant to sulfonamides and penicillins. It is effective against many Gram-negative bacteria and is especially useful for treatment of tularemia, plague, and tuberculosis. Highly purified streptomycin is nontoxic to humans and animals when given for short-term treatment of infections, but it does have a cumulative detrimental effect on a specific region of the nervous system when administered over long periods of time.

FIGURE 21.10
Selman A. Waksman, codiscoverer of the antibiotic streptomycin. He was awarded the Nobel Prize in 1952 for the discovery and development of this antibiotic.

Neomycin is the most toxic antibiotic in the aminoglycoside group. However, since it is poorly absorbed from the large bowel, it is sometimes given orally prior to certain types of intestinal surgery to help control the growth of flora in the large intestine. Neomycin is also a component of some topical preparations.

The Tetracyclines

The tetracyclines include *chlortetracycline, oxytetracycline, tetracycline, doxycycline,* and *minocycline.* They all have in common a chemical structure called a *naphthalene ring;* differences among the various kinds of tetracyclines are due to differences in the chemical groups attached to the naphthalene ring [FIGURE 21.11].

Tetracyclines are produced by species of the genus *Streptomyces.* They are active against a wide range of Gram-positive and Gram-negative bacteria, and they are especially useful for treatment of brucellosis, urinary tract infections caused by Gram-negative bacteria, and infections caused by mycoplasmas, rickettsias, and chlamydias. Some bacteria may be more susceptible to doxycycline and minocycline than they are to the other tetracyclines because these two compounds have a slightly broader antimicrobial spectrum than the other tetracyclines. Furthermore, these two compounds are better absorbed by the body, resulting in their maintaining higher and more prolonged levels in the bloodstream.

FIGURE 21.11

Tetracyclines, broad-spectrum antibiotics produced by *Streptomyces* species, differ slightly in chemical structure as shown in the positions labeled **W**, **X**, **Y**, and **Z** in this illustration.

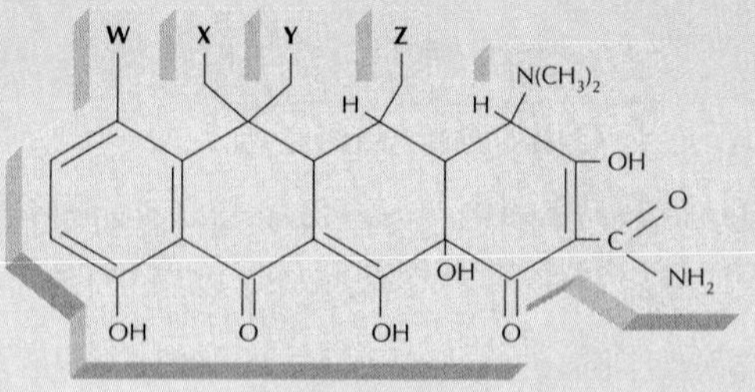

Tetracyclines

Antibiotic	Position on molecule			
	W	**X**	**Y**	**Z**
Tetracycline	H	CH_3	OH	H
Oxytetracycline	H	CH_3	OH	OH
Chlortetracycline	Cl	CH_3	OH	H
Minocycline	$N(CH_3)_2$	H	H	H
Doxycycline	H	CH_3	H	OH

The Polypeptide Antibiotics

Bacitracin and the *polymyxins* are included among the polypeptide antibiotics. They and the other members of this group are characterized chemically by their consisting of a chain of amino acids. Both bacitracin and the polymyxins are produced by bacteria in the genus *Bacillus*. Sometimes the chain is circular, as in polymyxin B [FIGURE 21.6].

Bacitracin is produced by the bacteria *B. subtilis* and *B. licheniformis*. It is effective against a wide variety of Gram-positive bacteria. However, because of its toxicity to human tissue its use is limited to topical applications.

Polymyxins are produced by the bacterium *Bacillus polymyxa*. This organism produces several different polymyxins, which have been named A, B, C, D, and E. Polymyxins are active against many Gram-negative bacteria, including *Pseudomonas aeruginosa*, but because they may cause severe toxic reactions such as nephrotoxicity and neurotoxicity in the host when administered internally, they are used mainly for topical application.

The Polyenes

A polyene compound is one that contains three or more double covalent bonds which join carbon atoms. The group includes the antibiotics *nystatin* [FIGURE 21.6] and *amphotericin B*.

Nystatin, produced by the bacterium *Streptomyces noursei*, was discovered by Hazen and Brown [FIGURE 21.12] in the 1950s. This antibiotic was the first to show

FIGURE 21.12

Elizabeth L. Hazen (left) and Rachel Brown, codiscoverers of nystatin, the world's first chemotherapeutic antibiotic for fungal diseases. The microorganism which produces nystatin was isolated from a soil sample in 1949 by Dr. Hazen, and she and Dr. Brown isolated and characterized this new antibiotic, which became available for chemotherapeutic use in the early 1950s.

promise for treatment of fungal infections. In spite of its useful antifungal properties, however, nystatin is toxic to human tissue and, consequently, is used only for treatment of skin or mouth infections. It is particularly useful for treating infections caused by the pathogenic yeast *Candida albicans*.

Amphotericin B, produced by *Streptomyces nodosus*, is a widely used antibiotic for treatment of very severe internal infections caused by certain pathogenic fungi. Unfortunately, amphotericin B also exhibits toxic properties and can cause kidney damage, and so the treatment of a patient must be closely monitored.

Other Antibiotics

Chloramphenicol. The structure of chloramphenicol is simple when compared with that of most other antibiotics [FIGURE 21.6]. It is produced by the bacterium *Streptomyces venezuelae*, but because of the simplicity of its structure it is more efficient and economical to manufacture by chemical synthesis.

Chloramphenicol is a broad-spectrum antibiotic. However, its use for chemotherapy is limited by its tendency to cause *aplastic anemia*, a condition in which the bone marrow fails to produce new blood cells. Despite this serious side-effect, chloramphenicol is useful for treatment of typhoid fever and some other serious infections, particularly when the causative microorganisms have developed resistance to other antibiotics.

ASK YOURSELF

Name several major groups of antibiotics on the basis of their chemical structure, and give an example of a specific antibiotic in each group.

MODE OF ACTION OF ANTIBIOTICS

Antibiotics act against microorganisms in a variety of ways. The major points of attack include:

1 Prevention of synthesis of bacterial cell-wall peptidoglycan
2 Damage to the cytoplasmic membrane
3 Interference with nucleic acid and protein synthesis

In the following section you will learn the mechanisms by which several important antibiotics destroy infectious microorganisms. The selective toxicity of the chemotherapeutic agent is based upon the differences between the procaryotic and eucaryotic cell structure and chemical composition.

Inhibitors of Cell-Wall Synthesis

The β-lactam antibiotics (penicillins and cephalosporins) affect the synthesis of the peptidoglycan component of bacterial cell walls. Without a rigid peptidoglycan "girdle" around a bacterial cell, the cell will usually die by taking up water, swelling, and bursting.

As you learned earlier, the biosynthesis of peptidoglycan involves a sequence of enzyme-catalyzed steps. Interference with any one of these steps can inhibit peptidoglycan synthesis. Penicillins and cephalosporins act by inhibiting the particular step in which cross-links are formed between the peptidoglycan chains [refer to FIGURE 12.7]. Without these cross-links the peptidoglycan has no rigidity and thus cannot provide a firm "coating" for the cell.

Another mode of action by penicillins is based on the fact that bacterial cell walls contain enzymes that can destroy peptidoglycan. This is because some peptidoglycan breakdown is necessary to allow newly made peptidoglycan to be added to the wall of a growing cell. Normally these degradative enzymes are controlled by natural inhibitors that also occur in the cell wall. However, in some bacteria, the addition of penicillin to the culture causes these inhibitors to be lost, thereby allowing the degradative enzymes to break down the peptidoglycan.

In the laboratory, bacterial cells that are susceptible to penicillins can be protected from destruction if their culture medium has a high osmotic pressure. For example, a high concentration of sucrose in the medium inhibits the cells from taking up water and bursting in the presence of penicillins. Under these conditions (i.e., a high-sucrose solution environment), bacteria that are normally rod-shaped, such as *Enterobacter aerogenes*, become spherical because they lack the rigid peptidoglycan that imparts a rod shape. Such spherical cells that result from peptidoglycan deprivation are called *spheroplasts* [FIGURE 21.13].

Some species of bacteria, such as the mycoplasmas, normally lack cell walls and thus cannot be inhibited by penicillins or cephalosporins. For example, primary atypical pneumonia caused by *Mycoplasma pneumoniae* is not treatable with penicillins.

FIGURE 21.13

The effect of β-lactam antibiotics on cell wall synthesis. **[A]** The normal morphology of the bacterium *Enterobacter aerogenes* grown for 8 h in a broth medium. **[B]** The same bacterium cultured in the same medium but containing 2 μg per ml of the antibiotic amdinocillin. The inhibition of cell wall synthesis results in the loss of rigidity of the cell wall covering the bacterium and hence the appearance of spherical bodies (spheroplasts), some of which collapse. **[C]** The normal appearance of *Escherichia coli*. **[D]** The appearance of *E. coli* cells after 30 min exposure to ceftazidime—a cephalosporin antibiotic—for a period of 30 min. Cells become elongated, spheroplasts form, and some cells lyse.

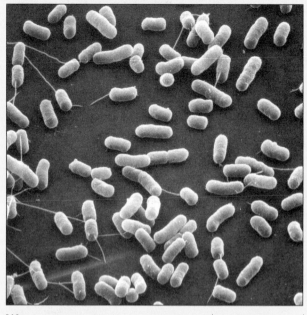

[A]   5 μm

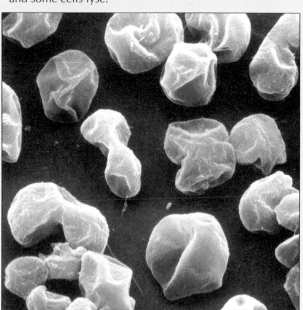

[B]   5 μm

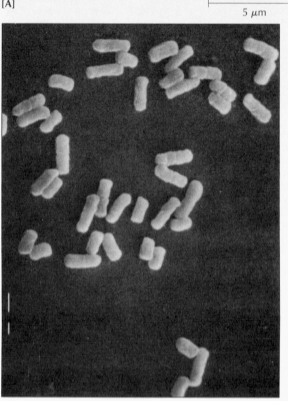

[C]   5 μm

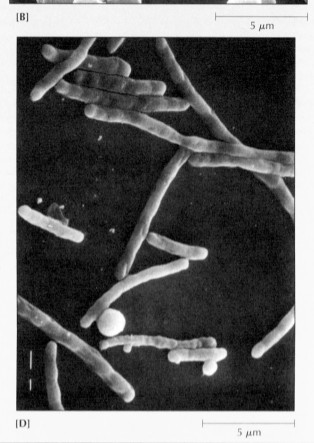

[D]   5 μm

Antibiotics That Damage the Cytoplasmic Membrane

Several polypeptide antibiotics, such as the *polymyxins*, have the ability to damage the cytoplasmic membrane of bacteria. Polymyxins are bactericidal because they disrupt the phospholipids that make up the structure of the membrane. This destroys the normal permeability characteristics of the membrane so that essential substances leak from the cells, resulting in cell death.

Polyene antibiotics such as *nystatin* and *amphotericin B* act on sterol components of membranes rather than on phospholipid components. Since most bacterial membranes do not contain sterols, they are not affected by polyenes, whereas the membranes of fungi (including yeasts) and animal cells do contain sterols and are susceptible.

Antibiotics That Inhibit Nucleic Acid and Protein Synthesis

The biosynthesis of DNA, RNA, and proteins involves a number of intricate biochemical reactions, as described in Chapter 13. Several important antibiotics owe their inhibitory action to interference with these reactions. The action of some of these antibiotics is as follows:

1 *Streptomycin* combines with the 30-S subunit of the bacterial ribosome and blocks the process of translation at its initial step [see FIGURES 13.8 and 13.9].
2 *Tetracyclines* combine with the 30-S ribosomal subunit in such a way as to prevent amino acid-*t*RNA molecules from attaching to the *m*RNA-ribosome complex [see FIGURES 13.8 and 13.9].
3 *Chloramphenicol* and *erythromycin* combine with

TABLE 21.1
Some Antibiotics Used for Chemotherapy of Bacterial and Fungal Infections

Antibiotic	Produced by	Active against	Mode of action	EFFECT Bactericidal	EFFECT Bacteriostatic
β-Lactams			Inhibit cell-wall synthesis		
Penicillins	*Penicillium* spp.	Gram-positive bacteria;			
Cephalosporins	*Cephalosporium* spp.	Gram-negative bacteria causing			
Monobactams	*Chromobacterium violaceum*	respiratory, intestinal, and urinary infections; penicillinase-		+	
Carbapenems	*Streptomyces cattleya*	producing bacteria			
Aminoglycosides			Induce abnormal protein synthesis		
Streptomycin	*Streptomyces griseus*	Tuberculosis infection			
Spectinomycin	*Streptomyces* sp.	Penicillin-resistant *Neisseria* *gonorrhoeae*			
Neomycin	*S. fradiae*	Inhibits intestinal bacteria		+	
Kanamycin	*S. kanomyceticus*	Most Gram-negative bacteria except *Pseudomonas*			
Gentamicin	*Micromonospora purpurea*	Active against a variety of Gram-positive and Gram-negative bacteria including *Pseudomonas*			
Tetracyclines	*Streptomyces* spp.	Broad spectrum—many Gram-positive and Gram-negative bacteria; also organisms such as *Mycoplasma*, *Rickettsia*, and *Chlamydia*	Interfere with protein synthesis		+
Macrolides					
Erythromycin	*Streptomyces erythreus*	Commonly encountered Gram-positive bacteria	Interferes with protein synthesis	+	
Lincomycin	*S. lincolnensis*	Gram-positive bacteria	Interferes with protein synthesis		+

the 50-S subunit of the bacterial ribosome in such a manner as to prevent assembly of amino acids into a protein chain [see FIGURES 13.8 and 13.9].

4 *Rifamycin* stops bacterial protein synthesis by inhibiting the DNA-dependent RNA polymerase that transcribes DNA into *m*RNA [FIGURE 13.6].

TABLE 21.1 presents in summary form a selected list of antibiotics, their mode of action, their antimicrobial spectra, and the microorganisms that produce them.

ASK YOURSELF

1 What are the various mechanisms by which antibiotics inhibit or kill microorganisms?

2 What is the mechanism by which each of the following inhibits or kills microorganisms: cephalosporins, nystatin, streptomycin?

DEVELOPMENT OF ANTIBIOTIC-RESISTANT BACTERIA

Some bacteria are normally resistant to a particular antibiotic, whereas others are susceptible to the same antibiotic. Even in those bacteria that are susceptible, however, mutant cells may arise that are no longer inhibited by the antibiotic. There are a number of different mechanisms that can account for the resistance of bacteria to antibiotics. These can be summarized as follows:

1 The bacterium may be able to make sufficient amounts of an enzyme that destroys or modifies the structure of the antibiotic. As mentioned earlier in this chapter, some bacteria make the enzyme penicillinase, which destroys the β-lactam ring of penicillins [FIGURE 21.9]. On the other hand, chloramphenicol can be inactivated by an enzyme that modifies the structure by adding an acetyl group to the molecule. Other antibiotics can be inactivated by enzymes that

Antibiotic	Produced by	Active against	Mode of action	EFFECT Bacteri-cidal	EFFECT Bacterio-static
Chloramphenicol (Chloromycetin)	*Streptomyces venezuelae*	Broad spectrum; severe Gram-negative infections	Interferes with protein synthesis		+
Polypeptides Colistin (Polymyxin E)	*Bacillus colistinus*	Most Gram-negative bacteria, including *Pseudomonas aeruginosa*	Deterioration of cell membrane		
Polymyxin B	*B. polymyxa*	Gram-negative bacteria; less effective than colistin	Deterioration of cell membrane	+	
Bacitracin	*B. subtilis*	Gram-positive, but not Gram-negative, bacteria	Inhibits cell-wall formation		
Vancomycin	*Streptomyces orientalis*	Gram-positive bacteria, including penicillinase-producing staphylococci and enterococci	Interferes with protein synthesis	+	
Viomycin	*Streptomyces griseus* var. *purpureus*	Tuberculosis infection	Interferes with protein synthesis	+	
Rifamycin	*Streptomyces mediterranei*	Tuberculosis infection	Interferes with protein synthesis	+	
Antifungal antibiotics Polyenes Nystatin	*Streptomyces noursei*	Fungal infections, particularly oral, skin, intestinal, and vaginal lesions due to *Candida*	Damages cell membrane	+	
Amphotericin B	*Streptomyces nodosus*	Deep-seated mycotic infections	Interferes with membrane function	+	
Griseofulvin	*Penicillium griseofulvin*	Fungal infections	Damages cell membrane		+

add phosphate groups or adenyl groups to the molecules.

2 The antibiotic may be unable to penetrate the bacterial cell surface. Thus the antibiotic cannot act on susceptible sites within the cell, such as ribosomes.

3 The bacterium may have an alternate biochemical pathway that bypasses the particular reaction that is inhibited by the antibiotic.

4 The bacterium may possess enzymes, ribosomes, or other cell components of a type that is not affected by the antibiotic.

Transmission of Antibiotic Resistance

When antibiotics were first used in chemotherapy, development of antibiotic-resistant microorganisms was infrequent. However, as antibiotics became widely used, resistance became much more of a problem as susceptible microbes were eliminated and the numbers of resistant microorganisms increased.

The initial appearance of a resistant bacterium in an otherwise susceptible population is often caused by a mutation in a single bacterial gene. The frequency of such initial mutations is low, usually occurring at rates of only one mutation in a population of several million cells. However, other bacteria can become antibiotic-resistant at a much higher frequency merely by acquiring a gene from a bacterium that is already resistant. The gene for resistance can be transmitted from a resistant cell to a susceptible cell by *conjugation*, as was described in Chapter 13. This process is called *transmissible antibiotic resistance.*

Transmission of antibiotic resistance by conjugation was first reported independently in 1958 by two Japanese microbiologists, Akiba and Ochiai. They had isolated pathogenic *Shigella dysenteriae* bacteria from patients with bacillary dysentery and found that some of the cells were resistant to sulfonamides, tetracyclines, streptomycin, and chloramphenicol. Other cells of the same strain of *S. dysenteriae* showed no such resistance. Where had the resistant cells acquired the genes for their resistance? Akiba and Ochiai showed that the genes had been acquired from conjugation with antibiotic-resistant *E. coli* cells that resided in the patients' intestinal tracts. Transfer of antibiotic resistance by bacterial conjugation has subsequently been observed in other species of bacteria and in other parts of the world. In many instances transmissible antibiotic resistance has made it very difficult to treat infections successfully.

We now know that the genes for transmissible antibiotic resistance are located on *conjugative R plasmids* ("R" for resistance) in bacteria such as *E. coli;* the plasmids can be readily transferred to various other bacterial cells (Chapter 13). Some organisms that are good recipi-

ents of R plasmids from an *E. coli* donor include species of *Enterobacter, Klebsiella, Salmonella,* and *Shigella.* Other species are weak recipients of these plasmids. These include species of *Pasteurella, Proteus,* and *Serratia.*

Antibiotic resistance, whether it arises by mutation or by conjugative transfer of R plasmids, is a serious problem for treatment of infectious diseases. Great efforts are being made to understand the mechanisms involved in resistance and how to prevent its occurrence. Currently, the development of resistance can be minimized in the following ways:

1 Avoid the indiscriminate use of antibiotics where they are likely to be of little or no therapeutic value.

2 Use sufficiently high dosages of the proper antibiotic to overcome an infection quickly. The less a pathogen is able to multiply, the lower the chance that a resistant mutant will arise.

3 Use a combination of antibiotics of proven effectiveness to overcome an infection quickly. It is far more difficult for a pathogenic microorganism to mutate to resistance against two antibiotics simultaneously than against a single antibiotic.

4 Switch to a different antibiotic as soon as an organism shows signs of developing resistance to the one used initially.

ASK YOURSELF

1 How do bacteria develop resistance to antibiotics?

2 How is resistance to an antibiotic transmitted to another bacterium?

3 What is the undesirable consequence of the indiscriminate use of antibiotics?

SYNTHETIC CHEMOTHERAPEUTIC AGENTS

At the beginning of this chapter you learned about Paul Ehrlich and his discovery of the antisyphilis agent salvarsan. Salvarsan is a **synthetic chemotherapeutic agent,** not an antibiotic, because it was made by chemical synthesis in a laboratory rather than produced by a microorganism. Since Ehrlich's time many other synthetic chemotherapeutic agents have been synthesized by chemists and chemical engineers. Some of these agents are widely used for treatment of infections caused by bacteria, viruses, or protozoa.

Synthetic Antibacterial Agents

Among the most useful synthetic antibacterial agents are the *sulfonamides*, *trimethoprim*, the *nitrofurans*, *isoniazid*, and *nalidixic acid*.

The Sulfonamides. You have already learned about Domagk's discovery of the antimicrobial activity of sulfanilamide. Sulfanilamide and other sulfonamides are able to inhibit a variety of bacteria by interfering with a particular biochemical reaction that is essential for the life of these bacteria. In order to understand how they do this, we must first examine the chemical structure of sulfonamides.

All sulfonamides have the same fundamental core structure [FIGURE 21.14A]. The various kinds of sulfonamides differ from one another only in other portions of the molecule [FIGURE 21.14B and C]. The core structure is important because it closely resembles the structure of a natural biochemical compound called **para-*aminobenzoic acid* (PABA)** [FIGURE 21.15A]. Many bacteria require PABA as a building block for an essential coenzyme called ***tetrahydrofolic acid (THFA)*** [FIGURE 21.15A]. Bacterial cells need THFA to make amino acids and thymidine, an essential component of DNA.

Because sulfonamides so closely resemble PABA, they are called ***structural analogs,*** or "phony" forms, of PABA. Bacterial enzymes can often be fooled into using a structural analog of a substrate instead of the real substrate. This usually results in *competitive inhibition of enzyme activity*. In the case of a sulfonamide, a bacterial enzyme called *dihydropteroate synthetase* is fooled into using the sulfonamide instead of PABA [FIGURE 21.15B]. The end result is that no THFA will be made by the cell.

Although sulfonamides inhibit the growth of many pathogenic bacteria, they do not inhibit human tissue cells. The reason for this selective action is that humans make THFA by a different biochemical pathway, a pathway that does not involve PABA at all. Instead, we use a vitamin called *folic acid*, found in various foods such as spinach. Our cells can reduce this folic acid directly to THFA [FIGURE 21.16]. Some bacteria can also do the same thing and therefore cannot be inhibited by sulfonamides.

Trimethoprim is a synthetic antibacterial agent that is not a sulfonamide but is often used in combination with sulfonamides. It is a structural analog of the pteridine portion of dihydrofolic acid (DHFA), and a bacterial enzyme called dihydrofolate reductase can easily be fooled into using it instead of DHFA. Human cells also have a dihydrofolate reductase, but the human enzyme has a different structure and trimethoprim does not fit readily onto the enzyme's active site. In fact, the human enzyme is several thousand times more resistant to inhibition by trimethoprim than is the bacterial enzyme.

FIGURE 21.14

Some examples of sulfonamides. **[A]** The basic structure of all sulfonamides; the differences among sulfonamides are in the chemical-group attachment in the position designated "R." **[B]** The sulfanilamide molecule has a hydrogen atom (H) in place of R. **[C]** The nature of the R group for several other sulfonamides.

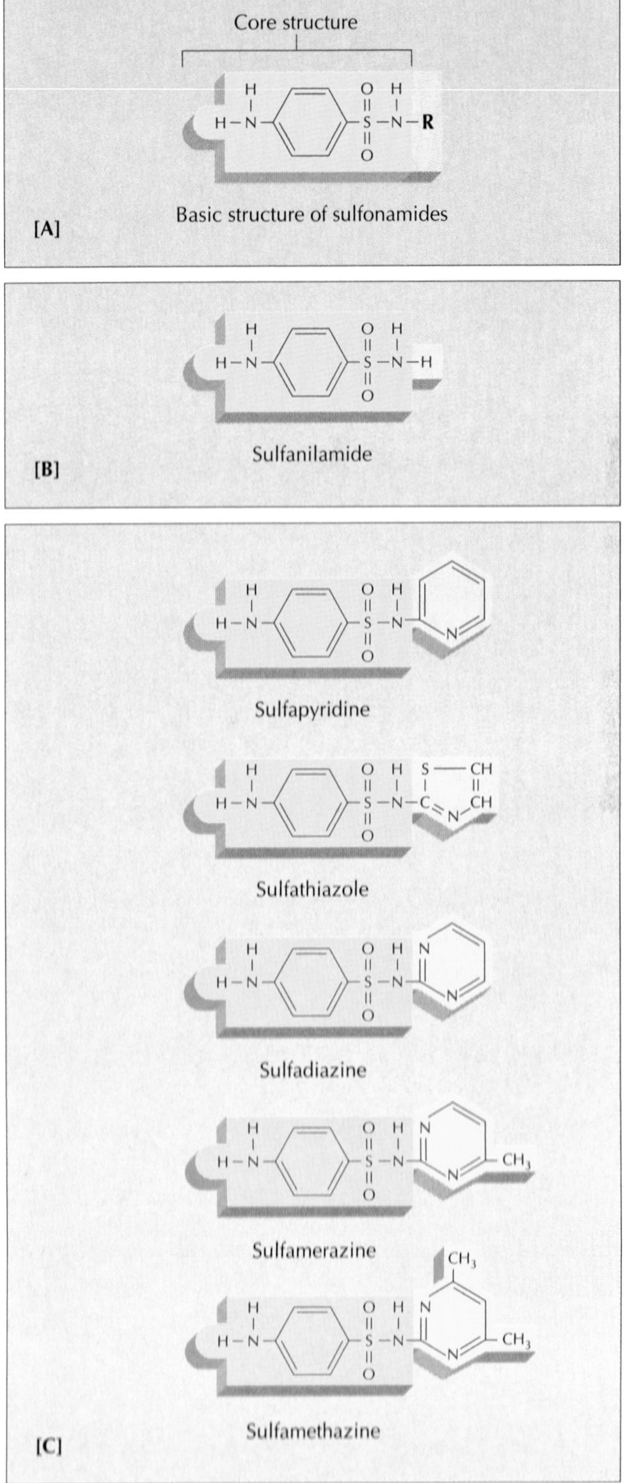

Basic structure of sulfonamides

[A]

Sulfanilamide

[B]

Sulfapyridine

Sulfathiazole

Sulfadiazine

Sulfamerazine

Sulfamethazine

[C]

FIGURE 21.15

[A] Structure of *para*-aminobenzoic acid (PABA) and tetrahydrofolic acid (THFA). [B] In the pathway for bacterial synthesis of THFA, the enzyme dihydropteroate synthetase can be fooled into using a sulfonamide instead of PABA. If this occurs, synthesis of THFA is inhibited.

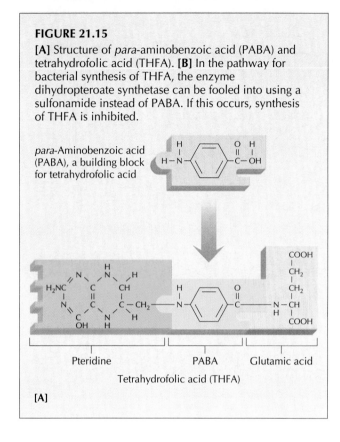

para-Aminobenzoic acid (PABA), a building block for tetrahydrofolic acid

Pteridine   PABA   Glutamic acid

Tetrahydrofolic acid (THFA)

[A]

FIGURE 21.16

Sulfonamides do not inhibit human cells, because human cells do not use PABA to make THFA. Instead, they make THFA by adding hydrogen atoms to the vitamin folic acid.

THFA synthesis by human cells

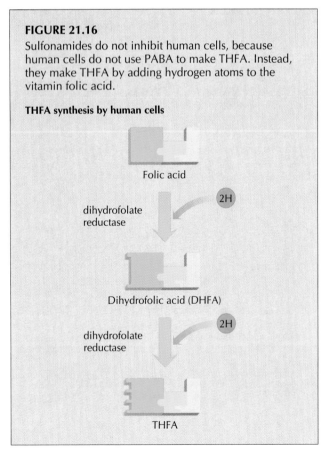

Folic acid

dihydrofolate reductase   2H

Dihydrofolic acid (DHFA)

dihydrofolate reductase   2H

THFA

THFA synthesis in bacteria

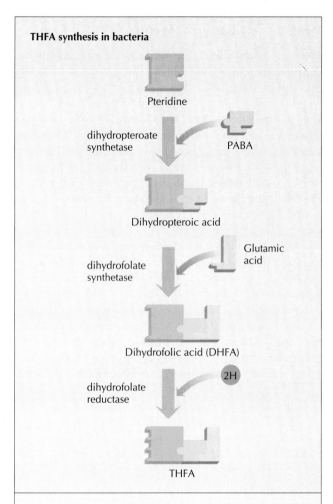

Pteridine

dihydropteroate synthetase   PABA

Dihydropteroic acid

dihydrofolate synthetase   Glutamic acid

Dihydrofolic acid (DHFA)

dihydrofolate reductase   2H

THFA

THFA synthesis is blocked by sulfonamides

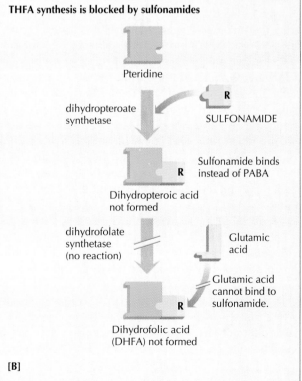

Pteridine

dihydropteroate synthetase   R   SULFONAMIDE

R   Sulfonamide binds instead of PABA

Dihydropteroic acid not formed

dihydrofolate synthetase (no reaction)   Glutamic acid

Glutamic acid cannot bind to sulfonamide.

R

Dihydrofolic acid (DHFA) not formed

[B]

However, long-term use of trimethoprim can sometimes affect human cells.

The Nitrofurans. The original compound from which nitrofurans are derived is *furfural* [FIGURE 21.17A]. Furfural can be prepared from corncobs and cornstalks, oat hulls, and other vegetable by-products. The ring structure that accounts for most of a furfural molecule is called a *furan ring*.

Furfural and other furan ring compounds have little antimicrobial activity. But in 1944, two American microbiologists, Dodd and Stillman, discovered that strong antibacterial properties could be conferred upon these compounds by adding a nitro group ($-NO_2$) to the furan ring, thereby creating a nitrofuran. Many kinds of nitrofurans have since been synthesized; three examples are shown in FIGURE 21.17B.

Nitrofurans inhibit protein synthesis and are effective against Gram-negative enteric bacilli, enterococci, several pathogenic protozoa, and some fungi. They are often used to treat infections of the urinary tract.

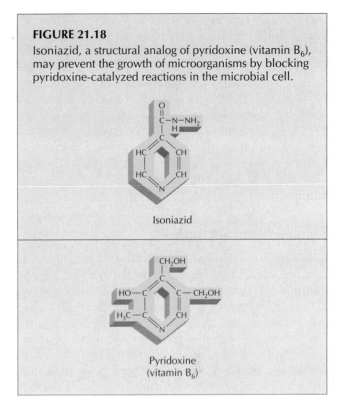

FIGURE 21.18
Isoniazid, a structural analog of pyridoxine (vitamin B₆), may prevent the growth of microorganisms by blocking pyridoxine-catalyzed reactions in the microbial cell.

Isoniazid

Pyridoxine (vitamin B₆)

FIGURE 21.17
Furfural **[A]** is the prototype of nitrofuran compounds. **[B]** Examples of chemotherapeutic derivatives prepared from furfural.

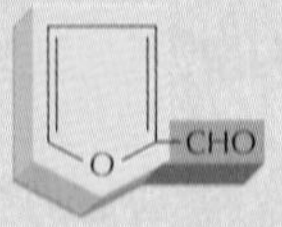

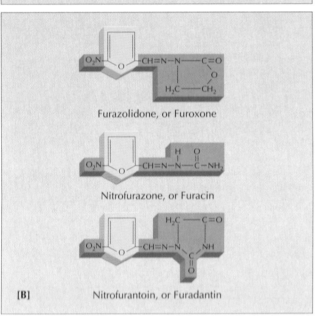

[A] Furfural

Furazolidone, or Furoxone

Nitrofurazone, or Furacin

[B] Nitrofurantoin, or Furadantin

FIGURE 21.19
Nalidixic acid is a synthetic antibacterial drug with a selective action against bacterial DNA synthesis.

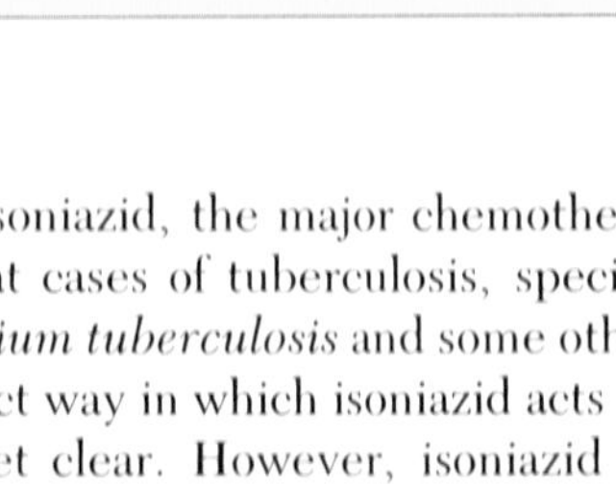

Isoniazid. Isoniazid, the major chemotherapeutic agent used to treat cases of tuberculosis, specifically inhibits *Mycobacterium tuberculosis* and some other mycobacteria. The exact way in which isoniazid acts on mycobacteria is not yet clear. However, isoniazid is a structural analog of *pyridoxine*, or vitamin B₆ [FIGURE 21.18], and also of nicotinamide, a component of the coenzyme NAD. Thus isoniazid may competitively block biochemical reactions involving these compounds.

The Quinolones. *Nalidixic acid* [FIGURE 21.19] is a quinolone that has the ability to inhibit DNA synthesis in various Gram-negative bacteria (see Chapter 13). Specifically, it inhibits DNA gyrase, an enzyme that causes conformational changes (winding and unwinding) in the highly twisted, compacted form of DNA in bacterial cells. These changes are required before the DNA can be replicated. Nalidixic acid is widely used for treatment of urinary tract infections.

Other quinolones are *cinoxacin, ciprofloxacin,* and *norfloxacin.* The latter two are fluorinated compounds and are active against bacteria that are resistant to nalidixic acid and cinoxacin.

Synthetic Antiviral Agents

Relatively few chemicals are available for treatment of viral infections. The reason lies in the fact that viruses multiply only within host cells and are dependent on host-cell metabolism. In order to attack a virus, a chemotherapeutic agent must be able to penetrate the infected host cell and selectively block the multiplication of the virus without inhibiting the metabolism of the host cell. Many chemicals can inhibit viral replication, but unfortunately most of them also inhibit host-cell metabolism.

The search for antiviral chemotherapeutic agents has focused mainly upon chemicals that block viral DNA or RNA synthesis. Most of these chemicals are structural analogs of purine or pyrimidine bases, which are part of the structure of DNA or RNA nucleotides (Chapter 1).

The analogs masquerade as legitimate building blocks and are inserted into the growing viral DNA or RNA molecule, resulting in a nonfunctional viral nucleic acid. The trick is to find compounds that inhibit nucleic acid synthesis by the virus to a much greater extent than they inhibit nucleic acid synthesis by the host cell. This has proved to be difficult.

One of the first effective antiviral chemotherapeutic agents discovered was *idoxuridine,* a structural analog of thymidine (thymine linked to deoxyribose). Idoxuridine was used for treatment of eye infections caused by herpesviruses. It has since been replaced by a more effective compound, *vidarabine* (ara-A), which is a structural analog of deoxyadenosine (adenine linked to deoxyribose). Another compound, *acyclovir,* is also used to inhibit herpesvirus nucleic acid synthesis. Acyclovir is an analog of deoxyguanosine (guanine linked to deoxyribose) and, when administered by intravenous injection, is highly effective for the treatment of genital herpes.

A compound called *amantadine* specifically inhibits the replication of influenza A viruses, but how it does this is not yet understood. Amantadine decreases the duration and severity of influenza type A, and when administered to healthy persons, it can prevent influenza type A from occurring.

Recently, a compound called *azidothymidine (AZT)* (also called *zidovudine*) has been approved for the treatment of acquired immunodeficiency syndrome (AIDS). AZT is a structural analog of thymidine. The AIDS virus uses the enzyme reverse transcriptase to make viral

---

TABLE 21.2
Some Examples of Synthetic Antiprotozoan Chemotherapeutic Agents

Chemotherapeutic agent	Disease	Causative agent
Quinacrine or metronidazole	Giardiasis (giardial dysentery)	*Giardia lamblia*
Metronidazole	Trichomoniasis	*Trichomonas vaginalis*
Pentamidine; suramin	African sleeping sickness (African trypanosomiasis)	*Trypanosoma gambiense* and *T. brucei*
Nitrofurfurylidine derivative	Chagas' disease (American trypanosomiasis)	*Trypanosoma cruzi*
Antimony sodium gluconate; pentamidine	Leishmaniasis	*Leishmania donovani* and *L. brasiliensis*
Metronidazole and diiodohydroxyquin	Amoebiasis (amoebic dysentery)	*Entamoeba histolytica*
Chloroquine	Malaria	*Plasmodium* spp.
Pyrimethamine plus trisulfapyrimidines	Toxoplasmosis	*Toxoplasma gondii*
Trimethoprim and sulfamethoxazole	Pneumocystosis (pneumonias)	*Pneumocystis carinii*

DNA, and this enzyme can be fooled into adding AZT to a growing strand of viral DNA. When this happens, the AZT blocks the addition of any more nucleotides to the DNA strand, thereby halting DNA synthesis [see FIGURE 23.18]. AZT acts selectively against the virus because human cells do not use reverse transcriptase to synthesize DNA. However, AZT can cause side effects in humans, such as bone marrow suppression that leads to low red and white blood cells counts. Studies are under way to modify the structure of AZT and reduce these toxic effects.

Synthetic Antiprotozoan Agents

Many chemical substances are available for the treatment of diseases caused by protozoa. However, one problem is that protozoa may exist in different forms (such as cysts) during stages of their life cycle (Chapter 10), and these forms may vary in their susceptibility to a chemotherapeutic agent. This variability needs to be considered when prescribing medication.

Some substances also exist that are effective against a number of bacteria as well as against protozoa. For example, *metronidazole* is an antiprotozoal agent active against *Trichomonas vaginalis* and *Entamoeba histolytica*. It is also active against anaerobic bacteria, including species of *Bacteroides*, *Clostridium*, *Peptococcus*, and *Peptostreptococcus*.

Some examples of chemotherapeutic agents used to treat diseases caused by protozoa are given in TABLE 21.2.

ASK YOURSELF

1 From the standpoint of "preparation," how does a synthetic chemotherapeutic agent differ from a chemotherapeutic antibiotic?

2 Name a synthetic therapeutic agent which is useful for the treatment of a disease caused by bacteria, by viruses, by protozoa.

ASSAY OF ANTIBIOTICS

Determination of the antibiotic content of a microbial culture, a patient's blood sample, an antibiotic tablet, or similar specimens can be done by chemical or biological methods. The method of choice depends on several factors, including the purity of antibiotic in a sample.

Chemical Assay

If an antibiotic occurs as part of a solid specimen, such as a powder or tablet, its concentration can be determined by a chemical assay method and expressed in micrograms of the antibiotic per milligram of the specimen. However, to be of value, the chemical assay must give results that correlate well with those obtained in biological assays (assays that indicate how much actual antimicrobial activity is present in the specimen). Chemical assay methods require less time to complete, but they are also less sensitive than biological methods. Moreover, they may not always be reliable, since antibiotics may degrade into biologically inactive forms that the chemical assay cannot distinguish from the active form.

Biological Assay

In a biological assay, living microorganisms are used to measure the amount of antimicrobial activity present in an antibiotic-containing specimen. This assay method is based upon comparing the antimicrobial activity of the specimen with that of a standard preparation of the antibiotic and is performed under precisely standardized conditions. It should be noted that the assay of an antibiotic in blood serum, urine, or tissue samples taken from a patient presents some special problems because (1) the quantity of antibiotic present is usually very small and (2) some of the antibiotic may have been inactivated by being bound to protein material in the specimen.

The unit of measurement for some antibiotics is arbitrary. For others it is established by international agreement, and for still others it is established by the U.S. Food and Drug Administration (FDA). For example, the international unit of penicillin is defined as that amount of penicillin that has antimicrobial activity equal to that present in 0.5988 microgram of an International Standard preparation of penicillin. This standard consists of a sample of pure penicillin G that contains 1667 units of activity per milligram.

The biological assay of antibiotics is performed by using either the tube-dilution technique or the disk-plate technique. In both of these methods, the amount of antibiotic in an "unknown" specimen is determined by comparing its antimicrobial activity with that of a standard known concentration of antibiotic. The procedure for carrying out a biological assay is illustrated in FIGURE 21.20.

FIGURE 21.20
The microbiological assay of an antibiotic using the tube-dilution technique. Two series of tubes are prepared: a "standard" set using tubes of media containing known (measured) amounts of the antibiotic, and a test sample set using tubes of media containing unknown amounts of the same antibiotic. The tubes are inoculated with a test bacterium, incubated, and then observed for growth. By comparing the endpoints of growth of the known (tube 6) and the unknown (tube 5), the antibiotic content of the sample can be determined.

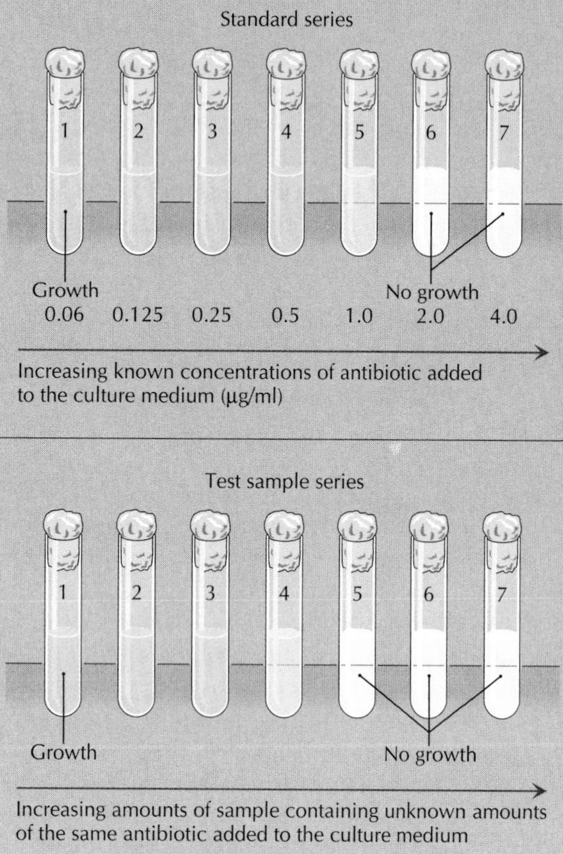

Standard series

Growth   No growth
0.06 0.125 0.25 0.5 1.0 2.0 4.0

Increasing known concentrations of antibiotic added to the culture medium (µg/ml)

Test sample series

Growth   No growth

Increasing amounts of sample containing unknown amounts of the same antibiotic added to the culture medium

ASK YOURSELF

What is the principle upon which the biological assay of antibiotics is based?

MICROBIAL SUSCEPTIBILITY TO CHEMOTHERAPEUTIC AGENTS

Microorganisms differ in their degree of susceptibility to chemotherapeutic agents. Furthermore, the susceptibil-

ity of a particular organism to a given agent may change with time. It is therefore important for the physician to know the identity of the microbe causing the infection, as well as its susceptibility to antibiotics, so that the specific chemotherapeutic agent that would give the most satisfactory results in treating the infection can be prescribed. To obtain this information, the clinical microbiology laboratory is called upon to identify the causative microorganism and to determine its susceptibility to various chemotherapeutic agents. From time to time during the course of therapy, the microbiology laboratory may be requested to determine whether any change has occurred in the susceptibility of the pathogen to the chemotherapeutic agent. The laboratory may use either of two techniques to provide this information—the *tube-dilution technique* or the *disk-plate technique.*

Tube-Dilution Technique

The tube-dilution method uses a series of tubes containing a sterile culture medium and various concentrations of each of a variety of antibiotics, very much as shown in FIGURE 21.20. All tubes are inoculated with the microorganism to be tested and then incubated. The microbiologist then examines the tubes to see which antibiotics have inhibited growth of the organism. For each antibiotic, the *lowest concentration that is able to completely prevent the growth of the microorganism* is determined; this is called the *minimum inhibitory concentration (MIC)* of the antibiotic. The antibiotics having the *lowest* MIC values would have the *highest* antimicrobial activity against the pathogen. This technique has been highly automated to provide convenience and rapid results when testing large numbers of specimens.

Disk-Plate Technique

In the disk-plate method, the microbiologist swabs an agar plate with the test organism and then places small paper disks impregnated with known amounts of several antibiotics upon the surface of the agar. After incubation, the plates are observed for clear zones around the disks [FIGURE 21.21]. A clear zone indicates that the antibiotic, which has diffused into the agar from the disk, has prevented the organism from growing. The absence of a clear zone means that the organism is resistant to the antibiotic.

The disk method for susceptibility testing currently recommended by the Food and Drug Administration is a highly standardized technique. The procedure specifies the amount of antimicrobial agent contained in each disk, as well as the culture medium, conditions of incubation, and other details. When the test is performed in

FIGURE 21.21

Steps in the disk-plate technique for the determination of the susceptibility of a bacterium to antibiotics. **[A]** A bacterial colony is "picked off" a Petri dish with a transfer needle and **[B]** the colony is dispersed in a few milliliters of sterile broth. **[C]** A sterile cotton swab is immersed in the broth suspension of bacteria and used to inoculate the surface of agar media in a Petri dish. **[D]** A mechanical device places small paper disks—each impregnated with a different antibiotic—on the surface of the inoculated plate (Petri dish). **[E]** After incubation, the Petri dish culture is examined for evidence of zones of inhibition around the antibiotic disks. When this test is performed under carefully controlled conditions, a relationship between the size of the zone of inhibition (clearing) and the susceptibility of the bacterium to the antibiotic which has produced the zone can be seen. In general, the larger the zone of inhibition, the more effective the antibiotic.

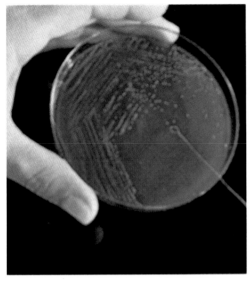

[A]

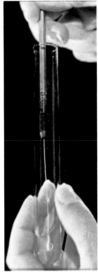

[B]

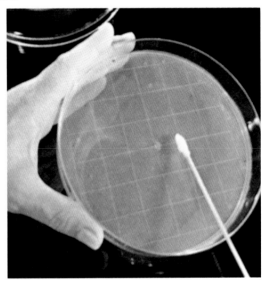

[C]

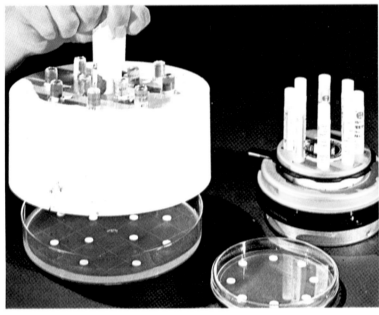

[D]

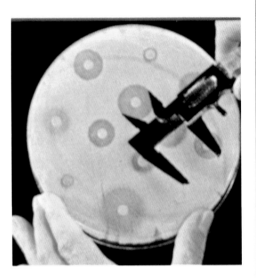

[E]

TABLE 21.3

Usual Susceptibility Patterns of Common Bacteria to Some Commonly Used Bacteriostatic and Bactericidal Antimicrobics

Antimicrobic	Bactericidal	Bacteriostatic	Staphylococcus aureus	Enterococci	Other streptococci	Neisseria	Haemophilus	Legionella	Mycoplasma	Escherichia coli	Proteus mirabilis	Other Proteus spp.	Klebsiella	Enterobacter	Serratia	Pseudomonas aeruginosa	Bacteroides fragilis	Other Gram-negative anaerobes	Clostridium	Rickettsia	Chlamydia	
Benzyl penicillin	+		◕[1]	⊘[C]	◑[1]	◑[1]	⊘	●	●	●	⊘	●	●	●	●	●	○[1]	○[1]	●	●	●	Narrow-spectrum agents
Penicillinase-resistant penicillins	+		○[1]	●	◑[2]	◑	●	●	●	●	●	●	●	●	●	●	●	●	●	●	●	
Erythromycin	±	+	◑[2]	◑[2]	◑[2]	◑	−	○[1]	○[1]	●	●	●	●	●	●	●	−	−	−	−	◑[2]	
Clindamycin	±	+	◑[2]	−	◑	●	●	−	−	●	●	●	●	●	●	●	○[1]	◑[1]	◑	−	−	
Vancomycin	+		○[2]	○[1]	○[2]	●	●	●	●	●	●	●	●	●	●	●	−	−	○[1]	−	−	
Ampicillin	+		◕[2]	◑[1]	◑[2]	◑[1]	◑[1]	●	●	◑	◑[1]	◑[1]	●	●	●	●	−	○[1]	●	●	●	
Piperacillin	+		−	○	○	−	○	●	●	−	◑[1]	◑[1]	◑[1]	◑[1]	◑[1]	◑[2]	◑[1]	−	−	●	●	Broad-spectrum agents
Cephalothin	+		◑[2]	●	◑[2]	−	●	●	●	◑	◑	●	◑[1]	●	●	●	◑	●	●	●	●	
Cefotetan	+		−	●	○[1]	○[1]	○	−	●	○[1]	○[1]	○[1]	○[1]	◑[2]	◑[1]	◑	−	●	●	●		
Cefoperazone	+		−	−	−	○	○	●	●	○[1]	○[1]	○[1]	○[1]	◑[2]	◑[2]	◑	−	●	●			
Imipenem	+		○[2]	○[2]	○[2]	○[1]	○[1]	−	●	○[1]	○[1]	○[1]	○[1]	○[1]	○[1]	○[1]	○[1]	−	−			
Aztreonam	+		●	●	●	○[1]	○[1]	−	●	◑[1]	◑[1]	◑[1]	○[1]	◑[1]	◑	●	●	●	−	−		
Gentamicin	+		◑	◕[C]	●	−	−	●	−	◑[1]	○[1]	○[1]	◑[1]	◑[1]	◑	●	●	●	−	−		
Amikacin	+		◑	◕[C]	●	−	−	●	−	◑[1]	○[1]	○[1]	○[1]	◑[1]	◑[1]	●	●	●	−	−		
Tetracycline		+	◑	●	◑	○	◑[2]	○[1]	○	◑	●	◑	◑	◑	●	◑	◑	◑	○[1]	○[1]		
Chloramphenicol		+	◑	◑	◑	◑	◑[2]	●	−	◑	◑	◑	◑	◑	●	◑[1]	○[2]	○	○[1]	−		
Ciprofloxacin	+		○	⊘	⊘	○[2]	−	−	●	○[1]	○[1]	○[1]	○[1]	○[1]	○[1]	◑[2]	●	●	−	−	⊘	
Sulfamethoxazole + trimethoprim	±	+	−	−	−	−	◑[1]	−	−	◑[1]	◑	◑	◑	◑	●	−	−	−	−	3	

Proportions of susceptible and resistant strains: ○ = 100% susceptible; ◕ = 25% resistant; ● = 100% resistant; ⊘ = intermediate susceptibility.

Abbreviations: −, no present indication for therapy or insufficient data; 1, antimicrobic of choice for susceptible strains; 2, second-line agent; 3, *C. trachomatis* sensitive, *C. psittaci* resistant; C, useful in combination of a β-lactam and an aminoglycoside.

These data reflect results in a single institution. Proportions of resistant strains may vary in different locations.

SOURCE: Reprinted by permission of the publisher from J. C. Sherris, ed., *Medical Microbiology: An Introduction to Infectious Diseases*, 2d ed., Chap. 13, p. 231. Copyright 1990 by Elsevier Science Publishing Co., Inc.

conformity with the FDA procedure, the clinical laboratory can determine whether the microorganism is resistant or susceptible to various antibiotics. The laboratory can also correlate the diameter of zones of inhibition with the MIC of the antibiotic for the particular microorganism.

In the routine testing of microorganisms to determine their susceptibility or resistance to antibiotics, various sets of antibiotics are recommended for use depending upon the identity of the suspected pathogen [TABLE 21.3].

ASK YOURSELF

1 Describe the tube-dilution and the disk-plate technique for determining microbial susceptibility to chemotherapeutic agents.

2 What is the significance of results of a microbial susceptibility test from the standpoint of treatment of patients?

NONMEDICAL USES OF ANTIBIOTICS

Antibiotics are used mainly for treatment of human and animal infections. However, there are some antibiotics that are effective against plant pathogens and are sometimes used for treatment of plant diseases, although the extent of this practice is limited by the cost of these antibiotics. Antibiotics have also been used for a number of *nonmedical* purposes, such as supplementation of animal feed, inhibition of bacteria in tissue cultures, and preparation of selective culture media.

Antibiotics as Animal Feed Supplements

Antibiotics are used as growth stimulants in poultry and livestock feeds. Commercially, the addition of tetracyclines or penicillin to swine or poultry feeds at the rate of 5 to 20 grams per ton of feed increases the rate of growth of young animals by at least 10 percent and sometimes much more.

The reason that low levels of antibiotics have a stimulatory effect on the growth of domestic animals is not well understood. One possible explanation is that the antibiotics may destroy pathogenic bacteria and other intestinal parasites that could cause mild forms of disease and retard growth and development. For example, it has been suggested that pigs respond dramatically to the addition of oxytetracycline to their diet because the antibiotic inhibits the growth of *Clostridium perfringens* in their intestines and thus prevents or reduces a chronic but low-grade toxic condition.

The practice of supplementing animal feed with antibiotics has raised the issue of potential widespread development of antibiotic-resistant bacteria [DISCOVER 21.2].

Antibiotics as Useful Additives to Microbiological Culture Media

Antibiotics are widely used to prevent bacteria from growing in tissue cultures and in embryonating chicken eggs which are used for the cultivation of viruses. They are also used to make culture media selective for certain pathogenic bacteria. For example, clinical microbiology laboratories often use a medium called *Thayer-Martin medium* as a selective medium for the isolation of the gonorrhea microbe, *Neisseria gonorrhoeae*, from clinical specimens. The medium contains the antibiotics vancomycin, colistin, and nystatin—which do not inhibit the growth of *N. gonorrhoeae* but do prevent the growth of many other bacteria and fungi that may be present in the specimen.

ASK YOURSELF

Describe several nonmedical uses of antibiotics.

21.2 ANTIBIOTICS IN ANIMAL FEEDS

Soon after antibiotics became widely used as chemotherapeutic agents it was discovered that low levels of penicillins or tetracyclines had a positive affect on animal growth. Subtherapeutic levels of these antibiotics added to animal feeds—200 g or less per ton of feed—promoted animal growth and improved the efficiency of feed conversion. This finding together with the rapid expansion of the production of animals for human food resulted in the widespread use of antibiotics in animal feeds. It is estimated that nearly one-half of the total annual production of antibiotics is used for farm animals.

The exposure of microorganisms to sublethal doses of antibiotics results in the development of strains that have increased resistance to these antibiotics. There is in fact a high prevalence of antimicrobial resistance among isolates of salmonellas from farm animals. The question of immediate concern becomes, What is the impact of this on human health? This question has been debated for several decades without a definitive answer.

In 1978 the Congress of the United States made an appropriation to the Food and Drug Administration designated for the National Academy of Sciences "to evaluate epidemiological approaches to the effects on human health of subtherapeutic use of antimicrobials in animal feeds."

A National Research Council Committee to Study the Human Health Effects of Subtherapeutic Antibiotic Use in Animal Feeds was appointed. Following an extensive investigation of available evidence, the committee concluded "that the postulated hazards to human health from the subtherapeutic use of antimicrobials in animal feeds were neither proven nor disproven."*

More recently (1987) the Institute of Medicine of the National Academy of Sciences was requested by the Food and Drug Administration to appoint a committee of experts to "investigate whether there are now sufficient data to resolve the public controversy surrounding the use of penicillin and tetracycline in animal feed." After an exhaustive study of available data, the committee was "unable to find a substantial body of *direct* evidence that established the existence of a definite human health hazard in the use of subtherapeutic concentrations of penicillin and tetracyclines in animal feeds."†

Thus a question which has been widely debated for several decades still remains unresolved, a question which the public at large might have anticipated would be easily answered by a simple yes or no. This is an example of the difficulties and complexities associated with the assessment of the impact of some broad applications of science and technology.

*The Effects on Human Health of Subtherapeutic Use of Antimicrobials in Animal Feeds, Committee to Study the Human Health Effects of Subtherapeutic Antibiotic Use in Animal Feeds, National Academy of Sciences, Washington, D.C., 1980.

†Human Health Risks with the Subtherapeutic Use of Penicillin or Tetracyclines in Animal Feed, Committee on Human Health Risk Assessment of Using Subtherapeutic Antibiotics in Animal Feeds, Institute of Medicine, National Academy Press, Washington, D.C., 1989.

SUMMARY

1 Chemotherapy was practiced for centuries before scientists understood how chemical agents worked against microorganisms.

2 Ehrlich was the first person to carry out a deliberate, systematic search for a laboratory-synthesized chemotherapeutic agent. His research resulted in the discovery of salvarsan. Nearly 30 years later, research by Domagk and also by Tréfouël and his colleagues resulted in the discovery of sulfonamides.

3 The discovery of penicillin by Fleming and the subsequent use of penicillin for treatment of war wounds introduced the modern era of antibiotics. A worldwide search for new antibiotics was initiated.

4 Not all antibiotics are suitable for therapeutic use. Chemotherapeutic agents must be able to kill or inhibit the infectious microorganism without harming the patient.

5 Chemotherapeutic antibiotics are produced by many species of bacteria in the genera *Streptomyces*, *Micromonospora*, *Nocardia*, *Micropolyspora*, and *Bacillus*. They are also produced by species of fungi in the genera *Penicillium*, *Aspergillus*, and *Cephalosporium*. New antibiotics continue to be discovered.

6 Antibiotics can be classified on the basis of their chemical structure—for example, as β-lactams, macrolides, aminoglycosides, tetracyclines, polyenes, or polypeptides.

7 Antibiotics act in one of three major ways: inhibition of cell-wall synthesis, damage to the cytoplasmic membrane, and interference with nucleic acid and protein synthesis.

8 Microorganisms can mutate to develop resistance against chemotherapeutic agents. This creates a serious problem in providing effective therapy to patients. In some instances, resistance is due to microbial enzymes that destroy antibiotics or inactivate them by altering their chemical structure. Transmissible antibiotic resistance is especially important because the genes for resistance are located on a plasmid that can be readily transferred from one bacterium to other, related bacteria through conjugation.

9 Several synthetic compounds are widely used for treatment of bacterial infections. Examples are sulfonamides, nitrofurans, isoniazid, and nalidixic acid.

10 Chemotherapy of viral infections is difficult because the virus replicates inside the host's cells. The chemotherapeutic compound must interfere with the multiplication of the virus and at the same time must not damage the host cell. Most antiviral compounds inhibit viral DNA or RNA synthesis; examples include vidarabine, acyclovir, and AZT.

11 Protozoa that cause infections characteristically have life cycles in which the parasite appears in different forms. Some of these forms may be more resistant to chemotherapeutic agents than others, and thus the chemotherapeutic agent must be administered at the proper time.

12 The potency or concentration of antibiotics and other chemotherapeutic agents can be assayed by either chemical or biological techniques. The susceptibility of bacteria to various antibiotics can be determined by either the tube-dilution technique or the disk-plate technique.

13 Nonmedical applications of antibiotics include their use as an animal feed supplement and as an ingredient of tissue-culture media and selective culture media.

KEY TERMS

para-aminobenzoic acid (PABA)
antibiotics
broad-spectrum antibiotics
chemotherapeutic agents
chemotherapy
disk-plate technique
β-lactamases
β-lactam ring
minimum inhibitory concentration (MIC)
natural penicillins
penicillin
penicillinases
Prontosil
salvarsan
semisynthetic penicillins
structural analogs
sulfonamides
synthetic chemotherapeutic agent
tetrahydrofolic acid (THFA)
tube-dilution technique

THE DAWN OF CHEMOTHERAPY

1 Which of the following persons synthesized an arsenic-containing compound that was useful in the treatment of syphilis? **(a)** Waksman; **(b)** Tréfouël; **(c)** Fleming; **(d)** Domagk; **(e)** Ehrlich.

2 Which of the following persons discovered that it was the sulfanilamide portion of the dye Prontosil that contained antimicrobial activity? **(a)** Waksman; **(b)** Tréfouël; **(c)** Fleming; **(d)** Domagk; **(e)** Ehrlich.

3 The modern era of antibiotic chemotherapy emerged following the discovery of

_____.

4 Fleming observed a zone of inhibition of *Staphylococcus aureus* around a contaminant colony of a(n) _____.

5 Antibiotics differ from substances such as salvarsan and sulfonamides in that they are produced by _____.

IDEAL QUALITIES OF A CHEMOTHERAPEUTIC AGENT

6 An antibiotic that inhibits many different kinds of bacteria is called a(n) _____ antibiotic.

7 Which one of the following characteristics is *undesirable* for an antibiotic being considered for use as a chemotherapeutic agent? **(a)** produces little change in the intestinal flora; **(b)** penetrates tissue; **(c)** is highly microbicidal; **(d)** produces few or no side effects; **(e)** becomes inactivated by stomach acids.

8 Which *two* of the following characteristics are *desirable* for an antibiotic being considered for use as a chemotherapeutic agent? **(a)** inhibits the host's normal microbial flora; **(b)** is readily soluble in body fluids; **(c)** has a narrow range of antimicrobial activity; **(d)** promotes development of resistant forms; **(e)** can be absorbed into the body from the intestinal tract.

ISOLATION OF ANTIBIOTIC-PRODUCING MICROORGANISMS FROM NATURE

9 Antibiotic-producing microorganisms have been isolated from which of the following? **(a)** soil; **(b)** air; **(c)** fresh or spoiled vegetables; **(d)** water; **(e)** all of the above.

10 In a screening procedure for new antibiotics, the first test is designed to detect _____ activity against a variety of microorganisms.

11 Before a new antibiotic can be used as a chemotherapeutic agent, it is important to determine that it is not _____ for animals and humans.

12 Of the genera of bacteria found to make antibiotics, the genus _____ has produced the largest number of useful antibiotics.

13 Which *three* of the following genera of antibiotic producers are *not* bacteria? **(a)** *Cephalosporium*; **(b)** *Aspergillus*; **(c)** *Micromonospora*; **(d)** *Nocardia*; **(e)** *Penicillium*.

14 Cyanobacterin is produced by: **(a)** *Bacillus polymyxa*; **(b)** a fungus; **(c)** an aquatic phototrophic bacterium; **(d)** *Bacillus pyocyaneus*; **(e)** an alga.

KINDS OF ANTIBIOTICS BASED UPON THEIR CHEMICAL STRUCTURE

15 The β-lactam ring is composed of how many atoms? **(a)** 3; **(b)** 4; **(c)** 5; **(d)** 6; **(e)** 8.

16 All penicillins contain a core structure called _____ acid.

17 Chemists are able to add various chemical side chains to the core compound of penicillins. This results in the creation of compounds called

_____ penicillins.

18 Penicillinases, also called _____, are enzymes that break down natural penicillins. The semisynthetic penicillin called

_____ has the advantage of being resistant to attack by these enzymes.

19 The cephalosporins belong to which of the following classes of antibiotics? **(a)** macrolides; **(b)** polyenes; **(c)** aminoglycosides; **(d)** β-lactams; **(e)** polypeptides.

20 Streptomycin and neomycin belong to the class of antibiotics called

_____ .

21 Match each antibiotic in the left-hand column with its correct class on the right.

_____ erythromycin

_____ doxycycline   **(a)** Polypeptides

_____ bacitracin   **(b)** Polyenes

_____ nystatin   **(c)** Macrolides

_____ amphotericin B   **(d)** Aminoglycosides

_____ neomycin   **(e)** Tetracyclines

Which two antibiotics in the above left-hand column are active against fungi?

_____ and _____ .

22 Which of the following antibiotics may cause aplastic anemia? **(a)** penicillin G; **(b)** chloramphenicol; **(c)** erythromycin; **(d)** oxytetracycline; **(e)** cephalothin.

MODE OF ACTION OF ANTIBIOTICS

23 Penicillins and cephalosporins are similar in their inhibitory action on bacterial cells; they both inhibit _____ synthesis.

24 Mycoplasmas are not inhibited by penicillins, because they: **(a)** produce penicillinase; **(b)** are Gram-positive; **(c)** are Gram-negative; **(d)** do not have cell walls; **(e)** are eucaryotes, not procaryotes.

25 Which one of the following antibiotics acts upon sterol-containing membranes? **(a)** Cephalothin; **(b)** amphotericin B; **(c)** streptomycin; **(d)** chloramphenicol; **(e)** oxytetracycline

26 Match the antibiotic on the left with its mode of action described on the right.

_____ streptomycin   **(a)** Combines with 50-S subunit of bacterial ribosome

_____ erythromycin   **(b)** Damages sterol-containing membranes

_____ nystatin   **(c)** Damages the cytoplasmic membrane of bacteria

_____ cephalothin   **(d)** Inhibits peptidoglycan synthesis

_____ polymyxin B   **(e)** Combines with 30-S subunit of bacterial ribosome

_____ rifamycin   **(f)** Inhibits bacterial DNA-dependent RNA polymerase

DEVELOPMENT OF ANTIBIOTIC-RESISTANT BACTERIA

27 Which of the following antibiotics express their antimicrobial action by interference with DNA/RNA synthesis? **(a)** penicillin; **(b)** tetracycline; **(e)** nystatin; **(d)** amphotericin-B; **(e)** cephalosporins.

586

28 Transmissible antibiotic resistance is due to: **(a)** special endospores; **(b)** transmissible mesosomes; **(c)** conjugative R plasmids; **(d)** resistance genes located on the bacterial chromosome; **(e)** mutation.

29 The transfer of antibiotic-resistance genes among bacteria was originally discovered in cells of *Shigella dysenteriae* which had acquired the genes from antibiotic-resistant cells of _____.

30 The development of antibiotic resistance can be minimized by: **(a)** avoiding indiscriminate use of antibiotics; **(b)** using a combination of antibiotics; **(c)** using sufficiently high dosages of antibiotics to overcome an infection quickly; **(d)** switching to another antibiotic as soon as an organism shows signs of developing resistance; **(e)** all of the above.

SYNTHETIC CHEMOTHERAPEUTIC AGENTS

31 Sulfonamides act by inhibiting the synthesis of the coenzyme _____ acid.

32 Sulfonamides owe their antimicrobial activity to the fact that they are similar in chemical structure to the compound _____.

33 Human and animal tissue cells are not inhibited by sulfonamides because they do not use PABA to make tetrahydrofolic acid; instead, they make it directly from _____ acid.

34 In 1944, Dodd and Stillman discovered that antimicrobial properties could be conferred upon furfural-like compounds by adding a(n) _____ group to the furan ring.

35 Isoniazid is a structural analog of _____ or _____.

36 Isoniazid is used mainly to treat patients who have the disease _____.

37 Nalidixic acid prevents bacterial DNA synthesis by inhibiting an enzyme called _____.

38 Antiviral chemotherapeutic agents are usually designed to block _____ or _____ synthesis.

39 AZT is a structural analog of _____ and is used to block viral DNA synthesis in patients who have _____.

40 Amantadine is used to treat patients with _____, whereas acyclovir is used to treat patients with _____.

41 Which two of the following are antiprotozoan chemotherapeutic agents? **(a)** chloroquine; **(b)** metronidazole; **(c)** gentamicin; **(d)** vancomycin; **(e)** ampicillin.

ASSAY OF ANTIBIOTICS

42 Chemical assays of antibiotics have the disadvantage of being

_____ sensitive than biological assays; moreover, they may

not be able to distinguish between _____ and

_____ forms of an antibiotic.

43 In a biological assay of the potency of an antibiotic preparation, the antimicrobial activity of the preparation is compared with that of a(n)

_____ preparation of the antibiotic.

MICROBIAL SUSCEPTIBILITY TO CHEMOTHERAPEUTIC AGENTS

44 In the tube-dilution technique, the smallest concentration of an antibiotic that completely inhibits growth of the test microorganism is called the

_____ .

45 If antibiotic A has an MIC of 2 μg/ml against a strain of *Salmonella typhi* and antibiotic B has an MIC of 50 μg/ml, which antibiotic would have the higher degree of activity against the bacterium? _____

46 When the disk-plate method is used in accordance with the FDA procedure, the diameter of the zone of inhibition around the antibiotic-impregnated disk can be correlated with the _____ of the antibiotic.

47 In both the tube-dilution technique and the disk-plate method, which one of the following *cannot* be determined? **(a)** the antibiotics that have high antimicrobial activity against the bacterium; **(b)** the antibiotics that have low antimicrobial activity against the bacterium; **(c)** the antibiotics that have no antimicrobial activity against the bacterium; **(d)** the antibiotics that will cause allergic reactions or other toxic side effects in the patient; **(e)** the susceptibility or resistance of the bacterium to various antibiotics.

NONMEDICAL USES OF ANTIBIOTICS

48 Low levels of antibiotics are added to poultry and livestock feeds for what purpose?

_____

49 A major concern about supplementing poultry and other animal feeds with antibiotics is that it could lead to development of _____ strains of microorganisms.

50 Bacterium X is susceptible to vancomycin, ampicillin, and nalidixic acid but is resistant to streptomycin, erythromycin, and nystatin. Which would you incorporate into a medium to help make the medium selective for the isolation of bacterium X from a clinical specimen?

1 Define the following terms: antibiotics, chemotherapy, and chemotherapeutic agents.

2 What contributions did each of the following persons make to chemotherapy: Ehrlich, Domagk, and Fleming?

3 What are the characteristics of an ideal chemotherapeutic agent?

4 Is every newly discovered antibiotic useful as a chemotherapeutic agent? Explain.

5 Describe the mode of action of a specific chemotherapeutic agent from each major chemical class of these compounds.

6 Explain how bacteria may develop resistance to an antimicrobial agent.

7 Outline a procedure by which you might isolate a new antibiotic from some natural environment such as soil. What laboratory evidence would you need to make a case that it is new and better than known antibiotics?

8 Describe a microbiological technique by which you could assay for the amount of an antibiotic in some specimen.

9 Assume that you are working in a clinical microbiology laboratory. The laboratory receives a sample of urine from a patient with a urinary tract infection. The urine contains large numbers of *Escherichia coli,* the microorganism often responsible for urinary tract infections. How would you determine which chemotherapeutic agents are most effective against this *E. coli* strain?

10 What are the objections to the use of low levels of antibiotic as a food preservative?

1 Prior to the sixth edition of *Bergey's Manual of Determinative Bacteriology* (1947), relatively few species of *Streptomyces* were recognized. Since then, hundreds of species have been included in subsequent editions of the manual. How can you explain this?

2 In terms of basic differences between procaryotic and eucaryotic cells, explain how a chemotherapeutic agent might be selectively toxic to a bacterial cell.

3 There are relatively few antiviral chemotherapeutic agents compared with antibacterial chemotherapeutic agents. What might account for this?

4 What is the purpose or goal of developing synthetic or semisynthetic antibiotics?

5 Why is it important to know the life cycle of a pathogenic protozoan agent before prescribing chemotherapy?

6 How might the development of antibiotic resistance among bacterial species be minimized?

7 Why might a chemotherapeutic agent for treatment of a protozoan disease have more potential undesirable side effects on the patient than a chemotherapeutic agent used to treat a bacterial infection?

8 What are the desirable features and the potential undesirable consequences of using low doses of antibiotics as an animal feed supplement?

IX

Microorganisms and Disease: Microbial Diseases

22

Nosocomial Infections

OBJECTIVES

After reading this chapter you should be able to

1 Define the term *nosocomial infection* and explain the importance of such infections.

2 Relate the contributions of Holmes, Semmelweis, Nightingale, Pasteur, and Lister to modern hospital practices.

3 Describe conditions under which both exogenous and endogenous infections might develop.

4 Explain the importance of surveillance and epidemiology as related to nosocomial infections.

5 Discuss possible sources of the microorganisms that cause nosocomial infections.

6 Identify the factors that contribute to the susceptibility of a hospitalized patient to infection.

7 List the microorganisms most often encountered in nosocomial infections.

8 Enumerate the practices and procedures used to break the cycle of infection.

9 Outline the components and activities of an effective control program.

10 Describe the responsibilities of the microbiology laboratory in an effective surveillance and control program.

OVERVIEW

Nosocomial infections are infections acquired in the hospital. The term *nosocomial* comes from the Greek words *nosos,* meaning disease, and *komeion,* meaning "hospital." Unfortunately, hospital-acquired infections occur at a high rate throughout the world. Many microorganisms that are relatively infrequent causes of disease in healthy individuals can become frequent causes of disease in hospital patients, whose normal immune defense mechanisms against infection have been weakened by such things as chemotherapy or major illness. These pathogens can come from a variety of sources in the hospital environment, including the air in a patient's room or an infected health care worker. However, most are opportunistic pathogens from the patient's own normal flora.

For a nosocomial infection to occur, there must be a source of infection, transmission of the causative agent, and a patient susceptible to that infection. This so-called cycle of infection must be broken to prevent hospital-acquired infections. Because of the frequency of nosocomial infections, all accredited hospitals are required to have an infection-control program. Infection control has many aspects, including surveillance for disease among patients and health care personnel and determination of the number and kinds of viable microorganisms in the hospital environment. To this end, hospital infection-control officers, infection-control committees, and laboratory staff work together to solve cases of nosocomial infection and prevent new cases. Successful infection control requires the education and cooperation of all hospital personnel.

HISTORICAL HIGHLIGHTS

Nosocomial infections have been a problem since hospitals were first established. To prevent the spread of disease during the eighteenth century, patients were isolated in fever hospitals, smallpox hospitals, tuberculosis sanitoriums, and "pest houses." These large, dingy hospitals were horrid, overcrowded places, with several patients occupying the same straw mat. Vermin and filth were everywhere, and infection spread rapidly from patient to patient. As F. H. Garrison described in his 1917 *History of Medicine*, conditions were such in 1788 at the Hôtel Dieu hospital in Paris that "septic fevers and other contagia were the rule, the average mortality rate about 20 percent and recovery from surgical operations a rarity." Notably, puerperal fever (childbed fever), the scourge of "lying-in" (maternity) hospitals, was a frequent and often fatal complication of childbirth.

By the mid-1800s, however, several health professionals had begun new infection-control measures that led to a dramatic drop in puerperal fever and other hospital-acquired infections. Oliver Wendell Holmes, Ignaz Philipp Semmelweis, Florence Nightingale, Louis Pasteur, and Joseph Lister were leaders in fighting these infections during the last half of the nineteenth century.

A poet, lawyer, and public figure, Oliver Wendell Holmes also studied medicine at Harvard and eventually became dean of Harvard Medical School. In 1843 he wrote a landmark paper, "The Contagiousness of Puerperal Fever," in which he stated that not only was puerperal fever contagious, but it was "frequently carried from patient to patient by physicians and nurses." Holmes suggested the following practical methods to help curb the spread of puerperal fever: (1) a physician involved in midwifery should not take any active part in postmortem examinations in cases of puerperal fever; (2) if a physician is present at such autopsies, he should wash thoroughly, change every article of clothing, and allow 24 hours or more to elapse before attending any birth or examining a patient; and (3) if a physician notices two cases of the fever in his own practice within a short period of time, he should stop practicing for at least a month. Holmes concluded his paper with the statement that "having puerperal fever cases in one's practice was not a misfortune but a crime."

While Holmes was trying to persuade his colleagues to use aseptic practices, Ignaz Philipp Semmelweis in Vienna was also studying puerperal fever [FIGURE 22.1A]. Like Holmes, Semmelweis had studied law before medicine. In 1846 he became an assistant at an obstetric clinic, where he observed that the ward on which medical students were trained had a much higher death rate than the ward on which nurses and midwives were trained. He also noted that the death rate declined when medical students were absent during the summer. Semmelweis often detected the odor of the autopsy room in the medical student's ward, and concluded that the medical students were inadvertently transferring materials from the autopsy room into the ward. Against strong opposition from other physicians, Semmelweis insisted that medical students must disinfect their hands and arms in a chlorine solution before entering the maternity ward—a procedure that reduced the death rate dramatically [FIGURE 22.1B]. Unfortunately, his methods still had not been accepted by other physicians when he died in 1865.

Rather than focusing only on aseptic technique, Florence Nightingale tackled the entire hospital and restructured the nursing profession in order to improve patient care and reduce nosocomial disease. Born to wealthy, socially prominent English parents, Nightingale was better educated than most men of her time. She learned several languages and was well versed in literature and mathematics. Her dream was to become a nurse, but her parents objected because of the appalling conditions in hospitals. During the 16 years it took Nightingale to overcome family opposition, she studied and analyzed nursing practices in several countries.

When the Crimean War began in the 1850s, she was about to assume the superintendent's position at Kings College Hospital. However, newspaper accounts of the high death rates in military hospitals and the inadequate care of wounded soldiers intervened to change the course of her life. An outraged public demanded action, and the secretary of war decided to send female nurses to military hospitals for the first time in English history. He asked Nightingale to lead the contingent as superintendent of the Female Nursing Establishment of the English General Hospitals in Turkey, and to bring order out of medical chaos.

Arriving at the end of 1854, the nurses found outrageous conditions in the Crimean hospitals, where patients were packed together in rooms lit by candles [FIGURE 22.2A]. There was no soap, water, linen, or decent food. An open sewer under one hospital building contained dead animals and was infested with rats. There were few medical supplies, and the death rate was over 50 percent! Many died of cholera and other infectious diseases, not from battlefield injuries. According to one account, during a 6-month period 73 percent of the soldiers in eight British regiments died from disease.

Fighting strong resistance from the military authorities who resented her gender and her autonomous authority, Nightingale nonetheless persevered. She established diet kitchens, a laundry, reading rooms, coffeehouses, recreation rooms—all under sanitary conditions [FIGURE 22.2B]. Despite all her administrative duties, she also assisted surgeons and made rounds to

FIGURE 22.1

[A] The Hungarian physician Ignaz Philipp Semmelweis (1818–1865) insisted that physicians and medical students wash their hands in a chlorinated solution before entering the obstetric ward and again before examining each patient. **[B]** Effect of hygienic hand disinfection as introduced by Semmelweis in May 1847 on maternal mortality at the K.K.I. Obstetric University Clinic in Vienna. Before introduction of disinfection procedure (red), after introduction (blue). *(From M. I. Rotter, "Hygienic Hand Disinfection," Infection Control 5:18-22, 1984.)*

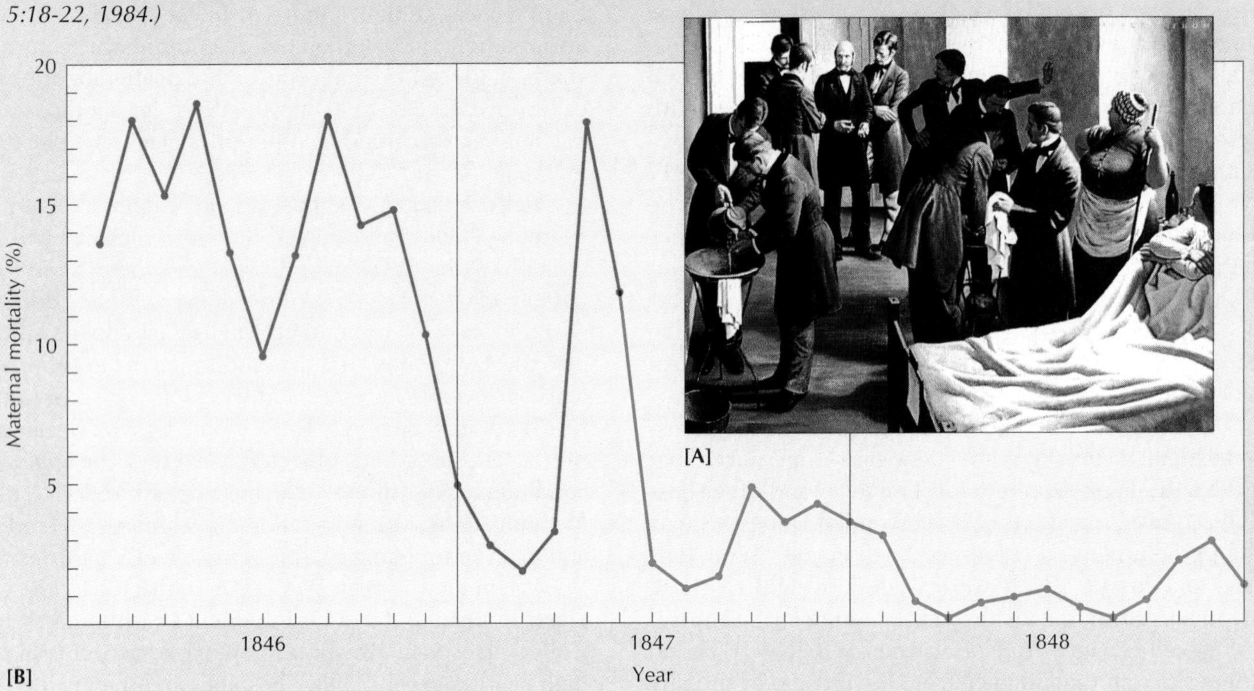

[A]

[B]

FIGURE 22.2

[A] Conditions in the military hospital on Florence Nightingale's arrival in Crimea. **[B]** Florence Nightingale instituted sanitary practices in military hospitals in 1854.

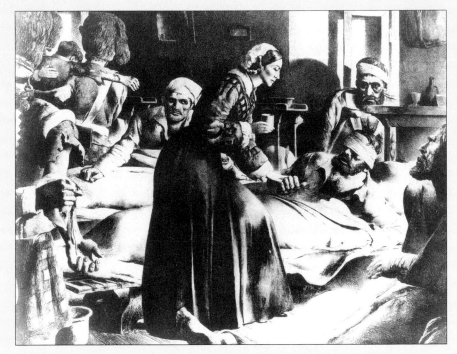

[A]

help the sickest patients. (Henry Wadsworth Longfellow immortalized her late-night visits with his 1857 poem "Lady with a Lamp.") Despite disappointments and frustrations, her success was documented by a drop in mortality to 2.2 percent within 6 months of her arrival!

After the war, Nightingale fought for improvement of medical care in military and civilian hospitals. Her methods were slow to be adopted but they eventually revolutionized hospital care. In addition to her patient-care reforms, she did extensive statistical analyses of mortality and sickness among military personnel, proving that sanitation was essential to health. She also established a school of nursing in London, and the old system of nursing by uneducated women or inmates was replaced by care from educated career women.

In retrospect, it is apparent that Nightingale, Semmelweis, and Holmes succeeded by reducing the transmission of pathogenic microorganisms within hospitals. Yet in their time the reasons for their success were not completely understood. Within a few years, however, Louis Pasteur and Joseph Lister had tied together the germ theory of disease and aseptic technique, as described earlier in this book. Pasteur's demonstrations between 1857 and 1876 left no doubt that the "infinitely small" play an "infinitely great role" in disease. In his germ theory of fermentation and of disease, Pasteur emphasized that microorganisms could be transmitted through the air. It was Lister, then a young surgeon in Glasgow, who realized the significance of Pasteur's studies and was convinced that microorganisms in the air

contaminated surgical wounds. His subsequent disinfection of operating rooms greatly reduced mortality among surgical patients.

The great reduction in deaths from infection, based on sanitation and antiseptic practices, was accelerated in 1935 with the introduction of sulfonamides, which were used to cure serious streptococcal and staphylococcal infections. Even more dramatic was the introduction of penicillin during World War II, followed by the discovery and use of other antibiotics. Unfortunately, this led to an attitude that nosocomial infections could be controlled by giving antibiotics to prevent these infections. Although the use of antibiotics did result in a rapid decline in the number of deaths due to hospital-acquired infections, there was no corresponding decline in the number of *cases* of hospital-acquired infection.

Reliance on antibiotics in combating infection has often resulted in relaxed aseptic technique and isolation precautions. The situation is made more serious by the increasing numbers of antibiotic-resistant strains of bacteria which have developed. For example, methicillin-resistant *S. aureus* (MRSA) was first detected in 1975 at the Royal Brisbane Hospital in Australia. The number of new patients infected increased from 1 in 1975 to 720 in 1987. Additionally, although resistant strains of *Enterobacter cloacae*, *Acinetobacter calcoaceticus*, and *Serratia marcescens* have not increased in number, they have caused major outbreaks in some hospitals. Widespread use and misuse of antibiotics in hospitals help to select for such strains. In the 1950s large, frequent out-

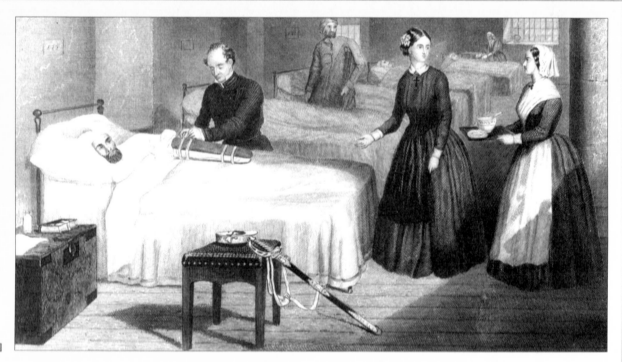

[B]

TABLE 22.1
Some Major Trends in the Occurrence of Nosocomial Infections (1980–1990)

Infection	Risk factor	Causative agent(s)	Occurrence
Pneumonia	Age; severity of underlying disease; surgery; ventilators; gastric infection	May be viruses, fungi, or bacteria Most common bacteria: antibiotic-resistant Gram-negative bacilli and *S. aureus*	0.5–1.0% admission
Bloodstream	Infusion therapy; central venous catheters	Coagulase-negative staphylococci, enterococci, and *Candida* *E. coli* and *S. aureus* BSI*	Increased 2- to 3-fold during 1980s Decreased
Surgical wound contamination	Illness; prosthetic vascular devices; type of surgery—colon, gastric, coronary, spinal fusion, and other	Staphylococci, endogenous aerobes and anaerobes, *Enterobacter* spp.	About 40% of all cases reported
Urinary tract	Prolonged use of catheter; female gender; absence of systemic antibiotics	*Proteus* and *Morganella* spp.	Most common (40% in surgical patients); three-fold increase in mortality
Fungal	Other diseases, e.g., BSI, SWI*, UTI*	*C. albicans,* spp. (79%) *Torulopsis* spp. (8%) *Aspergillus* spp. (1.3%)	Increased from 1.0 per 1000 to 2.9 per 1000 discharges
Viral	Transfusions; immunodeficiency; pregnancy; AIDS		Continues to increase

*BSI, bloodstream infection; SWI, surgical wound infection; UTI, urinary tract infection.
SOURCE: From the Third International Conference on Nosocomial Infections, Atlanta, Ga., July 31, 1990.

breaks of staphylococcal infections in the pediatric and surgical units of hospitals focused national attention on this problem.

In reviewing the history of hospital infection control, we should recall the comments of two great hospital reformers of the nineteenth century. Florence Nightingale said that "the very first requirement in a Hospital [is] that it should do the sick no harm." Sir James Y. Simpson stated that "in the treatment of the sick, there is ever danger in their aggregation, and safety only in their segregation." For these innovators and their professional successors, infection control became a cornerstone of hospital care. Unfortunately, hospital-acquired infections still cause problems, more than 100 years after Pasteur proved that microorganisms spread disease. An estimated 1 in 20 patients still develop nosocomial infections, and the incidence may be higher. Between 1979 and 1989, for example, the number of patients with *S. aureus* bacteremia (blood infection) increased from 40 to 138 per year; from 1980 to mid-1990 *C. albicans* infections increased from 1.0 to 2.9 per 1000 patient discharges.

In recent years nosocomial infections caused by fungi and viruses have increased in number, while patients with HIV infection and AIDS have become a major challenge to infection control. These and other newly described infectious diseases reinforce the need for infection-control practices to be flexible and ever-vigilant.

TABLE 22.1 lists the common classes of nosocomial infections and describes trends in their occurrence.

ASK YOURSELF

1 What is a nosocomial infection?

2 What was Semmelweis' concept of the manner in which hospital patients became infected, and what procedures did he institute to prevent spread of infections?

3 Who was Florence Nightingale, and what were her contributions to the control of infections?

4 What was the effect on general sanitation and antiseptic practices following the introduction and widespread use of chemotherapeutic agents such as sulfa drugs and antibiotics?

IMPORTANCE OF NOSOCOMIAL INFECTIONS

A leading cause of death in some countries, nosocomial infections pose a significant and costly health problem in hospitals throughout the world. The rate of hospital-acquired infections in the United States is approximately 50 infections per 1000 patients in acute-care institutions. Federal estimates indicate that 2 million patients will develop nosocomial infections annually. These patients average an extra week in the hospital plus loss of work time, adding significantly to the cost and pain of illness. Approximately 1 percent of all nosocomial infections in the United States directly cause death, and 3 percent contribute to death.

Because of the seriousness of nosocomial infections, the American Hospital Association (AHA) and the Centers for Disease Control (CDC) recommend that each hospital develop an infection-control plan. The Joint Commission on Accreditation of Hospitals also requires all accredited hospitals to have an infection-control program. Most infection-control programs include an infection-control committee, a clinical laboratory, an infection-control officer, a clearly understood isolation policy, and an ongoing staff education program.

One of the important activities of a control program is *surveillance*, the systematic observation and recording of cases of transmissible disease. To accomplish this, the National Nosocomial Infection Surveillance System (NNIS) was established in 1970 by the CDC to provide a national data base for nosocomial infections and to improve surveillance methods in acute-care hospitals. Participating hospitals send monthly reports of collected data to the CDC. By 1985, many hospitals began using the Interactive Data Entry and Analysis System (IDEAS) software to collate data. The CDC is shifting emphasis away from generalized nationwide statistics on infection rates to stress specific statistics, such as the operative procedure, site of infection, and most frequent pathogens in surgical wound infections [TABLE 22.2].

ASK YOURSELF

1 What are the essential features of an infection-control plan?

2 What is surveillance, and how is it accomplished?

TABLE 22.2

Microorganisms Responsible for Nosocomial Surgical Wound Infections (NSWI) in the United States (1986–1990)*

Operative procedure	Site of infection	Most frequent pathogen(s)
Vascular, cesarean section, abdominal hysterectomy, amputation, joint prosthesis, spinal fusion, and chest surgery (except cardiac)	Incisional	*S. aureus*, coagulase-negative staphylococci or *Enterococcus* spp.
Colon, gallbladder, gastric, small bowel, and abdominal	Incisional	Pathogens varied with Gram-negatives, especially *Enterobacter* spp. being more common
	Deep intraabdominal	*Enterococcus* spp., *E. coli*
Cesarean section, abdominal hysterectomy (removal of uterus)	Lining of uterus; vaginal cuff	*Enterococcus* spp., group B streptococci, *E. coli*
Coronary artery bypass graft and cardiac operation	Deep surgical wound	*S. aureus*, coagulase-negative staphylococci
Amputations, reduction of fracture, joint prosthesis (implant), spinal fusion, other back operations, vascular cardiac surgery	Deep surgical wound	*S. aureus*, *E. coli*
Deep surgical wound infection, chest operations, all other deep sites	Bloodstream	*S. aureus* and others

*These data relating the microorganism to the site of infection may help in recognition of emerging pathogens and in directing the way to developing preventive measures. Nosocomial infections in surgical patients account for about 40% of all infections reported to NNIS, of which 35% are surgical wound infections (SWI). To review the pathogens in SWI, 21,877 SWIs from 113 hospitals in NNIS were analyzed. Incisional infections accounted for more than 60% of all SWIs.

SOURCE: From the Third International Conference on Nosocomial Infections, Atlanta, Ga., July 31, 1990.

EPIDEMIOLOGY OF NOSOCOMIAL INFECTIONS

Epidemiology is the study of the factors that influence the occurrence and distribution of disease. The three factors necessary for an infection to occur are:

1 A source of microorganisms that can cause infection
2 A route of transmission of the microorganisms
3 A host susceptible to infection by the microorganisms

Sources of Microorganisms That Cause Nosocomial Infections

Reservoirs of infection can be either living organisms (usually humans, other animals, or insects) that harbor pathogens, or inanimate objects and substances that are contaminated with infectious microorganisms (called *fomites*). Infections may be classified in either of two general categories, depending on the source of infection:

1 *Exogenous infections.* These are caused by microbes from an external source, such as the environment, other persons, or fomites.
2 *Endogenous infections.* These are caused by microorganisms that are part of a person's own normal flora.

Exogenous Nosocomial Infections. Because of its special purpose, a hospital brings together patients, health care personnel, and visitors. Some of these individuals may carry infectious microorganisms; they may have active clinical infections or they may be healthy carriers who merely harbor infectious microorganisms. Hospital patients can acquire exogenous infections from such individuals.

Microorganisms that cause exogenous nosocomial infections also may come from the hospital environment. Some potential sources that have been implicated in nosocomial infections are air conditioners, floors, bedside water decanters, hand creams, body lotions, flowers in the patient's room, shaving brushes, utensils, dish mops, sponges, sinks, and water taps. Nosocomial infections have also been traced to contaminated medical equipment and fluids [FIGURE 22.3], including urinary catheters, oral thermometers, intravenous solutions, respiratory equipment, whirlpools, humidifiers, suction apparatus, and transducers (part of an electronic device used to monitor arterial blood pressure) [DISCOVER 22.1].

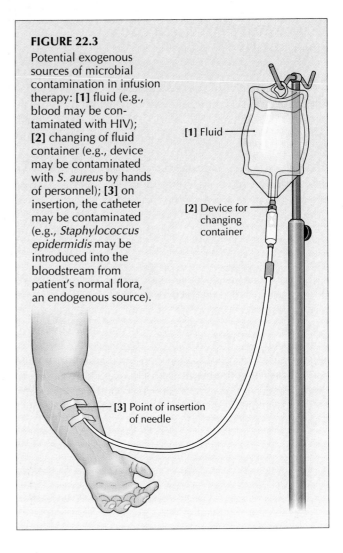

FIGURE 22.3
Potential exogenous sources of microbial contamination in infusion therapy: **[1]** fluid (e.g., blood may be contaminated with HIV); **[2]** changing of fluid container (e.g., device may be contaminated with *S. aureus* by hands of personnel); **[3]** on insertion, the catheter may be contaminated (e.g., *Staphylococcus epidermidis* may be introduced into the bloodstream from patient's normal flora, an endogenous source).

[1] Fluid
[2] Device for changing container
[3] Point of insertion of needle

Endogenous Nosocomial Infections. Although some nosocomial infections are exogenous, most are endogenous. Today's nosocomial infections are most commonly caused by bacteria found on the skin and mucous membranes (such as *Staphylococcus aureus*), the intestinal tract (such as *Escherichia coli* or *Streptococcus faecalis*), and other areas of the healthy human host [DISCOVER 22.2]. Many of these organisms are *opportunistic pathogens*—microbes that primarily infect hosts with weakened defense mechanisms. If a patient's normal defenses have been compromised, opportunistic pathogens may be able to multiply and cause an infection. The two greatest sources of opportunistic pathogens in hospitals are (1) the hands of health care personnel and (2) the skin, mucous membranes, saliva, feces, and urine of the patient.

FIGURE 22.4 summarizes the various sources of nosocomial infections.

FIGURE 22.4
Summary of sources of nosocomial infections.

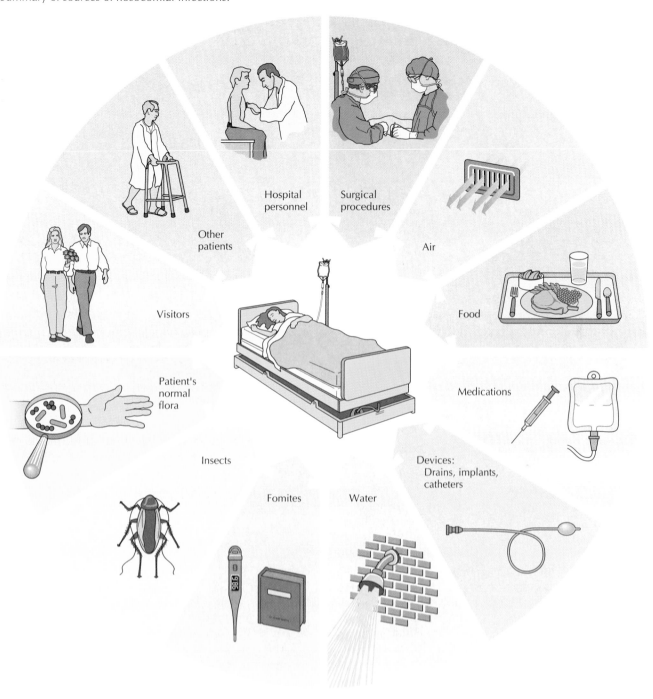

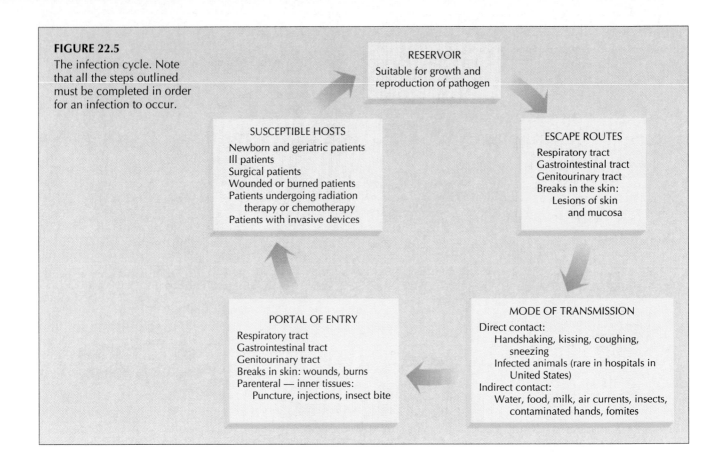

FIGURE 22.5
The infection cycle. Note that all the steps outlined must be completed in order for an infection to occur.

RESERVOIR
Suitable for growth and reproduction of pathogen

ESCAPE ROUTES
Respiratory tract
Gastrointestinal tract
Genitourinary tract
Breaks in the skin:
　Lesions of skin
　　and mucosa

MODE OF TRANSMISSION
Direct contact:
　Handshaking, kissing, coughing,
　　sneezing
　Infected animals (rare in hospitals in
　　United States)
Indirect contact:
　Water, food, milk, air currents, insects,
　　contaminated hands, fomites

PORTAL OF ENTRY
Respiratory tract
Gastrointestinal tract
Genitourinary tract
Breaks in skin: wounds, burns
Parenteral — inner tissues:
　Puncture, injections, insect bite

SUSCEPTIBLE HOSTS
Newborn and geriatric patients
Ill patients
Surgical patients
Wounded or burned patients
Patients undergoing radiation
　therapy or chemotherapy
Patients with invasive devices

Transmission of Infectious Microorganisms

The transmission of infectious microorganisms from one host to another and the subsequent infection of the new host may occur in a number of ways and is known as the *infection cycle* [FIGURE 22.5]. During the course of this cycle, pathogens may exit their reservoir in many ways.

Pathogenic microorganisms may escape into the air in droplets expelled from the nose and mouth during sneezing, coughing, or even talking. These droplets not only contaminate the air inhaled by other persons but may settle on inanimate objects, which then serve as fomites. Pathogens may also exit a host via the gastrointestinal tract and genitourinary tract, or by fluids exuded from skin and wound infections.

As the cycle continues, pathogenic microorganisms may be transmitted to susceptible persons in a variety of ways. They may be transmitted by direct contact (as in handshaking, kissing, or sexual contact), by contact with fomites, or by ingestion of contaminated water, food, or milk. In some instances pathogens may be taken up by an insect or other arthropod that later bites another host. Note that portals of entry of a pathogen into a new host usually parallel the escape routes just mentioned [FIGURE 22.5]. Specific diseases are described in later chapters, whose titles indicate the mode of transmission

of the infectious agents: "Sexually Transmitted Diseases," "Airborne Diseases," "Foodborne and Waterborne Diseases," "Arthropod-Borne Diseases," and "Wound and Skin Infections Acquired by Direct Contact."

Susceptibility of Patients to Infection

A number of factors are responsible for infection in hospitalized patients. For instance, infants and elderly patients often have a lower level of immunity than other patients, making them more vulnerable to infections. However, the normal antimicrobial defenses of *any* patient may become reduced by factors such as a concurrent infection, wounds, surgery, radiation, immunosuppressive agents, or procedures and instruments used on the body [FIGURE 22.6A and B]. Other conditions that may predispose a patient toward developing a hospital-acquired infection are listed in TABLE 22.3. AIDS is now considered one of the major concerns in infection control, as patients are susceptible to a frightening array of infections.

A patient's susceptibility to infection may be increased by clinical conditions and medical procedures that allow normal flora microorganisms to be transferred from their usual habitat to some other area of the pa-

22.1 *Candida parapsilosis* AS THE CAUSE OF NOSOCOMIAL INFECTIONS IN A PEDIATRIC HOSPITAL: A CASE STUDY

Between April 17 and May 8, 1985, nosocomial surveillance at a pediatric hospital identified four patients with blood samples from intravascular catheters (catheters inserted into blood vessels) that were positive for the yeast *Candida parapsilosis*.

Because no previous cluster of cases of *C. parapsilosis* fungemia (fungi in the blood) had been observed at the hospital, an epidemiological study of the disease began. First, the microbiology laboratory reports were reviewed for the 18 months before the reported cluster of cases of *C. parapsilosis* fungemia. The data confirmed that fungemia had occurred in a chronic pattern during these months.

Further studies revealed that the fungemia patients had been exposed to a central vascular catheter, to intravenous feeding, and to a blood monitoring device and transducer. A review of patient-care procedures found that, counter to hospital protocol, one vein had been used for multiple purposes, such as drawing blood, giving medication, and intravenous nutrition. When questioned, nurses recalled that solution had leaked from the venous nutrition therapy bags onto the surface of the transducer heads and then onto the floor. This fluid can provide a favorable growth medium for *C. parapsilosis*.

Another break in normal procedure was that, during busy periods in the in-

tensive care unit, the wiping of the transducer heads with a phenolic germicide solution before storage had been omitted. A microbiological survey of the patients, solutions, and medical devices confirmed that there was extensive contamination of the transducers with *C. parapsilosis*. On the basis of these results, the hospital instituted a procedure for ethylene oxide sterilization of blood pressure transducer heads between uses. (Sterile, disposable transducer heads are also available.) This was effective in controlling *C. parapsilosis* infections.

Adapted from *J. Clin. Microbiol.*, vol. 25, no. 6, June 1987, pp. 1029–1032.

TABLE 22.3

Factors Which Increase the Risk of Nosocomial Infections in Patients with Compromised Defenses

Predisposing factors	Basis for increased susceptibility	Most common types of infection
Invasive devices, arterial and urinary catheters, implants	Foreign body	Urinary tract infection, bacteremia, abscesses
Tissue transplant (kidney, heart, bone marrow)	Diminished cell-mediated immunity	Pneumonia, urinary tract infection, bacteremia
Extensive skin burns	Diminished cell-mediated immunity	*Pseudomonas* bacteremia
Malfunction or absence of spleen, sickle cell anemia	Impaired antibody synthesis	Pneumococcal bacteremia, meningitis
Bone marrow failure	Severe reduction in leucocyte count, low number of large leucocytes	Bacteremia, urinary tract infection, pneumonia
Malignant disorders	Immunodeficiency, fewer large leucocytes, impaired antibody synthesis	Bacteremia, urinary tract infection, pneumonia
HIV (AIDS) infection	Immunodeficiency	Pneumonia, many bacterial and fungal infections

---

tient's body and thereby become opportunistic pathogens [TABLE 22.4]. For example, *E. coli*, an inhabitant of the intestinal tract, may cause serious infection if introduced into the urinary tract. Urinary catheterization (the process of inserting a rubber or plastic tube called a *catheter* into the urinary tract to drain urine from the bladder) can sometimes introduce *E. coli* or other opportunistic pathogens into the bladder [FIGURE 22.7]. Urinary tract infections are the most common type of noso-

comial infection, and *E. coli* remains the most common single cause of hospital infections. Breaking the skin barrier by surgery, biopsy, injection, or withdrawal of a blood sample may allow normal skin bacteria such as *Staphylococcus aureus* and *S. epidermidis* to gain access to the underlying tissue and establish an infection. Other invasive procedures that may lead to infection include the implantation of prostheses—artificial body parts such as heart valves, pacemakers, or hip joints.

TABLE 22.4

Clinical Conditions and Procedures Associated with Compromised Host Defense Mechanisms

Condition or procedure	Opportunistic microorganism
Immunosuppressed (patient receiving chemical agents to reduce or inhibit antibody formation) kidney transplant recipients	*Aspergillus* spp.
General anesthesia; abdominal surgery	*Bacteroides fragilis*
Implanted prosthetic (artificial) heart valve; immunosuppressed graft recipients	*Candida albicans*
Urinary catheterization (a procedure to withdraw urine by inserting a catheter)	*Escherichia coli*
Lymphatic tissue malignancies such as Hodgkin's disease	*Cryptococcus neoformans*
Immunosuppressed allograft (tissue graft from nonidentical donor of the same species) recipient	Herpes simplex virus
Heart transplant recipients on antibiotic or immunosuppressive treatment	*Klebsiella* spp.
Immunosuppressed patient; prolonged use of steroids (therapeutic agents)	*Mycobacterium* spp.
Urinary catheterization; abdominal surgery	*Proteus* spp.
Decrease of leucocytes in cancer patients; blood cell–production disorders	*Pseudomonas aeruginosa*
Indwelling urinary catheter; continuous intravenous drip	*Serratia marcescens*
Intravenous catheters; implanted prostheses such as heart valve, devices for hand or eye	*Staphylococcus aureus*
Absence of spleen; multiple tumors	*Streptococcus pneumoniae*

FIGURE 22.6

Many factors can contribute to the increased chance of a patient's developing an infection in a hospital environment. Among these are **[A]** surgical procedures such as this one being performed in a shock trauma emergency room and **[B]** the equipment and instruments used in these procedures.

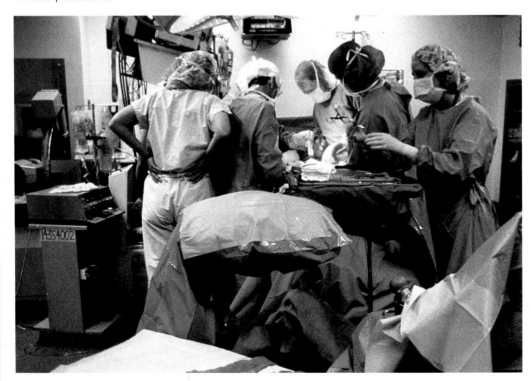

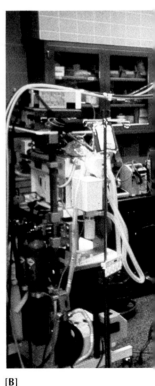

[A]   [B]

22.2 THE CAUSATIVE AGENTS OF NOSOCOMIAL INFECTIONS: CHANGE IN MICROBIAL ETIOLOGY

In 1986 the Centers for Disease Control reported the results of a study of 29,562 microbial isolates from nosocomial infection in the United States during 1984. They found that approximately one-half of the infections (57.3 percent) were caused by the following bacteria (with the most frequent site of infection): *Escherichia coli* (urinary tract), *Pseudomonas aeruginosa* (lower respiratory tract), enterococci (surgical wounds and respiratory tract), *Staphylococcus aureus* (surgical wounds), and *Klebsiella* spp. (lower respiratory tract). Other microorganisms identified as causative agents were species of *Proteus, Serratia, Bacteroides, Citrobacter, Enterobacter,* and *Candida.*

A similar study conducted from 1986 to 1989 revealed changes with respect to the etiology of nosocomial infections. For example, the incidence of *E. coli* infections decreased from 23 percent (in the early 1980s) to 16 percent in the 1986–1989 study. *Klebsiella pneumoniae* decreased from 7 percent to 5 percent and *Candida albicans* increased from 2 percent to 5 percent of the total infections. *Staphylococcus aureus, Pseudomonas aeruginosa, Enterobacter* spp., and enterococci had only minor

increases. Of major significance was the finding that the more recently isolated strains of bacteria have a higher resistance toward antimicrobial agents. "Taken as a whole, the shifts are away from the more easily treated pathogens toward more resistant pathogens with fewer options for therapy."*

*D. R. Schaberg, D. H. Culver, and R. P. Gaines, "Major Trends in the Microbial Etiology of Nosocomial Infection," *Am. J. Med.,* vol. 91, 3B–72S, Sept. 16, 1991.

Adapted from *Morbidity and Mortality Surveillance Summary* 35(no. 155):17ss–29ss, 1986.

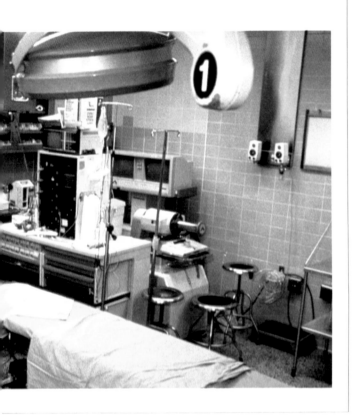

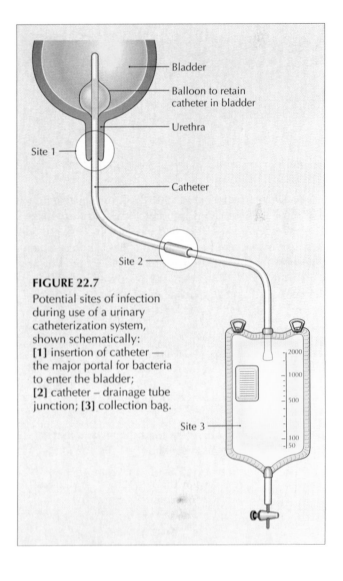

FIGURE 22.7
Potential sites of infection during use of a urinary catheterization system, shown schematically:
[1] insertion of catheter — the major portal for bacteria to enter the bladder;
[2] catheter – drainage tube junction; [3] collection bag.

Bladder

Balloon to retain catheter in bladder

Urethra

Site 1

Catheter

Site 2

Site 3

2000
1000
500
100
50

TABLE 22.5
Factors Affecting a Patient's Susceptibility to Infection

Factors	Examples
Inadequate cellular defenses	Very young patients Very old patients
Health status	Malnutrition Diabetes Chronic debilitating diseases Hematological disorders Renal diseases HIV (AIDS) infection Immunological deficiencies
Accidents	Severe debilitation Severe burns Shock
Surgery	Size of wound and amount of wound drainage Duration of operation Tissue trauma Length of hospitalization Foreign bodies—sutures, catheters, prostheses
Therapy	Antibiotic Radiation Steroid Immunosuppressive

Other factors affecting the susceptibility of a patient to infection are summarized in TABLE 22.5.

As shown earlier, in FIGURE 22.5, the cycle of infection must be completed in order for infection to occur. The pathogen must exit from the reservoir, have a mode of transmission, and have a portal of entry into a susceptible host. If the infectious agent is intercepted at any stage in this cycle, infection can be prevented. To break the cycle is the goal of infection control.

ASK YOURSELF

1 What factors influence the occurrence of a disease?

2 What are the sources of microorganisms that might infect a hospital patient?

3 What conditions of a patient make the patient more susceptible to acquiring an infection in the hospital?

BREAKING THE CYCLE OF INFECTION

Interruption of the cycle of infection is aimed primarily at transmission, because host and agent factors are more difficult to control.

Guidelines for the Prevention and Control of Nosocomial Infections

In 1980, the CDC initiated a series of recommendations for hospital personnel responsible for infection control. These guidelines are revised periodically as new knowledge of the epidemiology of infectious diseases becomes available. Topics covered in the guidelines include: hand washing and hospital environmental control; prevention of intravascular infections (blood infections), catheter-associated urinary tract infections, surgical wound infections, and nosocomial pneumonia; isolation precautions in hospitals; and infection control among hospital personnel. New or updated guidelines are developed as needed. For instance, in 1988 the guidelines were updated to cover the prevention of AIDS and other blood-borne diseases in health care personnel, and in July 1991, recommendations were made to minimize the possibility that health care workers could transmit HIV or hepatitis B virus to patients [DISCOVER 22.3]. Use of these guidelines can prevent many cases of infection. Unfortunately, too many health care personnel do not adhere strictly to such guidelines, according to the CDC compliance surveys.

Practices and Procedures Used to Break the Cycle of Infection

Methods used to stop the transmission of infection range from the relatively simple procedure of thorough hand washing to isolation of an infected patient, aseptic techniques, and proper sanitation, disinfection, and sterilization in the hospital setting. These measures can be very effective, but they must be used and enforced.

Hand Washing. Studies of microorganisms cultured from the hands of health care professionals prove that hand washing is the single most important procedure for preventing nosocomial infections. This simple procedure can greatly reduce the spread of pathogens from one patient to another. Mechanical removal of microorganisms by rubbing all surfaces of soap-lathered hands for at least 10 seconds and rinsing under running water before and after contact with each patient is usually adequate. Most

22.3 UPDATE: UNIVERSAL PRECAUTIONS FOR PREVENTION OF TRANSMISSION OF HUMAN IMMUNODEFICIENCY VIRUS, HEPATITIS B VIRUS, AND OTHER BLOOD-BORNE PATHOGENS IN HEALTH CARE SETTINGS

Health care workers (HCWs) need to consider *all patients* as potentially infected with human immunodeficiency virus (HIV) and/or other blood-borne pathogens such as hepatitis B virus (HBV). The increasing prevalence of HIV infection increases the risk that health care workers will be exposed to blood and other secretions from patients infected with the AIDS virus.

Every year since the 1983 edition of "Isolation Precautions," new guidelines have been developed and changes and additions have been made to earlier versions by the Centers for Disease Control (CDC). In 1987 "Recommendations for Prevention of HIV Transmission in Health-Care Settings" was added, and it was revised in 1988 to emphasize the need to treat blood and other body fluids from all patients as potentially infective. In 1989, guidelines were published to protect fire-service people, emergency medical technicians, paramedics, law-enforcement personnel—all public safety workers.

Despite adherence to the principles of universal precautions, certain invasive surgical and dental procedures have been implicated in transmission of HBV from infected HCWs to patients. Reported examples of exposure-prone procedures include certain oral, cardiothoracic, colon, and obstetric-gynecologic procedures.

To minimize the small risk that a health care worker might transmit HIV or HBV to a patient, the following measures were recommended by the Centers for Disease Control in July 1991:

1 All HCWs should adhere to universal precautions and comply with current guidelines for disinfection and sterilization of devices reused in invasive procedures.
2 Exposure-prone medical and dental invasive procedures should be identified.
3 HCWs who perform these procedures should know their HIV status.
4 Infected HCWs should not perform exposure-prone, invasive procedures unless, after review by an expert panel, they are permitted to do such procedures.
5 Patients should be told of the HCW's HIV status before performance of any exposure-prone procedure.

Since AIDS was first recognized and reported in 1981, more than 179,000 persons with AIDS have been reported in the United States to the CDC.

Epidemiologic evidence has implicated only blood, semen, vaginal secretions, and possibly breast milk in transmission of HIV. However, the virus has been isolated in saliva, tears, urine, and other body fluids and secretions.

Since medical history and examination cannot reliably identify all patients infected with this virus or other blood-borne pathogens, *universal blood and body fluid precautions*, recommended by the CDC should be used consistently in the care of *all patients*. Health care personnel should use these same rigid precautions in emergency-care settings, where the risk of blood exposure is increased and the infection status of the patient is unknown.

Universal precautions include:

1 Use of barrier protection—always use gloves when treating bleeding patients, when drawing blood, and for procedures involving contact with mucous membranes or potentially infectious material; wear masks, protective eyewear, and gowns if splashes of blood are likely.
2 Wash hands and skin immediately if contaminated, after removing gloves, and always before taking care of another patient.
3 Prevent injuries caused by needles and scalpels. Needle-stick exposure is the main route of transmission of HIV to workers. Needles should never be recapped, removed from disposable syringes, or bent or broken by hand. All sharp items should be placed in a puncture-resistant container, located as close as possible to the user, for disposal.
4 Minimize mouth-to-mouth resuscitation; always use a protective device.
5 Workers with weeping lesions should refrain from direct patient care and from handling patient-care equipment.
6 Pregnant health workers must be familiar with and must strictly adhere to precautions. The infant is also at risk of infection if the mother is infected.
7 All HCWs who are exposed to blood should receive HBV vaccine.

From *Morbidity and Mortality Weekly Report,* June 24, 1988, and July 12, 1991.

transient microorganisms are suspended in the soapy lather and rinsed away. Hands should be washed before caring for susceptible patients or newborn infants, before and after dressing wounds, and before performing invasive procedures. If hands come into contact with blood or blood-containing fluids, secretions from wounds, materials that contain pus, or any other suspect material, they should be washed for 2 to 3 minutes with a disinfectant.

In hospitals the "surgical scrub" is a routine procedure, but the specific steps may vary. However, all require scrubbing the lower arms and hands vigorously with soap and a brush for about 10 minutes, then rinsing under running water and with an antiseptic solution. The relative efficiency of antiseptics and disinfectants is described in Chapter 8; FIGURE 8.3 shows the comparative effects of various disinfectants on skin.

Isolation. As practiced in a hospital, *isolation* is the separation of a patient from other people and the care of that patient in an isolated environment. Hospital isolation policies are designed to prevent the spread of pathogenic organisms among patients, staff, and visitors.

The degree of isolation and the particular procedures to be followed are determined by the infection or condition that makes isolation necessary. Some practices include assigning the patient to a private room; wearing a mask, gown, and gloves; hand washing; using special procedures for equipment; and using universal precautions when dealing with blood or other infective materials. TABLE 22.6 summarizes the categories of hospital isolation procedures. Note that one category, reverse isolation precautions, differs from the others in that it is the *patient* who requires protection by isolation. This category applies to patients whose defense mechanisms

---

T A B L E 22.6
Categories of Isolation Precautions in Hospitals

Category of isolation	Examples of diseases requiring isolation	Routes of transmission
Strict isolation (to prevent transmission of highly contagious infections or highly deadly infections)	Diphtheria; smallpox; Lassa fever; pneumonic plague; chicken pox (varicella)	Air droplets
Contact isolation (to prevent spread of highly transmissible infections)	Gonococcal conjunctivitis; herpes simplex; influenza; colds; pneumonia; skin, wound, and burn infections	Close contact or direct contact
Respiratory isolation (to prevent short-distance or air droplet transmission)	Measles (rubeola); meningitis; mumps; whooping cough; pneumonia	Air droplets and direct and indirect contact
Tuberculosis isolation (to prevent transmission and protect the patient's privacy)	Pulmonary tuberculosis	Air droplets
Enteric precautions	Amoebic dysentery; cholera diarrhea; *Salmonella* gastroenteritis; shigellosis; hepatitis type A; typhoid fever	Direct or indirect contact with feces
Drainage and secretion precautions	Abscesses; burn infections; conjunctivitis; skin and wound infections	Direct or indirect contact with infected drainage or secretions
Universal blood and body fluid precautions	Acquired immunodeficiency syndrome (AIDS); hepatitis type B; malaria; syphilis	Direct or indirect contact with blood and blood-containing body fluids
Reverse isolation precautions (to prevent the patient from acquiring infections)	AIDS; Hodgkin's disease; patients who are immunosuppressed	Possibly all routes of transmission

FIGURE 22.8
An immunosuppressed patient protected by isolation in a hospital cubicle provided with a laminar airflow system to remove airborne microorganisms. The attendant wears gloves, masks, and gown to protect the patient from possible infection.

against infection have been compromised [FIGURE 22.8]. Isolation is an effective control method if carried out on all compromised patients, all infected patients, and all patients who harbor infectious agents but are not ill.

Asepsis. Asepsis is the exclusion of pathogenic and potentially pathogenic microorganisms to avoid infection. Two concepts of asepsis, medical and surgical, are practiced in hospitals.

Medical asepsis consists of all practices used to keep hospital personnel, patients, and the hospital environment as free as possible from infectious microorganisms. Hand washing, sanitary practices, and isolation procedures are but a few examples of the methods used to achieve asepsis. *Surgical asepsis* includes procedures that prevent microorganisms from gaining access to the surgical wounds and to tissues exposed during an operation. To achieve surgical asepsis, all instruments, gloves, surgical drapes, sutures, dressings, and other items that come into contact with a patient must be sterile. The operating room environment is sanitized and the microorganisms in the air are removed by passing the air through special filters combined with a laminar airflow system. In addition, operating room personnel scrub their hands and arms and put on sterile caps, gowns, masks, and gloves. The use of antiseptics helps reduce the number of microorganisms on the surface of the patient's skin.

Aseptic technique includes practices designed to prevent contamination by extraneous microorganisms and to reduce the numbers of those already present. Surgical asepsis is practiced in the operating room and in treatment procedures such as dressing wounds, catheterization, and intravenous therapy. The maintenance of asepsis is possible only if every person in the sterile area is responsible and conscientious in carrying out aseptic techniques.

Hospital Disinfection and Sterilization. The materials and equipment used for patient care can be divided into three categories—critical, semicritical, and noncritical—based on the risk of infection during their use:

1 Critical items include surgical instruments, cardiac catheters, implants, and any invasive items that are introduced into the bloodstream or other normally sterile areas of the body. Critical items must be sterilized.
2 Semicritical items include noninvasive instruments that come into contact with but do not penetrate body surfaces or mucous membranes, such as oral thermometers. These items must be meticulously cleaned and disinfected for reuse, unless disposables are used. The use of disposables is recommended.
3 Noncritical items are those that touch only intact skin, such as bedboards, crutches, and other medical accessories. They should be washed with a detergent.

Many hospitals have central supply units where most equipment and supplies are cleaned and sterilized. The effectiveness of the cleaning and sterilizing processes is monitored by the microbiology laboratory on a regular schedule. The physical and chemical agents used for accomplishing disinfection or sterilization are described in Chapters 7 and 8.

Most hospitals use disposable, presterilized instruments and materials, such as thermometers, syringes, hypodermic needles, gloves, and masks. The use of sterile disposable items not only decreases the time involved in cleaning, repairing, and sterilizing equipment but also reduces the chance of transmission of pathogens. For instance, before the widespread availability of sterile disposable hypodermic needles, hepatitis B virus and other blood-borne microbes were sometimes transmitted from infected individuals to healthy persons by nondisposable syringes and needles that were improperly sterilized after previous use. (Today, the spread of the AIDS virus among intravenous drug users is due mainly to the use of contaminated hypodermic needles. For this reason, some public health officials have advocated controversial programs to distribute free disposable sterile needles to intravenous drug users to help stop the spread of AIDS.) Despite the obvious advan-

FIGURE 22.9
Floor dust yielded these microorganisms. Cotton swabs were used to obtain samples from the floor surface and the plates were inoculated with the swabs. [A] Sample taken $4\frac{1}{2}$ h after morning mopping (mop water contained a sanitizing agent). [B] Sample taken immediately after midday mopping. [C] Sample taken 3 h after midday mopping.

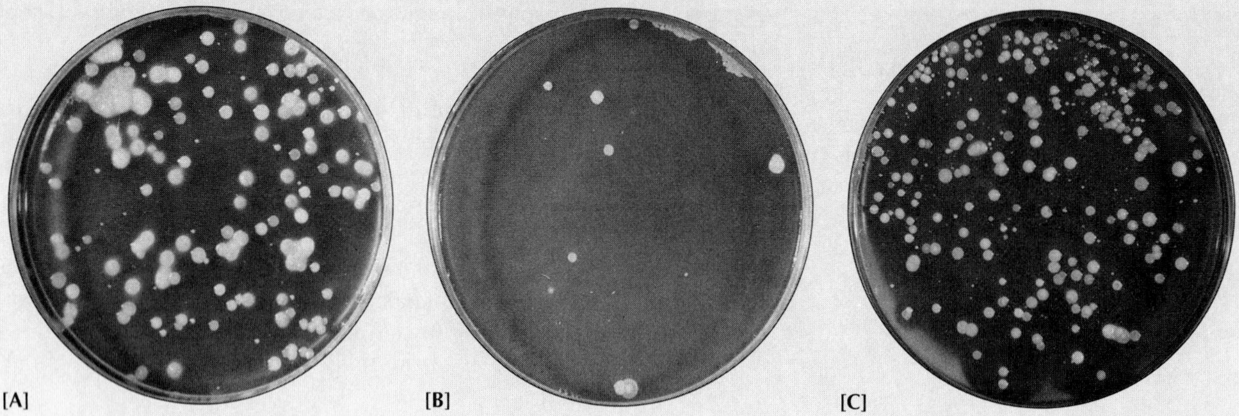

[A]   [B]   [C]

tages of using disposable equipment in hospitals and clinics, new problems have arisen concerning the disposal of increasing amounts of medical waste. Infective waste either should be incinerated or should be autoclaved before disposal in a sanitary landfill. In the past few years some hospital waste that was dumped in the ocean washed back onto beaches, causing much concern. Hospital wastes requiring special precautions include syringes and needles, all sharp objects, wastes from the microbiology and pathology laboratories, and blood specimens or blood products.

Hospital Environmental Sanitation. The goal of hospital environmental sanitation is to kill or remove microorganisms found on surfaces. Microbiologists periodically sample various surfaces to measure and identify the microbial population. The results obtained before and after surface cleaning can serve as an impressive teaching tool when instructing new hospital personnel [FIGURE 22.9].

Reduction of microbial contamination is accomplished best by a good scrubbing action using water and detergents. This is sufficient unless there is heavy contamination, when the use of sanitizers or disinfectants is necessary. To be effective, disinfectants and sanitizers must be used at adequate concentrations for a specified time. When cleaning floors in hospitals, the use of sanitizers helps to reduce microbial contamination of mop water. Mops should be washed and dried thoroughly each day to reduce contamination. A bucket of disinfectant solution and a wet rag are often used to clean and disinfect surfaces other than floors. The solution needs periodic replacement; otherwise, the cleaning solution

itself may actually contaminate the surface! It is best to clean surfaces other than floors by applying a dilute solution of disinfectant detergent onto the surface and then wiping with disposable wipes or clean cloths.

ASK YOURSELF

1 What determines the development of new guidelines by the CDC?

2 How can the cycle of infection be broken?

3 What are differences in medical and surgical asepsis?

4 Into what three categories of care is hospital equipment divided? Why?

SURVEILLANCE

Surveillance is the systematic observation and recording of cases of transmissible disease. This careful compilation of cases is the basis for an effective control program. Both the study of nosocomial infections and the development and assessment of effective control measures can be accomplished only by organized surveillance. Not only must data be collected continuously, but the data must be tabulated, analyzed, and reviewed. There should be one full-time person for every 300 to 500 beds to ensure adequate surveillance, investigation of clusters of infection, and infection-control activities. This person is normally a pathologist, an epidemiologist, or a nurse and is usually called an *infection-control officer (ICO)*.

Surveillance of Patients

Patient infection surveillance begins by including an infection data card in each patient's medical record. The following information is recorded on the card by the ICO:

1 Type of infection, if any, that is present upon admission to the hospital
2 Hospital-acquired infection, if any, including the site, date of onset, hospital section, and the sex and age of the patient
3 The pathogen isolated from the nosocomial infection
4 Surgical procedures or chemotherapeutic treatments that may have preceded the infection
5 The antibiotic given to control the infection
6 The time required to control the infection

Data from the daily reports of cultures isolated and identified by the microbiology laboratory, as well as data from clinical "rounds," are recorded on each patient's infection data card. (Rounds are the reviews of each patient's condition by doctors, nurses, an infection-control officer, or laboratory personnel.) Evaluation of this information may uncover new infections or clusters of infections. If so, there may be an immediate investigation into the source and mode of transmission of the infectious organism. These findings promote the development of better patient-care practices, the most important factor in controlling nosocomial diseases.

Surveillance of Health Care Personnel

As part of the surveillance of health care personnel, a preemployment physical examination should be required, and current immunization records should be reviewed for all hospital employees. Women of childbearing age, personnel in high-risk categories, and pediatric personnel should be informed of the possibility of infection and of the immunizations available. An employee health service and an ongoing education program should be available to alert staff to policies that protect both personnel and patients from preventable infections. Selective microbial culturing of samples from personnel may be necessary when investigating an outbreak of nosocomial disease.

Surveillance of the Hospital Environment

When the infection-control officer detects one or more new cases of infection, cultures from patients, personnel, and the hospital environment may be required to identify the reservoir of infection and eliminate the source of the pathogen. The case study in DISCOVER 22.1 is an example of such an investigation following the discovery of a cluster of infections in a pediatric hospital.

ASK YOURSELF

1 Why is organized surveillance necessary?
2 What information is gathered in a surveillance program to control nosocomial infections?

COMPONENTS OF A CONTROL PROGRAM

Effective patient care is the focal point for the prevention and control of nosocomial infections; it is also the reason for establishing an infection-control program. In most hospitals, an infection-control program is organized similar to the example in TABLE 22.7. When organized and implemented together, these components—the hospital policy-making committee, the infection-control committee, the microbiology laboratory, and the infection-control officer—make an effective control program. The Joint Commission on Accreditation of Hospitals insists that all infection-control policies be reviewed annually.

Infection-Control Committee

An efficient and effective infection-control committee is the most important element of an infection-control program. The committee usually consists of approximately 15 members, including the chairperson (hospital epidemiologist, microbiologist, or pathologist), the infection-control officer, and representatives from nursing services, hospital administration, the microbiology laboratory, and principal medical and surgical services.

The major responsibilities of the committee are:

1 Developing guidelines for patient care, and
2 Monitoring the effectiveness of the control program.

In order to perform successfully, an infection-control committee requires adequate data to assess the frequency and causes of nosocomial infections. The microbiology laboratory plays a major role in supplying these data.

TABLE 22.7
Organization of Infection-Control Program

HOSPITAL POLICY-MAKING COMMITTEE
Role: Develop policies for control of nosocomial infections

⇅

INFECTION-CONTROL COMMITTEE
Role: Develop guidelines for patient care; monitor effectiveness of control program

⇅

MICROBIOLOGY LABORATORY
Role: Isolate and identify organism(s); identify source of organism(s); monitor disinfection and sterilization procedures

⇅

INFECTION-CONTROL OFFICER
Role: Implement infection-control practices; surveillance and investigation of infections in patients and in personnel; maintain a continuing education program

---

Microbiology Laboratory

Records kept by the microbiology laboratory are a surveillance tool and data source, used for calculating infection rates and compiling infection reports. Proficiency in isolating and identifying microorganisms, determining drug resistance of isolates, and in reporting the results is essential for the early detection and treatment of nosocomial pathogens. DISCOVER 22.4 describes outbreaks of tuberculosis caused by multidrug resistant *Mycobacterium tuberculosis*.

Although environmental microbiological sampling (taking samples from the hospital environment) is done when needed to solve a problem, a certain amount of environmental surveillance should be carried out on a routine schedule [TABLE 22.8]. Such sampling should be coordinated with the objectives of the infection-control program. Sampling provides information that can be used to improve policies and methods for controlling environmental contamination.

ASK YOURSELF

1 What are the responsibilities of an infection-control program?

2 Of what importance is the microbiology laboratory in controlling nosocomial infections?

TABLE 22.8
Elements of a Minimal Environmental Surveillance Program in Hospitals

Supplies or equipment	Frequency of monitoring	Method of monitoring

Sterilizers:
  Steam
  Hot air
  Gas (e.g., ethylene oxide)
	
	Weekly
	Weekly
	Every load
		Bacterial spore strips (filter paper strips impregnated with spores)

Fluids	Monthly or semimonthly—random samples	Biologic test for toxic substances of microbial origin
Instruments	Weekly	Bacterial spore strips
Blood and intravenous fluids	Random sampling of lots or units	Sampling and culturing both aerobically and anaerobically
Inhalation therapy equipment	Intermittently	Sampling and culturing
Water and ice	If contamination suspected	Membrane-filter procedure (sampling and culturing)

22.4 OUTBREAKS OF MULTIDRUG-RESISTANT TUBERCULOSIS ON THE INCREASE

During 1990 and 1991, outbreaks of multidrug resistant tuberculosis (MDR-TB) in four hospitals (one in Miami and three in New York City) were investigated by the CDC in collaboration with the reporting hospitals and state and local health departments. The findings in this report illustrate the increased susceptibility of HIV (human immunodeficiency virus) infected persons, particularly those with severe immunodeficiency syndrome (AIDS), to life-threatening nosocomially transmitted TB. For example, of 29 patients diagnosed with MDR-TB in hospital A, 27 (93 percent) were known to be infected with HIV; 23 had AIDS and 21 of the 29 patients died a median of 7 weeks after diagnosis of MDR-TB. Most of the MDR-TB patients in all four hospitals in this study either were HIV-seropositive or had AIDS.

Laboratory tests performed on the isolates of *M. tuberculosis* from the patients, to determine their susceptibility to chemotherapeutic agents, revealed that the majority of strains were resistant to several drugs including isoniazid, streptomycin, rifamycin, and ethambutol.

One of the conditions which might have contributed to the delayed diagnosis and initiation of treatment is the relatively long time required for the laboratory isolation and identification of the causative agent and subsequent determination and reporting of the drug-susceptibility patterns of the isolates.

In all four hospitals, as a consequence of the time required to obtain results of laboratory tests, implementation of TB isolation precautions was delayed on admission of symptomatic TB patients. Before onset of TB, case patients were likely to have been hospitalized with other patients with infectious pulmonary MDR-TB.

In the course of this investigation, eight cases of TB were reported among health care workers who were associated with the care of case patients. Five were HIV-seropositive, one seronegative; and the serostatus of the other two was unknown.

These outbreaks underscore the need for early implementation of the following procedures for the prevention of TB transmission:

1 Early identification, isolation, and treatment of persons with active tuberculosis. This includes the use of the most rapid laboratory methods for isolation of the TB microorganism and the determination of the susceptibility of the isolates to chemotherapeutic agents. Results should be reported without delay.

2 Prevention of spread of infectious droplet nuclei to reduce the microbial contamination of indoor air. Initiate TB isolation precautions immediately for all patients suspected of having TB, and continue isolation procedures until clinical evidence and acid-fast smears indicate that infectiousness is under control.

3 Perform surveillance for TB transmission among other patients as well as health care workers.

From *Morbidity and Mortality Weekly Report*, Department of Health and Human Services, Public Health Service, August 30, 1991.

EDUCATION PROGRAM

A control program can be effective only if all the personnel involved know what is expected of them. General education classes for personnel should be scheduled twice monthly. Presentations should be structured for the particular group being addressed, such as food service and housekeeping personnel, laundry staff, nurses, or aides. During these classes new staff members can be educated, and policies and procedures can be reviewed and explained.

In-service teaching by the infection-control officer during surveillance rounds can be very effective. The most important ideas to convey in teaching are:

1 Need for understanding the guidelines and implementation of universal precautions and the epidemiology, modes of transmission, and prevention of infections including HIV and other blood-borne diseases

2 Infection-control and safety techniques to comply with infection-control policies

3 Hand washing and other basic aseptic techniques

4 Containment of infectious agents, and prevention of contamination

5 Personal responsibility and compliance with hospital regulations and all recommended protective measures

The continuing education program is one of the primary duties of the infection-control officer. An active educational program for all departments and all levels of the hospital staff is necessary to ensure the implementation of policies and practices for infection control.

ASK YOURSELF

What are the objectives of an effective education program to control nosocomial infections?

SUMMARY

1 Procedures to reduce nosocomial infections (infections acquired in the hospital) have been practiced since hospitals were first established. Oliver Wendell Holmes and Ignaz Philipp Semmelweis stressed hand washing between examinations of different patients, Louis Pasteur proved the germ theory of disease, Joseph Lister established the antiseptic system of surgery, and Florence Nightingale revolutionized hospitals by establishing sanitary conditions and professional nursing care.

2 Infections from an external source such as utensils and medical equipment are classified as *exogenous,* and infections caused by a patient's normal flora, such as microbes from the skin or urine, are termed *endogenous.*

3 Microbes that infect hosts who have weakened defense mechanisms caused by disease, surgery, radiation, and other medical treatment are opportunistic pathogens. *Klebsiella* species, *E. coli, P. aeruginosa, S. aureus,* and enterococci account for more than 57 percent of opportunistic pathogens isolated from patients. The greatest sources of these microorganisms are the hands of health care personnel and the patient's normal flora.

4 For infection to occur, the pathogen must exit from the source (reservoir), have a mode of transmission, and find a portal of entry into a susceptible host. To break this cycle of infection is the goal of infection control.

5 Growing concern over nosocomial infections in the past 20 years, because of their morbidity, mortality, and economic consequences, has stimulated hospitals to undertake organized activities aimed at surveillance and control. Infection surveillance and control programs have been established in most hospitals. The components of an infection-control program include:
An infection-control committee
A clinical microbiology laboratory
An infection-control officer
Effective patient care
Clearly understood isolation policies
Staff education programs

6 By reevaluating control measures on the basis of surveillance and analysis of data, new measures may be developed to prevent future occurrences of nosocomial infection. Studies are conducted by the Centers for Disease Control (CDC) to measure infection surveillance and control program activities related to patient care and practices with regard to changes in infection rate, and to evaluate the efficiency and cost-effectiveness of infection surveillance and control program activities. The CDC establishes guidelines and policies to aid hospitals in their efforts to control nosocomial infections.

7 The success of the infection-control program requires that all staff members know and practice the recommended policies and procedures.

8 As medical understanding of epidemiologic characteristics of diseases increases and as more infectious agents are identified, methods and practices for controlling nosocomial infections will need to be revised.

KEY TERMS

endogenous infections
epidemiology
exogenous infections
fomites
infection-control officer (ICO)
isolation (in hospitals)
medical asepsis
nosocomial infections
opportunistic pathogens
reservoirs of infection
surgical asepsis
surveillance (of infection)

1 The person who introduced sanitary practices in hospitals during the Crimean War was: **(a)** Semmelweis; **(b)** Holmes; **(c)** Fleming; **(d)** Nightingale; **(e)** Lister.

2 The names Holmes and Semmelweis are associated with: **(a)** the use of sulfonamides to cure infections; **(b)** the use of antibiotics to prevent nosocomial infections; **(c)** establishment of the germ theory of disease; **(d)** cleanliness and sanitation in hospitals; **(e)** establishment of immunization programs to prevent nosocomial infections.

3 The use of antibiotics in hospitals in the 1950s resulted in which *three* of the following? **(a)** decreased rates of nosocomial infections; **(b)** selection of antibiotic-resistant strains of bacteria; **(c)** effective prevention of nosocomial infections; **(d)** a decline in the number of deaths due to nosocomial infections; **(e)** relaxation of aseptic technique and isolation precautions.

4 The rate of hospital-acquired infections in the United States is approximately: **(a)** 0.33 per 1000 patients; **(b)** 1.0 per 1000 patients; **(c)** 50 per 1000 patients; **(d)** 33 per 1000 patients; **(e)** 330 per 1000 patients.

5 What percent of all nosocomial infections *directly* cause death? **(a)** 0.1; **(b)** 1.0; **(c)** 3; **(d)** 10; **(e)** 30.

6 Epidemiology is the study of the factors that influence the

_____ and _____ of disease.

7 Three conditions necessary for an infection to occur are:

(a) _____

(b) _____

(c) _____

8 Fomites are: **(a)** humans who carry an infectious microorganism; **(b)** insects that carry an infectious microorganism; **(c)** inanimate objects contaminated by an infectious microorganism; **(d)** visitors who bring infectious microorganisms into a hospital; **(e)** sanitizing detergents that have a foaming action.

9 Most nosocomial infections are caused by: **(a)** microorganisms from an external source; **(b)** microorganisms acquired from people with active clinical infections; **(c)** microorganisms that are part of the normal flora of the human body; **(d)** microorganisms that inhabit soil and water; **(e)** microorganisms in contaminated intravenous solutions.

10 An opportunistic pathogen is one that: **(a)** invariably causes disease in people who are exposed to it; **(b)** can escape from the body at the first opportunity; **(c)** is transmitted by direct contact; **(d)** is transmitted by airborne droplets; **(e)** causes disease mainly in persons whose normal defense mechanisms have been weakened.

11 Which of the following might compromise a person's normal defenses against infection? **(a)** surgery; **(b)** treatment with an immunosuppressive agent; **(c)** another infection; **(d)** malnutrition; **(e)** all of the above.

12 Which one of the following statements is incorrect? **(a)** The portal of entry of a pathogen into a new host usually parallels the escape route from the previous host. **(b)** Normal flora organisms may become pathogenic when transferred from their normal habitat into other areas of the host. **(c)** *E. coli* is the opportunistic pathogen most often associated with respiratory infections. **(d)** Breakage of the skin barrier may allow *S. aureus* to infect the underlying tissue. **(e)** Urinary catheterization may introduce opportunistic pathogens into the bladder, where they can cause infection.

13 The two greatest sources of opportunistic pathogens that can infect a hospital patient are: (1) the _____ of health care personnel and (2) the skin, mucous membranes, saliva, and urine of the _____.

BREAKING THE CYCLE OF INFECTION

14 The single most important procedure for preventing nosocomial infections is: **(a)** isolation of patients; **(b)** wearing a mask, gown, and gloves; **(c)** hand washing; **(d)** filtering air through a HEPA filter; **(e)** avoiding contact with blood or blood-containing materials.

15 Reverse isolation precautions would be most appropriate for which *one* of the following? **(a)** a patient who has a highly contagious disease; **(b)** a patient who has cholera or some other intestinal infection; **(c)** a patient who has tuberculosis or some other severe respiratory infection; **(d)** a heart transplant patient who is being treated with immunosuppressive agents; **(e)** a patient who has syphilis or some other sexually transmitted disease.

16 Which of the following would apply to *surgical asepsis*? **(a)** use of sterile instruments, gloves, sutures, and dressings; **(b)** surgical scrubs; **(c)** filtration of air in an operating room through a HEPA filter; **(d)** use of antiseptics on the patient's skin before making an incision; **(e)** all of the above.

SURVEILLANCE

17 _____ is the systematic observation and recording of the occurrence of transmissible disease and is the basis of an active hospital infection-control program.

18 The person assigned the responsibility for a hospital surveillance program is usually designated the _____, or ICO.

19 Which *one* of the following statements is false? **(a)** One ICO is required for every 300 to 500 beds for adequate surveillance. **(b)** Hospital personnel in high-risk categories should be informed of the possibility of infection and the immunizations that are available. **(c)** An infection data card is included in each patient's medical record. **(d)** Surveillance data need not be collected continuously; once a month is sufficient. **(e)** It may be necessary to culture samples not only from patients but also from hospital personnel when investigating an outbreak of nosocomial disease.

COMPONENTS OF A CONTROL PROGRAM

20 A(n) _____ committee is the most important element of a nosocomial disease control program.

21 The early detection of nosocomial pathogens depends to a great extent on the proficiency of the _____ laboratory in isolating and identifying microorganisms.

22 In a hospital, the policies established by the infection-control committee are required to be reviewed at least once every: **(a)** day; **(b)** week; **(c)** month; **(d)** year; **(e)** 10 years.

EDUCATION PROGRAM

23 In an infection-control program, education of hospital personnel is one of the primary duties assigned to the _____.

24 Which of the following statements apply to the continuing education program in a hospital? **(a)** The program is essential because the personnel involved in implementing the infection-control program have to know what is expected of them. **(b)** The program allows orientation of new staff members. **(c)** The program allows policies and procedures to be explained. **(d)** The particular group being addressed should be kept in mind when preparing for each class. **(e)** All of the above.

REVIEW QUESTIONS

1 Name and describe the contributions of four people who led the way to development of procedures for preventing transmission of disease in hospitals.

2 How can you account for a reservoir of antibiotic-resistant pathogens in hospitals?

3 Describe the steps in the cycle of infection, and indicate how this cycle might be broken.

4 Describe the conditions under which (1) an endogenous infection might develop and (2) an exogenous infection might develop.

5 Name at least four factors that may decrease the resistance of hospitalized patients to infection.

6 What is the value of using disposable sterile medical items such as hypodermic needles in a hospital?

7 What degree of isolation would be appropriate for a patient with (1) leukemia; (2) a wound infection; (3) tuberculosis; (4) pneumonia; (5) amoebic dysentery?

8 Name several practices or procedures in an operating room that would help to prevent infection of the patient.

9 Describe the special features of an educational program for controlling nosocomial infections.

10 Name the components of an active infection-control program, and indicate the function of each component.

DISCUSSION QUESTIONS

1 Assume that you are a member of the infection-control committee of a hospital and an outbreak of infections caused by staphylococci occurs. Outline a plan of investigation that might reveal the source of the organism causing the infections.

2 Certain procedures and practices on a hospital ward can be satisfied by disinfection, and others require sterilization. Give an example of each, and justify each.

3 Enumerate the practices and procedures that you would implement to break the ''cycle of infection'' on a hospital ward.

4 What are some common characteristics of the bacterial species that are most frequently the cause of nosocomial infections?

5 What role does the microbiology laboratory play in the program to control nosocomial infections?

Sexually Transmitted Diseases

OBJECTIVES

After reading this chapter you should be able to

1 Account for the high incidence of sexually transmitted diseases in the United States and other countries.

2 Assess the extent and significance of the current AIDS pandemic in the United States, Europe, and central Africa.

3 List the various means besides sexual contact by which diseases such as AIDS, gonorrhea, and syphilis can be acquired.

4 Explain how the AIDS virus multiplies and causes damage to the immune system, and how its multiplication can be retarded by the chemical compound AZT (azidothymidine), also called *zidovudine*.

5 Explain why the occurrence of Kaposi's sarcoma, *Pneumocystis carinii* pneumonia, and certain other diseases is usually indicative of a case of AIDS.

6 Compare the microbial agents that cause gonorrhea, syphilis, genital herpes, chlamydial infections, and other sexually transmitted diseases.

7 Describe the tests used in the laboratory diagnosis of sexually transmitted diseases.

8 Describe some of the serious complications that may result if patients with gonorrhea or syphilis are not effectively treated.

9 Distinguish between primary genital herpes and recurrent genital herpes.

10 List control measures that can limit the spread of sexually transmitted diseases.

OVERVIEW

The spread of most sexually transmitted diseases is currently out of control. Although most of these diseases are preventable with simple, careful behavior, they still affect millions each year. The various pathogenic bacteria, viruses, yeasts, and protozoa that cause these diseases can be directly passed from infected persons to healthy persons by sexual contact. Some of these agents can also be transmitted by other means, such as contaminated hypodermic needles or blood transfusions, and some can be acquired by infants born to infected mothers. Some sexually transmitted diseases cause minor symptoms, while others can lead to sterility or death.

The sexually transmitted diseases that are most prevalent in our society are AIDS, gonorrhea, syphilis, genital herpes, and chlamydial infections. AIDS is now recognized as being a *pandemic,* an epidemic of global proportions. Because of its high fatality rate and potential for rapid spread, it poses a threat to populations around the world. Some sexually transmitted diseases can be cured quite easily, but others, such as those caused by viruses, are presently difficult or impossible to cure.

Because treatments often are inadequate, prevention is essential. Preventive measures are based mainly on better education of the total population and, when possible, control of sources of infection and treatment of infected individuals with chemotherapeutic agents.

THE TYPES OF SEXUALLY TRANSMITTED DISEASES

Sexually transmitted diseases (STDs) represent a worldwide public health problem. In the United States alone, at least 8 to 10 million persons contract some form of STD each year. The STDs that are most prevalent in our society include gonorrhea, syphilis, genital herpes, chlamydial infections, trichomoniasis, type B hepatitis, and, most serious of all because of its extremely high mortality rate, AIDS (*acquired immunodeficiency syndrome*).

STDs were formerly called *venereal* diseases (from *Venus*, the Roman goddess of love). They occur most frequently in the most sexually active age group—15 to 30 years of age—but anyone who has sexual contact with someone who already has an STD is a potential victim. In general, the more sexual partners a person has, the more likely that person is to acquire an STD.

Some microorganisms that cause STDs also can be transmitted by nonsexual means, such as by contaminated hypodermic syringes and needles shared among intravenous drug users, and by transfusions with contaminated blood. Some also can be acquired by infants born to infected mothers.

Most STDs are caused by bacteria and viruses, but some are caused by yeasts and protozoa. TABLE 23.1 lists the various microorganisms that can be sexually transmitted and the diseases they cause.

ASK YOURSELF

1 Which STDs are most prevalent in our society?

2 In which age group do STDs occur most frequently?

3 Can some microorganisms that cause STDs be transmitted by means other than sexual contact?

SEXUALLY TRANSMITTED DISEASES CAUSED BY BACTERIA

Several STDs are caused by bacteria. Those most frequently encountered are gonorrhea, syphilis, and chlamydial infections.

Gonorrhea

During World War II the incidence of gonorrhea steadily increased in the United States, and by 1947 there were 265 reported cases of gonorrhea per 100,000 population. However, with the discovery that penicillin was effective in treating gonorrhea, some public health authorities predicted that the disease would eventually be eliminated. The incidence of gonorrhea did decline for a while, but then it took an upward turn and reached an all-time high of 468 per 100,000 in 1978. The main factors involved in this dramatic increase were as follows:

1 The introduction of oral contraceptives and contraceptive intrauterine devices.

2 An increase in the number of persons whose sexual activity is characterized by contact with a series of sex partners.

3 A decrease in use of spermicidal preparations and condoms (both of which afford some protection against gonorrhea).

4 The inability of public health agencies and physicians to trace all the contacts of the numerous carriers and clinically ill persons to prevent further transmission of the causative bacterium.

5 The emergence of penicillin-resistant strains of *Neisseria gonorrhoeae*, the bacterial species that causes the disease. (However, these penicillin-resistant strains are still relatively rare, about 0.5 percent of isolates.)

The incidence of gonorrhea in the United States has declined since 1978 but is still very high, with approximately 690,000 cases being reported each year, or 276 cases per 100,000 population. The actual rate is probably much higher because many cases are not reported. Reported male cases usually exceed reported female cases, because women who contract gonorrhea frequently do not have the painful symptoms that compel male patients to see a physician. Gonorrhea is prevalent throughout the world and occurs most often in large metropolitan areas and in the age group 15 to 24 years old.

The Causative Agent of Gonorrhea. Gonorrhea is caused by *Neisseria gonorrhoeae*, commonly called the **gonococcus.** The cells are aerobic Gram-negative nonmotile cocci that occur in pairs, with their adjacent sides flattened like a pair of coffee beans. In microscopic preparations made from clinical specimens, gonococci often are observed inside neutrophils, which ingest the bacteria by phagocytosis [FIGURE 23.1]. Gonococci grow best on "chocolate" agar, a blood-containing medium that has been heated to rupture the red blood cells (this heating turns the medium the color of chocolate). Cultures are incubated in an air atmosphere enriched with 5 to 10% carbon dioxide.

TABLE 23.1
Some Microorganisms That Are Sexually Transmitted and the Diseases They Cause

Organism	Characteristics	Disease
BACTERIA		
Neisseria gonorrhoeae	Cocci; Gram-negative; kidney-shaped cells occurring in pairs; aerobic	Gonorrhea; pelvic inflammatory disease (PID); arthritis; conjunctivitis in newborns
Treponema pallidum subspecies pallidum	Spirochetes; Gram-negative; microaerophilic; not cultivable on laboratory media	Syphilis; congenital syphilis
Chlamydia trachomatis	Coccoid organisms; Gram-negative; obligate intracellular parasites having a unique developmental cycle	Nongonococcal urethritis (NGU); cervicitis; pelvic inflammatory disease (PID); lymphogranuloma venereum; trachoma; conjunctivitis and pneumonia in newborns
Ureaplasma urealyticum, Mycoplasma genitalium	Pleomorphic bacteria that lack cell walls	Implicated in some cases of NGU
Mycoplasma hominis	Pleomorphic bacteria that lack cell walls	Implicated in some cases of PID
Haemophilus ducreyi	Rods; Gram-negative; facultative	Chancroid ("soft chancre")
Gardnerella vaginalis	Pleomorphic rods; Gram-variable; facultative	Bacterial vaginosis
Calymmatobacterium granulomatis	Pleomorphic rods; Gram-negative; facultative	Granuloma inguinale
Campylobacter cinaedi, C. fennelliae	Curved rods; Gram-negative; microaerophilic	Diarrhea and rectal inflammation in homosexual men
VIRUSES		
Human immunodeficiency virus (HIV)	Contains single-stranded RNA; belongs to the retrovirus group	Acquired immunodeficiency syndrome (AIDS)
Herpes simplex virus (HSV-2 and HSV-1)	Contains double-stranded DNA; belongs to the herpesvirus group	Genital herpes
Human papillomavirus type 6 (HPV-6)	Contains double-stranded DNA; belongs to the papovavirus group	Condyloma acuminata (genital warts)
Hepatitis B virus (HBV)	Contains double-stranded DNA	Type B hepatitis (serum hepatitis)
Cytomegalovirus (CMV)	Contains double-stranded DNA; belongs to the herpesvirus group	Congenital cytomegalic inclusion disease; CMV mononucleosis
Molluscum contagiosum virus	Contains double-stranded DNA; belongs to the poxvirus group	Genital molluscum contagiosum
YEASTS		
Candida albicans	Yeasts with pseudohyphae; form large, thick-walled chlamydospores	Candidiasis (moniliasis)
PROTOZOA		
Trichomonas vaginalis	Flagellated protozoan	Trichomoniasis

FIGURE 23.1

Neisseria gonorrhoeae causes infections of the human genitourinary tract. Shown is a Gram stain of *Neisseria gonorrhoeae* in the purulent (pus-containing) discharge from the urethra of a man with acute gonorrhea. The gonococci (arrow) are seen in their characteristic diplococcus arrangements within the cytoplasm of the pus cells (neutrophils). The large red objects in the field are the multilobed nuclei of the pus cells.

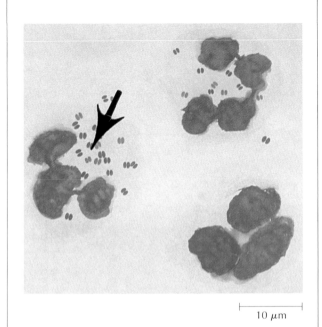

10 μm

Transmission of the Gonococcus.

N. gonorrhoeae is transmitted by sexual intercourse. It can also be acquired by a newborn infant from an infected mother during passage through the birth canal. This type of infection results in *gonococcal conjunctivitis*, an inflammation of the *conjunctiva*—the thin membrane that covers the surface of the eye and lines the inner surface of the eyelids. Gonococcal conjunctivitis can lead to corneal damage and blindness if not prevented or promptly treated. It is a standard practice in hospitals to place drops of silver nitrate solution or antibiotics into the eyes of newborn infants to prevent infection by gonococci and other pathogens. These other pathogens include *Chlamydia trachomatis, Haemophilus influenzae,* and *Streptococcus pneumoniae.*

Pathogenicity of the Gonococcus.

Gonococci initially attach to surface tissue cells of the host by means of *pili,* hairlike appendages that project from the bacterial cell surface; and by means of a protein called PII, located in the bacterium's outer membrane. Then the gonococci penetrate to the underlying tissue layers, where they multiply and cause tissue damage by means of a potent *endotoxin.* Not everyone exposed to gonorrhea contracts gonorrhea. The reason for this is not understood, but there is some evidence that the normal microbial flora of the genital organs may help to prevent infection.

In men, the primary site of infection is the *urethra,* the canal that carries urine from the bladder to the outside of the body [FIGURE 23.2]. The disease is usually

FIGURE 23.2

Anatomic organization of the male reproductive tract, and interrelationships with the urinary system (side view). The urethra functions to allow urine from the bladder and, alternatively, semen from the ductus deferens to pass to the outside of the body.

Seminal vesicle

Ejaculatory duct
Anal canal
Bulbourethral gland
Ductus deferens
Epididymis
Scrotum

Ureter
Bladder
Prostate gland
Urethra
Penis
Testis

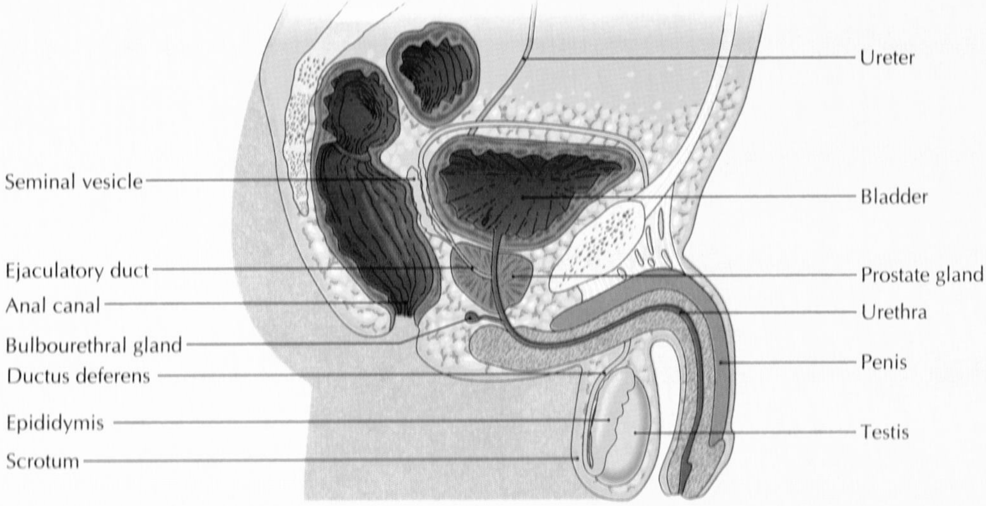

FIGURE 23.3

[A] Anatomic organization of the female reproductive tract and urinary system (side view). In the female, the urinary and reproductive duct systems are entirely separate. The ovaries produce the female sex cells, or eggs, which pass via the uterine tubes to the uterus. During mating, spermatozoa from a male are deposited within the vagina. Some spermatozoa pass to the uterus and, after the union of a spermatozoan with an egg, the fertilized egg undergoes a process of cell division and differentiation that eventually results in the formation of a fetus. **[B]** X-ray photograph (front view) of the genital tract of a woman with a gonococcal infection that has caused blockage of her right uterine tube (also termed the *fallopian tube* or *oviduct*). The other uterine tube, visible at the left, has not been obstructed.

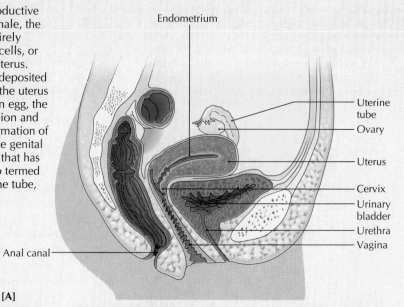

[A]

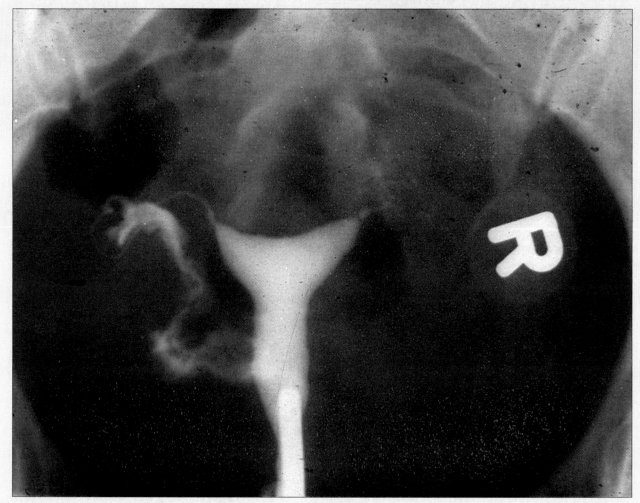

[B]

more obvious in men than women because of severe pain during urination and a yellowish, pus-containing discharge from the urethra. Sterility may result if the infection extends to the male reproductive system [FIGURE 23.2]—the *testes* (the egg-shaped glands which produce spermatozoa), the *prostate gland* (a gland which secretes a viscous, opalescent fluid into the urethra), and the *epididymis* (a coiled tube within which spermatozoa mature).

In women the primary site of infection is the *cervix*, the narrow, necklike portion of the *uterus* [FIGURE 23.3A]. Many women who are infected do not exhibit obvious symptoms and are **asymptomatic carriers.** Those who do have symptoms may experience painful urination, vaginal discharge, fever, and abdominal pain.

Pelvic inflammatory disease (PID) develops in approximately 10 to 20 percent of women with cervical gonorrhea. PID results from spread of the infection from the cervix to the *endometrium* (the lining of the uterus); the *uterine tubes* [FIGURE 23.3B], which carry eggs from the ovaries to the uterus; and to associated structures. PID is a major cause of female infertility and of *ectopic pregnancy*, an abnormal condition in which the fetus develops in a blocked uterine (fallopian) tube rather than within the uterus. PID can be caused not only by the gonococcus but by other microorganisms such as *Chlamydia trachomatis* (described later in this chapter).

Gonorrhea is not always confined to the genital and urinary tracts. In a few patients, the bacteria enter the bloodstream and cause fever, chills, and loss of appetite. They may then localize in various parts of the body; for instance, they can cause small red pustules to develop on the skin, or they can cause *arthritis*, an inflammation of the joints. Other complications include *endocarditis*, an inflammation of the heart valves, and *meningitis*, an inflammation of the *meninges*—the membranes that cover the brain and spinal cord.

Laboratory Diagnosis of Gonorrhea. A tentative diagnosis of gonorrhea can be made by finding Gram-negative diplococci inside neutrophils when clinical specimens are examined microscopically. A definitive diagnosis requires that the gonococci be isolated and their identity confirmed by laboratory tests. Gonococci are isolated on a chocolate agar medium that contains antibiotics to suppress the growth of normal flora bacteria. Biochemical tests used to identify gonococci include a positive oxidase test (the colonies turn black when exposed to tetramethylphenylenediamine reagent) and the development of an acidic reaction in glucose medium but not in maltose medium.

Treatment and Prevention of Gonorrhea. Penicillin is usually effective for treatment of gonorrhea. Spectinomycin, cefotaxime, or other antibiotics are used to treat cases caused by penicillin-resistant gonococci. Work is under way on a vaccine to prevent gonorrhea.

Syphilis

Syphilis is not as widespread as gonorrhea, but it is more dreaded because it is potentially more devastating to the body. The incidence of primary and secondary syphilis in the United States reached a peak of 73 cases per 100,000 during World War II. It fell to 4 per 100,000 in 1957 but then rose sharply again during the late 1950s and early 1960s and remained relatively stable at 10 to 14 cases per 100,000. In the early 1980s there was a rapid increase of the disease in heterosexuals. Some factors that may account for this increase include (1) a greater diversion of public health efforts toward other diseases, including AIDS; (2) the ineffectiveness of spectinomycin—frequently used to treat penicillin-resistant gonorrhea—against syphilis (which many gonorrhea patients may also have); (3) the difficulty of treating syphilis in those patients who also have AIDS; and (4) the increased exchange of sexual favors by drug users in order to obtain "crack" and other drugs.

The Causative Agent of Syphilis. Syphilis is caused by a microaerophilic spirochete called *Treponema pallidum* subspecies *pallidum*. The cells of this spirochete are thin and helically coiled, and are best observed by dark-field microscopy [FIGURE 23.4]. The organism has not been

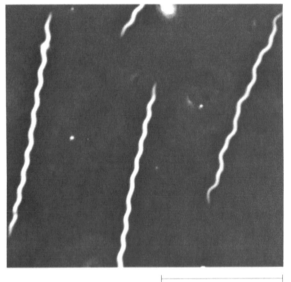

FIGURE 23.4
Treponema pallidum subspecies *pallidum* in exudate, as seen by dark-field microscopy. The spirochetes are tightly coiled cells.

5.0 μm

cultivated on laboratory culture media and can be grown—with difficulty—only in the testes of rabbits or in tissue cultures of rabbit epidermal cells. The spirochete attaches to the surface of host cells and has the ability to invade intact mucous membranes or abraded skin. The initial attachment to host cells is facilitated when the spirochetes become coated with *fibronectin*, a glycoprotein (protein with attached sugars) found in blood serum and on the surface of various mammalian tissue cells.

Transmission of the Syphilis Spirochete. Syphilis is acquired through sexual contact. Syphilis can also be a *congenital infection*—one acquired by a fetus within the uterus of its mother. The spirochetes pass from the mother's bloodstream to the fetus by crossing the *placenta*, the organ that links the fetus to the uterus and allows exchange of nutrients and waste products between mother and fetus. In most cases of congenital syphilis, the child is born healthy but develops symptoms of syphilis several weeks or months later [DISCOVER 23.1].

Pathogenicity of the Syphilis Spirochete. Syphilis occurs in several stages. The first stage is *primary syphilis,* which appears after an initial incubation period of 10 to 90 days and is characterized by a painless sore called a *chancre* on the genitals or other areas of the body [FIGURE 23.5A and B]. The chancre heals spontaneously in 25 to 40 days. *Secondary syphilis* develops 2 to 6 months later and is characterized by a generalized rash on the skin and mucous membranes [FIGURE 23.5C and D]. The rash disappears after 3 weeks to 6 months. At this point a *latent stage* may develop, which is a stage without symptoms. This may last from 3 to 30 years. The end of the latent stage is marked by the development of *tertiary syphilis,* in which the brain, spinal cord, and blood vessels are damaged. Patients with tertiary syphilis may experience failing memory, personality changes, headaches, delusions, poor coordination, blindness, loss of sensation and perception, impotency, loss of reflexes, and uncontrollable urination. Tertiary syphilis may also be accompanied by the development of disfiguring, tumorlike lesions called *gummas* on various parts of the body [FIGURE 23.5E and F].

Of untreated syphilis patients, approximately 25 percent exhibit a spontaneous cure, approximately 40 percent eventually develop signs and symptoms of tertiary syphilis but do not die of the disease, and approximately 35 percent die of tertiary syphilis. Persons who recover from syphilis can be reinfected upon subsequent sexual contact with an infected individual.

FIGURE 23.5

Clinical characteristics of the three stages of syphilis. **[A, B]** Primary syphilis. After an incubation period of 10 to 90 days during which the treponemes become distributed throughout the body, a painless sore called a *chancre* appears on the genitals **[A]** or other areas **[B]**. The chancre heals in 25 to 40 days. **[C, D]** Secondary syphilis, which develops after 2 to 6 months. A generalized rash appears on the skin **[C]** and mucous membranes **[D]**. The rash disappears after 3 weeks to 6 months. **[E, F]** Tertiary syphilis. Disfiguring, tumorlike lesions called *gummas* may appear on various parts of the body. Other aspects of tertiary syphilis include damage to the brain, spinal cord, and blood vessels.

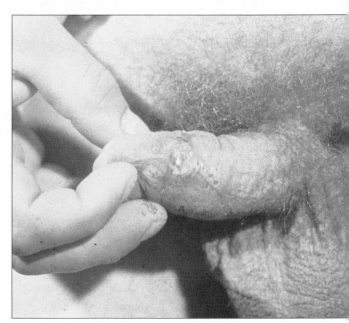

[A]

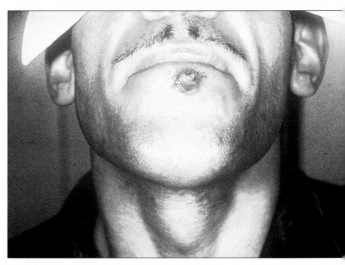

[B]

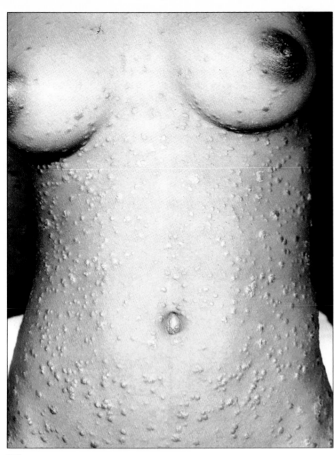

[C]

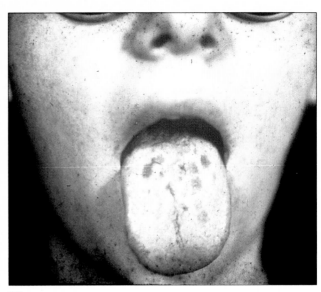

[D]

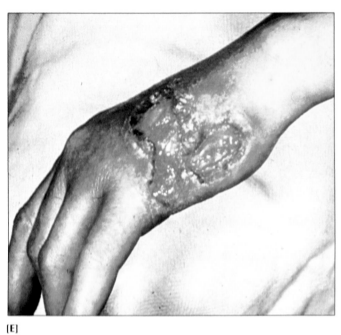

[E]

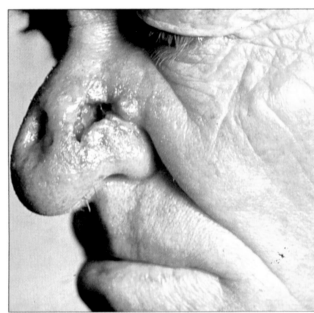

[F]

Laboratory Diagnosis of Syphilis. The quickest and most direct laboratory method of diagnosing syphilis uses dark-field microscopy to show the presence of numerous motile treponemes in the fluid from the chancre or from skin lesions. In the absence of a chancre or skin lesions, syphilis is diagnosed by demonstrating the presence of antibodies in the patient's serum which have formed in response to the infection. Simple serological screening tests are used initially for this purpose, such as the *rapid plasma reagin (RPR) test.* The RPR test is inexpensive and easy to perform, but it is a *nontreponemal* test; it does not detect antibodies against *T. pallidum* itself. Instead, it detects antibodies against an antigen called *cardiolipin*—a component of the cytoplasmic membrane of human and other mammalian cells. For unknown reasons antibodies against cardiolipin are formed in the blood of syphilitic patients; these antibodies are called *reagin.* When the serum from a syphilitic patient is added to a suspension of lipid particles containing cardiolipin, the reagin causes the particles to agglutinate [FIGURE 23.6].

However, reagin also may occur in patients with diseases such as malaria, lupus erythematosus, rheumatoid arthritis, and infectious mononucleosis. For this reason a positive RPR test must be confirmed by a *treponemal* test, which can detect antibodies against *T. pallidum* itself. These tests are more complex and more expensive than nonspecific tests because special procedures are required to grow the cells of *T. pallidum* as the antigen. The most widely used specific tests are the *fluorescent treponemal antibody (FTA) test* and the *microhemagglutination (MHA) test.*

The FTA test is an indirect fluorescent antibody test [refer to FIGURE 20.24] in which the antigen consists of *T. pallidum* cells fixed onto a microscope slide. If a patient's blood serum contains antibodies against *T. pallidum*, these antibodies (immunoglobulins) will bind to the treponemes on the slide. You then add fluorescent antibodies against human immunoglobulin. These will bind to the patient's antibodies (which were bound to the treponemes); their presence will make the treponemes glow when viewed under a fluorescence microscope. The MHA test is a passive hemagglutination test [see FIGURE 20.13] in which a small amount of the patient's serum is mixed with a suspension of red blood cells that have been coated with *T. pallidum* antigens. If the serum contains antibodies against *T. pallidum*, the antibodies will cause the red blood cells to agglutinate.

Treatment and Prevention of Syphilis. Penicillin is the antibiotic of choice for treatment of syphilis. The longer the disease progresses, the more difficult it is to cure. No vaccine is available for the prevention of syphilis, although research is in progress.

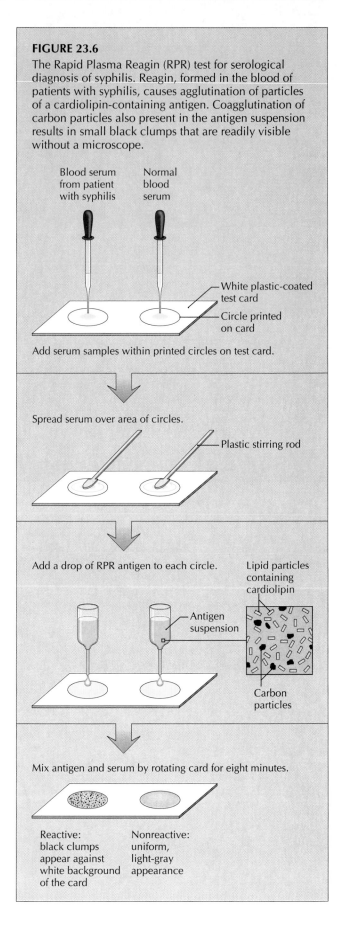

FIGURE 23.6

The Rapid Plasma Reagin (RPR) test for serological diagnosis of syphilis. Reagin, formed in the blood of patients with syphilis, causes agglutination of particles of a cardiolipin-containing antigen. Coagglutination of carbon particles also present in the antigen suspension results in small black clumps that are readily visible without a microscope.

Blood serum from patient with syphilis   Normal blood serum

White plastic-coated test card
Circle printed on card

Add serum samples within printed circles on test card.

Spread serum over area of circles.

Plastic stirring rod

Add a drop of RPR antigen to each circle.

Antigen suspension

Lipid particles containing cardiolipin

Carbon particles

Mix antigen and serum by rotating card for eight minutes.

Reactive: black clumps appear against white background of the card

Nonreactive: uniform, light-gray appearance

23.1 CONGENITAL SYPHILIS ON THE INCREASE IN THE UNITED STATES

In 1988, health departments reported to the Centers for Disease Control 691 cases of congenital syphilis in infants less than one year of age—the highest number since penicillin became widely used to treat syphilis in pregnant women in the early 1950s. In New York City alone, the number of reported cases of congenital syphilis increased more than 500 percent from 1986 through 1988—from 57 cases to 357 cases. Because congenital syphilis can be prevented by detection and treatment of syphilis early in pregnancy, such increases indicate gaps in syphilis control and prenatal care. Nationwide, as in New York City, the epidemiology of congenital syphilis parallels trends for early syphilis in women. In addition, almost half the infants with congenital syphilis reported to the Centers for Disease Control were delivered to mothers who received no prenatal care.

The increase in congenital syphilis in New York City parallels a 240 percent increase in the number of reported cases of primary and secondary syphilis in women—from 541 cases in 1986 to 1841 cases in 1988. Such increases have been linked elsewhere to use of cocaine or crack. In New York City, the proportion of mothers reporting use of cocaine increased from 1 per 1000 live births in 1981 to 21 per 1000 in 1988; no other drug has increased similarly in use.

The practice of having sex with a series of partners in exchange for drugs, especially cocaine or crack, now appears to play a major role in the transmission of syphilis. Because under these circumstances the identities of sex partners are often unknown, the traditional syphilis-control strategy of partner notification may not be effective—a failure that has been linked to congenital syphilis. In the New York City study, cocaine or crack use was also related to lack of prenatal care. Mothers of infants with congenital syphilis may not take advantage of the health care system fully.

Primary prevention of congenital syphilis will require innovative efforts to decrease syphilis incidence. Since drug users often do not use health care services, targeted screening programs may be necessary. For example, because untreated early syphilis is present in 2 percent of prisoners, many of whom are incarcerated for drug-related offenses, screening programs could be directed at that population. Innovative screening programs are especially important for detecting and treating syphilis in males.

Prevention of congenital syphilis will also require increased use of prenatal care. In all states, serological screening for syphilis is required during pregnancy; a second screening is recommended during the third trimester for high-risk populations, and follow-up and treatment must be assured. For example, in Orange County, California, rapid syphilis screening and treatment were instituted in 1986 in prenatal-care clinics so that women could be tested and treated during the same visit. As a result, congenital syphilis decreased from 12 cases in 1985 to one case each in 1987 and 1988.

Screening for syphilis at delivery is also recommended by the Centers for Disease Control for mothers who live in areas of high syphilis prevalence; it was recently mandated for all mothers by the state of New York. Since the consequences of nontreatment are grave and follow-up is often difficult, infants should not leave the hospital until the results of syphilis screening are known. Ideally, the mother's blood should be screened, because blood from the umbilical cord when used for screening may give either a false positive or a false negative result.

Adapted from *Morbidity and Mortality Weekly Report*, Dec. 8, 1989.

Chlamydia trachomatis Infections

Infections caused by *Chlamydia trachomatis* are the most prevalent of all STDs in the United States. An estimated 3 to 4 million Americans suffer from a chlamydial infection each year, and more than $1 billion in direct and indirect costs is spent on these infections annually.

The Causative Agent *C. trachomatis*. The Gram-negative bacterium *Chlamydia trachomatis* grows only within living host cells and has not been cultured on laboratory media. The organism has a unique developmental cycle, as described in Chapter 9 [see FIGURE 9.16].

Transmission of *C. trachomatis*. The strains of *C. trachomatis* that cause genital infections are transmitted by sexual contact. In addition, infants born to infected mothers can acquire serious chlamydial infections during the birth process. These newborns are at high risk of developing conjunctivitis and pneumonia.

Some strains of *C. trachomatis* cause *trachoma*, a type of conjunctivitis that is the single greatest cause of preventable blindness in the world. Trachoma is prevalent in many developing countries, particularly in the Middle East, north Africa, and northern India. It is acquired by direct contact or from contaminated inanimate objects and is not a sexually transmitted disease.

Pathogenicity of *C. trachomatis*. In women, most *C. trachomatis* infections occur without symptoms, but some infections lead to inflammation of the cervix. The organisms may spread from this site to the uterine (fallopian) tubes and associated structures to cause PID. *C. trachomatis* accounts for 25 to 50 percent of the 1 million recognized cases of PID in the United States each year.

In men, *C. trachomatis* is a common cause of *non-gonococcal urethritis* (NGU), a term used to describe a urethral inflammation that is caused by a microorganism other than *N. gonorrhoeae*. (Most cases of NGU are caused by *C. trachomatis*, but some are caused by other bacteria.) Symptoms of NGU mimic those of gonorrhea: painful urination and a discharge from the urethra.

Some strains of *C. trachomatis* can cause *lymphogranuloma venereum*, a severe sexually transmitted infection. This is an important disease in the tropics and semitropics, and many cases were brought back to the United States from Vietnam. Patients develop enlarged lymph nodes in the region of the anus and genitals, inflammation of the rectum, chills, fever, headache, and abdominal and joint pains.

Laboratory Diagnosis of *C. trachomatis* Infections. For diagnosis of *C. trachomatis*, clinical specimens are inoculated into tissue cultures and, after incubation, the tissue cells are stained by specific fluorescent antibody against *C. trachomatis*. This causes the inclusions that occur in *Chlamydia*-infected cells to become visible under a fluorescence microscope. In some instances fluorescent antibody staining can be done directly on clinical specimens that have been smeared onto a slide, providing a more rapid diagnosis.

Tetracycline, doxycycline, and erythromycin are among the antibiotics used to treat chlamydial infections. No vaccine against chlamydial infections is available.

Other Sexually Transmitted Diseases Caused by Bacteria

In addition to gonorrhea, syphilis, and chlamydial infections there are several other bacterial infections transmitted by sexual contact. Among these are chancroid, granuloma inguinale, and bacterial vaginosis.

Chancroid. Until recently, chancroid was thought to be common only in the tropics, but improved methods for isolating the causative bacterium have revealed that the disease occurs worldwide. Several large outbreaks were reported in North America during the 1980s. The disease is caused by *Haemophilus ducreyi*, a very small Gram-negative bacillus. Painful open sores appear on the genitals, usually within 5 to 7 days after exposure. These lesions may resemble those of syphilis, and laboratory diagnosis is required to differentiate the two diseases. This is done by isolating *H. ducreyi* from the sores on the genitals or from swollen lymph nodes in the groin. The disease can be treated effectively with erythromycin or other antibiotics.

Granuloma Inguinale. Granuloma inguinale is caused by *Calymmatobacterium granulomatis*, a Gram-negative rod. The disease involves the development of small, spreading, pus-filled ulcers on the genitals. It takes at least 3 months for the symptoms to appear; meanwhile, a great many people can be infected by a person harboring the causative agent before that person becomes aware that he or she has the disease. Granuloma inguinale can cause serious complications if left untreated, but antibiotics such as tetracycline can eliminate the infection.

Bacterial Vaginosis. Bacterial vaginosis, also called *nonspecific vaginitis*, is common in young women following puberty and is characterized by a vaginal discharge without pain or itching. It is believed to be caused by a bacterium called *Gardnerella vaginalis*, although various anaerobic bacteria may work in combination with it. *Gardnerella vaginalis* is a short, rod-shaped bacterium that stains Gram-negative to Gram-variable [FIGURE 23.7]. Infected males do not exhibit clinical symptoms but nevertheless are capable of transmitting the bacteria. Bacterial vaginosis can be treated with a drug called metronidazole.

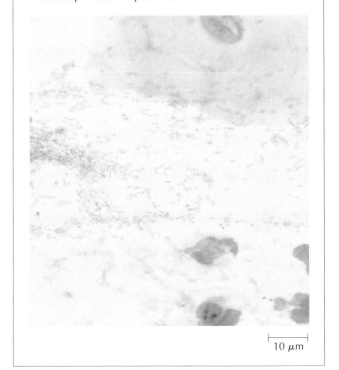

FIGURE 23.7

Gram-stained smear from a cervical specimen showing hundreds of short Gram-negative rod-shaped cells of *Gardnerella vaginalis*. The large red objects in the microscope field are pus cells.

10 μm

1 Which bacterial species cause the following diseases: gonorrhea, syphilis, pelvic inflammatory disease, nongonococcal urethritis, lymphogranuloma venereum, chancroid, granuloma inguinale, bacterial vaginosis? Which of these diseases can be caused by more than one kind of bacterium?

2 What is the primary site of gonococcal infection in the female? In the male? What are the characteristics of the following diseases: gonococcal arthritis, gonococcal urethritis, pelvic inflammatory disease, ectopic pregnancy, gonococcal conjunctivitis?

3 How is gonorrhea diagnosed in the laboratory? How is gonorrhea treated?

4 What are the differences in the symptoms that occur during the primary, secondary, and tertiary stages of syphilis? What is congenital syphilis, and how is it acquired?

5 What is the principle behind each of the following serological tests for syphilis: **(a)** the RPR test; **(b)** the FTA test; **(c)** the MHA test? How is syphilis treated?

6 What diseases can be caused by *Chlamydia trachomatis*? How are these diseases diagnosed in the laboratory? With what are they treated?

SEXUALLY TRANSMITTED DISEASES CAUSED BY VIRUSES

Sexually transmitted diseases caused by viruses include AIDS, genital herpes, type B hepatitis, and condyloma acuminata. Of these, AIDS unquestionably ranks as the most serious pandemic to confront modern society and the medical profession at the present time.

AIDS

The World Health Organization (WHO) estimates that 8 to 10 million adults and 1 million children worldwide are infected with the AIDS virus. By the year 2000, 40 million persons may be infected with the virus. More than 90 percent of these persons will reside in developing countries in sub-Saharan Africa, south and southeast Asia, Latin America, and the Caribbean. In addition, during the 1990s, the mothers or both parents of more

than 10 million children will have died from AIDS. If these predictions become reality, AIDS will rank among the greatest disease scourges experienced by the human race.

The first cases of AIDS in the United States probably occurred in the 1960s and 1970s, but AIDS was not recognized as a new kind of disease until 1981. By 1982 cases were reported in 15 states. At first the number of cases was quite low—158 men and one woman—but by 1983, 3000 cases of AIDS had been reported in adults from 42 states. The incidence has since increased at an alarming rate [FIGURE 23.8]. Of the 206,392 persons known to have contracted AIDS in the United States before December 31, 1991, 133,232 (64 percent) have died of the disease—approximately twice the number of American soldiers killed in the Vietnam war. Some estimates suggest that AIDS will soon become the second leading cause of death among men 25 to 44 years of age and that it is likely to become one of the five leading causes of death among women aged 15 to 44 years in the United States [DISCOVER 23.2].

In the United States AIDS first occurred mainly in homosexual and bisexual males, and this group still represents the highest proportion of AIDS cases overall [FIGURE 23.9]. However, the rate of increase in new AIDS cases within this group has decreased in recent years [FIGURE 23.10], presumably because of a change in behavioral patterns following the discovery of the modes of transmission of the virus.

Intravenous drug users, who traditionally share needles, are the group with the next highest incidence. In fact, in some areas of the United States intravenous drug users have become the group with the highest inci-

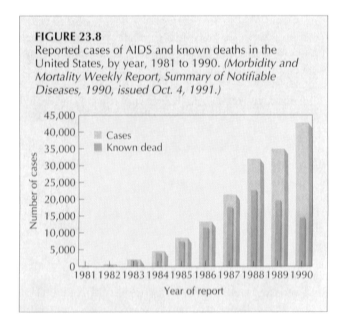

FIGURE 23.8
Reported cases of AIDS and known deaths in the United States, by year, 1981 to 1990. *(Morbidity and Mortality Weekly Report, Summary of Notifiable Diseases, 1990, issued Oct. 4, 1991.)*

FIGURE 23.9

Reported cases of AIDS by transmission category, United States, 1990. (*Morbidity and Mortality Weekly Report, June 7, 1991.*)

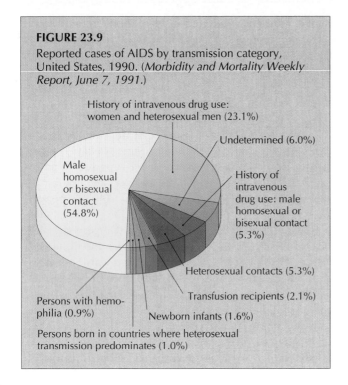

History of intravenous drug use: women and heterosexual men (23.1%)

Undetermined (6.0%)

History of intravenous drug use: male homosexual or bisexual contact (5.3%)

Male homosexual or bisexual contact (54.8%)

Heterosexual contacts (5.3%)

Transfusion recipients (2.1%)

Persons with hemophilia (0.9%)

Newborn infants (1.6%)

Persons born in countries where heterosexual transmission predominates (1.0%)

FIGURE 23.10

AIDS cases, by transmission category and year of diagnosis, United States, 1981–1990, based on cases reported through March 1991 and adjusted for reporting delays. In 1990 the greatest rates of increase occurred in heterosexuals and in infants born to infected mothers. A slowing in the rate of increase occurred among homosexual and bisexual men. The relatively few AIDS cases in recipients of transfused blood or blood products were due mainly to infection that occurred before screening of donated blood or heat treatment of the clotting factors given to hemophiliacs. These cases have been increasing in number because of the long period between infection with the HIV virus and onset of AIDS. (*Morbidity and Mortality Weekly Report, June 7, 1991.*)

Total cases, cases among homosexual or bisexual men (excluding intravenous drug users), and cases among women and heterosexual men reporting intravenous drug use

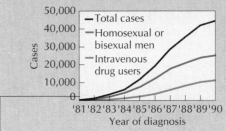

Cases among persons reporting heterosexual contact with persons with, or at high risk for, HIV infection

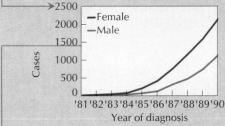

Cases among recipients of transfusions of blood or blood products

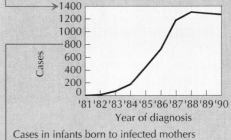

Cases in infants born to infected mothers

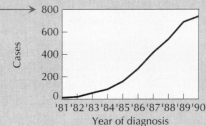

dence. Other groups—hemophiliacs receiving blood derivatives, blood transfusion recipients, heterosexuals, and infants born to infected mothers—have lower incidences [FIGURES 23.9 and 23.10].

In the United States and Europe the number of cases of AIDS acquired by heterosexual intercourse has been relatively low thus far (about 2 to 5 percent of the total cases), and, in 1991, the ratio between males and females with AIDS in the United States was approximately 7 : 1. However, the situation in developing countries such as those in central Africa is very different. There the disease is transmitted mainly by heterosexual contact, and the ratio between males and females is approximately 1 : 1.

The Causative Agents of AIDS. AIDS can be caused by either of two related viruses called HIV-1 and HIV-2 ("HIV" stands for *human immunodeficiency virus*). Scientists think it may be possible that other HIV viruses, still undiscovered, also cause AIDS. Virtually all AIDS cases in the United States are caused by HIV-1. In west Africa HIV-2 predominates, whereas in central Africa HIV-1 is predominant. Both types of HIV infect human cells in a similar manner and cause the same kind of severe damage to the patient's immune system.

The structure of HIV-1 is shown in FIGURE 23.11. The internal portion of HIV consists of single-stranded RNA and the enzyme *reverse transcriptase* (making HIV a *retrovirus*). These are contained within a protein capsid, which is surrounded by internal envelope protein 17

23.2 THE HIGH COST OF AIDS

AIDS is expensive, and the costs are expected to increase rapidly. The medical costs for a typical AIDS patient range from $50,000 to $150,000. It has been estimated that during the year 1991 there were approximately 174,000 AIDS patients in the United States requiring medical care (new cases and patients with old cases still living). The total funds required for medical care of AIDS patients in 1991, then, would be at least 174,000 × $50,000 = $8,700,000,000.

About a fifth of the people infected with HIV have no health insurance. Most of these persons seek treatment at public hospitals. Moreover, funds, space, and facilities for treatment of people with AIDS have been nearly exhausted in many large inner-city hospitals. Some of these hospitals may eventually face bankruptcy, and others have closed their emergency rooms.

To the direct medical costs must be added the indirect costs to society resulting from loss of productivity, wages, and future earnings due to premature deaths—costs that may be as high as $16,000,000,000 per year.

The significance of such gigantic figures is that, in addition to causing great human suffering and loss of life, this single disease will produce an enormous strain on the medical facilities and the financial resources of the entire nation if the epidemic continues to increase at its present rate.

FIGURE 23.11
Drawing of the structure of HIV, the virus that causes AIDS.

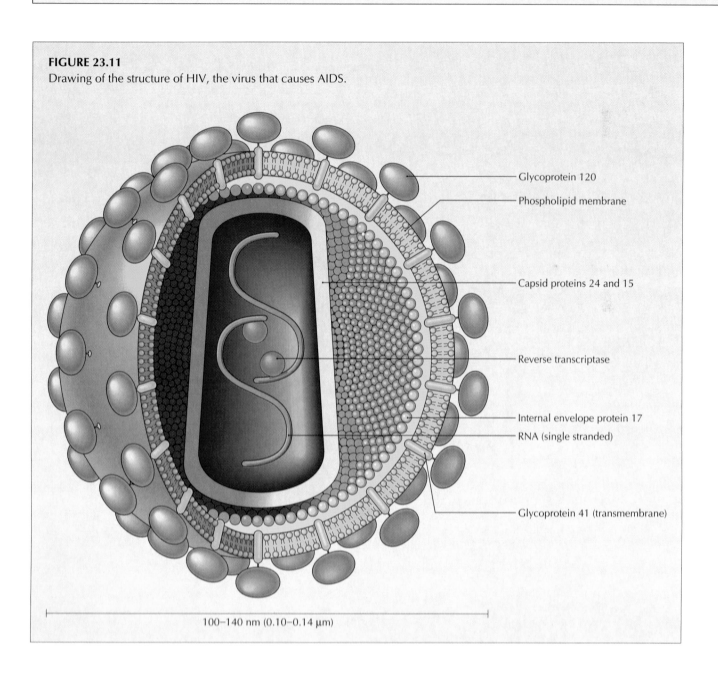

Glycoprotein 120

Phospholipid membrane

Capsid proteins 24 and 15

Reverse transcriptase

Internal envelope protein 17

RNA (single stranded)

Glycoprotein 41 (transmembrane)

100–140 nm (0.10–0.14 μm)

and a phospholipid membrane studded with glycoproteins. The glycoproteins allow the virus to attach to a chemical receptor called *CD4* on the surface of T4 lymphocytes ("helper T cells"; see Chapter 19). After binding to CD4 and entering a T4 lymphocyte, the virus loses its capsid, exposing its RNA. The reverse transcriptase then synthesizes a single strand of DNA that is complementary to the viral RNA. (Recall from Chapter 16 [see DISCOVER 16.2] that this enzyme differs from ordinary DNA polymerases because it uses an RNA strand instead of a DNA strand as the template for constructing a complementary strand of DNA.) The single-stranded DNA is enzymatically converted to double-stranded DNA, which is then integrated into the host cell's own DNA [FIGURE 23.12].

In this integrated form the virus is dormant and causes no damage to the infected cell. However, at some later date the virus becomes activated from its dormant state. When this activation occurs, the viral DNA directs the synthesis of new viral RNA and viral proteins. Then the RNA and proteins are assembled into numerous viral progeny, which are liberated from the surface of the host cell to infect other T4 lymphocytes. The host T4 lymphocyte is killed during this viral multiplication.

HIV also infects other cells in the body, such as the macrophages, the monocytes, and perhaps the microglial cells in the brain. Apparently these cells are not killed when they release new HIV, making them a potential reservoir for the virus. Scientists are still unraveling the mystery of which cells are affected by HIV.

FIGURE 23.12

Replication of HIV in a T4 lymphocyte. **[A]** Diagram showing the major steps in replication. A key step is the synthesis of a DNA strand complementary to the viral RNA, forming an RNA-DNA hybrid; this step is carried out by an enzyme called *reverse transcriptase*. The RNA-DNA hybrid is then converted to double-stranded DNA, which becomes integrated into the DNA of the host cell. Later, upon activation, the viral DNA directs the synthesis of viral RNA and viral proteins, which are then assembled into viral progeny. **[B]** Electron micrograph showing progeny HIV virions budding from the surface of an infected T4 lymphocyte. The virions are approximately 110 nm in diameter.

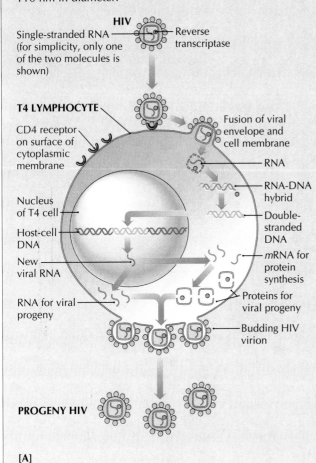

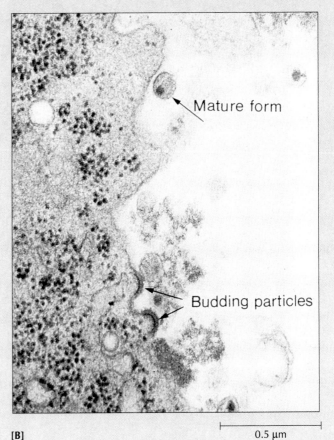

[A]   [B]   0.5 μm

In 1990, some researchers suggested that a mycoplasma bacterium contributes to AIDS by activating HIV, causing the virus to replicate itself and overwhelm the patient's immune system. Thus patients infected with the mycoplasma in addition to the virus would develop AIDS quickly. This provocative idea was received with considerable skepticism by most AIDS researchers, and it remains to be seen whether it can be confirmed.

Transmission of HIV. HIV is transmitted by both homosexual and heterosexual contact. In an infected male, the virus occurs in the *semen*, the fluid that carries the male sex cells. It also occurs in the blood of infected males and females, and in the vaginal secretions of infected females. During sexual contact, the virus gains entrance to the bloodstream of an uninfected individual, male or female, by means of microscopic breaks in the mucous membrane lining of the genital organs or rectum.

HIV also can be transmitted by residual contaminated blood on hypodermic needles and syringes that are shared among intravenous drug users [DISCOVER 23.3]. It is important to note that not only those who use so-called street drugs, but also those who use injectable substances such as steroids, can become infected if they share needles and syringes. HIV can be transmitted by blood transfusions with contaminated blood; however, the widespread screening of blood supplies by hospitals and blood banks has reduced such transmission to a very low level. Estimates made in 1989 suggested that the risk of contracting HIV infection by transfusion with one unit of screened blood ranged from 1 in 40,000 to 1 in 150,000.

Another route through which HIV can be acquired is from a mother to her infant. It can be transmitted either before birth or during exposure to blood or other infected fluids during passage through the birth canal. Not all children born to infected mothers become infected. There also are a few cases indicating that HIV can be transmitted in breast milk.

HIV occurs not only in the semen, vaginal secretions, and blood of infected individuals but also in the saliva, tears, urine, and feces. In view of this, one might think that the virus could be acquired from people with AIDS through the type of nonsexual, "casual" contact involved in daily life, such as handshaking or coughing. However, no known case of AIDS has ever been traced to casual contact with someone who has AIDS or HIV infection. Even in the families of AIDS patients there has been no evidence of transmission of the virus through the sharing of food, towels, cups, razors, and even toothbrushes.

Among doctors, nurses, and other health workers who have been exposed to HIV, infection has been extremely rare—associated only with such instances as being accidentally stuck with a contaminated needle or being spattered with blood when a rubber stopper was suddenly expelled from a blood-collection tube. Nevertheless, health care personnel are at a higher potential risk than the general population, and the CDC recommends that these persons use "universal precautions" in the care of all patients [see DISCOVER 22.3].

Pathogenicity of HIV. Individuals who are infected with the AIDS virus usually do not develop AIDS-related symptoms immediately. Therefore they may not be diagnosed as having AIDS until long after they become infected. This is because after the virus initially multiplies in the body, the person's immune system produces antibodies against the virus. These antibodies can control further viral multiplication for some period of time, often for several years. However, they do not completely eliminate the virus, because much of it exists as part of the genome of the host's T4 lymphocytes. The most insidious aspect of HIV infection is that, when a T4 cell carrying HIV becomes stimulated during an immune response, the HIV becomes activated, replicates, and kills the host T4 cell. Thus *the activation of the body's immune system contributes to the destruction of an essential component of the immune system, the helper T4 cells.* It is in this manner that the virus gradually gains ground and eventually damages the immune system to the point that the body can no longer hold the virus in check [FIGURE 23.13]. This is followed by development of clinical illness indicative of AIDS.

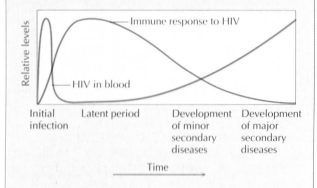

FIGURE 23.13

Interaction between HIV and the immune system. After initial infection the virus level in the blood is high, but it decreases as the patient develops an immune response to the infection. During the latent period, which may last for several years, HIV exists mainly as viral DNA integrated into the genome of T4 lymphocytes. Eventual destruction of the T4 cells damages the immune system to the point where it can no longer control multiplication of the virus. In the absence of a functional immune system, severe secondary diseases can readily occur.

Twenty to thirty percent of persons infected by the virus have developed AIDS within 5 years, but some individuals have remained healthy for up to 10 or more years. It is important to realize that although HIV-infected individuals may have no symptoms of AIDS, they nevertheless can transmit the virus to other persons, and so they are asymptomatic carriers.

In those who develop symptoms of AIDS, the illness is due to destruction of T4 lymphocytes during HIV multiplication. This destruction causes severe damage to the body's immune system, because T4 lymphocytes are needed for the normal functioning of other T lymphocytes and of B cells and macrophages. As a result, those with AIDS become highly vulnerable to *secondary infections* caused by various bacteria, protozoa, fungi, or viruses. The microorganisms that cause these secondary infections ordinarily have low pathogenicity and seldom cause disease in the general population. However, they frequently infect AIDS patients because these individuals have a deficient immune system. In addition, someone with AIDS may also suffer damage from HIV itself, because the virus can eventually attack the nervous system and cause damage to the brain. This damage may take years to develop, and the symptoms may show up as memory loss, indifference, loss of coordination, partial paralysis, or mental disorder.

Secondary Diseases Indicative of AIDS. A case of AIDS usually is signaled by the development of some secondary disease that indicates a defect in the immune system of the patient and that occurs in the absence of any other known cause of diminished resistance to that disease. These secondary diseases are often extremely serious and very difficult to cure. The two secondary diseases most common in AIDS patients are Kaposi's sarcoma and *Pneumocystis carinii* pneumonia [FIGURE 23.14]. These and other secondary diseases associated with AIDS are characterized as follows:

FIGURE 23.15
Purplish lesions of Kaposi's sarcoma on the heel and lateral foot.

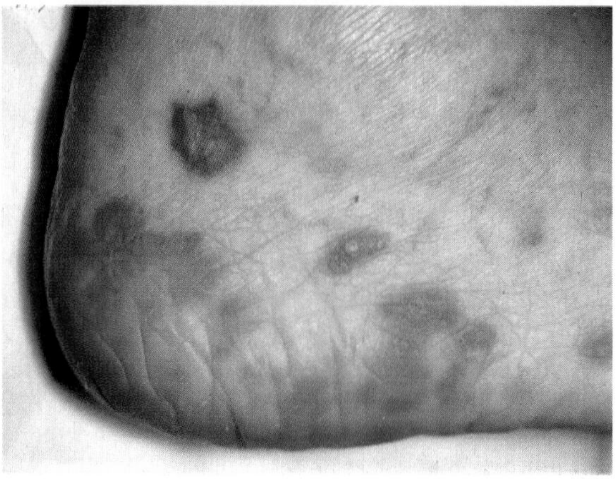

1 *Kaposi's sarcoma (KS)*, a type of cancer that begins as blue-violet or brownish blotches or bumps on the skin [FIGURE 23.15]. In patients who do not have AIDS, these skin lesions usually occur on the legs, develop slowly, and do not invade the rest of the body. In those with AIDS, however, the cancer spreads rapidly to the lungs, lymph nodes, intestinal tract, and sometimes even the brain. The cause of KS is uncertain, but recent studies suggest that HIV itself may be responsible. When an HIV gene was introduced into mice by genetic engineering techniques, the mice developed skin lesions that resembled the KS lesions seen in AIDS patients.

2 *Pneumocystis carinii pneumonia (PCP)*, a lung infection caused by a eucaryotic microorganism, *Pneumocystis carinii* [FIGURE 23.16]. Although this organism has long been thought to be a protozoan, recent

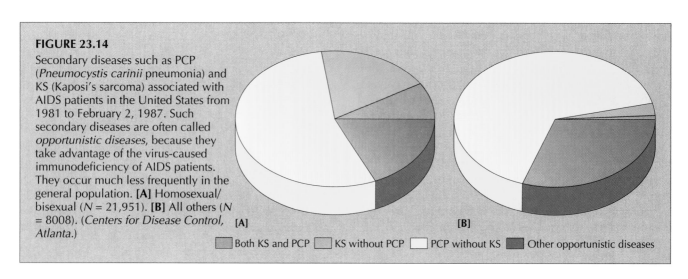

FIGURE 23.14
Secondary diseases such as PCP (*Pneumocystis carinii* pneumonia) and KS (Kaposi's sarcoma) associated with AIDS patients in the United States from 1981 to February 2, 1987. Such secondary diseases are often called *opportunistic diseases*, because they take advantage of the virus-caused immunodeficiency of AIDS patients. They occur much less frequently in the general population. **[A]** Homosexual/bisexual (*N* = 21,951). **[B]** All others (*N* = 8008). (*Centers for Disease Control, Atlanta.*)

[A] [B]

■ Both KS and PCP □ KS without PCP □ PCP without KS ■ Other opportunistic diseases

DISCOVER!

23.3 CAN MOSQUITOES TRANSMIT THE AIDS VIRUS?

It is known that small amounts of residual infected blood on contaminated hypodermic syringes and needles can transmit the AIDS virus (HIV) among drug users. For this reason there has been some concern as to whether mosquitoes or other arthropods may be involved in transmission of the virus. Some researchers have likened mosquitoes to "flying syringes" that could carry the virus from an infected individual to healthy persons.

Although theoretically the possibility does exist that insects may transmit the AIDS virus, present evidence suggests that such transmission is highly unlikely.

Studies of frequency and occurrence of AIDS have provided no evidence linking mosquitoes with the disease. For instance, if mosquitoes can transmit the virus, it is difficult to explain why the incidence of HIV infection or AIDS in children should be so low.

In laboratory studies, researchers at the Centers for Disease Control have shown that even in mosquitoes injected with HIV-contaminated blood, the virus survives for only one hour in the insects and does not multiply either in the mosquitoes or in tissue cultures of mosquito cells. Moreover, current efforts to transmit the virus from the insects to human cells in the laboratory have been unsuccessful.

FIGURE 23.16

Cysts of *Pneumocystis carinii* from a lung smear stained with toluidine blue. Note the "folded" cyst walls; this feature is of diagnostic value. Trophozoites are not apparent within the cysts by this stain.

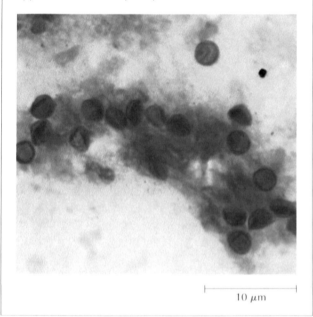

10 μm

studies indicate that it is probably a yeast. In persons who do not have AIDS the pneumonia is easily treated, but in AIDS patients it is much more difficult to treat. Moreover, approximately 20 percent of those who do respond usually have relapses. It is currently the most common cause of death among people with AIDS.

3 *Cytomegalovirus (CMV) infection*, which causes spots on the retina and can lead to blindness.

4 *Candidiasis*, caused by the yeast *Candida albicans* [FIGURE 23.17], which typically produces whitish patches ("cottage cheese plaques") on the soft palate, tonsils, and mucous membranes of the mouth.

5 *Toxoplasmosis*, caused by the protozoan *Toxoplasma gondii*. This organism infects 20 to 40 percent of the adult population in United States, but the infections are normally held in check by the immune response. When a person develops AIDS, however, the dormant cysts can become activated, allowing the parasite to infect the brain and other body organs.

6 *Cryptosporidiosis*, caused by protozoa in the genus *Cryptosporidium*. In persons with a normal immune system, this organism causes only a mild diarrhea that disappears in 1 to 2 weeks. In patients with AIDS the diarrhea is severe, long-lasting, and recurring, and can result in the loss of so much fluid that the patient can die of dehydration and malnutrition.

7 Infection by *Mycobacterium avium* and *Mycobacterium intracellulare*. These acid-fast bacilli resemble the causative agent of tuberculosis, *Mycobacterium tuberculosis*, but normally they have a much lower degree of pathogenicity. But in people with AIDS they often cause serious infections of the brain and other organs. Such infections are very difficult to treat because the bacilli are resistant to most of the antimicrobial agents used to treat tuberculosis.

Laboratory Diagnosis of HIV Infection. The laboratory tests most commonly used to detect infection by HIV are designed to identify *antibodies* that an infected person develops against HIV; they do not detect the virus itself. The antibodies usually appear in the blood within 1 or 2 months after the person becomes infected. An indirect ELISA test (Chapter 20) has been used widely, but it requires sophisticated equipment and takes 3 to 4 hours

FIGURE 23.17

Candida albicans, a yeast. The organism has a tendency to form pseudohyphae, chains of elongated budding cells. **[A]** In culture, clusters of blastospores and large round structures called *chlamydospores* are characteristically formed. **[B]** Gram stain of a section of human tissue showing *C. albicans*. **[C]** Candidiasis lesions on the tongue and lips of a 19-year-old male.

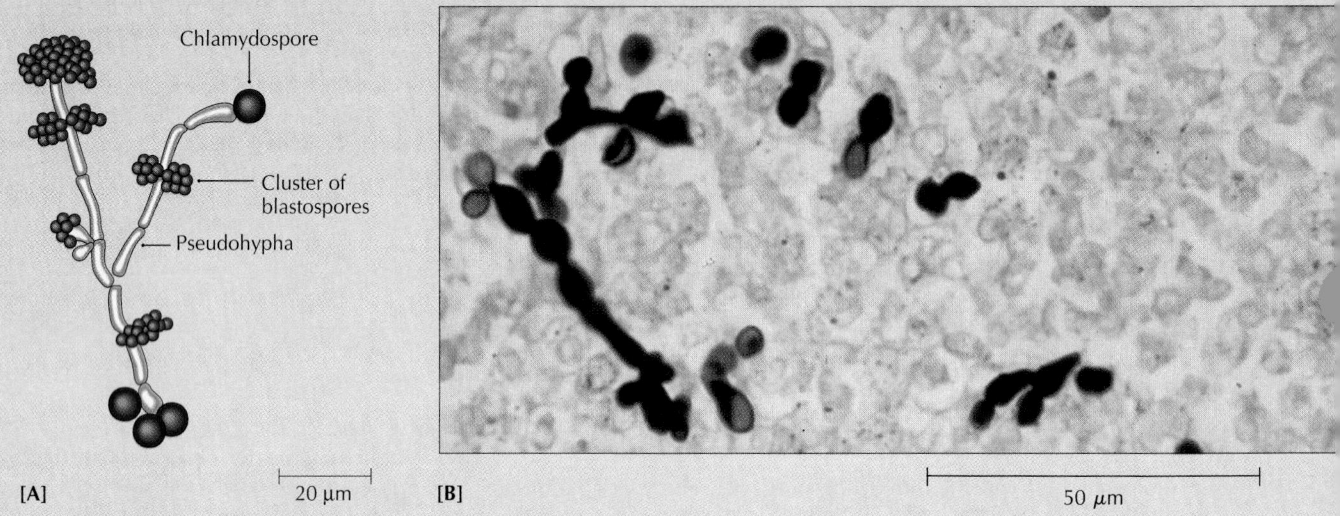

Chlamydospore

Cluster of blastospores

Pseudohypha

[A]   20 μm

[B]   50 μm

to perform. In 1988 a much simpler test to detect the antibodies was introduced which takes only 5 minutes. It is performed by placing a drop of blood on a plastic card, and then mixing the blood with microscopic white latex beads that have been coated previously with an HIV protein antigen. (The antigen is made by genetic engineering techniques instead of being extracted from the virus itself.) If antibodies against HIV are present in the blood, they will bind to the protein antigen and cause the latex beads to clump together.

Both the ELISA test and the latex bead test are highly sensitive and specific, but they occasionally can give a false positive result. For this reason, all positive tests require confirmation by a more specific and more expensive test that uses a procedure called a *Western blot*. This test detects and identifies antibodies against specific protein components of HIV. The test antigen used is a mixture of the HIV proteins prepared by disrupting purified HIV virions. The various proteins are separated by electrophoresis into a series of protein bands, which are then transferred to a strip of nitrocellulose paper. When the paper strip is treated with a patient's serum containing antibodies against HIV, the patient's antibodies will bind to the viral proteins on the paper. Then enzyme-linked antibodies against human immunoglobulins are placed on the paper, where they attach to the patient's antibodies. When the substrate for the enzyme is added, the enzyme will convert the substrate to a visible colored product. Thus a pattern of distinctive colored bands will appear on the paper strip. Each band shows where the patient's antibodies have reacted with a particular HIV protein component.

In the United States, all blood donated for use in blood transfusions is screened for the presence of antibodies against HIV. Because of this screening, transmission of the virus by transfusion with contaminated blood has become very rare.

One difficulty with tests that detect antibodies against HIV is that these antibodies take several weeks to several months to develop after a person has been infected. For this reason, other tests are being developed that can detect the presence of HIV itself. These tests should be used in conjunction with, not instead of, the tests for HIV antibodies. This is because the level of the virus in the blood is very low when the individual is producing antibodies against the virus. The virus levels in the blood remain low, sometimes for several years, until the immune system becomes so seriously damaged that it no longer can control the infection [see FIGURE 23.13]. During this latent period the only evidence of HIV infection may be viral DNA that has been integrated into the DNA of the infected T4 cells. One recently developed diagnostic test can detect very tiny amounts of this integrated viral DNA—amounts that fail to show up in ordinary tests. The new test uses a *polymerase chain reaction (PCR)*, an amplification technique by which billions of copies of DNA can be synthesized in a test tube from only a few initial copies [see DISCOVER

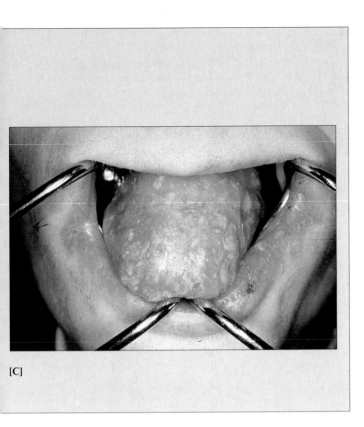

[C]

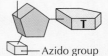

FIGURE 23.18
[A] Azidothymidine (AZT) resembles thymidine, a building block of DNA. [B] The reverse transcriptase of HIV is easily fooled into using AZT instead of thymidine; this causes termination of viral DNA synthesis.

Thymidine
(building block for DNA)

Azidothymidine (AZT)
(masquerades as thymidine)

[A]

Azido group

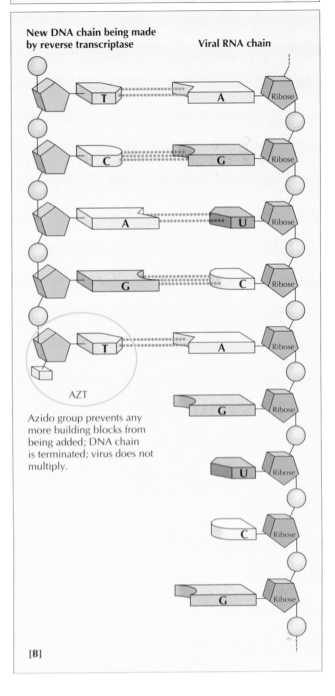

New DNA chain being made by reverse transcriptase

Viral RNA chain

AZT

Azido group prevents any more building blocks from being added; DNA chain is terminated; virus does not multiply.

[B]

13.1]. If a person is infected by HIV, even a tiny amount of viral DNA extracted from a test sample of that person's T4 cells can be amplified to the point where it can be detected easily by ordinary methods.

Some laboratory tests for diagnosing AIDS are designed to detect the damage that HIV causes to the immune system. These tests are based on demonstrating a decreased ratio of T4 lymphocytes (helper T cells) to T8 lymphocytes (suppressor T cells). In persons with AIDS, the T4:T8 ratio is abnormally low because T4 cells are destroyed by HIV but T8 lymphocytes are not attacked.

Treatment and Prevention of HIV Infection and AIDS.
Azidothymidine (AZT)—also called *zidovudine*—is a chemical compound that has been approved for treatment of AIDS patients and those with HIV infection. Although it does not cure the disease, it does retard multiplication of the virus and can prolong life. AZT interferes with the synthesis of viral DNA by masquerading as thymidine, a legitimate nucleotide building block of the DNA [FIGURE 23.18A]. The viral reverse transcriptase is easily fooled into incorporating the false building block into a growing DNA chain. After the AZT is incorporated, no additional nucleotides can be added, and viral DNA synthesis stops [FIGURE 23.18B]. AZT has little effect on human cells, because they use DNA polymerase, not reverse transcriptase, to make DNA. DNA polymerase is not so easily fooled into using AZT. How-

ever, 30 to 40 percent of patients treated with AZT may develop serious side effects, such as anemia, due to the toxicity of the drug to the bone marrow.

AZT is not only useful for treating severe cases of AIDS; it can also delay progression of the disease in infected persons who are in the early stages of AIDS and have only very mild symptoms. Moreover, when the chemical is administered to such persons, severe side effects are less likely to occur. Studies are under way to test the ability of the drug to delay onset of the disease in people who are infected but have not yet developed any symptoms. Unfortunately, the high cost of AZT will make it difficult to use the drug to treat large numbers of infected people.

A major research effort is under way to discover other chemotherapeutic agents against HIV infection and AIDS. In 1991, a drug called *dideoxyinosine (DDI)* was approved by the United States Food and Drug Administration (FDA) to be used mainly for AIDS patients who cannot tolerate or who no longer respond to AZT. It is significant that approval was granted even though DDI had not been subjected to all the rigorous clinical tests ordinarily required by the FDA. This was because of the extremely urgent need for chemotherapeutic agents to treat AIDS. DDI acts by inhibiting reverse transcriptase in a manner similar to AZT. Although it seems to be somewhat less active than AZT, it is also much less toxic to tissue cells and causes fewer adverse effects in the patient. Another potential agent that shows promise is a soluble, abbreviated version of the *CD4 glycoprotein,* produced by genetic engineering techniques. Its activity is based on the fact that HIV initiates infection by attaching to CD4 receptors on the surface of T4 lymphocytes. Theoretically, if soluble synthetic CD4 molecules were injected into someone infected with the virus, HIV would bind harmlessly to these decoy molecules instead of to T4 cells, thus neutralizing its infectivity [FIGURE 23.19]. Although the synthetic CD4 works well in test tube experiments, whether it is safe and effective for treating humans remains to be determined.

Several potential vaccines for prevention of AIDS are under intensive development. These vaccines are based on the principle that the glycoproteins of the HIV envelope, when injected into a noninfected person, may stimulate the production of antibodies that can prevent attachment of the virus to T4 lymphocytes. However, vaccine development is complicated by the fact that HIV undergoes frequent mutation and exhibits variability in its envelope proteins. This means that even if antibodies against a particular envelope protein are able to protect a person against one variety of HIV, they may not protect against varieties that have different envelope proteins. Some research groups are studying potential vaccines made from other, less variable portions of the virus. It

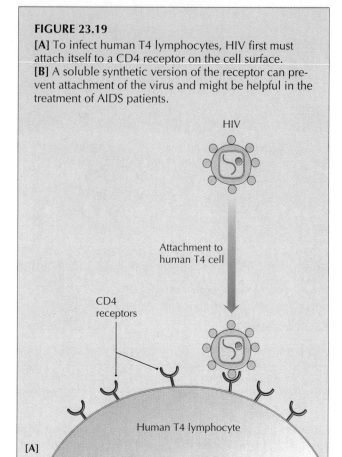

FIGURE 23.19
[A] To infect human T4 lymphocytes, HIV first must attach itself to a CD4 receptor on the cell surface.
[B] A soluble synthetic version of the receptor can prevent attachment of the virus and might be helpful in the treatment of AIDS patients.

HIV

Attachment to human T4 cell

CD4 receptors

Human T4 lymphocyte

[A]

Synthetic CD4 receptors

Human T4 lymphocyte

[B]

should be mentioned that many of the vaccines under study are not true vaccines in that they would not *prevent* HIV infection; instead, it is hoped they might keep already infected persons from developing AIDS.

Genital Herpes

Genital herpes is one of the most prevalent and well-known STDs. It is estimated that as many as 500,000 new cases of genital herpes occur each year in the United States, with the highest incidence occurring in young adults. It is characterized by alternating latent and active periods in an infected person. (Herpes infection can be deadly in people with AIDS because of their deficient immune system.)

The Causative Agents of Genital Herpes. About 80 percent of the cases are caused by *herpes simplex virus type 2 (HSV-2)*. A closely related virus, *herpes simplex virus type 1 (HSV-1)*, causes about 20 percent of genital herpes cases, but it is better known as the cause of "fever blisters," cold sores, and skin lesions on nongenital areas [FIGURE 23.20A].

Herpes simplex viruses contain double-stranded DNA enclosed within an icosahedral capsid. During viral replication, the nucleocapsids are assembled in the nucleus of the infected host cell. After assembly, each nucleocapsid passes out of the nucleus into the cytoplasm, and in the process it takes along a piece of nuclear membrane which forms a lipid envelope around the virus.

Transmission of Herpes Simplex Viruses. HSV-2 is transmitted by sexual intercourse, whereas HSV-1 is transmitted mainly by oral secretions. When HSV-1 causes genital herpes it is usually acquired by oral-genital contact.

HSV-2 infection in pregnant women can lead to serious and even fatal disease in newborn infants. During the birth process the virus can be acquired from the mother and can invade the skin, eyes, central nervous system, and visceral organs of the newborn [FIGURE 23.20B].

Pathogenicity of HSV-2. Primary genital herpes develops after an incubation period of 10 to 20 days. In women, small, painful, blisterlike lesions develop on the cervix, in the vagina [FIGURE 23.20C] and the urethra, and around the anus. In men, the lesions are on the penis, in the urethra, or around the anus. The lesions become crusted and heal without leaving scars. The virus is present in the lesions, and the disease is most contagious when the lesions are present. However, the

FIGURE 23.20

[A] Herpes simplex lesion on the lip of a patient, second day after onset. [B] Herpes simplex skin lesions in a newborn (age 12 h). [C] Primary genital herpes of the vagina, after the initial vesicles (blisters) have ruptured to form shallow ulcers (open sores). Many of the lesions have healed, but some ulceration remains.

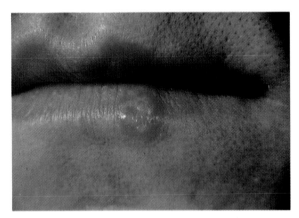

[A]

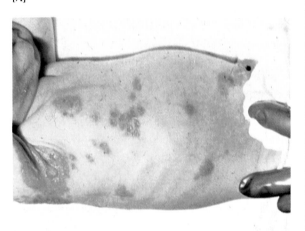

[B]

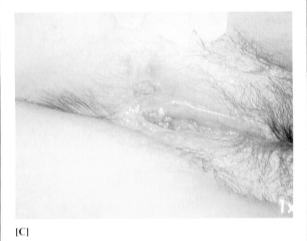

[C]

disease sometimes may be contagious even when the lesions are absent. Other manifestations of the disease include fever, painful urination, inflammation of the nearby lymph nodes, and genital soreness.

After the primary lesions disappear, the virus remains latent—which means it persists without causing symptoms of the disease. The latent period may range from a few weeks to a year or more; during this time the viral DNA persists in certain nerve cells. The virus can be reactivated periodically and travels down the nerves to infect cells in the skin, resulting in *recurrent genital herpes.* A patient may suffer from several such recurrences during a year. In women, recurrences usually involve the cervix; in men the lesions usually occur on the penis. Several studies have shown a definite link between genital herpes and cancer of the cervix or prostate, although whether HSV-2 actually causes the cancer has not been proven.

Pathogenicity of HSV-1. Unlike HSV-2, HSV-1 is often contracted by children, and by adulthood more than 50 percent of the population may harbor the virus. On initial contact with HSV-1, more than 90 percent of persons develop only a symptomless infection. The remainder may experience blisterlike eruptions in the mouth, an inflamed throat, cold sores, conjunctivitis, or skin lesions. Occasionally more severe and even fatal infections occur, such as encephalitis, an inflammation of the brain.

After the primary infection, HSV-1 often persists in the body in a latent form. The latent virus may be reactivated by environmental factors such as heat or cold, by hormonal or emotional disturbances, or by other stimuli. Patients may develop superficial blisterlike lesions such as cold sores and fever blisters. HSV-1 infections also have been related to head and neck cancers, but whether the virus actually causes these cancers is not certain.

Laboratory Diagnosis of Genital Herpes. The best laboratory evidence for diagnosing HSV-2 infection is the isolation of the virus in cell culture. When the cell culture is exposed to fluorescent antibodies against the virus, any cells that are infected by the virus will glow under a fluorescence microscope. In more rapid but less specific tests, scrapings from skin or mucous membrane lesions are stained with special dyes to indicate the presence of characteristic tissue cells called *multinucleated giant cells,* which occur in infections caused by HSV and certain other viruses.

Treatment and Prevention of Genital Herpes. Like all virus-caused diseases, genital herpes cannot be cured with antibiotics. However, a chemical compound called *acyclovir* greatly retards multiplication of the virus, thus shortening the course of the disease and preventing the development of new lesions. Depending on the severity of the disease, acyclovir is administered topically, orally, or intravenously. Acyclovir inhibits the synthesis of viral DNA by masquerading as the purine guanine. Acyclovir acts selectively against the virus because the host cells are much less likely to incorporate the false purine into their DNA. No vaccines against HSV are presently available.

Other Sexually Transmitted Diseases Caused by Viruses

In addition to AIDS and genital herpes, there are other sexually transmitted diseases caused by viruses. Among these the most significant are type B viral hepatitis and condyloma acuminata (genital warts).

Viral Hepatitis, Type B. Type B hepatitis, also known as *serum hepatitis,* is an infection of the liver and blood caused by *hepatitis B virus (HBV).* Approximately 21,000 cases of type B hepatitis are reported each year in the United States, but many other cases go unreported and the total number of cases is undoubtedly much higher.

HBV contains double-stranded DNA and is surrounded by a lipid envelope. It is transmitted in the same manner as the AIDS virus: through sexual contact with an infected person, through transfusion of contaminated blood or blood products, through contaminated hypodermic syringes and needles, and from mothers to offspring. At present, intravenous drug users are the group with the highest risk of contracting type B hepatitis.

Type B hepatitis is characterized by weakness, nausea, vomiting, abdominal discomfort, fever, and jaundice. The disease is rarely fatal, and most individuals recover spontaneously within 2 to 6 weeks; however, in 5 to 10 percent of patients the virus persists in the body for many years. Such persons may have chronic (persistent) hepatitis or they may merely be asymptomatic carriers. About 200 million people worldwide have chronic HBV infections, and because their blood can contain infectious virus, it must not be used for blood transfusions. Blood banks and hospitals routinely screen blood for the presence of HBV antigens.

HBV is also the probable cause of *primary hepatic carcinoma,* a type of cancer which is rare in the United States but common in certain areas of Africa, southeast Asia, and other regions.

A very effective vaccine against hepatitis type B has been developed through genetic engineering from a harmless surface antigen of the virus [see DISCOVER 14.1]. Vaccination programs have focused mainly on health care workers who are exposed to blood. Unfortunately, the risk group that accounts for most cases of type B hepatitis, the intravenous drug users, is not being reached effectively by current immunization programs.

Condyloma Acuminata (Genital Warts). Genital warts are caused by certain sexually transmitted viruses of the human papillomavirus (HPV) group. The warts occur as large, moist, pinkish to brown masses, usually in clusters and occasionally in cauliflowerlike arrangements, on or within the male or female genital organs or around the anus. Effective treatment usually can be accomplished by use of chemicals such as podophyllin solution or by physical means such as freezing, burning, or surgical removal. There is circumstantial evidence that genital warts may sometimes lead to cancer of the cervix.

ASK YOURSELF

1 What is the extent and significance of the current AIDS pandemic in the United States and central Africa? What differences are there in the distribution of cases within the populations of these areas?

2 In what ways other than sexual contact can HIV be transmitted? In what ways is it *not* transmitted?

3 How does HIV multiply and cause damage to the immune system? Why may years elapse between infection by HIV and the development of AIDS?

4 What secondary diseases are usually indicative of AIDS? Why?

5 What laboratory tests are used to detect the presence of antibodies against HIV in a person's blood? Why is the PCR method helpful in detecting the presence of HIV in a person's T4 cells?

6 How is the multiplication of HIV retarded by AZT?

7 Which viruses cause genital herpes? How does primary genital herpes differ from the recurrent form? How is the disease diagnosed in the laboratory? What chemical agent is used to treat the disease, and how does it act?

8 How does the transmission of HBV compare with that of HIV? What are the characteristics of type B hepatitis? Is a vaccine available against this disease?

9 What causes condyloma acuminata? What are the distinctive characteristics of this disease?

SEXUALLY TRANSMITTED DISEASES CAUSED BY YEASTS AND PROTOZOA

Relatively few STDs are caused by fungi and protozoa, but those that are can be problematic. *Candida* vaginitis and urethritis are caused by a yeast, and trichomoniasis is caused by a zooflagellate protozoan.

Vaginal Candidiasis

The yeast *Candida albicans* [see FIGURE 23.17] is part of the normal flora of the mouth, gastrointestinal tract, and vagina. Its multiplication usually is suppressed by other normal flora organisms and by normal body defenses. A decrease in body defenses due to some debilitating disease such as diabetes, or an alteration of the normal microbial flora by antibiotic therapy, can lead to uncontrolled growth of the yeast (see Chapter 17 and the section "Secondary Diseases Indicative of AIDS" in this chapter). Among the various *Candida* infections that can occur under these conditions is a vaginitis (inflammation of the vagina) characterized by a thick, cheeselike discharge [FIGURE 23.21]. Another condition caused by *C. albicans* is urethritis in both women and men. Men can develop the urethritis following sexual contact with women having *Candida* vaginitis; in women, the urethritis results from an extension of the vaginitis. Recurring vaginitis is not uncommon. *Candida* vaginitis can be treated with nystatin, clotrimazole, or miconazole; *Candida* urethritis is treated with amphotericin B.

FIGURE 23.21
Gram stain of the vaginal discharge from a patient with vaginal candidiasis, showing yeast forms of *Candida albicans* (dark ovals), some of which are budding. Also present are pus cells and various rod-shaped bacteria.

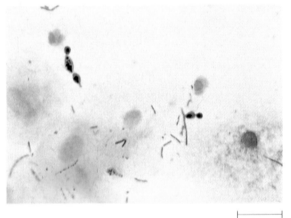

20 μm

Trichomoniasis

An estimated 2.5 to 3 million Americans contract trichomoniasis each year. The disease is caused by a protozoan, *Trichomonas vaginalis* [FIGURE 23.22A].

The symptoms of trichomoniasis may appear within 4 to 20 days after exposure. In women the infection may be asymptomatic or it may be a vaginitis characterized by severe genital itching and an offensive-smelling vaginal discharge. The disease is annoying but does not lead to serious complications. In men, trichomoniasis is usu-ally asymptomatic except in cases involving the seminal vesicles and prostate gland.

Laboratory diagnosis of trichomoniasis is made by microscopic examination of the discharge [FIGURE 23.22B] or by culturing the protozoan. Patients can be treated effectively with metronidazole.

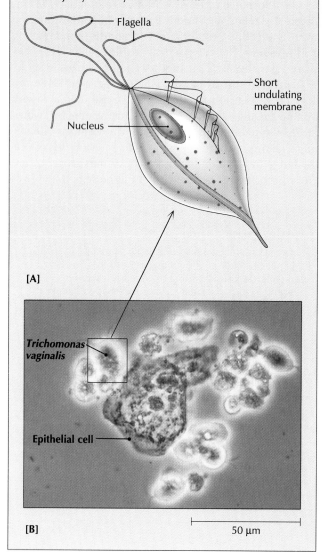

FIGURE 23.22

[A] *Trichomonas vaginalis*, the protozoan that causes trichomoniasis. **[B]** Phase-contrast photomicrograph of a wet mount of the vaginal discharge from a patient with trichomoniasis. Many live cells of *Trichomonas vaginalis* can be seen surrounding a large epithelial cell. The protozoan is readily recognized by its characteristic jerky motility in wet mounts.

Flagella · Short undulating membrane · Nucleus · [A] · *Trichomonas vaginalis* · Epithelial cell · [B] · 50 μm

ASK YOURSELF

1 What microorganism causes vaginal candidiasis? What factors may allow the disease to develop?

2 How is vaginal candidiasis diagnosed in the laboratory? What chemical agents can be used to treat the disease?

3 What is the causative agent of trichomoniasis? How is the disease diagnosed in the laboratory? With what agent can the disease be treated?

CONTROL OF STDs

The spread of most STDs is out of control. In view of the absence of vaccines against STDs, there appears to be little hope for control through immunization. At present, other approaches must be used to control STDs.

Control of Sources of Infection

One approach is based on the identification of infected individuals by public health agencies and physicians, so that measures can be instituted to prevent further transmission of the agent.

Effective Treatments

With STDs caused by bacteria, yeasts, or protozoa, chemotherapeutic agents can be used to cure infected individuals, thereby eliminating the sources of transmission. However, no cure is available for STDs that are caused by viruses. Complicating this approach is the fact that many persons who have an STD may not have symptoms and therefore are unlikely to seek treatment.

Public Education

The spread of STDs can be decreased through effective education. This involves education programs that emphasize the serious clinical consequences of STDs and describe how the risk of contracting these diseases can be minimized.

Halting the spread of AIDS is unquestionably the paramount STD control problem today. As indicated earlier, unless the current pandemic can be halted, AIDS seems likely to become one of the most devastating disease scourges ever experienced by the human race. Widespread immunization against AIDS is one hope for prevention, but a vaccine is not yet available, and even if one is developed it may be years before it is ready for wide use. In the absence of a vaccine, various public health policy measures have been proposed for controlling the sources of infection. However, some of these proposals have raised important legal and ethical questions involving the balance between health needs and individual rights. For instance, there currently are debates over whether the testing of persons to see if they are infected should be done on a mandatory or a voluntary basis, whether such testing should be restricted to only certain segments of the population, and whether test results can lead to discriminatory practices.

At present, the main approach to controlling AIDS is public health education about the disease. The importance of this approach now has been recognized at the highest levels of the United States government, as indicated by the following statement made by President Ronald Reagan in 1987:

What our citizens must know is this: America faces a disease that is fatal and spreading, and this calls for urgency, not panic. It calls for compassion, not blame. And it calls for understanding, not ignorance. It's also important that Americans not reject those who have the disease, but care for them with dignity and kindness. This is a battle against disease, not against our fellow Americans.

In view of the fact that HIV can be acquired in a variety of ways—by both heterosexual and homosexual contact, by shared syringes and needles, by unscreened transfusion blood, and by transmission to infants at or before birth from infected mothers—it is important that public health education efforts be directed toward *all segments of the population*, not merely toward those traditionally considered high-risk groups. It is *behavior* that puts one at risk, not membership in a particular "group." For instance, as part of the public education program in the United States, the U.S. Department of Health and Human Services mailed a highly informative booklet called *Understanding AIDS* to every postal customer in the nation in 1988. State and local public health agencies are also engaged in massive public education programs. These programs describe the types of personal behavior known to be either risky or safe with regard to HIV infection. The following is an example taken from an educational brochure.

RISKY BEHAVIOR

Sharing drug needles and syringes

Anal sex, with or without a condom

Vaginal or oral sex with someone who shoots drugs or engages in anal sex

Sex with someone you don't know well (a pickup or prostitute) or with someone you know has several sex partners

Unprotected sex (without a condom) with an infected person

SAFE BEHAVIOR

Not having sex

Sex with one mutually faithful, uninfected partner

Not shooting drugs

SOURCE: From U.S. Department of Health and Human Services, *Understanding AIDS*, 1988.

We must remember, however, that HIV infection and AIDS is a pandemic, and it is essential that a worldwide effort be undertaken to control the pandemic. Toward this end, the World Health Organization (WHO) is presently coordinating a global program against AIDS. More than 150 countries already have established national committees and programs aimed at controlling this pandemic. These programs are concerned not only with public education but also with facilitating research on AIDS, improving diagnostic procedures, screening blood donors, and providing compassionate care and treatment of patients. Although these initial efforts are encouraging, their effectiveness will depend upon long-term commitment and funding, and the results will not be evident for several years.

ASK YOURSELF

1 What are three approaches for the control of STDs other than the development of potential vaccines?

2 With regard to AIDS, what kinds of questions have arisen in the United States about proposals for public health policy measures for controlling the sources of infection?

3 Toward which segments of the United States population should public health education efforts about AIDS be directed?

4 What global efforts are being made to control the AIDS pandemic?

SUMMARY

1 The incidence of STDs is very high, especially among persons 15 to 30 years old. The STD currently receiving the greatest attention worldwide is AIDS and HIV infection. Some microorganisms that cause STDs may also be transmitted by contaminated syringes and needles shared among drug users and by blood transfusion, and some can be acquired by infants born to infected mothers.

2 Gonorrhea is caused by a Gram-negative diplococcus, *Neisseria gonorrhoeae*. The primary site of infection in females is the cervix; in males it is the urethra. Spread of the infection to the uterine tubes and other regions of the female genital tract can lead to PID, a major cause of sterility. Other complications include arthritis, endocarditis, meningitis, and, in newborn infants, gonococcal conjunctivitis.

3 Syphilis is caused by the spirochete *Treponema pallidum* and occurs in three stages: primary, in which the chancre occurs; secondary, characterized by skin and mucous membrane lesions; and tertiary, in which damage to the brain, spinal cord, and blood vessels may occur, as well as disfiguring lesions called gummas. A latent stage may intervene between the secondary and tertiary stages.

4 *Chlamydia trachomatis* infections are widespread but are usually asymptomatic in women; however, they can lead to PID. Infants who acquire the organism from their mothers may develop conjunctivitis and pneumonia. In men, *C. trachomatis* is a major cause of nongonococcal urethritis (NGU).

5 Other STDs caused by bacteria include chancroid, caused by *Haemophilus ducreyi*; granuloma inguinale, caused by *Calymmatobacterium granulomatis*; and bacterial vaginosis, caused by *Gardnerella vaginalis*.

6 Among the STDs caused by viruses, the most threatening is AIDS, which is caused by HIV-1 and HIV-2. HIV can be transmitted by sexual contact, by contaminated needles and syringes shared among drug users, by contaminated blood products, and from infected mothers to their unborn infants. HIV is *not* spread by the casual contacts that occur during daily life. The virus severely damages the immune system by destroying T4 lymphocytes, making a person highly susceptible to secondary diseases such as Kaposi's sarcoma and *Pneumocystis carinii* pneumonia, which are relatively rare in the general population. HIV itself can cause delayed brain damage. Although there is no cure for AIDS or HIV infection, the chemical compound AZT can retard multiplication of the virus.

7 Genital herpes is caused by HSV-2 and, to a lesser extent, HSV-1. Following primary genital herpes, the virus becomes latent and then can become reactivated periodically to cause recurrent genital herpes. Infection in pregnant women can lead to serious and even fatal disease in newborn infants.

8 Other sexually transmitted diseases caused by viruses include hepatitis type B and condyloma acuminata (genital warts).

9 Trichomoniasis is caused by a flagellated protozoan, *Trichomonas vaginalis*. The yeast *Candida albicans* causes vaginitis and urethritis.

10 The spread of most STDs is presently out of control. In the absence of vaccines, approaches to control are based on control of the sources of infection, on effective treatment, and on public awareness. At present, control of AIDS is based mainly on public education programs, which should be directed toward all segments of the population.

KEY TERMS

acyclovir
asymptomatic carrier
azidothymidine (AZT)
cardiolipin
CD4 glycoprotein
congenital infection
dideoxyinosine (DDI)
fluorescent treponemal antibody (FTA) test
gonococcus
gummas
microhemagglutination (MHA) test
pandemic
polymerase chain reaction (PCR)
rapid plasma reagin (RPR) test
reagin

REVIEW GUIDE

1 STDs were formerly called _____ diseases.

2 Some STDs may be spread by means other than sexual contact. These include which *three* of the following? **(a)** airborne droplets produced by coughing and sneezing; **(b)** contaminated hypodermic syringes and needles shared among drug users; **(c)** transfusions with contaminated blood; **(d)** drinking contaminated food and water; **(e)** acquisition by infants born to infected mothers.

3 Which one of the following did *not* contribute to the increase in the incidence of gonorrhea? **(a)** an increased use of oral contraceptives and contraceptive intrauterine devices; **(b)** an inability to trace the contacts of carriers and patients with clinical cases; **(c)** a decreased use of spermicidal preparations; **(d)** the emergence of penicillin-resistant strains of gonococci; **(e)** an increased use of condoms.

4 Which one of the following best describes *Neisseria gonorrhoeae*? **(a)** Gram-positive cocci in pairs; **(b)** Gram-negative rods in pairs; **(c)** Gram-negative cocci in chains; **(d)** Gram-negative cocci in pairs; **(e)** Gram-positive cocci in chains.

5 "Chocolate agar" is a medium that contains: **(a)** chocolate; **(b)** vitamins; **(c)** heated blood; **(d)** cocoa bean derivative; **(e)** iron salts.

6 Drops of silver nitrate solution or antibiotics are placed in the eyes of newborn infants to prevent a disease called gonococcal _____.

7 A gonococcus binds a host cell by means of the gonococcal: **(a)** capsule; **(b)** cell wall; **(c)** pili; **(d)** flagella; **(e)** endotoxin.

8 In men, the primary site of infection by gonorrhea is the _____; in women it is the _____.

9 Which of the following may result in infertility when a microbial infection spreads from the vagina and cervix to the endometrium, uterine tubes, and associated structures? **(a)** conjunctivitis; **(b)** PID; **(c)** pneumonia; **(d)** endocarditis; **(e)** meningitis.

10 The abnormal condition in which the fetus does not develop within the uterus of the mother is called _____.

11 The medium used for isolation of gonococci is a "chocolate" agar that contains _____ that suppress the growth of the other bacteria.

12 The antibiotic that is usually effective for treatment of gonorrhea is _____.

13 Syphilis is much _____ (more, less) prevalent than gonorrhea.

14 Syphilis is caused by a microorganism that can be classified as a **(a)** Gram-positive rod; **(b)** Gram-negative coccus; **(c)** spirochete; **(d)** Gram-positive coccus; **(e)** virus.

15 Match the type of syphilis on the left with the appropriate description on the right.

_____ tertiary syphilis
_____ secondary syphilis
_____ congenital syphilis
_____ primary syphilis

(a) Syphilis acquired by a fetus within the uterus of the mother
(b) Stage of syphilis in which a chancre develops
(c) Stage of syphilis in which damage to the brain, spinal cord, and blood vessels occurs
(d) Stage of syphilis in which a generalized rash appears on the skin

16 Observation of *T. pallidum* in the fluid from a chancre would best be done by _____ microscopy.

17 The antigen used in the RPR test is **(a)** *Treponema pallidum;* **(b)** cardiolipin; **(c)** a protein; **(d)** the patient's serum; **(e)** a suspension of bacterial cells.

18 The most widely used *treponemal* tests for the serological diagnosis of syphilis are the (select *two* answers): **(a)** MHA test; **(b)** RPR test; **(c)** FTA test; **(d)** rabbit inoculation test; **(e)** MPN test.

19 There are 3 to 4 _____ (hundred, thousand, million) cases of chlamydial infection each year in the United States.

20 Which *two* of the following apply to trachoma? **(a)** It is the single greatest cause of preventable blindness in the world. **(b)** It is an infection of the urethra. **(c)** It is a severe infection characterized by enlarged lymph nodes in the region of the anus and genitals. **(d)** It is a conjunctivitis. **(e)** It is a sexually transmitted disease.

21 Infants born to *Chlamydia*-infected mothers are at high risk of developing two disease conditions, namely, _____ and _____.

22 *C. trachomatis* accounts for what percent of the 1 million recognized cases of PID in the United States each year? **(a)** 1–10; **(b)** 25–50; **(c)** 70–90; **(d)** 95–99; **(e)** 100.

23 Match each disease listed on the right with the causative organism on the left.

_____*Haemophilus ducreyi*   **(a)** Bacterial vaginosis

_____*Calymmatobacterium granulomatis*   **(b)** Chancroid

_____*Gardnerella vaginalis*   **(c)** Granuloma inguinale

SEXUALLY TRANSMITTED DISEASES CAUSED BY VIRUSES

24 Which one of the following statements is correct? **(a)** Intravenous drug users are the group with the second highest percentage of AIDS cases in the United States. **(b)** At present, AIDS occurs only in the United States. **(c)** In central Africa, AIDS is spread mainly by homosexual contact. **(d)** In the United States, AIDS is spread mainly by heterosexual contact. **(e)** In the United States, AIDS occurs only in homosexual or bisexual men and drug abusers.

25 "HIV" is the abbreviation for _____.

26 Which *two* of the following do *not* occur in an HIV virion? **(a)** single-stranded RNA; **(b)** surface glycoproteins; **(c)** double-stranded DNA; **(d)** reverse transcriptase; **(e)** phospholipid membrane; **(f)** core proteins; **(g)** single-stranded DNA.

27 HIV attacks certain lymphocytes called _____ lymphocytes.

28 Reverse transcriptase synthesizes a strand of DNA that is complementary to a strand of viral _____.

29 The single-stranded viral DNA made by reverse transcriptase is converted to double-stranded DNA, which is then integrated into the _____.

30 Which *two* of the following statements are *false*? **(a)** No known case of AIDS has ever been traced to casual contact with AIDS patients during everyday life. **(b)** As a result of damage by HIV to the body's immune system, an AIDS patient is unable to resist infection by microorganisms of even relatively low pathogenicity. **(c)** If a person infected by HIV has no disease symptoms, that person cannot transmit the virus to other persons. **(d)** HIV can be found in the blood, semen, or vaginal fluid of infected persons but not in other body fluids or secretions. **(e)** The AIDS virus can be acquired by an infant born to an infected mother.

31 The following question refers to secondary diseases that are usually indicative of AIDS. Match each description on the right with the appropriate item on the left.

_____ *Cryptosporidium*

_____ CMV

_____ *Pneumocystis carinii*

_____ *Mycobacterium avium-intracellulare group*

_____ *Candida albicans*

_____ *Toxoplasma gondii*

_____ Kaposi's sarcoma

(a) Yeast that causes a lung infection called PCP

(b) Cancer that begins as blue-violet or brownish blotches or bumps on the skin

(c) A yeast that causes cottage cheese-like plaques in the mouth

(d) Protozoan that causes a severe, recurrent diarrhea

(e) Virus that causes spots on the retina of the eye

(f) Protozoan that invades the brain

(g) Acid-fast bacilli that infect the brain and other organs

32 The indirect ELISA test that is used to detect infection by HIV actually detects the presence of **(a)** *Pneumocystis carinii;* **(b)** HIV; **(c)** the antibodies that develop against the AIDS virus; (d) the lesions of Kaposi's sarcoma; **(e)** brain damage caused by the AIDS virus.

33 Which one of the following statements is true regarding the latex bead test to detect antibodies against HIV? **(a)** The beads have been previously coated with HIV antibodies. **(b)** The test detects the presence of HIV in a person's blood. **(c)** Antibodies against HIV in the person's blood cause the beads to agglutinate. **(d)** The test takes several hours to perform. **(e)** A positive test is indicated by the appearance of a pattern of distinctive colored bands on a nitrocellulose paper strip.

34 A technique that allows billions of copies of HIV DNA to be synthesized in a test tube from only a few initial copies of the DNA is called: **(a)** Western blot; **(b)** ELISA technique; **(c)** CD4; **(d)** T4:T8 ratio; **(e)** PCR.

35 AZT inhibits synthesis of single-stranded viral _____ by the enzyme _____ .

36 Eighty percent of the cases of genital herpes are caused by _____ (HSV-1, HSV-2) and the remainder are caused by _____ (HSV-1, HSV-2).

37 Which *two* of the following occur in HSV-1 and HSV-2? **(a)** single-stranded DNA; **(b)** reverse transcriptase; **(c)** lipid envelope; **(d)** an icosahedral nucleocapsid; **(e)** single-stranded RNA.

38 Latent HSV-2 can be reactivated periodically and can travel down the _____ to infect cells in the skin, resulting in _____ genital herpes.

39 Which *two* statements about acyclovir are true? **(a)** It stimulates antibody production against HSV. **(b)** It cures genital herpes. **(c)** It retards the multiplication of HSV-2. **(d)** It masquerades as an amino acid during viral DNA synthesis. **(e)** It does not greatly affect synthesis of host-cell DNA.

40 The modes of transmission of hepatitis virus B most closely resemble those of which other virus? **(a)** *Treponema pallidum;* **(b)** HIV; **(c)** HSV-2; **(d)** poliovirus; **(e)** human papillomaviruses.

41 The vaccine against hepatitis type B consists of a harmless _____ of the virus.

42 Genital warts are caused by a virus belonging to which group of viruses? **(a)** herpesviruses; **(b)** human papillomaviruses; **(c)** adenoviruses; **(d)** retroviruses; **(e)** picornaviruses.

SEXUALLY
TRANSMITTED
DISEASES CAUSED BY
YEASTS AND
PROTOZOA

CONTROL OF STDs

43 Which of the following is caused by a yeast? **(a)** chancroid; **(b)** vaginal candidiasis **(c)** trichomoniasis; **(d)** condyloma acuminata; **(e)** granuloma inguinale.

44 In question 43, which one of the diseases listed is caused by a protozoan? _____

45 The spread of most STDs is presently _____ (under, out of) control.

46 In the absence of vaccines against most STDs, the present approaches to control involve (1) control of sources of infection, (2) effective treatment, and (3) _____ .

47 With regard to the control of AIDS, government and state public health education programs should be aimed at: **(a)** all segments of the population; **(b)** only blood bank personnel; **(c)** only health care personnel; **(d)** only members of high-risk groups; **(e)** only persons with Kaposi's sarcoma or *Pneumocystis carinii* pneumonia.

REVIEW QUESTIONS

1 Explain why there was a great increase in the incidence of gonorrhea despite the discovery that penicillin was effective in treating the disease.

2 Which STDs can be acquired by means other than sexual contact?

3 Which STDs present a health risk not only for adults but also for fetuses and newborn infants?

4 What types of damage to the body can occur in gonorrhea?

5 What are the stages of syphilis, and what happens in each stage?

6 What diseases can be caused by *Chlamydia trachomatis*?

7 What are the ways in which HIV is transmitted? What are the ways in which it is *not* transmitted?

8 What problems are there in developing an effective vaccine against AIDS?

9 Exactly why are AIDS patients unusually prone to develop diseases such as Kaposi's sarcoma, *Pneumocystis carinii* pneumonia, and *Mycobacterium avium-intracellulare* infections?

10 What is the importance of reverse transcriptase (1) in the multiplication of HIV and (2) in the treatment of AIDS patients by AZT?

DISCUSSION QUESTIONS

1 STD agents may sometimes cause asymptomatic infections. Why should we worry about such infections if there are no symptoms?

2 STDs caused by bacteria can often be cured. What is there about viral-caused STDs that makes them so much more difficult to cure?

3 What seems to be the fundamental research strategy for developing synthetic chemical agents to treat diseases such as genital herpes and AIDS?

4 In screening individuals for syphilis, why aren't only treponemal tests such as the FTA and MHA tests used, since a positive screening test for syphilis must be confirmed by a treponemal test anyhow?

5 Since antibiotics are available for treatment of syphilis and gonorrhea, why is it important that syphilis and gonorrhea be effectively diagnosed and treated as early as possible?

6 In what ways might basic research on the structure and composition of HIV lead to applied benefits?

7 If you were the director of a global program to control AIDS, what actions would you take, considering that the pandemic is increasing in magnitude and assuming that no vaccine is likely to become available in the near future?

Airborne Diseases

OBJECTIVES

After reading this chapter you should be able to

1 Give specific examples of airborne infections caused by bacteria and indicate how these infections differ with regard to causative agent, symptoms, treatment, and prevention.

2 Explain why influenza pandemics occur in cycles.

3 Indicate the differences in the vaccines used against *Haemophilus* meningitis, diphtheria, tuberculosis, and influenza.

4 Explain why it is possible for a person to have several colds during a single year.

5 Explain the value of serotyping pathogenic microorganisms such as *Streptococcus pyogenes* and influenza viruses.

6 List several different diseases caused by *Streptococcus pyogenes* and indicate how these diseases differ from one another with respect to the symptoms produced and the body sites affected.

7 Give the identifying features of *Streptococcus pyogenes*, *Mycobacterium tuberculosis*, *Legionella pneumophila*, and *Histoplasma capsulatum*.

8 Name several airborne infections caused by fungi and list the identifying morphological features of the causative agents.

OVERVIEW

Some pathogenic microorganisms can be transmitted through the air by tiny droplets or dust particles that are invisible to the naked eye. The microbe-laden droplets or particles can be inhaled by a healthy individual and cause an infection. Such airborne infections may be caused by bacteria, viruses, or fungi. The microorganisms may be transmitted from infected humans, or from environmental sources such as dust from contaminated bedding or soil. Examples of airborne infection include streptococcal sore throat, tuberculosis, the common cold, influenza, histoplasmosis, and many others. Airborne infections may be restricted to the respiratory tract or they may spread to other areas of the body. Active immunization programs have dramatically decreased the incidence of certain airborne infections such as diphtheria, measles, and rubella ("German measles").

Although every disease has certain unique and interesting aspects, it is not possible in an introductory textbook to describe every disease in detail. Therefore this chapter will concentrate on relatively few diseases, chosen to exemplify both the principles of airborne transmission and important aspects of host-pathogen interactions.

MODE OF TRANSMISSION OF AIRBORNE PATHOGENS

People may become infected by inhaling pathogenic microorganisms that are present in the air. Some airborne pathogens can come from other people who are ill or are convalescing from illness, or from asymptomatic carriers. Others can come from environmental sources such as water and soil. A great deal of research has been done on how microorganisms get into the air and on the factors affecting their survival and transmission.

Aerosols

The term *aerosol* used in connection with airborne infections refers to a spray of small and large droplets which may contain microorganisms. Aerosols can be generated from human sources or environmental sources.

Aerosols Generated from Human Sources. Microorganisms that cause respiratory infections occur in secretions from the nose and throat of infected individuals. When a person coughs or sneezes, an aerosol is expelled [FIGURE 24.1]. The larger droplets (10 μm or more in diameter) can be inhaled by people nearby, or they can settle onto clothing and other inanimate objects. If these objects are disturbed, they may resuspend microorganisms that can infect people. The small droplets (1 to 4 μm in diameter)

can also be inhaled directly, but the water in these droplets tends to evaporate quickly, leaving *droplet nuclei* (a residue of solid material, including microorganisms). Droplet nuclei that contain living microorganisms can remain suspended in air for hours or days, travel long distances, and serve as a continuing source of infection.

The larger droplets, when inhaled, usually are trapped on the moist mucus layer covering the surfaces of the nasal cavity and the nasopharynx [FIGURE 24.2A]. The microorganisms carried by these droplets may be able to penetrate the mucus layer, attach themselves to the tissue cells underneath, and multiply. However, some may be swept along by the downward flow of mucus and attach to the tissue cells that line the oropharynx, or they may be swallowed and eventually destroyed by the high acidity of the stomach.

The smaller droplets and droplet nuclei are less likely to be trapped in the nasopharynx; instead, they may reach the alveoli of the lungs and be retained there [FIGURE 24.2B]. Macrophages in the lungs can often destroy the microorganisms that reach the lungs.

The likelihood that pathogens can be transmitted by droplets or droplet nuclei is greatest when people are crowded together, because this increases the number of microorganisms being expelled into air in a confined space. It is not surprising that the frequency of airborne infections is usually greatest during the cold months of the year, when people tend to be crowded indoors [FIGURE 24.3]. Moreover, airborne diseases usually occur in epidemic form, attacking large numbers of people in a short time.

FIGURE 24.1
[A] High-speed photograph of a spray of droplets expelled by sneezing. [B] The simple use of a handkerchief can trap potentially dangerous aerosol droplets.

[A]

[B]

FIGURE 24.2

Organization of the respiratory tract. **[A]** Air taken in through the nose or mouth reaches the lungs by means of the trachea. During swallowing, the epiglottis covers the larynx so that food will pass to the esophagus rather than the trachea. The trachea terminates in branches called *bronchi*, which form smaller branches called *bronchioles* that terminate in the alveoli, or air sacs, of the lung. **[B]** The alveoli are surrounded by a network of blood vessels, allowing the blood cells to exchange oxygen for carbon dioxide, a waste product of metabolism. For clarity, these vessels are shown only on the right cluster of alveoli.

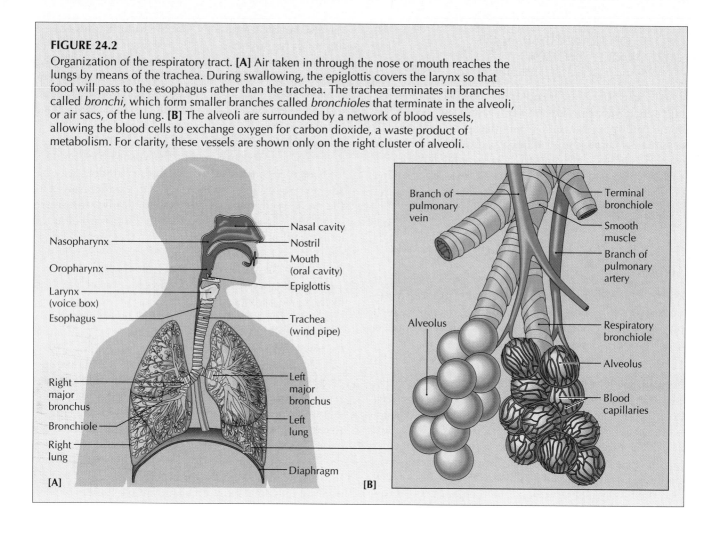

Some microorganisms that cause respiratory infections are unable to survive long outside the body. For example, the measles virus is quickly inactivated outside the body. Transmission of these microorganisms depends upon rapid airborne transfer of large droplets from one person to another, or by even more direct transfer, as by kissing. Other pathogenic microorganisms, such as the bacterium that causes tuberculosis, can survive for long periods outside the body.

Aerosols Generated from Environmental Sources. Some human infections result from the airborne transmission of microorganisms from an environmental source rather than from infected persons. For example, some epidemics of Legionnaires' disease have been attributed to aerosols generated from the contaminated water of air-conditioning equipment, and from mist sprays used in grocery stores to keep vegetables fresh. Environmental aerosols also may explain how humans acquire *Mycobacterium intracellulare*, which causes a respiratory disease resembling tuberculosis but is not transmitted from person to

person. This organism is a frequent inhabitant of fresh and brackish waters in the southeastern United States, and it has been shown that it can be ejected into the air in significant numbers by air bubbles that rise through the water and burst at the surface. Another potential source of airborne microorganisms is the aerosolization produced by a high-speed drill in a dental office.

Infectious Dust

Humans may become infected by inhaling *infectious dust,* which is dust containing pathogenic microorganisms. Infectious dust may arise from human or environmental sources.

Infectious Dust Generated from Human Sources. Nasal or throat secretions on a handkerchief eventually dry, leaving a residue of material. Similarly, when a person

FIGURE 24.3

Reported cases of varicella (chicken pox) per 100,000 population in the United States from 1982 to 1991. The highest incidence occurs in the colder months, which is characteristic of an airborne infection. For instance, the peak incidence for 1986 was reached between March and May. (*Morbidity and Mortality Weekly Report, Summary of Notifiable Diseases, United States, 1990, issued Oct. 4, 1991.*)

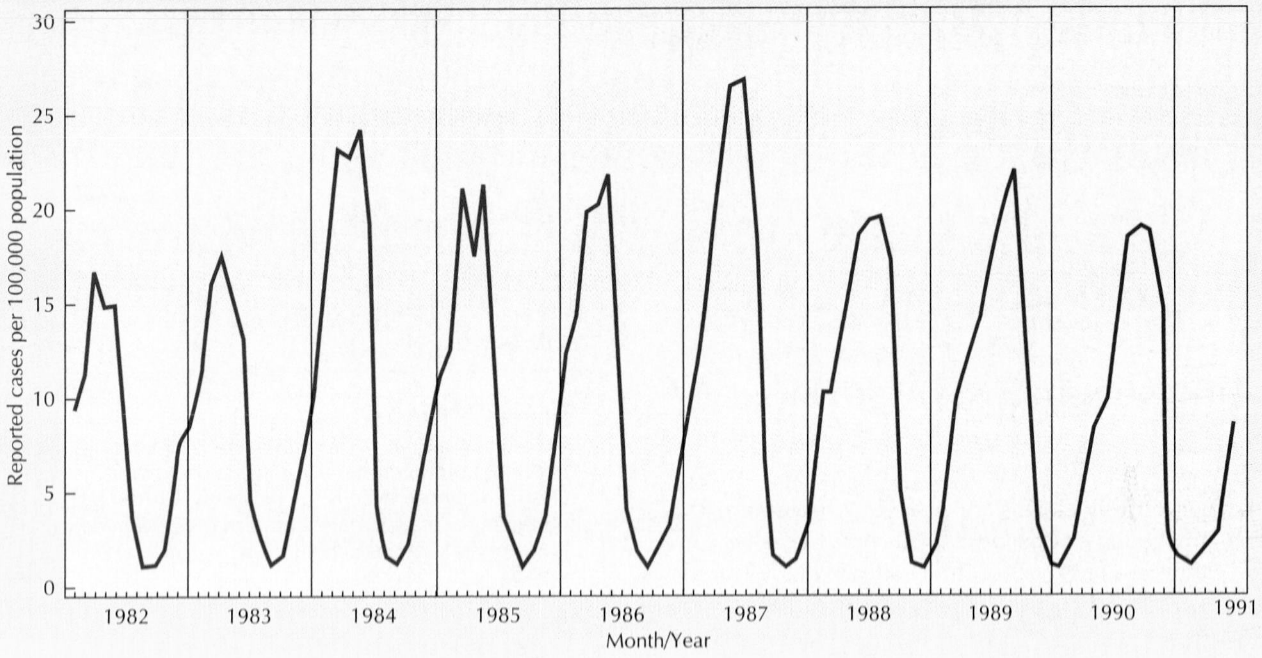

sneezes or coughs, the large aerosol droplets that are expelled settle onto surfaces such as bedclothes or the floor, where they evaporate and leave a residue. Disturbance of these residues—by handling a dried handkerchief, by bed making, or by sweeping the floor—can generate dust particles that may add pathogenic microorganisms to the circulating air. Dust-borne spread of infection is enhanced when people move about in poorly ventilated areas. Some pathogenic microorganisms are able to survive for relatively long periods in dust. This creates a significant hazard, particularly in hospitals, where it can contribute to nosocomial diseases (Chapter 22). TABLE 24.1 indicates the bacterial content of air samples from various environments.

Infectious Dust Generated from Environmental Sources. Some airborne pathogens inhabit soil and are not transmitted from person to person; instead, they are transmitted by inhaling dust arising from this soil. For instance, the fungus that causes histoplasmosis usually is acquired by this means.

ASK YOURSELF

1 How are aerosols generated from human sources? How do they transmit pathogenic microorganisms from person to person? How are aerosols generated from environmental sources? What is the relationship between aerosol droplets and droplet nuclei?

2 What happens to the larger aerosol droplets when they are inhaled? What happens to the smaller droplets and droplet nuclei?

3 How can infectious dust be generated from human sources? How can it be generated from environmental sources?

4 What are two examples of diseases whose causative agents are transmitted by dust or aerosols from environmental sources?

TABLE 24.1
Bacterial Counts in Air from Different Environments

Environment	BACTERIA-CARRYING PARTICLES PER CUBIC FOOT OF AIR	
	Peak value	Lowest value
Civilian hospital during bed making	2000	81
Crowded military canteen	230	50
Crowded typists' office	65	20
Poorly ventilated factory shop	30	15
Large, oily engineering shop	25	5
Fresh air on the outskirts of a town	6	0.25

SOURCE: Data from F. P. Ellis and E. F. Raymond, "Studies in Air Hygiene," *Med. Res. Council (GB), Spec. Rep. Ser. 262,* 1948.

AIRBORNE INFECTIONS CAUSED BY BACTERIA

Many airborne infections are caused by bacterial pathogens. Infections caused by *Streptococcus pyogenes* are interesting not only because they affect millions of people worldwide each year, but also because of the variety of diseases caused by this single organism and because of the puzzling conditions that may follow a primary infection, such as rheumatic fever and acute glomerulonephritis. Tuberculosis is a disease which exemplifies the importance of a cell-mediated immune response. Legionnaires' disease is particularly interesting because of the environmental sources of the causative organism.

Streptococcal Pharyngitis and Related Streptococcal Diseases

Streptococcal pharyngitis, commonly called *streptococcal sore throat*, is characterized by an acute inflammation of the pharynx. If a red skin rash accompanies the pharyngitis, the disease is known as *scarlet fever*. At least a quarter of a million cases of streptococcal pharyngitis or scarlet fever occur each year in the United States.

Biology and Differentiation of Streptococci. As mentioned in Chapter 9, streptococci are Gram-positive cocci that occur in long or short chains or in pairs [FIGURE 24.4A]. They obtain energy by fermenting sugars, and they do not carry out respiration. They require a sugar and several amino acids and vitamins in their culture medium in order to grow. Most species can grow in the presence of air, but some are anaerobic.

FIGURE 24.4
Cells and colonies of *Streptococcus pyogenes*.
[A] Photomicrograph of a Gram stain showing arrangement of the cells in chains. **[B]** Close-up photograph of subsurface colonies of *S. pyogenes* on blood agar, showing β hemolysis.

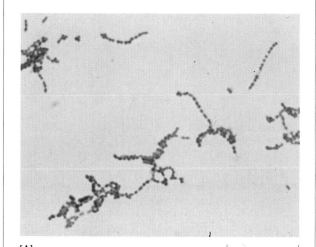

[A]   20 μm

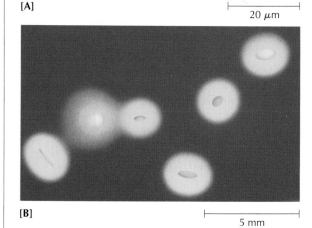

[B]   5 mm

The *Streptococcus* species that are associated with humans are listed in TABLE 24.2. When grown on blood agar, some of these streptococci are *β-hemolytic* [FIGURE 24.4B], others are *α-hemolytic*, and others are *nonhemolytic* [see FIGURE 18.2]. Streptococci can also be divided into antigenic groups on the basis of a carbohydrate antigen that is located in the cell wall [FIGURE 24.5]. These antigenic groups are called *Lancefield groups* and are designated by letters of the alphabet. Streptococci that belong to group A all share the same antigenic substance, or cell-wall carbohydrate; the organisms in group B possess a different carbohydrate; and so forth. Notice from TABLE 24.2 that some Lancefield groups contain more than one species. Biochemical tests are required to differentiate the species within a group.

Streptococcus pyogenes, which belongs to Lancefield group A, causes over 90 percent of human streptococcal infections. These infections include pharyngitis, scarlet fever, rheumatic fever, erysipelas, impetigo contagiosum, and poststreptococcal glomerulonephritis.

Transmission of *S. pyogenes*. Humans are the natural reservoir of *S. pyogenes*. The organisms are carried in the nasopharynx and are spread primarily by sneezing and coughing. Unfortunately, *S. pyogenes* may survive for several weeks in mucoid material expelled from the throat; this dried material can be disturbed, spreading the organisms even further.

To determine the origin and manner of spread of an outbreak of a disease such as streptococcal pharyngitis or scarlet fever, it often is useful to determine whether the *same strain* of *S. pyogenes* is responsible for all the cases. For example, suppose that an epidemic of streptococcal pharyngitis occurs in one part of a city and a few days later a second outbreak occurs elsewhere in the city. Are the two outbreaks caused by a single strain of *S. pyogenes* that was transported across the city, or is each outbreak caused by a different strain with a separate origin? Such questions could be answered easily if each streptococcal strain were to carry some sort of identification, like the numbers emblazoned on football uniforms. Streptococcal cells obviously do not carry such numbers, but they do have an *M protein* on their cell walls that can serve the same function [FIGURE 24.5]. As a species, *S. pyogenes* has 70 different types of M proteins, but each strain of *S. pyogenes* has only one of these 70 types. This allows us to classify strains of *S. pyogenes* into *serotypes*—antigenically different types, based on which M protein is present. For example, if two outbreaks of streptococcal pharyngitis are both caused by M type 45, this would strongly indicate that the same strain is involved. However, if one outbreak is caused by M type 45 and the other by M type 57, then the two outbreaks must be caused by different strains of *S. pyogenes*.

Pathogenicity of *S. pyogenes*. *S. pyogenes* produces a number of substances that contribute to its infective ability. Among these substances are the following:

1 The M protein on the cell wall is important because (a) it is responsible for attachment of the streptococci to the cells of the throat and (b) it is *antiphagocytic*, which means that it enables the streptococci to resist being engulfed by phagocytes such as neutrophils.

2 *Streptolysin O (SLO)* is a streptococcal toxin that is inactivated by oxygen (hence the "O" in its name). It has the ability to kill cells by inserting its crescent- or horseshoe-shaped polymers into cell membranes, thereby forming small holes that allow cell contents to leak out. For example, it can damage red blood cells and thus is a *hemolysin*, causing β-hemolysis on blood-agar plates that are incubated anaerobically. In

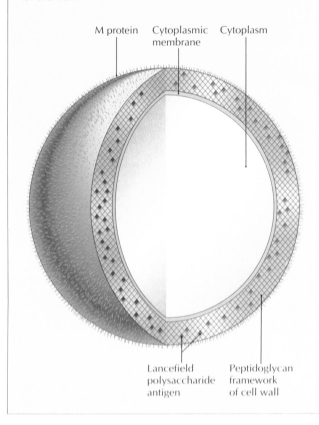

FIGURE 24.5

Diagram of a streptococcal cell. The carbohydrate antigen used to identify the Lancefield group to which the strain belongs occurs in the cell wall. The M protein antigen used to identify which serotype the strain belongs to occurs as a "fuzz" on the outer surface of the wall.

M protein   Cytoplasmic   Cytoplasm
                membrane

Lancefield   Peptidoglycan
polysaccharide framework
antigen   of cell wall

TABLE 24.2
Some Members of the Genus *Streptococcus*

Group and species	Lancefield group	Hemolysis on blood agar	Pathogenicity and other features
PYOGENIC GROUP			
S. pyogenes	A	β	Pharyngitis, scarlet fever, erysipelas, impetigo, cellulitis, gangrenous myositis, pneumonia, sinusitis, otitis media, mastoiditis, rheumatic fever, poststreptococcal glomerulonephritis.
S. agalactiae	B	β, α, or none	Found in genital and intestinal tracts of healthy adults and infants. In newborn infants, causes meningitis, septicemia, and pneumonia. In adults, causes urinary tract infections, wound infections, and otitis media.
"Human C"	C	β	Respiratory tract, skin and wound infections, endocarditis, meningitis, and urinary tract infections.
INTESTINAL STREPTOCOCCI			
S. faecalis	D	None or β	Found in feces of humans and animals; insects; plants. Causes urinary tract infections and endocarditis.
S. faecium	D	α or none	Found in feces of humans and animals; insects; and plants.
S. bovis	D	Weak α or none	Alimentary tract of cow, sheep, and other ruminants. Occasionally occurs in large numbers in human feces. Can cause endocarditis in humans.
S. avium	Q and usually also D	α or none	Feces of chickens, dogs, pigs, humans. May cause appendicitis, otitis media, and abscesses of brain.
VIRIDANS GROUP (HUMAN ORAL STREPTOCOCCI)			
S. salivarius	K or none	α or none	Found in mouth (on tongue or in saliva) and in feces. Can cause endocarditis.
S. sanguis	H	α	Found in dental plaque and in lower numbers in other parts of the mouth. Can cause endocarditis.
S. mitior	H, O, K, or none	α	Found in saliva, dental plaque, sputum, feces. The most frequent cause of endocarditis.
S. milleri	F, G, C, A, or none	None or β	Abscesses in mouth, liver, brain, female genital tract, appendix. Sometimes causes bacteremia. In healthy persons, it is found in the mouth (especially on the surface of the teeth and in the gingival crevice), nasopharynx, throat, vagina, and feces.
S. mutans	None	None	Primary cause of dental caries.
S. oralis	None	α	Found in mouth.
S. mitis	None or H	α	Found in saliva, sputum, and feces. May cause endocarditis.
PNEUMOCOCCI			
S. pneumoniae	None	α (aerobic); β (anaerobic)	Lobar pneumonia, meningitis, otitis media, and, less frequently, abscesses, conjunctivitis, pericarditis, and arthritis.
ANAEROBIC STREPTOCOCCI			
S. morbillorum		α or none	Human clinical specimens and intestinal contents; has been isolated from a lung abscess.
S. hansenii		None	Found in human feces.
S. pleomorphus		None	Intestines of chickens and occasionally human feces.
S. parvulus		None	Found in human respiratory tract.

a patient's body, however, SLO acts mainly as a *leucocidin,* killing host phagocytes. *Streptolysin S (SLS)* is another hemolysin produced by *S. pyogenes;* it kills leucocytes in the same manner as SLO. However, SLS is oxygen-stable (hence the "S" in its name), and, unlike SLO, it can cause β-hemolysis on *aerobically* incubated blood-agar plates.

3 Some strains of *S. pyogenes* produce an *erythrogenic toxin,* which causes the red skin rash characteristic of scarlet fever. Only strains of *S. pyogenes* that harbor a particular type of bacteriophage can produce the erythrogenic toxin.

Streptococcal pharyngitis is a disease characterized by fever, enlargement of the lymph nodes of the neck, and a red, raw, and often bleeding throat surface [FIGURE 24.6]. Scarlet fever is similar but is accompanied by a skin rash that may extend to all parts of the body, appearing on the first or second day after onset of the infection. Streptococcal pharyngitis or scarlet fever can give rise to various complications following the primary infection, such as infections of the middle ear, mastoid bone, sinuses, or lungs. Rheumatic fever or poststreptococcal glomerulonephritis may also occur.

Rheumatic fever is a disease that follows approximately 3 percent of untreated cases of streptococcal pharyngitis or scarlet fever. Signs and symptoms of rheumatic fever usually begin about 2 to 3 weeks after the respiratory infection and include inflammation of the joints, involuntary jerking movements, pea-sized nodules that develop beneath the skin, and reddened areas with raised edges on the skin. However, the most important characteristic of the disease is degeneration of the heart valves. With each subsequent streptococcal infection, the degree of heart damage increases markedly. Rheumatic fever occurs most frequently in the preadolescent age group (3 to 10 years of age) and is a cause of death in the 5- to 20-year-old age group. The incidence of acute rheumatic fever in the United States has declined markedly during the last 20 years, probably because of accurate diagnosis and treatment of cases of streptococcal pharyngitis and scarlet fever and the use of penicillin as a preventive agent [DISCOVER 24.1]. At present there are approximately 160 reported cases per year, but in 1970 there were over 3000 cases. The disease is much more prevalent in third world countries, where it is thought to account for 25 to 49 percent of all cardiovascular disease.

Two puzzling features of rheumatic fever are that antibiotics are ineffective in curing it and, although the heart valves are inflamed, streptococci are usually not present on the heart tissue or in the blood. For these reasons rheumatic fever is considered to be *an inflammation but not an infection* of the heart valves. The explanation of this seeming paradox is still not fully understood, but it likely has an immunological basis. For instance, because a similarity exists between certain *S. pyogenes* antigens and heart tissue antigens, the antibodies against the microbe might cross-react with heart tissue and cause inflammation of that tissue.

Acute poststreptococcal glomerulonephritis (AGN), also called *Bright's disease,* is a kidney disease that may occur within 1 to 3 weeks after an *S. pyogenes* infection of the throat or skin. One sign of the damage to the kidney is the presence of blood in the patient's urine. Only certain M-protein serotypes of *S. pyogenes* are associated with AGN. The disease can occur in up to 15 percent of persons who have had a prior *S. pyogenes* infection, and its incidence is highest in children. *S. pyogenes* is not present at the site of kidney damage, and, like rheumatic fever, *AGN is an inflammation rather than an infection.* Exactly how the disease occurs is not yet understood, but it probably has an immunological basis.

Infective endocarditis differs from rheumatic fever in that (1) it is caused mainly by α-hemolytic streptococci [TABLE 24.2], not by *S. pyogenes;* (2) the streptococci adhere to and grow directly on the heart valves; and (3) it can be treated successfully with antibiotics. Persons whose heart valves have been damaged previously by rheumatic fever or by congenital heart disease are especially prone to develop endocarditis.

FIGURE 24.6

Throat of a patient with streptococcal pharyngitis (strep sore throat), showing localized redness at back of throat and edema (swelling) of tonsils at both sides.

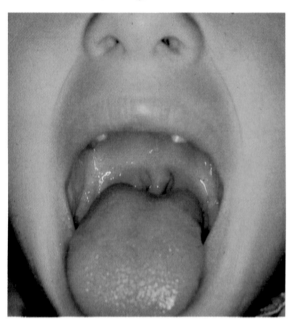

FIGURE 24.7
Red, swollen lesions of erysipelas on the face of a patient.

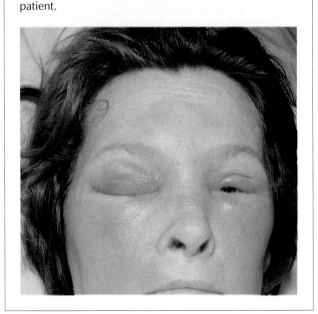

Erysipelas is a skin infection caused by S. *pyogenes*. Entry of S. *pyogenes* into the skin is favored by the occurrence of wounds, cuts, abrasions, sores, fungal skin infections, or other types of damage to the skin. The skin becomes bright-red and swollen, especially on the face [FIGURE 24.7] or legs. The streptococci may originate from the patient's own respiratory tract, from an asymptomatic carrier, or from contaminated linens, dressings, and other inanimate objects. Control is best accomplished by good personal hygiene and by preventive treatment with antibiotics following known exposure.

Impetigo contagiosum is another skin infection caused by S. *pyogenes*, with *Staphylococcus aureus* often causing additional infection later. The S. *pyogenes* strains involved usually are not those that cause pharyngitis. Pus-filled blisters appear most commonly on the face and hands but may cover the body. They eventually develop thick crusts. The streptococci are transmitted by direct contact with a patient or contaminated objects. Because children are usually susceptible, epidemics are likely to spread rapidly through schools and camps unless controlled by good sanitary and hygienic practices.

Puerperal fever is a streptococcal infection associated with childbirth. It is an infection of the uterus of the mother and is a serious and often fatal disease. Before the germ theory of disease was established, maternity wards in some hospitals were looked upon as the "vestibule of death" because of the prevalence of puerperal fever. Later it was found that the disease could be controlled by aseptic obstetrical practices. The streptococci may come from the patient's respiratory, genital, or in-testinal tract, or from the skin or hands of the patient or her attendants. Antibiotics can be used to reduce the possibility of infection.

Laboratory Diagnosis of S. *pyogenes* Infections. It is important that S. *pyogenes* infections be diagnosed promptly and effectively treated in order to prevent complications such as rheumatic fever. An accurate diagnosis cannot be made from clinical information alone; laboratory data are required. Laboratory techniques usually consist of isolating the organism and identifying it as belonging to Lancefield group A. However, other techniques have been developed recently to extract the group A antigen directly from material on a swab of the inflamed area and identify it by a sensitive ELISA test (see Chapter 20).

When S. *pyogenes* cannot be isolated from the patient (for example, in cases of rheumatic fever and post-streptococcal glomerulonephritis), the development of an immune response in the patient provides strong circumstantial evidence that the patient either has, or recently has had, an S. *pyogenes* infection. This immune response can be demonstrated by finding a marked increase in the level of antibodies against streptolysin O in the patient over a period of days or weeks.

Treatment and Prevention of S. *pyogenes* Infections. The antibiotic usually used for treatment of S. *pyogenes* infections is penicillin, since no penicillin-resistant strains of S. *pyogenes* have been found. Erythromycin can be used to treat patients who are allergic to penicillin. Antibiotic treatment should be continued for some days after the symptoms have subsided to ensure complete elimination of the streptococci. This reduces the risk of complications such as rheumatic fever. No active immunization methods are available for prevention of S. *pyogenes* infections. ***Chemoprophylaxis*** (the use of chemicals such as antibiotics to prevent disease) is advisable for at least 5 years after a patient has had rheumatic fever, to prevent recurrences.

Tuberculosis

Tuberculosis is a slowly progressive disease of humans that often becomes well established before symptoms become apparent. It is estimated that 10 million to 15 million persons in the United States may be infected, although most never become ill. There were 137,000 reported cases in 1948, but the incidence of clinical tuberculosis in the United States has decreased steadily over the years. However, there are still about 26,000 new cases each year, and recent data suggest that the disease is now on the rise. In 1989 there was a 5 percent increase in the number of cases over the previous year,

24.1   ACUTE RHEUMATIC FEVER AT A NAVY TRAINING CENTER

Between December 15, 1986, and July 15, 1987, ten cases of acute rheumatic fever were identified among recruits at the Naval Training Center in San Diego, California. This outbreak was the first at the center in over two decades.

All patients were male and ranged from 19 to 31 years of age. All had joint inflammation and fever, and three patients had heart inflammation. One patient had sought treatment for sore throat and was diagnosed as having group A streptococcal pharyngitis, but he did not complete an oral penicillin regimen.

Throat cultures from four of the patients were positive for group A streptococci when they were hospitalized for acute rheumatic fever.

For approximately 15 years, intramuscular penicillin G was given to all incoming recruits at the Naval Center as a preventive measure against streptococcal infection. However, the practice was discontinued in 1980 because of a perceived decrease in the risk for rheumatic fever. The Marine Corps Recruit Depot adjacent to the Naval Center had used penicillin G as a preventive measure

continuously since the mid-1960s. No cases of rheumatic fever were reported at the Marine Depot during the time of the outbreak at the Naval Center, although streptococcal pharyngitis was epidemic.

Mass prophylaxis (preventive measures) with penicillin G has been reinstituted at the Naval Center. All incoming recruits except those allergic to penicillin now receive 1.2 million units intramuscularly.

Adapted from *Morbidity and Mortality Weekly Report,* Feb. 26, 1988.

and in the first 41 weeks of 1990 there was another 9 percent increase. Some of these new cases occur in AIDS patients, whose weakened immune systems cannot halt the growth of the bacilli. Despite these increases, the incidence of tuberculosis in the United States and other industrialized countries is relatively low compared with that in many developing countries, where tuberculosis is a major cause of death.

Biology of Mycobacteria. *Mycobacterium tuberculosis* and *Mycobacterium bovis* are the causative agents of tuberculosis. Other *Mycobacterium* species are also pathogenic for humans and cause serious diseases [TABLE 24.3]. The cells of *M. tuberculosis* and *M. bovis* are slender, straight or curved rods, and, like other mycobacteria, they exhibit acid-fast staining [see FIGURES 9.30 and 24.8]. Cultivation requires special culture media such as Löwenstein-Jensen coagulated egg medium and Middlebrook 7H12 agar. The organisms grow very slowly, taking 2 to 3 weeks or more to form visible colonies.

Transmission of *M. tuberculosis* and *M. bovis*. *M. tuberculosis* is almost exclusively a parasite of humans and has an airborne mode of transmission. It usually causes *pulmonary tuberculosis*, an infection of the lungs, although it is capable of infecting any tissue or organ of the body. *M. bovis* is primarily a pathogen of cattle, transmitted to humans via raw milk from infected animals. Because it is ingested rather than inhaled, *M. bovis* causes tuberculosis of body sites other than the lungs, such as the intestinal tract, lymph nodes, bones, and joints. It is rarely found in cases of tuberculosis in the United States, because of the widespread use of milk pasteurization, which destroys the organism. However, it is an important pathogen in countries where raw milk is consumed.

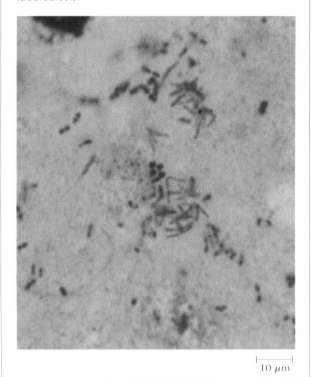

FIGURE 24.8
Mycobacterium tuberculosis stained red with Ziehl-Neelsen acid-fast stain of sputum from a patient with tuberculosis.

10 µm

Pathogenicity of *M. tuberculosis*. Pulmonary tuberculosis begins when *M. tuberculosis* lodges within an air sac in the lungs. The bacteria are rapidly engulfed by macrophages but are not destroyed; instead, they multiply slowly within these phagocytes. The first evidence of infection is development of a hypersensitivity to the bacte-

TABLE 24.3
Some *Mycobacterium* Species Pathogenic for Humans

Group and species	Clinical significance
TUBERCULOSIS GROUP	
M. tuberculosis	Causes tuberculosis
M. bovis	Causes tuberculosis
LEPROSY GROUP	
M. leprae	Causes leprosy; has never been cultivated on laboratory media but can be grown in armadillos and in the footpads of mice
RUNYON GROUPS*	
I	
M. kansasii	Causes a tuberculosislike disease
M. marinum	Causes skin papules and sores; contracted from swimming in fresh or salt water
II	
M. scrofulaceum	Causes lymphadenitis (lymph node disease) in children
M. xenopi	Causes a chronic pulmonary infection
III	
M. avium/M. intra-cellulare group	Causes tuberculosislike disease in adults and lymphadenitis in children; causes severe secondary infections in AIDS patients; resistant to the antimicrobial agents used to treat tuberculosis
M. malmoense	Causes pulmonary infection
IV	
M. fortuitum	Causes a tuberculosislike disease
M. chelonei	Possible cause of a chronic respiratory disease

*Many of the species in these four Runyon groups live in aquatic and soil environments and are probably acquired by humans from inhalation of dust or aerosols from these environments; they do not appear to be transmissible from person to person.

ria after about a month. The hypersensitivity can be detected by the ***tuberculin test,*** in which an extract of proteins from *M. tuberculosis* is injected into the skin. A positive test is indicated by a red, swollen zone at the site of the injection within 48 hours.

If a person who has previously been tuberculin-negative becomes tuberculin-positive, this indicates that the person has become infected during the interim. Although such infections often remain subclinical (without any disease symptoms), the individual should be treated with appropriate antimicrobial agents to ensure that clinical tuberculosis does not develop.

In untreated infections, antibody formation in response to the infectious agent (humoral immunity) is ineffective. The only effective type of immunity is *cell-mediated* immunity. As a cell-mediated immune response develops in the infected individual, specific T lymphocytes migrate toward the bacilli lodged in the lung. Upon contact with the bacilli, these lymphocytes release soluble substances that attract macrophages to the area and convert them to *activated macrophages*, which have increased amounts of hydrolytic enzymes and other antibacterial substances. After engulfing the

mycobacteria, the activated macrophages are able to halt the intracellular growth of the bacteria (but do not kill them). Eventually a small, pearl-gray nodule called a ***tubercle*** forms. It consists of the mycobacteria surrounded by several concentric layers of macrophages and an outer layer of lymphocytes. The bacilli usually become dormant within the tubercle and the infection remains subclinical. Tuberculin tests will continue to give positive reactions as long as the dormant bacilli exist in the body—usually for a lifetime, unless the infection is eliminated by antimicrobial agents.

In about 10 percent of untreated infections, cell-mediated immunity does not develop strongly enough to stop the multiplication of the tubercle bacilli. The initial tubercle becomes larger and more tubercles develop. The macrophages and lung tissue cells inside the enlarged tubercles begin to die because of toxic lipids from the mycobacteria or lack of oxygen circulation. Then they fuse together to form a cheeselike mass of dead tissue. Eventually several tubercules coalesce to form an area of dead tissue large enough to show up on a chest x-ray. As the area of dead tissue expands it may erode the wall of a bronchus, so that acid-fast bacilli begin to appear in the *sputum,* the mucus coughed up by the patient. As the disease progresses, the patient exhibits loss of appetite, fatigue, weight loss, night sweats, and a persistent, worsening cough. If a blood vessel in the lungs is damaged, the bacilli may invade the bloodstream and be transported to various parts of the body, causing numerous tubercles to develop at these sites. Death ultimately results when sufficient damage has occurred in the lungs or other vital organs.

Reactivation tuberculosis is the type of tuberculosis most prevalent today in the United States. In this disease the dormant bacilli from an old subclinical primary infection are no longer held in check by cell-mediated immunity, and they begin to proliferate. This form of the disease occurs most often in elderly persons whose resistance has been lowered by factors such as malnutrition, alcoholism, or other stresses. It also occurs frequently in people with AIDS.

Laboratory Diagnosis of Tuberculosis. In the microbiology laboratory, a tentative diagnosis of pulmonary tuberculosis can be made by detecting acid-fast bacilli in smears of sputum [FIGURE 24.8]. However, a definitive diagnosis depends upon isolating the bacilli from the patient and identifying them as being a virulent strain of *M. tuberculosis.* This involves demonstrating that the bacilli synthesize the vitamin niacin, reduce nitrates to nitrites, and form serpentine *cords* (cable-like arrangements of the bacilli) when growing on laboratory media [FIGURE 24.9].

Treatment and Prevention of Tuberculosis. Patients with tuberculosis can usually be treated effectively by a combination of antimicrobial agents. The most common agent is *isoniazid,* which is normally used in combination with rifampin. Other antituberculosis drugs include pyrazinamide, *para*-aminosalicylic acid, ethambutol, and streptomycin. Treatment must be extended over a year or more because of the chronic nature of the disease and the slow penetration of the chemical agent into the tubercles.

BCG vaccine is used widely throughout the world—but not in the United States—to prevent tuberculosis. It consists of live cells of an **attenuated strain** of *M. bovis* that was isolated in 1908 by the French microbiologists Calmette and Guérin. (An "attenuated" strain has lost its ability to cause disease.) Injection of the harmless BCG strain into a tuberculin-negative individual (usually an infant) induces cell-mediated immunity against tuberculosis; it is 60 to 80 percent effective. Immunization usually does not have adverse effects, although swollen lymph nodes may occur in 10 percent of those vaccinated. The BCG organism may grow and cause infection in approximately one person in 1 million vaccinated; those in whom it does so usually have immune systems weakened by disease or treatment with immunosuppres-

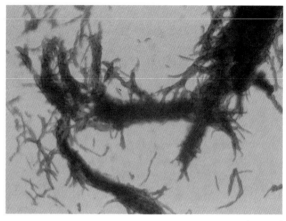

FIGURE 24.9

Photomicrograph of cords—cable-like arrangements of parallel bacilli—formed during growth of *Mycobacterium smegmatis,* a harmless species. They resemble the cords made by virulent strains of *Mycobacterium tuberculosis.* Acid-fast stain.

50 μm

sive drugs. BCG vaccine is not used in the United States, because the risk of *M. tuberculosis* infection is very low, and because the recipients become tuberculin-positive. This prevents use of the tuberculin test in early detection of individuals infected with *M. tuberculosis.*

Legionnaires' Disease

Legionnaires' disease was first described in 1976 after an outbreak of illness at an American Legion convention in Philadelphia. One hundred eighty-two persons were affected and 29 of those died. The cause of the outbreak remained a mystery for months. Despite many attempts, the causative microbe could not be seen in, or isolated from, specimens of diseased lung tissue. However, it could be propagated by inoculating diseased tissue into guinea pigs. Later the microbe was grown successfully in live chick embryos and was found to be a small rod-shaped bacterium. Eventually microbiologists at the Centers for Disease Control in Atlanta were able to grow colonies of the bacterium on special agar media. Once the organism had been isolated, it became clear that Legionnaires' disease was not a new disease. For instance, in 1957, a mysterious outbreak of pneumonia in Austin, Minnesota had affected 78 persons and caused two deaths. Retrospective serological studies indicate that this was an outbreak of Legionnaires' disease.

Legionnaires' disease occurs in both epidemic and sporadic forms. Although epidemics have attracted the most attention, the sporadic cases outnumber the epidemic cases. It has been estimated that 25,000 to 50,000 sporadic cases may occur in the United States each year. Outbreaks of Legionnaires' disease have been reported in at least 15 other countries.

Biology of *Legionella pneumophila*. More than 20 species of the genus *Legionella* have been described, and probably all are pathogenic. The best known species is *L. pneumophila* [FIGURE 24.10]. Legionellas are aerobic Gram-negative rod-shaped bacteria that require, among other nutrients, the amino acid cysteine for growth. This requirement is unusual among Gram-negative aerobic bacteria.

Transmission of *L. pneumophila*. Unlike many other airborne pathogens, legionellas do not seem to be transmitted from person to person. The organism has been isolated from the water of lakes and reservoirs, where it can grow inside the cells of certain protozoa. It has also been isolated from the water of air-conditioning cooling towers and condensers, and from shower heads and pipes of hot water plumbing systems, especially systems with "dead ends" in which warm water can stagnate. Humans probably acquire the organism by inhaling aerosols generated from these environmental sources [DISCOVER 24.2]. Hospitals must pay special attention to eliminating *Legionella* from their plumbing and air-conditioning systems, because persons who are ill or who are being treated with agents that suppress immune responses may have an increased susceptibility to infection.

Pathogenicity of *L. pneumophila*. *L. pneumophila* can cause two kinds of diseases. The first, Legionnaires' disease, is a severe pneumonia characterized by fever, chills, and a dry cough. Sometimes there are also chest pain, abdominal pain, vomiting, diarrhea, and mental confusion. The disease tends to occur most frequently in men above the age of 50. The fatality rate in untreated cases is 15 percent or higher. The second type of disease is termed *Pontiac fever* (named after an outbreak that occurred in Pontiac, Michigan). Pontiac fever is a milder, nonfatal disease characterized by fever, chills, headache, dry cough, and muscle pain. The disease is self-limiting, and complete recovery without treatment occurs within a week.

Laboratory Diagnosis of *Legionella* Infections. The definitive method of diagnosing *Legionella* is to isolate the bacterium from respiratory secretions, using an agar medium containing (among other ingredients) the amino acid cysteine and finely ground charcoal. The function of the charcoal is to destroy toxic hydrogen peroxide, which is formed when some of the cysteine oxidizes spontaneously in the presence of oxygen. Identification of an isolate as a legionella is based mainly on its requirement for cysteine. Since isolation may take several days, fluorescent antibody staining can be used to quickly detect the bacteria in clinical specimens from the patient. However, this method is less sensitive than the culture method. Also, the development of an immune response in the patient, as indicated by a marked increase in the level of specific antibodies in the patient over a period of time, provides strong circumstantial evidence of a *Legionella* infection. However, the patient may take several weeks to develop these antibodies.

Treatment and Prevention of Legionnaires' Disease. Erythromycin is the antibiotic of choice for treatment of Legionnaires' disease.

No vaccine against Legionnaires' disease is available. To eliminate *Legionella* bacteria from institutional water systems, the level of chlorination of water supplies should be increased, dead ends in the plumbing should be eliminated, and hot water tanks should be heated to at least 70°C for 72 hours.

Other Airborne Diseases Caused by Bacteria

Many other serious airborne infections are caused by bacteria. Some of these infections, the bacteria that cause them, and their treatment and prevention, are listed in TABLE 24.4. Photomicrographs of some of the causative agents are shown in FIGURE 24.11.

FIGURE 24.10
Electron micrograph of the Legionnaires' disease organism, *Legionella pneumophila*. Note that the bacillus has a polar flagellum.

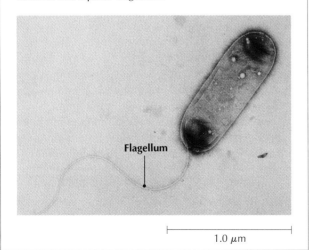

Flagellum

1.0 μm

FIGURE 24.11

Some bacterial agents of airborne infections. **[A]** *Corynebacterium diphtheriae*, the cause of diphtheria. The cells are stained with Albert's stain to show the dark metachromatic granules. **[B]** Electron micrograph of an ultrathin section through a microcolony of *Chlamydia psittaci*, the cause of psittacosis, in the cytoplasm of a tissue cell. Shown are the elementary bodies, initial bodies (now called *reticulate bodies*), and forms that are intermediate between the two. The membrane of the intracellular vacuole containing the chlamydias has been ruptured. **[C]** *Streptococcus pneumoniae*, showing the swollen, distinct capsules that become visible upon addition of specific antibodies against the capsular polysaccharide. **[D]** Gram stain of *Haemophilus influenzae*.

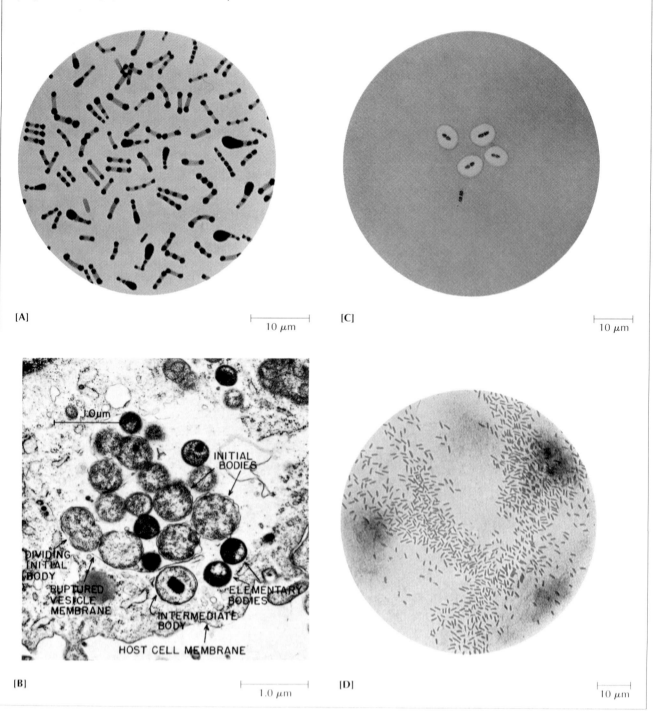

TABLE 24.4
Some Airborne Infections Caused by Bacteria

Disease	Causative agent	Pathogenicity	Treatment and prevention
Pneumococcal pneumonia	*Streptococcus pneumoniae.* Gram-positive cocci in pairs, surrounded by a poly-saccharide capsule that resists phagocytosis. 84 capsular serotypes exist. Colonies are α-hemolytic on blood-agar plates incubated aerobically.	The major cause of bacterial pneumonia. Fatality rates are high in persons age 65 or older. Symptoms include chills, fever, and chest pain. Air sacs of the lungs fill with fluid in which pneumococci multiply. Neutrophils attempt to engulf the cocci but are often hindered by the antiphagocytic bacterial capsules. Cells make pneumolysin O, an oxygen-labile hemolysin that damages host-cell membranes. From the lungs the cocci may invade the bloodstream.	Pencillin is usually effective, but some pneumococcus strains are resistant to it. A vaccine is available and consists of the purified capsular material from the 23 most frequent sero-types. Mainly given to elderly persons.
Diphtheria	*Corynebacterium diphtheriae.* Gram-positive rods, often arranged in parallel like a picket fence. The cells contain metachromatic granules when stained with methylene blue.	Causes localized throat infection; makes a powerful exotoxin that kills throat tissue cells and causes an exudate to form that can block the trachea and cause the patient to suffocate. The toxin also circulates in the blood and can kill the patient by damaging the kidneys, the nerves, and especially the heart.	Antitoxin is adminis-tered to neutralize the toxin. Vaccination of infants has reduced the incidence of diphtheria dramatically. The vaccine consists of a toxoid made from diphtheria exotoxin.
Pertussis (whooping cough)	*Bordetella pertussis.* Short Gram-negative rods.	Bacteria attach to the surface tissue of bronchi and cause a localized infection. The patient develops a severe cough that ends with a "crowing" sound, or "whoop." The coughing may be accompanied by vomiting, lack of oxygen in the blood, and hemorrhages of the nose, eyes, and even brain. Deafness and other permanent damage may occur.	Erythromycin is the antibiotic of choice. Vaccination of infants and children has greatly reduced the incidence of the disease. The vaccine consists of killed cells of *B. pertussis.*
Primary atypical pneumonia (walking pneumonia)	*Mycoplasma pneumoniae.* Gram-negative pleomorphic cells that lack a cell wall and thus are not susceptible to penicillin.	Lung infection characterized by a gradual onset with headache, sore throat, fever, and cough. The mortality rate is less than 1 percent. *M. pneumoniae* may cause 25 percent of all pneumonias in young adults and 9 percent of pneumonias in children.	Tetracycline is the antibiotic of choice. No vaccine is available.
Haemophilus meningitis	*Haemophilus influenzae.* Gram-negative rod that requires heme and nicotinamide adenine dinucleotide (NAD) to grow. Cells have a poly-saccharide capsule that resists phagocytosis. Six capsular serotypes exist; serotype b causes nearly all cases of *Haemophilus* meningitis among children.	*Haemophilus* meningitis is the most frequent kind of meningitis in children between 6 weeks and 2 years of age. The fatality rate in untreated cases is 90 to 100 percent. The organisms initially grow in the nasopharynx. An endotoxin probably helps to damage the surface tissue, and the bacteria penetrate to reach the underlying blood vessels. The bacteria are transported by the blood to the meninges, where they cause a severe inflammation.	A combination of ampicillin and chloram-phenicol is used for treatment. A vaccine is available and consists of purified capsular polysaccharide of serotype b that has been chemically linked to diphtheria toxoid. It is given to infants in a three-dose series at 2, 4, and 6 months of age.
Meningococcal meningitis	*Neisseria meningitidis.* Gram-negative cocci in pairs. A polysaccharide capsule occurs and in-hibits phagocytosis dur-ing infection. Serotypes are based on type of capsule; A, B, C, and Y are the most common.	The bacteria can be harbored in the nasopharynx without causing disease; however, they may gain access to the bloodstream and be carried to the meninges, where they cause a severe inflammation. Patients have a headache, fever, pain in the neck and back, loss of mental alertness, and sometimes a skin rash. Death can occur within 24 h.	Penicillin is the antibiotic of choice. A vaccine is available consisting of the capsular polysaccha-rides from serotypes A, C, Y, and W135. No vaccine is available against serotype B.

24.2 LEGIONNAIRES' DISEASE IN WAYNE COUNTY, MICHIGAN

Fourteen cases of pneumonia with high fever were identified among approximately 380 persons who attended a church banquet at a hotel on April 27, 1985, in Wayne County, Michigan. Three of the cases were fatal. There was laboratory evidence of *Legionella* infection in seven of the cases, including all the fatal cases. No common exposures other than attending the banquet were identified. Samples for laboratory analysis were obtained from the hotel's drinking water, a nearby swimming pool and whirlpool, and the 12 functioning air-conditioning ventilation units. *L. pneumophila* was isolated from samples obtained from the external surfaces of the cooling coils of the two air-conditioning units that supplied the banquet hall.

Merely recovering *Legionella* bacteria from an environmental site does not prove that the bacteria caused an outbreak of infection. *Legionella* organisms are frequently isolated from water sources unrelated to human disease. The air-conditioning units in the Michigan hotel may have been involved, but, if so, it is difficult to explain why only one other suspected case of pneumonia was identified among more than 800 persons who attended 12 other banquets held at the same hotel between April 25 and May 10. This anomaly illustrates the sort of problem one often encounters in attempting to trace an outbreak of Legionnaires' disease to a specific source.

Adapted from *Morbidity and Mortality Weekly Report*, June 14, 1985.

Disease	Causative agent	Pathogenicity	Treatment and prevention
Psittacosis	*Chlamydia psittaci.* Obligate intracellular parasite with developmental cycle. Mainly a pathogen of various birds and domestic fowls.	Acquired by inhalation of infectious dust from infected bird feces. Poultry workers may contract the infection. In humans the disease may range from a mild respiratory infection to a severe pneumonia that may involve the central nervous system.	Tetracyclines, sulfonamides, and erythromycin are effective. No vaccine is available.

ASK YOURSELF

1 What are the functions of the virulence factors of *Streptococcus pyogenes*? What practical use can be made of the M protein? Why are rheumatic fever and acute poststreptococcal glomerulonephritis not considered infections?

2 What sequence of events occurs in infections caused by *Mycobacterium tuberculosis*? How does the patient's immune response determine the outcome? How does BCG vaccine function?

3 What are the sources of *Legionella* bacteria? How can *Legionella* infections be prevented?

4 How are streptococcal pharyngitis, rheumatic fever, tuberculosis, and Legionnaires' disease diagnosed in the clinical microbiology laboratory?

5 What are the causative agents of pneumococcal pneumonia, diphtheria, pertussis, primary atypical pneumonia, psittacosis, *Haemophilus* meningitis, and meningococcal meningitis?

AIRBORNE INFECTIONS CAUSED BY VIRUSES

Several airborne infections are caused by viruses. Of these, the common cold and influenza are particularly interesting because of their widespread occurrence and the many antigenic types of causative viruses involved.

The Common Cold

The common cold is a mild infection of the upper respiratory tract. It is the most prevalent infectious disease of humans and is worldwide in its distribution. It is during winter months adults have an average of 6 to 8 colds per 1000 persons per day; the rate in summer is about one-third of that in winter.

Biology of Cold Viruses. A number of viruses can cause the common cold. Of these, the rhinoviruses (from the Greek word *rhis*, "nose") are the most frequent [FIGURE 24.12]. Rhinoviruses consist of an icosahedral protein capsid which encloses single-stranded RNA. Rhinoviruses grow best at a temperature of 33°C instead of body temperature (37°C). This helps to explain why rhinoviruses are restricted to the respiratory tract and do not invade the internal organs of the body. There are at present at least 115 serotypes of rhinoviruses, and immunity against one type does not prevent infection by another type. This is the main reason why a person may have several colds a year.

FIGURE 24.12
Electron micrograph of purified rhinovirus.

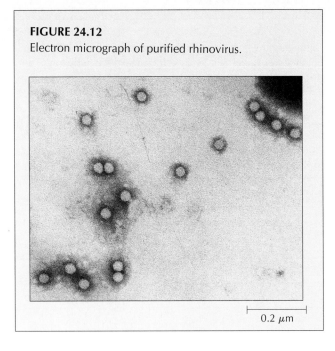

0.2 µm

Coronaviruses cause about 15 percent of common colds. They are so named because large particles of glycoprotein project from the surface of the virions, giving the appearance of a crown, or corona [FIGURE 24.13]. Coronaviruses have a helical nucleocapsid composed of protein and single-stranded RNA; the nucleocapsid is surrounded by a lipid envelope. Unlike rhinoviruses, coronaviruses have only two antigenic types. However, immunity that is developed in response to a coronavirus infection is relatively short-lived (approximately one year), and an individual can be reinfected later by the same antigenic type.

FIGURE 24.13
Electron micrograph of coronavirus OC 43.

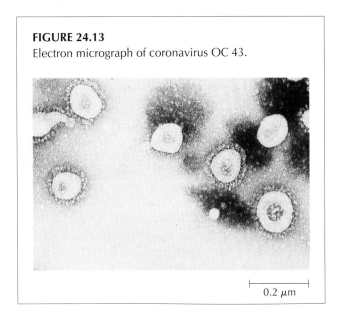

0.2 µm

Transmission of Cold Viruses. There is no basis for the popular belief that sharp changes in temperature or wetness predispose a person to get a cold. Colds are contracted by exposure to a cold-causing virus. The main cold-causing viruses, rhinoviruses, are shed in high concentrations in nasal secretions and can be spread by aerosols. However, their main mode of transmission appears to be through *hand-to-hand transmission*. A high proportion of persons infected with rhinoviruses have virus-contaminated nasal secretions on their hands, and the virus can be transferred by contact to the hands of uninfected individuals. These individuals then may place their contaminated fingers in contact with nasal mucous membranes or the conjunctiva of the eye. A person suffering from a cold should wash his or her hands frequently with soap and water, especially after disposing of handkerchiefs contaminated with nasal secretions.

Pathogenicity of Cold Viruses. Viral multiplication occurs in the cells that line the surface of the nasal passages and pharynx. After an incubation period of 12 to 72 hours, the cold develops as an acute infection of the nose, throat, sinuses, trachea, and bronchi, lasting approximately 2 to 7 days. Symptoms include nasal discharge, nasal congestion, sneezing, coughing, a sore or scratchy throat, hoarseness, and sometimes a slight fever. During the acute phase of the cold, large amounts of virus appear in the nasal secretions. Serotype-specific antibodies of the secretory IgA type also appear in the nasal secretions.

Although the common cold is itself a relatively mild disease, it may affect a patient's normal resistance to bacterial invasion of the sinuses and the middle ear. This may explain why bacterial sinusitis and otitis media (inflammation of the sinuses and middle ear, respectively) develop in a small proportion of cold cases.

Laboratory Diagnosis, Treatment, and Prevention of the Common Cold. The common cold is usually diagnosed by its symptoms rather than by laboratory methods. There is no specific treatment for the common cold. Supportive measures such as adequate rest, warm clothing, and aspirin are recommended and serve to increase the patient's comfort. Liberal intake of fluids, such as fruit juices, is helpful. Since colds are caused by viruses, antibiotics have no place in the treatment of uncomplicated colds. Antihistamines have only a minimal effect in reducing nasal secretions. Whether large doses of vitamin C are beneficial is debatable.

Because there are so many serotypes of rhinoviruses, a vaccine against the common cold is not yet feasible. Antibodies, however, do appear in response to a rhinovirus infection, and they afford protection against the specific rhinovirus serotype for up to 2 years. As mentioned previously one of the most effective ways to prevent a cold is thorough hand washing and avoiding contact with persons who are infected.

Influenza

It is common for influenza to occur as an *epidemic*, which is a sudden increase in the number of cases within a particular country or region. Epidemic influenza, or "flu," as it is commonly known, is one of the most familiar examples of airborne infection. There are three antigenic types of the influenza virus—A, B, and C. Epidemics of influenza occur in cycles: those caused by type A influenza virus strains commonly follow a 2- to 3-year cycle, while those caused by type B strains have a 4- to 6-year cycle. Type C strains rarely, if ever, give rise to epidemics; they cause subclinical infections or small outbreaks of influenza among children.

In addition to epidemics, influenza can occur in pandemics, which are epidemics of worldwide proportions. Pandemics illustrate the enormous geographic range and the rapid spread that airborne disease can achieve. Great pandemics of influenza have occurred at intervals of 10 to 30 years or even longer; they are caused by type A influenza virus strains.

Biology of Influenza Viruses. Influenza viruses have a core of single-stranded RNA contained within a helical capsid. The capsid is wound up to form a rounded mass and is covered by a lipid envelope from which protein spikes project [FIGURE 24.14]. These spikes are *hemagglutinins* (H proteins), so named because they allow attachment of the virus to red blood cells and other host cells. Also projecting from the lipid envelope are mushroom-shaped protrusions composed of *neuraminidase* (N proteins). This enzyme can degrade the protective mucus layers of mucous membranes, allowing attachment of the virus to the underlying tissue cells.

Influenza A viruses can be classified into subtypes on the basis of the H protein and N protein they possess. So far, 13 major types of H proteins (H1 to H13) and 9 types of N proteins (N1 to N9) have been identified in influenza A viruses from humans, animals, and birds. In influenza A viruses isolated from humans, only three of these H proteins (H1, H2, and H3) and two types of N proteins (N1 and N2) have been identified. H and N proteins can occur in different combinations to yield various subtypes of influenza A viruses. For instance, the strain that caused the worldwide human "Asian flu" epidemic in 1957 was of the A(H2N2) subtype, whereas the strain that caused the "Hong Kong flu" epidemic in 1968 was of the A(H3N2) subtype. During the 1989–1990 in-

FIGURE 24.14

[A] Diagram showing the structure of influenza virus and the location of the H and N proteins. The helical nucleocapsid is in eight segments, each composed of protein and an internal single-stranded segment of RNA. The location of an RNA strand is shown in one nucleocapsid segment. [B] Electron micrograph (negative stain preparation) of influenza virus particles.

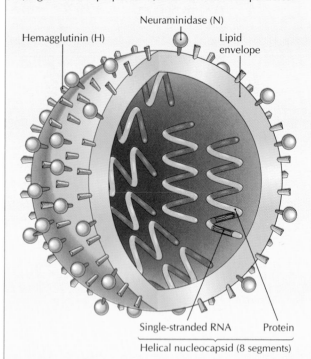

Neuraminidase (N)
Hemagglutinin (H)
Lipid envelope
Single-stranded RNA   Protein
Helical nucleocapsid (8 segments)
80–120 nm (0.08–0.12 μm)

[A]

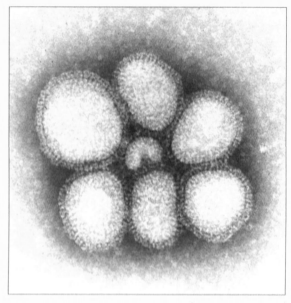

[B]   0.1 μm

fluenza season, strains of the A(H3N2) subtype caused most of the epidemics worldwide.

The H and N antigens of an influenza virus have practical importance because antibodies against them can prevent attachment of the virus to host cells, and recovery from influenza will confer a degree of active natural immunity on a population. However, antibodies formed by a host population against one antigenic subtype of influenza A virus, for example, A(H2N2), do not protect against other subtypes which may develop by mutation, such as A(H3N2). Moreover, within a particular influenza virus subtype, such as A(H3N2), varieties having different antigenic properties may develop. For instance, during the 1990–1991 influenza season three antigenically distinct varieties of A(H3N2) viruses were isolated worldwide. If the antigenic differences between varieties are sufficiently great, then antibodies formed against one variety will react poorly with another variety. It is because of the occurrence of new subtypes and new varieties of influenza A viruses that pandemics occur in populations that had been previously immune to an older subtype or variety [DISCOVER 24.3].

Transmission of Influenza Viruses. Large amounts of influenza virus are present in the respiratory secretions of patients and can be transmitted to uninfected individuals by aerosols and *fomites* (inanimate objects that harbor pathogenic microorganisms, such as a handkerchief that has been contaminated by a patient). A single infected person can transmit the virus to a large number of susceptible persons, accounting for the "explosive" nature of epidemics.

Laboratory Diagnosis of Influenza. For diagnosis of influenza, sputum specimens and specimens obtained by swabbing the nose and throat are inoculated into cultures of appropriate host cells, such as canine kidney cells. After incubation, influenza virus can be detected by its ability to agglutinate red blood cells added to the culture, or by its ability to alter the surface of the infected cells so that red blood cells will now bind to this surface. Alternatively, the presence of viral antigens in the host cells can be detected by using specific fluorescent antibodies.

Pathogenicity of Influenza Viruses. Virus multiplication is usually restricted to tissue in the upper respiratory tract. The death and sloughing off of the cells lining these mucous membranes may be responsible for many of the symptoms, such as congestion and increased secretion. Influenza is characterized by a clear nasal dis-

charge, fever, chills, headache, muscle pains, sore throat, coughing, and a marked weakness and exhaustion. In patients with influenza, body temperature usually rises rapidly to 100 to 104°F, and sometimes to 106°F, within 12 hours of the onset of symptoms (compared with the slight fever that accompanies the common cold). The fever usually lasts 3 days, but it can persist for up to 8 days. Complete convalescence may require one or more weeks.

Influenza causes a decreased resistance to infection by other microbial pathogens, and there is a tendency to develop a secondary pneumonia caused by bacteria such as *Streptococcus pneumoniae*, *S. pyogenes*, *Staphylococcus aureus*, and *Haemophilus influenzae*. Many of the deaths attributed to influenza are due to such secondary infections.

Treatment and Prevention of Influenza. Treatment for uncomplicated influenza involves supportive measures such as bed rest. As with any viral infection, no chemotherapeutic agent can cure influenza. The chemotherapeutic agent **amantadine** can shorten the duration of the disease by about 50 percent. However, it may cause side effects such as insomnia, dizziness, or difficulty in concentrating. Active immunization with a vaccine consisting of formaldehyde-inactivated strains is presently the most effective means of prevention. Live attenuated influenza virus vaccines, which have greater immunogenic properties, are currently being developed. A mixture of the various antigenic subtypes most likely to cause infection is used to prepare the inactivated vaccine, since immunity is subtype-specific. The composition of the vaccine is reevaluated annually so that the particular subtypes and varieties predominant at the time will be included. Maximum protection requires annual immunization, since the protective immunity lasts only 3 to 6 months. It is particularly important that high-risk persons, such as elderly individuals, receive immunization before the beginning of the "flu season" each year.

Other Airborne Infections Caused by Viruses

Both the common cold and influenza are infections of the respiratory tract. However, there are other airborne viral diseases that affect areas of the body other than the respiratory system. TABLE 24.5 summarizes some of the main features of these diseases, and FIGURE 24.15 illustrates their clinical manifestations. It is one of the triumphs of medical science that one of the most deadly of these diseases, *smallpox*, has now been completely eradicated from the world [DISCOVER 24.4].

24.3 WHY DO INFLUENZA PANDEMICS KEEP HAPPENING?

In 1918–1919 a strain of type A influenza virus caused the deadliest influenza pandemic on record, killing more than 20 million persons. At the time, microbiologists did not know how to isolate and characterize the virus. In the 1950s evidence showed that the deadly strain probably belonged to a particular antigenic variety of the A(H1N1) subtype. This evidence was based on the fact that if a person recovers from influenza, that person's blood serum will continue to contain antibodies against the particular viral subtype that caused the infection. A survey of the blood serum of persons born between 1918 and 1929 revealed that antibodies against the particular variety of A(H1N1) were present. They were not present in the serum of persons born after that period. Such surveys provide an *immunological record* of the influenza virus strains that predominated at various times in the past.

Type A influenza viruses are notorious for their ability to undergo antigenic change with time and to give rise to new viral subtypes. Unfortunately, antibodies produced against the old subtypes provide little protection against the new subtypes.

Marked changes in the H and N antigens of influenza A viruses occurred in 1947, 1957, 1968, and 1977, giving rise to the subtypes A(H1N1), A(H2N2), A(H3N2), and A(H1N1), respectively. These changes resulted in epidemics and sometimes pandemics of influenza. For instance, after the emergence of the A(H2N2) subtype in 1957, influenza spread widely throughout China and then to Hong Kong and other parts of the world. When it reached the United States nearly half the population became ill and more than 8000 persons died. However, even before this pandemic occurred, microbiologists had found that the blood serum of many persons 70 to 90 years old *already contained antibodies against the new A(H2N2) strain*. This was of considerable interest because a moderately severe influenza pandemic occurred in 1889 and the immunological record indicated that an A(H2N2) strain had probably caused it.

In 1968 the A(H3N2) subtype appeared in Hong Kong, and a moderately severe pandemic occurred. In 1977, still another subtype emerged, A(H1N1) (similar to the subtype that had been prevalent in 1947); it caused a pandemic which, fortunately, was relatively mild.

The sequence in which these viral subtypes have emerged suggests that antigenic variation in type A influenza virus may occur in a *repeating* or *cyclic* fashion rather than as an endless progression of new subtypes. For instance, in 1976 at Fort Dix, New Jersey, a strain was isolated having the antigenic subtype A(H1N1). This strain was antigenically similar to the one thought to be responsible for the deadly 1918 pandemic. Public health authorities feared that this strain might cause a serious pandemic, but, fortunately, it failed to gain predominance over the A(H3N2) strains that were still prevalent.

How do new influenza virus subtypes arise? We know that type A influenza viruses occur naturally in a number of birds (particularly waterfowl) and mammals such as swine and horses, as well as humans. When different subtypes infect the same animal host, genetic recombinants may occur: some of the genes from one virus strain may replace those within another strain, giving rise to a new viral subtype. This might account in part for the plethora of subtypes which complicate the production of effective influenza vaccines year after year.

ASK YOURSELF

1 Which viruses can cause the common cold? Why can a person have several colds a year?

2 What is the best way to prevent a cold?

3 How are influenza type A viruses classified into subtypes?

4 Why do influenza pandemics occur in cycles?

5 What does a vaccine against influenza contain? Why must the components be changed periodically?

6 What differences are there between the vaccines used against influenza and those used against tuberculosis, pneumococcal pneumonia, meningococcal meningitis, *Haemophilus* meningitis, and diphtheria?

7 What are the causative agents of chicken pox, herpes zoster, measles, German measles, mumps, and smallpox?

TABLE 24.5
Some Airborne Infections Caused by Viruses

Disease	Causative agent	Pathogenicity	Occurrence and prevention
Chicken pox (varicella)	Varicella-zoster virus, a herpesvirus	The virus multiplies in the respiratory tract and regional lymph nodes, reaches the blood, and spreads to all parts of the body. Fever and headache precede development of skin rashes, which eventually become blisters.	Mainly a mild infection of children. About 170,000 cases occur annually in the United States. Epidemics are most frequent in winter and spring. No vaccine is yet available but a live, attenuated vaccine is currently being tested.
Herpes zoster (shingles)	Varicella-zoster virus	Herpes zoster occurs as a result of activation of latent virus from a previous varicella infection, and is characterized by a blisterlike skin eruption and a very painful inflammation of the sensory nerves.	Herpes zoster occurs mainly in adults.
Measles (rubeola)	Rubeola virus, a paramyxovirus	Measles is a severe, highly contagious disease. The virus multiplies in the upper respiratory tract and in the conjunctiva of the eye early in the course of the disease. It is then disseminated by the blood to the intestinal tract, urinary tract, skin, and central nervous system. Symptoms include fever, coldlike symptoms, cough, conjunctivitis, and a red, blotchy skin rash. Small bluish-white spots (Koplik's spots) occur on the mucous membranes of the cheeks and lips.	Occurs mainly in children but can also occur in adults who escaped childhood infection. Immunization decreased the incidence of measles dramatically (e.g., 3396 cases in 1988 in the United States compared with an annual average of 526,000 cases in 1950–1962); however, it has since risen markedly (28,000 cases in 1990) due to fewer children being vaccinated. The vaccine consists of live attenuated rubeola virus.
German measles (rubella)	Rubella virus, a togavirus	Rubella is a highly contagious but mild disease unrelated to common measles (rubeola). After initial multiplication in the upper respiratory tract, the virus becomes distributed by the blood to the skin, lymph nodes, and joints. Symptoms include fever, swollen lymph glands, and sometimes a rash on the face and other parts of the body. When rubella occurs in early pregnancy it can cause serious congenital abnormalities or death of the fetus. During the 1964–1965 epidemic in the United States, rubella caused 30,000 fetal deaths, and more than 20,000 children were born with heart disease, mental retardation, and defects in vision and hearing.	Highest incidence is in children and adolescents. Since widespread immunization was begun in 1968, the incidence has decreased dramatically. There are now about 1100 cases a year in the United States. The vaccine consists of live attenuated rubella virus.

24.4 WILL SMALLPOX RETURN?

Smallpox has caused death, blindness, and disfigurement for thousands of years. During the seventeenth and eighteenth centuries smallpox was the most devastating disease in the western world. Even the Americas were not spared: during the eighteenth century, smallpox epidemics in the city of Boston affected as much as 52 percent of the population.

By the twentieth century smallpox had been eradicated from many countries. The last case of smallpox in the United States occurred in 1949. However, the disease still smoldered in many parts of the world, especially in areas of Africa, Asia, and South America.

In 1966 the World Health Organization instituted a "grand strategy" directed toward total eradication of the disease. Unlike many other infections, smallpox had certain features that made eradication seem possible: (1) the virus was restricted to humans and did not occur in other hosts such as wild or domestic animals; (2) it was not harbored by healthy individuals, nor did it cause latent or "hidden" infections; (3) it did not undergo antigenic variation; and (4) an effective vaccine was available.

The grand strategy was implemented on a worldwide basis and involved several tactical aspects:

1 Systematic mass vaccination
2 Prompt and regular reporting of all cases, even those merely suspected to be smallpox, by all existing health facilities
3 Investigation of all cases to determine the sources of infection
4 Establishment of laboratory techniques to test clinical specimens so that preliminary diagnoses of smallpox could be confirmed
5 Containment of the disease by intensive vaccination programs in those areas where cases or outbreaks occurred, together with the isolation of smallpox patients and disinfection of bedclothes and other inanimate objects capable of transmitting the infection

So far, the strategy appears to have been successful. No cases of smallpox have appeared anywhere in the world since 1977. The last case occurred in Merka, Somalia, on October 13 of that year.

Disease	Causative agent	Pathogenicity	Occurrence and prevention
Mumps	Mumps virus, a paramyxovirus	The virus multiplies initially in the upper respiratory tract and then is distributed by the blood throughout the body. The disease is characterized by painful swelling, particularly of the parotid glands; salivary glands, testes, ovaries, pancreas, and other glands may be involved. The most feared complication in males is *orchitis*, infection of the testes.	Most cases occur in 5- to 15-year-old children, but some can occur in adults, in whom the infection may be more serious. Since widespread immunization against mumps was begun in 1967, the incidence of the disease in the United States has decreased dramatically. There are now about 5300 cases per year. The vaccine consists of live attenuated mumps virus.
Smallpox (variola)	Variola virus, a poxvirus. There are two variants: *variola major* causes severe illness with a 25 to 50% mortality rate, and *variola minor* causes a much milder disease with less than 1% mortality.	The virus is transmitted by droplet infection. From the respiratory tract it invades the lymph nodes and later the blood, which distributes it throughout the body. Symptoms include fever and a skin eruption characterized by papules or pustules that become enlarged and filled with fluid. As the pustules regress, scabs are formed, leaving craterlike scars.	In the past, smallpox has been one of the great disease scourges of humans; however, no cases have occurred in the world since 1977. The vaccine consists of live vaccinia virus, a virus antigenically similar to smallpox virus; however, vaccination is no longer done, because the disease has been eradicated.

[A]

FIGURE 24.15

Clinical manifestations of some airborne infections caused by viruses. **[A]** Patient with smallpox, photographed in Africa. **[B]** Chicken pox (varicella): lesions on chest and shoulder. **[C]** Measles (rubeola): skin lesions at third day of illness. **[D]** Measles (rubeola): inside surface of a patient's cheek, showing small bluish-white spots (Koplik's spots) at fifth day of illness. **[E]** German measles (rubella): rash on back of an 11-month-old child. **[F]** Mumps in a child, showing diffuse lymphedema of anterior neck or mumps virus infection of thyroid.

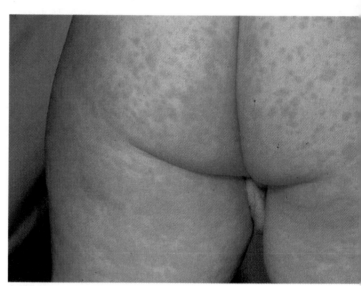

[C]

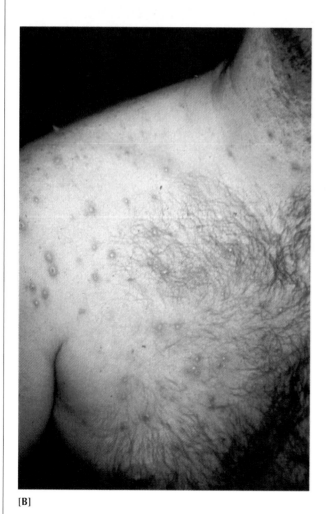

[B]

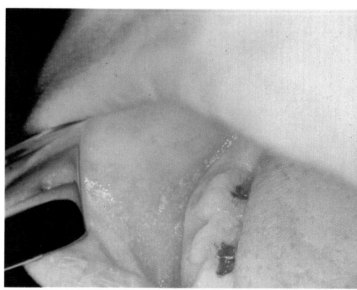

[D]

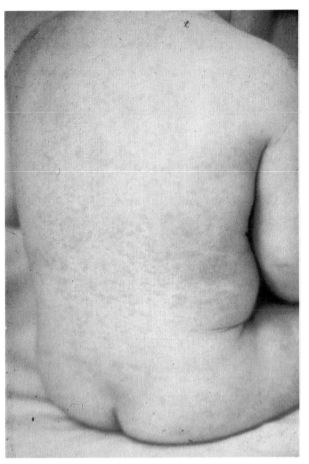

[E]

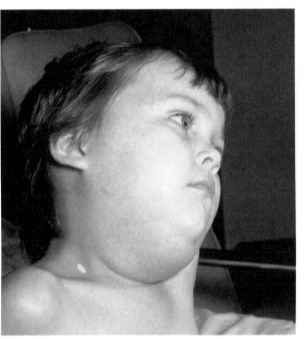

[F]

AIRBORNE INFECTIONS CAUSED BY FUNGI

Several airborne infections are caused by fungi living in soil or dead vegetation. Spores or hyphal fragments can be inhaled, or they can enter the body through a wound or a break in the skin. Inhaled organisms usually cause lung infections, but occasionally they become *disseminated*, spreading through the body to produce a generalized, or systemic, infection that is often fatal.

Cell-mediated immunity is the body's primary defense mechanism against fungal infections, and disseminated fungal infections tend to occur in patients who have a decreased level of cell-mediated immunity. For instance, AIDS patients are prone to develop the disseminated forms of histoplasmosis or coccidioidomycosis. Other chronic debilitating diseases such as tuberculosis, cancer, diabetes, and leukemia can also result in decreased resistance to fungal diseases. In this chapter histoplasmosis has been selected to exemplify many of the characteristic features of airborne infections caused by fungi. The disease demonstrates the importance of cell-mediated immunity in preventing infection from progressing to a deadly disseminated form.

Histoplasmosis

Histoplasmosis is caused by a fungus called *Histoplasma capsulatum*. Many persons are infected by this organism, but only rarely does the infection progress to the disseminated and potentially fatal form. In the United States it is estimated that at least 40 million persons are infected and that about half a million additional persons are infected each year. Of these, only about 55,000 to 200,000 show disease symptoms and only 25 to 100 die of the disease.

Estimates of the widespread occurrence of infection are based on the fact that infected individuals develop a hypersensitivity against the organism, much like that seen in tuberculosis, as discussed earlier. This hypersensitivity can be detected by the **histoplasmin test**, a skin test that is very similar to a tuberculin test—except that the antigen for the test is an extract of *H. capsulatum*. Skin tests using histoplasmin have revealed that, in the United States, *H. capsulatum* infection occurs most frequently in persons living along the St. Lawrence, Ohio, Mississippi, and Rio Grande river valleys. In some of these regions up to 90 percent of the inhabitants may give a positive skin reaction by the time they reach age 20. High skin reactivity also occurs in other regions of the world.

Biology of *Histoplasma capsulatum*. Normally found in the soil as a mold, *H. capsulatum* is a dimorphic fungus: in the body or in a 37°C laboratory incubator, it grows as a yeast, with oval budding cells; but at 25 to 30°C it grows as a mold, with hyphae that bear conidia. Some of the conidia of *H. capsulatum* have a smooth surface; others, called *tuberculate conidia,* have stubby projections [FIGURE 24.16A and B]. Like many other pathogenic fungi, *H. capsulatum* grows very slowly; it may take 2 to 4 weeks or more for colonies to develop on agar media.

Transmission of *H. capsulatum*. The habitat of *H. capsulatum* is soil, particularly soil containing bird or bat excrement that has accumulated for several years. This excrement greatly enhances growth of the fungus, probably because of its high content of nitrogenous compounds. Humans become infected after they inhale the conidia or hyphal fragments present in soil dust. This dust comes from sites such as blackbird roosts, pigeon roosts, and chicken houses, or caves and attics frequented by bats [DISCOVER 24.5].

Pathogenicity of *H. capsulatum*. After being inhaled, *H. capsulatum* is ingested by lung macrophages, in which it survives and multiplies. *Pulmonary histoplasmosis* may occur as an asymptomatic infection or with symptoms ranging from mild to severe. The symptoms include fever, headache, chills, cough, and chest pain, and sometimes weakness, weight loss, and muscle pain. The lesions in the lung resemble the tubercles formed in patients with tuberculosis, and, as with tuberculosis, a cell-mediated immune response occurs that is usually able to halt the multiplication of the organisms.

Disseminated histoplasmosis is the most serious kind of histoplasmosis and occurs in persons whose immune system is weak or compromised. The disease occurs in one of three clinical forms—the acute, the intermediate, and the chronic forms. The *acute form* is the most severe and occurs mainly in infants, in AIDS patients, in patients taking immunosuppressive drugs, or in patients with cancer of the lymphatic system. The microorganisms pass (probably inside macrophages) from the lungs to the spleen, liver, lymph nodes, or bone marrow. Ultimately every organ of the body can become infected. The patient has a continuous high fever, enlarged liver and spleen, enlarged visceral lymph nodes, and often nausea, vomiting, and diarrhea. Without treatment, the disease is fatal within a few weeks of onset.

The *intermediate form* of disseminated histoplasmosis also occurs in adults and infants, but it has more moderate symptoms. Eventually, however, vital organs such as the adrenal glands and the brain become severely damaged. Without treatment, death normally occurs within a year. The *chronic form* is the mildest form and

FIGURE 24.16

Histoplasma capsulatum. **[A]** Photomicrograph of a culture in the saprophytic phase, showing numerous tuberculate macroconidia. **[B]** Close-up photomicrograph of two tuberculate macroconidia. **[C]** Smear from human tissue showing numerous oval cells of *Histoplasma capsulatum* in the cytoplasm of a macrophage. The large dark object is the nucleus of the macrophage. Giemsa stain.

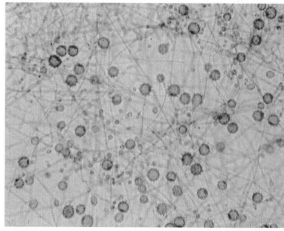

[A]   50 μm

[B]   10 μm

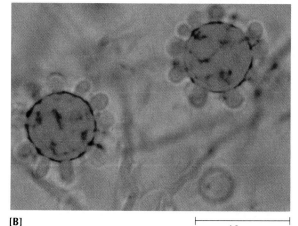

Nucleus

Histoplasma capsulatum

[C]   10 μm

24.5 OUTBREAK OF HISTOPLASMOSIS AT A SCHOOL

During the first two weeks of May 1970, an outbreak of histoplasmosis occurred among students, faculty, and staff of a junior high school in Delaware, Ohio. During this period the school absentee rate went from its usual baseline level of about 60 per day to a high of 245 per day (in a total enrollment of 872). Forty percent (354) of the students were clinically ill, and 85 percent had serological tests positive for *Histoplasma capsulatum*. None of 45 other persons living on the blocks surrounding the school became ill with a similar illness.

The illness was generally mild in nature and was characterized primarily by fever, bodily discomfort, headache, and chest pain. Other symptoms included muscle pain, sore throat, cold-like symptoms, nausea, vomiting, and loss of appetite. In about two-thirds of the cases the illness lasted a week or less, although in a few, illness was prolonged.

Investigation uncovered only one event which could be implicated as the source of exposure to *H. capsulatum* for persons at the school. On April 22, 24, and 25, groups of students at the school had conducted a series of cleanup activities associated with Earth Day. These consisted of raking and sweeping in a courtyard which was known to be a blackbird roost. Large amounts of dust were raised during these activities. The school's forced-air ventilation system had its intake in the courtyard, and by use of airflow study techniques, it was demonstrated that aerosols raised in these areas could be distributed throughout the building. *H. capsulatum* was cultured from four of eight soil samples from the courtyard and from one of the ventilation system fans. None of 80 soil samples from elsewhere around the building were positive.

The courtyard was treated over the Labor Day weekend with three separate applications of 3 percent formalin, a procedure demonstrated to be effective in eradicating this fungus from soil.

Adapted from *Morbidity and Mortality Weekly Report*, Oct. 17, 1970.

---

occurs mainly in adults. It can persist for many years and is characterized by gradual loss of weight, weakness, fatigue, and sometimes an intermittent fever.

Laboratory Diagnosis of Histoplasmosis. Histoplasmosis can be confused easily with many other diseases, especially tuberculosis, and laboratory procedures are essential for accurate diagnosis. Stained tissue specimens from biopsy or surgery samples, spinal fluid, and blood may reveal the presence of oval yeast cells [FIGURE 24.16C]. Specimens are inoculated onto Sabouraud's dextrose agar containing antibiotics to suppress bacteria and common fungal contaminants. The inoculated medium is incubated at 25°C for up to 12 weeks and periodically examined for the characteristic tuberculate conidia. Conversion to the yeast form can be accomplished by growing the organisms at 37°C.

Patients with histoplasmosis develop serum antibodies against the organism. Although these antibodies do little to stop the infection, the demonstration of an increasing level of the antibodies in the patient over days or weeks provides the physician with strong circumstantial evidence of an active *Histoplasma* infection. Various serological tests are available for estimating the levels of antibody.

Treatment and Prevention of Histoplasmosis. In most cases of histoplasmosis the patient recovers spontaneously and no treatment is required. Severe cases can be treated with amphotericin B and ketoconazole.

No vaccine is available against histoplasmosis.

Other Airborne Infections Caused by Fungi

Other airborne infections caused by fungi are described in TABLE 24.6, and some morphological features of the organisms are illustrated in FIGURE 24.17.

ASK YOURSELF

1 What is the relation between the level of cell-mediated immunity and the occurrence of disseminated fungal infections?

2 What are the similarities between the histoplasmin test and the tuberculin test?

3 What is the source of *Histoplasma capsulatum* in nature? What are the characteristic morphological features of this microorganism?

4 Why are laboratory methods needed to diagnose a case of histoplasmosis? How is the laboratory diagnosis done?

5 What are the causative agents of blastomycosis, paracoccidioidomycosis, coccidioidomycosis, and cryptococcosis?

TABLE 24.6
Some Airborne Mycotic Infections

Disease	Causative organism	Characteristics of the organism	Characteristics of the infection
Blastomycosis	*Blastomyces dermatitidis* (*Ajellomyces dermatitidis*)	Dimorphic: grows as a mold at 25°C and as a yeast at 37°. Habitat: unknown.	The infection resembles pulmonary tuberculosis. It is characterized by tubercle-like lesions in the lungs, but the infection can spread to any organ. The disease occurs only in the United States and Canada, most commonly among rural males aged 30 to 50. Disseminated infections are often fatal, even with treatment. The organism is not spread from humans or other animals to humans.
Paracoccidi-oidomycosis	*Paracoccidioides brasiliensis*	Dimorphic: grows as a mold at 25°C and as a yeast at 37°C. Habitat: presumably soil.	The infection occurs most frequently in South America. Clinically, it is similar to blastomycosis. Lesions are commonly found not only in the lungs but also in the mouth and intestinal tract and in the lymph nodes of the neck.
Coccidioido-mycosis	*Coccidioides immitis*	In the body the organism occurs as large spherules containing many endospores. In laboratory culture at 25 and 37°C, the organism grows as a mold and produces numerous arthrospores. Habitat: soil.	The arthrospores are highly infectious and occur in the soil of certain regions of the southwestern United States and Central and South America. The disease is usually a mild, transitory infection of the lungs. The rare (but often fatal) disseminated form usually involves the meninges, bones, and skin.
Cryptococcosis	*Cryptococcus neoformans* (*Filobasidiella neoformans*)	Budding yeastlike cells that are surrounded by a large capsule. Habitat: soil, and also avian excrement, such as pigeon droppings.	The organism may infect any part of the body but usually starts in the lungs and spreads through the bloodstream. Infection of the brain and meninges usually causes death unless treated. Immunosuppressed persons, such as those with leukemia, Hodgkin's disease, or AIDS, are particularly susceptible to infection. The disease occurs worldwide.

FIGURE 24.17

Some pathogenic fungal species causing airborne infections.

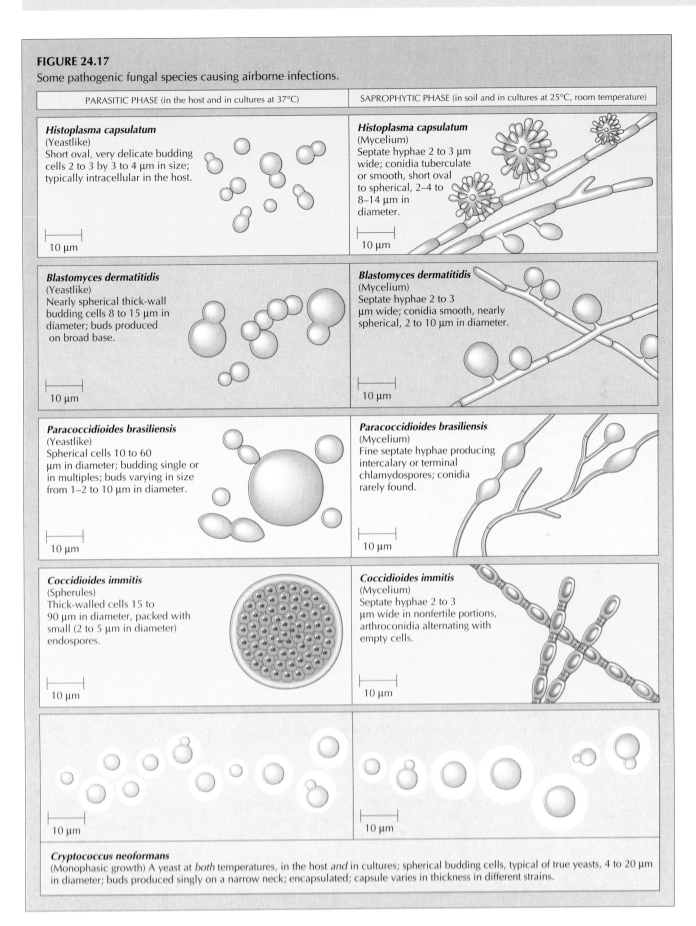

PARASITIC PHASE (in the host and in cultures at 37°C)	SAPROPHYTIC PHASE (in soil and in cultures at 25°C, room temperature)
Histoplasma capsulatum (Yeastlike) Short oval, very delicate budding cells 2 to 3 by 3 to 4 μm in size; typically intracellular in the host.	**Histoplasma capsulatum** (Mycelium) Septate hyphae 2 to 3 μm wide; conidia tuberculate or smooth, short oval to spherical, 2–4 to 8–14 μm in diameter.
10 μm	10 μm
Blastomyces dermatitidis (Yeastlike) Nearly spherical thick-wall budding cells 8 to 15 μm in diameter; buds produced on broad base.	**Blastomyces dermatitidis** (Mycelium) Septate hyphae 2 to 3 μm wide; conidia smooth, nearly spherical, 2 to 10 μm in diameter.
10 μm	10 μm
Paracoccidioides brasiliensis (Yeastlike) Spherical cells 10 to 60 μm in diameter; budding single or in multiples; buds varying in size from 1–2 to 10 μm in diameter.	**Paracoccidioides brasiliensis** (Mycelium) Fine septate hyphae producing intercalary or terminal chlamydospores; conidia rarely found.
10 μm	10 μm
Coccidioides immitis (Spherules) Thick-walled cells 15 to 90 μm in diameter, packed with small (2 to 5 μm in diameter) endospores.	**Coccidioides immitis** (Mycelium) Septate hyphae 2 to 3 μm wide in nonfertile portions, arthroconidia alternating with empty cells.
10 μm	10 μm
10 μm	10 μm

Cryptococcus neoformans

(Monophasic growth) A yeast at *both* temperatures, in the host *and* in cultures; spherical budding cells, typical of true yeasts, 4 to 20 μm in diameter; buds produced singly on a narrow neck; encapsulated; capsule varies in thickness in different strains.

674

SUMMARY

1 Aerosols can be produced during coughing or sneezing. Large aerosol droplets transmit infectious microbes for short distances; small droplets or droplet nuclei can transmit them for much longer distances. Aerosols or respiratory tract secretions may dry onto surfaces, such as textiles. Infectious dust can be generated when these surfaces are disturbed.

2 Streptococcal pharyngitis and scarlet fever are caused by *S. pyogenes,* which is β-hemolytic and belongs to Lancefield group A. Serotyping is based on the M proteins. Virulence factors of *S. pyogenes* include the M proteins, streptolysin O (SLO), streptolysin S (SLS), and the erythrogenic toxin. Complications of streptococcal pharyngitis include rheumatic fever and poststreptococcal glomerulonephritis, both of which appear to have an immunological basis. Other *S. pyogenes* infections include erysipelas, impetigo contagiosum, and puerperal fever. The large number of *S. pyogenes* serotypes makes a vaccine impractical.

3 Tuberculosis is caused by *Mycobacterium tuberculosis,* which is airborne, and *Mycobacterium bovis,* which is transmitted by drinking contaminated raw milk. The first evidence of infection is development of hypersensitivity to the organisms, as indicated by a change from tuberculin-negative to tuberculin-positive skin tests. The bacilli may remain dormant within tubercles or, in persons having poor cell-mediated immunity, may continue to grow, causing clinical tuberculosis. Reactivation tuberculosis can occur if the bacilli from an old subclinical infection are no longer held in check. Active immunization with BCG vaccine is practiced in many countries but not in the United States.

4 Many species of *Legionella* exist; of these, *L. pneumophila* has been the most studied. Legionellas are acquired from environmental sources. *L. pneumophila* causes two diseases: Legionnaires' disease, which is a severe pneumonia, and Pontiac fever, which is a mild respiratory infection. No vaccine is available.

5 Other airborne diseases caused by bacteria include pneumococcal pneumonia, diphtheria, whooping cough, meningococcal meningitis, *Haemophilus* meningitis, primary atypical pneumonia, and psittacosis.

6 The common cold is caused mainly by rhinoviruses and coronaviruses. There are at least 115 serotypes of rhinoviruses. Rhinoviruses can be spread by aerosols but are mostly spread by hand-to-hand transmission. There is no specific treatment for the common cold, and a vaccine is not yet feasible, because of the large number of viral serotypes.

7 Influenza epidemics occur in cycles. Pandemics are caused by type A strains and occur every 10 to 30 years. Influenza viruses belong to different serotypes based on hemagglutinin and neuraminidase antigens. Patients with influenza have a decreased resistance to other pathogens and tend to develop secondary bacterial pneumonia. Amantadine can be used to treat influenza. A vaccine is available and consists of killed influenza virus.

8 Other airborne infections caused by viruses include chicken pox (varicella), measles (rubeola), German measles (rubella), and mumps. Smallpox now has been eradicated.

9 Histoplasmosis is caused by a dimorphic fungus, *Histoplasma capsulatum,* which is acquired by inhaling the conidia or hyphal fragments from soil dust. Many persons are infected but few develop respiratory disease and even fewer develop the disseminated infection. Infected persons have a positive histoplasmin skin test.

10 Other systemic fungal infections include cryptococcosis, blastomycosis, paracoccidioidomycosis, and coccidioidomycosis.

KEY TERMS

aerosol
amantadine
attenuated strain
BCG vaccine
chemoprophylaxis
droplet nuclei
erythrogenic toxin
hemagglutinins
histoplasmin test
infectious dust
isoniazid
Lancefield groups
leucocidin
M protein
neuraminidase
serotypes
sputum
streptolysin O (SLO)
streptolysin S (SLS)
tubercle
tuberculate conidia
tuberculin test

MODE OF
TRANSMISSION OF
AIRBORNE
PATHOGENS

1 The spray of small and large droplets that are expelled during sneezing or coughing is called: **(a)** a fomite; **(b)** infectious dust; **(c)** droplet nuclei; **(d)** an aerosol; **(e)** bacteria.

2 Which *two* of the following statements are correct? **(a)** Aerosols can be generated not only by humans but also from environmental sources. **(b)** The larger droplets from an aerosol tend to remain suspended in the air for long periods and can transmit pathogenic microorganisms over long distances. **(c)** The frequency of most airborne infections tends to be highest during the warm months of the year. **(d)** The smaller droplets in an aerosol evaporate quickly, leaving droplet nuclei which can transmit pathogenic microorganisms over long distances. **(e)** All airborne infections involve person-to-person transmission of the causative agent.

3 Disturbance of dried material containing pathogenic microorganisms can generate

_____ .

AIRBORNE
INFECTIONS CAUSED
BY BACTERIA

4 Match the term on the left with the appropriate description on the right.

_____ SLO
_____ SLS
_____ erythrogenic toxin
_____ M protein
_____ erysipelas
_____ rheumatic fever
_____ infective
    endocarditis
_____ Lancefield antigen
_____ poststreptococcal
    glomerulonephritis

(a) Caused by α-hemolytic streptococci growing on heart valves
(b) Oxygen-stable hemolysin and leucocidin
(c) Responsible for attachment of *S. pyogenes* to throat cells
(d) Inflammation of the heart valves caused by *S. pyogenes*
(e) Carbohydrate located in the streptococcal cell wall
(f) Responsible for the rash of scarlet fever
(g) Oxygen-sensitive hemolysin and leucocidin
(h) Skin infection caused by *S. pyogenes*
(i) Kidney inflammation caused by *S. pyogenes*

5 *S. pyogenes* cells are Gram-_____-hemolytic cocci that form long chains; they belong to Lancefield group _____ .

6 Which *two* of the following species of *Streptococcus* inhabit the human intestine? **(a)** *S. pyogenes*; **(b)** *S. mutans*; **(c)** *S. sanguis*; **(d)** *S. faecalis*; **(e)** *S. faecium*.

7 The primary causative agent of dental caries is: **(a)** *S. pyogenes*; **(b)** *S. mutans*; **(c)** *S. agalactiae*; **(d)** *S. faecalis*; **(e)** *S. salivarius*.

8 Which *two* of the following statements apply to M proteins? **(a)** They occur in the cytoplasm of *S. pyogenes*. **(b)** They are used for serotyping strains of *S. pyogenes*. **(c)** They inhibit phagocytosis. **(d)** There are 15 kinds. **(e)** They are inactivated by oxygen.

9 Rheumatic fever is an inflammation but not a(n) _____ of the heart valves, and antibiotics _____ (are, are not) effective in curing the disease.

10 Which *two* of the following diseases caused by *S. pyogenes* probably have an immunological basis? **(a)** impetigo contagiosum; **(b)** poststreptococcal glomerulonephritis; **(c)** streptococcal pharyngitis; **(d)** puerperal fever; **(e)** rheumatic fever.

11 Puerperal fever is an infection of what part of the body? **(a)** intestinal tract; **(b)** skin; **(c)** uterus; **(d)** liver; **(e)** kidney.

12 In the laboratory diagnosis of rheumatic fever, it is usually not possible to isolate

S. pyogenes. However, an increase in the level of _____

against SLO indicates that the patient has, or recently had, an *S. pyogenes* infection.

13 The outstanding morphological feature of mycobacteria that differentiates them from other bacteria is that: **(a)** they are Gram-positive; **(b)** they are rod-shaped; **(c)** they have no cell wall; **(d)** they are acid-fast; **(e)** they are nonmotile.

14 *Mycobacterium tuberculosis* is transmitted by airborne means from person to

person, but *Mycobacterium bovis* is not; it is transmitted by _____.

15 The causative agent of leprosy is _____ (genus, species).

16 Match the item on the left with the appropriate description on the right.

_____tubercle

_____tuberculin

_____sputum

_____BCG vaccine

_____isoniazid

_____acid-fast bacilli seen in a smear of the patient's sputum

(a) Used to treat tuberculosis

(b) Name of the test that detects hypersensitivity toward *M. tuberculosis*

(c) Pearl-gray nodule formed in the tissues of a person infected with *M. tuberculosis*

(d) Mucus that is coughed up

(e) An attenuated strain of *M. bovis*

(f) Basis for a tentative laboratory diagnosis of pulmonary tuberculosis

17 The only effective type of immunity toward tuberculosis is

_____ immunity.

18 The type of tuberculosis most prevalent today in the United States is

_____ tuberculosis.

19 *Legionella pneumophila* is an aerobic Gram-_____ rod-

shaped bacterium that requires the amino acid _____ to grow.

20 Which of the following is the only correct statement? **(a)** *L. pneumophila* is transmitted from person to person. **(b)** Pontiac fever is more severe than Legionnaires' disease. **(c)** Legionnaires' disease is not believed to have existed before 1976. **(d)** Erythromycin is the antibiotic of choice for treating Legionnaires' disease. **(e)** Humans acquire *L. pneumophila* mainly by drinking contaminated water.

21 Match the item on the left with the appropriate statement on the right.

_____Corynebacterium diphtheriae

_____Bordetella pertussis

_____Neisseria meningitidis

_____Mycoplasma pneumoniae

_____Chlamydia psittaci

_____Streptococcus pneumoniae

_____Haemophilus influenzae

(a) Gram-negative rod that causes meningitis in children

(b) The patient develops a severe cough that ends with a crowing sound, or "whoop"

(c) Gram-negative cocci with polysaccharide capsule

(d) Gram-positive rods that produce a powerful exotoxin

(e) Acquired by inhaling infectious dust derived from bird feces

(f) Gram-positive cocci with 84 capsular serotypes

(g) Bacteria that lack a cell wall

AIRBORNE
INFECTIONS CAUSED
BY VIRUSES

22 The two main kinds of viruses that can cause the common cold are the

_____ viruses and the _____ viruses.

23 The major mode of transmission of rhinoviruses is by: **(a)** aerosols; **(b)** infectious dust; **(c)** hand-to-hand transmission; **(d)** drinking infected raw milk; **(e)** droplet nuclei.

24 Which of the following is *least* effective in the treatment of the common cold? **(a)** liberal intake of fluids; **(b)** adequate rest; **(c)** aspirin; **(d)** antibiotics; **(e)** warm clothing.

25 There is no vaccine available to prevent the common cold because: **(a)** rhinoviruses do not stimulate production of antibodies; **(b)** there are too many serotypes of rhinoviruses; **(c)** rhinoviruses grow best at 33°C instead of 37°C; **(d)** the common cold seldom causes absence from work and school.

26 Influenza pandemics are caused by type _____ influenza viruses.

27 Influenza viruses: **(a)** have an icosahedral nucleocapsid with a core of double-stranded DNA; **(b)** lack a lipid envelope; **(c)** have a helical nucleocapsid with a core of single-stranded RNA; **(d)** have an icosahedral nucleocapsid with a core of double-stranded RNA; **(e)** have a helical nucleocapsid with a core of single-stranded DNA.

28 The component of an influenza virus that allows attachment of the virus to a host

cell is called _____ , whereas the component that degrades

the mucus layer of a mucous membrane is called _____ .

29 The periodic occurrence of influenza pandemics is attributable to: **(a)** the ineffectiveness of antibodies against one viral subtype to protect against new subtypes; **(b)** the long time it takes for the virus to spread around the world and return to its starting point; **(c)** a periodic change in the host for the virus; **(d)** the tendency of the virus to attack only elderly people; **(e)** the periodic disappearance of the virus for years at a time.

30 The chemical agent called _____ has been approved in the United States for treatment of influenza.

31 Match the item on the left with the appropriate description or statement on the right.

(a) No cases in the world since 1977

(b) Results from activation of latent virus from a previous varicella infection

_____ chicken pox

_____ herpes zoster

_____ rubeola

_____ rubella

_____ mumps

_____ smallpox

(c) When it occurs in early pregnancy it can cause congenital abnormalities or death of the fetus

(d) Characterized by painful swelling, particularly of the parotid glands; orchitis may occur in males

(e) Koplik's spots may occur on the mucous membranes of the cheeks and lips

(f) Varicella

AIRBORNE
INFECTIONS CAUSED
BY FUNGI

32 Airborne infections caused by fungi are transmitted mainly by: **(a)** aerosols from person to person; **(b)** inhaling spores or hyphal fragments from soil or dead vegetation; **(c)** drinking contaminated water; **(d)** objects such as handkerchiefs that are contaminated with respiratory secretions; **(e)** AIDS patients.

33 The primary body defense mechanism against fungal infections is immunity of the _____ type.

34 *H. capsulatum* grows as a _____ (yeast, mold) at 37°C and as a _____ (yeast, mold) at 25°C.

35 Pulmonary histoplasmosis is a disease that most closely resembles pulmonary _____, and the lesions in the lungs resemble _____.

36 The type of histoplasmosis in which the organisms invade virtually every organ of the body is called _____ histoplasmosis and is most likely to occur in persons whose _____ system is weak or compromised.

37 The major distinguishing characteristic of *H. capsulatum* grown at 25°C is the occurrence of: **(a)** septate hyphae; **(b)** tuberculate conidia; **(c)** pseudohyphae; **(d)** spherules; **(e)** budding cells.

38 The antibiotic _____ can be used to treat severe cases of histoplasmosis.

39 Match the item on the left with the appropriate statement on the right.

_____ cryptococcosis

_____ blastomycosis

_____ paracoccidioido-
mycosis

_____ coccidioidomycosis

(a) Caused by budding yeastlike cells that are surrounded by a large capsule; the disease has a worldwide distribution

(b) In the body the causative agent occurs as large spherules containing many internal spores

(c) The yeast form of the dimorphic fungus consists of cells with a single bud; the disease occurs only in the United States and Canada

(d) The yeast form of the dimorphic fungus consists of cells with multiple buds; the disease occurs most often in South America

REVIEW QUESTIONS

1 Most airborne infections are spread from person to person but some are not. Give two examples of those that are not and explain how the causative agents are transmitted.

2 What is the value of determining the Lancefield group to which a streptococcal isolate belongs?

3 Why is M-protein serotyping done of isolates of Lancefield group A streptococci?

4 How does rheumatic fever differ from infective endocarditis? Why are antibiotics ineffective in curing rheumatic fever but effective in curing infective endocarditis?

5 Give examples of four vaccines that are used to immunize people against various airborne infections. Explain how they can prevent these infections.

6 Why don't rhinoviruses invade the internal organs of the body such as the liver, brain, or kidneys?

7 What variations occur among strains of influenza viruses, and what is the importance of these variations?

8 What measures could prevent an outbreak of Legionnaires' disease in a hospital? Why are hospitals particularly concerned about eliminating *L. pneumophila* from their plumbing and air-conditioning systems?

9 In a tuberculosis infection, what is a tubercle and what type of immune response of the patient causes it?

10 What similarities are there between the tuberculin test and the histoplasmin test? What is the significance of a positive test?

11 What antimicrobial agents are used to treat streptococcal pharyngitis? Tuberculosis? Legionnaires' disease? Influenza? Histoplasmosis?

DISCUSSION QUESTIONS

1 If you are unable to isolate pathogen "X" from a patient whom you suspect to be infected by this pathogen, what other laboratory evidence might you be able to obtain to support the diagnosis?

2 Considering the factors that led to the eradication of smallpox from the world, do you think it would be possible to eradicate Legionnaires' disease? Tuberculosis? Histoplasmosis? The common cold? Explain your answers.

3 Suppose you discovered a new pathogenic bacterium or virus. What approaches might you use to "tag" different isolates of this disease agent so you could trace the origin of outbreaks of the disease?

4 Why might AIDS patients be especially prone to develop reactivation tuberculosis or a disseminated fungus infection?

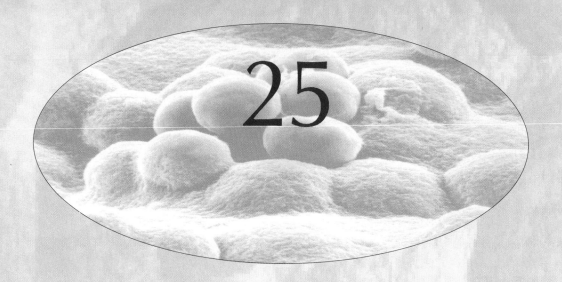

25

Foodborne and Waterborne Diseases

OBJECTIVES

After reading this chapter you should be able to

1 Differentiate between a food *poisoning* and a food-borne *infection*.

2 Explain how the sequence of events leading to staphylococcal food poisoning differs from that leading to botulism.

3 Describe the mode of action of the exotoxin produced by *Clostridium botulinum*.

4 Differentiate typhoid fever from *Salmonella* gastroenteritis.

5 Name the probable causative agent of antral gastritis and ulcers and explain how it grows in the stomach despite the stomach's acidity.

6 List several bacterial agents that can cause diarrhea and name the specific diseases they cause.

7 Explain how polioviruses are able to cause paralytic poliomyelitis and how immunization with the Salk vaccine or the Sabin vaccine can prevent this disease.

8 Name two viral agents that cause diarrhea in humans and differentiate between them.

9 Describe three protozoa that cause intestinal infections in humans and explain how they are transmitted to uninfected persons.

10 Summarize the sequence of events leading to brain damage in a patient infected by the tapeworm *Taenia solium*.

11 Give the mode of transmission of the roundworm *Trichinella spiralis* and indicate how trichinosis can be prevented.

OVERVIEW

Inadequate cooking or improper storage of food, as well as poor sanitary conditions in food preparation, can cause uncomfortable and even serious diseases due to presence of pathogenic microorganisms. The contamination of water by pathogen-containing materials such as feces can also cause disease. There are two major categories of foodborne diseases caused by microorganisms: food poisoning and foodborne infections. *Food poisoning* occurs when a microorganism produces a toxin in a food; when people consume the food, the ingested toxin causes damage to the body. *Foodborne infections* occur when the pathogen is ingested and grows within the body. Foodborne infections are usually diseases of the intestinal tract, although other areas of the body may be affected.

Waterborne infections occur when an infectious microorganism is acquired through consumption of water contaminated by fecal matter containing pathogens from humans or animals. When these pathogens contaminate a municipal water supply or other source of drinking water used by many people, outbreaks of intestinal disease tend to be of the epidemic type, affecting a large number of people in a short period of time. The finding that a particular source of drinking water is the common factor linking the various cases helps to trace the origin of such epidemics.

Bacteria, viruses, protozoa, and helminths have all been implicated in foodborne and waterborne disease. While many of these diseases are gastrointestinal in nature, some may affect other parts of the body, such as the muscles, the nervous system, or organs such as the heart. The distinction between foodborne infections and waterborne infections often is not sharply defined. This is because some pathogens (for example, the typhoid bacillus) can be transmitted by either food or water. Relatively simple methods of sanitation can prevent the spread of such diseases by preventing contamination of food and water sources.

There are many different kinds of foodborne and waterborne infections, each with its unique and interesting aspects. Because it is not possible in an introductory textbook to describe each of these in detail, relatively few diseases have been chosen to exemplify the principles of transmission of disease through food or water, as well as the important features of the interactions between pathogen and host.

THE HUMAN GASTROINTESTINAL TRACT

Since most foodborne and waterborne infections affect the intestinal tract, you need to understand the structure and function of this portion of the human body.

Structure and Function of the Gastrointestinal Tract

The gastrointestinal tract is basically a tube approximately 15 feet long that extends from the mouth to the anus [FIGURE 25.1]. When you ingest food, you first chew it to break up the pieces into smaller particles. After being mixed with saliva and swallowed, these particles pass along the pharynx and esophagus to the stomach. The stomach secretes hydrochloric acid to help break the food into much smaller particles and even into individual molecules, such as protein or polysaccharide molecules. The stomach also secretes enzymes that degrade protein molecules into small peptide fragments. Fats, being water-insoluble, are not degraded in the stomach.

The food then passes from the stomach to the small intestine, where the final stages of digestion occur. Fats are rendered water-soluble by bile secreted into the small intestine from the *gallbladder*. Bile is a detergent that acts much like laundry detergents used to solubilize greasy stains on clothing. The polysaccharide, protein, and fat molecules are broken down by enzymes into monosaccharides, amino acids, fatty acids, and glycerol. These molecules are absorbed into the bloodstream by first passing across the tissue cells that line the inner surface of the intestinal wall. The bloodstream distributes the nutrients throughout the body. Vitamins, minerals, and water are also absorbed into the bloodstream from the small intestine.

Muscular movements of the small intestine cause the undigested material still in the small intestine to move slowly toward the large intestine. Here, the enormous numbers of bacteria that are part of the normal flora cause further breakdown of food substances. The large intestine temporarily stores undigested food and concentrates it by absorbing more water from it. By the muscular activity of the rectum, the material is then eliminated through the anus as the feces, or excrement.

Gastroenteritis and Diarrhea

Many pathogenic bacteria transmitted by feces-contaminated food or water can cause *gastroenteritis,* an acute inflammation of the gastrointestinal tract (particularly the small intestine and/or the large intestine). One of the most common symptoms of gastroenteritis is *diarrhea,* which is characterized by an increased water content in the feces (watery stools). Diarrhea is ultimately the result of either (1) a decreased absorption of fluid from the intestinal tract, or (2) an increased secretion of fluid derived from the patient's blood into the intestinal tract, which is a reversal of the normal process of water absorption. If the diarrhea is severe, as it may be in some intestinal infections, it can lead to dehydration of the body, increased acidity of the blood, and *hemoconcentration,* a thickening of the patient's blood. To prevent dehydration, the patient may need to be treated by intravenous administration of fluids and salts.

In intestinal infections, diarrhea may be caused by the action of an *enterotoxin* (from the Greek *enteron,* "gut"). An enterotoxin is an exotoxin (protein toxin that is secreted from microbial cells) that stimulates secretion of water and salts (ultimately derived from the patient's blood) into the intestine. In the case of one well-studied type of enterotoxin, the toxin works by activating *adenylate cyclase,* an enzyme that catalyzes the formation of a special form of adenosine monophosphate (AMP) from adenosine triphosphate (ATP). This special form of AMP is called *cyclic AMP:*

$$ATP \xrightarrow{\text{adenylate cyclase}} \text{cyclic AMP} + \text{pyrophosphate}$$

Cyclic AMP plays a regulatory role in tissue cell metabolism. When adenylate cyclase is activated in the cells that line the intestine, the level of cyclic AMP in these cells becomes abnormally high. This in turn causes the cells to secrete large amounts of fluid and salts into the channel of the intestine, resulting in diarrhea. The enterotoxins of *Vibrio cholerae, Campylobacter jejuni,* and some strains of *Escherichia coli* act by stimulating adenylate cyclase. Other enterotoxins may act differently, and some are not yet understood.

FIGURE 25.1
Anatomy of the gastrointestinal system.

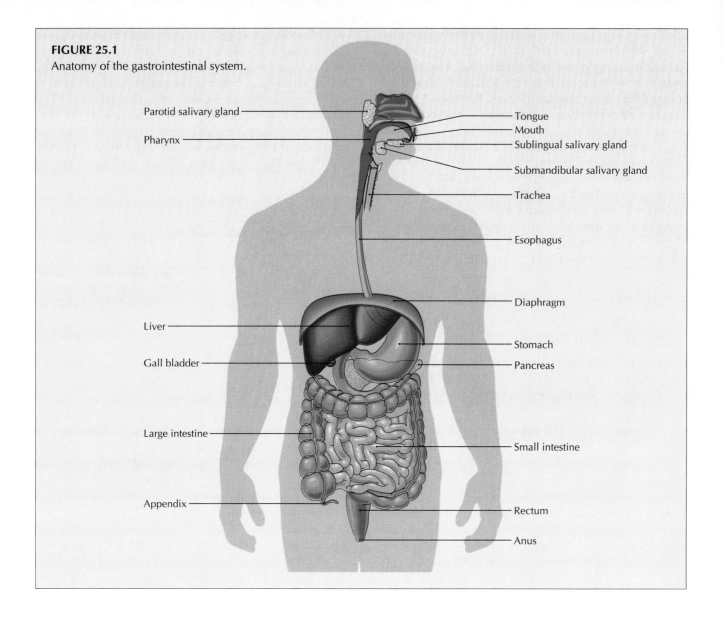

Parotid salivary gland

Pharynx

Tongue

Mouth

Sublingual salivary gland

Submandibular salivary gland

Trachea

Esophagus

Diaphragm

Liver

Stomach

Gall bladder

Pancreas

Large intestine

Small intestine

Appendix

Rectum

Anus

ASK YOURSELF

1 What functions do the mouth, stomach, small intestine, large intestine, and rectum have in food digestion?

2 What is the function of bile in food digestion? Where does the bile come from?

3 What is gastroenteritis? What is diarrhea, and what may it result from? Why is intravenous administration of fluid and salts sometimes necessary in treating severe cases of diarrhea?

4 What are enterotoxins, and how do they function? What is the relationship of some enterotoxins to adenylate cyclase?

FOOD POISONINGS

Food poisoning occurs when people consume food containing a toxin made by a microorganism.

There are several kinds of food poisoning caused by microbes; the most familiar examples are staphylococcal food poisoning and botulism. Staphylococcal food poisoning is one of the most common. On the other hand, the most dreaded food poisoning is botulism, because of the particularly deadly toxin produced by the causative agent. Because of these, careless storage or handling of food can cause very unpleasant, and sometimes dangerous, symptoms.

Staphylococcal Food Poisoning

Caused by the bacterium *Staphylococcus aureus*, staphylococcal food poisoning is one of the most common types of food poisoning. Many thousands of cases occur each year in the United States, most of which could be prevented easily by using simple precautions in preparing and storing food.

Biology of *Staphylococcus aureus*. *S. aureus* cells are Gram-positive cocci arranged in characteristic clusters [FIGURE 25.2]. Staphylococci can grow well under aerobic and anaerobic conditions, but they generally do not compete well with other microorganisms present in foods. However, if the other organisms are destroyed during cooking, staphylococci that subsequently contaminate the cooked food may grow well. Thus foods that have been cooked prior to staphylococcal contamination are the ones most often associated with staphylococcal food poisoning.

Only certain strains of *S. aureus* can cause food poisoning, namely, those that produce an enterotoxin. As little as 1 μg (0.000001 gram) of the *S. aureus* enterotoxin can cause food poisoning in a human. An enterotoxin-producing strain of the bacterium may make one or more of five antigenically distinct types of the enterotoxin.

FIGURE 25.2

Staphylococcus aureus (Gram stain). Note that the cells are arranged in irregular clusters.

10 μm

How Staphylococcal Food Poisoning Occurs. Human carriers are responsible for contaminating food with an enterotoxin-producing strain of *S. aureus*. Most carriers are not ill and merely harbor the staphylococci in or on their bodies, usually in the nose. But sometimes the hands of a carrier may have an obvious staphylococcal infection such as a boil. (Skin and wound infections caused by *S. aureus* are described in Chapter 27.) The events leading to staphylococcal food poisoning are usually as follows:

1 The hands of the carrier become contaminated with nasal secretions.
2 The carrier's hands inoculate the food during its preparation.
3 The food is stored for several hours without being properly refrigerated. During this period the staphylococci multiply and produce the enterotoxin.
4 The food is consumed, raw or cooked. Cooking does not destroy the enterotoxin. It is heat-stable and can withstand boiling for 30 minutes or more.

The foods most likely to be involved in this type of food poisoning are milk products, custards, processed meat spreads, cream puff fillings, sandwich spreads, poultry stuffing, and potato salad. Symptoms occur within 1 to 6 hours after consumption of the food; they include severe nausea, vomiting, and moderate diarrhea, but usually no fever. The disease usually lasts for less than 12 hours, and although the symptoms are extremely unpleasant, the disease is rarely if ever fatal.

Laboratory Diagnosis of Staphylococcal Food Poisoning. When patients develop the aforementioned symptoms, finding more than 10,000 *S. aureus* bacteria per gram of a suspected food is strong circumstantial evidence of staphylococcal food poisoning. Conclusive diagnosis of staphylococcal food poisoning is based on demonstration that the enterotoxin is present in the food. Sensitive immunological tests have been developed for this purpose.

Prevention of Staphylococcal Food Poisoning. The best general preventive measures are to use sanitary precautions when preparing all perishable foods and to refrigerate the food at temperatures below 6 to 7°C. Food should not be allowed to stand for several hours at room temperature before serving.

Botulism

Although botulism is relatively rare (only about 120 cases occurring each year in the United States), the disease has a high fatality rate. Botulism is caused by the bacterium *Clostridium botulinum*, which produces an exotoxin that is the most potent of all known poisons. As little as 0.000033 μg (0.000000000033 g) of this toxin can kill a mouse, or, stated in more dramatic fashion, 1 gram is enough to kill approximately 30 billion mice. Botulism occurs in three forms: *food poisoning botulism*, *infant botulism*, and *wound botulism*. Of these, infant botulism is the most common form.

Biology of *Clostridium botulinum*. *C. botulinum* cells are anaerobic Gram-positive rods that produce heat-resistant endospores [FIGURE 25.3A]. Strains are classified into 7 serotypes, A through G, based on which antigenically distinct form of botulinum toxin is produced. Human botulism is caused by serotypes A, B, E, and (rarely) F. Serotypes C and D cause botulism in chickens, ducks, horses, and cattle, while serotype G has not yet been proved to cause disease.

In *C. botulinum* types C and D, the gene for the exotoxin is not located on the bacterial chromosome. Instead, it is present in the DNA of a temperate bacteriophage found inside the bacteria. It is not known whether toxin production by the other types of *C. botulinum* is coded for by bacteriophage genes.

Food Poisoning Botulism. The name *botulism* comes from the Latin *botulus* (sausage). In the eighteenth century the disease was first associated with the consumption of sausages. Since then, many other foods have been found to cause this type of food poisoning. This is because foods can easily become contaminated by *C. botulinum* endospores, which occur widely in soil and in some marine and lake sediments. If the food is an *uncooked, processed food* such as cured ham or smoked fish, inappropriate storage of the food may allow the spores to germinate, the bacteria to grow, and the toxin to be produced. Anaerobic conditions must exist within the food for this to happen. If the spore-contaminated food is a *canned food*, insufficient heat treatment during the canning process may allow some of the spores to survive. (Note the heat resistance of *C. botulinum* spores in TABLE 7.1.) During storage, these spores may germinate and toxin may be produced within the anaerobic interior of the can or jar. Most cases of botulism are associated with home-canned foods; only rarely are commercially canned foods involved [DISCOVER 25.1].

When food containing the toxin is eaten, the toxin passes to the intestine. The digestive enzymes in the intestine do not destroy the toxin, which is absorbed into the bloodstream and carried by the blood throughout the body. The toxin causes an inability to operate various muscles (a flaccid paralysis). Initially the patient may experience blurred or double vision due to paralysis of eye muscles, or difficulty in speaking and swallowing due to paralysis of pharyngeal muscles. As the disease

FIGURE 25.3
[A] *Clostridium botulinum* cells and endospores (Gram stain). Note that the endospores do not stain by the Gram method. [B] The toxin neutralization test is used to detect the presence of botulinum exotoxin in a sample of a patient's blood, stool, or vomitus, or in a sample of food suspected of containing the toxin. Some mice are injected intraperitoneally with the sample; others are injected with a combination of the sample and botulinum antitoxin. If the toxin is present, the mice receiving the sample plus antitoxin will live while the ones receiving only the sample will die.

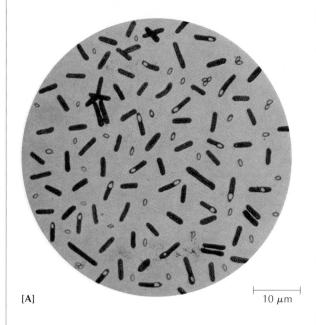

[A]   ⊢ 10 μm ⊣

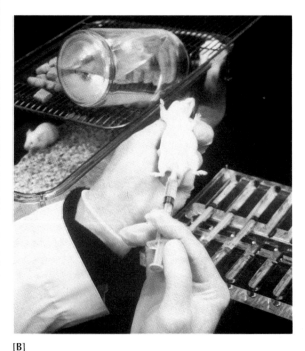

[B]

25.1 RESTAURANT-ASSOCIATED BOTULISM FROM BOTTLED MUSHROOMS

Eleven suspected cases of botulism were reported in Vancouver, British Columbia, between February 18 and February 22, 1987. Five of the patients were hospitalized; three had to be placed on mechanical respirators. All had eaten in the same waterfront restaurant on February 13, 14, or 16. An epidemiological study showed a strong correlation between the botulism cases and eating chanterelle mushrooms bottled in the restaurant or eating a lobster and red snapper meal that contained the mushrooms. Botulinum toxin was not identified in blood serum samples from the patients; however, one specimen of liquid from the bottled mushrooms contained type A botulinum toxin. Restaurant personnel estimated that three bottles of the mushrooms had been used between February 13 and February 16; restaurant records revealed that 31 persons had eaten mushrooms between February 12 and February 17. The restaurant was closed on February 18.

Although restaurants are not frequent sources of botulism outbreaks, they represent a risk of widespread public exposure to contaminated foods. For instance, while foods served in restaurants were associated with only 4 percent of the botulism outbreaks reported in the United States between 1976 and 1984, they were responsible for 42 percent of the individual cases during that period. In addition, restaurant-associated outbreaks in major transportation centers may result in widely distributed cases whose origin may not be recognized for a long time.

Adapted from *Morbidity and Mortality Weekly Report*, Feb. 27, 1987.

progresses, the muscles of the chest and diaphragm are affected, causing great difficulty in breathing or even death from respiratory failure.

Botulinum toxin causes paralysis by its action as a nerve poison, or **neurotoxin.** It affects the ability of nerves to stimulate muscles. Normally, for muscle contraction to occur, a nerve impulse travels along a nerve fiber to the *neuromuscular junction,* the area of contact between the end of the nerve fiber and the muscle to be stimulated. There the end of the nerve fiber secretes a chemical called *acetylcholine,* which initiates muscle contraction. In patients with botulism, the neurotoxin binds to the nerve fiber near the neuromuscular junction and prevents the fiber from secreting acetylcholine; thus the muscle cannot contract, and paralysis occurs.

Infant Botulism. Infant botulism is not a food poisoning but instead an *infection.* This is because the clostridia produce the toxin *while they grow within the body.* The disease occurs as follows:

1 An infant ingests spores of *C. botulinum* from some food or environmental source. Honey contaminated with spores has been implicated as one source; doubtless there are many others.
2 The spores germinate in the infant's intestine. *Clostridium botulinum* does not ordinarily grow in the human intestine, because it cannot compete with the normal flora bacteria. However, in some infants 2 weeks to 6 months old, the intestinal flora is not yet well developed, and *C. botulinum* may grow and produce toxin.

The symptoms of infant botulism include excessive sleeping, poor head control, sluggish reflexes, and generalized weakness. In severe cases respiratory failure and death can occur.

Wound Botulism. The rare type of botulism known as *wound botulism* is also an infection. If *C. botulinum* spores enter a wound, and if appropriate anaerobic conditions exist, then the spores may germinate and enough toxin can be made to cause the symptoms of botulism.

Laboratory Diagnosis of Botulism. Foodborne botulism is diagnosed in the laboratory by demonstrating the presence of toxin in the patient's blood serum, gastric contents, or feces, or in a sample of the food suspected to contain the toxin. This is done with a toxin-neutralization test. The test is based on the ability of botulinum antitoxin to neutralize the lethal effect of the toxin when the test sample is injected into mice [FIGURE 25.3B].

In cases of infant botulism, presence of the toxin is usually demonstrable in the infant's feces. However, *C. botulinum* itself can often be isolated from a fecal specimen.

Treatment and Prevention of Botulism. Patients with botulism are treated with *polyvalent botulinum antitoxin,* which is a combination of antitoxins against toxin types A, B, and E. The antitoxin neutralizes any free toxin that is still circulating in the blood. Treatment must begin as soon as possible, because once the bloodborne toxin binds to nerve cells it can no longer be neutralized. Some patients may have to be placed on a mechanical respirator to prevent death from respiratory failure.

Careful quality control by the food-processing industry has greatly diminished cases of botulism caused by commercial foods. The greatest danger comes from home canners who do not pay close attention to proper canning procedures. Unfortunately, food that contains botulinum toxin may appear or smell normal. However, any food can be made safe from botulism by heating it in a manner that will raise the entire food volume to a temperature of 100°C for 10 min; this will destroy the toxin.

Other Types of Food Poisoning

***Bacillus cereus* Food Poisoning.** Some strains of *Bacillus cereus* can cause a "short-incubation" type of food poisoning that resembles staphylococcal food poisoning. Patients experience nausea and vomiting within 1 to 6 hours after consuming the poisoned food; diarrhea is usually absent. As in staphylococcal food poisoning, the symptoms are caused by a heat-stable enterotoxin. *Bacillus cereus* food poisoning is associated most often with consumption of fried or boiled rice, but it has been linked to other foods as well, such as mashed potatoes and spaghetti.

Mycotoxin Food Poisoning. Various fungi can produce poisonous substances called *mycotoxins*, which can produce severe disease symptoms. Poisoning caused by consumption of certain mushrooms, such as *Amanita virosa* [FIGURE 25.4], is a familiar example. Poisonous substances can also be produced by microscopic fungi growing on food products such as grains, peanuts, coffee beans, tobacco, and country-cured hams.

Ergotism is a type of mycotoxin poisoning that occurred frequently during medieval times. For instance, in A.D. 943, more than 40,000 deaths in France were apparently due to an outbreak of ergotism. Several outbreaks in Russia, England, France, and India have been reported during the twentieth century. *Ergot* is a mycotoxin produced by *Claviceps purpurea*, an ascomycete fungus that grows on moist rye and other grains. When consumed by humans, ergot can cause seizures, mental disorders, gangrene of the toes and fingers, and sometimes death. Ergot consists of several nitrogen-containing organic compounds, some of which have useful medicinal properties. An example is *ergotamine*, a drug used to prevent migraine headaches.

Various species of *Penicillium*, *Alternaria*, and *Aspergillus*, and other molds, also can produce mycotoxins. Most of these substances are potent mutagens and carcinogens; two of the most potent belong to a group of compounds called the *aflatoxins*. (This name comes from their initial discovery in peanut meal contaminated with *Aspergillus flavus*.) On the basis of animal studies, it seems that aflatoxins are a potential danger to human health. They may be one of the factors responsible for the high incidence of liver cancer in tropical Africa and Asia.

ASK YOURSELF

1 Why is a bacterial food poisoning not considered to be a bacterial infection?

2 What are the biological characteristics of *Staphylococcus aureus*? What is the source of the enterotoxin-producing strains of this organism?

3 What are the symptoms of staphylococcal food poisoning? How can this type of food poisoning be prevented?

4 What are the biological characteristics of *Clostridium botulinum*? Where do *C. botulinum* endospores occur in nature? What toxin does *C. botulinum* produce, and what is its mechanism of action?

5 What are the differences between the three types of botulism? Which type is the most prevalent? Which types are *not* food poisonings?

6 What is the method of laboratory diagnosis of botulism? What treatment is there for the disease? How can botulism be prevented?

7 What are mycotoxins, and what kinds of microorganisms produce them? What are aflatoxins? What is ergot?

FIGURE 25.4

Amanita virosa, a causative agent of mushroom poisoning, is indigenous to the northern hemisphere. After ingesting the fungus, people develop painful abdominal cramps, diarrhea, and vomiting in 8 to 12 h. The fungus contains two highly poisonous peptides, phalloidin and amanitin, which attack cells of the liver and the lining of the small intestine. About 10 to 15 percent of the patients die of liver failure.

FOODBORNE AND WATERBORNE INFECTIONS CAUSED BY BACTERIA

In foodborne or waterborne infections caused by bacteria, the microorganisms enter the body through consumption of food or water contaminated by fecal matter from humans or animals. Foodborne and waterborne diseases are usually diseases of the intestinal tract, although other areas of the body may be affected. Only a few examples of the many kinds of foodborne and waterborne infections are included in this discussion. *Salmonella* gastroenteritis is of particular interest because of its widespread occurrence, the variety of sources of contamination, and the antigenic complexity of the organisms. Another bacterial infection called *typhoid fever* is a serious disease with special features not found in *Salmonella* gastroenteritis. *Campylobacter* gastroenteritis is now recognized as the most frequent kind of bacterial gastroenteritis worldwide, and the causative bacteria have unusual physiological features that complicate their isolation from patients. *Helicobacter*, discovered in 1983, has been linked to gastritis and peptic ulcers in humans; it is currently the subject of intense research.

Salmonella Gastroenteritis and Typhoid Fever

Salmonella gastroenteritis is caused by bacteria of the genus *Salmonella*. (This genus was named after an American bacteriologist, Daniel E. Salmon, in 1900 and has no relationship to salmonid fish.) About 40,000 to 70,000 cases of *Salmonella* gastroenteritis are reported each year in the United States, but the actual number may be much higher because many cases are not reported. The incidence of the disease varies with the season: the greatest number of cases occur from July through October, and the fewest are reported from December through May. This is because the bacteria are more likely to multiply in food at warm temperatures that prevail in the summer and early fall.

Typhoid fever is caused by one particular salmonella serotype, *Salmonella typhi*. Today only about 400–600 cases of typhoid fever occur annually in the United States, but large epidemics occurred in the past before pasteurization of milk, chlorination of water supplies, and sewage treatment became widely established. Even in more recent years, lapses in sanitation have led to some large typhoid epidemics. For example, in 1973 at a camp for migrant farm workers in Dade County, Florida, 230 persons contracted typhoid fever from drinking feces-contaminated water. Although the camp's water supply had supposedly been disinfected by chlorination, the chlorinator apparatus was defective at the time of the epidemic.

Biology of *Salmonella* Bacteria. As mentioned in Chapter 9, salmonellas are Gram-negative facultative rods with peritrichous flagella [FIGURE 25.5]. They are members of the family *Enterobacteriaceae* and are closely related to the genera *Escherichia* and *Shigella*. There is only one species in the genus—*Salmonella enterica*—but more than 2000 serotypes of this species exist, all of them pathogenic for humans and often animals. Even though the serotypes belong to a single species, their names are traditionally written as if they were different species (for example, *Salmonella typhimurium*). Each serotype is characterized by a particular combination of **O antigens** and **H antigens.** O antigens are heat-stable polysaccharides located on the surface of the bacterial cell wall [see FIGURE 4.19]. They are designated by numbers 1 to 67. The H antigens are flagellar proteins, and, unlike O antigens, they are easily destroyed by heat treatment. There are two major categories of H antigens, called phase 1 and phase 2. Each phase 1 antigen occurs in only a few serotypes and is designated by a letter, a to z (z_i to z_{59}). Fewer kinds of phase 2 antigens occur, but they are widely distributed among *Salmonella* serotypes and are usually designated by numbers. TABLE 25.1 gives examples of some frequently encountered *Salmonella* serotypes and the particular combination of H and O antigens that defines each serotype.

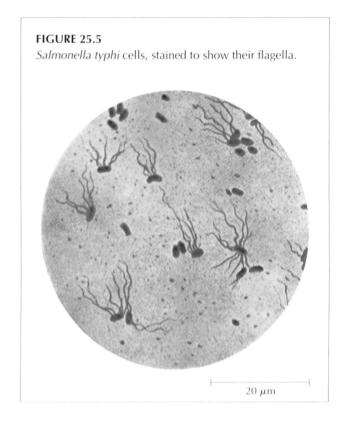

FIGURE 25.5
Salmonella typhi cells, stained to show their flagella.

20 μm

TABLE 25.1
Some *Salmonella* Serotypes Commonly Encountered in Human Infections

| Serotype name* | O antigens | H ANTIGENS | | Human disease |
		Phase 1	Phase 2	
S. paratyphi A	1,2,12	a	—	Paratyphoid fever or gastroenteritis
S. typhimurium	1,4,5,12	i	1,2	Gastroenteritis or septicemia
S. choleraesuis	6,7	c	1,5	Gastroenteritis
S. typhi	9,12	d	—	Typhoid fever
S. enteritidis	1,9,12	g,m	—	Gastroenteritis

*The names of *Salmonella* serotypes are traditionally written as if they were different species; however, they all belong to a single species.

Transmission of Salmonellas. Humans are infected by salmonellas almost exclusively through the consumption of contaminated food or water. The foods most commonly involved are cream-containing pastries, ground meats, sausages, poultry, commercially prepared beef roasts, and eggs.

Humans can spread salmonellas to other humans. Asymptomatic carriers and ill persons may excrete salmonellas in their feces, and the salmonellas may contaminate their hands. If persons with contaminated hands are involved in food preparation, they may inoculate salmonellas into the food. If the food is stored in a warm place for several hours, the bacteria may multiply to numbers high enough to cause disease in those who eat the food. Human feces may also contaminate water supplies and cause *Salmonella* infections. For instance, during the early part of the twentieth century, many outbreaks of typhoid fever were traced to the consumption of oysters harvested from waters contaminated by human feces.

The main source of many salmonellas is animals, not humans. Many *Salmonella* serotypes infect chickens, turkeys, ducks, rodents, cats, dogs, turtles, and other animals [DISCOVER 25.2]. Poultry and poultry products, especially raw or inadequately cooked eggs, are implicated in approximately half of all *Salmonella* gastroenteritis outbreaks [FIGURE 25.6]. Meats, particularly beef and pork, are responsible for about 13 percent of outbreaks. Infected eggs, poultry, and meats are most likely to cause outbreaks when stored without adequate refrigeration. Also, particles of infected raw meat or poultry left on improperly cleansed kitchen utensils and cutting boards can serve as a continuing source of infection.

FIGURE 25.6
Cycle of *Salmonella typhimurium* infection in chickens. [1] Badly infected egg which produces no chick; [2] moderately infected egg which gives rise to an infected chick [4] which dies; [3] lightly infected egg from which an infected chick [5] is hatched, survives, and grows into a bird which may continue to excrete salmonellas.

25.2 TURTLE-ASSOCIATED *SALMONELLA* GASTROENTERITIS

On June 6, 1986, two cases of turtle-associated *Salmonella* gastroenteritis were reported in Ohio. A 2-year-old boy became ill with fever, abdominal pain, and bloody diarrhea 4 days after his mother had purchased a pet turtle from a pet store. His 4-year-old brother developed similar symptoms the next day.

Stool cultures from both boys yielded *Salmonella typhimurium*. Following investigation by the Ohio Department of Health, *S. typhimurium* was isolated from the turtle in the bowl in the children's home.

When investigators from the Food and Drug Administration and the Ohio Department of Health visited the pet store, no more turtles were available. The store owner had purchased the turtles from a local distributor who sells reptiles primarily to local universities and other institutions for scientific pur-poses. The invoice for the sale of the turtles to the pet store stated that the turtles were to be used for scientific purposes only.

Local health departments in Ohio were notified that turtles might be for sale illegally in their jurisdiction. No other cases of turtle-associated *Salmonella* gastroenteritis have been reported in Ohio.

Pet turtles are estimated to have caused 14 percent of reported cases of *Salmonella* gastroenteritis in humans in the early 1970s. Consequently the inter-state and intrastate commercial distribution of turtles having a shell diameter less than 4 inches was banned in 1975, except for scientific, educational, or exhibitional purposes. After this ban went into effect, turtle-associated *Salmonella* gastroenteritis in the United States became rare.

Turtles are easily infected with *Salmonella* from the environment and can acquire the organism in the egg stage or after the eggs have hatched. Treating turtle eggs with gentamicin has been proposed as a means of producing *Salmonella*-free turtles, but the efficacy of the technique in practice has not yet been established. The technique may promote gentamicin resistance in *Salmonella*, as a similar technique has done when used in treating turkey eggs. Furthermore, uninfected baby turtles can easily acquire *Salmonella* from other turtles or from the environment after hatching. Turtles also harbor *Campylobacter*, *Aeromonas*, and other potential pathogens. They are not appropriate pets for small children.

Adapted from *Morbidity and Mortality Weekly Report*, Nov. 28, 1986.

***Salmonella* Gastroenteritis.** Large numbers of salmonellas must be ingested to produce gastroenteritis, because many of the cells are rapidly eliminated from the gastrointestinal tract. But if the remaining bacteria multiply to sufficient numbers, the symptoms of gastroenteritis appear. Eight to forty-eight hours after eating food contaminated with salmonellas, patients experience a sudden onset of abdominal pain accompanied by watery diarrhea. The stools may occasionally contain mucus or blood. Frequent nausea and vomiting, as well as a fever of 100 to 102°F, are common. These symptoms are probably caused by the endotoxins of the salmonellas or by the production of an enterotoxin. The symptoms usually subside within 2 to 5 days. However, sometimes the disease can be fatal in patients who are very young or very old, because of their lower resistance to infection.

Typhoid Fever. Typhoid fever is caused by only one *Salmonella* serotype, *S. typhi* [TABLE 25.1]. *S. typhi* occurs only in humans and is transmitted only by food or water contaminated by human feces. Typhoid fever differs from *Salmonella* gastroenteritis in being mainly an infection of the bloodstream. Although the typhoid bacilli initially reach the intestine after being ingested, they attach to and penetrate the intestinal wall, multiply in the nearby lymph nodes, and eventually invade the bloodstream. Here, many of the bacilli are lysed by the combined action of antibodies and complement. The endotoxin that is liberated from these lysed bacteria causes the patient to develop a high fever.

A few of the bacteria escape lysis when they are removed from the blood through the phagocytic action of macrophages in the liver, spleen, lymph nodes, and bone marrow. Typhoid bacilli are not killed when engulfed by macrophages; instead, they survive and multiply within these cells. Moreover, when they are *inside* the macrophages, they are *protected from attack by antibodies*. Only cell-mediated immunity may eventually be able to kill these bacilli. This can happen if some of the normal macrophages are converted, through the action of lymphokines, to *activated macrophages*, which have an increased microbicidal activity.

After multiplying in the macrophages of the liver, some typhoid bacilli pass to the gallbladder, which is immediately adjacent to the liver [FIGURE 25.1]. They are then carried along to the intestine by the bile secreted by the gallbladder. At that point they multiply in the intestine and sometimes cause diarrhea.

A patient who recovers from typhoid fever generally will continue to excrete the bacilli in the feces for several weeks. However, some persons excrete the organisms for months or years, or even for life, making them ***chronic carriers.*** Chronic typhoid carriers usually have "nests" of typhoid bacilli that persist indefinitely in the

FIGURE 25.7

Salmonella typhimurium and *Escherichia coli* growing on a plate of deoxycholate agar. The medium is selective for Gram-negative intestinal bacteria. It is also a differential medium, in that lactose fermenters (such as *E. coli*) form red colonies and non-lactose fermenters (such as salmonellas) form colorless colonies.

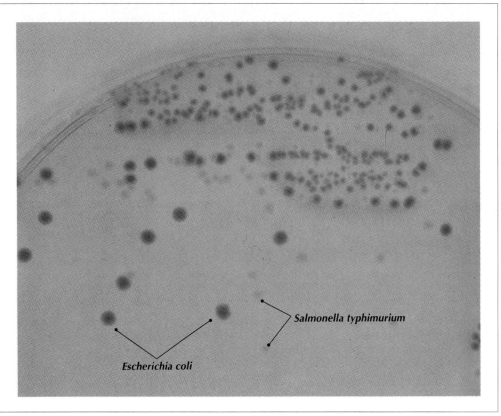

Salmonella typhimurium

Escherichia coli

gallbladder, although some chronic carriers harbor the typhoid bacilli in the urinary bladder and excrete the bacilli in urine instead of in feces.

Paratyphoid fever is similar to typhoid fever but is a milder disease. It can be caused by several serotypes of *Salmonella*, such as *S. paratyphi A* [TABLE 25.1], *S. schottmuelleri*, and *S. hirschfeldii*.

Laboratory Diagnosis of *Salmonella* Infections. A definitive diagnosis of *Salmonella* gastroenteritis depends on isolating the bacteria from the patient's feces. Selective or differential media, such as deoxycholate agar medium [FIGURE 25.7], are available for this purpose. The isolates are then identified by biochemical and serological methods. Identification of the isolate's particular serotype depends on determining which O and H antigens are present.

The diagnosis of typhoid fever differs somewhat from that of *Salmonella* gastroenteritis, because, during the first week of illness, *S. typhi* is much more likely to be isolated from the patient's blood than from the feces. By the third week, however, the organisms have largely disappeared from the blood and are best isolated from the feces.

Treatment of *Salmonella* Infections. Most patients with *Salmonella* gastroenteritis require no treatment. How-

ever, if diarrhea is severe, intravenous administration of fluids and salts may be necessary to prevent dehydration.

Patients with typhoid fever are treated with ampicillin, chloramphenicol, or amoxicillin. Prolonged antibiotic treatment is needed to cure the disease, because antibiotics have difficulty in reaching typhoid bacilli inside the macrophages. Typhoid bacilli can be eliminated from chronic typhoid carriers by treatment with ampicillin, but in some instances surgical removal of the gallbladder may be the only effective measure.

Prevention of *Salmonella* Infections. Since most cases of *Salmonella* gastroenteritis result from the ingestion of contaminated food, the following measures can prevent infection:

1 Adequate cooking of foods from animal sources to kill salmonellas that may be present
2 Suitable refrigeration temperatures for holding food, so that salmonellas do not multiply to high numbers
3 Protection of food from contamination by rodents, flies, and other animals that may carry salmonella-contaminated materials
4 Periodic analysis of stool samples from food handlers by public health personnel to detect carriers

5 Periodic inspection of food-processing plants by public health personnel to detect contamination of food products by salmonellas
6 Good personal sanitary and hygienic practices

Once a case of foodborne salmonella infection is discovered, it should be reported to public health authorities so that suitable measures can be implemented to prevent an epidemic.

There is no effective immunization against infection by salmonellas, except against typhoid fever. This is because of the large number of *Salmonella* serotypes that would have to be included in a vaccine. Typhoid fever, however, is caused by only one serotype, and two vaccines are available. One consists of killed cells of S. *typhi* and is administered by injection. The other vaccine was only recently licensed for use and consists of a live, attenuated strain of S. *typhi* (i.e., a strain that has lost its virulence); it is administered orally, in the form of capsules that can be swallowed. However, routine immunization against typhoid fever is no longer recommended for persons in the United States, because typhoid fever has become relatively rare. Immunization is now given only when a person has come into contact with a known typhoid fever patient in the community, or if a person plans to travel to an area where typhoid fever is prevalent.

CAMPYLOBACTER AND HELICOBACTER INFECTIONS

Campylobacter bacteria are among those microorganisms that can cause great discomfort in the human digestive system. *Campylobacter jejuni* had long been suspected as a cause of diarrhea in humans, but it was not until 1972 that scientists developed methods that could isolate *C. jejuni* from diarrheic stools. Recent surveys suggest that *C. jejuni* infections may be twice as frequent as *Salmonella* infections.

Antral gastritis refers to inflammation of the *antrum*, or non-acid-secreting portion of the stomach. This disease condition occurs worldwide, and its incidence increases with age. In the United States the average age of patients is 40 to 60 years old. *Peptic ulcers* are eroded areas on the wall of the stomach or duodenum accompanied by gradual disintegration and death of the tissue. Until recently, factors such as alcohol, smoking, aspirin-like drugs, worry and stress, or reflux of bile from the duodenum into the stomach were thought to be potential causes of antral gastritis and peptic ulcers. However, there is now strong circumstantial evidence that a bacterium actually causes these disease conditions. First isolated in Australia, this bacterium was initially named *Campylobacter pylori* because it closely resembled campylobacters in many ways. However, ribosomal RNA sequencing studies have since shown that the organism is not a true campylobacter, and recently it was reclassified into a new genus, *Helicobacter*. *Helicobacter pylori* is currently the subject of intense research throughout the world. Among the factors that implicated this bacterium as a cause of antral gastritis and ulcers were (1) the frequent presence of *H. pylori* in patients compared with its relative scarcity in healthy persons, (2) the effectiveness of antimicrobial agents such as bismuth salts and antibiotics in curing patients, (3) the discovery that the bacterium produces a cytotoxin (a toxin that kills tissue cells), and (4) the development of antral gastritis in two human volunteers who consumed cultures of *H. pylori*.

Biology of *Campylobacter jejuni* and *Helicobacter pylori*. The genus *Campylobacter* contains several species that are pathogenic for humans [TABLE 25.2], but *C. jejuni* and *H. pylori* have received the greatest attention. Campylobacters and helicobacters are Gram-negative vibrioid cells (curved cells with a twist; FIGURE 25.8A and B) that have polar flagella. Most, including *C. jejuni*, have a single flagellum at one or both ends of the cell. However, *H. pylori* has a tuft of four to six flagella. Moreover, these flagella are *ensheathed*, with each one covered by a thin membrane that is an extension of the outer membrane of the cell wall. Such flagella are unusual and have been described in only a few other bacterial species. The function of the sheath is not known.

The outstanding physiological characteristic of campylobacters and helicobacters is that they are *microaerophilic*; although they use oxygen, they cannot grow with the level of oxygen present in air (21% oxygen). To culture a campylobacter, it is necessary to decrease the oxygen level in the culture vessel below 21%. Most clinical laboratories grow campylobacters and helicobacters in a gaseous atmosphere containing 6% oxygen, 10% carbon dioxide, and 84% nitrogen.

C. jejuni produces both an enterotoxin and a cytotoxin. Both these toxins are probably involved in causing the gastroenteritis. *H. pylori* produces a cytotoxin which probably causes tissue damage in patients with gastritis or ulcers, although this is not yet certain.

Transmission and Pathogenicity of *Campylobacter jejuni* and *Helicobacter pylori*. *C. jejuni* is transmitted by contaminated food or water; animal feces are the major source of contamination. *C. jejuni* is a part of the normal intestinal flora of cattle, sheep, dogs, cats, poultry, and other animals, and it is likely that outbreaks of infection occur when feces from these animals reach food or water

TABLE 25.2
Some Species of *Campylobacter* and *Helicobacter* Associated with Human Disease

Species	Pathogenicity
C. jejuni	Part of the normal intestinal flora of cattle, sheep, dogs, cats, poultry, and other animals; causes gastroenteritis in humans
C. coli	Part of the normal intestinal flora of pigs and poultry; causes gastroenteritis in humans
C. fetus subspecies *fetus*	Causes sporadic abortion in cattle and sheep and blood infections in humans
C. lari	Occurs in intestines of seagulls, humans, dogs, horses; occasionally causes blood infections in humans
C. hyointestinalis	Causes proliferative ileitis in pigs and diarrhea in calves; occasionally causes blood infections in humans
C. cinaedi	Part of the normal flora of hamsters; causes inflammation of the rectum in homosexual men; also has been isolated from the blood and feces of children and adult females
C. fennelliae	Causes inflammation of the rectum in homosexual men
C. cryaerophila	Causes abortions in pigs, cattle, horses, and sheep; occasionally causes blood infections in humans
C. concisus	Isolated from humans with periodontal disease, but its pathogenicity is unknown
C. upsaliensis	Isolated from dogs with and without diarrhea; also associated with gastroenteritis and blood infections in humans
H. pylori	Probable causative agent of antral gastritis and peptic ulcer disease in humans

supplies. Several epidemics have been traced to contaminated water. *C. jejuni* is often present on poultry carcasses, and undercooked poultry is an important source of infection.

H. pylori occurs only in humans, but how it is transmitted from person to person is not yet known.

Most *C. jejuni* gastroenteritis occurs 2 to 4 days after ingestion of contaminated food or water. Patients experience fever, diarrhea, and abdominal pain. In many cases the diarrheic stools contain blood. Patients may excrete the organism in the feces for 2 to 3 weeks. In addition to infecting the intestinal tract, *C. jejuni* may also penetrate the intestinal wall and invade the patient's bloodstream.

H. pylori is not an acid-tolerant organism and prefers a pH of 8. Thus microbiologists could not understand at first how this organism could grow within the human stomach, which is highly acidic. However, they discovered that the organism resides in the layer of mucus which covers and protects the epithelial cells lining the stomach. It swims within the mucus layer and becomes attached to the surface of the epithelial cells, where it multiplies [FIGURE 25.8B]. Unlike *C. jejuni*, *H. pylori* does not invade the tissues or bloodstream.

In addition to being protected from stomach acid by the mucus layer, *H. pylori* can protect itself by breaking down *urea*, a nitrogenous waste product of tissue cell metabolism. Body cells excrete this waste product into the bloodstream for transport to the kidneys, which then remove it and add it to urine. However, some urea can pass from the bloodstream through the epithelial cell layer of the stomach into the gastric fluid. In fact, gastric fluid contains urea at about half the concentration found in the blood. This urea is the substrate for a powerful enzyme called *urease*, made by *H. pylori*:

$$H_2N\!\!-\!\!CO\!\!-\!\!NH_2 + H_2O \xrightarrow{\text{urease}} 2NH_3 + CO_2$$
$$\text{Urea} \qquad\qquad\qquad\qquad \text{Ammonia}$$

The ammonia produced in this reaction is alkaline and helps protect *H. pylori* from stomach acid. Moreover, in 1990 researchers found that the ammonia liberated by *H. pylori* urease was directly toxic to gastric epithelial cells growing in laboratory culture. Therefore, the urease of *H. pylori* may be partially responsible for the gastric tissue injury that is associated with *H. pylori* infection.

Laboratory Diagnosis of *C. jejuni* and *H. pylori* Infection. Laboratory diagnosis of *C. jejuni* consists of isolating the bacterium from the patient's stools. This is done by using a selective agar medium containing antibiotics that suppress the growth of normal intestinal bacteria but do not affect the growth of *C. jejuni*. Cultures are incubated at 42°C under microaerophilic conditions.

FIGURE 25.8

[A] *Campylobacter jejuni*, showing vibrioid cells. The cells are 0.2 to 0.5 μm wide and 0.5 to 5.0 μm long. Two or more cells that are linked together may have a spiral, gull-wing, or S shape. Crystal violet stain. **[B]** Drawing of *Helicobacter pylori* growing on the surface of epithelial cells lining the antrum of the stomach and in the overlying mucus layer. The mucus layer helps to protect the acid-sensitive bacteria. *H. pylori* cells are 0.5 to 1.0 μm wide and 2.5 to 5.0 μm long.

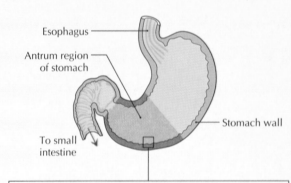

[A]   10 μm

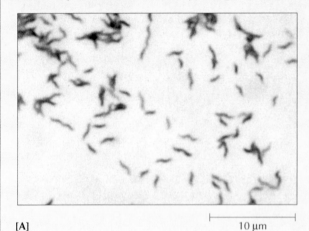

Esophagus

Antrum region of stomach

To small intestine

Stomach wall

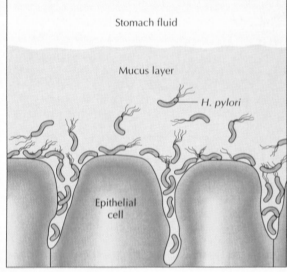

Stomach fluid

Mucus layer

H. pylori

Epithelial cell

[B]

(Most *Campylobacter* species grow best at 30 to 37°C; *C. jejuni* is one of the exceptions that grow best at 42°C.) Identification of an isolate is usually based on biochemical tests such as the ability of *C. jejuni* to hydrolyze sodium hippurate to sodium benzoate and glycine.

Diagnosis of *H. pylori* gastritis can be done by the *urea breath test*. The patient ingests some urea that contains the radioactive isotope ^{14}C ($[^{14}C]$ urea) instead of the normal ^{12}C. After 100 min the patient's breath is tested for the evolution of radioactive carbon dioxide ($^{14}CO_2$). This comes from the action of the *H. pylori* urease; the radioactive CO_2 is absorbed from the stomach into the bloodstream and is later released in the lungs. (A recent modification of the breath test uses ^{13}C instead of ^{14}C. This may possibly be safer, since ^{13}C is nonradioactive; however, its detection requires the use of an expensive instrument called a mass spectrometer.) A second method for diagnosis involves the insertion of a fiber-optic device through the mouth and esophagus into the stomach. This device can be used to excise and retrieve a tiny piece of tissue from the stomach wall. The tissue specimen can then be examined microscopically for the presence of *H. pylori* bacteria, or it may be tested biochemically to see whether it contains urease activity.

Treatment and Prevention of *C. jejuni* and *H. pylori* Infection. Severe cases of *C. jejuni* gastroenteritis are treated with the antibiotic erythromycin. Replacement of lost fluid and salts may be required to prevent dehydration.

H. pylori gastritis and ulcers have been treated successfully with antimicrobial agents such as bismuth subsalicylate and by antibiotics such as amoxicillin. Recurrence of *H. pylori* after a month or so is common, and scientists are looking for better long-term treatments.

No vaccine is available for immunization against *C. jejuni* and *H. pylori*. Prevention of *C. jejuni* gastroenteritis is best accomplished by properly cooking and storing food, by drinking only pasteurized milk, and by drinking water from an uncontaminated source. Ways to prevent *H. pylori* infection are not known, since the mode of transmission of the organism has not been identified.

Other Foodborne and Waterborne Infections Caused by Bacteria

Several other important foodborne and waterborne infections are caused by bacteria. Some of these infections and their causative agents are listed in TABLE 25.3, and photomicrographs of some of the agents are shown in FIGURE 25.9.

TABLE 25.3
Some Additional Foodborne and Waterborne Infections Caused by Bacteria

Disease	Agent and transmission	Pathogenicity	Occurrence and prevention
Cholera	*Vibrio cholerae* (Gram-negative, facultative curved rod, motile by a polar flagellum). Transmitted mainly by water supplies contaminated by human feces. Can also be foodborne.	After infection, the vibrios bind to the intestinal wall, multiply, and secrete an enterotoxin. The vibrios do not penetrate the intestinal wall or invade body tissues, but the enterotoxin causes a very severe diarrhea. The patient may lose as much as 10 to 12 liters of fluid a day and becomes severely dehydrated. Treatment involves replacing the lost fluid and salts.	Chronic foci of infection exist in India (Bengal) and Nepal; in recent years the disease has been prevalent in southeast Asia, Africa, and the Middle East. Occurs only rarely in the United States. A vaccine is available for short-term immunization; it consists of killed whole cells. The best prevention is sanitary treatment of water supplies.
Vibrio parahaemolyticus gastroenteritis	*Vibrio parahaemolyticus* (Gram-negative, facultative curved rod, motile by a single polar flagellum). A marine bacterium that needs NaCl in its medium to grow. Acquired by consumption of uncooked or inadequately cooked seafood (fish and shellfish).	The mechanism of pathogenicity is unknown but may be due to a hemolysin (Kanagawa hemolysin). Patients experience an "explosive" watery diarrhea and sometimes fever, chills, and headache. Symptoms usually last about a day. Most cases do not require treatment.	Major outbreaks occasionally occur in the United States. The disease may account for 20% of diarrhea cases in less developed countries. The best prevention is to cook seafood adequately to kill the vibrios.
Yersinia gastroenteritis	*Yersinia enterocolitica* and *Y. pseudotuberculosis* (Gram-negative, facultative rods with peritrichous flagella). Grow slowly at 37°C and rapidly at 25°C. Mainly pathogens of various animals, which probably serve as the initial source of foodborne and, rarely, waterborne human infection.	The bacteria can penetrate the intestinal wall and invade nearby lymph nodes. Patients experience diarrhea, nausea, fever, and abdominal pain that mimics appendicitis. The mechanism of pathogenicity is unknown, but *Y. enterocolitica* makes a heat-stable enterotoxin that may contribute to the diarrhea. Patients may spread the disease to other humans via feces.	*Y. pseudotuberculosis* infections are rare and occur mainly in Europe and Scandinavia. *Y. enterocolitica* infections are more common and occur worldwide. There are no specific preventive measures.
Traveler's diarrhea	Various microorganisms may cause this disease, but the most important is *Escherichia coli* (Gram-negative, facultative rod with peritrichous flagella).	Although *E. coli* is part of the normal intestinal flora of humans, some strains can cause "traveler's diarrhea." The stools are watery and do not contain blood or mucus. A heat-labile enterotoxin is produced that resembles the cholera toxin, and also a heat-stable toxin that resembles that produced by *Y. enterocolitica*.	The disease often occurs in Americans traveling to other countries. Prevention: drinking boiled or treated water and avoiding salads and raw vegetables.

Disease	Agent and transmission	Pathogenicity	Occurrence and prevention
Traveler's diarrhea *(continued)*	*E. coli* is spread by contaminated water and food. Source: human feces.	Other, non-toxin-producing *E. coli* strains may cause a disease resembling shigellosis (see below), and still others may cause a type of infantile diarrhea.	Prevention: drinking boiled or treated water and avoiding salads and raw vegetables.
Shigellosis (bacillary dysentery)	*Shigella dysenteriae, S. flexneri, S. boydii, S. sonnei* (Gram-negative, facultative rods that are nonmotile). Have O antigens but not H antigens. Cause waterborne and, less often, foodborne infections. Source: human feces.	All strains can cause damage by growing in the tissue of the wall of the large intestine. Some strains produce an enterotoxin called the "shiga" toxin. Patients have diarrhea with blood and mucus in the stools; fever may also occur. In severe cases replacement of lost fluids and salts may be necessary. Antibiotics (ampicillin or tetracycline) can shorten the illness.	Approximately 17,000 cases of shigellosis occur annually in the United States; *S. sonnei* and *S. flexneri* are the main species. Most cases occur in infants and preschool children. Prevention is best achieved by purification of water supplies.
Clostridium perfringens gastroenteritis	*Clostridium perfringens* (Gram-positive anaerobic rods that form endospores). Causes foodborne gastroenteritis. Source: meat and poultry.	Raw meat and poultry may often contain spores of *C. perfringens,* and these may survive cooking. If the cooked meat or poultry is then incubated at 43–47°C for at least 2 h, the spores can germinate and *C. perfringens* can actively multiply in the food. When the food containing the clostridia is eaten, the clostridia multiply to enormous numbers within the intestinal tract and then form spores. During sporulation, the bacteria make an enterotoxin that causes cramps, diarrhea, nausea, and vomiting. Symptoms begin 8 to 24 h after eating the food and last about 12 to 18 h.	One of the most common types of gastroenteritis. Fortunately, the disease is relatively mild. Prevention is based on measures to prevent multiplication of the clostridia during postcooking periods. The meat should either be freshly cooked and eaten hot, or, if the cooked meat must be stored, it should be chilled rapidly and later reheated immediately before serving.
Listeriosis	*Listeria monocytogenes* [Gram-positive, facultative short rod, motile (at 25°C but often not at 37°C) by peritrichous flagella]. Widely distributed in water, mud, sewage, vegetation, and animal and human feces. Some outbreaks have been associated with consumption of contaminated milk and cheese.	In the body the organism lives mainly within macrophages. It makes a hemolysin that is similar to SLO. Infections range from mild and flulike to severe or fatal forms. An infected pregnant mother can transmit the organism to the fetus in utero, and the infant, if born alive, can develop a severe and often fatal septicemia or meningitis. In adults, meningitis is the most common severe form of the disease.	The disease tends to occur mainly in newborns and in adults whose immune system has been weakened, as by alcoholism or by immunosuppressive drugs such as are used to treat cancer patients. No vaccine is available. Prevention is based on elimination of infected animal reservoirs, avoidance of infected animals or animal products, and early diagnosis and treatment of the disease in pregnant women.

FIGURE 25.9

Bacterial agents of some of the intestinal infections listed in TABLE 25.3 **[A]** *Vibrio cholerae*, Gram stain. **[B]** *Yersinia enterocolitica*, Gram stain. **[C]** *Escherichia coli* appears as glowing green rods in a fluorescent antibody–stained section of intestine from an 8-month-old child suffering from chronic diarrhea. **[D]** Microscopic appearance of a stained stool specimen from a patient with shigellosis, showing pus cells, red blood cells, and many rod-shaped cells of *Shigella* bacteria. **[E]** *Clostridium perfringens*, vegetative cells, Gram stain.

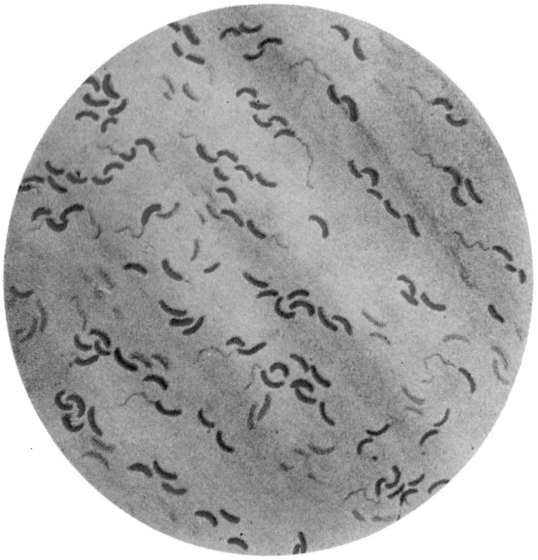

[A]   20 μm

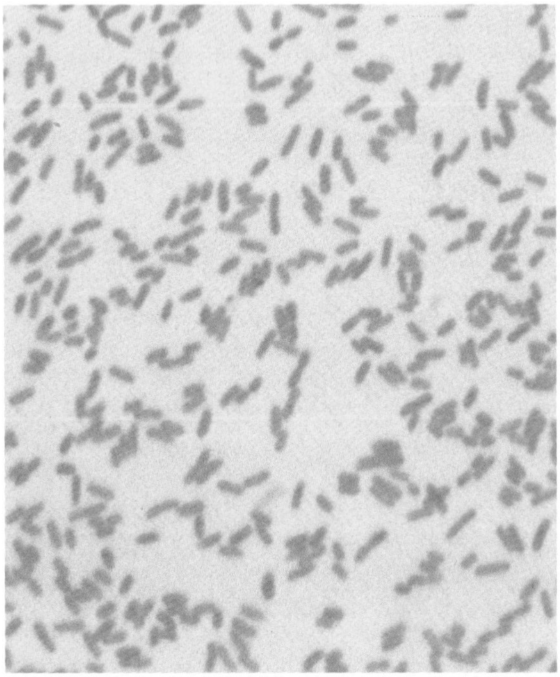

[B]   20 μm

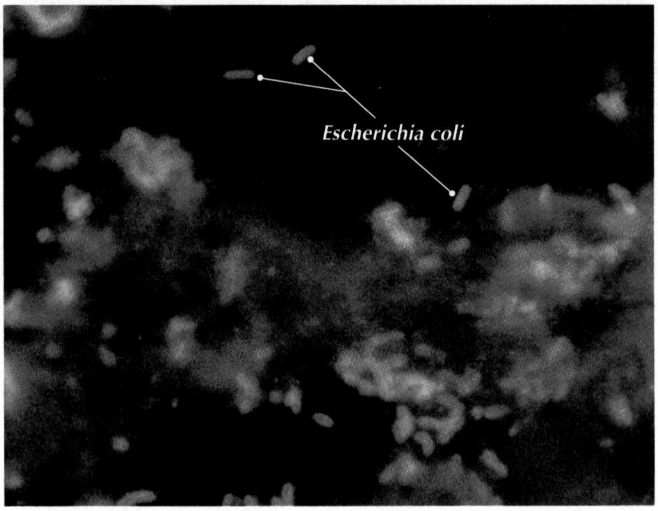

[C]   *Escherichia coli*   20 μm

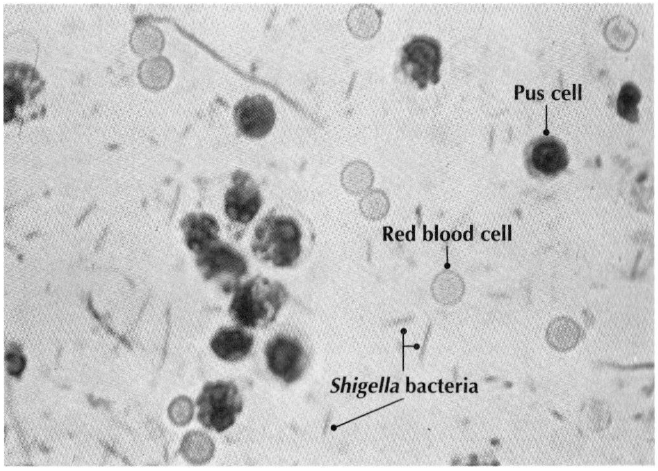

[D]   Pus cell   Red blood cell   *Shigella* bacteria   20 μm

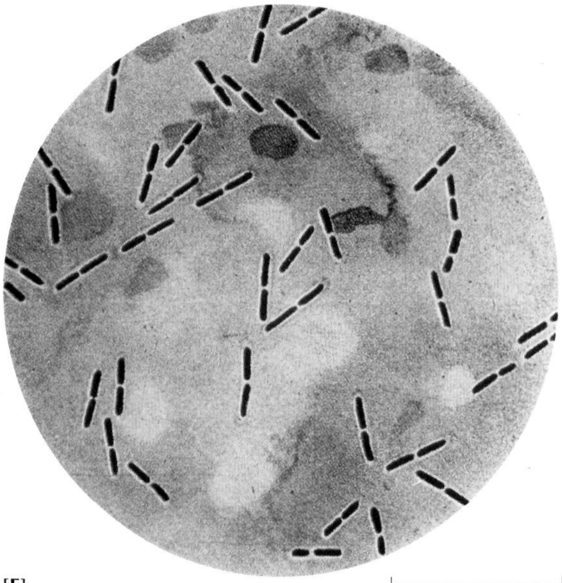

[E]   50 μm

ASK YOURSELF

1 What are the biological characteristics of salmonellas? How many serotypes exist, and what antigens are used to define each serotype? Where do salmonellas occur in nature? What are "chronic carriers"?

2 In what ways does *Salmonella* gastroenteritis differ from typhoid fever? How does the laboratory diagnosis of these diseases differ?

3 How can *Salmonella* gastroenteritis be prevented? How can typhoid fever be prevented?

4 What are the biological characteristics of *Campylobacter jejuni* and *Helicobacter pylori*? Where do these two species occur in nature? What special gaseous conditions are required for their cultivation in the laboratory?

5 How can *H. pylori* grow in the stomach if the organism is not acid-tolerant?

6 How does the laboratory diagnosis of *C. jejuni* gastroenteritis differ from that of *H. pylori* gastritis? What treatments are available for these diseases?

7 What other foodborne and waterborne infections occur in humans, and which bacterial species cause them?

FOODBORNE AND WATERBORNE INFECTIONS CAUSED BY VIRUSES

Several viruses cause foodborne and waterborne infections. Some, such as rotaviruses and Norwalk viruses, infect only the intestine and cause gastroenteritis. Others such as the hepatitis A virus can pass from the intestinal tract to the bloodstream and be carried to other areas of the body. The poliovirus initially infects the intestine. It then may invade the central nervous system and is a particularly serious example of a food- or waterborne virus that can cause problems beyond the intestine.

Paralytic Poliomyelitis

Paralytic poliomyelitis is a particularly dreaded disease. Fatality rates are sometimes as high as 10 percent of the cases, but even if a patient survives, he or she may be left severely crippled. One well-known example was President Franklin D. Roosevelt, who acquired paralytic poliomyelitis as an adult and could walk only with the greatest difficulty for the rest of his life.

There are now only about 7 cases or so of paralytic poliomyelitis per year in the United States. But prior to 1955, before the first successful vaccine was licensed, 15,000 to 20,000 cases occurred annually [FIGURE 25.10]. However, poliomyelitis is still far from con-

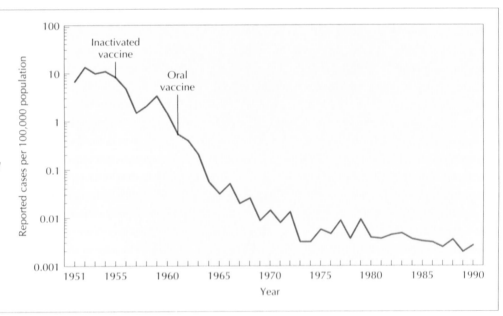

FIGURE 25.10

Reported cases of paralytic poliomyelitis per year per 100,000 population, United States, 1951–1990. Note that the y axis is a logarithmic scale. (*Morbidity and Mortality Weekly Report, Summary of Notifiable Diseases, United States, 1990, issued Oct. 4, 1991.*)

quered. Although it is now rare in countries with mass immunization programs, this disease remains a major problem in other areas of the world. There are at least 40 developing countries, with a total population of 400 million, in which poliomyelitis has not been brought under control. In these countries tens of thousands of cases are reported each year.

Biology of Polioviruses. The viruses that cause poliomyelitis have an icosahedral nucleocapsid [FIGURE 25.11] with a core of single-stranded RNA. Polioviruses are classified into three serotypes: 1, 2, and 3. To be immunized against poliomyelitis, a person must be immunized against all three serotypes, because antibodies against one type will not prevent infection by the other two.

Transmission of Polioviruses. Polioviruses are excreted in the feces of infected humans, and their major mode of transmission is by fecal contamination of hands or food, or of water supplies. However, polioviruses also occur in nose and throat discharges of patients and can be transmitted by airborne means.

Pathogenicity of Polioviruses. Polioviruses multiply initially in the mucous membranes of the intestine or the pharynx (depending on the route of transmission) and then penetrate to nearby lymph nodes and eventually to the bloodstream. In most instances the disease is without symptoms, but in 4 to 6 percent of cases, *nonpara-lytic poliomyelitis* occurs, in which the patient develops fever and stiffness or pain in the neck and back muscles. In about 0.1 percent of cases, *paralytic poliomyelitis* occurs—the virus is carried by the blood to the central nervous system and infects the cells in the gray matter of the spinal cord. Damage to these nerve cells causes paralysis of the various muscles that they control.

Frequently paralysis is preceded by muscle pain, usually in the neck or back. The patient often tries to relieve this pain by moving the affected area. However, within 1 to 3 days a flaccid paralysis occurs, and the patient can no longer move various muscles. The muscles of any limb or combination of limbs can be affected, and quadriplegia (paralysis of all four limbs) may occur. Interestingly, the sense of feeling in a paralyzed limb is retained. Other areas of the body may also be affected; for instance, some patients find it difficult to talk, swallow, or breathe.

Paralysis in some areas of the body may disappear within a few months, particularly if the paralysis was not severe. Paralysis that is still present after 9 months is usually permanent.

Laboratory Diagnosis of Poliomyelitis. Laboratory diagnosis involves isolating the virus from the feces of the patient and identifying it as a poliovirus. The virus can be isolated in tissue cultures of human or monkey cells. It is necessary to show that the isolated virus is not one of the harmless vaccine strains of poliovirus (see the paragraphs that follow) that occur in the feces of many persons.

Prevention of Poliomyelitis. Two vaccines are available for immunization against poliomyelitis. The **Salk vaccine** is a "killed" vaccine: it consists of the three serotypes of virulent poliovirus, all inactivated by chemical treatment. It is administered in a series of three intramuscular injections and is 70 to 90 percent effective. The Salk vaccine stimulates production of serum antibodies in the bloodstream. These antibodies cannot prevent a virulent strain of poliovirus from initially multiplying in the intestine, but they do prevent poliovirus in the bloodstream from reaching the spinal cord and causing paralysis. The second type of vaccine is the **Sabin vaccine,** an easily administered oral vaccine that is nearly 100 percent effective. It consists of live attenuated strains of the three serotypes. These attenuated strains infect the intestinal tract, but, unlike virulent strains, they do not cause paralytic disease. Instead, they produce a long-lasting immunity by stimulating the formation of secretory IgA antibodies in the intestine and also serum antibodies in the bloodstream. The intestinal secretory antibodies can prevent the primary intestinal infection by neutralizing the infectivity of virulent strains that a person may later encounter.

FIGURE 25.11
Electron micrograph of negatively stained poliovirus serotype 1 showing the icosahedral shape of the capsids. The stain has penetrated into the interior of some of the virions (arrow).

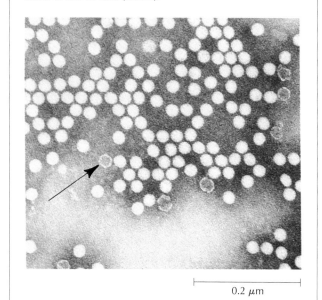

0.2 μm

The vaccine presently used in the United States is the Sabin vaccine. Its use is not entirely without risk. Occasionally the type 3 mutant strain reverts to virulence, which may result in vaccine-associated paralytic poliomyelitis. However, the incidence of this is extremely low (0.03 cases per 100,000 vaccinations) in comparison with the disease rates of 7 to 13 per 100,000 population seen prior to vaccination programs [see FIGURE 25.10].

Other Foodborne and Waterborne Infections Caused by Viruses

Common examples of other foodborne and waterborne infections caused by viruses include diarrhea caused by rotaviruses and the Norwalk group of viruses, and a liver infection called *viral hepatitis type A*.

Rotavirus Diarrhea. Rotaviruses have been recognized as major causes of acute diarrhea in infants and children in many parts of the world. The World Health Organization (WHO) has estimated that, on a worldwide basis, rotaviruses are responsible for one-half of the cases of infantile diarrhea requiring hospitalization.

Rotaviruses owe their name to their unusual wheel-like shape, caused by two concentric icosahedral capsids surrounding the double-stranded RNA [FIGURE 25.12]. Rotaviruses occur in humans and animals and are probably transmitted to healthy individuals by feces-contaminated food or water. After reaching the intestinal tract, they multiply extensively in the tissue of the small intestine, and the patient may have fever, vomiting, and a watery diarrhea. In severe cases death can result from dehydration of the body.

Laboratory diagnosis is done by demonstrating presence of the virus in the patient's feces with electron microscopy or immunological methods. Alternatively, circumstantial evidence can be obtained by showing that the patient is actively producing serum antibodies against the virus in response to the infection. No vaccine is yet available against rotavirus diarrhea.

Norwalk Gastroenteritis. It has been estimated that approximately one-third of all outbreaks of gastroenteritis may be due to the Norwalk group of viruses. This group consists of related viruses that have been observed by electron microscopy in feces from patients affected by epidemic gastroenteritis [FIGURE 25.13]. These viruses are designated by names such as the "Norwalk agent" (first described in an outbreak of disease in Norwalk, Ohio, in 1972), the "Snow Mountain agent," the "Hawaii agent," the "Ditchling agent," and so forth. Virologists

FIGURE 25.13
Electron micrograph of the Norwalk agent.

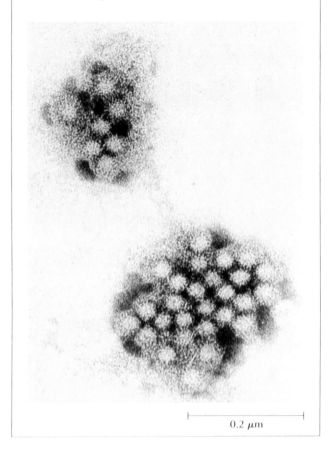

0.2 μm

FIGURE 25.12
Electron micrograph of negatively stained rotavirus double-shelled virions.

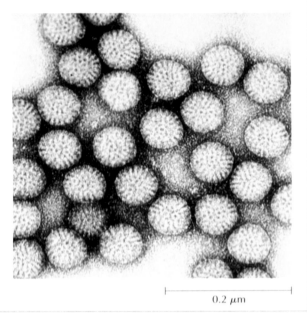

0.2 μm

have not been able to isolate and culture any of these viruses in the laboratory. However, studies with human volunteers who were fed bacteria-free filtrates from stool specimens containing these viruses have shown that the viruses do cause gastrointestinal illness.

Norwalk agent and related viruses have an icosahedral shape and contain single-stranded RNA. They are transmitted by feces-contaminated water or food, and infection can occur in any age group and at any season of the year. Symptoms include nausea, vomiting, abdominal cramps, and often diarrhea. Laboratory diagnosis is done by electron microscopy to demonstrate presence of the viruses in the patient's feces. Immunological tests can also be used to detect the presence of the viral antigens in the feces. No vaccine is yet available for prevention of Norwalk gastroenteritis.

Viral Hepatitis Type A. Viral hepatitis type A has also been called acute *epidemic hepatitis* and *infective hepa-*

titis. About 30,000 cases are reported annually in the United States. The disease tends to occur in nursery schools, mental institutions, and all establishments or societies where there is a high risk of fecal contamination of water or food.

The hepatitis type A virus (HAV) has an icosahedral nucleocapsid and contains single-stranded RNA. It is transmitted by water or food contaminated with human feces. For instance, infection has often been associated with the consumption of raw or inadequately cooked oysters, clams, and mussels from contaminated waters.

After HAV reaches the intestinal tract it infects the surface lining of the intestinal wall, spreads to adjacent cells, and then invades the bloodstream, which carries it to the liver. Initial symptoms are loss of appetite, fatigue, abdominal discomfort, and fever. Later, jaundice occurs, which is indicative of liver damage. Jaundice is a condition in which the skin and mucous membranes turn a yellow color. With viral hepatitis type A, the jaundice

TABLE 25.4
Hepatitis Viruses

Name	Mode of transmission	Structure
Hepatitis type A virus (HAV)	Ingestion of fecally contaminated food or water	Virions have icosahedral capsid and contain RNA.
Hepatitis type B virus (HBV)	Transfusion of contaminated blood or blood products; contaminated hypodermic syringes and needles; sexual contact; mothers to offspring (see Chapter 23)	Virions have lipid envelope and contain DNA.
Hepatitis type C virus (HCV); also called classic non-A, non-B (classic NANB)	Similar to that for type B	Virions have icosahedral capsid and contain RNA.
Hepatitis type D virus (HDV); also called the delta agent	Similar to that for type B	Virions have lipid envelope and contain RNA. *They require a concurrent infection by type B hepatitis virus in order to replicate.* This is because the envelope of type D consists of HBsAg (the envelope component of type B virus) yet type D virus cannot make this component. Unlike type B virus, the nucleic acid of type D is RNA.
Hepatitis type E virus (HEV); also called epidemic or enterically transmitted non-A, non-B (ET-NANB)	Similar to that for type A	Virions are icosahedral and contain RNA.

persists for 1 to 3 weeks. Fortunately, hepatitis type A is rarely fatal, and recovery occurs gradually over a period of 2 to 6 weeks.

Laboratory diagnosis is based on detection of the virus in the patient's feces by electron microscopy, by serological tests for viral antigens, or by demonstrating that the patient is actively producing serum antibodies against HAV. No vaccine is presently available.

A number of other viruses cause hepatitis [TABLE 25.4]. However, only type E is spread in the same manner as type A—by ingestion of fecally contaminated water. In 1956, type E virus caused an epidemic that affected 29,300 people in India, and it has since caused epidemics in India, Nepal, Burma, north Africa, and Mexico. No type E epidemics have been reported in the United States.

ASK YOURSELF

1 What makes paralytic poliomyelitis a particularly dreaded disease?

2 What are the biological characteristics of polioviruses? How many serotypes occur?

3 How can an initial intestinal infection by a poliovirus lead to paralytic disease?

4 What vaccines are available against poliomyelitis, and how does each one function?

5 In what ways do rotaviruses, Norwalk viruses, and hepatitis type A virus differ from one another? How are the diseases caused by these viruses diagnosed in the laboratory?

FOODBORNE AND WATERBORNE INFECTIONS CAUSED BY PROTOZOA

Several protozoa cause intestinal illness. One of the most important is *Entamoeba histolytica*, which causes amoebiasis, or amoebic dysentery. Other examples include *Giardia lamblia*, which causes giardiasis, and *Balantidium coli*, the causative agent of balantidiasis.

Amoebiasis (Amoebic Dysentery)

It is estimated that more than 10 percent of the world's population is infected by *E. histolytica*. Although relatively few persons develop clinical symptoms, there still

are approximately 10 million clinical cases and 34,000 deaths worldwide each year. In the United States approximately 4 percent of the population is infected, and 3000 to 7000 clinical cases are reported each year. Some segments of the population have a much higher incidence of amoebiasis than others, such as male homosexuals, AIDS patients, and recent immigrants from countries where amoebiasis is prevalent.

Biology, Transmission, and Pathogenicity of *Entamoeba histolytica*. The infectious form of *E. histolytica* is a nonmotile, dormant form called a *cyst* [FIGURE 25.14A]. The cysts are excreted in the feces of infected individuals and can be transmitted to uninfected persons by feces-contaminated water or food. The cysts, which are not destroyed by the digestive juices of the stomach, pass to the small intestine. Then an amoeba emerges from each cyst (*excysting stage*) and undergoes division to produce four new amoebas [FIGURE 25.14B]. The amoebas pass to the large intestine and multiply in the intestinal wall, where they cause disintegration of the tissue cells. By using the nutrients liberated from the destroyed tissue cells, the amoebas grow much larger until they are about 20 to 30 μm in diameter. These large, active amoebas are called **trophozoites**, a term used to describe the active, motile, feeding stage of a protozoan. A single *E. histolytica* trophozoite can ingest several red blood cells [FIGURE 25.14A]. The tissue destruction caused by the trophozoites can lead to a severe diarrhea with blood and mucus (and the trophozoites) appearing in the stools. The trophozoites may even penetrate the intestinal wall and invade other parts of the body, such as the liver, lungs, or brain. In the large intestine, some of the trophozoites are converted to cysts; these are excreted in the patient's feces and can be transmitted to other individuals, where the cycle can begin anew.

Laboratory Diagnosis of Amoebiasis. Laboratory diagnosis depends on the microscopic demonstration of the presence of *E. histolytica* in stool specimens. The search for the organism should be made as soon as possible after the stool is passed in order to find living, motile trophozoites. Diagnosis requires that the organisms be differentiated from various nonpathogenic amoebas which may occur in the human intestinal tract.

Treatment and Prevention of Amoebiasis. Amoebiasis is treated with a combination of metronidazole and diiodohydroxyquin. Prevention of the disease depends on the recognition and treatment of chronically infected persons who transmit the infective cysts, and on proper methods of water purification and waste disposal. Travelers should not rely on chlorine tablets to kill the cysts in drinking water; the only reliable treatment is to boil the water.

FIGURE 25.14

[A] *Entamoeba histolytica*, the parasitic amoeba that causes amoebiasis in humans. The large cells are active trophozoites stained with Giemsa stain. Some red blood cells can be seen within their cytoplasm. The small cell is a cyst, stained with iodine. Four nuclei can be seen within the cyst. [B] Life cycle of *E. histolytica*. A person may ingest food or water contaminated with infective mature cysts. Excystation occurs within the intestine of the host, releasing progeny amoebas, which become active amoebas (trophozoites). The trophozoites can penetrate the intestinal wall and invade the bloodstream, resulting in infection of the liver and other organs. Continued multiplication of the organisms in the intestinal wall is accompanied by tissue destruction, and the accompanying diarrheic stools are often tinged with blood. Cysts are passed in the feces and can subsequently infect other humans.

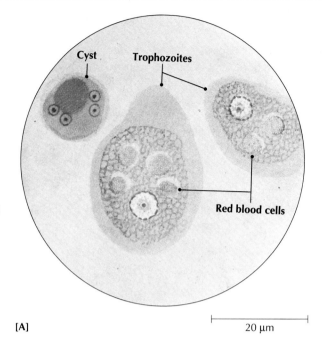

[A]

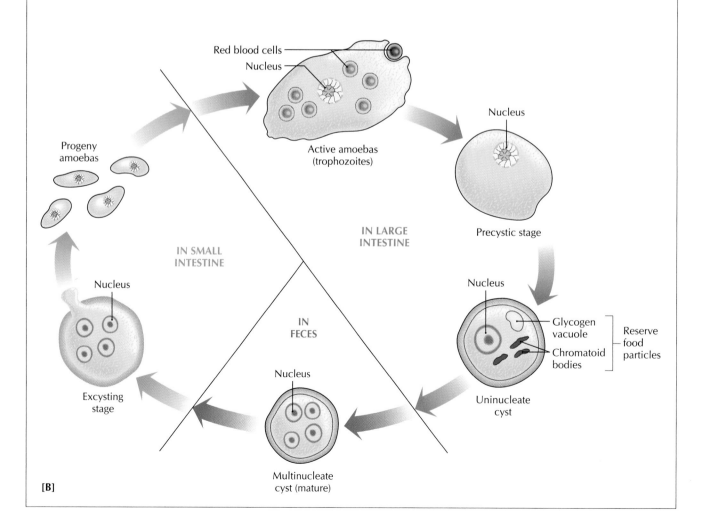

[B]

Other Foodborne and Waterborne Infections Caused by Protozoa

Giardiasis. Giardiasis is caused by *Giardia lamblia*, the only *flagellated protozoan* known to cause intestinal disease in humans. The disease is found worldwide and often occurs in travelers to foreign countries who drink untreated water or eat uncooked foods washed or prepared in contaminated water. In the United States, at least 4 percent of the population is infected, and al-

though most infected individuals do not show any disease symptoms, at least 15,000 to 26,000 clinical cases of giardiasis occur annually. The infectious cysts of the protozoan are usually transmitted by fecally contaminated water supplies, but foodborne transmission of the disease also has been reported. *G. lamblia* can invade and destroy the surface tissue cells of the duodenum, the first portion of the small intestine. Patients with clinical disease experience diarrhea and cramps, abdominal distension and tenderness, weight loss, anemia, and decreased absorption of nutrients. Both a trophozoite stage and a cyst stage of the protozoan can be found in the patient's feces [FIGURE 25.15].

Giardiasis is treated with quinacrine hydrochloride. Prevention of the disease is based on good personal hygiene and on elimination of the cysts from water supplies. Chlorination can kill cysts in water supplies but is not always reliable, because of various factors that can decrease its efficacy. For this reason water supplies also should be treated to remove particulate matter.

Balantidiasis. Balantidiasis is caused by *Balantidium coli*, the only *ciliated protozoan* known to cause human disease. *B. coli* can be up to 200 μm in length and is the largest of the various parasitic protozoa that may be found in the human intestine. It is often present in hogs, and humans become infected through water or food contaminated by the cysts present in swine feces. *B. coli* resides primarily in the channel of the intestine and obtains food by consuming bacteria. Most infections do not cause any symptoms, but occasionally a bloody diarrhea may occur. The infection is treated with tetracycline.

FIGURE 25.15

[A] Trichrome stain of a fecal specimen showing a *Giardia lamblia* trophozoite. [B] Cyst of *G. lamblia*, trichrome stain.

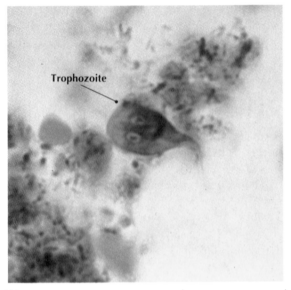

Trophozoite

[A]   20 μm

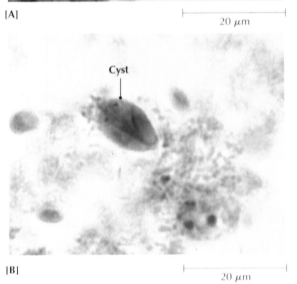

Cyst

[B]   20 μm

ASK YOURSELF

1 What is the causative organism of amoebiasis, and how is it transmitted? What is its life cycle? How is amoebiasis diagnosed in the laboratory? What treatment is available? How can the disease be prevented?

2 What is the only flagellated protozoan known to cause intestinal disease in humans? How is it transmitted? How is the disease treated? What can be done to prevent the disease?

3 What is the only ciliated protozoan known to cause human disease? How is it transmitted? With what are patients treated?

FOODBORNE AND WATERBORNE INFECTION CAUSED BY HELMINTHS

Some foodborne and waterborne infections are caused by parasitic worms, or **helminths**—multicellular parasitic animals that have elongated, soft bodies. Helminths are classified into two main groups: (1) the **flatworms,** which are flattened in cross section, and (2) the **nematodes,** or roundworms, which are round in cross section.

The flatworms are divided into two main categories. The **cestodes,** or tapeworms, have adult forms that are long and narrow and resemble a measuring tape. Examples are the beef and pork tapeworms of the genus *Taenia,* which are discussed in this chapter. The **trematodes,** or flukes, have adults that are leaf-shaped. Examples are the blood flukes, which belong to the genus *Schistosoma* and cause schistosomiasis; these are transmitted by direct contact with water containing the infectious stage of the parasites, and not by ingestion of food or water.

Examples of nematodes include pinworms, whipworms, and *Trichinella spiralis,* which causes trichinosis.

Tapeworm Infections

Tapeworms are so called because they resemble a long, flat ribbon that is divided into segments called *proglottids.* An adult tapeworm in the human intestine may be up to 30 ft long [FIGURE 25.16A]. It feeds by absorbing soluble nutrients along its entire outer surface. The "head" of a tapeworm is a *scolex,* a structure with cuplike suckers used to anchor the worm to the intestinal wall [FIGURE 25.16B]. The worm grows at the "neck" region just behind the scolex; here, new proglottids are formed which push back the older proglottids. Each mature proglottid of a tapeworm contains a complete sexual reproductive system, with both male and female reproductive organs [FIGURE 25.16C]. As the proglottids move farther toward the posterior end of the worm, the uterus in each proglottid becomes filled with eggs, each about 35 µm in diameter. Eventually each proglottid breaks up, releasing the eggs in large numbers.

Two species of tapeworms are important in human disease: the pork tapeworm, *Taenia solium,* and the beef tapeworm, *Taenia saginata.* Swine or cattle become infected by ingesting food or water contaminated with human feces that contain tapeworm eggs. The eggs hatch in the animal's intestine and develop into larvae, which then penetrate the intestinal wall and infect various parts of the animal. There they develop into dormant encysted forms called **cysticerci**—small, fluid-filled sacs about 10

to 20 mm in diameter, each containing a scolex. If a human consumes inadequately cooked pork or beef containing the cysticerci [FIGURE 25.16D], each cysticercus can develop into an adult tapeworm that attaches to the person's intestinal wall and grows. The infection may result either in no obvious symptoms or in intestinal discomfort and loss of appetite.

T. solium (but not *T. saginata*) can cause a much more serious disease called *cysticercosis.* This can occur if *T. solium* eggs, which are excreted by an infected person, are transmitted by the fecal-oral route to an uninfected person. A patient can even be *reinfected* by the eggs from his or her *own* feces. After the eggs are ingested, they develop into larvae that invade the patient's body and form cysticerci in the tissues. Sometimes the cysticerci may be formed in the patient's eyes and affect vision, or in the patient's brain, where they can cause headache, muscular paralysis, and seizures.

Laboratory diagnosis of tapeworm infections is based on finding the eggs and proglottids in the patient's feces using a light microscope. Tapeworm infections are treated with the chemical agent niclosamide.

Trichinosis

Approximately 60 to 130 cases of trichinosis occur annually in the United States. However, it is estimated that 4 percent of the population is infected by the causative agent, *Trichinella spiralis,* without showing clinical symptoms.

T. spiralis is a roundworm that parasitizes the intestinal tracts of a variety of animals, including swine. Animals become infected by eating the flesh of other infected animals; for example, pigs may consume garbage containing scraps of infected raw or undercooked meat derived from infected animals. Such meat contains the larvae of *T. spiralis,* which can remain alive for years in an encysted form [FIGURE 25.17].

Humans usually become infected by eating undercooked pork and, less often, horsemeat that contains the cysts [DISCOVER 25.3]. In Arctic regions the disease is often caused by eating undercooked meat from bears, seals, and walruses. Whether a patient will develop clinical disease, and whether the disease symptoms will be mild or severe, depends on the number of cysts ingested. After reaching the patient's intestine, the worm larvae are liberated from the cysts by the digestive juices, attach themselves to the intestinal wall, and develop into adult male and female worms. At this time the patient may experience diarrhea, nausea, vomiting, and fever. Later, the male and female worms mate and the females produce hundreds of small larvae. The larvae penetrate into muscle tissue throughout the body, particularly the muscles of the tongue, larynx, diaphragm,

FIGURE 25.16

[A] Adult *Taenia saginata*, the beef tapeworm, from a human intestine. The ruler at the bottom is 11.5 cm long. [B] The scolex of *Taenia solium*, the pork tapeworm. The scolex is about 1 mm in diameter and possesses cuplike suckers and small hooklets that anchor the worm to the intestinal wall. The scolex of *T. saginata* lacks hooklets. [C] A single segment, or proglottid, of *T. solium*. The dark area is the highly branched uterus. A mature proglottid contains both male and female reproductive organs and can produce many fertilized eggs, from which larvae can hatch. [D] Cysticerci of *T. solium* in a sample of pork ("measly pork"). The cysticerci are fluid-filled bladderlike cysts about 1 to 2 cm in diameter and contain the worm larvae.

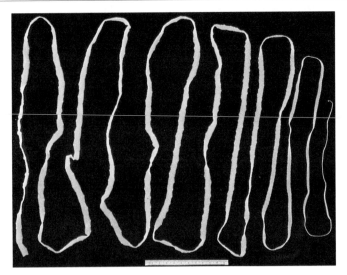

[A]

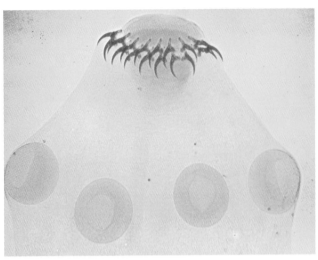

[B]

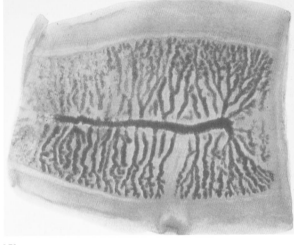

[C]

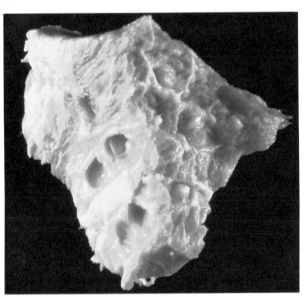

[D]

FIGURE 25.17

Thin section of pork showing a cyst containing a coiled worm of the species *Trichinella spiralis*, the causative agent of trichinosis.

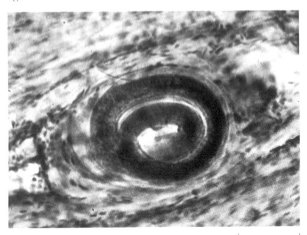

20 μm

and eye. If there are large numbers of larvae, they can cause extensive tissue damage. Patients may experience severe muscular pain and tissue swelling, and death may occur if the muscle tissue of the heart is severely damaged or if the central nervous system is invaded. The larvae eventually coil up and become enclosed by a cyst wall, and the patient's condition gradually improves.

Laboratory diagnosis is done by detecting specific antibodies against *T. spiralis* in the patient's serum. Unfortunately, no chemotherapeutic agents are available that can kill the larvae already in muscle tissue. The best protection against trichinosis is to cook all meat products thoroughly, especially pork.

Other Intestinal Infections Caused by Helminths

Pinworm Infections. Pinworm infections of humans are extremely common worldwide and usually occur in children. A single species, *Enterobius vermicularis*, is responsible. The eggs of this worm are carried to the mouth by fingers contaminated when patients scratch the anus, which itches intensely when worms are present in the area. Contaminated clothing and bed linens also are sources of the eggs. After being ingested, the eggs hatch into larvae, which migrate to the large intestine and mature into adult worms 2 to 13 mm long. After mating, the female worms emerge from the anus at night and deposit thousands of eggs that adhere to the skin or bedclothes. Microbiologists diagnose the infection by detecting eggs trapped on sticky tape that has been pressed against the anal region. In some instances, particularly at night, adult worms can be observed emerging from the anus. Infections can be treated effectively with drugs such as mebendazole or pyrantel pamoate.

Whipworm Infections. Infections caused by *Trichuris trichiura* (whose shape resembles a buggy whip) occur worldwide, but most commonly in tropical and subtropical regions. It is estimated that more than 500 million people are infected. Eggs are ingested with feces-contaminated food or water. In the small intestine they hatch into larvae, which later migrate to the large intestine and mature into adult worms that can be as long as 50 mm. The adults attach themselves to the intestinal lining, where they may damage the blood capillaries and tissues. After mating, each female worm lays up to 6000 eggs, which are excreted in the feces. The eggs are noninfective at first, but under proper soil conditions they become infective within 3 to 6 weeks. Infections may be asymptomatic, or they may include mild to severe symptoms such as nausea, vomiting, and diarrhea. Diagnosis is based on microscopic detection of eggs in the patient's stools. Patients usually are treated with the drug mebendazole, although this is not always effective.

***Ascaris* Infections.** Health officials estimate that the large nematode *Ascaris lumbricoides* infects nearly 1 billion persons in the world, especially in tropical and subtropical areas. Its elaborate life cycle inside the host begins with eggs ingested via feces-contaminated water or food, particularly raw vegetables. The ingested eggs develop into larvae which migrate from the small intestine to various tissues of the body and eventually return to the small intestine. In about 8 to 10 weeks, the larvae mature in the small intestine into adult worms 15 to 35 cm long. After mating, each female lays about 200,000 eggs—which hatch into larvae that penetrate the intestinal wall, enter the bloodstream, and move to the lungs. There the larvae may damage the air sacs, and patients typically have a dry cough, fever, and difficulty in breathing. After two weeks the larvae ascend from the lungs to the mouth, where they are swallowed. They thus reach the small intestine, where they mature into adult worms. Symptoms caused by adult worms occur mainly in children and include loss of appetite, loss of weight, and intestinal discomfort. Occasionally, the adult worms may be so numerous that they form a mass that obstructs the large intestine. *Ascaris* eggs excreted in the feces become infective in 2 or 3 weeks and can remain infective in soil for months or years. Laboratory diagnosis is based on microscopic detection of eggs in stool samples. Treatment includes drugs such as pyrantel pamoate and mebendazole, which can eliminate the adult worms from the intestine.

ASK YOURSELF

1 What are helminths, and into what two main groups are they classified?

2 What two tapeworm species are important in human disease? How are they transmitted? What sequence of events occurs in the human body during an infection? What makes cysticercosis a serious disease?

3 Where is *Trichinella spiralis* found in nature? How do humans become infected? What sequence of events occurs in the human body in infection with trichinosis? How can the disease be prevented?

4 How do humans become infected by pinworms? Whipworms? *Ascaris lumbricoides*? What symptoms occur in infections caused by these helminths?

25.3 HORSEMEAT-ASSOCIATED TRICHINOSIS IN FRANCE, TRACED TO CONNECTICUT

In August and October 1985, two outbreaks of trichinosis associated with consumption of horsemeat occurred in France. A brief report of one of these outbreaks follows.

During August 1985, several cases of trichinosis were diagnosed in Melun, a small town located 30 miles southeast of Paris. Shortly thereafter, several more cases were diagnosed from a southern district of Paris. An investigation was undertaken to determine the extent and source of this outbreak. Three hundred twenty-five individuals met the case definition of trichinosis. The investigation implicated horsemeat as the source of the outbreak. All 325 patients reported consuming horsemeat before onset of illness, and 99 percent of them had eaten it raw or rare. Family members of patients who did not eat any horsemeat but shared other food with the patients did not become infected with trichinosis.

Although several butchers in Paris and Melun sell horsemeat, all patients had purchased their horsemeat exclusively from one of two shops between July 22 and August 5. The butchers from these two shops and their families were also infected with trichinosis. Records indicated that each shop received half of a single horse carcass on July 22. The carcass had been shipped as "fresh meat" to France from a slaughterhouse in Connecticut that ships 8000 to 9000 horses to Europe each year. The establishment is inspected by the U.S. Department of Agriculture, but inspection did not include examination of meat samples for *Trichinella*. Because horses are obtained by the slaughterhouse from multiple sources and are not individually identified on leaving the processing plant, the implicated horse could not be traced to the farm of origin. No meat from the implicated horse was available for inspection.

Horsemeat has rarely been implicated as a source of trichinosis. The first reported outbreaks due to this meat source occurred in Italy in 1975 and in France in 1976. In both instances, the infected horsemeat was imported from eastern Europe. How horses become infected with trichinosis is unknown. Horses are commonly observed to be herbivorous; however, experimental studies prompted by the outbreak in Italy indicate that horses will ingest meat placed in their feed and will become infected with trichinosis when fed infective larvae. The unusually large number of cases involved in the 1985 outbreak is related to the body size of the implicated animal species (the carcass of the horse was 613 lb) and the preference among French consumers for raw or lightly cooked horsemeat, prepared as steaks, in soups, or ground ("steak tartare").

Little is known about *Trichinella* infection in horses in the United States, but it is assumed to be extremely rare. Between late October and December 31, 1985, samples from 20,000 horses killed in the United States were examined for *Trichinella*, with negative results. Trichinosis in horses in the United States would presumably represent an unlikely health hazard because few citizens eat horsemeat, and those who do probably cook it. Since 1975, 30 to 289 trichinosis cases have been reported in the United States per year, approximately 80 percent of which have been associated with the ingestion of pork.

Adapted from *Morbidity and Mortality Weekly Report,* May 9, 1986.

GENERAL CONTROL MEASURES FOR PREVENTION OF FOODBORNE AND WATERBORNE INFECTIONS

Factors that contribute to foodborne and waterborne infections are thoroughly understood, and there are well-established, effective methods for control of these infections. These are simple, inexpensive measures that should be practiced by anyone responsible for food preparation or water supplies.

Control of Foodborne Infections

The factors contributing to foodborne infections are:

1 Inadequately cooked food
2 Improper holding time and temperatures for the food (between preparation and ingestion)
3 Contaminated equipment
4 Poor personal hygiene
5 Inadequate preservation methods

Inadequate cooking can be a particular problem in cooking large birds or roasts, since their size increases the time required for sufficient heat penetration. Without high enough temperatures or sufficient cooking time, either the microorganisms (including parasites) are not killed, or heat-sensitive toxins such as botulinum toxin are not destroyed.

Improper holding temperatures for food, such as warm room temperatures, can allow the multiplication of some foodborne pathogens. To prevent this, adequate chilling and refrigeration facilities are essential. Long-term storage of food is best done at freezing temperatures. When holding food for short periods, the following generalization should be observed:

0 to 7°C: relatively safe for holding food
10 to 50°C: very dangerous range, because it supports the rapid growth of many pathogenic microorganisms
60 to 100°C: another relatively safe range for holding food, since it destroys vegetative cells of bacteria

The contamination of food by microorganisms from equipment can be prevented or minimized if proper sanitary practices are employed. Growth of microorganisms can be controlled with chemical agents, such as those used in washing equipment (Chapter 8). Leftover food should be removed promptly from work surfaces and utensils in food preparation areas.

Good personal hygiene is of great importance in the control of foodborne diseases. It is especially significant in controlling foodborne infections caused by microorganisms that have a fecal-oral route of entry into the host. It is obvious that food handlers should not have open wound infections such as boils. Not so obvious are food handlers who may be carriers of pathogenic microorganisms without exhibiting any clinical symptoms. Such carriers constitute an important problem in the control of not only foodborne disease but also waterborne and respiratory diseases. Carriers have usually had the disease caused by the organisms they harbor, but in some cases the attack was so mild that it passed without notice. Carriers are often unaware of their condition until an outbreak of disease is traced to them. The carrier state, fortunately, can be determined by use of appropriate laboratory tests; carriers may then be treated with chemotherapeutic agents to eliminate the pathogenic organisms.

The major control measure is to prevent the contamination of water supplies. This can be achieved by sanitary measures such as purification of drinking water supplies and proper disposal of human wastes (Chapter 29). It is mainly through improved sanitation and strict control of water supplies that the incidence of waterborne diseases has decreased dramatically in the United States, Canada, and other developed countries during the past few decades.

ASK YOURSELF

1 What are the five general factors that can lead to foodborne infections?

2 What measures can be taken to prevent foodborne infections?

3 What is the cycle of transmission that must be understood in order to prevent waterborne infections?

4 What measures can be taken to prevent waterborne infections?

Control of Waterborne Infections

Control of waterborne diseases is directed toward disrupting the following cycle:

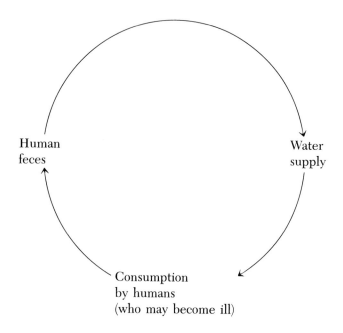

Human feces

Water supply

Consumption by humans (who may become ill)

SUMMARY

1 Gastroenteritis is often accompanied by diarrhea, which can result in dehydration of the body, increased acidity of the blood, and hemoconcentration. Treatment of a diarrheic patient may require intravenous replacement of the lost fluids. In intestinal infections diarrhea is usually caused by microbial enterotoxins, which stimulate secretion of water and salts into the intestine.

2 There are two major categories of foodborne diseases caused by microorganisms: food poisoning and foodborne infection. In food poisonings, the bacterial agents produce a toxin in a food. When people consume the food, they ingest the toxin, which then causes the disease symptoms. In foodborne infections, the pathogen itself is ingested and grows within the body.

3 In staphylococcal food poisoning, it is usually a nasal carrier who inoculates the food with the enterotoxin-producing strain of *S. aureus*. In food poisoning botulism, soil is the source of the heat-stable endospores of *C. botulinum* that contaminate food. *C. botulinum* produces a neurotoxin that binds to nerve fibers and causes muscular paralysis. Food can be rendered safe by boiling, which destroys the toxin. (Infant botulism is not a food poisoning, but an infection in which the neurotoxin is formed by *C. botulinum* growing within an infant's intestine. *Wound botulism* is an infection in which *C. botulinum* grows in the damaged tissue of a wound and produces the neurotoxin.)

4 Foodborne and waterborne infections caused by bacteria include *Salmonella* gastroenteritis, typhoid fever, *Campylobacter* gastroenteritis, and a number of other diseases. *Helicobacter pylori* is the probable causative agent of antral gastritis and peptic ulcers, but its mode of transmission is not yet known.

5 Foodborne and waterborne infections by viruses include the following: paralytic poliomyelitis, caused by polioviruses; rotavirus diarrhea; Norwalk gastroenteritis; and hepatitis type A. Polioviruses multiply initially in the intestinal wall, penetrate the wall, and enter the bloodstream. They may reach the central nervous system and cause nerve damage that results in paralysis. Immunization can be accomplished with either the Salk vaccine (killed virus) or the Sabin vaccine (live attenuated virus).

6 Foodborne and waterborne infections caused by protozoa include the following: amoebiasis (cysts of the amoeba *Entamoeba histolytica* are transmitted from human to human by the fecal-oral route); giardiasis (*Giardia lamblia* is the only flagellated protozoan known to cause intestinal disease in humans); and balantidiasis (*Balantidium coli* is the only ciliated protozoan known to cause human disease).

7 Foodborne and waterborne infections caused by helminths include *Taenia* infections and trichinosis. *Taenia saginata* and *Taenia solium* tapeworms are ribbon-shaped and may be several meters in length. Cysts can be ingested with inadequately cooked beef or pork and develop into adult tapeworms that attach to the intestinal wall and grow. Ingestion of the eggs of *T. solium* leads to the development of larvae that can invade the body and form cysts, sometimes in the eye or brain. Trichinosis is usually acquired by eating inadequately cooked pork containing encysted larvae of *Trichinella spiralis*. From the intestine the larvae may invade muscle tissue throughout the patient's body. Other intestinal infections caused by helminths include pinworm, whipworm, and *Ascaris* infections.

KEY TERMS

cestodes
chronic carriers
cysticerci
enterotoxin
flatworms
foodborne infections
food poisoning
gastroenteritis
H antigens
helminths
nematodes
neurotoxin
O antigens
polyvalent botulinum antitoxin
Sabin vaccine
Salk vaccine
trematodes
trophozoites
waterborne infections

THE HUMAN
GASTROINTESTINAL
TRACT

1 In the large intestine, undigested material becomes more concentrated as

_____ is absorbed from it.

2 Match the item on the left with the statement or description on the right.

_____ diarrhea

_____ gastroenteritis

_____ absorption

_____ small intestine

_____ hemoconcentration

(a) Where the final stages of digestion occur

(b) Nutrient molecules pass from the intestine into the blood

(c) Characterized by watery stools

(d) Thickening of the blood due to fluid loss

(e) Acute inflammation of the gastrointestinal tract

3 Some enterotoxins act by stimulating production of an enzyme called

_____, which catalyzes the formation of cyclic AMP from ATP.

FOOD POISONINGS

4 Only those strains of *S. aureus* that produce a(n) _____ can cause staphylococcal food poisoning.

5 Which *two* of the following statements are true? **(a)** Most carriers of enterotoxin-producing strains of *S. aureus* have obvious infections on their hands. **(b)** The *S. aureus* enterotoxin is produced within the body after the food is eaten. **(c)** Staphylococcal food poisoning is almost never fatal. **(d)** Symptoms of staphylococcal food poisoning usually begin about 24 h after consumption of the food. **(e)** The *S. aureus* enterotoxin is not destroyed by boiling for 30 min.

6 The best preventive measure against staphylococcal food poisoning is to

_____ all perishable food.

7 Of the three types of botulism, _____ botulism is the most common.

8 Which *two* of the following statements are true? **(a)** The main source of the endospores of *C. botulinum* is human feces. **(b)** *C. botulinum* types A, B, E, and F cause botulism in humans. **(c)** Most cases of food poisoning botulism occur in commercially canned foods. **(d)** The toxin produced by *C. botulinum* is a neurotoxin. **(e)** The main action of botulinum toxin is to cause diarrhea.

9 *C. botulinum* may be able to grow in an infant's intestinal tract if the infant's

_____ is not yet well developed.

10 Infant botulism is an infection, not a food poisoning, because the toxin is produced not in a food but instead in _____.

11 The test to determine whether botulinum toxin is present in a patient's blood serum or a food sample is: **(a)** an ELISA test; **(b)** a toxin-neutralization test; **(c)** a slide agglutination test; **(d)** an immunodiffusion test; **(e)** an in vitro test.

12 Some strains of *Bacillus* _____ can cause a type of food poisoning that resembles staphylococcal food poisoning.

13 Mycotoxins are produced by: **(a)** mycobacteria; **(b)** algae; **(c)** fungi; **(d)** mycoplasmas; **(e)** alkaloids.

14 Name a mycotoxin having a component that is used to treat migraine headaches: **(a)** aflatoxin; **(b)** ergot; **(c)** *Amanita virosa* toxin; **(d)** *Aspergillus flavus* toxin; **(e)** tetradotoxin.

15 Match the item on the left with the description on the right.

      (a) Consists of killed typhoid bacilli

_____ chronic carrier

      (b) A heat-stable polysaccharide located on the surface of
the bacterial cell wall

_____ endotoxin

_____ O antigen

      (c) A flagellar protein

_____ H antigen

      (d) Excretes a pathogenic microorganism for months,
years, or life

_____ typhoid vaccine

      (e) Causes the fever response in typhoid fever

16 Although humans can spread salmonellas to other humans, the main source of many salmonellas is _____.

17 Which *two* of the following are false? **(a)** Large numbers of salmonellas must be ingested to produce gastroenteritis. **(b)** If food contaminated with salmonellas is stored in a warm place for several hours, the salmonellas may multiply to high numbers. **(c)** *S. typhi* infects both humans and animals. **(d)** In typhoid fever, endotoxins liberated from lysed typhoid bacilli in the blood cause the fever. **(e)** During the first week of typhoid fever infection, *S. typhi* is much more likely to be isolated from the feces than from the blood.

18 No vaccine is available against *Salmonella* gastroenteritis because of the large number of _____ that would have to be included.

19 Chronic typhoid carriers harbor persistent nests of typhoid bacilli in the gallbladder or sometimes in the _____ bladder.

20 The major bacterial species that causes gastroenteritis is: **(a)** *C. coli*; **(b)** *C. fetus*; **(c)** *H. pylori*; **(d)** *C. jejuni*; **(e)** *C. upsaliensis*.

21 The probable causative agent of antral gastritis and peptic ulcers is: **(a)** *C. jejuni*; **(b)** *C. coli*; **(c)** *H. pylori*; **(d)** *C. concisus*; **(e)** *C. hyointestinalis*.

22 The main physiological characteristic of campylobacters that must be considered when isolating and culturing them is that they are: **(a)** anaerobes; **(b)** aerobes; **(c)** halophiles; **(d)** microaerophiles; **(e)** psychrophiles.

23 The enzyme synthesized by *H. pylori* that helps to protect this bacterium from stomach acid is: **(a)** alkaline phosphatase; **(b)** urease; **(c)** beta-galactosidase; **(d)** acid phosphatase; **(e)** glucose-6-phosphate dehydrogenase.

24 *H. pylori* gastritis can be treated with bismuth salts or with _____.

25 The major source of contamination of food or water by *C. jejuni* is: **(a)** human feces; **(b)** undercooked poultry; **(c)** asymptomatic human carriers; **(d)** animal feces; **(e)** stomach fluid.

26 Match the item on the left with the statement or description on the right.

      (a) Traveler's diarrhea

_____ *Vibrio parahaemolyticus*

      (b) Produces an enterotoxin when it sporulates in the intestine

_____ *Escherichia coli*

_____ *Shigella* species

      (c) The patient may lose as much as 10 to 12 liters of fluid a day

_____ *Clostridium perfringens*

      (d) Bacillary dysentery

_____ *Yersinia enterocolitica*

      (e) Patients may develop abdominal pain that mimics appendicitis

_____ *Vibrio cholerae*

      (f) May be present in inadequately cooked seafood

27 Paralytic poliomyelitis is now rare in the United States, mainly because of the establishment of a(n) _____ program.

28 Polioviruses have a(n) _____ shape, and their genetic material consists of _____-stranded _____.

29 Although polioviruses initially multiply in the intestinal tract, they may eventually cause muscular paralysis by infecting the cells in the gray matter of the: **(a)** large intestine; **(b)** lymph nodes; **(c)** spinal cord; **(d)** small intestine; **(e)** muscles.

30 Select the *two* correct answers: **(a)** The Sabin vaccine consists of killed poliovirus strains. **(b)** The Salk vaccine consists of live attenuated poliovirus strains. **(c)** The Salk vaccine can stimulate production of serum antibodies but not intestinal secretory antibodies. **(d)** The vaccine presently used in the United States is the Salk vaccine. **(e)** The Sabin vaccine is administered orally.

31 The World Health Organization estimates that one-half of all cases of infantile diarrhea requiring hospitalization are due to _____ viruses.

32 The wheel-like shape of rotaviruses is due to their having: **(a)** double-stranded RNA; **(b)** two concentric icosahedral capsids; **(c)** double-stranded DNA; **(d)** 6 serotypes; **(e)** a circular type of RNA.

33 The "Snow Mountain agent," "Hawaii agent," and "Ditchling agent" refer to viruses of the _____ group.

34 Although viruses of the Norwalk group can be seen in a patient's feces by electron microscopy, they have never been _____.

35 In hepatitis type A, HAV initially multiplies in the surface lining of the intestinal wall and spreads to adjacent cells. It then invades the bloodstream, which carries it to the _____.

36 Match the item on the left with the description on the right.
_____ amoebiasis
_____ giardiasis
_____ balantidiasis
_____ trophozoite
_____ cyst

(a) Nonmotile, dormant form of a protozoan
(b) Disease caused by a flagellated protozoan
(c) Disease caused by a ciliated protozoan
(d) Active, motile, feeding stage of a protozoan
(e) Amoebic dysentery

37 A protozoan-caused intestinal infection that is transmitted by ingestion of water or food contaminated by cysts that are present in hog feces is: **(a)** trichinosis; **(b)** amoebiasis; **(c)** balantidiasis; **(d)** giardiasis; **(e)** cystitis.

38 Match the item on the left with the description on the right.
_____ scolex
_____ proglottid
_____ hermaphrodite
_____ cysticercus
_____ *Trichinella spiralis*

(a) Example of a roundworm
(b) A segment of a tapeworm
(c) A fluid-filled sac containing a scolex
(d) Organism that has both male and female reproductive organs
(e) The "head" of a tapeworm

39 Ingestion of the cysticerci of *T. saginata* or *T. solium* can lead to the development of a long adult tapeworm in the patient's _____.

40 A patient whose intestine contains an adult *T. solium* can be reinfected by the eggs of this worm, and this can lead to a serious disease called _____.

41 Trichinosis is usually acquired by eating inadequately cooked _____ that contains the encysted form of *T. spiralis*.

42 In which one of the following is there a stage in the helminth's life cycle in which the larvae reach the lungs, ascend to the mouth and are swallowed, and then mature into adults in the patient's intestine? **(a)** whipworm infection; **(b)** pinworm infection; **(c)** trichinosis; **(d)** *Ascaris* infection; **(e)** tapeworm infection.

43 Which one of the following is characterized by helminth eggs gaining access to the mouth via fingers that become contaminated when the patient responds to intense itching of the anus? **(a)** whipworm infection; **(b)** pinworm infection; **(c)** trichinosis; **(d)** *Ascaris* infection; **(e)** tapeworm infection.

GENERAL CONTROL MEASURES FOR PREVENTION OF FOODBORNE AND WATERBORNE INFECTIONS

44 In order to kill pathogenic microorganisms, the cooking of large birds or roasts must be done thoroughly because of the problem of heat _____.

45 Long-term storage of food is best done at: **(a)** 0 to 7°C; **(b)** 7 to 10°C; **(c)** 10 to 50°C; **(d)** 100°C; **(e)** freezing temperatures.

46 Persons who are carriers of a pathogenic microorganism often do not exhibit any clinical symptoms. They can be proved to be carriers only by appropriate _____.

47 The major control measure for waterborne infections is to prevent _____.

REVIEW QUESTIONS

1 Is staphylococcal food poisoning an infection? Is infant botulism a food poisoning? Explain your answers.

2 The term *Salmonella food poisoning* is sometimes used instead of *Salmonella gastroenteritis* by newspapers when reporting outbreaks. Is this correct? Explain your answer.

3 What special conditions are used when isolating *Campylobacter jejuni* from diarrheic stools?

4 What is the "urea breath test," and what is it used for?

5 Which pathogenic agents described in this chapter are transmitted mainly from animals to humans? Which are transmitted only from human to human?

6 In what ways does the hepatitis type A virus described in this chapter differ from the hepatitis type B virus described in Chapter 23?

7 What evidence implicates *Helicobacter pylori* as the causative agent of antral gastritis?

8 Explain how humans can become infected by *Entamoeba histolytica*, *Giardia lamblia*, and *Balantidium coli*.

9 How can you protect yourself from getting botulism from home-canned foods? From getting trichinosis from pork?

10 Since there is a vaccine against typhoid fever, why isn't there also a vaccine against *Salmonella* gastroenteritis?

DISCUSSION QUESTIONS

1 Assume that you have isolated a Gram-negative rod-shaped bacterium that gives biochemical reactions typical of *Salmonella typhi*. What can you do to prove that the isolate is *S. typhi* and not some other salmonella that is biochemically similar to *S. typhi*?

2 Suppose that you have isolated a strain of *C. botulinum* from the stool of an infant with botulism. Mice injected with the toxin produced by the culture die within 3 days. Describe a laboratory procedure by which you could determine the *particular antigenic type* of this toxin.

3 Assess the benefits and risks of the Sabin vaccine for immunization against poliomyelitis. Should the vaccine continue to be used in the United States?

4 Several of the foodborne and waterborne diseases discussed in this chapter have a relatively low incidence in the United States and other industrialized countries but are prevalent in developing or third world countries. What factors might account for this?

5 Suppose you wish to develop a vaccine against *H. pylori* gastritis and ulcers. Since the bacteria do not invade the tissues or bloodstream, what problems might you encounter? Would a vaccine still be possible? (*Note:* Cholera bacteria [TABLE 25.3] also do not invade the tissue or bloodstream, yet a vaccine exists against cholera.)

26

Arthropod-Borne Diseases

OBJECTIVES

After reading this chapter you should be able to

1 Explain what is meant by a "biological vector" and list the major kinds of arthropods that serve as such vectors.

2 List three arthropod-borne diseases that represent major global health problems of the past and present, and indicate how these diseases can be controlled.

3 Name the causative agents of six microbial infections transmitted by arthropods and the arthropod vector for each agent.

4 Give the sequence of events leading to an epidemic of plague.

5 Describe the relationship between *Ixodes* ticks and the spirochete that causes Lyme disease.

6 Distinguish between the urban cycle of yellow fever and the sylvatic cycle of yellow fever.

7 Describe the life cycle of the protozoa that cause human malaria and explain how these protozoa are transmitted from human to human.

8 Explain how a filaria infection can lead to a disfiguring disease called *elephantiasis*.

OVERVIEW

Other than humans themselves, *arthropods* are the most important source of human disease. Arthropods are invertebrate animals with jointed limbs and a segmented body that is generally covered with a chitinous shell. Examples include spiders, centipedes, crabs, lobsters, barnacles, ticks, and insects. Arthropods constitute the largest assemblage of species in the zoological world. More than 900,000 species of arthropods are known and thousands more remain to be classified.

Some arthropods, particularly various ticks, lice, fleas, mites, flies, and mosquitoes, can serve as agents of transmission of pathogenic microorganisms to humans. Arthropod-borne infections have an extensive distribution over the face of the globe. Through the centuries, diseases such as plague, yellow fever, and malaria have produced untold suffering, economic loss, and death in the human population.

There are a great variety of arthropod-borne diseases of humans, and each disease has interesting and unique features. However, this chapter will concentrate on a few diseases which exemplify the principles of disease transmission by arthropods, as well as the interactions among the pathogen, the arthropod, and the human host.

715

ARTHROPODS AS DISEASE VECTORS

Arthropods may serve as vectors for pathogenic microorganisms. A *vector* is an organism, such as an insect, that transports a pathogenic microorganism. Some arthropods are **mechanical vectors,** merely transmitting pathogens that adhere to their mouthparts or legs. The common housefly, *Musca domestica,* is the classic example: it can become contaminated with pathogens from feces and transmit them to food or other objects. Diseases mechanically transmitted by houseflies include gastroenteritis, poliomyelitis, amoebiasis, and other intestinal diseases. However, in most arthropod-borne diseases, the arthropod serves as a **biological vector,** one in which the pathogen undergoes a period of growth or development within the arthropod, as in epidemic typhus or malaria. In some instances the pathogenic microorganism may even be transmitted to subsequent generations of the arthropod by being incorporated into the eggs produced by the female *(transovarian passage).* For example, the ticks that are biological vectors of *Rickettsia rickettsii,* the causative agent of Rocky Mountain spotted fever, readily transmit the rickettsia to their offspring.

ASK YOURSELF

1 How can an arthropod act as a mechanical vector? What is one example of such a vector?

2 How can an arthropod act as a biological vector? What is one example of such a vector?

3 How do the ticks that are biological vectors of *Rickettsia rickettsii* transmit the organism to subsequent generations of ticks?

ARTHROPOD-BORNE INFECTIONS CAUSED BY BACTERIA

Many diseases caused by arthropod-borne bacteria are serious and often life-threatening. Lyme disease, which was not discovered until 1975, may result in nervous system disorders and a debilitating arthritis. Rocky Mountain spotted fever, found only in North and South America, has a high mortality rate unless promptly treated, but it is difficult to diagnose because it resembles several other diseases. Of all the arthropod-borne diseases caused by bacteria, plague is the most notable because it has caused the greatest suffering and death, occasionally spreading around the globe. Although the incidence of plague has declined in recent years, history shows that it has often subsided before, only to return with an even greater ferocity. Thus we can never afford to relax preventive measures against this and other arthropod-borne diseases.

Plague

Plague pandemics ravaged Asia and Europe for centuries. The Great Plague, which started in A.D. 542, was reputedly responsible for over 100 million deaths in 50 years. The Black Death, a great plague pandemic of the fourteenth century, was considered the worst catastrophe ever to strike Europe, and perhaps even the world. It caused the death of an estimated one-third of the world's population at the time.

History records 45 other plague pandemics between the years 1500 and 1720. Plague occurred mainly in parts of Asia in the eighteenth and nineteenth centuries, but in 1871 a great pandemic began in central Asia and spread to other parts of the world. In India alone during the years 1898–1918 it was responsible for 10 million deaths. Plague subsided after the 1920s, but flare-ups still occur when preventive measures are not used, as in

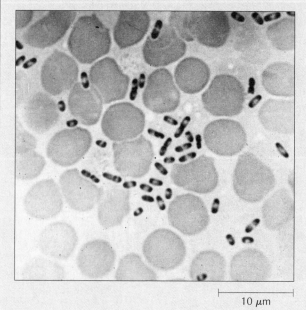

FIGURE 26.1
Yersinia pestis organisms exhibit a bipolar, or "safety pin," appearance in this smear of mouse blood. The large round objects are red blood cells.

10 μm

26.1 MAN TOSSES DEAD SQUIRREL AT WIFE, DEVELOPS PLAGUELIKE DISEASE

In 1981, while hiking near Taos, New Mexico, a New York man found a dead squirrel, picked it up, and tossed it at his wife as a prank. Nine days later, after the couple had returned to their home in Manhattan, the man developed a high fever and pain in his legs and in the lymph glands of his groin. Bubonic plague was suspected, probably carried by a flea living on the dead squirrel's body. However, the hospital epidemiologist subsequently decided that it was extremely unlikely the patient actually had bubonic plague and that there was no threat of transmission of his illness to others. The patient responded well to antibiotic treatment.

Although this case was a false alarm, between 4 and 40 plague cases do occur each year in the United States in the southwestern and western regions, caused by human contact with the wild rodent reservoir. In 1988, for instance, 15 cases of plague were reported—one in Texas, four in Colorado, seven in New Mexico, one in Arizona, and two in California.

One of the California cases occurred in a 19-year-old Army recruit, who was hospitalized with a fever, a bubo in the groin region, and multiple insect bites on both legs. He recovered after treatment with tetracycline and chloramphenicol. His exposure to *Yersinia pestis* probably occurred during military training in Monterey County. A field investigation of the area discovered a high incidence of local California ground squirrels with infected fleas. In another case, a 30-year-old New Mex- ico man contracted plague while skinning a cottontail rabbit in Colorado.

If you are planning a vacation in a wilderness area in the southwestern and western United States, you should check with state and local health departments to see whether parks are closed for any health reasons. There also are common- sense precautions you can take when visiting a wilderness area. Avoid any contact with rodents, including prairie dogs and ground squirrels. Never handle sick or dead rodents or other mammals. If you find such animals, report them to local health authorities, park rangers, or campground supervisors.

Adapted from *New York Times*, March 5, 1981, p. B4; *Morbidity and Mortality Weekly Report*, Oct. 28, 1988.

---

times of war. For instance, in Vietnam during the 1960s plague caused as many as 10,000 deaths a year.

Today plague occurs chronically in certain areas of Africa, Asia, and the Americas. No human epidemics have ever occurred in the United States, but a few sporadic cases—usually between 4 and 40—occur each year in the western United States because of occasional human contact with infected wild rodents that inhabit the region [DISCOVER 26.1].

The Biology of *Yersinia pestis*. Plague is caused by *Yersinia pestis*, a nonmotile facultative Gram-negative rod. When the cells are stained by special methods such as Wayson's method, they exhibit **bipolar staining.** This means that they have deeply stained areas at both ends, giving the cells a safety pin-like appearance [FIGURE 26.1]. In the laboratory, *Y. pestis* grows best at 25°C; this is unlike most pathogenic bacteria, which prefer 37°C. *Y. pestis* produces several substances that may contribute to its pathogenicity: (1) a capsule, which inhibits phagocytosis; (2) a complex of two cell-wall proteins, the **V** and **W** *proteins*, which also inhibits phagocytosis; (3) an endotoxin; and (4) a protein toxin called the **murine toxin**, which can damage the mitochondria of the tissue cells of rats, mice, and other animals that are susceptible to plague. However, the precise properties of *Y. pestis* that are responsible for its high virulence are not known.

Transmission and Pathogenicity of *Y. pestis*. Plague is mainly a disease of wild rodents, which form the *reser-* *voir of infection.* (This term is applied to the hosts in which the pathogen lives in nature and which serves as a continuing source of the pathogen.) Plague is spread from rodent to rodent by fleas that infest these animals. In the United States, plague made its first appearance in 1900 at the seaport of San Francisco, being imported by rats on ships. The domestic rats of the city were soon infected, and the disease spread to various wild rodents such as ground squirrels, prairie dogs, and wood rats. In this manner plague moved eastward from the Pacific coast, and today it is widespread among various wild rodents in the southwestern United States. A few sporadic human infections occur every year among people who have been bitten by infected fleas from rodents.

The great human plague epidemics of the past have followed a definite sequence of events [FIGURE 26.2]. Domestic rats, those that inhabit the human environment, may contract plague via fleas from infected wild rodents. An epidemic of plague then occurs among the domestic rats, the plague bacilli being transmitted from rat to rat by the rat flea *Xenopsylla cheopis* [FIGURE 26.3]. When *X. cheopis* bites an infected rat it ingests a blood meal which contains enormous numbers of plague bacilli. An enzyme made by the bacilli then causes the blood to clot in the flea's digestive tract. This clot prevents any food from passing along the digestive tract, and the flea becomes very hungry. When the rat dies of plague, the hungry flea leaves the corpse and may try to attack a human host. However, because of the blockage in the flea's digestive tract, the human blood that is in-

FIGURE 26.2
Sequence of events leading to epidemics of bubonic and pneumonic plague.

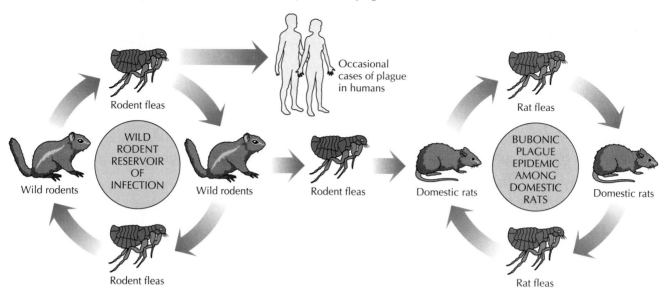

FIGURE 26.3
The rat flea *Xenopsylla cheopis* (adult female).

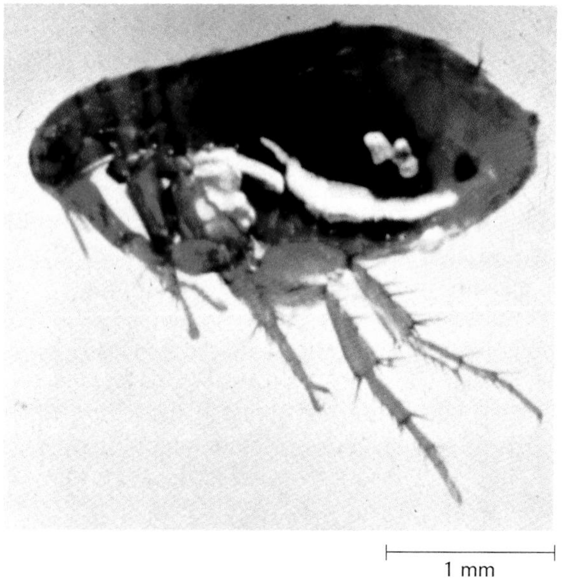

1 mm

gested cannot pass along the flea's digestive tract. Instead, it merely becomes mixed with some of the plague bacilli and is regurgitated back into the bite, thereby inoculating the person.

The most common form of plague in humans is the bubonic form, which is characterized by chills, fever, nausea, vomiting, general weakness, and swollen, infected lymph glands—the sites where the plague bacilli initially multiply. (An enlarged lymph gland is called a *bubo;* hence the name *bubonic plague.*) In untreated cases of bubonic plague, the mortality rate is approximately 50 percent if the infection remains restricted largely to the lymph glands. However, the bacteria may pass from the infected lymph glands to the bloodstream and cause a *septicemia,* a serious condition characterized by active bacterial multiplication in the blood. In untreated cases of plague septicemia the mortality rate is 100 percent. In approximately 15 percent of plague cases a *primary* septicemia occurs; this is a septicemia without preliminary infection of the lymph glands. This can happen if the plague bacilli enter the victim's bloodstream directly and begin to multiply.

After an initial case of bubonic plague develops, the disease can be transmitted from person to person by *human fleas or human body lice.* However, this type of transmission requires heavily louse- or flea-infested populations, which are common under wartime conditions and were common in temperate regions such as Europe before the advent of sanitation.

In approximately 10 to 15 percent of untreated cases of bubonic plague, the infection spreads to the lungs and the patient develops a severe pneumonia. The sputum coughed up by the patient contains bacilli and is thin, watery, and streaked with blood. Untreated cases of pneumonic plague have a mortality rate of 100 percent. Pneumonic plague is much more contagious than bubonic plague, because the bacilli can be transmitted from person to person through air by aerosols [FIGURE 26.4]. If you think of how easily airborne infections such as influenza can spread among a population, you can understand how a pneumonic plague epidemic could become widespread and catastrophic.

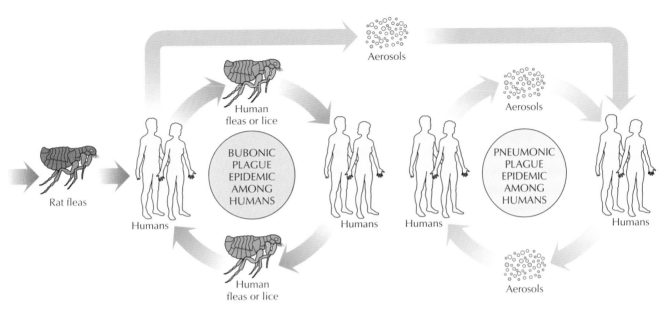

FIGURE 26.4

Rare copy of a 1921 proclamation from the Medical and Sanitary Department of the Chinese Eastern Railway. The document was distributed during a pneumonic plague epidemic in Manchuria in which 9000 persons died. The upper portion is in Russian; the bottom is in Chinese. The document explains that pneumonic plague "is caused by a microbe invisible to the naked eye . . . which is in the sputum of an infected person, who, by expectorating or coughing, can infect people living with him, or those who come into contact with him." Also described are the disease symptoms and various preventive measures, such as the wearing of cloth facial masks.

Laboratory Diagnosis. A presumptive laboratory diagnosis of plague can be made by staining clinical specimens (blood, sputum, or the fluid from buboes) to demonstrate the presence of bipolar-staining bacilli. The fluorescent antibody technique is also used for rapid detection of *Y. pestis*, especially in sputum from patients with pneumonic plague. A confirmed diagnosis is made by isolating *Y. pestis* and identifying it by biochemical and immunologic tests.

Treatment and Prevention of Plague. Streptomycin is effective for treatment of plague. Prevention of plague depends first upon control and elimination of domestic rats and rat fleas; it is impractical to eliminate the wild rodent reservoirs of infection. Other preventive measures include immunization programs and elimination of human fleas and lice. Vaccines consisting of killed whole cells or live attenuated strains of *Y. pestis* are available. The vaccines stimulate development of antibodies against the capsule and V and W antigens, thereby enhancing phagocytosis. Vaccination is available for persons traveling to regions where plague is prevalent, who work in close contact with wild rodents, or who do laboratory work with live cultures of plague bacilli.

Rocky Mountain Spotted Fever

Despite its name, Rocky Mountain spotted fever (RMSF) occurs throughout the temperate zones of the western hemisphere, and in the United States it is far more prevalent in the east than in the west [FIGURE 26.5]. RMSF occurs mainly in the summer months and in persons engaged in outdoor pursuits, because such persons are most likely to be bitten by the tick vector.

The Biology of *Rickettsia rickettsii*. *Rickettsia rickettsii* is the causative agent of RMSF. This microbe is a Gram-negative rod-shaped bacterium that is obligately parasitic, growing in the nucleus and cytoplasm of host cells. In the laboratory it is usually cultured in embryonated

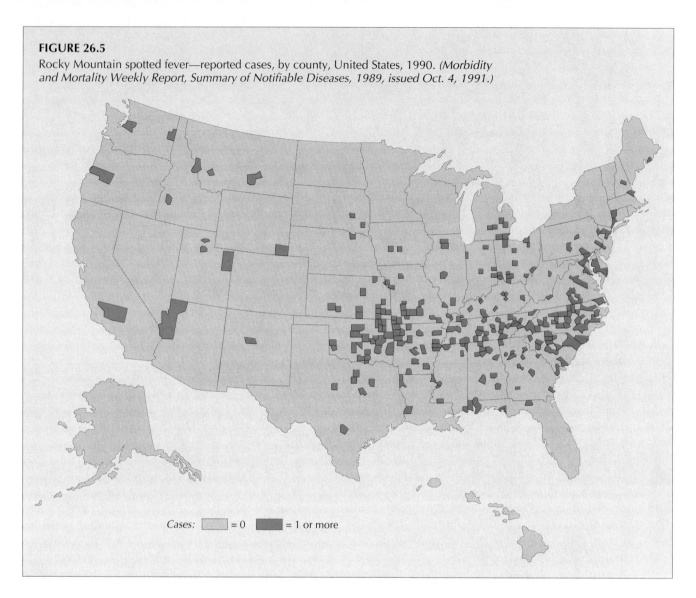

FIGURE 26.5

Rocky Mountain spotted fever—reported cases, by county, United States, 1990. *(Morbidity and Mortality Weekly Report, Summary of Notifiable Diseases, 1989, issued Oct. 4, 1991.)*

Cases: ☐ = 0   ■ = 1 or more

chicken eggs, where it grows within the cells of the yolk sac membrane [FIGURE 26.6 A and B]. It can also be cultured in tissue cell cultures or in laboratory animals. Laboratory work with this species can be extremely hazardous unless extreme safety precautions are used, because a very small number of cells can cause infection.

Transmission and Pathogenicity of *Rickettsia rickettsii*. In the eastern United States, *R. rickettsii* is transmitted mainly by the American dog tick, *Dermacentor variabilis* [FIGURE 26.7]; in the west it is transmitted by the wood tick, *Dermacentor andersoni;* and in Texas and Louisiana it is transmitted by the Lone Star tick, *Amblyomma americanum.* These ticks serve not only as vectors but also as the reservoir of infection. *R. rickettsii* is not pathogenic for its tick host and is passed to the tick offspring by transovarian passage. The rickettsias are widely distributed throughout the body of a tick, and transmission to humans or animals occurs via infected

saliva during biting, or by tick feces rubbed into the bite. Although the ticks constitute the primary reservoir of infection, there is also an animal reservoir of infection (wild rabbits, and dogs, sheep, and rodents) in which the disease is perpetuated by tick-borne transmission.

The incubation period for RMSF is usually one week, after which there is a sudden onset of symptoms: chills, high fever, severe frontal headache, and muscular pain. *R. rickettsii* multiplies preferentially within endothelial cells—the cells that form the walls of blood capillaries. The rickettsias damage the capillary walls, allowing fluid and even whole blood to leak out into the surrounding tissue. Leakage of whole blood (hemorrhaging) within the skin causes a rash that develops within 1 to 5 days after the patient is bitten by an infected tick [FIGURE 26.8]. The rash consists of numerous round, tiny, purplish-red spots, which appear first on the ankles and wrists and then the rest of the body. More serious than the rash is the damage that may occur to internal

FIGURE 26.6

[A] Method of culturing rickettsias in embryonated chicken eggs. [B] Photomicrograph of *Rickettsia rickettsii* (numerous tiny red rods) in a smear from the yolk sac membrane of an inoculated chicken egg. Gimenez stain.

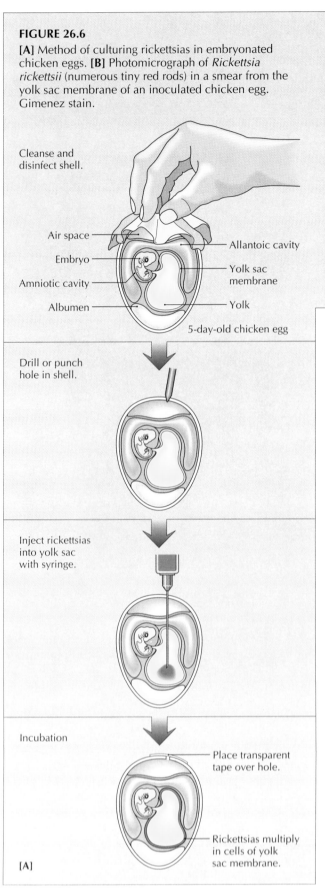

Cleanse and disinfect shell.

Air space
Embryo
Amniotic cavity
Albumen

Allantoic cavity
Yolk sac membrane
Yolk

5-day-old chicken egg

Drill or punch hole in shell.

Inject rickettsias into yolk sac with syringe.

Incubation

Place transparent tape over hole.

Rickettsias multiply in cells of yolk sac membrane.

[A]

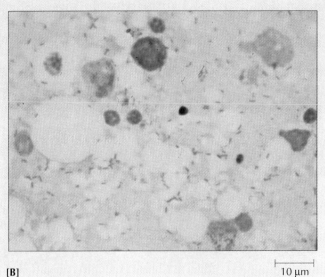

[B]   10 µm

FIGURE 26.7

Dermacentor variabilis, the American dog tick.

1 mm

organs such as the brain, kidneys, and heart; this damage is due to multiplication of the rickettsias in the blood capillaries of these organs.

Because of the skin rash, an initial diagnosis of measles, scarlet fever, or other diseases is sometimes made before RMSF is suspected. In untreated cases, the symptoms grow more severe and the patient may become drowsy and then go into a coma. Death usually results from shock and cardiorespiratory failure. When untreated, the mortality rate of RMSF is about 20 percent.

FIGURE 26.8
[A] Face of a female child with Rocky Mountain spotted fever, showing 9-day-old rash. [B] Wrist and hand of a child with Rocky Mountain spotted fever.

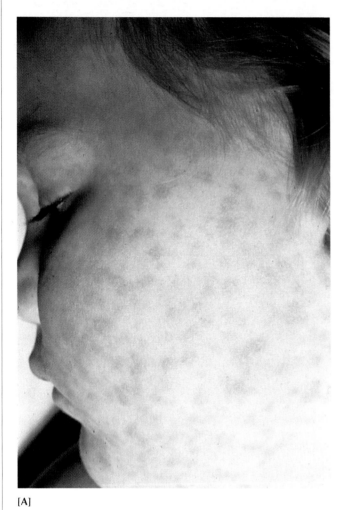

[A]

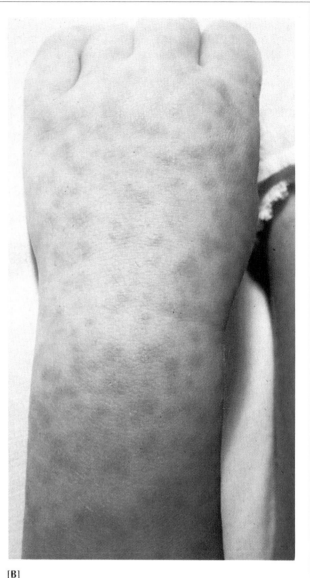

[B]

Laboratory Diagnosis, Treatment, and Prevention of RMSF. Although *R. rickettsii* can be isolated from blood specimens, this requires special laboratory facilities. For this reason, laboratory confirmation of RMSF is usually based either on fluorescent antibody identification of rickettsias in skin specimens or on demonstration of serum antibody production by the patient in response to the infection.

Prompt treatment with tetracycline in the early stages of RMSF is essential. Most fatalities occur because of delay in administering the proper antibiotic. Individuals who may be exposed to ticks should inspect themselves regularly for ticks or tick bites. If a tick has attached itself to the skin, it can be made to release itself by applying drops of gasoline, lighter fluid, or alcohol, or by bringing a heated object, such as the end of a heated

needle, close to (but not touching) the tick. The tick can then be removed by forceps or by fingers that have been protected with paper or cloth. Care should be taken never to crush the tick. There is at present no commercially available vaccine against RMSF.

Lyme Disease

Lyme disease was first discovered during an investigation of several hundred cases of a mysterious infection in the village of Old Lyme, Connecticut, in 1975. About 4 percent of the population contracted the infection. Although the disease was initially thought to be a form of rheumatoid arthritis, it is now known to be caused by a tick-borne spirochete. Since 1982—the year the United States began collecting statistics on Lyme disease—

more than 14,000 cases of Lyme disease have been reported in the United States. The number of reported cases increased nearly fivefold from 1982 to 1987, but this was likely due to an improved awareness and recognition of the disease, rather than to an increased incidence.

In the United States, Lyme disease occurs mainly in the northeastern states from Massachusetts to North Carolina, but it has also occurred in some midwestern and western states. Cases have also been reported in Germany, Switzerland, France, and Australia. The disease affects all age groups and both sexes. The incidence is highest in the summer months, because this is the period of greatest outdoor exposure to the tick vector.

The Biology of *Borrelia burgdorferi*. *Borrelia burgdorferi*, the causative agent of Lyme disease, is a microaerophilic spirochete that is 2 to 20 μm long but only 0.18 to 0.25 μm wide. The organisms are difficult to see with a light microscope because of their thinness; however, one good way to visualize them is by treating them with specific fluorescent antibodies, which bind to the spirochetes and cause them to glow when observed with a fluorescence microscope [FIGURE 26.9]. *B. burgdorferi* can be cultivated in the laboratory on complex culture media.

Transmission of *B. burgdorferi*. *B. burgdorferi* occurs mainly in wild white-footed mice, in deer, and in ticks of

FIGURE 26.9

Borrelia burgdorferi, the causative agent of Lyme disease. The spirochetes are stained with fluorescent antibody.

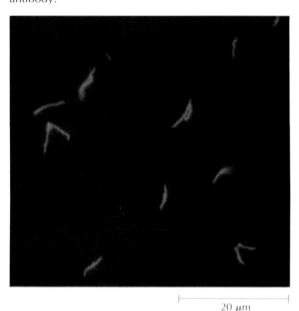

20 μm

FIGURE 26.10

The tick *Ixodes dammini*, a vector of Lyme disease, showing the larval (smallest), nymph (intermediate size), and adult (largest) stages.

1 mm

the genus *Ixodes*, such as *Ixodes dammini* [FIGURE 26.10]. The ticks transmit the spirochete to humans. The life cycle of *Ixodes dammini* covers a 2-year period [FIGURE 26.11]. In the spring of the first year, the tick eggs develop into immature forms called *larvae*. The larvae feed only once during a 2-day period and ingest the blood of various mammals, especially white-footed mice. In the fall the larvae enter a resting stage which lasts until the following spring. Then they develop into a second and only slightly larger immature form called *nymphs*. The nymphs feed only once during a 3- to 4-day period, again preferably upon white-footed mice. As fall approaches, the nymphs develop into the *adult stage*, and the adults feed upon large mammals, especially white-tailed deer. While attached to these deer, the adult ticks mate and the female later produces eggs, thus completing the cycle.

Humans can be bitten by the ticks at any stage of the life cycle; however, they are most likely to be bitten by the larval and nymph forms. These forms are so small as to be practically invisible to the naked eye. *Borrelia burgdorferi* is injected into the skin of a human victim

FIGURE 26.11

The 2-year life cycle of *Ixodes dammini*. Each year is represented with a different color. Humans are bitten most often by the larvae and nymphs.

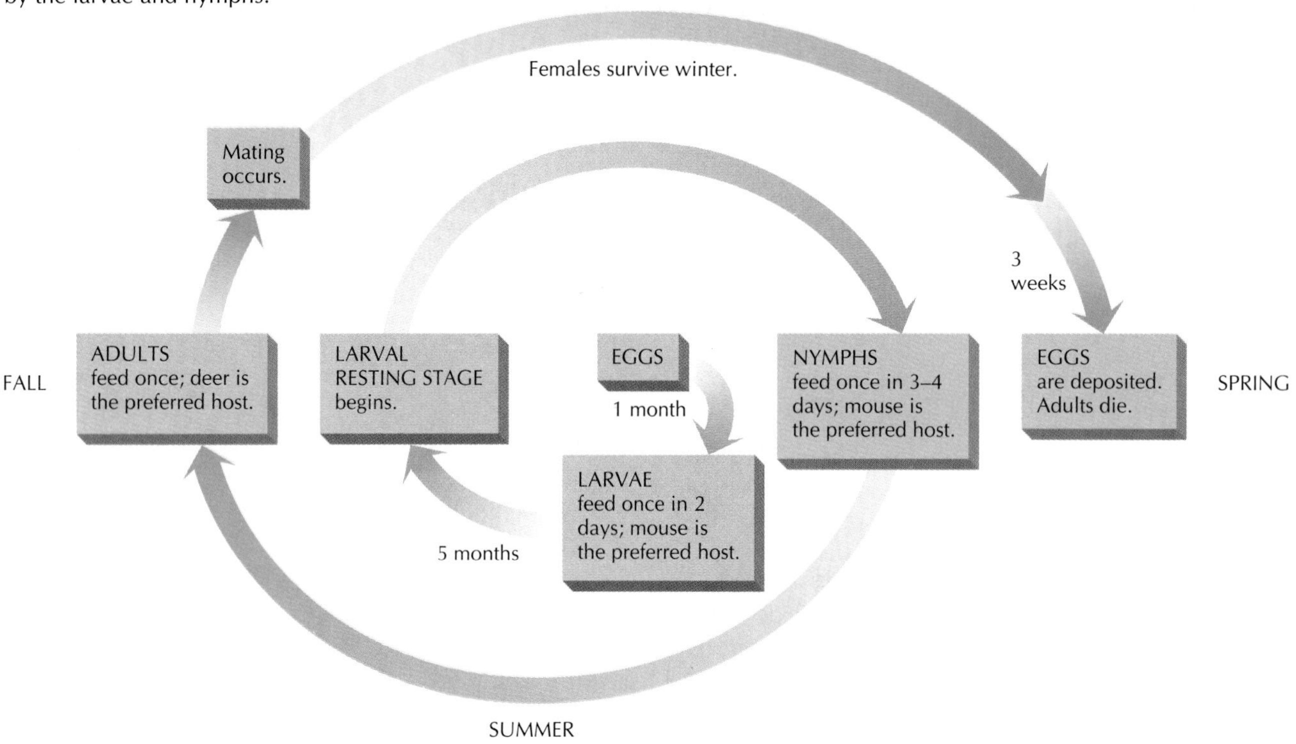

WINTER

Females survive winter.

Mating occurs.

3 weeks

FALL

ADULTS feed once; deer is the preferred host.

LARVAL RESTING STAGE begins.

EGGS

1 month

NYMPHS feed once in 3–4 days; mouse is the preferred host.

EGGS are deposited. Adults die.

SPRING

LARVAE feed once in 2 days; mouse is the preferred host.

5 months

SUMMER

either by infective tick saliva during biting, or by infective tick fecal material that is deposited on the skin and rubbed into the bite. Domestic animals such as dogs, cats, horses, and cattle can also get Lyme disease. Moreover, these animals can increase the risk of infection to pet owners, farmers, or ranchers by carrying infected *Ixodes* ticks [DISCOVER 26.2].

Some microbiologists have wondered whether Lyme disease is really a "new" disease or merely an old disease that has been newly recognized. Researchers discovered some interesting clues in 1990 when they examined 97 alcohol-preserved specimens of *Ixodes dammini* ticks that had been collected from 1945 through 1951. By using the PCR technique (described in Chapter 13), the researchers were able to detect *B. burgdorferi* DNA in 13 ticks collected from eastern Long Island, New York. In other words, these ticks carried the spirochete 25 to 35 years before Lyme disease was first recognized as a distinct disease in 1975. This suggests that Lyme disease in humans occurred in the United States much earlier than previously thought.

Pathogenicity of *B. burgdorferi*. After *B. burgdorferi* gains access to the tissues of a human victim, there is an incubation period of 3 to 32 days before symptoms of Lyme disease appear. The illness usually begins with the

FIGURE 26.12

An example of the characteristic red-ringed skin lesion called *erythema chronicum migrans*, which occurs in persons with Lyme disease.

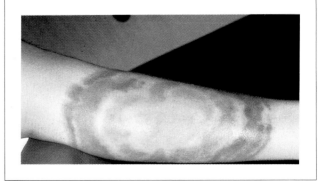

development of a red papule at the site of the tick bite. This lesion expands to form a characteristic red-ringed skin rash called ***erythema chronicum migrans (ECM)*** [FIGURE 26.12] In approximately half of the patients, several concentric red rings may develop within the outer ring, giving a "bull's-eye" appearance. Other ECM lesions may develop in addition to the primary one. The ECM lesions usually last for several weeks.

26.2 LYME DISEASE IN MONMOUTH COUNTY, NEW JERSEY

Although Lyme disease was first recognized in Old Lyme, Connecticut, other areas have since been reported to have unusually high infection rates. One of these areas was Monmouth County, New Jersey. Of 117 cases of Lyme disease in New Jersey from 1978 to 1982, 57 occurred within Monmouth County in an area whose total population was only 1.1 percent of the population of the entire state. Thirty of the cases occurred in persons working or living at a military facility. A comparison of patients from the military facility who had worked indoors (in an office, with outdoor movement confined to paved or lawn areas) with those who had worked outdoors (in woods, brush, and tall grass away from the lawns and paved areas) showed that the incidence of Lyme disease was significantly higher for those who had worked outdoors.

Some factors that might have contributed to the high incidence of Lyme disease at the military facility are: (1) the location of the facility in a wooded area; (2) a relatively high mammal population, especially deer, inside the fenced facility; and (3) an unusually high density of the *Ixodes dammini* tick vector, with more than 70 percent of the ticks infected with *Borrelia burgdorferi*. A high tick density and tick infection rate might also have contributed to the high incidence of Lyme disease in other areas of the county.

Adapted from *Am. J. Epidemiol. 120*: 387–394, 1984.

ECM is often accompanied by other symptoms that may develop to various degrees and in various combinations. The most common symptoms include fatigue, fever, chills, headache and backache, stiff neck, and muscle and joint pain.

The spirochetes eventually reach the brain, and within several weeks or months about 15 percent of patients develop meningitis, which may be accompanied by excruciating headache and neck pain. There may be abnormalities of the nervous system that last for years, ranging from a mild tingling sensation in the limbs to encephalomyelitis (inflammation of the central nervous system), partial paralysis, or mental deterioration. Within several weeks after the beginning of the disease, about 8 percent of patients show cardiac involvement indicated by heartbeat irregularity, dizziness, or shortness of breath; this may last from 3 days to 6 weeks. Within 2 weeks to 2 years after the beginning of the disease, about 80 percent of patients develop arthritis, and eventually the knees or other large joints may become swollen and painful. The arthritis may last for weeks or months and disappear, then reappear.

Much of the damage to the body caused by *B. burgdorferi* has been attributed to the endotoxin in the outer membrane of the spirochete. The endotoxin is believed to stimulate macrophages to produce interleukin-1, a regulator of the body's immune response (see Chapter 13). Overproduction of this regulator could account for the fever, skin rash, and arthritis that are characteristic of Lyme disease.

Laboratory Diagnosis, Treatment, and Prevention of Lyme Disease. Although *B. burgdorferi* can be cultured occasionally from patients, diagnosis of Lyme disease in the laboratory is usually based on the antibody response of the patient to the infection (that is, demonstration that the patient is producing an increasing level of serum antibodies against *B. burgdorferi* over a period of days or weeks).

Tetracycline is the antibiotic of choice for treating patients in the early stages of Lyme disease. For patients having neurological involvement or arthritis, administration of high doses of penicillin is usually effective.

No commercial vaccine is available for prevention of Lyme disease. However, in 1990 an experimental vaccine was developed that protected laboratory mice against *B. burgdorferi* infection. Nonimmunized laboratory mice, when inoculated with *B. burgdorferi*, develop a disease in 1 or 2 weeks that resembles Lyme disease in humans. The vaccine used to immunize mice consisted of a protein found in the outer membrane of *B. burgdorferi*. The gene for the spirochetal protein was cloned in *Escherichia coli*, which made it possible to produce larger quantities of the vaccine. Whether the vaccine can be used to protect humans remains to be seen. At present, the best prevention is to wear protective clothing when hiking or playing in wooded areas known to be tick-infested. Tick repellents used on clothing may also be helpful. People should also be aware of the typical early symptoms of infection, such as the characteristic skin rash.

Other Arthropod-Borne Infections Caused by Bacteria

TABLE 26.1 lists some other arthropod-borne infections caused by bacteria. Note that these infections are caused mainly by rickettsias and borrelias.

Of the diseases listed in TABLE 26.1, epidemic typhus stands out as one of the greatest disease scourges of the human race. Typhus has often accompanied natural disasters, war, and famine. As related by microbiologist Hans Zinsser in his book *Rats, Lice and History* (New

TABLE 26.1

Representative Bacterial Diseases of Humans Transmitted by Arthropods as Biological Vectors

Disease	Causative agent (geographic distribution)	Biological vector and animal reservoir	Arthropod-pathogen-human interrelationship
Epidemic relapsing fever	*Borrelia recurrentis,* a spirochete (Asia, Africa, Latin America)	Human body louse (*Pediculus humanus*) Reservoir: none.	Pathogen multiplies in tissues of louse; humans inoculated by crushing louse on skin.
Endemic relapsing fever	*Borrelia hermsii* and other *Borrelia* spirochetes (worldwide)	Ticks (*Ornithodoros* spp.) Reservoir: the ticks themselves and also wild rodents and other small animals.	Pathogen multiplies throughout body of tick; transovarian passage occurs; humans are inoculated by tick saliva or tick feces.
Epidemic typhus	*Rickettsia prowazekii,* a rickettsia (Africa, Central and South America, southeastern United States)	Human body louse (*Pediculus humanus*) Reservoir: usually none; however, *R. prowazekii* has been found recently in flying squirrels in the southeastern United States.	Pathogen multiplies in tissues of louse; the louse excretes the rickettsias in its feces; humans are inoculated by rubbing the louse feces into bite.
Scrub typhus	*Rickettsia tsutsugamushi,* a rickettsia (Asia, Australia, Pacific islands)	Red mites (*Trombicula* spp.) Reservoir: wild rodents.	Pathogen multiplies in gut of mite; transovarian passage occurs; humans infected through bite of larval mite.
Murine typhus	*Rickettsia typhi,* a rickettsia (worldwide)	Rat flea (*Xenopsylla cheopis*) Reservoir: rats and mice.	Pathogen multiplies in lining of the flea's midgut; humans infected through bite.
Rickettsialpox	*Rickettsia akari,* a rickettsia (United States, Russia, Korea, Africa)	Mouse mite (*Allodermanyssus sanguineus*) Reservoir: house mice.	Pathogen multiplies in gut of mite; humans infected through bite.
Trench fever	*Rochalimaea quintana,* a rickettsialike bacterium that can be grown on a blood-agar medium (Europe, Africa, North America)	Human body louse (*Pediculus humanus*) Reservoir: none.	Pathogen multiplies in midgut of louse; humans inoculated by louse feces or by crushing louse on skin.

York: Atlantic Monthly Press, 1935), typhus affected the course of western civilization on several occasions. In 1489–1490, when the forces of King Ferdinand and Queen Isabella of Spain were fighting with the Moors for possession of Granada, typhus caused the death of 17,000 Spanish soldiers, compared with only 3,000 soldiers killed in combat. Typhus also achieved prominence in northern Italy during the early part of the sixteenth century, when Charles V of Spain and Francis I of France were disputing the leadership of Europe. Suc-

cess in this dispute depended on controlling the immense influence of the Pope in Rome. By 1527, Spain had conquered many Italian cities, sacked Rome, and made the Pope a prisoner. However, the French army then began to recoup its losses by reconquering many cities from Spain. This alarmed the Spanish army, which hurried to fortify the next French target—the city of Naples. However, bubonic plague had reduced the Spanish army by this time to fewer than 11,000 men. These soldiers soon found themselves besieged by

28,000 French troops. After more than a month of siege, the Spanish army was very close to surrendering, which would have greatly affected the subsequent history of Europe. But then epidemic typhus struck suddenly, killing more than half the French army and its commanding general. Most of the remaining French were destroyed by Spanish troops. This gave Spain control over Italy and the Pope, and, as stated by Hans Zinsser in *Rats, Lice and History,* "In 1530 Charles V was crowned ruler of the Roman Empire at Bologna by the power of typhus fever."

Typhus epidemics also had decisive effects on the war in the Balkans in the sixteenth century, on the Thirty Years' War, and on the Napoleonic campaigns. Typhus was also the major cause of death during the Irish famine of 1845–1850 and the cause of many deaths in both World War I and World War II. In Japan and Korea, 30,000 cases were reported in 1946 and 1947. At present, the disease is confined mainly to a few areas in Africa, Central America, and South America. Although it is practically nonexistent in the United States, flying squirrels in the southeastern United States can harbor typhus rickettsia, and a few rare cases of human typhus in this region might be attributable to these squirrels and their arthropod parasites.

ASK YOURSELF

1 What is the reservoir of infection for *Yersinia pestis?* For *Rickettsia rickettsii?* For *Borrelia burgdorferi?*

2 What sequence of events precedes an epidemic of bubonic plague? How does an epidemic of pneumonic plague occur?

3 What differences are there in the biological properties of the causative agents of plague, Rocky Mountain spotted fever, and Lyme disease? What are the biological vectors of these bacteria?

4 What accounts for the seasonal incidence of Rocky Mountain spotted fever and Lyme disease?

5 What is the life cycle of *Ixodes dammini,* and how is it related to Lyme disease?

6 How are plague, Rocky Mountain spotted fever, and Lyme disease diagnosed in the laboratory? What treatments are available for these diseases?

7 What are the causative agents of epidemic relapsing fever, endemic relapsing fever, epidemic typhus, scrub typhus, murine typhus, rickettsialpox, and trench fever?

ARTHROPOD-BORNE INFECTIONS CAUSED BY VIRUSES

A number of important arthropod-borne infections are caused by viruses. Of these, yellow fever has the greatest global importance and has received the most attention. At the beginning of the twentieth century, nothing was known about the causative agent of this deadly disease, making prevention difficult. As described in the following paragraphs, careful scientific study and heroic volunteers finally made it possible to curb this viral disease.

Yellow Fever

For more than 200 years after the first known outbreak in the Yucatán Peninsula in 1648, yellow fever was one of the great disease scourges of the world. It was especially prevalent in Central and South America. During the nineteenth century, at least half a million cases occurred in the eastern United States. As late as 1905, New Orleans and other southern American ports had an epidemic of at least 5000 cases and many deaths. The last indigenous case in the United States occurred in 1911; the last imported case occurred in 1923. The disease is still widespread in the tropical regions of South America and Africa.

Before scientists understood how yellow fever was transmitted, most people thought that contact with the clothing, bedding, and possessions of yellow fever victims was responsible for transmitting the disease. In 1900, Walter Reed, a United States Army surgeon, took charge of a commission to investigate the cause of yellow fever. Working in Cuba, Reed and his staff used volunteers and carefully controlled experiments to show unequivocally that exposure to objects in contact with patients did not cause disease in healthy volunteers. Even volunteers who slept in bedclothes and pajamas soiled with the blood and black vomit of yellow fever victims failed to develop yellow fever.

The scientists found instead that yellow fever developed only in persons bitten by mosquitoes that had previously fed upon yellow fever patients. Several of the volunteers in this part of the experiment died. The commission also showed that infected blood from a patient could transmit the causative agent when injected into volunteers, even when the blood was first passed through a filter that retained bacteria. Thus the unknown agent was not a bacterium, but a virus. Subsequent mosquito-control programs virtually eliminated epidemic yellow fever from Cuba and areas of Central and South America—and made it possible to complete the Panama Canal.

The Causative Agent of Yellow Fever. The yellow fever virus [FIGURE 26.13] belongs to the flavivirus group. It is 38 nm in diameter, and it has an icosahedral capsid 25 to 30 nm in diameter that encloses single-stranded RNA and is surrounded by a tight-fitting lipid envelope. The virus has the ability to multiply within the tissues of various mosquitoes as well as in tissues of humans and monkeys.

Transmission of Yellow Fever Virus. Yellow fever results from two basically different cycles of virus transmission, the *urban* (epidemic) *cycle* and the *sylvatic* (jungle) *cycle*, as shown in FIGURE 26.14A. In the urban cycle, the virus is transmitted from person to person by bites of the *A. aegypti* mosquito [FIGURE 26.14B]. The blood meal taken from a yellow fever patient contains the virus, which multiplies for 10 to 15 days in the mosqui-

to's intestinal tissue. Then the virus appears in the salivary glands, and the mosquito can transmit it to a healthy individual. Once infected, the mosquito is able to transmit the virus for the rest of its life.

Sylvatic yellow fever is caused by the same virus but occurs in wild animals, mainly monkeys. The virus is transmitted among them, and sometimes to humans, by mosquitoes other than *A. aegypti*. In the rain forests of South and Central America, treetop mosquitoes belonging to the genera *Haemagogus* and *Sabethes* carry out transmission in the wild animal reservoir. When humans enter the jungle, sporadic cases or local outbreaks of yellow fever may occur because of mosquito bites. In Africa, the mosquito-monkey cycle is maintained by *Aedes africanus*, a species that seldom feeds on humans. However, another species, *Aedes simpsoni*, feeds upon monkeys that invade village gardens, and it can transmit the virus to humans. The threat of yellow fever always exists in urban areas of the tropical and semitropical regions because of the existence of the sylvatic cycle. Once yellow fever is introduced into an urban area, the urban human-mosquito-human cycle can be reinitiated and can lead to an epidemic. Although yellow fever is widespread in South America and Africa, it has never invaded Asia, despite the widespread occurrence of human-biting *A. aegypti* mosquitoes. The reason is unknown.

Pathogenicity of the Yellow Fever Virus. The yellow fever virus causes a disease that affects the liver, the kidney, and other internal organs. The incubation period of yellow fever is usually 3 to 6 days. The fully developed disease consists of three clinical periods: (1) *infection*, which is coincident with the presence of the virus in the blood and is marked by headache, backache, muscular pains, fever, nausea, and vomiting; (2) *remission*, during which the symptoms subside; and (3) *intoxication*, in which the temperature again rises, stomach bleeding occurs (as indicated by black vomit), albumin appears in the urine (evidence of kidney damage), and jaundice occurs (evidence of liver damage). The fatality rate for yellow fever is 25 to 50 percent.

Laboratory Diagnosis of Yellow Fever. Laboratory diagnosis is done either by detecting an increase of specific antibodies in the patient's blood serum or by isolating the virus. The virus can be isolated by inoculating the patient's blood serum into the brains of infant mice.

Treatment and Prevention of Yellow Fever. There is no specific antiviral therapy for yellow fever, and treatment involves minimizing damage to the body, as, for example, by kidney dialysis, blood replacement, and administration of oxygen. Urban yellow fever can be prevented by eradicating *A. aegypti* mosquitoes or by suppressing their numbers to the extent that they no longer perpetu-

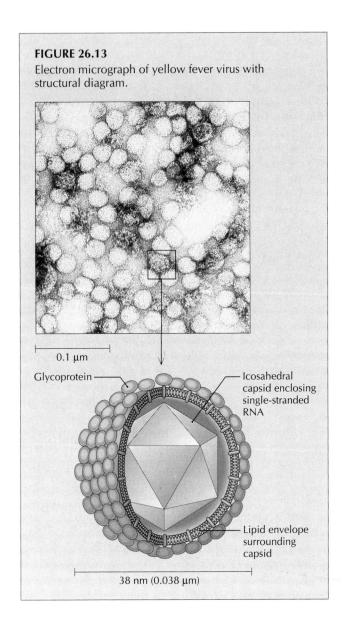

FIGURE 26.13

Electron micrograph of yellow fever virus with structural diagram.

0.1 μm

Glycoprotein

Icosahedral capsid enclosing single-stranded RNA

Lipid envelope surrounding capsid

38 nm (0.038 μm)

FIGURE 26.14
[A] Relationship between the sylvatic and urban transmission cycles of yellow fever.
[B] The mosquito *Aedes aegypti*, which transmits the yellow fever virus from human to human. Length, 3 to 6 mm.

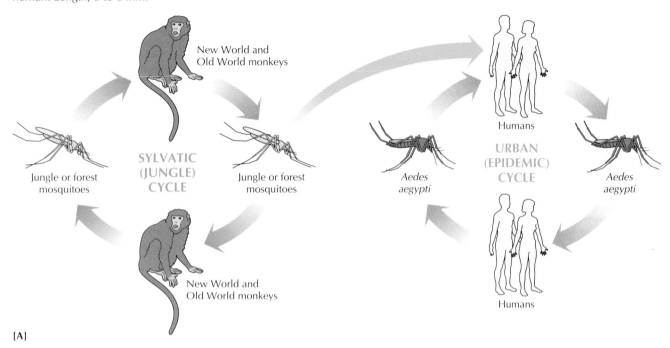

New World and Old World monkeys

SYLVATIC (JUNGLE) CYCLE

Jungle or forest mosquitoes

Jungle or forest mosquitoes

New World and Old World monkeys

Humans

URBAN (EPIDEMIC) CYCLE

Aedes aegypti

Aedes aegypti

Humans

[A]

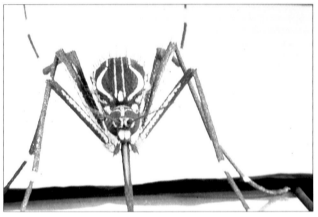

[B]

ate infection. Control of sylvatic yellow fever is impractical because the jungle cycles maintain a reservoir of virus. However, humans can be immunized against the disease. The vaccine consists of an attenuated strain of the virus. Vaccination is recommended for persons aged 6 months or older who are traveling or living in areas where yellow fever infections still occur.

Other Arthropod-Borne Infections Caused by Viruses

Other examples of viral diseases of humans that are transmitted by arthropods are listed in TABLE 26.2. Note that many of these diseases are types of encephalitis, diseases characterized by inflammation of the brain. Viral encephalitis often begins with a headache, fever, and weakness; later developments include mental confusion, paralysis of one side of the body, deterioration of speech and memory, and coma. The various types of viral encephalitis are caused by different viruses and have different geographic distributions. Also notice from TABLE 26.2 that mosquitoes and ticks are the main vectors involved in the transmission of arthropod-borne viruses.

ASK YOURSELF

1 What were Walter Reed's contributions to our understanding of yellow fever?

2 What differences are there between the urban and sylvatic cycles of yellow fever? What mosquito species are involved in each cycle?

3 How can yellow fever be prevented? What type of vaccine is available?

4 What other human diseases are caused by arthropod-borne viruses? What types of arthropods transmit these viruses?

TABLE 26.2
Representative Viral Diseases of Humans Transmitted by Arthropods as Biological Vectors

Disease	Causative agent (geographic distribution)	Principal vectors and animal reservoir
Dengue fever	A flavivirus (tropical and subtropical regions of the world)	Mosquitoes (*Aedes aegypti, A. albopictus*) Reservoir: other *Aedes* species maintain a sylvatic cycle in monkeys, similar to that of yellow fever.
Eastern equine encephalitis	An alphavirus (eastern North America)	Mosquitoes (*Culex melanura* and *Aedes* spp.) Reservoir: wild birds.
Western equine encephalitis	An alphavirus (western North America)	Mosquitoes (*Culex tarsalis*) Reservoir: wild birds.
St. Louis encephalitis	A flavivirus (United States)	Mosquitoes (*Culex pipiens* and other *Culex* spp.) Reservoir: wild birds.
Venezuelan equine encephalitis	An alphavirus (Central and South America and southern United States)	Several kinds of mosquitoes Reservoir: horses, rodents.
Colorado tick fever	An orbivirus (western United States)	Ticks (*Dermacentor andersoni*) Reservoir: small mammals.
Tick-borne encephalitis	A flavivirus (Russia and northern Europe)	Ticks (*Ixodes ricinus* and others) Reservoir: small wild mammals and birds.
Crimean-Congo hemorrhagic fever	A bunyavirus (central Asia)	Ticks (*Hyalomma marginatum* and others) Reservoir: many mammals.
Murray Valley encephalitis	An alphavirus (Australia)	Mosquitoes (*Culex annulirostris* and others) Reservoir: birds.
West Nile fever	A flavivirus (Africa, Europe, Middle East)	Mosquitoes (probably *Culex* spp.) Reservoir: birds.

ARTHROPOD-BORNE INFECTIONS CAUSED BY PROTOZOA

Of the various arthropod-borne infections caused by protozoa, malaria has been known from antiquity and has probably been the single greatest disease scourge of the human race. Malaria exemplifies the fact that you must know the life cycle of a pathogenic protozoan in order to understand how the parasite causes disease. Knowing the life cycle may also help you find potential ways to prevent the disease.

Malaria

On a global scale, malaria is one of the most common infectious diseases of humans. Each year more than 150 million people become ill with malaria and 3 million die. At present the disease is widely distributed in Africa, Asia, and Latin America.

In the United States, malaria has been associated mainly with the return of military personnel from areas where the disease is prevalent. For instance, in 1966–1972, a high incidence of malaria occurred in veterans returning from Vietnam [FIGURE 26.15]. Although the

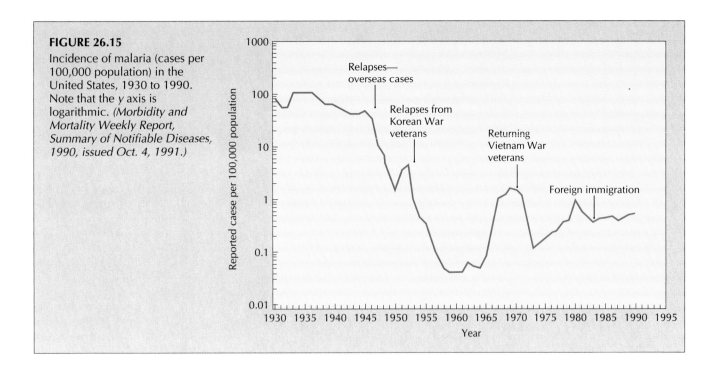

FIGURE 26.15

Incidence of malaria (cases per 100,000 population) in the United States, 1930 to 1990. Note that the y axis is logarithmic. *(Morbidity and Mortality Weekly Report, Summary of Notifiable Diseases, 1990, issued Oct. 4, 1991.)*

case rate subsequently declined, it rose again after 1974. This increase has been associated mainly with travelers to, or immigrants from, areas of the world where malaria is prevalent, particularly Nigeria, Mexico and other countries of Central America, and New Guinea. Malaria is rarely contracted within the United States itself.

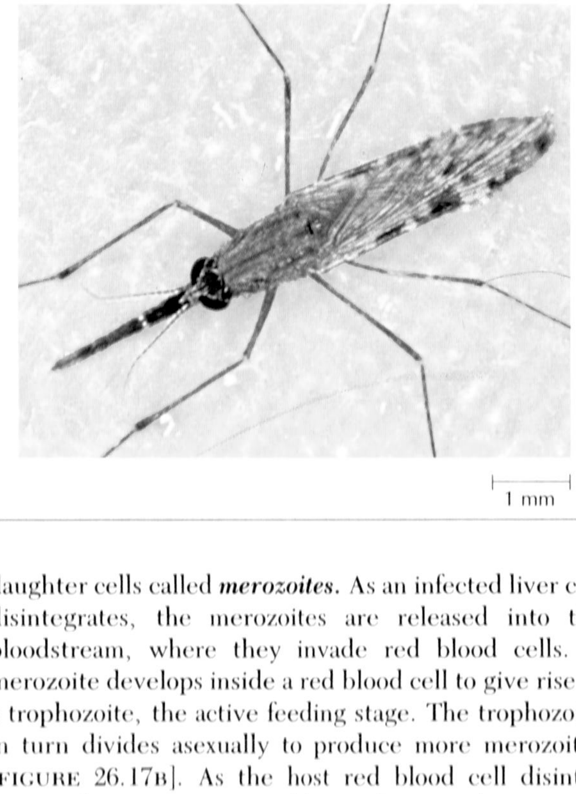

The Causative Agents of Malaria. The protozoa that cause malaria are sporozoans belonging to the genus *Plasmodium*. Malaria is caused by more than 50 species of *Plasmodium*, but only four species cause malaria in humans; the rest attack several hundred other animal hosts. The four species that cause human malaria are *P. falciparum, P. vivax, P. malariae,* and *P. ovale. P. falciparum* causes the most serious form of the disease.

Human malaria protozoa can be grown in the laboratory in a thin layer of human red blood cells over which a complex serum-containing medium is slowly flowing. The protozoa are microaerophilic and grow best under an atmosphere containing 3 percent oxygen and 1 percent carbon dioxide. Oxygen levels of 17 to 21 percent inhibit growth.

Transmission and Life Cycle of Malaria Protozoa. *Plasmodium* protozoa are transmitted to humans by mosquitoes of the genus *Anopheles* [FIGURE 26.16]. The saliva of an infected *Anopheles* mosquito contains *sporozoites*, sickle-shaped infective forms of the protozoa. When the mosquito bites a human, the sporozoites are injected into the bloodstream of the victim and quickly reach the liver [FIGURE 26.17A]. There they divide asexually inside the liver cells and give rise to numerous round

FIGURE 26.16

The mosquito *Anopheles gambiae*, a vector of malaria.

1 mm

daughter cells called **merozoites.** As an infected liver cell disintegrates, the merozoites are released into the bloodstream, where they invade red blood cells. A merozoite develops inside a red blood cell to give rise to a trophozoite, the active feeding stage. The trophozoite in turn divides asexually to produce more merozoites [FIGURE 26.17B]. As the host red blood cell disintegrates, the merozoites are liberated to attack more red blood cells, producing more merozoites that attack more red blood cells, and so on (the **erythrocytic cycle;** FIGURE 26.17A.)

FIGURE 26.17
[A] The life cycle of malaria protozoa. [B] Wright's stain of a blood smear showing a red blood cell filled with merozoites of *Plasmodium vivax* just prior to disruption of the cell.

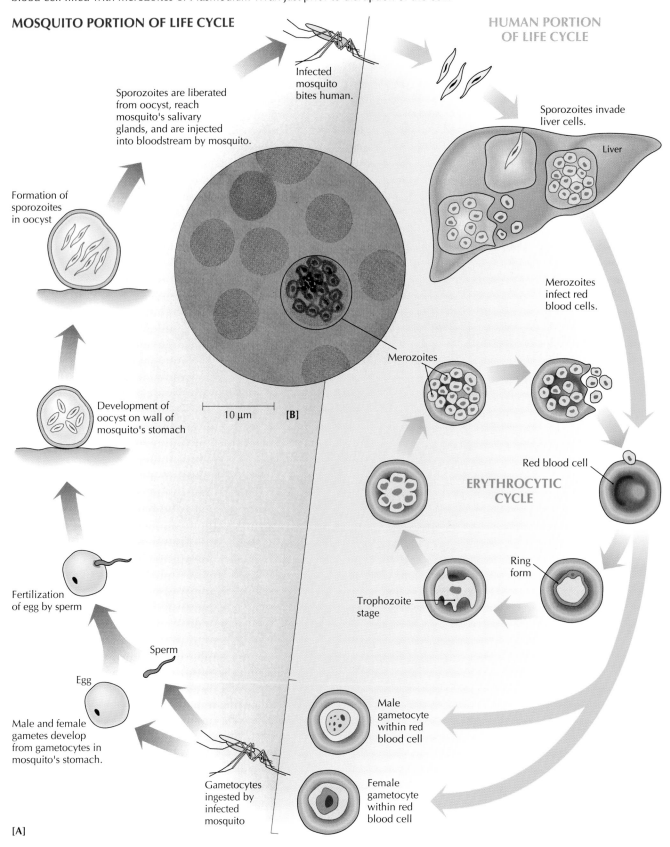

MOSQUITO PORTION OF LIFE CYCLE

HUMAN PORTION OF LIFE CYCLE

Infected mosquito bites human.

Sporozoites are liberated from oocyst, reach mosquito's salivary glands, and are injected into bloodstream by mosquito.

Sporozoites invade liver cells.

Liver

Formation of sporozoites in oocyst

Merozoites infect red blood cells.

10 μm   [B]

Merozoites

Development of oocyst on wall of mosquito's stomach

Red blood cell

ERYTHROCYTIC CYCLE

Ring form

Fertilization of egg by sperm

Trophozoite stage

Sperm

Egg

Male gametocyte within red blood cell

Male and female gametes develop from gametocytes in mosquito's stomach.

Gametocytes ingested by infected mosquito

Female gametocyte within red blood cell

[A]

Some of the merozoites that infect red blood cells develop into male and female sexual cells called *gametocytes.* When an uninfected *Anopheles* mosquito bites a person with malaria, it ingests blood containing the gametocytes. In the stomach of the mosquito, the gametocytes develop into free male and female gametes—*egg* cells and whiplike *sperm* cells. After the sperm cell fertilizes an egg, the zygote passes to the outside of the mosquito's stomach lining, where it develops into an encysted form called an *oocyst* [see FIGURE 10.31]. Sporozoites develop within the oocyst and, when mature, migrate to the mosquito's salivary glands, from which they can be injected by a mosquito bite into the bloodstream of a new victim to begin the cycle all over again.

Pathogenicity of Malaria Protozoa. The symptoms of malaria occur during the asexual erythrocytic cycle and may be caused by release of a *pyrogen,* a fever-inducing substance, from the injured cells. The symptoms usually begin 10 to 16 days after infection by mosquitoes. The patient experiences bed-shaking chills followed by recurrent fevers, sweating, headache, and muscular pain. The cycles of fever vary according to the *Plasmodium* species causing the infection. The symptomatic periods usually last fewer than 6 hours. The spleen becomes enlarged and tender [FIGURE 26.18]. Eventually the patient becomes weak and exhausted, and an anemia develops due to destruction of the red blood cells by the *Plasmodium* merozoites. The pattern of periodic illness interspersed with periods of well-being is characteristic of benign malaria, caused by *P. vivax, P. ovale,* and *P. malariae.* If not treated, benign malaria usually subsides spontaneously and recurs at a later date.

In patients with malignant falciparum malaria (caused by *P. falciparum*), the fever and symptoms are usually more persistent and also include tissue swelling in the brain and lungs and blockage of kidney activity. Malignant malaria has a high fatality rate if not treated promptly. This is due in part to the high rate of reproduction of the asexual form of the protozoan within red blood cells. The small veins and capillaries of the heart become clogged with parasitized red blood cells, and effective coronary blood flow and cardiac function are diminished.

Laboratory Diagnosis of Malaria. The typical symptoms of malaria mimic a variety of other human infections, and a definitive diagnosis depends upon demonstration that the parasite is present in blood smears from patients [FIGURE 26.19]. Detection of specific antibodies in a patient's blood serum can also be done using serological tests; however, antibodies are usually not detectable until after the second week of infection.

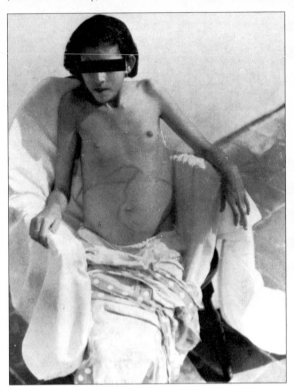

FIGURE 26.18
Malaria-infected youngster with enlarged spleen (outlined on belly).

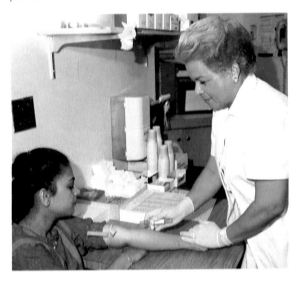

FIGURE 26.19
Malaria worker about to draw a blood sample from a woman in Bombay, India. The blood sample will be examined microscopically for the presence of malaria protozoa.

TABLE 26.3

Representative Protozoan Diseases of Humans Transmitted by Arthropods as Biological Vectors

Disease	Causative agent (geographic distribution)	Biological vector and animal reservoir	Arthropod-pathogen-human interrelationship
Chagas' disease	*Trypanosoma cruzi* (continental Latin America)	Reduviid bugs (*Triatoma* spp., *Panstrongylus* spp.) Reservoir: armadillos, opossums, dogs, cats, and other animals	Pathogen multiplies in hindgut of bug; humans infected by rubbing bug's feces into the bite.
African trypanosomiasis (sleeping sickness)	*Trypanosoma brucei* subspecies *gambiense* (west and central Africa) *T. brucei* subspecies *rhodesiense* (east and central Africa)	Tsetse flies (*Glossina* spp.) Reservoir: antelopes and other wild game animals in Africa	Pathogen multiplies in midgut and passes to salivary glands; humans are infected by bite.
Kala-azar	*Leishmania donovani* (China, India, Africa, Mediterranean area, continental Latin America)	Sandflies (*Phlebotomus* spp.) Reservoir: wild rodents and other wild animals; dogs	Pathogen multiplies in midgut and reaches mouthparts of fly; humans infected through bite.
Oriental sore	*Leishmania tropica* and *L. major* (Mediterranean area to western India)	Same as above	Same as above
Espundia	*Leishmania brasiliensis* (Mexico to northern Argentina)	Same as above	Same as above

Treatment of Malaria. For over 100 years, quinine was the only drug available for treating malaria patients. In World War II it was replaced by quinacrine, which was later supplanted by chloroquine and primaquine, the current anti-*Plasmodium* agents of choice. Primaquine destroys the protozoa as they multiply in the liver, while chloroquine destroys merozoites in the blood. The combination of these two anti-*Plasmodium* agents is very effective against susceptible malaria protozoan strains found in Africa, India, and Central America. However, beginning in 1959, chloroquine-resistant strains of *P. falciparum* have appeared in many countries. The combination of quinine sulfate plus pyrimethamine is used to treat chloroquine-resistant falciparum malaria.

Prevention of Malaria. One approach to the control of malaria is based on elimination of the insect vector that transmits the protozoan. Eradication of the mosquito requires destruction of its breeding areas and killing of the larval stages and adults. These are not easy tasks, because some mosquitoes develop resistance to insecticides, the behavioral patterns of others prevent their contact with insecticides, and in certain areas it is impossible to eliminate the breeding of mosquitoes.

At the individual level of control, netting can be used around sleeping areas; houses can be screened; and mosquito boots, insecticides, and mosquito repellents can be used. This type of control, of course, can be used for the prevention of all arthropod-borne diseases. Malaria can also be prevented by the same drugs that are used for treatment of infected patients. For instance, travelers to areas where chloroquine-susceptible malaria is prevalent are advised to take chloroquine phosphate. A combination of sulfonamides and pyrimethamine can be used to prevent chloroquine-resistant falciparum malaria.

It is likely that only mass immunization programs will permit the ultimate eradication of malaria. Unfortunately, there is no commercial vaccine presently available against malaria, although some are under development. One of the difficulties is that the malaria protozoa usually are not free in the bloodstream; instead, *they live mainly inside liver cells or red blood cells where antibodies cannot reach them.* Nevertheless, several approaches to development of a malaria vaccine are presently under intense investigation [DISCOVER 26.3].

Other Arthropod-Borne Infections Caused by Protozoa

TABLE 26.3 lists several other protozoan diseases of humans transmitted by arthropods as biological vectors. FIGURE 26.20 shows organisms of one genus of these causative agents.

26.3 WORKING TOWARD A MALARIA VACCINE

It has been difficult to control malaria by mosquito eradication; moreover, some malaria protozoa have become resistant to the usual antimalarial chemotherapeutic agents. For these reasons, an effective vaccine is urgently needed to help stop the spread of malaria. Several ingenious approaches to developing a vaccine are now under investigation. The following approaches are based on a knowledge of the life cycle of malaria protozoa and on modern genetic engineering techniques.

(1) A sporozoite is covered by a thick coat consisting of a protein called the *CS protein*. Antibodies against CS protein are known to destroy the infectivity of sporozoites. After a mosquito injects malaria sporozoites into a human, the sporozoites are in the bloodstream for only a few minutes before disappearing into liver cells. It is during this brief period that the antibodies would attack the sporozoites. Through genetic engineering, it is now possible to obtain unlimited quantities of CS protein. The protein has been tested for its ability to induce immunity against malaria in people, but so far the results have been disappointing. Possible reasons are: (1) if even a single sporozoite escapes destruction, the infected person will still develop malaria, and (2) sporozoites have the ability to vary their type of CS protein, so that a vaccine composed of one type of CS protein will not protect against sporozoites that make a variant type.

(2) It may be possible to make a vaccine that can stimulate antibodies against the *merozoite* stage of the protozoan. These antibodies might be able to prevent the erythrocytic cycle from occurring in the patient, since merozoites liberated from one red blood cell are free in the blood for a few minutes before invading another red blood cell. However, it is difficult to determine which of the many antigens of a merozoite can stimulate production of antibodies that can effectively block merozoite invasion of red blood cells.

(3) Another approach directed against the erythrocytic cycle is based on the fact that, after a merozoite invades a red blood cell and begins to develop into its ring and trophozoite stages, some antigens of the growing protozoan *are inserted into the cytoplasmic membrane of the infected host cell*. If a vaccine could stimulate production of antibodies against these membrane antigens, the antibodies would destroy the entire infected red blood cell before the protozoan inside had a chance to mature.

(4) Still another approach is to develop a vaccine that can stimulate production of antibodies against the *gametes* of the protozoan. These antibodies would not directly protect people from getting malaria, because the gametes occur only in mosquitoes. However, *the antibodies would stop mosquitoes from transmitting the infection to healthy individuals*. If a mosquito ingests blood from a malaria patient who has been immunized to produce antibodies against the gametes, the antibodies that are taken in with the blood meal would destroy the gametes that subsequently develop in the mosquito's stomach. This would render the mosquito noninfective. Widespread immunization of a population against the protozoan gametes might be able to break the human-mosquito-human transmission cycle.

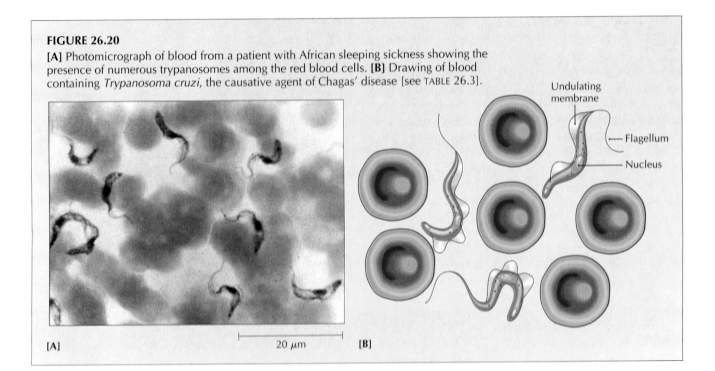

FIGURE 26.20

[A] Photomicrograph of blood from a patient with African sleeping sickness showing the presence of numerous trypanosomes among the red blood cells. **[B]** Drawing of blood containing *Trypanosoma cruzi*, the causative agent of Chagas' disease [see TABLE 26.3].

Undulating membrane

Flagellum

Nucleus

[A]   20 μm   [B]

ASK YOURSELF

1 Which genera and species of protozoa cause malaria?

2 Which part of the life cycle of malaria protozoa occurs in mosquitoes? Which part occurs in humans?

3 How can malaria be treated? How can it be prevented?

4 What problems are there in developing a vaccine against malaria?

5 What protozoan agents cause Chagas' disease, African sleeping sickness, kala-azar, oriental sore, and espundia? What types of arthropods transmit these agents?

ARTHROPOD-BORNE INFECTIONS CAUSED BY HELMINTHS

Filarias are pathogenic nematodes (helminths) that are transmitted to humans by the bites of arthropods. The general term *filariasis* is used to describe the various infections caused by filarias. Filariasis constitutes a major global health problem, with millions of people infected in the tropical and subtropical regions of the world.

Filariasis

TABLE 26.4 lists various specific diseases caused by filarias. Of these, Bancroft's filariasis, caused by *Wuchereria bancrofti*, is the most widespread, occurring in approximately 250 million people throughout the tropical and subtropical regions of the world.

Transmission and Life Cycle of *Wuchereria bancrofti*. Like many of the diseases mentioned earlier in this chapter, *W. bancrofti* is transmitted to humans by infected mosquitoes. The mosquito transmits the larval stage of the filaria when biting a human victim. After entering the tissues of the human, the sausage-shaped larvae invade the lymph nodes and mature into white, threadlike male and female adult worms. These may be as long as 40 mm (male worm) and 100 mm (female worm). The adult worms can live in the lymph nodes of the patient for years. After mating, the female produces *microfilarias*, small, threadlike forms about 0.25 mm long, which are discharged into the bloodstream in large

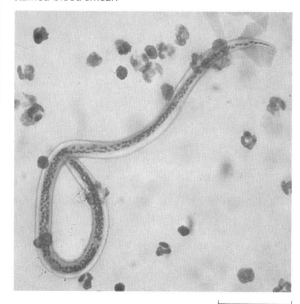

FIGURE 26.21
Microfilaria of *Wuchereria bancrofti* as seen in a stained blood smear.

50 μm

FIGURE 26.22
Elephantiasis in a patient with chronic bancroftian filariasis.

TABLE 26.4
Filariases

Disease	Filarial agent (geographic distribution)	Arthropod vector
Bancroft's filariasis	*Wuchereria bancrofti* (tropical and subtropical regions throughout world)	Mosquitoes (*Aedes* spp., *Culex* spp., *Anopheles* spp.)
Brugian filariasis	*Brugia malayi* (southeast Asia)	Mosquitoes (*Anopheles* spp., *Mansonia* spp.)
	B. timori (Indonesia)	*Anopheles barbirostris*
Loasis	*Loa loa* (Africa)	Horse- or deerflies (*Chrysops* spp.)
Onchocerciasis	*Onchocerca volvulus* (Africa, Central and South America)	Blackflies (*Simulium* spp.)
Tetrapetalonemiasis	*Tetrapetalonema perstans* (Africa, South America)	Midges (*Culicoides* spp.)
	T. streptocerca (Africa)	Midges (*Culicoides* spp.)
Ozzard's filariasis	*Mansonella ozzardi* (Central and South America)	Midges (*Culicoides* spp.)

numbers [FIGURE 26.21]. For unknown reasons, this usually occurs during the nighttime.

If an uninfected mosquito subsequently bites an infected human, it ingests microfilarias as it takes in the blood meal. The microfilarias then penetrate the muscle tissue of the arthropod and develop into larvae. The larvae eventually reach the mouthparts of the mosquito and can then be transmitted by the insect to another human.

Pathogenicity of *W. bancrofti*. Many patients with microfilarias in the bloodstream may show no symptoms of infection. When symptoms occur, they are due to damage to the lymphatic system of the patient. The lymphatic system can be described as follows. Body tissues are permeated by a network of blood capillaries which supply oxygen and nutrients to the tissue cells. Blood capillaries have very thin walls, and some of the fluid portion of the blood invariably leaks out into the tissues. Such fluid, called *lymph*, would cause the body tissues to become swollen with excess fluid. The lymphatic system is a system of thin-walled tubular vessels that collect the lymph and eventually return it to the blood circulatory system. In persons with filariasis, the microfilarias may cause obstruction of the lymphatic vessels. Some parts of the body become grossly swollen, particularly the genital organs and the legs—a condition called *elephantiasis* [FIGURE 26.22].

Laboratory Diagnosis, Treatment, and Prevention of Bancroft's Filariasis. Laboratory diagnosis depends on microscopic detection of microfilarias in nighttime blood specimens from the patient. Also, serological tests can detect antibodies that are formed in response to the infection.

Treatment involves oral administration of diethylcarbamazine. This chemical will decrease the numbers of microfilarias in the bloodstream of a patient. However, it does not kill the adult worms. Prevention is best achieved by the use of screens, nets, and insect repellents in areas where Bancroft's filariasis is prevalent.

ASK YOURSELF

1 What are filarias? What type of arthropod vectors can transmit them to humans?

2 What is the life cycle of *Wuchereria bancrofti*? What are microfilarias?

3 How can elephantiasis result from Bancroft's filariasis?

738

SUMMARY

1 Arthropods are invertebrate animals with jointed limbs and a segmented body that is generally covered with a chitinous shell. Some arthropods can serve as either mechanical vectors or biological vectors of disease. They may transmit pathogenic bacteria, viruses, protozoa, or nematodes (helminths).

2 Plague is caused by *Yersinia pestis,* a Gram-negative bacillus that exhibits bipolar staining. Plague is mainly a disease of wild rodents, and in the United States, it is widespread among wild rodents in the southwestern regions. Fleas can transmit plague bacilli from infected wild rodents to domestic rats, and from the domestic rats to humans. Human-to-human transmission can occur via body lice or human fleas, but if pneumonic plague occurs the plague bacilli can spread by airborne means.

3 Rocky Mountain spotted fever (RMSF) is caused by the bacterium *Rickettsia rickettsii,* which is transmitted to humans by dog ticks or wood ticks. The ticks serve not only as vectors but also as the main reservoir of infection. RMSF is characterized by a spreading skin rash that first begins on the ankles and wrists.

4 Lyme disease is caused by the spirochete *Borrelia burgdorferi,* which is transmitted by *Ixodes* ticks. The ticks have a 2-year life cycle involving larval, nymph, and adult stages. The preferred hosts of the ticks are white-footed mice and deer. A characteristic early symptom of Lyme disease is development of a skin rash called *erythema chronicum migrans.*

5 Other arthropod-borne diseases caused by bacteria include epidemic and endemic relapsing fever, epidemic typhus, scrub typhus, rickettsialpox, murine typhus, and trench fever.

6 Arthropod-borne infections caused by viruses include yellow fever, caused by a flavivirus transmitted to humans by the mosquito *Aedes aegypti.* Two basically different cycles of transmission occur, an urban cycle and a sylvatic cycle.

7 Other arthropod-borne diseases caused by viruses include dengue fever, Colorado tick fever, Crimean-Congo hemorrhagic fever, and West Nile fever, as well as various kinds of viral encephalitis such as eastern equine encephalitis and Venezuelan equine encephalitis.

8 Malaria is an arthropod-borne disease caused by four species of the protozoan genus *Plasmodium. P. falciparum* causes the most severe form of malaria. Malaria sporozoites are transmitted to humans by *Anopheles* mosquitoes. The sporozoites invade liver cells and develop into merozoites, which then enter an erythrocytic cycle. When the gametocytes of the protozoan are ingested by a mosquito, they develop into gametes in the mosquito's stomach. After a sperm fertilizes an egg, the egg develops into an oocyst, in which sporozoites develop. The mosquito can then transmit the sporozoites to another human victim. Efforts to control malaria by eliminating the mosquito vector have proved difficult, and a vaccine against malaria is urgently needed. Vaccine development is complicated by the fact that malaria protozoa live mainly inside body cells, where antibodies cannot get to them.

9 Other protozoan diseases that are transmitted by arthropods include Chagas' disease, African trypanosomiasis, kala-azar, oriental sore, and espundia.

10 Filarias are pathogenic nematodes that are transmitted by the bite of an arthropod. Bancroft's filariasis is caused by *Wuchereria bancrofti,* the larvae of which are transmitted to humans by mosquitoes. In the body the adult worms produce numerous microfilarias. When the microfilarias are ingested by a mosquito they develop into larvae and can be transmitted by the mosquito to other human victims. One of the symptoms of Bancroft's filariasis is elephantiasis, in which some parts of the body, particularly the genital organs and the legs, become greatly swollen because of a blockage of the patient's lymphatic system.

KEY TERMS

arthropods
biological vector
bipolar staining
bubo
elephantiasis
erythema chronicum migrans (ECM)
erythrocytic cycle of malaria
filarias
gametocytes
lymph
mechanical vectors
merozoites
microfilarias
murine toxin
oocyst
pyrogen
reservoir of infection
septicemia
sporozoites
sylvatic cycle of yellow fever
transovarian passage
urban cycle of yellow fever
V and W proteins

**ARTHROPODS AS
DISEASE VECTORS**

1 A vector which transmits a pathogen that adheres to its mouthparts or legs is a(n)

_____ vector, whereas a vector in which the pathogen un-

dergoes a period of growth or development is a(n) _____

vector.

2 Transovarian passage refers to the transmission of a pathogenic microorganism to subsequent generations of an arthropod by being incorporated into the

_____ produced by the female.

**ARTHROPOD-BORNE
INFECTIONS CAUSED
BY BACTERIA**

3 Match the item at the left with the most appropriate description at the right.

_____ the Black Death   **(a)** The reservoir of plague

_____ bipolar staining   **(b)** Complex that prevents phagocytosis

_____ V and W proteins   **(c)** Fourteenth century pandemic

_____ *Xenopsylla cheopis*   **(d)** Enlarged lymph gland

_____ bubo   **(e)** Rat flea

_____ wild rodents   **(f)** A major morphological feature of *Y. pestis*

4 Arrange the following in the correct order to account for an epidemic of pneumonic plague:
(a) A bubonic plague patient develops pneumonic plague, which spreads from human to human by aerosols.
(b) Rat fleas transmit plague bacilli from rats to humans.
(c) Rodent fleas transmit plague bacilli from infected wild rodents to domestic rats.
(d) Rodent fleas transmit plague bacilli among wild rodents.
(e) Rat fleas transmit plague bacilli among domestic rats.

5 Rocky Mountain spotted fever is most prevalent in the

_____ (eastern, western) part of the United States and

occurs mainly during the _____ (winter, summer) months.

6 The primary reservoir of Rocky Mountain spotted fever is: **(a)** wild rodents; **(b)** *Dermacentor andersoni, Dermacentor variabilis,* and *Amblyomma americanum;* **(c)** *Rattus rattus* and *Rattus norvegicus;* **(d)** *Pediculus humanus* and *Pulex irritans;* **(e)** *Xenopsylla cheopis.*

7 In patients with Rocky Mountain spotted fever, the skin rash usually appears first on: **(a)** the chest; **(b)** the abdomen; **(c)** the face; **(d)** the back; **(e)** the wrists and ankles.

8 Lyme disease is caused by a _____ (coccus, rod, vibrio, spirochete) called *Borrelia burgdorferi,* which is transmitted to humans by

_____ (lice, ticks, mosquitoes, fleas) of the genus *Ixodes.*

9 Lyme disease occurs mainly in the United States in the: **(a)** northeast; **(b)** midwest; **(c)** northwest; **(d)** south; **(e)** southwest.

10 In the initial stages of Lyme disease, erythema chronicum migrans may occur, which is a type of: **(a)** meningitis; **(b)** pneumonia; **(c)** skin rash; **(d)** jaundice; **(e)** blood disorder.

11 The lipopolysaccharide of *B. burgdorferi* is believed to stimulate macrophages to

overproduce an immune regulator called _____.

12 Epidemic typhus has been one of the greatest disease scourges of the human race. The disease is caused by a bacterium called _____ (genus, species) and is transmitted to humans by _____ (ticks, fleas, lice, mites).

13 The borrelias that cause epidemic relapsing fever are transmitted to humans by _____, whereas those that cause endemic relapsing fever are transmitted by _____.

ARTHROPOD-BORNE INFECTIONS CAUSED BY VIRUSES

14 The most serious arthropod-borne viral disease of the tropics is _____ (malaria, yellow fever, rabies).

15 The relationship between *Aedes aegypti* and epidemic yellow fever was first discovered in 1900–1901 by _____ and his colleagues.

16 Place the letter for each of the following items after either urban yellow fever *or* sylvatic yellow fever. Urban yellow fever: _____. Sylvatic yellow fever: _____.
(a) Transmission is from human to mosquito to human.
(b) Wild monkeys constitute the reservoir of infection.
(c) Transmission to humans is by mosquitoes other than *A. aegypti*.
(d) Control is more difficult because of the wild animal reservoir that perpetuates the infection.
(e) Can be controlled relatively easily by eradicating *A. aegypti*.

17 In patients with yellow fever, the occurrence of albumin in the urine is indicative of damage to the _____, jaundice is indicative of damage to the _____, and black vomit is indicative of _____.

18 The vaccine against yellow fever consists of _____.

19 Arthropod-borne diseases caused by viruses other than the yellow fever virus are transmitted by mosquitoes and _____.

ARTHROPOD-BORNE INFECTIONS CAUSED BY PROTOZOA

20 Human malaria is caused by four species of _____ (*Trypanosoma, Leishmania, Plasmodium, Toxoplasma*) protozoa.

21 Which of the following causes the most severe symptoms? **(a)** *P. vivax;* **(b)** *P. falciparum;* **(c)** *P. malariae;* **(d)** *P. ovale;* **(e)** none of the above; they all cause equally severe symptoms.

22 With regard to their relationship to oxygen, malaria protozoa are: **(a)** aerobic; **(b)** anaerobic; **(c)** facultatively anaerobic; **(d)** microaerophilic; **(e)** aerobic to anaerobic.

23 Match the item at the left with the appropriate description at the right.

(a) A fever-inducing substance released from injured body cells

_____ sporozoites

_____ merozoites

_____ gametocytes

_____ oocyst

_____ trophozoite

_____ pyrogen

(b) The infective forms of malaria protozoa that are injected into a human by a mosquito

(c) Structure in which sporozoites develop on the wall of a mosquito's stomach

(d) Male and female sexual cells of malaria protozoa, formed in the blood of a malaria patient

(e) The active feeding stage of a malaria protozoan that develops within an infected red blood cell

(f) Round forms of malaria protozoa that invade red blood cells

24 The two chemical agents most widely used to treat malaria are: **(a)** penicillin and streptomycin; **(b)** chloramphenicol and ampicillin; **(c)** chloroquine and primaquine; **(d)** tetracycline and penicillin; **(e)** vancomycin and cephalothin.

25 Chagas' disease and African trypanosomiasis are caused by protozoan species of the genus _____ _(Plasmodium, Trypanosoma, Leishmania)_. Kala-azar, oriental sore, and espundia are caused by protozoa of the genus

_____ _(Plasmodium, Trypanosoma, Leishmania)_.

26 Match the disease on the left with the arthropod vector on the right.

_____ Chagas' disease

_____ malaria

_____ sleeping sickness

_____ kala-azar

(a) Mosquitoes

(b) Sandflies

(c) Reduviid bugs

(d) Tsetse flies

ARTHROPOD-BORNE INFECTIONS CAUSED BY HELMINTHS

27 Filariasis occurs mainly in the _____ (temperate; tropical and subtropical) regions of the world.

28 Which one of the following is _not_ a vector for filarias? **(a)** mosquitoes; **(b)** horse- or deerflies; **(c)** blackflies; **(d)** midges; **(e)** ticks.

29 Bancroft's filariasis is caused by a filaria belonging to the genus: **(a)** _Brugia;_ **(b)** _Loa;_ **(c)** _Wuchereria;_ **(d)** _Mansonella;_ **(e)** _Tetrapetalonema._

30 After mating occurs between the male and female adult forms of _W. bancrofti,_ the female produces numerous _____, which enter the bloodstream.

31 After being ingested by a mosquito, the microfilarias of _W. bancrofti_ develop into _____, which can then be transmitted to humans.

32 The function of the lymphatic system in the human body is to collect a fluid called _____ and return it to the

_____ system.

33 Microfilarias may cause obstruction of the lymphatic vessels, resulting in grossly swollen areas of the body—a disease condition called

_____.

REVIEW QUESTIONS

1 What is meant by a biological vector? What is meant by a reservoir of infection?

2 Give an example of an infectious disease in which the causative agent is a bacterium that is transmitted by: **(a)** rat fleas; **(b)** human body lice; **(c)** mites; **(d)** *Ixodes* ticks; **(e)** American dog ticks.

3 Give three examples of infectious diseases in which the causative agents are viruses that are transmitted by mosquitoes.

4 Give an example of an infectious disease in which the causative agent is a protozoan that is transmitted by: **(a)** tsetse flies; **(b)** mosquitoes; **(c)** reduviid bugs.

5 Rocky Mountain spotted fever and Lyme disease are both transmitted by arthropods. In what ways do these arthropods differ? In what ways do the causative agents differ?

6 What is the reservoir of infection for *Yersinia pestis?* Describe the sequence of events leading from the reservoir of infection to an epidemic of human plague.

7 What is meant by urban and sylvatic yellow fever?

8 How can a filarial infection lead to elephantiasis?

9 What type of skin lesion is particularly characteristic of Lyme disease?

DISCUSSION QUESTIONS

1 Since only a relatively few cases of plague occur in the United States each year, do you think plague could be eradicated from the United States? Give your reasoning.

2 Could an epidemic of bubonic plague occur in the United States? If so, how and where would it be most likely to occur? Could an epidemic of pneumonic plague occur in the United States? Explain your answer.

3 Lyme disease is known to have existed at least as far back as 1962, yet the disease was first described in 1975. What kind of laboratory evidence might a microbiologist obtain that would indicate that the disease existed prior to 1975?

4 Why is it important to know the life cycle of arthropods that transmit pathogenic microorganisms? Give examples to support your answer.

5 Which of the various approaches toward developing a vaccine against malaria do you think are the most promising? Why?

6 With what other diseases might a case of Rocky Mountain spotted fever be confused on the basis of clinical signs and symptoms? Why? If you were the examining physician, why would you think it important to check the patient for tick bites, or to inquire whether the patient had been bitten recently by a tick?

Wound and Skin Infections
Acquired by Direct Contact

OBJECTIVES

After reading this chapter, you should be able to

1 List the sources of the microorganisms that gain entrance into the body through wounds, surgical incisions, or other kinds of breaks in the skin.

2 Describe two wound infections caused by endospore-forming anaerobic bacteria.

3 Describe the mechanism of action of tetanus exotoxin.

4 Explain why *Staphylococcus aureus* is a frequent cause of postoperative infections.

5 Differentiate between the modes of transmission of tetanus, staphylococcal infections, and tularemia.

6 Explain why rabies is a particularly feared disease.

7 Describe the rabies vaccine and how it is used to prevent rabies.

8 Give the life cycle and mode of transmission of hookworms.

9 Explain what is meant by a "ringworm infection" and indicate whether or not it is actually caused by worms.

10 Differentiate between a dermatomycosis and a subcutaneous mycosis.

OVERVIEW

Few microorganisms can penetrate unbroken skin. However, pathogenic microorganisms may enter the body easily through abrasions, cuts, or wounds caused by automobile accidents, gunshot wounds, battle injuries, and other injuries. Surgical incisions are also wounds and may become contaminated, leading to postoperative infections.

Wounds can be contaminated by microbes that are already present on the surface of the skin, on the object that inflicted the wound, or in aerosol droplets that settle onto the wound. Wound-contaminating microorganisms may also come from soil, clothing, human feces, or the urine, feces, and flesh of infected animals.

Wound and skin infections can be caused by various bacteria, viruses, helminths, and fungi. However, it is not possible in an introductory text to describe every disease and its causative agent in detail. Therefore this chapter will concentrate on a few representative diseases which not only demonstrate the principles of transmission by direct contact but also reveal important mechanisms by which pathogenic microorganisms can injure a human host.

TRANSMISSION OF MICROBIAL AGENTS OF WOUND AND SKIN INFECTIONS

As mentioned in Chapters 17 and 18, the unbroken skin is an effective mechanical barrier to infectious agents. However, if this barrier is damaged in some way, microorganisms can reach the interior tissues and may cause serious infections. This may happen after the skin has been cut or has been wounded in some other manner, or even as a result of tiny cracks and abrasions on the surface of the skin. It is also possible for some microorganisms to enter the body through hair follicles, sebaceous glands, or sweat glands.

A break in the skin can be contaminated by organisms such as staphylococci that are already present on the skin. However, there are many other sources of pathogens that can invade a wound. Microbes such as *Streptococcus pyogenes* can be carried to an exposed wound by large aerosol droplets expelled during sneezing or coughing. Contaminating organisms may also come from soil, feces, or the patient's own fingers or clothing. For instance, the major causative agent of gas gangrene, *Clostridium perfringens*, is a normal inhabitant of the intestinal tract of humans and animals. Similarly, the spores of *Clostridium tetani*, the causative agent of tetanus, are common in animal feces and soil. Wound contamination from these sources frequently occurs when there are traumatic injuries, such as automobile accidents, gunshot wounds, and wounds received by soldiers on the battlefield.

Surgical incisions also result in a break in the skin barrier. It is therefore important to prevent such incisions from becoming contaminated during or after an operation. For instance, staphylococci could gain entrance to the body via an incision. Surgical wounds may also become infected from environmental sources such as aerosols and infectious dust in the operating room or in the hospital ward, or from contact with articles such as bedpans and bedclothes.

Some pathogens can be acquired through cuts in skin from the tissues, saliva, urine, or feces of infected animals. Diseases caused by these pathogens usually have an occupational incidence, being associated mainly with hunters, veterinarians, butchers, and slaughterhouse workers. Examples are brucellosis, tularemia, and anthrax.

ASK YOURSELF

1 What might be the source of staphylococci that contaminate a wound?

2 How can aerosols contaminate a wound with pathogenic microorganisms? What is the source of bacteria that cause gas gangrene? Where do the spores of *Clostridium tetani* occur in nature?

3 How may wound infections be acquired in hospitals?

4 With what occupations are brucellosis, tularemia, and anthrax mainly associated?

BACTERIAL INFECTIONS TRANSMITTED THROUGH A BREAK IN THE SKIN

Many different kinds of bacteria are able to cause an infection after invading tissue through a break in the skin. Some of these infections are caused by anaerobic bacteria; these include tetanus and gas gangrene. Others may be caused by aerobic or facultative bacteria, such as *Staphylococcus aureus* or *Francisella tularensis*. Each type of infection has distinctive and characteristic features.

Infections Caused by Anaerobic Bacteria

Three general factors, either separately or in combination, contribute to the development of anaerobic conditions in a wound and thus to the growth of pathogenic anaerobic bacteria: (1) crushed or mechanically damaged tissue and blood clots, which lack blood circulation and rapidly become anaerobic; (2) aerobic or facultative bacteria that contaminate the wound and use up oxygen, creating anaerobic conditions; and (3) toxic or irritant chemicals introduced into the wound by dirt or soil that kill tissue cells, thereby causing the tissue to become anaerobic. Some typical examples of wounds that are likely to lead to anaerobic infections include jagged shrapnel wounds in soldiers on the battlefield, crushed or torn limbs resulting from an automobile accident, wounds contaminated by dirty hands and instruments, and wounds caused by human or animal bites.

Of the various infections caused by anaerobes, tetanus and gas gangrene are particularly interesting because they exemplify two entirely different ways by which pathogens cause disease. In a tetanus infection,

FIGURE 27.1

Fuchsin–methylene blue stain of *Clostridium tetani*. The typical drumstick shape of the bacteria is due to the formation of a spherical endospore at one end of the cell. Many free endospores are also visible as separate round objects in the field.

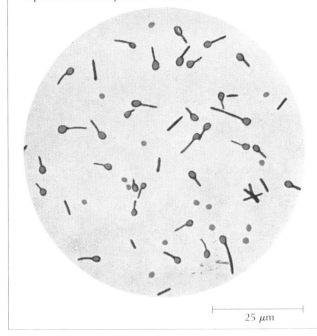

25 μm

the organisms remain localized at their site of entry into the body, but they secrete a deadly exotoxin that reaches a person's central nervous system. In contrast, the bacteria that cause gas gangrene spread readily from the initial site of entry; as they spread, they secrete toxins that kill the surrounding tissue.

Tetanus. Tetanus is a disease with a high fatality rate. Fortunately, it is relatively rare in the United States, with only about 50 to 90 cases occurring each year. However, it is prevalent in countries lacking immunization programs, and in some underdeveloped tropical countries it is one of the 10 leading causes of death. In such countries tetanus is particularly important as a killer of infants born to nonimmunized mothers; tetanus in the newborn, called *neonatal tetanus*, can occur if, during delivery, the cut surface of an infant's umbilical cord becomes contaminated by dirt or fecal matter.

Tetanus is caused by *Clostridium tetani*, a Gram-positive anaerobic rod that forms a large, round endospore at one end of the cell. This spore gives the organism a characteristic drumstick appearance [FIGURE 27.1]. *Clostridium tetani* occurs in the intestinal tracts of herbivorous animals such as horses and cattle and is also widely distributed in soil. *Clostridium tetani* may grow

in wounds that provide favorable anaerobic conditions, but it does not spread through the tissues; instead, it remains localized and secretes a *neurotoxin* (a nerve poison). The toxin becomes bound to nearby motor nerves and then travels along these nerves to the central nervous system. This toxin is extremely potent: one gram would be sufficient to kill approximately 25 billion laboratory mice.

To understand the action of tetanus toxin, you must first understand how muscular movements of various parts of the body occur. A muscular movement usually involves a cooperative action between two muscles, one muscle opposing the other. If both muscles contracted at the same time, no movement would be possible, because one muscle would counteract the other (such counteraction is the basis of isometric body exercises). Normally, however, one muscle is prevented from contracting because an inhibitory chemical secreted in the central nervous system inactivates the nerve cells controlling that muscle. This process is illustrated in FIGURE 27.2.

If tetanus neurotoxin reaches the central nervous system, it *prevents secretion of the inhibitory chemical*. This means that opposing sets of muscles may now contract simultaneously and in an uncontrollable fashion. This results in rigid muscular spasms that may be powerful enough to break bones and tear tissue. Tetanus symptoms include painful and violent contractions of the muscles, usually of the neck and jaw (restricting opening of the mouth and giving rise to the term *lockjaw*). Death usually results from respiratory failure brought on by an inability of the patient to control the diaphragm and muscles of the chest involved in breathing. The mortality rate of tetanus is high—55 to 65 percent. Treatment involves administration of muscle relaxants and antitoxin. The antitoxin is given to neutralize any toxin that has not yet become fixed to nerve tissue. (Toxin that is already fixed cannot be neutralized.)

Active immunization against tetanus is done with a vaccine made of toxoid (formaldehyde-inactivated toxin), which stimulates the body to produce antitoxin. Booster immunization should be given every 10 years to maintain an adequate level of antitoxin. If a person who has never been immunized receives a wound that could lead to tetanus, it would take too long to produce immunity by using toxoid. Instead, such a person should receive tetanus *antitoxin* containing preformed antibodies, to provide immediate protection.

Gas Gangrene. Gas gangrene is typically a disease of the battlefield and, like tetanus, results from contamination of wounds. It is relatively rare in civilian life because wounds that might give rise to gas gangrene are likely to receive prompt treatment under normal conditions.

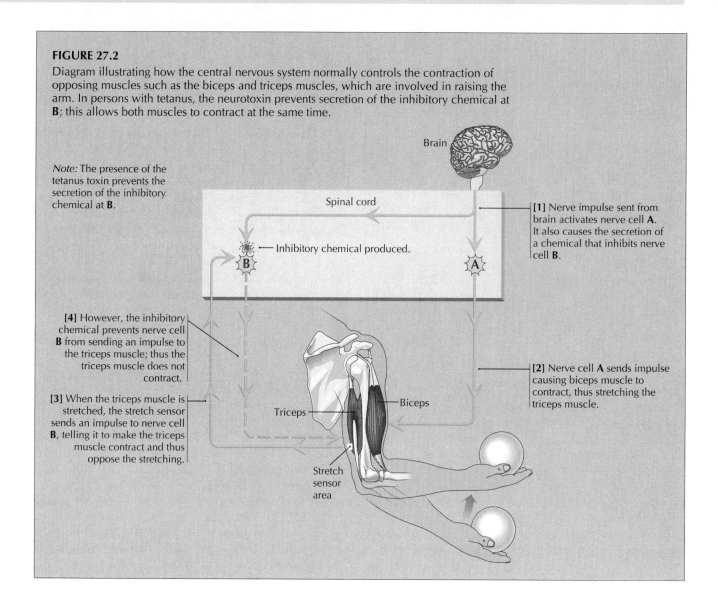

FIGURE 27.2

Diagram illustrating how the central nervous system normally controls the contraction of opposing muscles such as the biceps and triceps muscles, which are involved in raising the arm. In persons with tetanus, the neurotoxin prevents secretion of the inhibitory chemical at **B**; this allows both muscles to contract at the same time.

Note: The presence of the tetanus toxin prevents the secretion of the inhibitory chemical at **B**.

Brain

Spinal cord

Inhibitory chemical produced.

B

A

[1] Nerve impulse sent from brain activates nerve cell **A**. It also causes the secretion of a chemical that inhibits nerve cell **B**.

[4] However, the inhibitory chemical prevents nerve cell **B** from sending an impulse to the triceps muscle; thus the triceps muscle does not contract.

[3] When the triceps muscle is stretched, the stretch sensor sends an impulse to nerve cell **B**, telling it to make the triceps muscle contract and thus oppose the stretching.

Triceps

Biceps

Stretch sensor area

[2] Nerve cell **A** sends impulse causing biceps muscle to contract, thus stretching the triceps muscle.

Although several *Clostridium* species can cause gas gangrene, the most frequent cause is *C. perfringens* type A [see FIGURE 25.9E]. You have already learned that this organism is an enterotoxin-producing agent of foodborne infections (Chapter 25). However, *C. perfringens* type A produces several other exotoxins, the most important of which is the **α toxin**. This toxin is both a cytotoxin and a hemolysin, and it acts by damaging the cytoplasmic membranes of tissue cells and red blood cells. In biochemical terms, it is a *lecithinase,* an enzyme that catalyzes the breakdown of *lecithin,* an important phospholipid component of human cell membranes.

Clostridium perfringens is normally present in low numbers in the human intestine, where it is harmless; however, wounds can become contaminated by fecal material present on hands or clothing. As the clostridia begin to grow, their toxins kill the surrounding healthy tissue. The dead tissue becomes anaerobic and supports the growth of more clostridia, which release more toxins that kill more tissue and allow the organisms to spread further [FIGURE 27.3]. Another factor that contributes to the rapid spread of *C. perfringens* is the large amount of *hydrogen gas* produced by the bacteria. The pressure of this gas causes muscle sheaths to separate from the muscles, and the space resulting from this separation can be filled in rapidly by fluid containing the clostridia. By this means *C. perfringens* can invade the entire length of a muscle in a very short time.

Prevention of gas gangrene depends on three measures: (1) surgical removal of dead tissue and blood clots from the wound; (2) administration of antitoxin; and (3) administration of antibiotics to stop the growth of the bacteria. For treatment of clinical cases, amputation of an affected limb is sometimes the only way to stop the spread of the highly invasive clostridia to the rest of the body. However, an alternative treatment called *hyper-*

FIGURE 27.3
Gas gangrene that developed in a patient's leg stump following amputation.

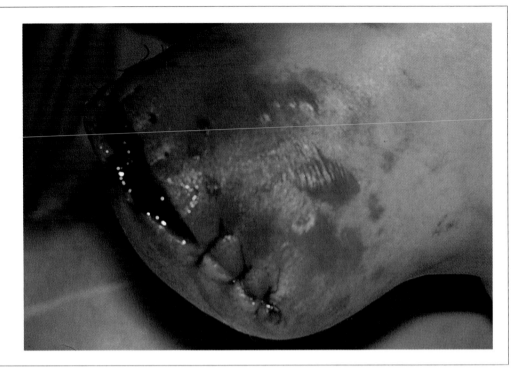

baric oxygen is sometimes effective. In this treatment, the patient is placed in a chamber containing pure oxygen gas under pressure several times a day for brief periods. This treatment causes a high level of tissue oxygenation that may halt the growth of the clostridia. However, neither amputation nor hyperbaric oxygen treatment can save the life of the patient if the clostridial toxins have already become widely distributed throughout the body by the bloodstream. Mortality rates for untreated cases of gas gangrene range from 40 to 60 percent.

Infections Caused by Aerobic and Facultative Bacteria

A variety of infections are caused by aerobic or facultative bacteria that gain access to the body through a break in the skin. Two well-known examples are *Staphylococcus aureus* infections and tularemia. These provide an interesting contrast in terms of transmission of their causative agents. Whereas humans themselves are usually the source of *S. aureus* infections, wild and domestic animals are the source of *Francisella tularensis*, the bacterium that causes tularemia.

***Staphylococcus aureus* Infections.** *Staphylococcus aureus* cells are facultative Gram-positive cocci arranged in irregular clusters [see FIGURE 25.2]. In Chapter 25 you learned about the *S. aureus* enterotoxin that causes the

symptoms of staphylococcal food poisoning. However, *S. aureus* makes several toxins and other substances that contribute to its ability to cause wound infections [TABLE 27.1].

Staphylococcus aureus commonly inhabits the skin's surface and the nasopharynx. It can cause infections if it enters the body through a break in the skin [FIGURE 27.4], and it is a common cause of infections following surgery. Alternatively, staphylococci may enter the body through a hair follicle and form a localized and sometimes painful nodule called a *furuncle* or *common boil* at the base of the follicle. The infection may penetrate more deeply and expand to form a cluster of boils called a *carbuncle*. Carbuncles are usually restricted to the neck or upper back. Whether staphylococci enter the body through a break in the skin or through a hair follicle, they usually do not spread readily from the site of entry. Instead, they tend to remain in place, multiply, make various toxins, and kill the surrounding tissue cells. The general term for the type of lesion produced by staphylococci is **abscess.** (Abscesses can also be caused by various other bacteria besides staphylococci; for instance, the anaerobic Gram-negative bacillus *Bacteroides fragilis* commonly causes this type of lesion.)

An abscess is much like a walled-off fort; it is a cavity in the tissues that contains dead tissue, neutrophils, and the growing bacteria. An insoluble protein, **fibrin,** which is formed during the clotting of blood or blood plasma, is deposited at the periphery of the abscess. Fibrin deposi-

FIGURE 27.4
Staphylococcus aureus can cause infection if it enters the body through a break in the skin. **[A]** Staphylococcal infection on a patient's back. **[B]** Staphylococcal wrist infection.

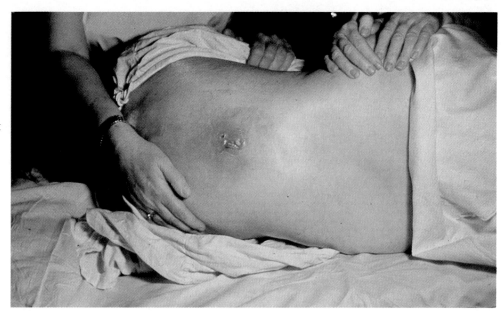

[A]

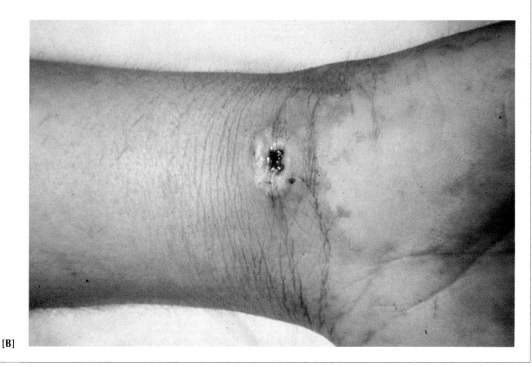

[B]

tion may be aided by staphylococcal *coagulase* [TABLE 27.1]. Neutrophils are present in the abscess because they can actively migrate past the fibrin barrier. They eventually accumulate to such great numbers that they form a white, pasty mass called *pus.* Although the neutrophils are often effective in destroying the staphylococci by phagocytosis [FIGURE 27.5], they can be killed by the various *leucocidins* produced by the staphylococci [TABLE 27.1]. Phagocytosis works best when specific antibodies against the bacteria are present; unfortu-

nately, there is no blood circulation within an abscess, and antibodies from the bloodstream can penetrate the abscess only by a slow diffusion process. Antibiotics have similar difficulty in reaching the bacteria, and a patient may have to be treated with antibiotics for a prolonged period to cure the infection.

Although *S. aureus* does not readily spread through tissues, the bacteria can sometimes be carried by the bloodstream or within neutrophils to sites far removed from the original abscess. Nearly any organ or tissue may

TABLE 27.1
Some Toxins and Other Virulence Factors Produced by *Staphylococcus aureus*

Toxin or factor	Action
Alpha toxin	Hemolysin; cytotoxin; leucocidin; damages cell membranes, possibly by a proteolytic action.
Beta toxin	Hemolysin; leucocidin; the toxin is an enzyme that destroys the phospholipid sphingomyelin, a component of the membranes of red blood cells and other cells.
Gamma toxin	Hemolysin; leucocidin; mechanism of action unknown.
Delta toxin	Hemolysin; leucocidin; disrupts cell membranes by a detergentlike action.
Panton-Valentine leucocidin	Leucocidin; forms pores in the membranes of leucocytes.
Exfoliative toxins A and B	Responsible for "scalded skin syndrome," a severe skin disease in which large sheets of epidermis peel away leaving moist, red, denuded areas.
TSS toxin-1	Associated with toxic shock syndrome.
Coagulase	Causes blood plasma to clot, i.e., causes soluble blood fibrinogen to be converted to a network of insoluble filaments of fibrin; virulent strains of *S. aureus* are usually coagulase-positive, but just how coagulase contributes to virulence is not clear.
Lipase	Catalyzes breakdown of fats and oils on skin, in sebaceous gland secretions, and in blood plasma; virulent strains of *S. aureus* are usually lipase-positive, but just how lipase contributes to virulence is not clear.
Enterotoxin	Responsible for symptoms of staphylococcal food poisoning (see Chapter 25).
β-Lactamase	Enzyme that causes breakdown of penicillin, thus rendering the bacteria penicillin-resistant; the ability to produce β-lactamase is one reason why today nearly all hospital strains of *S. aureus* are penicillin-resistant; the gene for the β-lactamase is usually located on a plasmid within the staphylococcal cell.

FIGURE 27.5

Microscopic view of human blood stained with Wright's stain, showing two neutrophils (arrows) which have engulfed staphylococci that were added to the blood sample. The staphylococci appear as dark-purple dots in the cytoplasm of the neutrophils; the lobed nuclei of the neutrophils are light purple. Numerous red blood cells are also present in the field.

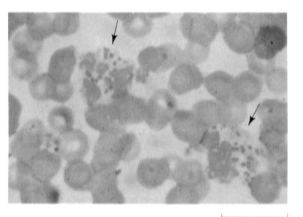

20 μm

serve as a site for a secondary infection, leading to severe complications such as chronic osteomyelitis, a bone infection that is very difficult to treat because of poor penetration of the affected area by antibiotics. Other complications include staphylococcal pneumonia, meningitis, endocarditis, and abscesses in the brain, kidney, spleen, liver, pancreas, or other organs.

Toxic shock syndrome (TSS) is a disease that has received much attention in recent years. It was first described in 1978 but probably occurred long before then. The disease occurs mainly in young women during a menstrual period, but males also occasionally develop TSS as a complication from an *S. aureus* infection. The symptoms are caused by an exotoxin called **TSS *toxin-1*** and include fever, diarrhea, vomiting, shock, and a sunburnlike skin rash. The death rate is presently about 3 to 4 percent. In women, TSS has been associated with the use of highly absorbent tampons, which may provide an environment for staphylococcal growth and toxin formation. Because of this possibility, less absorbent tampons are now being manufactured, and this might explain why the incidence of TSS has decreased considerably since 1982.

The treatment of staphylococcal infections is complicated not only by the poor penetration of antibiotics into abscesses but also by resistance of the staphylococci toward various antibiotics. Many clinical isolates of *S. aureus* are resistant to several antibiotics. Usually the genes responsible for this multiple antibiotic resistance are located on one or more plasmids. For instance, most clinical isolates of *S. aureus* are resistant to penicillin because they produce a β-lactamase, or penicillinase. This is unfortunate, because penicillin, unlike many other antibiotics, is bactericidal rather than bacteriostatic. Certain semisynthetic penicillins, such as methicillin, are not destroyed by β-lactamase and can be effective in treating penicillin-resistant staphylococcal infections. However, for unknown reasons some strains of *S. aureus* are resistant to *all* β-lactam antibiotics, including methicillin. Vancomycin, which is not a β-lactam antibiotic, is usually effective against these strains.

Tularemia. Tularemia is caused by the bacterium *Francisella tularensis* and is mainly a disease of wild animals. It is found in most countries north of the equator. About 150 to 300 cases of human tularemia occur each year in the United States. Over 90 percent of human cases are contracted from direct contact with infected wild rabbits. However, *F. tularensis* has been isolated from many other wild animals such as squirrels, mice, rats, muskrats, beavers, foxes, deer, and birds, and also from domestic animals such as sheep, cattle, horses, and cats. It also occurs in various arthropods such as ticks, deerflies, mites, blackflies, and mosquitoes, which can serve as vectors for transmission of the infection from animals to humans. In ticks, *F. tularensis* can be transmitted from generation to generation by transovarian passage.

Francisella tularensis is a Gram-negative aerobic rod 0.2 μm wide by 0.2 to 0.7 μm long. It has the ability to penetrate small abrasions on human skin and can be transmitted to persons such as hunters and trappers whose hands come into contact with the flesh of infected animals [DISCOVER 27.1]. It can also be transmitted to persons who work outdoors and are bitten by an infected tick or other arthropod.

In the most common form of tularemia, a papule initially appears on the skin of the fingers or hands within 3 to 5 days. This papule, at the site of entry of *F. tularensis* into the body, eventually becomes an open sore [FIGURE 27.6]. The patient develops swollen lymph glands, back pain, headache, chills, fever, and general weakness, and some patients may develop a skin rash. The bacteria multiply mainly within macrophages, and granulomas are often produced in internal organs. As with tuberculosis, cell-mediated immunity is the only type of immunity that is effective against the bacteria. The death rate from tularemia is relatively low (less than 1 percent of cases), but patients may take as long as 2 to 4 weeks or more to recover from the disease.

Francisella tularensis is very difficult to isolate from clinical specimens, and laboratory diagnosis of tularemia usually depends instead on demonstrating an immune response to the infection, as indicated by the patient's production of an increasing concentration of specific antibodies over a period of time.

Tularemia can be treated with streptomycin. The disease can be prevented by avoiding contact with wild animals, particularly rabbits, especially if the animals appear to be ill. Gloves may help hunters and trappers to avoid infection during skinning and dressing of animals. A vaccine consisting of a live, attenuated strain of *F. tularensis* is available for persons whose occupations put them at high risk.

Other Bacterial Infections Transmitted Through a Break in the Skin

Other infections caused by bacterial pathogens that enter the body through a wound or other break in the skin are listed in TABLE 27.2, together with the specific modes of transmission and the characteristic disease symptoms. Micrographs of some of the bacterial species are shown in FIGURE 27.7. FIGURE 27.7D shows a large lesion on a patient's neck that resulted from an anthrax infection.

FIGURE 27.6
Primary tularemia lesion that developed on the hand of a muskrat trapper in Vermont.

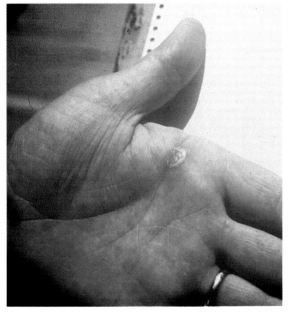

FIGURE 27.7

Micrographs of some of the bacterial pathogens listed in TABLE 27.2. **[A]** *Bacteroides fragilis*, Gram stain. **[B]** *Brucella melitensis*, Gram stain. **[C]** Blood smear taken from a sheep that died of anthrax, showing capsulated *Bacillus anthracis* cells (rod forms surrounded by a clear area). The large round objects in the field are blood cells. **[D]** Cutaneous anthrax that has developed on a patient's neck. **[E]** *Leptospira interrogans* cells, stained by silver impregnation. The cells have extremely fine helical coils that can barely be seen with a light microscope. The ends of the cells often have a characteristic "shepherd's crook" configuration. **[F]** Electron micrograph of *L. interrogans* cells showing the helical coils.

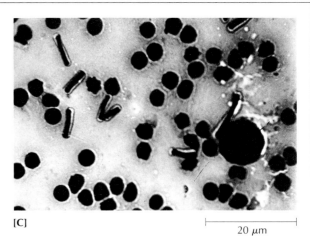

[C]

20 μm

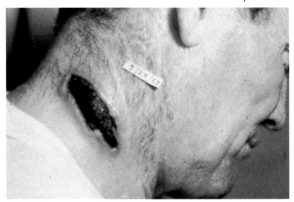

[D]

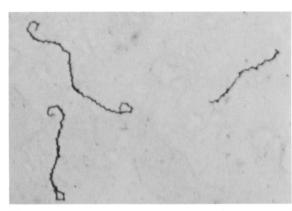

[E]

5 μm

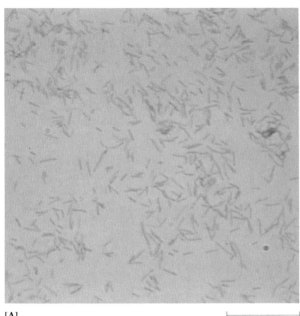

[A]

50 μm

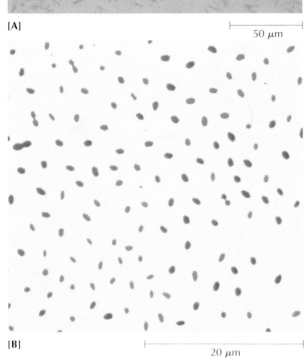

[B]

20 μm

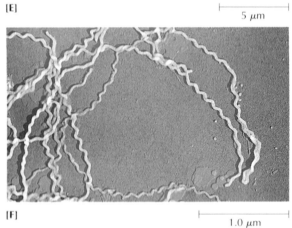

[F]

1.0 μm

TABLE 27.2
Some Bacterial Infections of Humans That Are Transmitted Through Breaks in the Skin

Disease	Causative agent	Mode of transmission	Characteristics of disease
Anaerobic abscesses	*Bacteroides fragilis* and other anaerobic Gram-negative non-spore-forming rods	These bacteria are normal inhabitants of the intestine, oral cavity, nasopharynx, vagina, and urethra. If they gain access to internal tissues, as by wounds, bowel surgery, human or animal bites, dental extractions, uterine damage during abortion surgery, or similar means, severe infections may result.	Abscesses may be formed in any part of the body but usually near some skin or mucosal surface that provided the portal of entry to the internal tissues. Effective chemotherapeutic agents include clindamycin, imipenem, and metronidazole.
Brucellosis	*Brucella abortus*, *B. melitensis*, and *B. suis*; aerobic Gram-negative nonmotile rods	Brucellas are mainly pathogens of cattle (*B. abortus*), sheep and goats (*B. melitensis*), and swine (*B. suis*). They can be transmitted to humans by consumption of unpasteurized milk, direct contact with the infected flesh of animals, or inhaling aerosols generated during processing of infected meat. *B. suis* is the most prevalent species today; infections occur mainly in veterinarians, butchers, and slaughterhouse workers.	Generalized aches and pains of the muscles and joints, chills and night sweats, and a prolonged fever which continues into a chronic stage. The bacteria grow mainly inside macrophages, and cell-mediated immunity is the only effective type of immunity. Brucellosis is a debilitating disease but is usually not fatal. Live attenuated vaccines are available for immunizing animals but not humans.
Anthrax	*Bacillus anthracis*, a facultative Gram-positive endospore-forming rod	Anthrax occurs mainly in cattle and sheep. Humans can contract cutaneous anthrax through scratches and abrasions by handling infected animals or infected hides, wool, and horn. Pulmonary anthrax is contracted by inhaling dust generated during the combing or sorting of raw wool contaminated with anthrax spores.	Cutaneous anthrax begins as a localized papule that develops into an open sore on the skin; the organisms eventually invade the bloodstream, grow to large numbers, and produce an exotoxin that seems to act on the central nervous system to cause respiratory failure. Pulmonary anthrax begins as a localized lung infection and, like cutaneous anthrax, progresses to a bloodstream infection. Mortality rates are high in untreated cases. A live attenuated vaccine is available for immunization of animals but not humans.
Leptospirosis	*Leptospira interrogans*, an aerobic spirochete	Rats, mice, dogs, and other animals are the natural hosts and excrete the spirochetes in their urine. Humans are infected by handling objects contaminated with infected animal urine or by swimming in urine-contaminated water; the spirochetes penetrate skin abrasions and mucous membranes.	The spirochetes multiply initially in the bloodstream and are carried to all parts of the body, causing flulike symptoms and jaundice. The organisms eventually localize in the kidneys and may cause kidney failure. In severe cases, survival of the patient may depend on use of a blood dialysis machine that takes over the function of the kidneys. Vaccines consisting of killed leptospiras are available for immunization of animals but not humans.

27.1 TULAREMIA: THE CASE OF THE "GOOD LUCK CHARMS"

On November 15, 1977, a 19-year-old man went deer hunting with friends and relatives in central Washington state. While on the trail two days later, he found a partially dismembered dead rabbit. The hunter amputated the front paws for good luck charms and gave them to another hunter in the party.

The rabbit had been handled with bare hands that were bruised and scratched from the hunter's work as an automobile mechanic. Festering sores on his hands, legs, and knees were noted on November 19. Spiking fevers followed a day later. He was cared for at home until December 11, when his phy-sician admitted him to a local hospital because of continued bouts of fever and a weight loss of 10 pounds. By December 14 the fevers had subsided, and the patient was discharged.

A blood specimen drawn on December 16 was sent to the state's public health laboratory to be tested for the presence of antibodies indicative of tularemia, brucellosis, or a rickettsial infection. The serum showed a high level of antibodies against *Francisella tularensis.* A 10-day course of antibiotic therapy was started on December 21. The patient remained well with no evidence of relapse.

Despite repeated attempts to elicit a history of exposure of the patient to wild rabbits, none was obtained until after Christmas, when the patient's grandfather remembered the rabbit paw incident. This suggested that the portal of entry of *F. tularensis* into the body had probably been scratches on the hands. The recipient of the "good luck charms" did not become ill. However, he had discarded the paws, and so they could not be recovered for bacteriological analysis.

Adapted from *Morbidity and Mortality Weekly Report,* March 28, 1978.

Disease	Causative agent	Mode of transmission	Characteristics of disease
Rat-bite fever	Either *Spirillum minus,* a Gram-negative, polar-flagellated spirillum that can be cultured only in mice and guinea pigs; or *Streptobacillus monilifor-mis,* a Gram-negative non-motile facultative rod that is highly variable in shape	Both *S. minus* and *S. monilifor-mis* commonly occur in the oral cavity of rats; they enter the human body through a bite from these rodents. The disease has its highest incidence in inner-city ghettos with poor sanitation and large rat populations.	Fever and chills develop, lymph glands near the entry site become swollen and painful, and a skin rash occurs. A severe arthritis may also occur in *S. moniliformis* infections. Mortality rates in untreated cases range from 6 to 10 percent. No vaccine is available.
Pseudomonas infections	*Pseudomonas aeruginosa* is the most common pathogenic species. It is an aerobic Gram-negative rod with 1 to 3 polar flagella. It produces a distinctive blue-green water-soluble pigment in cultures.	*P. aeruginosa* is an opportunistic pathogen that occurs widely in the environment: in soil, water, sewage, and plants, for example. In hospital wards it may occur in water pitchers, flower vase water, respiratory ventilators, hot tubs, sponges, sinks, humidifiers, body lotions, hand creams, contaminated wound dressings, bedclothes, contaminated urine, and many other items.	*P. aeruginosa* causes many nosocomial infections, particularly burn infections, wound infections, and infections of the urinary tract. Immunocompromised patients are at the greatest risk. Almost any part of the body can be infected. Initial localized infections can lead to invasion of the bloodstream. In cystic fibrosis patients, the organism often causes a severe and often fatal pneumonia. *P. aeruginosa* makes exotoxin A, which inhibits protein synthesis in the same manner as diphtheria toxin; it mainly affects the liver. Several other toxins are also produced. The organism is usually resistant to most antibiotics, but tobramycin or gentamicin plus ticarcillin, carbenicillin, azlocillin, mezlocillin, or piperacillin may be effective. No vaccine is available.

ASK YOURSELF

1 What three general factors contribute to the development of anaerobic conditions in a wound?

2 How does tetanus toxin cause uncontrollable muscle spasms? Of what does tetanus vaccine consist?

3 What is the mechanism of action of the α toxin of *Clostridium perfringens*? If a person has a wound conducive to development of anaerobic conditions, how can gas gangrene be prevented?

4 What is the nature of the characteristic lesion formed in infections caused by *Staphylococcus aureus*? What toxin is responsible for toxic shock syndrome? Why are most staphylococcal infections resistant to treatment with penicillin?

5 Where does *Francisella tularensis* occur in nature? How do people become infected by this organism?

6 What bacteria cause each of the following: anaerobic abscesses, brucellosis, anthrax, leptospirosis, and rat-bite fever?

VIRAL INFECTIONS TRANSMITTED THROUGH A BREAK IN THE SKIN

Many viral infections can be transmitted to humans through wounds or breaks in the skin. Of these, probably none is regarded with as much fear and horror as rabies. Rabies also is of special interest because it is one of the few infectious diseases in which a person can be immunized *after* being infected by the causative agent.

Rabies

Rabies in humans is a rare disease, but it is particularly feared because of the especially horrible suffering of the victims and because, after the symptoms begin, the disease is almost invariably fatal. The great microbiologist Louis Pasteur never forgot his childhood recollection of a rabid wolf that had terrorized his district in 1831. He always remembered the sight of the wounds on one of the bitten men being cauterized with a red-hot iron at the smithy near his father's house. Such recollections were undoubtedly a factor in directing his research in later years toward rabies, research which eventually culminated in the discovery of the first effective vaccine against the disease.

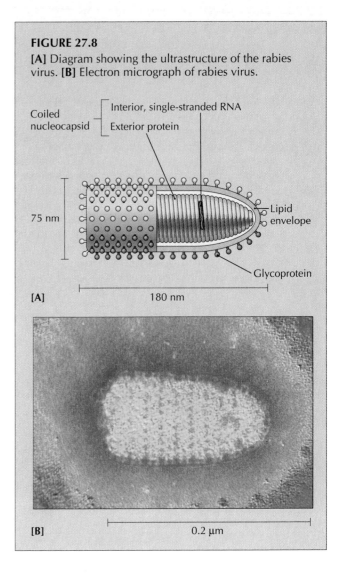

FIGURE 27.8

[A] Diagram showing the ultrastructure of the rabies virus. [B] Electron micrograph of rabies virus.

Biology of the Rabies Virus. Although rabies has been known for centuries, the morphological and chemical features of the virus were first described in the 1960s. The virus belongs to the rhabdovirus family and is a large, enveloped, bullet-shaped virus that contains single-stranded RNA [FIGURE 27.8]. Only one antigenic type is known to exist.

Transmission of the Rabies Virus. Rabies is primarily a disease of animals, and transmission of the rabies virus to humans occurs through the bite of an infected animal or through contact of abraded skin with the saliva of an infected animal. Dogs, cats, bats, and skunks are the most frequent sources of human infection, but many other wild and domestic animals may also be infected. Public awareness of this disease has increased as wild animals such as raccoons and foxes have invaded suburban communities in larger numbers; some of these animals have been rabid [DISCOVER 27.2].

27.2 RABIES EXPOSURE IN A NURSING HOME—ONTARIO, CANADA

On August 15, 1986, a woman reported to a private veterinarian that a fox had had direct contact with her female dog and its four puppies on the front porch of her farmhouse. The veterinarian advised her either to destroy the dogs or to have them quarantined on her premises, but failed to report the contact with a potentially rabid animal to the federal veterinarian as legally required. On August 20 the owner delivered the four puppies to a local animal shelter. She neglected to mention the fox contact to the staff. That afternoon, two of the puppies were taken to a nursing home and introduced to most of the residents and staff and several visitors.

Within 24 hours, all four puppies had been adopted, by four different families. On August 24, one of the pups had diarrhea and vomiting and was taken to a veterinary clinic; it died on August 29. A second pup became ill on August 28 and died on August 31. The brain in each case was submitted for rabies testing. On September 4 and 5, the Health Unit was notified that both puppies were positive for rabies. Furthermore, there was strong evidence that one of the rabid

puppies was one of the two taken to the nursing home. The remaining two puppies were traced and destroyed. They were subsequently found to be negative for rabies. The owner's dog was placed under a federal quarantine for a 6-month period but did not develop symptoms.

With the assistance of the Regional Health Unit staff, the nursing home immediately prepared lists of those individuals who had definitely been in contact with the rabid pup, those who definitely had not been in contact, and those for whom the contact was uncertain. In addition, two press releases were issued by the Health Unit because of the large number of people who had been in contact with the rabid puppies. Individuals were encouraged to question their children to determine whether they had had contact with the pups and, if so, to consult their family physician. The press releases were followed by a survey of all households near the homes that had adopted the two rabid animals. It was learned that one of the rabid pups had been placed in a carriage with two babies.

In total, 134 Canadians received

postexposure treatment with rabies vaccine and rabies immune globulin. These included 60 nursing home contacts, 62 neighborhood contacts (mostly children), six veterinary clinic staff members, and six animal shelter staff personnel. Also, one boy visiting from England and four vacationers from Massachusetts had been exposed; all were vaccinated.

The average cost of a course of rabies immune globulin and vaccine ranges from $400 to $700 per person, depending on body weight. The total cost of the preventive treatments provided by the Ontario Ministry of Health was estimated at $65,000.

This incident emphasizes the problem that may result from failure to report the rabies risk from animals and the need to immunize pets against rabies before they have contact with large numbers of people. If the fox contact had been reported promptly, the large number of treatments and the consequent expense and anxiety might have been avoided.

Adapted from *Morbidity and Mortality Weekly Report Supplement, Rabies Surveillance 1986,* issued Aug. 28, 1987.

Pathogenicity of the Rabies Virus. After a human has been infected, the symptoms of rabies usually appear in about 3 to 8 weeks; however, they may take as little as 6 days or as long as 1 year to appear. The length of the incubation period reflects the time required for the virus to reach the central nervous system and depends largely on the severity and location of the bite. It has been estimated that only 5 to 15 percent of all persons bitten by a rabid animal actually contract the disease. The virus attacks the central nervous system, and the initial disease symptoms in humans include severe headache and high fever, followed by hyperactivity, disorientation, hallucinations, and alternating stages of excitement and depression. Brief periods of hyperactivity alternate with periods of calm and are characterized by agitation, thrashing about, running, biting, or other unusual behavior. Patients have difficulty in swallowing, and slight stimuli, such as the sight of water, can incite painful muscular spasms in the throat and chest, resulting in gagging, choking, and fear. (The term *hydrophobia,* "dread of water," is sometimes used to describe rabies.) Death due to respiratory failure or heart failure occurs 3 to 20

days after onset of symptoms, and is usually preceded by paralysis or convulsive seizures.

Treatment and Prevention of Rabies. After rabies symptoms develop, no effective treatment for the disease is known, although intensive care may postpone the fatal outcome. However, a person who has been bitten recently by a rabid animal and who has not yet developed symptoms can be treated *to prevent the virus from reaching the central nervous system.* If the patient is immunized within 2 days of the bite, the disease can almost always be prevented. Such preventive treatment is possible only because of the long incubation period of rabies. The preventive treatment includes: (1) administration of *immune human or horse globulin* to provide an immediate source of antibodies against the virus (although the immunity lasts for only about 14 days), and (2) administration of a *rabies vaccine* to stimulate active, long-lasting antibody production by the patient.

If a person has been bitten by an animal suspected of having rabies, it is important to confirm that the animal is rabid so that the human victim can receive preventive

TABLE 27.3
Some Viral Infections of Humans That Can Be Transmitted through a Break in the Skin by Direct Contact

Disease	Causative agent	Disease characteristics in humans
Orf	A poxvirus that causes an infection of sheep and goats	Blisters develop at the site of abrasions on the hands or face; nodules and swollen lymph glands may eventually develop.
Molluscum contagiosum	A poxvirus	Children develop small papules on the skin of the face, trunk, or limbs. The virus can also be transmitted sexually.
Milker's nodules	Milker's node virus, a poxvirus that produces blisters on the udder of cattle	Painless, watery small nodules are produced on the skin.
Eczema herpeticum; herpetic whitlow; herpes gladiatorum	Herpes simplex virus type 1 (HSV-1)	Blisters form on the skin; eczema herpeticum can be potentially fatal in young children, herpetic whitlow is a primary infection of the finger and may occur in dentists, and herpes gladiatorum may be acquired by wrestlers through skin abrasions.
Common warts	Various human papillomaviruses	Skin lesions are flesh-colored to brown papules 2 to 10 mm in diameter with a pitted or speckled surface; they may coalesce to form large lesions. The virus is acquired through minute skin abrasions.
Lymphocytic choriomeningitis	An arenavirus that causes an infection of house mice	A nonfatal meningitis; viral transmission is believed to occur by direct contact with infected mice or by mouse bites.
Lassa fever	An arenavirus that causes an infection of *Mastomys natalensis*, an African rodent	A particularly deadly disease that occurs in west Africa. Viral transmission is believed to occur by direct contact with the urine and excreta of the infected rodents.
Kuru	A *prion*, or unconventional virus (see Chapter 16); occurs among the Fore people of New Guinea	A slowly developing disease of the central nervous system. It is associated with the practice of cannibalism. Viral transmission probably occurs through breaks in the skin during handling of infected tissues.

FIGURE 27.9

Nerve cell containing several Negri bodies (dark oval structures), which are diagnostic of rabies. They consist of ribonucleoprotein components of the rabies virus.

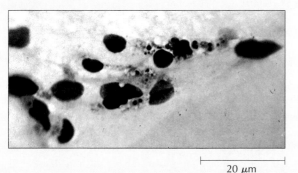

20 μm

treatment. Wild animals suspected of being rabid are tested by several means: (1) microscopic detection of rabies virus in brain tissue from the animal by specific fluorescent antibodies; (2) isolation of the virus from the saliva, urine, spinal fluid, or tissues of the animal by inoculation into the brains of mice; and (3) microscopic demonstration of characteristic round granules called **Negri bodies,** ribonucleoprotein components of the virus found in the cytoplasm of the nerve cells of the animal's brain [FIGURE 27.9]. If a domestic dog or cat is suspected of having rabies, the animal can be tested by these laboratory procedures or, alternatively, it can be kept under quarantine for at least 10 days to see if it develops clinical symptoms.

The rabies vaccine that is presently used is called *human diploid cell vaccine (HDCV).* It is prepared from rabies virus propagated in cultures of human tissue cells and consists of either inactivated whole virus or fragments of inactivated virus.

Other Wound and Skin Infections Caused by Viruses

Some other viral infections that can be acquired through skin abrasions are listed in TABLE 27.3, together with their agents and descriptions of the diseases. Laboratory workers should be especially aware that many other viruses, including the AIDS virus, may be acquired by direct contact with clinical specimens such as blood from infected patients, and that appropriate safety precautions should be used in dealing with such specimens.

ASK YOURSELF

1 What is the shape and composition of the rabies virus?

2 How do people become infected by the rabies virus? What accounts for the relatively long incubation period? What symptoms are produced in patients with rabies?

3 What treatment is given to people who have been bitten a short time earlier by a rabid animal? What makes it possible to immunize these patients against rabies? Of what does the present rabies vaccine consist?

4 What are several other viral infections of humans in which the causative agent is transmitted through a break in the skin?

HELMINTH INFECTIONS TRANSMITTED THROUGH CONTACT WITH THE SKIN

Although most helminths are transmitted by ingestion or by the bites of arthropods, hookworms are transmitted by direct contact with skin. It is interesting that these nematodes (roundworms) apparently can penetrate *unbroken* human skin, especially the tender skin between the toes. Certain trematodes (flatworms) called *blood flukes*, or **schistosomes**, can also penetrate unbroken human skin.

Hookworm Infections

It is estimated that about one-fourth of the world's population is infected with hookworms, mainly in the tropics and subtropics. In the United States, clinical hookworm disease was once common in rural areas of the southeastern states but has become relatively rare in recent years. Nevertheless, up to 10 percent of the population in some of these states may be infected (although not ill). The two hookworm species of greatest importance are the human parasites *Ancylostoma duodenale* and *Necator americanus*.

Life Cycle of Hookworms. Hookworms are acquired during direct contact with soil contaminated with the larvae [FIGURE 27.10A]. Contact for a period of at least 5 to 10 minutes is required for the larvae to penetrate the skin. The larvae are then carried by the bloodstream to the lungs and make their way up the trachea, or windpipe, to the mouth, where they are swallowed. After reaching the small intestine, the larvae anchor them-

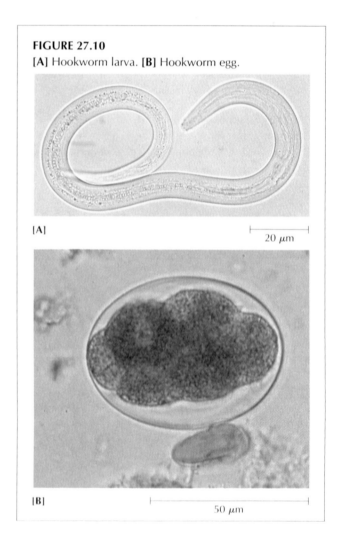

FIGURE 27.10
[A] Hookworm larva. [B] Hookworm egg.

[A]   20 μm

[B]   50 μm

selves to the intestinal wall and obtain nourishment by sucking blood from the blood capillaries. They eventually mature into sexually active adults, and after mating, a female worm produces a large number of eggs, about 7000 daily [FIGURE 27.10B]. The eggs are excreted in the stools of the patient and may enter the soil, where, if soil conditions are appropriate, they hatch into larvae. The larvae can then penetrate the skin of another human victim.

Pathogenicity of Hookworms. A patient with hookworm infection initially experiences intense itching and burning at the site of skin penetration, and papules develop that later become blisters [FIGURE 27.11]. Symptoms caused by the adult worms in the small intestine include abdominal pain, diarrhea, and loss of weight. Moreover, the patient loses blood when the worms suck it from blood capillaries. When the worms later attach to other sites in the intestine, blood continues to ooze from the previous wounds in the intestinal wall. The extent of blood loss from the patient depends on the number of worms causing the infection. If the rate at which the patient's body replaces the lost blood is less than the rate of blood loss, then the patient develops an *anemia*, a lack of red blood cells and their oxygen-containing pigment hemoglobin. A severe anemia can result in general weakness and even congestive heart failure.

Laboratory Diagnosis, Treatment, and Prevention of Hookworm Infections. Serious hookworm infection is indicated by egg counts of more than 1200 per milliliter, as determined by microscopic examination of the patient's stool.

Hookworm disease can be treated effectively with the chemical agents mebendazole and pyrantel pamoate. Prevention of the disease is best accomplished by proper disposal of human feces and by not going barefoot on soil.

Schistosomiasis

Schistosomiasis is one of the greatest disease scourges of the tropics, second only to malaria. More than 200 million people have the disease, mainly in Asia, South America, and Africa. Although as many as 400,000 persons are estimated to be infected in the United States, the disease is not transmissible in this country and occurs only in persons who have previously lived or traveled in other regions of the world.

Life Cycle of Schistosomes. Schistosomiasis is caused by blood flukes of the genus *Schistosoma*. The three major species are *S. mansoni*, *S. japonicum*, and *S. haematobium*, each having a specific geographic distribution. One portion of the life cycle of schistosomes occurs in certain freshwater snails [FIGURE 27.12]. Each *Schistosoma* species is dependent on a particular kind of snail. (Schistosomiasis is not transmissible in the United States because these particular snails do not occur there.) Humans become infected by contact with water containing *cercariae*—the infective forms of the schisto-

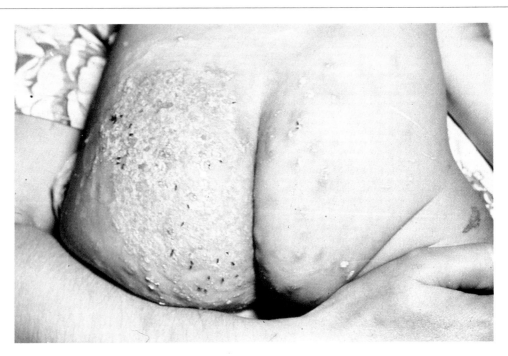

FIGURE 27.11
Child's buttocks infected with hookworms.

FIGURE 27.12
Life cycle of schistosomes.

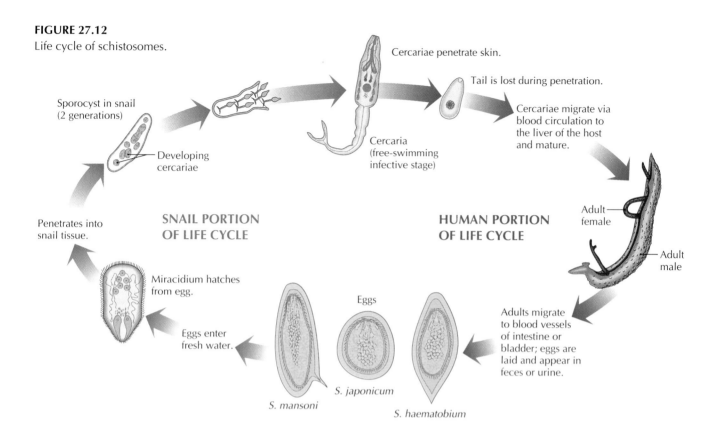

Sporocyst in snail
(2 generations)

Developing
cercariae

Cercariae penetrate skin.

Tail is lost during penetration.

Cercaria
(free-swimming
infective stage)

Cercariae migrate via
blood circulation to
the liver of the host
and mature.

**SNAIL PORTION
OF LIFE CYCLE**

**HUMAN PORTION
OF LIFE CYCLE**

Penetrates into
snail tissue.

Adult
female

Adult
male

Miracidium hatches
from egg.

Eggs

Adults migrate
to blood vessels
of intestine or
bladder; eggs are
laid and appear in
feces or urine.

Eggs enter
fresh water.

S. japonicum

S. mansoni

S. haematobium

FIGURE 27.13
Adult stage of
*Schistosoma
mansoni.*

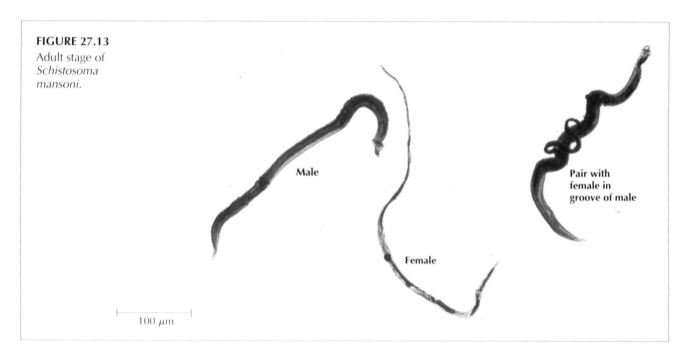

Male

Female

Pair with
female in
groove of male

100 μm

---

somes. These motile, fork-tailed forms, which emerge by the hundreds from an infected snail, can penetrate a person's skin by means of enzymes that break down the skin. The cercariae lose their tails during penetration, pass into the underlying tissues, and are carried by the bloodstream to the blood vessels of the liver. There they mature in 4 to 12 weeks (the time depends on the species) to become adult worms, 1 to 2 cm in length. The adults occur in pairs, with the female living in a long groove on the male [FIGURE 27.13]. The adults mate and

FIGURE 27.14
Egg of *Schistosoma mansoni*. Eggs of this species have a projecting "spine."

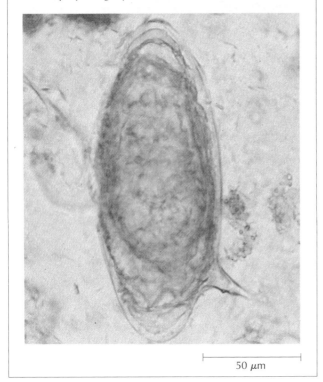

50 μm

then migrate to small blood vessels on the outside wall of the intestines (in the case of S. *mansoni* and S. *japonicum*) or urinary bladder (in the case of S. *haematobium*). The female lays numerous eggs, which are 40 to 70 by 100 to 175 μm in size [FIGURE 27.14]. After the eggs pass through the wall of the intestine or bladder, they are excreted in the feces or urine of the patient. When the feces or urine reaches fresh water, the eggs hatch to produce *miracidia*, which are motile by means of cilia and can penetrate snails. Sporocysts then develop within the snail's tissue, and in 4 to 6 weeks, motile cercariae emerge from the snail and the cycle begins again.

Pathogenicity of Schistosomes. Patients with schistosomiasis experience diarrhea, fever, loss of appetite, loss of weight, severe abdominal pain, and anemia. Severe damage may occur to the liver, the intestinal wall, the bladder wall, and often the lungs, heart, and brain. The major damage occurs during egg deposition and extrusion of the eggs from the patient's body. When some of the eggs become trapped in the tissues, the patient's body attempts to wall off these eggs. A cell-mediated immune response occurs, with the formation of granulomas similar to those occurring in tuberculosis (Chapter 24). The granulomas and scar tissue formed in response

to the infection may eventually become extensive enough to obstruct the flow of blood through blood vessels, or urine through the bladder.

Laboratory Diagnosis, Treatment, and Prevention of Schistosomiasis. A definitive diagnosis of schistosomiasis depends on demonstration of the presence of schistosome eggs by microscopic examination of the patient's feces or urine. In the case of fecal specimens, a special technique called the *Kato thick smear* is used to clarify the slide preparation so that the schistosome eggs can be seen more readily. Effective treatment of schistosomiasis is accomplished by oral administration of praziquantel, a recently developed antihelminthic drug.

There is presently no vaccine against schistosomiasis. Current research on the prevention of the disease includes development of potential vaccines, treatment of patients to stop the excretion of the schistosome eggs, control of snail populations, and establishment of various sanitary measures.

ASK YOURSELF

1 What are the two hookworm species of greatest importance?

2 What is the life cycle of hookworms? How can hookworms cause a severe anemia? With what can patients be treated?

3 What are the three most important species of schistosomes?

4 What is the life cycle of schistosomes? Why is schistosomiasis not a transmissible disease in the United States?

5 What treatment is available for patients with schistosomiasis?

SKIN AND WOUND INFECTIONS CAUSED BY FUNGI

Some pathogenic fungi have the ability to infect hair, nails, or the superficial layers of the skin. These infections are referred to as *dermatomycoses,* and the fungi that cause them are called *dermatophytes.* Other pathogenic fungi can invade the *subcutaneous tissue* (the tissue underlying the skin); these fungi cause infections called *subcutaneous mycoses.* Subcutaneous mycoses are far more serious than dermatomycoses and can result in extensive tissue destruction.

Dermatomycoses

Dermatomycoses are often called ***ringworm,*** on the basis of an early mistaken notion that worms or lice caused the skin infections and also because the skin lesions are more or less circular with an inflamed border that gives a ring-like appearance [FIGURE 27.15].

Biology of Dermatophytes. Many species of dermato-phytes (fungi that infect the skin) are known; some of the most common ones, and the infections they cause, are listed in TABLE 27.4. These species are differentiated on the basis of various morphological features, such as the size and shape of the asexual spores, pigmentation of the mycelium, and the occurrence of special hyphal struc-tures and arrangements. The morphological features of two common dermatophytes are shown in FIGURE 27.16.

The correlation of a particular dermatophyte species with a characteristic disease is difficult because a single

FIGURE 27.16
Some cases of ringworm of the scalp (tinea capitis) are caused by various species of the fungal genus *Microsporum,* such as **[A]** *M. canis* and **[B]** *M. gypseum.* The large spindle-shaped or elliptical macroconidia (spores) attached to the hyphae are characteristic of these species. Such macroconidia are formed during growth on laboratory media and are used to differentiate between the genera of derma-tophytes.

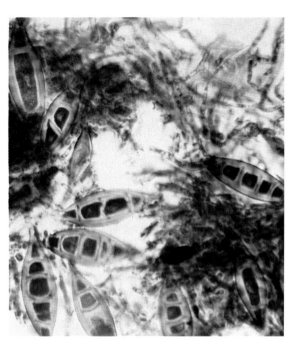

[A]   25 μm

[B]   25 μm

FIGURE 27.15
Ringworm lesions on a patient's back. This infection was caused by *Trichophyton verrucosum.*

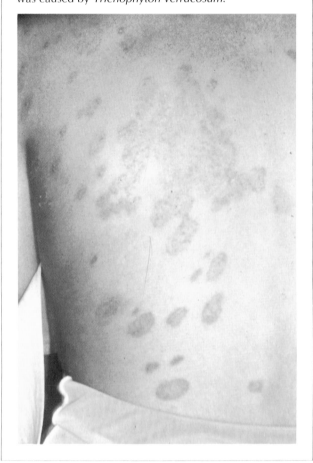

FIGURE 27.17

[A] A case of ringworm of the scalp (tinea capitis) caused by *Trichophyton mentagrophytes*.
[B] Photomicrograph of *T. mentagrophytes* showing grapelike clusters of round microconidia and several large, club-shaped macroconidia.

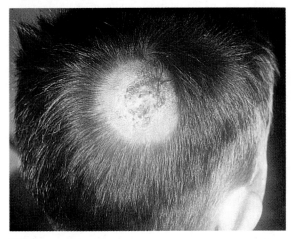

[A]

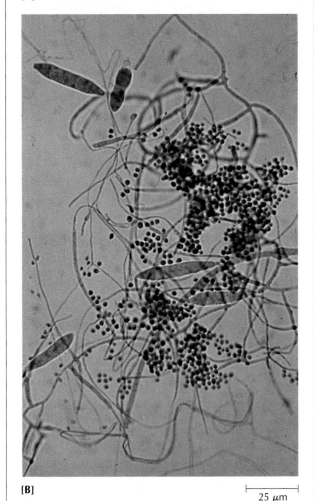

[B]   ⊢————⊣
                                      25 µm

FIGURE 27.18

This case of ringworm of the nails (tinea unguium, or onychomycosis) was caused by *Trichophyton rubrum*.

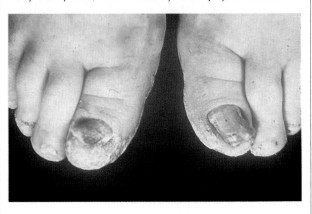

FIGURE 27.19

This case of tinea pedis was caused by *Trichophyton rubrum*.

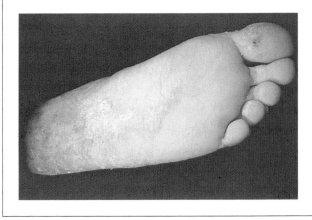

species can cause a variety of clinical symptoms. Furthermore, the same clinical disease can be caused by different species of dermatophytes. For these reasons, dermatologists often describe the infections by a terminology based on the part of the body involved. The first word used in this terminology is *tinea*, which means "small insect larva" and originated from the mistaken notion that these infections were caused by insects. For example, *tinea capitis* is ringworm of the scalp [FIGURE 27.17]; *tinea unguium*, or *onychomycosis*, is ringworm of the nails [FIGURE 27.18]; and *tinea pedis* is ringworm of the feet [FIGURE 27.19]. The type of tinea pedis in which scaling between the toes occurs is often termed *athlete's foot*.

TABLE 27.4
Some Common Fungi That Attack Skin, Nails, or Hair

Groups of fungi	Species	Occurrence and disease
Epidermophyton	*E. floccosum*	Causes infections of the skin and nails on fingers and toes.
Microsporum	*M. audouinii*	Causes epidemic ringworm of the scalp in children.
	M. canis	Common cause of infection of skin and hair on cats, dogs, and other animals; causes tinea capitis in children.
	M. gypseum	Occurs as a saprophyte in the soil and as a parasite on lower animals; occasionally found in ringworm of the scalp in children.
Trichophyton	Gypseum subgroup	
	T. mentagrophytes	Primarily a parasite of the hair.
	T. rubrum	Causes ringworm on many parts of the body; infects hair and scalp.
	T. tonsurans	Infects hair and scalp.
	Faviform subgroup	
	T. schoenleinii,	These fungi cause ringworm of the skin and scalp and glabrous
	T. violaceum	skin in humans; *T. verrucosum* causes ringworm in cattle also.
	T. ferrugineum	
	T. concentricum	
	T. verrucosum	
	Rosaceum subgroup	
	T. megnini	Causes ringworm of the human scalp.
	T. gallinae	Causes an infection in chickens.
Miscellaneous	*Piedraia hortae*	Causes an infection of the hair and scalp characterized by hard, black concretions; black piedra.
	Trichosporon beigelii	Causes an infection similar to the above, except that the concretions are white; white piedra.
	Malassezia furfur	Causes tinea versicolor, a generalized fungus infection of the skin covering the trunk and sometimes other areas of the body.
	Candida albicans	Causes candidiasis of skin, mucous membranes, and nails.

Transmission of Dermatophytes. Dermatophytes are commonly transmitted by direct contact with infected animals or people, or with inanimate objects contaminated with the fungi. Undamaged skin is a fairly effective barrier against infection, but skin abrasions can help dermatophytes to initiate infection. However, even unbroken skin can be infected by dermatophytes. Contributory factors are the quantity of fungi involved during exposure, the warmth of the skin, the chemical composition of the fluid from sweat glands and sebaceous glands, genetic factors that make some people more likely to become infected than others, and—most important of all—moisture. A "waterlogged" skin is far more vulnerable to infection than is dry skin, and this is why the sweat-laden, moist feet of athletes are susceptible to infection by dermatophytes.

Pathogenicity of Dermatophytes. After gaining access to the skin, dermatophytes spread radially in the outer layer of the epidermis by means of branching hyphae and occasional arthrospores. The outer layer of the epidermis consists of dead surface cells that are continually being replaced from below. The main chemical constituent of this outer layer is a tough protein called **keratin.** Dermatophytes have the ability to digest this protein, which helps them spread through the skin. Skin lesions caused by metabolic products of the fungi are characterized by irritation, scaling, local reddening and swelling, and inflammation at the circular spreading edge. Hair and nails also contain keratin, and some dermatophytes can infect these areas [FIGURE 27.20]. However, dermatophytes are unable to invade the living tissue below the outer keratinized layer, and dermatophyte infec-

FIGURE 27.20
Black piedra is a fungus infection of hair caused by *Piedraia hortae*. It is characterized by dark-brown or black nodules on the hair shaft, as shown in this photomicrograph.

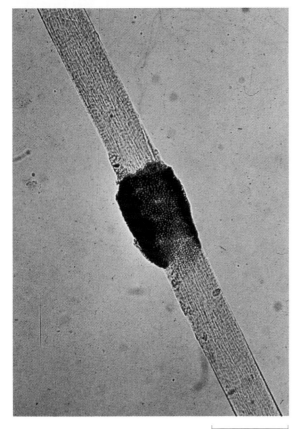

100 μm

tions, although very annoying, are relatively mild infections and are not life-threatening.

Laboratory Diagnosis of Dermatomycoses. Scrapings from infected skin, nails, or hair are prepared as wet slide mounts in potassium hydroxide (KOH) solution for microscopic detection of the fungi. The KOH makes the specimen transparent and increases the visibility of the fungal hyphae and fungal spores. Scrapings are also inoculated onto culture media that contain antibiotics to inhibit bacteria and saprophytic fungi, which otherwise would rapidly overgrow the slow-growing dermatophytes.

Treatment and Prevention of Dermatomycoses. Chronic dermatomycoses can be treated by oral administration of the antibiotic griseofulvin, which becomes concentrated in keratinized body tissues. Other chemotherapeutic agents for topical application include tolnaftate, haloprogin, and miconazole.

Prevention of dermatomycoses is difficult because of the widespread distribution of the causative fungi. Bathhouses at public swimming pools and common shower areas can be sources of infection.

Subcutaneous Mycoses

Subcutaneous mycoses are more severe than dermatomycoses because the causative microorganisms can attack the living tissue below the skin. One example of a subcutaneous mycosis is mycetoma, a serious disease in which destruction of skin, subcutaneous tissue, connective tissue, muscle, and even bone can occur.

FIGURE 27.21
A case of mycetoma caused by *Streptomyces somaliensis.*

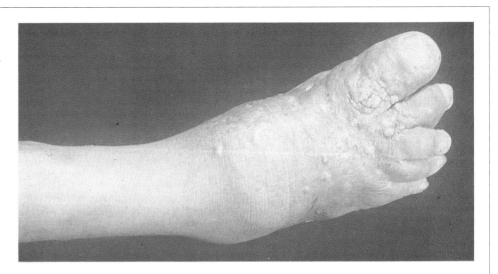

Mycetoma. Mycetoma occurs mainly in the tropics and subtropics but is not limited to these areas. The causative agents are various soil fungi or soil bacteria that gain access to subcutaneous tissue through a wound. The fungal species include *Madurella grisea, Madurella mycetomatis, Pseudallescheria boydii,* and others. The bacterial species are aerobic actinomycetes such as *Nocardia asteroides, N. brasiliensis, Actinomadura madurae, A. pelletieri,* and *Streptomyces somaliensis.*

Infection usually occurs on a foot and begins with a small, painless papule. As the microorganism spreads through the tissues, multiple abscesses and cavities develop from which pus drains to the skin surface. This pus contains tiny granules 0.2 to 3.0 mm in diameter, composed of the fungal or bacterial hyphae. Eventually the foot becomes a swollen, deformed mass of destroyed tissue and is subject to secondary infection by various bacterial pathogens [FIGURE 27.21]. In advanced cases of mycetoma the foot may have to be amputated.

A tentative identification of the causative agent is based on the color of the granules in the pus—red, pink, white, black, or yellow. However, precise identification depends on culturing the causative agent. It is important to determine early in the diagnosis whether the microorganism is a fungus or a bacterium. Bacterial mycetoma can be treated with chemotherapeutic agents such as penicillin or sulfonamides, whereas fungal mycetoma is much more difficult to treat, even with chemical agents that are effective against other kinds of fungal infections.

ASK YOURSELF

1 How do dermatomycoses differ from subcutaneous mycoses? Which of the two categories is the more serious?

2 What terminology is used for dermatomycoses? Is *ringworm* an accurate term?

3 What is the relation between dermatophytes and keratin? What chemotherapeutic agents can be used to treat dermatomycoses?

4 What kinds of microorganisms cause mycetoma? Are they all eucaryotes? Why is it important to determine the kind of causative agent in each case? How can laboratory identification be done?

5 What may happen to a patient's foot if a case of mycetoma becomes advanced?

SUMMARY

1 A break in the skin can be contaminated by organisms from many sources, including the skin itself, aerosol droplets, infectious dust, soil, human feces, animal urine and feces, or direct contact with the flesh of infected animals.

2 Infections caused by anaerobic bacteria are favored by crushed tissue and blood clots, contaminating aerobic or facultative bacteria, and toxic or irritant chemicals. Anaerobic infections include the following: tetanus, caused by *Clostridium tetani;* and gas gangrene, caused by various *Clostridium* species, especially *C. perfringens*. Tetanus neurotoxin prevents the secretion of the inhibitory chemical that normally prevents two opposing muscles from contracting at the same time. *C. perfringens* spreads rapidly through tissues and produces α toxin, which is a lecithinase.

3 Infections caused by aerobic and facultative bacteria include *Staphylococcus aureus* infections. *S. aureus* is a common inhabitant of the skin and nasopharynx and can easily gain access to wounds or surgical incisions. The organism produces a variety of toxins, and typically the infections are characterized by abscesses. Toxic shock syndrome occurs mainly in young women during a menstrual period. Treatment of *S. aureus* infections is complicated by the multiple antibiotic resistance of many strains.

4 Tularemia is caused by the bacterium *Francisella tularensis*. It is mainly a disease of wild animals and is acquired by direct contact, as during skinning of animals by hunters and trappers. Other bacterial infections whose agents are transmitted through wounds or breaks in the skin include *Bacteroides fragilis* infections, brucellosis, anthrax, leptospirosis, and rat-bite fever.

5 Rabies is a viral infection transmitted through the bite of an infected animal. After a long incubation period the virus reaches the central nervous system; during the incubation period a victim can be immunized with immune globulin and a vaccine consisting of live attenuated virus.

6 Other viral infections of humans that can be transmitted through a break in the skin include orf, molluscum contagiosum, milker's nodules, herpetic infections, common warts, lymphocytic choriomeningitis, Lassa fever, and kuru.

7 Hookworms are nematodes whose larvae from feces-contaminated soil can penetrate human skin. The larvae pass to the lungs, windpipe, and mouth, where they are swallowed and reach the small intestine. They develop into adults and produce many eggs, which are excreted in the feces. The bloodsucking ability of the adults can cause a patient to develop a severe iron-deficiency anemia. Certain trematodes (flatworms) called *blood flukes,* or schistosomes, can also penetrate unbroken human skin.

8 Dermatomycoses, or ringworm infections, are superficial fungal infections of nails, hair, or the keratinized outer layer of the skin. The ability to digest keratin helps the dermatophytes to spread along skin, hair, or nails. Subcutaneous mycoses are more severe than dermatomycoses and can be caused by fungi or by actinomycete bacteria. An example is mycetoma, which is characterized by extensive destruction of tissue and bone in the foot.

KEY TERMS

abscess
α toxin of *C. perfringens*
cercariae
dermatomycoses
dermatophytes
fibrin
hydrophobia
hyperbaric oxygen
keratin
lecithin
lecithinase
lockjaw
miracidia
Negri bodies
pus
ringworm
schistosomes
subcutaneous mycoses
subcutaneous tissue
tinea
TSS toxin-1 of *S. aureus*

REVIEW GUIDE

1 A cut or wound can be easily contaminated by staphylococci because these organisms are commonly present on the _____.

2 The causative agent of gas gangrene is a normal inhabitant of the human: **(a)** nasopharynx; **(b)** large intestine; **(c)** skin; **(d)** mouth; **(e)** stomach.

3 Wounds may be contaminated by *Streptococcus pyogenes* present in

_____ that are expelled during coughing or sneezing.

4 Which of the following statements best applies to infections acquired by contact with the tissues, urine, or feces of infected *animals*? **(a)** They have a low mortality rate. **(b)** They are characterized by person-to-person transmission. **(c)** They have an occupational incidence. **(d)** They have a high mortality rate. **(e)** They are usually postoperative infections.

5 Which *three* of the following favor development of anaerobic conditions in a wound? **(a)** presence of blood clots and crushed tissue; **(b)** removal of mechanically damaged tissue; **(c)** presence of aerobic or facultatively anaerobic bacteria; **(d)** lack of blood circulation in the damaged area; **(e)** absence of dirt or soil.

6 The drumstick shape of *Clostridium tetani* is due to the occurrence of a(n)

_____ at one end of the cell.

7 Tetanus neurotoxin prevents the secretion of a(n) _____ that would otherwise act to stop opposing muscles from contracting at the same time.

8 The vaccine against tetanus consists of: **(a)** antitoxin; **(b)** killed cells of *C. tetani;* **(c)** toxoid; **(d)** preformed antibodies; **(e)** a live attenuated strain of *C. tetani.*

9 Match the item at the left with the most appropriate description at the right.

_____ tetanus toxin

_____ α toxin of *C. perfringens*

_____ hydrogen gas

_____ hyperbaric oxygen

_____ lockjaw

(a) Lecithinase

(b) Used in treatment of cases of gas gangrene

(c) Acts on the central nervous system

(d) Can separate muscle sheaths from muscles and allow spread of *C. perfringens*

(e) Another name for tetanus

10 Which one of the following does *not* apply to gas gangrene? **(a)** The causative organism spreads rapidly through tissues. **(b)** Amputation of a limb may be required to save a patient. **(c)** Gas gangrene is most often a disease of the battlefield. **(d)** The infection usually remains localized at the site of the wound. **(e)** The α toxin of *C. perfringens* is a hemolysin and cytotoxin.

11 Match the item at the left with the most appropriate description at the right.

_____ alpha, beta, gamma, and delta toxins of *S. aureus*

_____ coagulase of *S. aureus*

_____ β-lactamase of *S. aureus*

_____ exfoliatins A and B of *S. aureus*

_____ TSS toxin-1 of *S. aureus*

(a) Toxic shock syndrome

(b) Conversion of soluble fibrinogen to insoluble fibrin

(c) Breaks down penicillin

(d) Hemolysins and leucocidins

(e) Scalded skin syndrome

12 The typical lesion caused by *S. aureus* is a "walled fort" called a(n)

_____.

13 Antibodies and antibiotics have difficulty in reaching bacteria within an abscess because there is no _____ within an abscess.

14 In women, toxic shock syndrome has been associated with the use of highly absorbent _____.

15 *Francisella tularensis* can be transmitted to humans by direct contact with infected animals and also by the bites of infected _____.

16 Which one of the following would be most likely to contract tularemia? **(a)** office workers; **(b)** sewer workers; **(c)** hunters and trappers; **(d)** persons over 65 years of age; **(e)** children under 5 years of age.

17 Match the organism at the left with the appropriate description at the right.

_____ *Bacteroides fragilis*

_____ *Brucella suis*

_____ *Bacillus anthracis*

_____ *Leptospira interrogans*

_____ *Streptobacillus moniliformis* and *Spirillum minus*

(a) Rat-bite fever
(b) Anaerobic abscesses
(c) Acquired by swimming in water contaminated by animal urine
(d) Endospore former that can cause a skin or lung infection that progresses to a fatal infection of the blood
(e) Gram-negative rod that is transmitted to humans by direct contact with infected swine

VIRAL INFECTIONS TRANSMITTED THROUGH A BREAK IN THE SKIN

18 The first person to develop a vaccine against rabies was

_____.

19 The rabies virus: **(a)** is icosahedral and contains single-stranded DNA; **(b)** has a lipid envelope and contains double-stranded DNA; **(c)** is bullet-shaped and contains single-stranded RNA; **(d)** is icosahedral and contains single-stranded DNA; **(e)** is icosahedral and contains double-stranded RNA.

20 Human rabies usually has an incubation period of 3 to 8 weeks before the virus reaches the _____ system.

21 A person who has been bitten by a rabid animal is treated with: **(a)** antibiotics; **(b)** Negri bodies; **(c)** fluorescent antibodies; **(d)** rabies vaccine and immune globulin; **(e)** interleukin-2.

22 Match the disease at the left with the appropriate description at the right.

_____ kuru

_____ common warts

_____ Lassa fever

_____ milker's nodules

_____ lymphocytic choriomeningitis

(a) Caused by papillomaviruses
(b) Acquired by direct contact with house mice or by mouse bites
(c) Associated with cannibalism in New Guinea
(d) Caused by a poxvirus that infects the udder of cattle
(e) Caused by an arenavirus that infects rodents in west Africa

23 *Ancylostoma duodenale* and *Necator americanus* are the two species of

_____ that are most important in human infections.

24 For hookworm infection to occur, contact of the skin with larvae-containing soil must be for a period of at least: **(a)** 0 to 5 seconds; **(b)** 5 to 10 seconds; **(c)** 5 to 10 minutes; **(d)** 30 minutes.

25 Because of the ability of hookworms to suck blood from the capillaries of the intestinal wall, patients may develop a severe _____.

26 Schistosomes are (select *three* of the following): **(a)** nematodes; **(b)** flatworms; **(c)** trematodes; **(d)** blood flukes; **(e)** roundworms.

27 The three most important *Schistosoma* species are

S. _____, *S.* _____, and

S. _____.

28 The infective forms of schistosomes (select *two* of the following): **(a)** are free-swimming cercariae; **(b)** are miracidia; **(c)** emerge by the hundreds from infected snails; **(d)** are the eggs; **(e)** are the adult worms.

29 The reason that schistosomiasis is *not transmissible* in the United States is mainly which one of the following? **(a)** high levels of sanitation; **(b)** mass immunization programs against schistosomiasis; **(c)** absence of the appropriate kinds of snails; **(d)** high resistance of the population to the disease; **(e)** none of the above: the disease *is* transmissible in the United States.

30 Fungi that cause superficial skin infections are called: **(a)** dermatomycoses; **(b)** subcutaneous mycoses; **(c)** ringworms; **(d)** dermatophytes; **(e)** tinea.

31 Tinea unguium is: **(a)** ringworm of the feet; **(b)** ringworm of the scalp; **(c)** ringworm of the hair; **(d)** athlete's foot; **(e)** ringworm of the nails.

32 The most important factor favoring infection by a dermatophyte is

_____.

33 Dermatophytes have the ability to digest a tough protein called

_____.

34 Mycetoma is a severe subcutaneous mycosis that usually occurs on the: **(a)** hand; **(b)** foot; **(c)** face; **(d)** trunk; **(e)** scalp.

35 Mycetoma can be caused not only by fungi but also by bacteria called aerobic

_____.

REVIEW QUESTIONS

1 List all the ways by which a wound could become contaminated by an infectious microorganism.

2 What conditions favor the development of an anaerobic infection such as tetanus or gas gangrene?

3 Contrast the mode of action of the major toxin of *C. tetani* with that of *C. perfringens*.

4 Explain the basis for using hyperbaric oxygen to treat a case of gas gangrene.

5 What is an abscess, and why is it difficult to treat diseases characterized by abscess formation, even when using the correct antibiotic?

6 Which infections described in this chapter are acquired by contact with the tissues, saliva, urine, or feces of *animals*?

7 If a person has been bitten by an animal suspected of having rabies, it is important to confirm that the animal is rabid so that the human victim can receive preventive treatment. How can this be done?

8 What is the infectious form of a schistosome? Where does it occur in nature?

DISCUSSION QUESTIONS

1 If a person has a wound conducive to development of anaerobic conditions, why is surgical removal of dead tissue and blood clots the *most important* of the three measures that are used to prevent gas gangrene?

2 An immune response to an infection usually benefits the patient. How, then, is it that a person's immune response to infection by schistosomes may cause extensive damage to the body?

3 Why is laboratory identification of the causative agent essential in order to provide the proper treatment of a case of mycetoma?

4 Earlier vaccines against rabies, including Pasteur's original vaccine, contained not only inactivated virus but also some nerve tissue from the animals used to propagate the virus. Why do you suppose that some individuals who were given these vaccines, although they did not develop rabies, did develop a severe and often fatal encephalomyelitis (inflammation of the brain and spinal cord)? (*Note:* The present human diploid cell vaccine does not contain nerve tissue and does not induce encephalomyelitis.)

5 From a practical viewpoint, why is it important to know the life cycles of parasites such as schistosomes and hookworms?

6 How is it that some pathogenic microorganisms that tend to "stay put" and not spread readily through the body are able to cause serious diseases such as toxic shock syndrome and tetanus?

X

Microbial Ecology

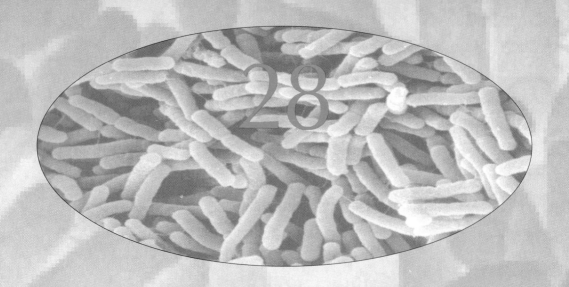

Microbiology of the Soil and the Atmosphere

OBJECTIVES

After reading this chapter you should be able to

1 Explain how the soil environment supports the growth of microorganisms.

2 Describe laboratory methods that are used to count the microorganisms present in soil and understand the limitations of each method.

3 Characterize the various groups of microorganisms that inhabit the soil.

4 Compare the microorganisms in soil with those that inhabit the rhizosphere.

5 Identify the kinds of interactions that occur among soil microorganisms.

6 Describe the roles of microorganisms in the nitrogen, carbon, and sulfur cycles.

7 Explain the importance of microorganisms for degrading herbicides and pesticides.

8 Describe the microorganisms present in the atmosphere and their origin, dissemination, and survival.

9 Discuss the importance of the microorganisms in the atmosphere.

OVERVIEW

Soil teems with microscopic life. A teaspoon of fertile garden soil may contain billions of microorganisms—bacteria, fungi, algae, protozoa, and viruses. Two words characterize the microbial flora of soil—abundant and diverse. One researcher estimated that the weight of the microflora living in the top 15-cm layer of soil in one hectare (2.47 acres) is between 0.5 and approximately 4 metric tons. Macroscopic forms of life also abound, such as earthworms, nematodes, mites, and insects, and also the root systems of plants. Thus soil is a very complex living environment.

Directly or indirectly, animal wastes and the dead bodies of animals and tissues of plants eventually enter the soil. In time they all disappear, transformed into substances that enrich the soil. Microorganisms are responsible for these transformations, converting dead plant and animal matter into simple inorganic substances that nourish plants. The plants then serve as nourishment for animals. By serving as a link between animals and plants, microorganisms play a key role in maintaining life on earth.

In this chapter you will learn about the kinds of microorganisms that inhabit the soil and how they bring about important biochemical changes. They are essential to several biochemical processes that recycle important elements such as sulfur, nitrogen, and carbon. You also will learn about the microorganisms of the air, because many aerial microorganisms come from the soil. Soil may harbor pathogenic microorganisms, depending on the nature of animal and plant tissues and wastes it contains. These microorganisms may cause infections, as you learned in Chapter 27.

THE SOIL ENVIRONMENT

Soil is the region on the earth's crust where geology and biology meet, the land surface that provides a home to plant, animal, and microbial life.

If you compare the physical and chemical characteristics of soil from deserts, forests, marshlands, swamps, grazing pastures, and farmland, it becomes evident that vast differences exist among them. Soils are characterized by *horizons*, parallel layers of various thicknesses and structures [FIGURE 28.1]. Each horizon differs from that above or below it in such properties as the organic and mineral content, color, texture, structure, porosity, and pH. These properties in turn influence the moisture content, gaseous content, and biological content of the horizon. For example, a horizon that is rich in organic matter has great biological activity and is quite different from one that is made up of bedrock and has little organic matter and low biological activity.

Organic matter enters soil from various sources. For instance, cellulose, lignin, and glycans such as pectin come from the dead remains of plants. Proteins come from the dead remains of animals, chitin from the exoskeletons of insects, and complex polysaccharides from the cell walls of fungi and other microorganisms. Animal urine and feces also contribute organic material. The organic matter of soil can be classified into three groups: *insoluble*, *soluble*, and *microbial*. For instance, a soft, brownish, amorphous substance called *humus* is classified as insoluble organic matter.

Humus is formed during the microbial decomposition of plant and animal residues; it includes the mass of microorganisms involved in the decomposition of these substrates. Humus is beneficial to soil because it improves soil structure, provides for the slow release of nutrients, increases the soil's buffering capacity, and increases its water-holding capacity.

The soluble organic compounds in soil include the degradation products of the complex polymers of plant and animal tissue and microbial cells, such as sugars from cellulose, phenolics from lignin, and amino acids from proteins.

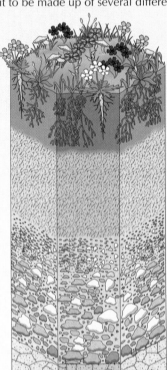

FIGURE 28.1

Soil horizons. An examination of a profile of soil shows it to be made up of several different *horizons* or layers.

Horizon A:
Topsoil. Organic debris in various stages of decomposition, including humus; living organisms, including soil microbial flora, plant roots, and insects; minerals.

Horizon B:
Subsoil. Fine particles and minerals.

Horizon C:
Parent material. Weathered mineral materials excluding bedrock; partially broken-down inorganic materials.

Horizon D:
Bedrock. Unweathered rock.

ASK YOURSELF

1 How are soils characterized?

2 What differences exist in properties of various layers of soil?

3 From what is humus formed, and how does it benefit the soil?

ENUMERATION AND ISOLATION OF SOIL MICROORGANISMS

Because microorganisms are crucial in maintaining the productivity of soil, it is imperative that microbiologists understand the magnitude and diversity of this microbial population [FIGURE 28.2]. No single laboratory technique can reveal the total microbial population of a soil sample. This is because of the great diversity of microorganisms that inhabit soil. Some of the techniques that are used to estimate the numbers and kinds of soil microorganisms include the *agar-plate culture technique*, *direct microscopic examination*, and the *enrichment culture technique*.

FIGURE 28.2

Sizes of various soil organisms and their respective locations in the soil structure. Most organisms live exclusively in pores, which individually constitute a fractional part of the fine microstructure of the soil.

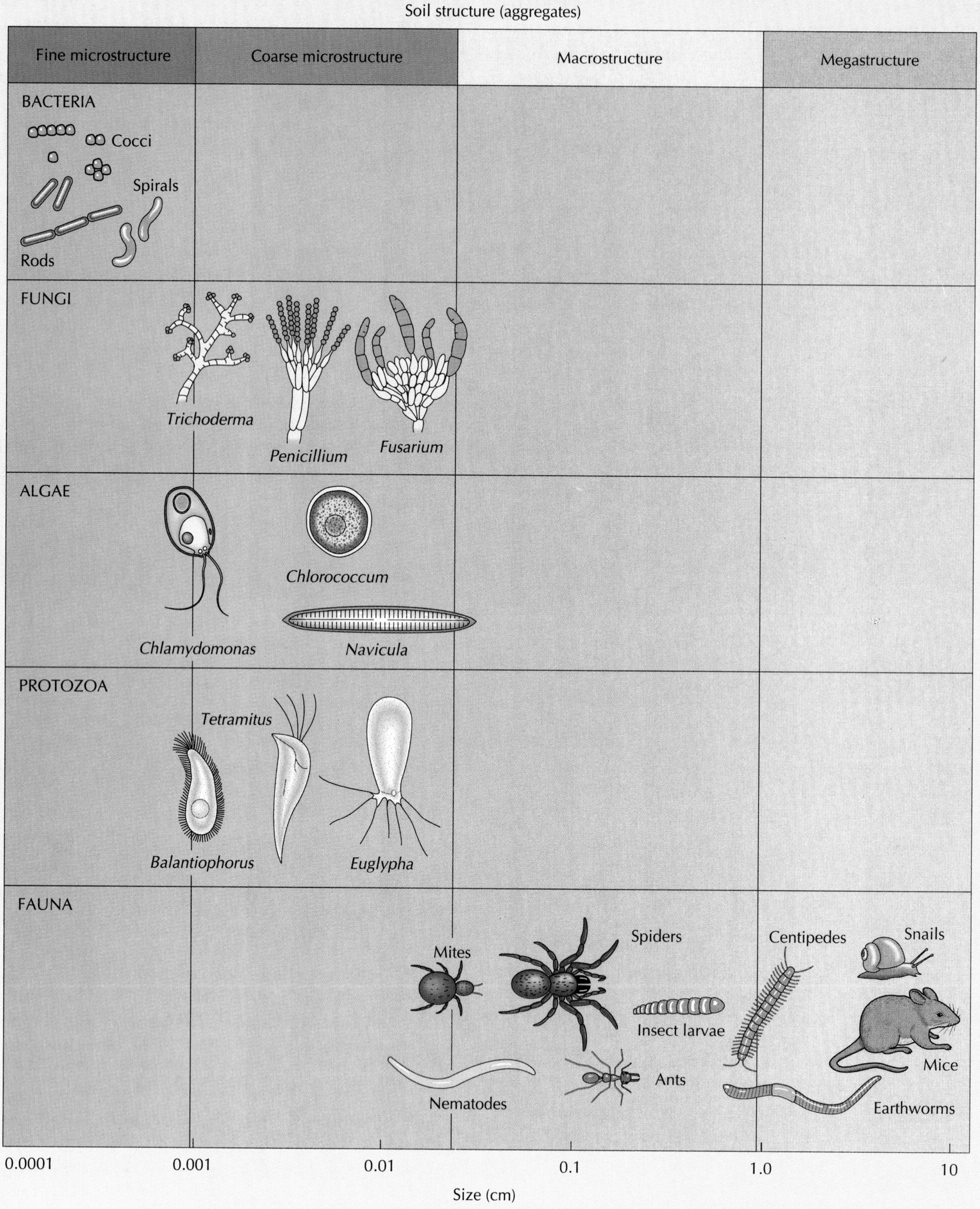

FIGURE 28.3
Colonies of microorganisms which have developed on agar medium that was inoculated with a soil sample and then incubated at room temperature.

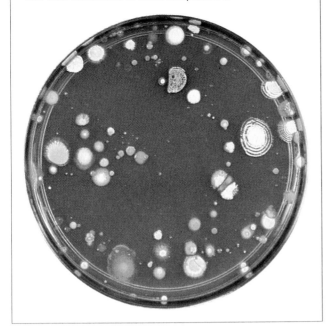

Agar-Plate Culture Technique

In the agar-plate culture technique, dilutions of the soil sample are added to tubes of a melted and cooled agar medium and the contents of the tubes are poured into Petri dishes. Alternatively, the dilutions may be spread over the surface of plates of the solidified agar medium to permit colonies to develop [FIGURE 28.3]. From the numbers of colonies that develop on the plates, we can calculate the number of living organisms per gram of soil. However, only a portion of the total microbial population will be able to grow under any specific set of cultural conditions provided. For example, if you use nutrient agar and incubate the plates at 25°C in an air atmosphere in the dark for 48 hours, you will not be able to detect the following kinds of microbes:

Anaerobes and microaerophiles, because they are poisoned by an air atmosphere
Strict thermophiles and psychrophiles, because they do not grow at 25°C
Photoautotrophs, because they require light as an energy source
Chemoautotrophs, because they prefer inorganic nutrients

Many nutritionally fastidious heterotrophs, because they may require special nutrients not present in nutrient agar
Slow-growing organisms, because they may take a week or more to grow into visible colonies

Even if you use several different media and cultural conditions, it will still be difficult to estimate the total microbial population. This is because of the overlapping that occurs among physiological groups. For example, facultative organisms can grow aerobically and anaerobically, some autotrophs can use organic sources of nitrogen, some phototrophs can grow heterotrophically in the dark, and some thermophiles can grow at mesophilic temperatures.

Direct Microscopic Examination

For direct microscopic examination, a dilution of a soil sample is spread in a thin film on a glass slide. After fixing and staining the film, the microorganisms can be enumerated by microscopic examination. Although this method can be used to estimate the total microbial population, special staining techniques are necessary to distinguish living from dead microorganisms. Moreover, it is often difficult to distinguish microscopic soil particles from microbial cells.

Scanning electron microscopy has been used to search for microorganisms in soil. This kind of direct observation can provide interesting information about microorganisms in their natural habitat.

Enrichment Culture Technique

The enrichment culture technique does not provide quantitative information on the microbial flora present in any given sample. Instead, it helps isolate microorganisms that are able to metabolize a particular substrate and that may be present in very small numbers in the original sample. For example, assume that you wish to isolate soil microorganisms that can degrade a phenolic-type compound such as p-hydroxybenzoic acid [FIGURE 28.4]. You would first prepare a medium in which p-hydroxybenzoic acid is the only source of carbon (the energy source). A sample of soil would then be inoculated into the first of a series of flasks and that flask is then placed in an incubator. After several days of incubation, some material is transferred from the first flask into a second flask. This process is repeated a number of times. After incubation of the last inoculated flask in this series, material from this flask is transferred to an agar medium containing p-hydroxybenzoic acid as the sole

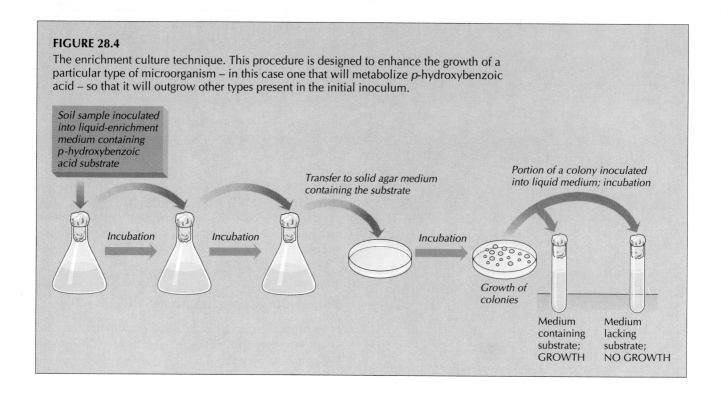

FIGURE 28.4
The enrichment culture technique. This procedure is designed to enhance the growth of a particular type of microorganism – in this case one that will metabolize *p*-hydroxybenzoic acid – so that it will outgrow other types present in the initial inoculum.

carbon source. After incubation, colonies will develop on the agar that may consist of *p*-hydroxybenzoic acid-utilizing microbes. To confirm this, a small amount of each colony to be tested is inoculated into liquid medium that either contains the *p*-hydroxybenzoic acid substrate or does not contain it. After incubation, growth will occur only in the medium containing the substrate, if the enrichment process has selected for and promoted the growth of *p*-hydroxybenzoic acid-utilizing microbes.

Enrichment culture techniques are not foolproof. For example, failure to isolate the desired metabolic type of microorganism might be due to the lack of a required vitamin; on the other hand, degradation of a complex substrate may result from the action of more than one species of microorganism.

ASK YOURSELF

1 Why and how do we enumerate microbes that inhabit the soil?

2 What techniques are used to estimate the numbers and kinds of soil microorganisms?

3 What kinds of bacteria from a soil sample would not be recovered by inoculating a nutrient agar plate that is then incubated at 30°C?

SOIL MICROORGANISMS

The numbers and kinds of microorganisms present in soil depend on many environmental factors:

1 Amount and type of nutrients available
2 Available moisture
3 Degree of aeration
4 Temperature
5 pH
6 Practices and events that may add large numbers of microorganisms to the soil, such as application of manure or sewage sludge and the occurrence of floods; or those that may remove microorganisms, such as dust storms

The presence of roots and the extent of the root system in soil also affect the numbers and kinds of microorganisms present, as discussed later in this chapter. This is called the *rhizosphere effect* (from the Greek *rhiza*, "root").

Interactions among microbial species also have an important effect on the microbial population in soil. For instance, predatory protozoa and antibiotic-producing actinomycetes may eliminate certain species of microorganisms. On the other hand, cellulose- and protein-decomposing bacteria may provide nutrients for less versatile biochemical species by breaking down these complex molecules into smaller, more readily metabolized ones.

Bacteria

Bacteria account for the largest portion of the microbial population of soil, in both numbers and variety [TABLE 28.1]. Direct microscope counts as high as several billion bacteria per gram of soil have been reported, but plate counts from the same samples yield only a fraction of this number (millions). The reason for this discrepancy, as stated earlier, is that (1) the direct microscope method does not distinguish between dead cells and living cells, and (2) there is such a great variety of nutritional and physiological kinds of bacteria in soil that no single set of cultural conditions can support the growth of every viable cell. Indeed, there are undoubtedly many kinds of soil bacteria that have not yet been isolated and identified.

Most soil bacteria are heterotrophic, and spore-forming bacilli are common. Species of *Bacillus*, *Clostridium*, *Arthrobacter*, *Pseudomonas*, *Rhizobium*, *Azotobacter*, and *Nitrobacter* are generally present. Actinomycete bacteria including species of *Nocardia*, *Streptomyces*, and *Micromonospora*—as many as millions per gram—are present in dry, warm soils. These organisms are responsible for the characteristic musty or earthy odor of a freshly plowed field. Actinomycetes can degrade many complex substances and thus are important in improving soil fertility. Actinomycetes are noted for their ability to make antibiotics in the laboratory, but detectable amounts of antibiotics are rarely found in soil. It is possible that antibiotics can be present and active only in localized areas immediately surrounding the actinomycete cells.

Cyanobacteria, the oxygen-producing photosynthetic bacteria, play a key role in the transformation of rock to soil. They can grow on the surfaces of freshly exposed rocks, and their cells accumulate as organic deposits. This establishes a nutrient base that supports the growth of other bacterial species. These in turn pave the way for growth of other bacteria and fungi. Meanwhile, acids produced during microbial metabolism dissolve the mineral constituents of the rock. The gradual accumulation of organic matter and dissolved minerals continues until conditions are suitable for the growth of lichens, then mosses, then higher plants. Cyanobacteria, as you will see later, also help provide nitrogen to certain crops.

Fungi

Hundreds of different species of fungi inhabit the soil. They are most abundant near the soil surface, where oxygen is readily available. Some of the more common species of fungi in soil are *Penicillium*, *Mucor*, *Rhizopus*, *Fusarium*, *Cladosporium*, *Aspergillus*, and *Trichoderma*. The physical and chemical (nutrient) conditions in soil will dictate the predominant species. An example is the soil pH, as shown in TABLE 28.2.

TABLE 28.1

Approximate Numbers of Organisms Commonly Found in Soils*

Organism[†]	Estimated numbers/g
Bacteria (other than actinomycetes)	3,000,000 to 500,000,000
Actinomycetes	1,000,000 to 20,000,000
Fungi (other than yeasts)	5,000 to 900,000
Yeasts	1,000 to 100,000
Algae	1,000 to 500,000
Protozoa	1,000 to 500,000
Nematodes	50 to 200

*The figures for bacteria, actinomycetes, fungi, and yeasts are based on plate counts and refer to viable cells, spores, or fragments of mycelia able to grow on the plating media.
[†]In addition to these there are large numbers of slime molds (myxomycetes), viruses or phages of bacteria, plants, insects and other arthropods, earthworms, mycoplasmas, and other organisms.
SOURCE: J. P. Martin and D. D. Focht, "Biological Properties of Soils," in L. F. Elliott and F. J. Stevenson, eds., *Soils for Management of Organic Wastes and Waste Waters*, American Society of Agronomy, Madison, Wis., 1977.

TABLE 28.2

Numbers of Bacteria and Fungi in Soil Fertility Plots at Riverside, California, in Relation to Soil pH

Soil pH	Bacteria (millions/gm)	Fungi (thousands/gm)
7.5	95	180
7.2	58	190
6.9	57	235
4.7	41	966
3.7	3	280
3.4	1	200

SOURCE: J. P. Martin and D. D. Focht, "Biological Properties of Soils," in L. F. Elliott and F. J. Stevenson, eds., *Soils for Management of Organic Wastes and Waste Waters*, American Society of Agronomy, Madison, Wis., 1977.

Fungal counts have been reported ranging from thousands to hundreds of thousands per gram of soil. Fungi are very active in decomposing the complex organic constituents of plant tissues such as cellulose, lignin, and pectin. Moreover, the accumulation of mold mycelia improves the physical structure of soil by increasing the *crumble structure*. This refers to the binding together of fine soil particles to form larger, water-stable aggregates. The mycelium penetrates through the soil, forming a network that entangles the small particles.

Yeasts are most likely to occur in the soils of vineyards, orchards, and apiaries, since they are abundant on the leaves, stems, and fruit that drop onto the soil.

Algae

The algal population of soil is usually smaller than the population of either bacteria or fungi. The major kinds of algae present are the green algae *Chlorophyta* and the diatoms *Chrysophyta*. Because they are photoautotrophic, algae are predominantly near the soil surface. In a rich, fertile soil, the biochemical activities of algae are much less important than those of bacteria and fungi. In some situations, however, algae can perform important beneficial changes. For example, on barren and eroded lands they may initiate the accumulation of organic matter because of their photosynthetic activities. Algae, when growing in association with fungi, can help transform rock material into soil.

Protozoa and Viruses

The number of protozoa in moist, rich soils ranges from a few hundred to several hundred thousand per gram. Most soil protozoa feed upon bacteria and other organic material.

Some soil bacteria contain bacterial viruses (bacteriophages). Plant and animal viruses also occur sporadically in soil in tissues of dead plants and animals and in animal wastes.

ASK YOURSELF

1 What factors affect the numbers and kinds of microorganisms in soil?

2 What role do cyanobacteria play? Explain.

3 How do the following compare in numbers in soil, and how may they affect soil: bacteria, fungi, algae, protozoa, viruses?

THE RHIZOSPHERE

The *rhizosphere* is the region where soil and plant roots make contact. The number of microorganisms on and around roots is greater than that in root-free soil; the kinds of microorganisms in the rhizosphere also differ from those in root-free soil [FIGURE 28.5]. Electron microscope techniques allow microbiologists to observe microorganisms directly on root surfaces [FIGURE 28.6]. In the rhizosphere, bacteria are the predominant microorganisms. Their growth is stimulated by nutrients such as amino acids and vitamins released from the root tissue. Bacteria that require amino acids for growth occur in greater numbers in the rhizosphere than in root-free soil. The products of microbial metabolism that are released into the rhizosphere stimulate the growth of the plants. Thus, an exchange of nutrients occurs between the plant root system and the microorganisms. The rhizosphere is a tremendously complex biological sys-

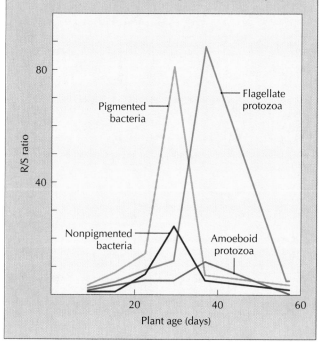

FIGURE 28.5

The ratio between the number of microorganisms in the rhizosphere (R) and the corresponding number of microbes in the soil (S) away from the root system (R/S ratio). The R/S ratios shown here depict the rise and fall of bacterial and protozoan populations within the rhizosphere, during development of *Sinapsis alba* (mustard plant). Note that at the beginning and at the end of plant growth, the R/S ratio is very low, indicating that the populations of microorganisms in the soil and in the rhizosphere are of nearly the same magnitude. During the active growth phase, however, the microbial population is considerably higher in the region of the rhizosphere.

FIGURE 28.6

The microbial flora in the rhizosphere as seen in scanning electron micrographs of epidermal root cells. In this study, plants were removed from a forest preserve, and special precautions were taken to recover root systems with as little mechanical damage as possible to the tissues. The root systems were dissected from the plants and representative specimens were selected for electron microscopy. **[A, B]** Fungal hyphae and bacteria on the epidermal cells of *Ammophilia arenaria* (beach grass). **[C]** Bacteria on the epidermis of a barley root. **[D]** Root hair, epidermal cell, and bacteria.

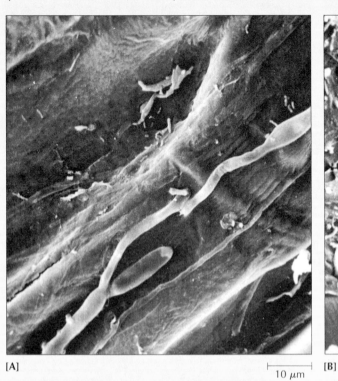

[A] 10 μm

[B] 10 μm

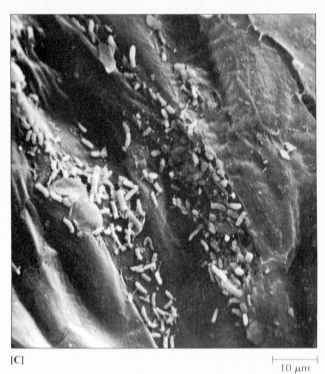

[C] 10 μm

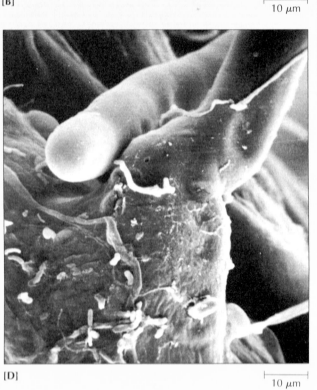

[D] 10 μm

tem, and there is a great deal yet to be learned about its plant-microbe interactions [DISCOVER 28.1].

INTERACTIONS AMONG SOIL MICROORGANISMS

Symbiosis is a condition in which the individuals of a species live in close association with individuals of another species. In soil, symbiotic relationships are common because of the enormous numbers of microorganisms that are sharing the same environment. Organisms living symbiotically may interact in various ways. In some instances the interactions are beneficial to one or more of the species involved; in others the interaction may be inhibitory. For example, one species may inhibit another by competing with it for available nutrients or by forming toxic metabolic products. On the other hand, the metabolic end products of one species may serve as nutrients for growth of another species. The interactions in a symbiotic relationship often cannot be deduced from pure-culture studies, and many have been discovered only by experiments in which two or more species of microorganisms are deliberately cultured together. Unfortunately, relatively few studies of this kind have been done compared with pure-culture studies.

The different ways in which symbiotic organisms interact have been given specific descriptive labels: *mutualism, commensalism, antagonism, competition, parasitism,* and *predation.*

Mutualism

Mutualism is the form of symbiosis in which each organism benefits. The manner in which the benefit is derived depends on the particular interaction, as shown in the following examples.

Lichens are composite microorganisms—they consist of an alga or a cyanobacterium growing in intimate association with a fungus. Lichens occur on rocks [FIGURE 28.7], tree bark, and many other substrates that may be unsuitable for growth of other organisms. Many lichens can grow at the low temperatures found at high altitudes or in polar environments. For example, "reindeer mosses" are lichens which serve as food for herbivorous animals in Arctic regions, and they may cover

FIGURE 28.7
[A] A red lichen, *Caloplaca elegans*, growing on a rock. [B] Two different kinds of lichens, *Pseudoparmelia caperata* (green) and *Umbilicaria pustulata* (brown), growing on a rock.

[A]

[B]

many miles of land with ankle-deep growth. Lichens may occur in many colors: white, black, red, orange, yellow, and green.

A simple lichen is made up of a top layer of tightly woven fungal mycelium, a lower layer of the alga or cyanobacterium, and a bottom layer of fungal mycelium [FIGURE 28.8]. The bottom layer may attach to the substrate directly or by means of short, twisted strands of hyphae that serve as anchors. Some lichens have a more

28.1 AN EXPERIMENTAL TECHNIQUE TO OBSERVE INTERACTIONS IN THE RHIZOSPHERE

Field studies of microorganism-root interactions pose problems when one wishes to assess the effect of specific microbial populations. For example, it is not feasible to distribute an inoculum of microorganisms evenly throughout the plant-root system of a plant grown conventionally in the soil.

Recently, Peter G. Hartel and his colleagues at the University of Georgia have described a Styrofoam cup-membrane assembly designed especially for the study of microorganism-root interactions. In this technique membranes of appropriate porosity are used to physically separate the root system from the soil while allowing the passage of water and nutrients through the membranes.

A cross section of the Styrofoam assembly is shown in the accompanying illustration [A], which consists of three nested 450-ml Styrofoam cups. The top cup is cut in half lengthwise; the top half of this cup is covered vertically with a membrane of 10-μm pore size. The middle cup (with bottom removed) holds the two top halves together—soil is added to each of the top halves. Seedlings are planted between the membrane surfaces and incubated, as shown in photo [B].

After suitable incubation, the top cup is removed and opened at the membrane surface. Root hairs attach to the 10-μm pore size membrane as shown in photo [C]. In experiments to study microorganism-root interactions, the inoculum of microorganisms is evenly dispersed into the soil in the cup halves and the two halves of the top cup are rejoined as in the original setup. Plants are incubated and observed for growth responses and the microbiological changes in the soil portion determined.

Adapted from Peter G. Hartel et al. and the American Society for Microbiology, *Applied and Environmental Microbiology*, May 1989, pp. 1291–1294.

[A] Cross section of the Styrofoam three-nested-cup assembly. [B] Cup assembly with 14-day-old tomato plant. [C] Cup assembly opened at membrane interface.

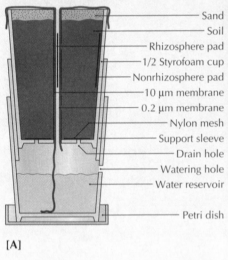
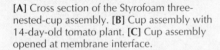

- Sand
- Soil
- Rhizosphere pad
- 1/2 Styrofoam cup
- Nonrhizosphere pad
- 10 μm membrane
- 0.2 μm membrane
- Nylon mesh
- Support sleeve
- Drain hole
- Watering hole
- Water reservoir
- Petri dish

[A]

[B]

[C]

complex structure. For example, some may have a midlayer of fungus directly below the algal layer; this midlayer may act as a reservoir for stored food.

In this association, the photosynthetic activities of the alga or cyanobacterium provide the fungus with necessary organic compounds. The fungus in turn protects its photosynthetic partner from desiccation. Its mycelium provides a firm base for growth and prevents removal of the alga or cyanobacterium by wind and rain.

Microorganisms may also form mutualistic relationships with plants; perhaps the most common example is that of nitrogen-fixing bacteria growing in the roots of legumes (described later in this chapter). Another example of mutualism is the root-fungus associations called **mycorrhizae** that occur on most plants. Mycorrhizae are of two types: *ectotrophic*, or growing on the outside surface of the roots; and *endotrophic*, or growing within the plant roots.

Ectomycorrhizae are characterized by a fungal growth of mycelia that forms a sheath around the feeder roots of the plant [FIGURE 28.9]. The fungi involved belong to the basidiomycete group—those that form mushrooms. The fungus hyphae penetrate the cells of the outer root surface; single hyphae extend outward from

FIGURE 28.8

Structure of a lichen. **[A]** Diagrammatic representation of algal and fungal physical relationships in a foliose lichen. **[B]** A portion of a longitudinal section through the thallus of the foliose lichen, *Physica* sp.

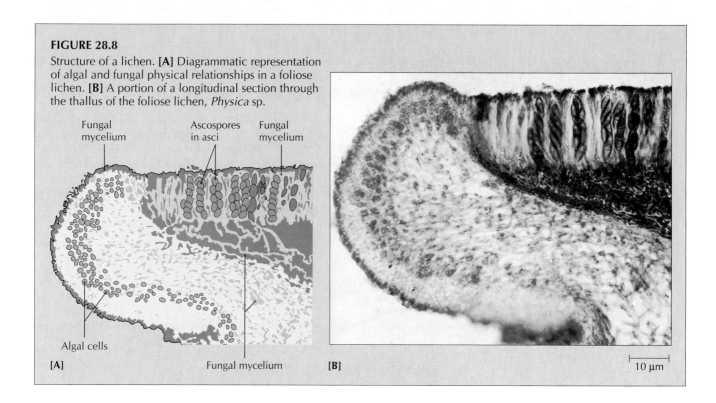

[A]

[B]

10 µm

FIGURE 28.9

Mycorrhizae: A plant root-fungus association. **[A]** Ectomycorrhizae. The fungus develops a layer of mycelia (white areas) at the tips of the feeder roots on a shortleaf pine plant. **[B]** Endomycorrhizae. The hyphae of the fungus grow between and penetrate the epidermal and cortical cells of plant feeder roots and form highly branched structures called arbuscules which are clearly seen in this cross section of a feeder root. The plant uses the arbuscules as a nutrient source and the fungus, in return, derives its nutrients from the plant.

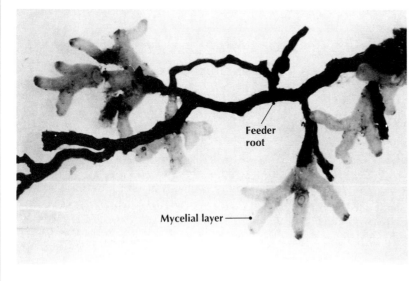

[A]

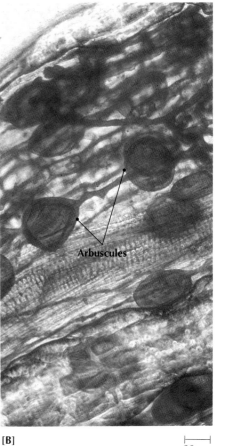

[B]

20 µm

the roots into the soil. The fungus obtains nutrients from the plant, and the plant receives nutrients (especially minerals) and water through the fungus. This association is of particular significance in mineral-deficient soils and occurs primarily on the roots of conifers such as pine and spruce trees.

The second type, the endomycorrhizae, occur in numerous crop plants such as corn, wheat, and legumes and trees such as maple, citrus, holly, and dogwood. The hyphae of the fungus penetrate the surface cells of the feeder roots and form highly branched structures called *arbuscules* within the root tissue [FIGURE 28.9B]. The arbuscules are digested, releasing nutrients to the plant. The fungus in turn derives nutrients from the plant tissue. Basidiomycetes are the most common type of fungi involved in this association.

Commensalism

Commensalism is an association in which one organism benefits and the other is not affected. For example, many fungi can degrade cellulose to glucose, and then bacteria—most of which cannot degrade cellulose—can use this glucose. The fact that many nutritionally fastidious bacteria occur in soil suggests that their growth and survival may depend upon the synthesis and excretion of vitamins and amino acids by less fastidious species.

Another example of commensalism is the ability of a combination of species to attack a particular substrate when an individual species cannot. For instance, lignin, a major chemical constituent of wood, is usually resistant to degradation by pure cultures of microorganisms under laboratory conditions. However, the lignin in forest soil is readily degraded by the mixed microbial population present in the soil, particularly by the fungi. The ability of a combination of microorganisms to degrade a substance may have important practical applications.

Antagonism

Antagonism is the inhibition of one species of organisms by another. Antibiotic production by microorganisms is the classic example of microbial antagonism [FIGURE 28.10A]. However, there are many other forms of antagonism. For instance, some fungi produce cyanide in concentrations that are toxic to other microorganisms, and some algae produce antibacterial fatty acids. The methane, sulfides, and volatile sulfur-containing compounds that are produced by some soil microorganisms can inhibit other species.

Myxobacteria and streptomycetes are noted for their ability to secrete powerful *lytic enzymes*, enzymes that degrade the cell walls or other protective surface layers

of other bacteria [FIGURE 28.10B]. The degraded cell material, as well as internal substances released from the lysed organism, may serve as nutrients for myxobacteria, streptomycetes, and other microorganisms.

Competition

The fact that soil is inhabited by many different species of microorganisms suggests that there is likely to be active *competition* among some of these species for available nutrients. As the supply of nutrients decreases, the rapidly growing species deprive those that grow more slowly of food. This phenomenon can result in major fluctuations in the composition of the microbial population.

Parasitism

Parasitism is an interaction in which one organism lives in or on the body of another organism. The parasite is dependent upon the host and lives in intimate physical contact and metabolic association with the host. It feeds on the cells, tissues, or fluids of the host, and the host is usually harmed in the process (although not necessarily killed). All major groups of plants, animals, and microorganisms are susceptible to attack by microbial parasites. Examples of parasitism of microorganisms include bacteriophages, which replicate only within bacterial cells; and chytrid fungi (Chytridiomycetes, described in Chapter 10), which parasitize algae as well as other fungi and plants. A motile zoospore of a chytrid fungus attaches to an algal cell and forms protrusions that penetrate the host cell to obtain nutrients. Meanwhile, the zoospore on the outside of the host cell grows in size and eventually becomes a zoosporangium that produces more zoospores.

Predation

Predation is an association in which one organism, the predator, feeds on and digests another organism, the prey. For instance, some protozoa feed upon bacteria and some algae, in a process called *grazing*. There are also some fungi that attack and destroy nematodes.

For many years microbiologists did not believe that any bacteria preyed upon other bacteria, and discovery of *Bdellovibrio* bacteria by Heinz Stolp and Mortimer Starr in 1963 caused great excitement. As you learned in Chapter 6, a bdellovibrio can penetrate and grow within the periplasmic space of a host bacterium. In the process, the host bacterium is destroyed. Bdellovibrios are widespread in soil and sewage and may affect the kinds and numbers of other bacteria in these environments.

FIGURE 28.10

[A] Antibiotic activity of microorganisms from the soil. In each of the Petri dish cultures shown, an isolate (bacteria from soil) was streaked across the upper portion of the nutrient agar and the lower region was inoculated with the fungus *Rhizoctonia solani,* a plant pathogen. Note that each of the bacterial isolates prevent the growth of the fungus (clear, central region). [B] Lysis of a cyanobacterium by a myxobacter. Shown in this series is a sequence of lysis of a *Nostoc* filament by the myxobacter.

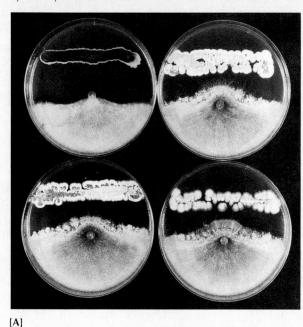

[A]

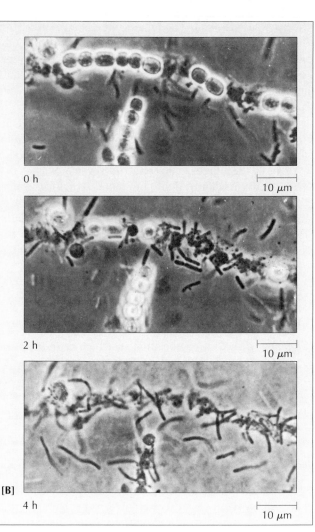

0 h   10 μm

2 h   10 μm

[B]

4 h   10 μm

ASK YOURSELF

What kinds of symbiotic interactions occur among soil microbes? Between plants and soil microbes?

THE ROLE OF MICROORGANISMS IN RECYCLING

Planet Earth functions as a closed system, with the overall quantity of matter remaining constant. However, changes in the chemical states of matter occur, continuously producing forms ranging from simple chemical elements to complex compounds constructed of these elements. Some forms of life, especially plants and many microorganisms, use simple inorganic compounds as nutrients. Animals, on the other hand, require more complex organic compounds for their nutrition. Life on earth is dependent on the cycling of chemicals from their elemental states to inorganic compounds, then to organic compounds, and back into their elemental states. The biochemical reactions whereby organic compounds are broken down to inorganic compounds or their constituent elements is called *mineralization.* Microorganisms are essential to these chemical transformations. The following sections illustrate this phenomenon with nitrogen, carbon, and sulfur.

ASK YOURSELF

1 Why is it necessary to recycle resources on planet Earth?

2 What occurs during the process of mineralization?

BIOCHEMICAL TRANSFORMATIONS OF NITROGEN AND NITROGEN COMPOUNDS

The overall transformations of nitrogen and nitrogen-containing compounds can be summarized in a sequential series of reactions called the *nitrogen cycle* [FIGURE 28.11]. In this cycle, atmospheric nitrogen gas is converted to ammonia and then to amino acids, which are used for the biosynthesis of complex nitrogen-containing organic compounds such as proteins. The proteins are then degraded to simpler organic compounds, namely, peptides and amino acids, which are in turn converted to inorganic nitrogen compounds such as ammonia, nitrites, and nitrates. The nitrates are converted to atmospheric nitrogen gas, thus completing the cycle. Microorganisms play a key role in several steps of the nitrogen cycle, beginning with the conversion of atmospheric nitrogen to ammonia.

FIGURE 28.11

The nitrogen cycle. Note the role of many different microorganisms involved in the process of recycling nitrogen in our environment.

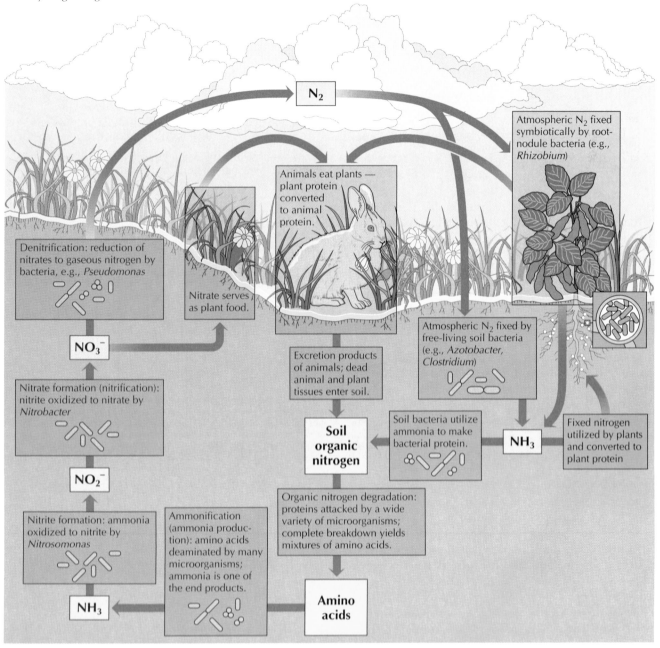

Nitrogen Fixation

Nitrogen fixation is the conversion of atmospheric nitrogen (N_2) to ammonia—a substance required for biosynthesis of amino acids. Although ammonia can be made industrially by chemical synthesis, the process is expensive, is limited to industrialized countries, and accounts for only about one-third of the total nitrogen fixed annually on the earth. The remaining two-thirds is fixed by living organisms. Of all living organisms, only certain species of bacteria can fix nitrogen.

The Nitrogenase Complex. The bacteria that fix nitrogen possess **nitrogenase,** a complex of two enzymes—one an iron-containing protein and the other a molybdenum-containing protein. Together, these two enzymes catalyze the following reaction:

$$N_2 + 6H^+ + 6e^+ + 12ATP \xrightarrow[\text{(nitrogenase)}]{\text{enzyme}}$$

Atmospheric nitrogen

$$2NH_3 + 12ADP + 12P_i$$

Ammonia   Phosphate

The ammonia produced is usually in the form of the ammonium ion, NH_4^+, which is formed when ammonia dissolves in water:

$$NH_3 + H_2O \longrightarrow NH_4^+ + OH^-$$

The reaction catalyzed by nitrogenase not only requires a source of electrons for reducing N_2 to NH_3; it also requires large amounts of energy in the form of ATP. Moreover, nitrogenase is very easily inactivated by oxygen. Some nitrogen-fixing bacteria are anaerobes and normally live in oxygen-free environments. However, others are aerobes that have to use various means to keep oxygen away from the nitrogenase inside their cells. For instance, an *Azotobacter* cell respires so rapidly (reduces oxygen to water so quickly) at the cell surface that the interior of the cell remains oxygen-free. On the other hand, the aerobic nitrogen fixer *Derxia gummosa* has a normal rate of respiration but makes a thick capsule that surrounds the cell. This capsule slows down the diffusion of oxygen from the air to the cells.

For many years microbiologists found it difficult and expensive to measure the nitrogenase activity of bacteria. However, in the 1960s researchers found a rapid, relatively inexpensive technique called the **acetylene reduction test** to measure nitrogenase activity. This simple test is based on the observation that nitrogenase interacts with compounds having triple covalent bonds, such as acetylene gas, as follows:

$$HC \equiv CH + 2H \xrightarrow[\text{(nitrogenase)}]{\text{enzyme}} H_2C = CH_2$$

Acetylene   Ethylene

The comparable reaction with nitrogen is:

$$N \equiv N + 6H \xrightarrow[\text{(nitrogenase)}]{\text{enzyme}} 2NH_3$$

The test is performed by adding the bacteria to be assayed for nitrogenase activity to a closed vessel containing some acetylene gas. After a period of incubation ranging from 30 minutes to several days, a sample of gas is removed and analyzed by *gas chromatography* to see whether ethylene has been formed. The amount of ethylene produced is a measure of the nitrogenase activity of the bacteria.

Nonsymbiotic Nitrogen Fixation. Nitrogen-fixing bacteria can be classified as either *nonsymbiotic* nitrogen fixers, which live freely and independently in soil, or *symbiotic* nitrogen fixers, which fix nitrogen only when they live in association with certain plants.

Estimates of the amount of nitrogen fixed by nonsymbiotic nitrogen-fixing bacteria range from 20 to 50 lb/acre annually. This process is of great importance in flooded rice fields, barren or new rock surfaces, and virgin or cultivated arid soils. Bacteria that can carry out nonsymbiotic nitrogen fixation are listed in TABLE 28.3. Among the most important are *Azotobacter* species and the cyanobacteria, which are aerobic, and *Clostridium pasteurianum*, which is a spore-forming anaerobe; these organisms are widely distributed in soils.

T A B L E 28.3
Some Examples of Nonsymbiotic Nitrogen-Fixing Bacteria

Bacterial genera/species	Physiological characteristics	
Azotobacter chroococcum *Beijerinckia indica* *Derxia gummosa*	Heterotrophic	Aerobes
Cyanobacteria	Photosynthetic	
Clostridium spp. *Desulfovibrio* spp.	Heterotrophic	Anaerobes
Chromatium vinosum *Chlorobium thiosulfatophilum* *Rhodospirillum rubrum* *Rhodomicrobium vannielii*	Photosynthetic	

Symbiotic Nitrogen Fixation. Symbiotic nitrogen fixation is of particular importance to agriculture. In many cases plants derive great benefit from the nitrogen-fixing bacteria that live in association with them, as in the *Rhizobium*-legume, *Anabaena-Azolla*, *Frankia*–alder tree, and other systems.

The most efficient and best-studied system of symbiotic nitrogen fixation is that of *Rhizobium* bacteria growing in nodules attached to the roots of legumes (plants that bear seeds in pods), such as soybeans, peas, and clover. In order to achieve effective nitrogen fixation in the *Rhizobium*-legume system, it is necessary to select the proper strain of *Rhizobium* bacteria [FIGURE 28.12]. It has been estimated that the amount of nitrogen fixed by a legume crop ranges between 50 and 500 lb/acre.

Rhizobia are capable of invading the root-hair cells of the host plant and establishing a mutualistic partnership [FIGURE 28.13]. Initially, the bacteria cause an "infection thread" to be formed in a root-hair cell. The infection thread allows the bacteria to penetrate deeper into the root tissue and infect the cells there. The infected root cells enlarge and divide at an increased rate, leading to the formation of large masses of cells, called *root nodules*. The *Rhizobium* bacteria within these nodules fix N_2 to NH_3, and some of the NH_3 is used by the plant to make amino acids. In turn, the plant not only provides nutrients for the bacteria but also protects their nitrogenase from oxygen. It does this by surrounding the bacteria with a red, oxygen-binding pigment called *leghemoglobin*. This pigment resembles the hemoglobin of animal blood in many respects, and it limits the amount of oxygen that reaches the bacteria.

The *Anabaena-Azolla* system involves an association between the water fern *Azolla* and the cyanobacterium *Anabaena* [FIGURE 28.14]. The association is of great importance in rice paddies, where nitrogen is frequently a limiting nutrient. The water fern is allowed to grow in the rice paddy area, and the nitrogen-fixing cyanobacterium provides ammonia that the fern uses to make amino acids and proteins. When the fern crop dies, the microbial decomposition of its proteins provides the inorganic nitrogen needed for growth of the rice plants.

In the *Frankia*–alder tree system, actinomycete bacteria of the genus *Frankia* grow within the root nodules of alder trees and certain shrubs. Although these root nodules had been observed for more than a century, it was not until 1978 that the *Frankia* bacteria were isolated in pure culture and shown to be nitrogen-fixing organisms. Alder trees are capable of growing on impoverished soil; it is likely that the association with *Frankia* species provides the nitrogen that makes this possible.

A more recently discovered system of symbiotic nitrogen fixation is that of grasses, wheat, corn, and other plants growing in association with the species of *Azospirillum*. The azospirilla invade the root tissue; fix nitrogen, which feeds the plant; and in turn derive food from the plant tissue. Nodules are not formed as they are in the *Rhizobium*-legume system. This discovery suggests that it may be possible to extend the practice of symbiotic nitrogen fixation to a broader range of plants.

Nitrogen Fixation and Genetic Engineering. Microbiologists using molecular biology techniques have characterized the genes responsible for nitrogen fixation. These

FIGURE 28.12
Different strains of rhizobia have different effects on the growth of clover. Tests are carried out on Crimson clover in the following manner: Seeds are planted in sterile sand contained in a jar. The sand is then inoculated with the bacteria. Each jar contains a solution of nutrients—except nitrogen—which diffuses through the sand. Thus the extent of growth is indicative of the amount of nitrogen being supplied by the bacteria. [A] was not inoculated; [B], [C], and [D] were inoculated with different strains of rhizobia. Note the difference in growth response.

FIGURE 28.13
The stages of infection of a legume root-hair with rhizobia bacteria and the resulting formation of root nodules.

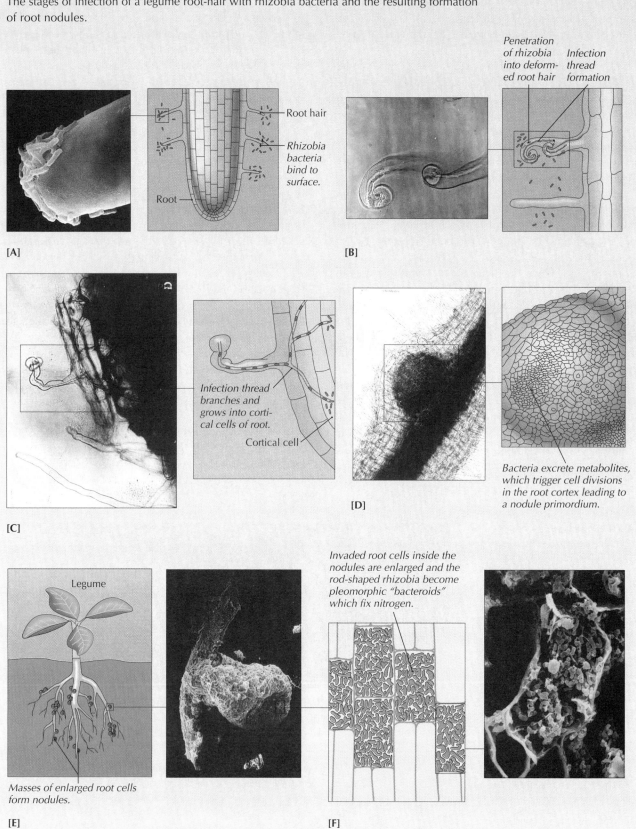

[A]

Root hair

Rhizobia bacteria bind to surface.

Root

[B]

Penetration of rhizobia into deform-ed root hair *Infection thread formation*

[C]

Infection thread branches and grows into cortical cells of root.

Cortical cell

[D]

Bacteria excrete metabolites, which trigger cell divisions in the root cortex leading to a nodule primordium.

[E]

Legume

Masses of enlarged root cells form nodules.

[F]

Invaded root cells inside the nodules are enlarged and the rod-shaped rhizobia become pleomorphic "bacteroids" which fix nitrogen.

FIGURE 28.14

The nitrogen-fixing relationship between the aquatic fern, *Azolla* spp., and the cyanobacterium, *Anabaena azollae*. **[A]** A leaf of the azolla plant flattened to show the two lobes of the leaf. The smaller dorsal lobe contains the dark-colored cavity where the *Anabaena azollae* symbiont resides. **[B]** Scanning electron micrograph of *Anabaena* filaments (chains of cells) in the dark cavity.

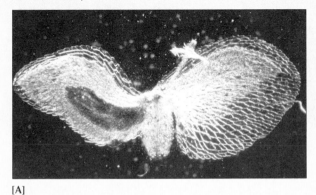

[A]

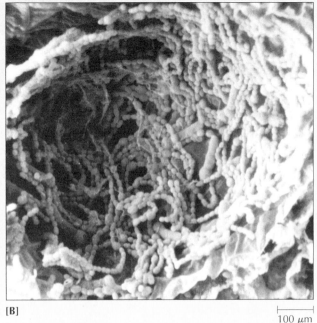

[B]

100 μm

genes include not only those for the nitrogenase complex but also several others that are needed for regulation of nitrogenase activity. Advances in genetic engineering have suggested some exciting ways in which the capacity for nitrogen fixation might be enhanced or inserted into other types of plants. The complete set of genes for nitrogen fixation has been cloned from *Klebsiella pneumoniae* and transferred into *Escherichia coli*. Further research along these lines is likely to expand the use of nitrogen fixation, by developing bacteria that can live on other plants and fix nitrogen. Development of a symbiotic nitrogen-fixing system for cereal crops similar to the *Rhizobium*-legume system could greatly enhance crop yields.

Proteolysis

Plants use the ammonia produced by symbiotic and non-symbiotic nitrogen fixation to make their amino acids and, eventually, plant proteins. Animals eat the plants and convert the plant protein into animal protein. Eventually plants and animals die; during their decomposition in the soil, the nitrogen contained in their proteins is released. The first step in this release is *proteolysis*, the enzymatic breakdown of proteins.

Proteolysis is the job of microorganisms that secrete *proteinases*, enzymes that split protein molecules into smaller units. Each unit is called a *peptide* and consists of two or more amino acids. The peptides are in turn attacked by *peptidases*, which release the individual amino acids. The overall reaction may be summarized as follows:

$$\text{Proteins} \xrightarrow{\text{proteinases}} \text{peptides} \xrightarrow{\text{peptidases}} \text{amino acids}$$

Powerful proteinases are made by many fungi and by some bacteria, particularly certain species of *Clostridium*, *Pseudomonas*, and *Bacillus*. Peptidases occur much more widely among microorganisms. Peptones, which are partially hydrolyzed proteins made from meat, casein, or soybean protein, are a common constituent of culture media; they provide a readily available source of nitrogen for heterotrophic microorganisms.

Amino Acid Degradation: Ammonification

Amino acids released during proteolysis undergo *deamination*, which is the removal of the nitrogen-containing amino (—NH₂) group. Microbes accomplish deamination of amino acids by various reactions, but one of the end products is always ammonia. For example, the deamination of alanine can take place in the following manner:

$$\underset{\text{Alanine}}{CH_3-\underset{\overset{|}{NH_2}}{CH}-COOH} + \tfrac{1}{2}O_2 \xrightarrow[\text{deaminase)}]{\text{enzyme}\ \text{(alanine}} \underset{\text{Pyruvic acid}}{CH_3-\underset{\overset{\|}{O}}{C}-COOH}$$

$$+\ \underset{\text{Ammonia}}{NH_3}$$

The production of ammonia is termed *ammonification*; thus, deamination results in ammonification.

Nitrification

After ammonification has occurred, some bacteria can convert the ammonia to nitrate by a process called **nitrification.**

During the Napoleonic Wars in the nineteenth century, France was unable to import saltpeter (mineral nitrates) for the manufacture of gunpowder. To solve this difficulty, the French prepared compost beds consisting of soil mixed with animal waste, vegetable matter, ashes, and other materials. They aerated this mixture by turning over the compost heaps from time to time. Then, after lengthy incubation, they extracted crude saltpeter from the compost mixture with hot water. We now know that this production of nitrate occurred because of the activity of nitrifying bacteria, but at the time the role of microorganisms in the process was not understood. It was only later, in 1877, that nitrification was discovered to be a biological process. Pure cultures of nitrifying bacteria were first isolated in 1890 by the Russian microbiologist Sergei Winogradsky.

Nitrification occurs in two steps; each step is performed by a different group of bacteria.

Step 1: Oxidation of ammonia to nitrite by *ammonia-oxidizing bacteria:*

$$2NH_3 + 3O_2 \longrightarrow 2HNO_2 + 2H_2O$$

Ammonia   Nitrous acid

$$\downarrow \text{ ionization}$$

$$H^+ + NO_2^-$$

Nitrite ion

Step 2: Oxidation of nitrite to nitrate by *nitrite-oxidizing bacteria:*

$$NO_2^- + \tfrac{1}{2}O_2 \longrightarrow NO_3^-$$

Nitrite ion   Nitrate ion

Nitrifying bacteria (ammonia-oxidizing bacteria and nitrite-oxidizing bacteria) are aerobic Gram-negative autotrophs. They obtain their carbon from carbon dioxide, and they derive the energy needed to fix carbon dioxide by oxidizing NH_3 or NO_2^-.

Nitrifying bacteria are common inhabitants of soil, sewage, and aquatic environments, but they cannot be isolated easily in the laboratory. This is due to their slow growth and low numbers in soil and other environments. Consequently, microbiologists use an enrichment technique to increase their numbers in a mixed population before trying to isolate them in pure culture. An example of an enrichment medium for nitrifying bacteria is given in TABLE 28.4. This medium is completely inorganic and provides either ammonia or nitrite as the only source of nitrogen for growth.

TABLE 28.4

Composition of Medium for Isolation of Nitrifying Bacteria Using Enrichment Culture Technique

Ingredients	g/liter
$(NH_4)_2SO_4$	2.0
K_2HPO_4	1.0
$MgSO_4$	0.5
$FeSO_4$	0.4
NaCl	0.4
$CaCO_3$	1.0
$MgCO_3$	1.0

Ammonia-oxidizing bacteria have various shapes (rods, cocci, spirals, or lobular forms). Observed by electron microscopy, they usually have an extensive system of membranes inside the cells. Some species of ammonia oxidizers are *Nitrosomonas europaea, Nitrosovibrio tenuis,* and *Nitrosococcus nitrosus* (note that all the genus names have the prefix *Nitroso-*).

Nitrite-oxidizing bacteria have cell shapes similar to those of ammonia oxidizers. Only a few species have been isolated: among these are *Nitrobacter winogradskyi* and *Nitrospina gracilis* (note that all the genus names have the prefix *Nitro-*).

Assimilatory Nitrate Reduction: Nitrate to Ammonia

After nitrate has been formed by nitrification, many heterotrophic bacteria are capable of converting it back into ammonia by **assimilatory nitrate reduction.** This process typically occurs under aerobic conditions and has the function of supplying the cell with ammonia for amino acid biosynthesis. Assimilatory nitrate reduction involves several reactions, but the overall reaction is as follows:

$$NO_3^- + 8e^- + 9H^+ \longrightarrow NH_3 + 3H_2O$$

Nitrate   Ammonia

Denitrification: Nitrate to Nitrogen Gas

Some bacteria are capable of reducing nitrates to gaseous nitrogen, a process called **denitrification.** Denitrification occurs only under anaerobic conditions, such as occur in waterlogged soils. The nitrate serves as the terminal electron acceptor for an electron-transport system, and the energy liberated by the electron-transport system is used in ATP synthesis. In denitrification, the reduction of nitrate to nitrogen gas occurs by a sequence of reactions in which various intermediate compounds are formed:

$$2NO_3 \longrightarrow 2NO_2 \longrightarrow 2NO \longrightarrow N_2O \longrightarrow N_2$$

Nitrate   Nitrite   Nitric oxide   Nitrous   Nitrogen
(questionable   oxide   gas
intermediate)

Many bacteria can carry out denitrification; some examples are species of *Agrobacterium*, *Alcaligenes*, *Bacillus*, *Thiobacillus*, and *Pseudomonas*. As useful as denitrification may be to these bacteria for energy production, from the standpoint of agriculture denitrification is undesirable; it results in loss of nitrogen from the soil and consequently a decline in nutrients for plant growth.

Environmental conditions have a significant effect on the level of denitrification. For example, the process is enhanced in soil having an abundance of organic matter, elevated temperatures (25 to 60°C), and a neutral or alkaline pH.

ASK YOURSELF

1 What series of reactions make up the nitrogen cycle?

2 What is nitrogen fixation, and what reaction does nitrogenase catalyze?

3 What is the difference between nonsymbiotic and symbiotic nitrogen fixation?

4 What are three examples of symbiotic nitrogen fixation?

5 What are the following processes: proteolysis, deamination, ammonification, nitrification, assimilatory nitrate reduction, and denitrification?

BIOCHEMICAL TRANSFORMATIONS OF CARBON DIOXIDE AND OTHER CARBON COMPOUNDS

Like the nitrogen cycle, the biochemical transformations of carbon dioxide and other carbon compounds can be viewed as a cyclic sequence of reactions [FIGURE 28.15]. Carbon dioxide from the atmosphere is fixed during photosynthesis into simple organic compounds, from which complex compounds such as cellulose are made. Eventually these complex compounds are degraded to smaller

molecules, which are then oxidized to form carbon dioxide, thus completing the cycle. It has been estimated by the U.S. Department of Agriculture that the atmosphere above the surface of an acre of soil contains 20 tons of carbon dioxide and that the living organisms in the same area return 20 tons to the atmosphere each year.

Carbon Dioxide Fixation

Carbon dioxide fixation is the conversion of carbon dioxide (CO_2) into organic compounds. The general reaction is:

$$CO_2 + 4H \xrightarrow{\text{enzymes}} (CH_2O)_x + H_2O$$

Carbohydrate

Green plants are the most important agents of carbon dioxide fixation, but algae, cyanobacteria, purple and green phototrophic bacteria, and chemoautotrophic bacteria can also fix carbon dioxide. These organisms are autotrophs, and most of them use the Calvin cycle for CO_2 fixation (Chapter 12). Many heterotrophic bacteria are also able to fix CO_2 to some extent, although they cannot use it as their major source of carbon. The following is an example of how some heterotrophs fix CO_2:

$$CH_3COCOOH + CO_2 \xrightarrow{\text{enzymes}} HOOCCH_2COCOOH$$

Pyruvic acid   Oxaloacetic acid

Cellulose Degradation

Plants use some of the carbohydrate that is formed from CO_2 fixation to make complex organic compounds such as cellulose, a water-insoluble long-chain polymer of glucose. Wood normally contains 40 to 50% cellulose; other major constituents are lignin (20 to 30%) and hemicelluloses (10 to 30%). When plants die, these complex substances are degraded by soil microorganisms. In the soil beneath most natural systems of vegetation, such as forest land, the amount of organic material remains approximately the same from year to year. This is because of the balance established between the amount of dead plant material deposited on the soil and the capacity of the soil microorganisms to degrade this material [FIGURE 28.16].

Cellulose is the most abundant organic material in plants, and it is readily attacked by many species of bacteria and fungi in soil. These microorganisms initially use the enzyme cellulase to break down cellulose to molecules of cellobiose, a disaccharide that contains two glucose units.

$$\text{Cellulose} \xrightarrow[\text{(cellulase)}]{\text{enzyme}} \text{many cellobiose molecules}$$

FIGURE 28.15
The carbon cycle, showing the role of microorganisms.

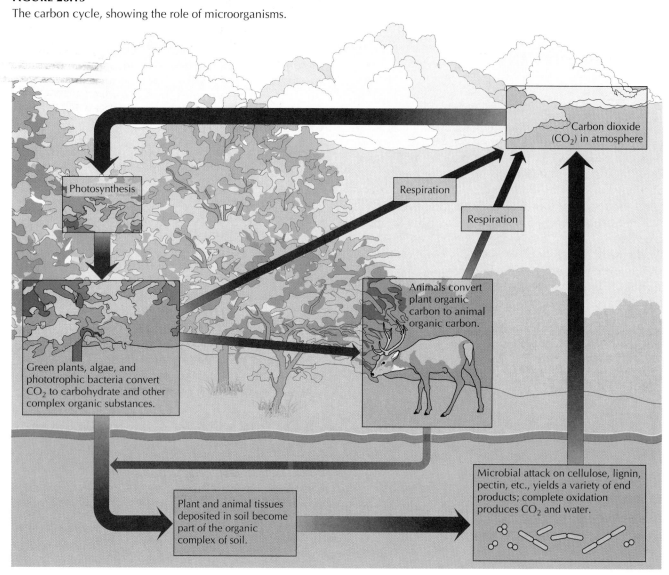

Then another enzyme, β-glucosidase, splits the cellobiose into glucose.

$$\text{Cellobiose} \xrightarrow[\text{(\beta\text{-glucosidase})}]{\text{enzyme}} 2 \text{ glucose}$$

The glucose can then be metabolized by many kinds of microorganisms. The complete oxidation of glucose yields CO_2 and H_2O:

$$\text{Glucose} + 6O_2 \xrightarrow{\text{enzymes}} 6CO_2 + 6H_2O$$

Similar degradation pathways occur for the other major plant tissue substances, such as hemicellulose and lignin. Carbon dioxide is produced not only from the breakdown of carbohydrates, but also from the break-down of the amino acids produced by proteolysis and from the fatty acids produced by the breakdown of lipids.

ASK YOURSELF

1 What are the steps or sequence of reactions in the carbon cycle?

2 How is CO_2 converted into organic compounds?

3 What are the products of cellulose degradation by microbes?

FIGURE 28.16

The decomposition of component substrates of oak leaf litter.

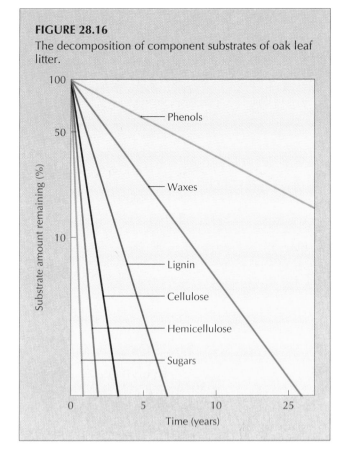

This is an aerobic, chemoautotrophic process in which acid is produced, reducing the pH of alkaline soils. This is important in the control of potato scab and rot diseases caused by *Streptomyces* bacteria that are inhibited by low pH.

2 Plants utilize the sulfur in sulfates for the synthesis of sulfur-containing amino acids (cystine, cysteine, and methionine), which are essential components of some proteins. When the plants die, soil microorganisms degrade the plant proteins that reach the soil, releasing the amino acids. These are further degraded by enzymes called **desulfurases,** as shown in the following equation; note that the sulfur is released in the form of hydrogen sulfide (H_2S).

$$\begin{array}{c} CH_2SH \\ | \\ HC-NH_2 + H_2O \\ | \\ COOH \end{array} \xrightarrow[\text{desulfurase)}]{\text{enzyme (cysteine}} \begin{array}{c} CH_3 \\ | \\ C=O \\ | \\ COOH \end{array} + NH_3 + H_2S$$

Cysteine   Pyruvic acid   Hydrogen sulfide

3 Sulfate can be reduced to hydrogen sulfide by various soil microorganisms. For example, the anaerobic bacterium *Desulfotomaculum* can carry out the following reaction:

$$8H + CaSO_4 \xrightarrow{\text{enzymes}} H_2S + Ca(OH)_2 + 2H_2O$$

Calcium sulfate   Calcium hydroxide

4 Some species of green and purple phototrophic bacteria can oxidize the hydrogen sulfide that is produced by sulfate reduction and amino acid decomposition. This oxidation process results in the formation of elemental sulfur:

$$CO_2 + 2H_2S \xrightarrow[\text{light}]{\text{enzymes;}} (CH_2O) + H_2O + 2S$$

Carbohydrate

BIOCHEMICAL TRANSFORMATIONS OF SULFUR AND SULFUR COMPOUNDS

Like nitrogen and carbon, sulfur passes through a cycle of transformations mediated by microorganisms [FIGURE 28.17]. Some microorganisms oxidize various sulfur compounds; others reduce them. Some of the biochemical changes in the sulfur cycle may be summarized as follows:

1 Sulfur in its elemental form cannot be used by plants or animals. However, some bacteria can oxidize it to sulfate (SO_4^{2-}), a form of sulfur readily used by all forms of life. An example of such an organism is the autotroph *Thiobacillus thiooxidans*, which carries out the following reaction:

$$2S + 2H_2O + 3O_2 \longrightarrow 2H_2SO_4$$

Elemental sulfur   Sulfuric acid

$$\downarrow \text{ionization}$$

$$2H^+ + SO_4^{2-}$$

Sulfate ion

ASK YOURSELF

1 What are the steps in the sequence of reactions in the sulfur cycle?

2 How is the elemental form of sulfur changed so that it can be used by plants or animals?

3 How is hydrogen sulfide derived from plant or animal proteins?

4 How is elemental sulfur formed from hydrogen sulfide?

FIGURE 28.17
The sulfur cycle, showing the role of microorganisms.

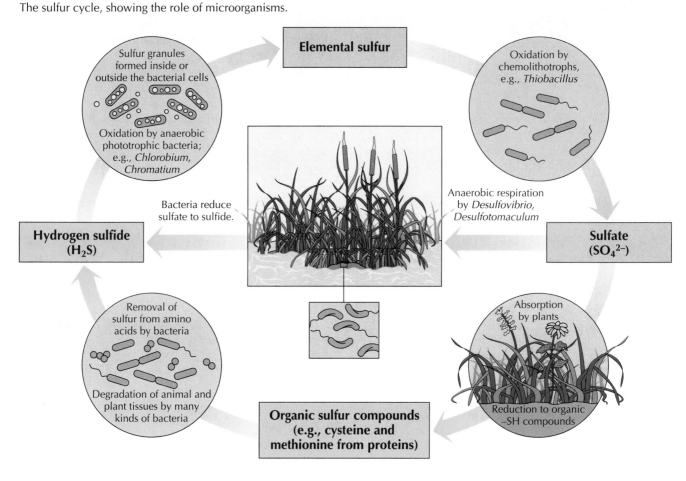

BIOCHEMICAL TRANSFORMATIONS OF OTHER ELEMENTS AND THEIR COMPOUNDS

You have learned about the chemical transformations that occur in the nitrogen, carbon, and sulfur cycles. The central theme of all these transformations is the continual synthesis, degradation, and resynthesis of compounds in a cyclical manner. The chemical state of each element changes, but the total global supply of the element remains constant.

Similar cyclic processes occur with phosphorus, iron, and the other elements that are essential for life. In each instance, microorganisms play a key role in transforming the chemical state of the element so that it becomes available and usable by the organisms in the next step of the cyclic process.

ASK YOURSELF

1 What other elements have cyclic processes similar to the nitrogen, carbon, and sulfur cycles?

2 Why are microorganisms important in these cycles?

BIODEGRADATION OF HERBICIDES AND PESTICIDES

Herbicides are chemical substances that kill plants, particularly weeds. *Pesticides*, as the name denotes, are chemical substances that kill pests. In the context of soil, we think of pests as the insects, fungi, and nematode worms that cause damage to field crops. Thus we can more specifically name substances classified as pesticides, such as *insecticides*, *fungicides*, and *nematocides*.

28.2 THE BIOCIDES: BIOLOGICAL CONTROL OF INSECTS

The introduction of DDT in 1939 for the control of insects initiated the development and production of many new chemical compounds for this purpose. Several years passed before the damaging effect of DDT on the environment was recognized and highlighted in 1962 by Rachel Carson's book *Silent Spring*. By 1972, federal restrictions were implemented for the use of DDT and other compounds of organic chlorine because of their harmful effects upon animals and the environment in general.

The growing awareness of practices affecting the environment has increased the public's sensitivity to the potential damages associated with extensive use of chemical insecticides in modern agriculture. Contamination of groundwater, pollution of streams with the resulting damage to aquatic vegetation, and development of resistance to these chemicals by insects and the resulting need for increased dosages are some of the problems associated with the widespread use of chemical insecticides.

An attractive alternative method for controlling insects that damage plants is application of microorganisms that infect and kill specific insects without harming the plant. *Bacillus thuringiensis*

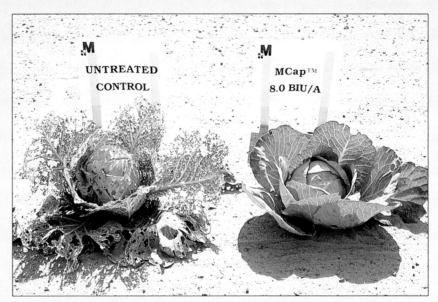

(commonly referred to as *Bt*) has been used commercially for several years to control lepidopterous insects (scaly winged insects such as moths, butterflies, and skippers). The accompanying photo shows protection of cabbage plants via treatment with *Bt*. *B. thuringiensis* is also used to control the gypsy moth, which is very destructive to trees; the gypsy moth has been responsible for the destruction of large forests. *Bacillus*

popillae and *B. lentimorbus* are used to control the Japanese beetle. Some new varieties of turf grass are protected from foraging insects by application of fungi of the genus *Acremonium*. In recent experiments at the University of Wisconsin, a bacterium was isolated from soil that was effective in controlling "damping off" and "root rot"—diseases of alfalfa and soybeans that are caused by a fungus.

Although the wide-scale application of herbicides and pesticides to crops can improve crop yields, it raises questions about the short- and long-term effects of these substances on the environment and on human health. Are they degraded by soil microorganisms, and if so, how rapidly? Do they affect soil microorganisms, and if they do, is the effect temporary or permanent? Do they constitute a form of pollution that passes from the soil to streams and rivers, and do they affect aquatic plant and fish life? Do they pose a health hazard to humans? These are some of the questions that are of concern to soil scientists, biologists, environmentalists, and the general public.

An ideal pesticide would be one that destroys the pest quickly and then is degraded to nontoxic substances as quickly as possible. Because soil is the "sink" that receives the pesticide, we depend upon soil microorganisms to degrade the pesticide's chemical constituents.

Some recent studies have suggested that using genetically engineered strains of normal soil bacteria may hasten pesticide degradation [FIGURE 28.18]. An attractive alternative to the use of chemical pesticides is the use of microorganisms that attack and destroy insects [DISCOVER 28.2]. These are discussed in Chapter 31.

ASK YOURSELF

1 What adverse environmental conditions may result from application of herbicides and pesticides to crops?

2 What are the characteristics of an ideal pesticide?

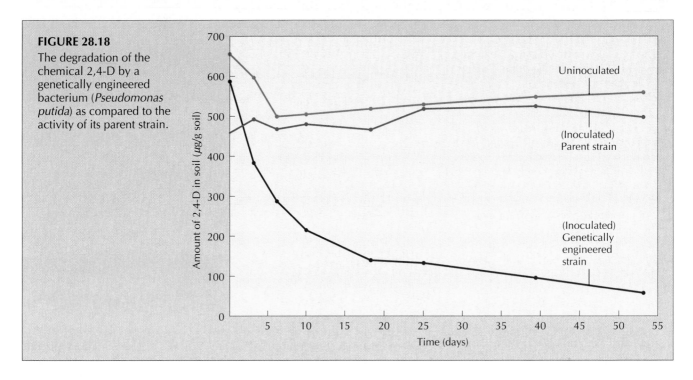

FIGURE 28.18
The degradation of the chemical 2,4-D by a genetically engineered bacterium (*Pseudomonas putida*) as compared to the activity of its parent strain.

MICROBIOLOGY OF THE ATMOSPHERE

The microbial population of the atmosphere is transient and variable. Air is not a medium in which microorganisms grow, but it is a carrier of dust and droplets that may be laden with microorganisms. Microorganisms may be carried on dust particles, in large droplets that settle out quickly, and in the droplet nuclei that remain when small liquid droplets evaporate. Organisms introduced into the air may be transported a few feet or many miles. Some airborne microorganisms die in a matter of seconds; others survive for weeks, months, or longer. The ultimate fate of airborne microorganisms is governed by a complex set of circumstances that include humidity, temperature, the amount of sunlight, and the size of the particles bearing the microorganisms. The nature of the microorganisms is also important. For instance, organisms that form spores or cysts are likely to survive in the atmosphere for long periods.

Techniques for Microbiological Sampling of Air

One technique for the microbiological sampling of air is simply to expose a Petri dish containing an agar medium to the air for a designated period of time. When the dish is incubated, microorganisms that have settled on the agar surface grow into colonies. However, this method gives only a rough approximation of the numbers and kinds of airborne organisms. Two kinds of laboratory devices can provide more quantitative data: solid impingement devices and liquid impingement devices [FIGURE 28.19].

Solid impingement devices draw a stream of air rapidly through narrow slits or holes in a metal plate. As airborne microorganisms pass at high velocity through the slits or holes, they impinge on and stick to the surface of an agar medium located just beneath the metal plate. When the agar medium is incubated, the organisms multiply and form colonies, which then can be counted. Liquid impingement devices draw air through a broth medium or other liquid in which the organisms become trapped. Portions of the liquid are then plated or cultured to determine the microbial content.

Origin of the Microorganisms of the Atmosphere

The earth's surface—both land and water—is the source of microorganisms in the atmosphere. Winds create dust from soil, and the dust particles carry soil microorganisms into the air. In addition, water droplets containing microorganisms can originate at the surface of oceans, bays, and other natural bodies of water and enter the atmosphere. Most of these droplets are produced by the bursting of air bubbles at the water's surface. The top 0.1 mm of the water's surface is called the *microlayer* and contains many more microorganisms than the deeper layers. Bubbles that emerge from the microlayer may contribute significantly to the microbial population in the atmosphere above water. The distribution of mi-

FIGURE 28.19

Air sampling devices. **[A]** A solid impingement apparatus (sieve sampler). Air is drawn through small holes in the metal cover; particles striking the agar medium adhere to its surface. **[B]** A liquid impingement device. Air is drawn through a suitable liquid which entraps any particles. Samples of the liquid are then cultured to determine the microbial content.

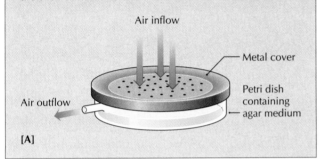

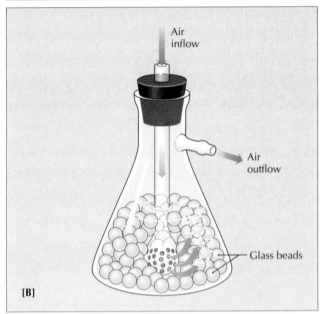

croorganisms in the air above the sea at different distances from land is shown by the data in TABLE 28.5.

In addition to this global origin of atmospheric microorganisms, various industrial, agricultural, and municipal processing facilities have the potential of producing microbe-laden aerosols. Some examples are (1) sprinkler irrigation of crops and forest land with the effluent from sewage-treatment plants, (2) large grain-threshing operations, (3) trickling-filter beds in sewage-treatment plants, and (4) abattoirs where animals are butchered.

Kinds of Microorganisms Present in the Atmosphere

Algae, protozoa, yeasts, molds, and bacteria have been isolated from the air near the earth's surface. An example of the microorganisms found in an urban atmosphere is shown in FIGURE 28.20. The samples were taken from an industrial area over a period of several months. Mold spores constituted the largest portion of the microorganisms, particularly spores of the genus *Cladosporium*. The bacteria were spore-forming and non-spore-forming Gram-positive bacilli, Gram-positive cocci, and Gram-negative bacilli.

Bacteria and mold spores have been found at high altitudes above the earth's surface. Air turbulence disseminates the microorganisms, and airstreams carry them for great distances. The data in TABLE 28.6 provide evidence of the dispersion of microorganisms at high altitudes. Relatively little research has been done on upper-air organisms, but in one study researchers determined the concentration of microorganisms in air masses between Montreal, Canada, and London, England. They took samples at altitudes of 2700 to 3000 m, over land and ocean. The results indicated that viable bacteria

TABLE 28.5

Number of Bacteria and Molds That Developed on Plates of Seawater and Freshwater Media Exposed to Air for 1 h at Different Distances from Land

Distance from land (nautical miles)	SEAWATER MEDIUM		FRESHWATER MEDIUM		RATIO SW/FW	
	Bacteria	Molds	Bacteria	Molds	Bacteria	Molds
0–10	45	115	20	200	2.25	0.57
10–150	48	79	13	69	3.69	1.14
150–400	71	20	39	36	1.82	0.56

SOURCE: Data from C. E. Zobell, "Microorganisms in Marine Air," *Aerobiology, AAAS Publ. 17*, 1942.

TABLE 28.6
Types of Bacteria and Molds Isolated from Upper Air

Height (ft)	Bacteria (genera)	Molds (genera)
1,500–4,500	Alcaligenes Bacillus	Aspergillus Macrosporium Penicillium
4,500–7,500	Bacillus	Aspergillus Cladosporium
7,500–10,500	Sarcina Bacillus	Aspergillus Hormodendrum
10,500–13,500	Bacillus Kurthia	Aspergillus Hormodendrum
13,500–16,500	Micrococcus Bacillus	Penicillium

SOURCE: Data from B. E. Proctor and B. W. Parker, *J. Bacteriol.* 36:180, 1938.

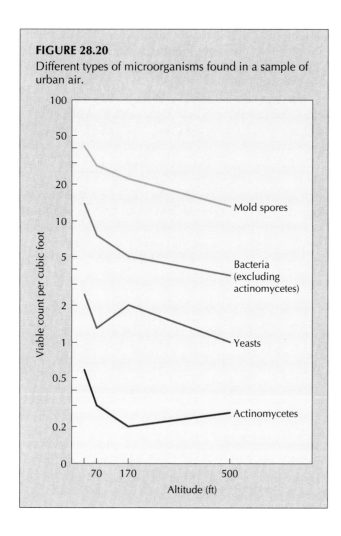

FIGURE 28.20
Different types of microorganisms found in a sample of urban air.

and fungi were present at these altitudes all the way across the North Atlantic. The bacteria were Gram-positive cocci, Gram-negative rods, Gram-positive pleomorphic rods, and aerobic spore formers. The fungi were identified as species of *Cladosporium, Alternaria, Pullularia, Penicillium, Botrytis,* and *Stemphylium. Cladosporium* was the most abundant species over land as well as sea.

ASK YOURSELF

1 How are microorganisms carried in the atmosphere?

2 What circumstances govern the fate of airborne microorganisms?

3 How can the number of microorganisms in a sample of air be determined?

4 What is the source of microorganisms in air, and what kinds are found in air?

SUMMARY

1 The physical and chemical characteristics of different soils vary widely, and the variations have a direct influence on the number and kinds of microorganisms in soil.

2 Representatives of all forms of microbial life occur in soil.

3 The agar-plate culture technique, direct microscopic technique, and enrichment culture technique are used to enumerate and isolate microorganisms from soil. Because of the great diversity of physiological types of microorganisms in soil, no single technique will reveal the total microbial population.

4 Of the microorganisms in soil, bacteria are predominant; a rich garden soil may contain millions to a few billion bacteria per gram. Fungi, algae, and protozoa number in the tens to hundreds of thousands per gram.

5 Microorganisms in soil exist as communities, and various interactions can occur among these communities. These interactions include mutualism, commensalism, antagonism, competition, parasitism, and predation.

6 The maintenance of life on earth is completely dependent upon the continual reutilization of chemical compounds and elements. This recycling depends upon key chemical reactions carried out by microorganisms. Microorganisms play a particularly important role in mineralization, the conversion of organic compounds into inorganic compounds.

7 The nitrogen cycle involves nitrogen fixation, that is carried out by bacteria that contain the nitrogenase complex. There are nonsymbiotic nitrogen fixers such as *Azotobacter* and symbiotic nitrogen-fixing bacteria such as *Rhizobium*. Other steps in the nitrogen cycle include proteolysis, ammonification, nitrification, assimilatory nitrate reduction, and denitrification.

8 Similar cyclic biochemical processes occur with carbon, sulfur, phosphorus, iron, calcium, and the other elements that are essential for life. In each instance, microorganisms play a key role in transforming the chemical state of the element so that it becomes available and usable at the next step in the cyclic process.

9 The wide-scale use of herbicides and pesticides in agriculture and gardening has resulted in the pollution of soil and water by these toxic substances. Some soil microorganisms can decompose these substances. Biological insecticides, or microorganisms that attack insect pests, may provide a useful alternative to chemical herbicides and pesticides.

10 Microorganisms can enter the atmosphere from soil and from the microlayer surface of oceans and other bodies of water. In the atmosphere they can be transported very long distances and at high altitudes. Airborne microorganisms can be enumerated by various methods, including solid impingement devices and liquid impingement devices. The most prevalent species present in the atmosphere are spore formers, both bacteria and fungi.

KEY TERMS

acetylene reduction test
ammonification
antagonism
assimilatory nitrate reduction
carbon dioxide fixation
commensalism
competition
deamination
denitrification
desulfurases
horizons, of soil
humus
lichens
mineralization
mutualism
mycorrhizae
nitrification
nitrogenase
nitrogen fixation
parasitism
predation
proteolysis
rhizosphere
symbiosis

THE SOIL
ENVIRONMENT

1 Soil can be defined as the region of the earth's crust where the sciences of

_____ and _____ meet.

2 The different horizontal layers or profiles that make up soil are referred to as

_____ .

3 The presence of humus improves soil by increasing retention of

_____ , improving _____ , and

maintaining a reserve of _____ for microorganisms and
plants.

ENUMERATION AND
ISOLATION OF SOIL
MICROORGANISMS

4 The three principal laboratory techniques used to determine the microbial flora of

soil are: **(a)** _____ ; **(b)** _____ ;

(c) _____ .

5 Which of the following statements are true with reference to procedures for the
enumeration of microorganisms in soil?
(a) All physiological types can be grown by one plate culture procedure.
(b) Microscopic examination of a soil specimen does not ordinarily distinguish dead
from living microbial cells.
(c) The method of choice for isolating a bacterial species from soil with unique biochemical characteristics is the enrichment culture technique.
(d) All species of soil microorganisms can be isolated and enumerated by the enrichment culture technique.
(e) Agar-plate cultures made from samples of soil reveal only a portion of the total
microbial flora.

SOIL
MICROORGANISMS

6 The microorganisms most numerous in soil are: **(a)** viruses; **(b)** bacteria; **(c)** fungi;
(d) algae; **(e)** protozoa.

7 Match the most appropriate description on the right with each term on the left.

_____ streptomycetes   **(a)** Transform rock to soil
_____ fungi   **(b)** Active decomposers of cellulose
_____ yeasts   **(c)** Graze on bacteria
_____ protozoa   **(d)** Prevalent in vineyards
_____ cyanobacteria   **(e)** Soil actinomycetes

8 Algae and cyanobacteria can improve fertility of barren soil because they are photosynthetic; moreover, many cyanobacteria can also fix

_____ .

9 Algae and cyanobacteria are located near the surface of soil because of their re-

quirement for _____ .

THE RHIZOSPHERE

10 The rhizosphere is the region where soil and _____
make contact.

11 Bacteria that require amino acids occur in _____
(lesser, greater) numbers in the rhizosphere than in root-free soil.

INTERACTIONS
AMONG SOIL
MICROORGANISMS

12 The condition in which the individuals of a species live in close association with

individuals of another species is called _____ .

13 Match the most appropriate term or description on the right with each term on the left.

_____ mutualism

_____ antagonism

_____ commensalism

_____ predation

_____ parasitism

(a) Fungi degrade cellulose; bacteria utilize the glucose

(b) Protozoa grazing on bacteria

(c) Lichens

(d) Bacteriophages

(e) Lytic enzymes of myxobacteria

14 Which of the following microbial associations involve fungi as one partner of the association?

(a) mycorrhizae   **(c)** legumes/rhizobia   **(e)** predation by *Bdellovibrio* spp.

(b) lichens   **(d)** reindeer mosses

15 In the type of symbiosis called _____, one species benefits and the other is not affected.

16 In the type of symbiosis called _____, one species inhibits another species.

17 Actinomycetes may inhibit other bacteria because of their production of

_____.

18 Myxobacteria secrete enzymes that can _____ other bacteria.

19 The type of symbiosis in which one organism lives in or on another organism at

the expense of the other is called _____.

20 Members of the bacterial genus _____ are able to attach to and lyse other Gram-negative bacteria.

21 In terms of symbiosis, all viruses are obligate intracellular

_____.

THE ROLE OF MICROORGANISMS IN RECYCLING

22 The planet Earth is not supplied with any significant amounts of elements or chemical compounds from outside sources; thus it is a

_____ system, and maintenance of life on earth is dependent on the _____ of chemical compounds and elements.

23 The conversion of organic compounds to inorganic compounds or their constituent

elements is called _____.

BIOCHEMICAL TRANSFORMATIONS OF NITROGEN AND NITROGEN COMPOUNDS

24 Proteins are degraded to peptides by enzymes called

_____, and peptides are degraded to amino acids by

enzymes called _____.

25 The enzyme alanine deaminase catalyzes a reaction between alanine and oxygen

to form the products _____ and

_____.

26 _____ is the process by which ammonia is oxidized to nitrate.

27 Nitrification occurs in two stages: (1) the oxidation of ammonia to

_____ and (2) the oxidation of

_____ to nitrate.

28 The genera of bacteria that oxidize ammonia to nitrite have the prefix

_____, whereas the genera that oxidize nitrite to nitrate

have the prefix _____.

29 During the Napoleonic Wars, the French prepared niter beds consisting of soil mixed with organic waste matter; in these beds, proteolysis and ammonification oc-

curred initially; this was followed by _____, which resulted

in formation of the _____, which was needed for gunpowder manufacture.

30 The conversion of nitrates to gaseous nitrogen is called

_____.

31 Denitrification is undesirable in agriculture because it results in

_____.

32 Denitrification is favored under conditions where oxygen is

_____.

33 The reduction of gaseous nitrogen to ammonia is called

_____.

34 The enzyme complex responsible for symbiotic nitrogen fixation is called

_____.

35 The gas _____ inactivates the enzyme responsible for
symbiotic nitrogen fixation.

36 Two elements, molybdenum and iron, are components of the enzyme in the

_____ complex.

37 Among nitrogen-fixing bacteria are the oxygenic phototrophic bacteria, which are

commonly called _____, and the nonoxygenic phototrophic

bacteria, which are commonly called the _____ and

_____ bacteria.

38 A chemotrophic soil bacterium which is an anaerobic spore former and has been studied extensively for its ability to fix nitrogen is the species

_____.

39 An example of a genus of aerobic nonsymbiotic nitrogen fixers is

_____.

40 Members of the genus _____ fix nitrogen symbiotically in association with the roots of legumes.

41 Rhizobia attach to the _____ of plant roots, invade the host plant cells, and cause the plant cells to enlarge and multiply; the result is the development of abnormal growths on the roots, called

_____.

42 The type of symbiosis that occurs between rhizobia and legumes is called

_____.

43 The *Anabaena-Azolla* association contributes to the fertility of

_____.

44 Species of the bacterial genus _____, in association with alder trees, can fix nitrogen symbiotically.

45 Which of the following genera do not contain species that fix nitrogen symbiotically?
(a) *Rhizobium*   **(c)** *Nitrobacter*   **(e)** *Anabaena*
(b) *Clostridium*   **(d)** *Frankia*

46 Match each description on the right with the correct term on the left.
_____ proteolysis   **(a)** Converts gaseous nitrogen to ammonia
_____ deaminase   **(b)** Converts substrate to peptides
_____ peptidase   **(c)** Converts substrate to ammonia and organic acid
_____ nitrification   **(d)** The conversion of ammonia to nitrate
_____ nitrogenase   **(e)** Converts substrate to amino acids

BIOCHEMICAL
TRANSFORMATIONS
OF CARBON DIOXIDE
AND OTHER CARBON
COMPOUNDS

47 Algae, cyanobacteria, and _____ phototrophic bacteria are capable of fixing carbon dioxide.

48 The general reaction for carbon dioxide fixation is:

$$CO_2 + 4H \longrightarrow (\underline{\hspace{5cm}})_x + H_2O$$

49 One example of a reaction whereby heterotrophic organisms can fix carbon dioxide is:

$$CO_2 + \text{pyruvic acid} \longrightarrow \underline{\hspace{5cm}}$$

50 Degradation of organic compounds (to carbon dioxide) is carried out mainly by two general groups of microorganisms, _____ and

_____.

51 The most abundant organic material in plants is _____.

52 Cellulose is hydrolyzed to cellobiose by the enzyme

_____, and the cellobiose is in turn hydrolyzed to

_____ by the enzyme β-glucosidase.

53 The major constituents of woody plants are _____,

_____, and _____.

804

54 Which of the following compounds or groups of compounds is unlikely to have its origin in the microbial dissimilation of cellulose? **(a)** glucose; **(b)** cellobiose; **(c)** carbon dioxide; **(d)** hexoses; **(e)** amino acids.

55 End products of complete oxidation of glucose are

_____ and _____.

BIOCHEMICAL
TRANSFORMATIONS
OF SULFUR AND
SULFUR
COMPOUNDS

56 The oxidation of elemental sulfur is carried out by bacteria such as *Thiobacillus thiooxidans,* which performs the following reaction:

$2S + 2H_2O + 3O_2 \longrightarrow 2$ _____

57 Sulfate is assimilated by plants into sulfur-containing amino acids such as

_____.

58 Members of the genus *Desulfotomaculum* can respire anaerobically with sulfate as the terminal electron acceptor; the end product of this anaerobic respiration is the

compound _____.

59 Purple and green sulfur bacteria use _____ as an electron donor for photosynthesis, thereby forming elemental sulfur.

60 Which of the following statements are true?
(a) One dissimilation product of sulfur-containing amino acids is H_2S.
(b) Thiobacilli are green or purple sulfur bacteria.
(c) Elemental sulfur is assimilated into amino acids by plants.
(d) *Thiobacillus thiooxidans* is an autotroph.
(e) *Rhodospirillum* is a nonsulfur purple bacterium.

BIOCHEMICAL
TRANSFORMATIONS
OF OTHER ELEMENTS
AND THEIR
COMPOUNDS

61 In the cyclic transformations of phosphorus, iron, calcium, and other elements essential for life, _____ play a key role in transforming the chemical state of the element so that it becomes available for the next step in the cyclic process.

BIODEGRADATION
OF HERBICIDES AND
PESTICIDES

62 A desirable characteristic of an effective herbicide is rapid

_____ by soil microorganisms.

63 The term "*Bt*" refers to _____.

64 Two species of the genus *Bacillus* used to control the Japanese beetle are

_____ and _____.

MICROBIOLOGY OF
THE ATMOSPHERE

65 Which of the following air-sampling techniques provides the least information in terms of quantitative results? **(a)** nutrient-agar settling Petri dish; **(b)** sieve sampler; **(c)** slit sampler; **(d)** membrane filter; **(e)** liquid impingement device.

66 Among molds recovered from the atmosphere, species of the genus

_____ predominate.

67 The two major sources of airborne microorganisms are

_____ and _____.

68 Which of the following genera of microorganisms is least likely to occur at altitudes of several thousand feet? **(a)** *Cladosporium*; **(b)** *Bacillus*; **(c)** *Neisseria*; **(d)** *Aspergillus*; **(e)** *Penicillium*.

REVIEW QUESTIONS

1 Outline three methods for determining the microbial flora of a sample of soil. Compare the three with respect to the portion of the total flora they would reveal.

2 What generalizations can you make with respect to the total number and the different kinds of microorganisms that occur in soil? Comment on the influence that the physical and chemical characteristics of soil have on the microbial flora.

3 Characterize the following microbial interactions, and cite a specific example for each: symbiosis, commensalism, mutualism, antagonism, parasitism, predation.

4 Compare the microbial flora of soil in the region of the rhizosphere to that in the area outside the rhizosphere.

5 What is meant by *mineralization?* Give an example.

6 Assume that some protein material is buried in the soil. Trace the changes it may undergo as a result of microbial attack. Identify bacteria capable of bringing about each of the changes.

7 Distinguish between symbiotic and nonsymbiotic nitrogen fixation. Name several genera of bacteria that are nonsymbiotic nitrogen fixers; name three genera of microorganisms that are symbiotic nitrogen fixers.

8 Do all the species and strains of rhizobic bacteria fix nitrogen equally well on all legume plants? Explain.

DISCUSSION QUESTIONS

1 The late Dr. Charles Thom, one of America's great mycologists and soil microbiologists, in a speech entitled "A Microbiologist Digs in the Soil," remarked, "The demonstration that soil, instead of being all dead harbors millions of organisms, releases that flight of imagination which pictures the soil as a sort of Lilliputian Zoo in which some magic hand . . . set free every grade of minute but rapacious monster to go roaring after the next lesser grade as lawful prey." Cite several examples that provide evidence to substantiate this generalization.

2 Why is it difficult to obtain a reasonably accurate estimate of the total viable microbial population in a sample of soil?

3 What is the relationship between the growing practice of "recycling" of waste in cities throughout the United States and the microbiological recycling processes that occur in nature?

4 Assume that scientists will, in the near future, develop strains of bacterial species that fix nitrogen in association with grain crops such as corn and wheat. How will this benefit the environment? The economy?

5 Lignin is a major constituent of plant tissue, particularly woody tissue. Deposited in or on soil, lignin is decomposed. However, when lignin is extracted from woody tissue and inoculated with microorganisms and incubated under laboratory conditions, the lignin is relatively resistant to microbiological degradation. What might account for the difference between what occurs under natural conditions and under laboratory conditions?

6 What is the fate of herbicides and pesticides that are applied to agricultural crops?

7 What conditions influence the occurrence of and the spread of microorganisms in the atmosphere?

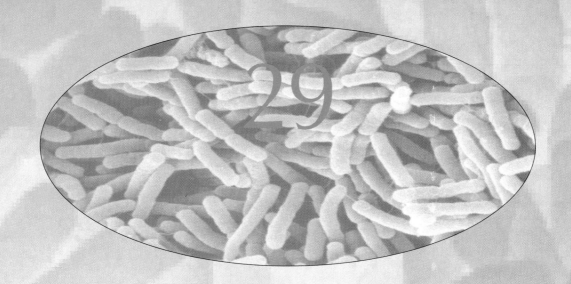

Microbiology of Natural Waters, Drinking Water, and Wastewater

OVERVIEW

Moisture on our planet undergoes continuous circulation, supplying the water all living things need. It enters the earth's atmosphere by evaporation from lakes, streams, and oceans, and by transpiration from the leaves of plants. Then it precipitates back onto the earth in the form of snow, hail, and rain. While a drop of water may appear simple, it really is quite complex, often containing chemicals and microorganisms of many kinds. These microorganisms can change the chemical substances found in water; they also provide nutrients for other aquatic organisms.

Water used by humans comes from natural freshwater sources such as wells, lakes, and rivers. To be safe to drink, this water (except that from individual wells providing good-quality water) must be treated to eliminate potential disease-producing microorganisms. Water-purification plants are designed for this purpose.

Wastewater, or sewage, is water already used by humans at home or at work; it must be treated prior to its disposal. Microorganisms play a major role in wastewater treatment by degrading a large portion of the organic materials present and by decomposing other undesirable chemical substances.

NATURAL WATERS

The earth's moisture circulates to and from the atmosphere in a process called the **hydrologic cycle.** This term refers to the passage of water into the atmosphere by evaporation from the oceans and other surface waters and by transpiration (evaporation from leaf surfaces) from plants, and the subsequent precipitation of moisture in the atmosphere in the form of rain, snow, or hail that falls back to earth [FIGURE 29.1; DISCOVER 29.1]. In this cycle, natural waters can be classified into three major categories, based on their location:

1 Atmospheric water: water contained in clouds and precipitated as rain, snow, or hail
2 Surface water: bodies of water such as lakes, streams, rivers, and oceans

3 Groundwater: water beneath the surface of the earth where all pores of the soil as well as spaces in and among rocks are saturated

Natural waters can serve as habitats for many microorganisms. They may be *freshwater habitats* such as lakes, ponds, springs, swamps, and rivers; *marine habitats* (the oceans); or *estuarine habitats,* the regions between freshwater sources and the oceans. An *estuary* is a semienclosed coastal body of water that has free connection with the open sea. The marine environment is by far the largest of the aquatic habitats.

The study of microorganisms in freshwater, marine, and estuarine environments is called *aquatic microbiology.* Microbiologists who specialize in this area of research must take into account the many physical and chemical characteristics of these various aquatic environments.

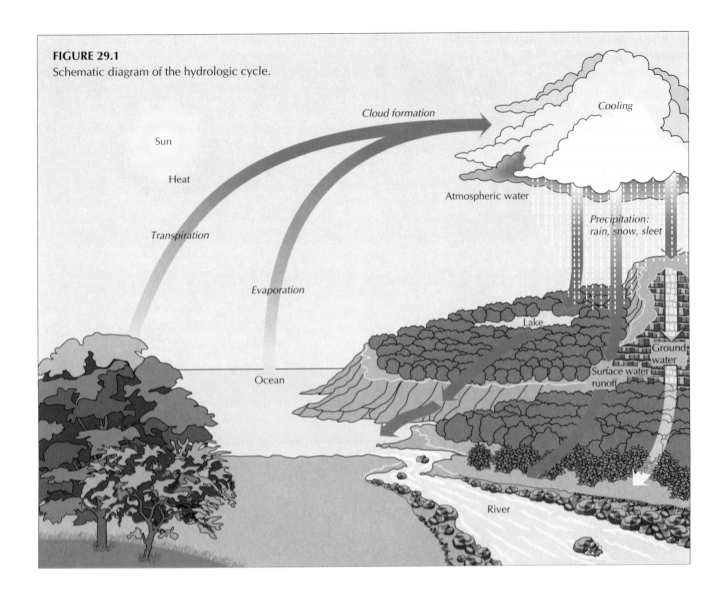

FIGURE 29.1
Schematic diagram of the hydrologic cycle.

29.1 THE JOURNEY OF A WATER DROP

The recycling characteristics of the earth's moisture are captured in this essay entitled "Journey of a Water Drop," written by a sixth-grade student in Public School 63, New York City.

> I am millions of years old. I've experienced life, I've explored the earth and I've traveled through space. I am of many drops, forming one. I sailed on the slave ships, the cargo ships, I attended the Boston Tea Party and I boarded the "Titanic". I have been written of many times. For I am the source of life. I am a drop of water.

From Bruce M. Kantrowitz, *The Second Wave and Other Tales: Getting the Most from Our Coastal Resources*, New York Sea Grant Institute Annual Report 1976–1977. Albany, New York: New York Sea Grant Institute, 1977, p. 6.

ASK YOURSELF

1 What is the hydrologic cycle?
2 What are three categories of natural waters?

THE AQUATIC ENVIRONMENT

The kinds of microorganisms found in an aquatic environment are, to a large extent, determined by the physical and chemical conditions that prevail in that environment. These environmental conditions vary from one extreme to another in terms of such factors as temperature, light, pH, and nutrients.

Temperature

Temperatures of surface waters range from 0°C in polar regions to 40°C in equatorial regions. Beneath the surface, more than 90 percent of the marine environment is below 5°C, a condition favorable for the growth of psychrophilic microorganisms.

Some thermophilic bacteria have been isolated from anaerobic sediments near cracks in the ocean floor. For instance, the archaeobacterium *Pyrodictium occultum* was isolated from a submarine field near the island of Vulcano, Italy, where water as hot as 103°C was flowing from cracks in the sea floor. Laboratory studies have shown that *P. occultum* has an optimum growth temperature of 105°C (5° above the boiling point of water) and that it does not grow at all below 82°C. *P. occultum* is an anaerobic autotroph that grows by forming hydrogen sulfide (H_2S) from hydrogen gas (H_2) and elemental sulfur (S). *Pyrobaculum organotrophum* is a representative of a new group of hyperthermophilic archaeobacteria isolated from seas in different parts of the world [FIGURE 29.2]. Species in this genus grow optimally at 100°C; they are Gram-negative rods, strict anaerobes, and motile by flagella. Microbiologists are still discovering new kinds of microorganisms capable of living at these very high temperatures.

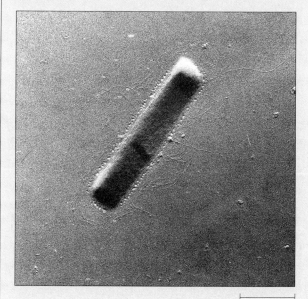

FIGURE 29.2

Pyrobaculum organotrophum, one of a new group of hyperthermophilic archeobacteria isolated from boiling neutral to alkaline solfataric waters in the Azores, Iceland, and Italy. Bacteria in this group grow optimally at 100° C.

1.0 μm

Hydrostatic Pressure

Hydrostatic pressure is the pressure at the bottom of a vertical column of water. It increases with water depth at the rate of 1 atmosphere of pressure (14.7 lb/in^2) for every 32.8 ft (10 m). At great depths, such as near the ocean floor, the hydrostatic pressure is enormous and can cause many changes that affect biological systems, such as changes in the rates of chemical reactions, the solubility of nutrients, and the boiling point of water.

Barophilic organisms are organisms that cannot grow at normal atmospheric pressures and require high hydrostatic pressures. Some barophilic bacteria have been isolated from Pacific Ocean trenches at depths of 1000 to 10,000 m. Their isolation requires special sampling equipment that maintains the high pressure on the sample from the time it is taken until, and during, the culture period. In general, barophilic bacteria grow best at pressures slightly less than the pressure of the site from which they were isolated, and almost all must be incubated at a psychrophilic temperature (about 2°C).

Light

Most forms of aquatic life depend, directly or indirectly, upon the metabolic products of photosynthetic organisms. The principal photosynthetic organisms in most aquatic habitats are algae and cyanobacteria; their growth is restricted to the upper layers of waters through which light can penetrate. The depth of the water layer in which photosynthesis occurs is called the *photic zone.* The size of this zone varies, depending upon such local conditions as position of the sun, the season, and especially the turbidity of the water. Generally the photosynthetic activity is confined to the upper 50 to 125 m of a body of water, depending upon its clarity.

Salinity

The salinity, or sodium chloride concentration, of natural waters ranges from near zero in fresh water to saturation (32% NaCl) in salt lakes such as the Great Salt Lake in Utah. Seawater contains approximately 2.75% NaCl; the total concentration of salts (NaCl plus other salts) in seawater varies between 3.3 and 3.7%. Besides NaCl, the principal salts found in water are sulfates and carbonates of sodium and the chlorides, sulfates, and carbonates of potassium, calcium, and magnesium. The concentration of salts is usually less in shallow offshore regions and near river mouths. In estuaries, salt concentration varies from top to bottom, upper end to lower end (mouth), and season to season, creating ever-changing conditions for the forms of life inhabiting these bodies of water. Most marine microorganisms are halophilic; they grow best at NaCl concentrations of 2.5 to 4.0%. On the other hand, microorganisms from lakes and rivers are usually inhibited by NaCl concentrations greater than 1%. The growth responses of three bacterial types to different levels of salinity are shown in FIGURE 29.3.

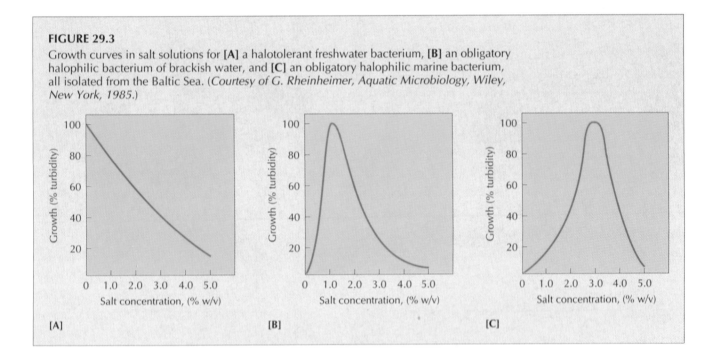

FIGURE 29.3
Growth curves in salt solutions for **[A]** a halotolerant freshwater bacterium, **[B]** an obligatory halophilic bacterium of brackish water, and **[C]** an obligatory halophilic marine bacterium, all isolated from the Baltic Sea. (*Courtesy of G. Rheinheimer, Aquatic Microbiology, Wiley, New York, 1985.*)

Turbidity

There is a marked variation in the clarity of surface waters. The Adriatic Sea is sparkling clear at great depths, whereas the Mississippi River is very turbid. The suspended material responsible for water turbidity includes (1) particles of mineral material, which come from coastal erosion; (2) *detritus,* which is particulate organic matter such as fragments of cellulose, hemicellulose, and chitin from decomposing plant and animal matter; and (3) suspended microorganisms. The greater the turbidity of water, the less the penetration of light, and the less the depth of the photic zone. Particulate matter also serves as a surface to which microorganisms adhere. Many species of bacteria attach themselves to a solid surface in order to colonize [FIGURE 29.4]; such bacteria are called *epibacteria.* This phenomenon of adherence has been described in Chapter 17. Particulate matter also serves as a substrate that can be metabolized by microorganisms.

Hydrogen Ion Concentration (pH)

Aquatic microorganisms usually grow best at pH 6.5 to 8.5. The pH of seawater is 7.5 to 8.5, and most marine microorganisms grow best on culture media adjusted to pH 7.2 to 7.6. Lakes and rivers may show a wider range in pH depending upon local environmental conditions. For example, archaeobacteria have been isolated from salt lakes in Africa where the pH is 11.5; other species of archaeobacteria have been found to grow at a pH of 1.0 or less.

Nutrients

The amount and kind of organic and inorganic materials (nutrients) present in an aquatic environment significantly influence microbial growth. Nitrates and phosphates are common inorganic constituents, and they promote the growth of algae. Excessive amounts of nitrates and/or phosphates can cause an overgrowth of algae in a body of water to the extent that the massive growth depletes the oxygen supply of the water, suffocating all other aquatic life. The quantity of nutrients in a body of water is referred to as the *nutrient load* of an environment. Near-shore waters, which receive domestic wastewater containing organic and inorganic compounds, are subject to intermittent variations in their nutrient load, whereas the open sea has a nutrient load that is comparatively low and stable. Industrial wastes may also contribute antimicrobial substances to estuaries and coastal waters. Mercury and other heavy metals

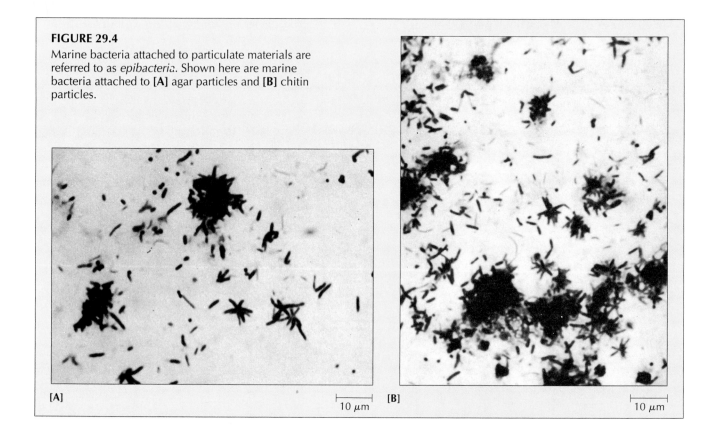

FIGURE 29.4
Marine bacteria attached to particulate materials are referred to as *epibacteria.* Shown here are marine bacteria attached to **[A]** agar particles and **[B]** chitin particles.

[A]   10 μm

[B]   10 μm

from industrial wastes may inhibit the growth of some microorganisms, while simultaneously permitting the growth of resistant forms. For example, many pseudomonads can survive in environments containing mercury. They convert mercury into methyl mercury, a volatile substance which escapes into the atmosphere, thereby removing mercury from the aquatic environment.

ASK YOURSELF

1 What are the major environmental conditions which influence the microbial flora of aquatic environments?

2 What is the distinctive feature of barophilic microorganisms?

3 What is the common metabolic feature between cyanobacteria and algae?

4 What is meant by *nutrient load* in aquatic microbiology?

DISTRIBUTION OF MICROORGANISMS IN THE AQUATIC ENVIRONMENT

Microorganisms in the aquatic environment may occur at all depths—ranging from the surface to the very bottom of ocean trenches. The upper layers—especially the surface film—and the bottom sediments contain the larger numbers of microorganisms, particularly in deep waters.

The collection of floating and drifting microbial life in the surface regions of ponds, lakes, and oceans is called *plankton*. The plankton population may be primarily algae and cyanobacteria *(phytoplankton)* or it may consist predominantly of protozoa and other microscopic animal life *(zooplankton)*. Phototrophic microorganisms are regarded as the most important plankton because they are *primary producers* of organic matter via photosynthesis. Most phytoplanktonic organisms can maintain their location in the photosynthetic zone by being motile. Others possess an unusual structural feature or contain oil droplets or gas vacuoles, which gives them buoyancy [FIGURE 29.5]. A multitude of conditions—such as sunlight, winds, tides, currents, nutrients, and ingestion by higher forms—may affect the numbers and types of organisms in the planktonic population.

Microbial inhabitants at the bottom of a body of

water are called *benthic organisms* and collectively referred to as the **benthos.** The *benthic zone* is the richest region of an aquatic system in terms of numbers and kinds of microorganisms. In addition, many aquatic microorganisms inhabit the gut of marine animals such as whales and fish.

Freshwater Environments

The microbiology of freshwater environments is a part of the science of *limnology,* which is the comprehensive study of all organisms living in lakes, ponds, and streams.

Lakes and Ponds. Lakes and ponds have characteristic zones or layers [FIGURE 29.6]. These zones can be described as follows:

1 The *littoral zone* is the zone along the shore, where light penetrates to the bottom. There is a large amount of rooted vegetation.
2 The *limnetic zone* is the upper region in open areas away from the shore. Its depth is determined by the depth of effective light penetration (called the *compensation level*).
3 The *profundal zone* refers to the deeper regions of the open water. Photosynthetic activity decreases progressively in this zone.
4 The *benthic zone* is the soft mud or ooze at the bottom.

Both the profundal zone and the benthic zone are populated largely by heterotrophic organisms. When the benthic zone is composed primarily of organic material, the majority of organisms will be anaerobes that decompose this material. In contrast, the limnetic and littoral zones contain a greater variety of types of microorganisms. Moreover, in terms of the synthesis of organic compounds from inorganic substances, the limnetic and littoral regions are the most *productive* regions. Productivity is affected by the chemical characteristics of the lake or pond and the nature of materials imported from streams and rivers.

Lakes and ponds in temperate climates have significant seasonal changes in their microbial populations due to stratification, the lack of mixing of the water. In the summer, the top layers tend to be warmer and less dense than the lower regions. In the winter, the situation is reversed, because ice, which is less dense than water, collects on top. Such stratification acts as a barrier to nutrient and oxygen exchange, especially in still water. However, in the spring and fall, mixing of upper and lower layers occurs, and this often results in massive algal growth called a *bloom* [FIGURE 29.7].

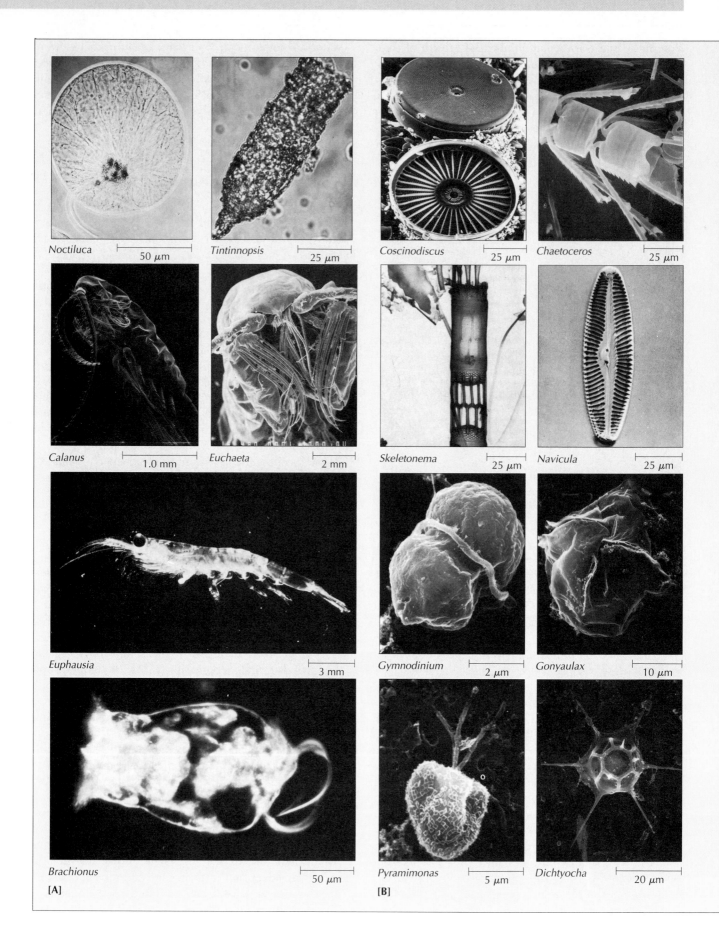

Noctiluca   50 μm

Tintinnopsis   25 μm

Coscinodiscus   25 μm

Chaetoceros   25 μm

Calanus   1.0 mm

Euchaeta   2 mm

Skeletonema   25 μm

Navicula   25 μm

Euphausia   3 mm

Gymnodinium   2 μm

Gonyaulax   10 μm

Brachionus   50 μm

[A]

Pyramimonas   5 μm

[B]

Dichtyocha   20 μm

FIGURE 29.5

Marine zooplankton, phytoplankton and bacteria.
[A] Zooplankton comprises an extremely diverse animal population ranging from the microscopic, unicellular organisms (shown are the dinoflagellate *Noticula* and the ciliate *Tintinnopsis*), to the multicellular metazoans (shown are the copepods *Calanus* and *Euchaeta*, the euphausid "krill" *Euphausia* and the rotifer *Brachionus*). All species shown are found in Puget Sound on the Pacific coast. **[B]** Phytoplankton is made up of algae which are uniquely adapted to the marine environment. Shown are the centric diatoms *Coscinodiscus, Skeletonema,* and *Chaetoceros* as well as the pennate diatom *Navicula*. *Gymnodinium* is an example of an unarmored dinoflagellate while *Gonyaulax* is an armored species. Also represented in the phytoplankton group are the flagellates. Shown here is a green flagellate (probably *Pyramimonas*) and the skeleton of the golden brown silicoflagellate *Dichtyocha*. All species shown are from Puget Sound. **[C]** Gas-vacuolate bacteria (predominantly Gram-negative rods) have been isolated from the Antarctic sea ice as well as from the underlying water column. Top: phase-contrast wet mount. Bottom: transmission electron microscopy. The clear (white) areas are gas vacuoles.

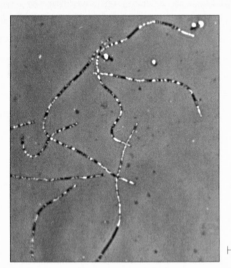

10 μm

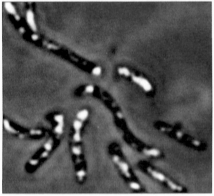

2 μm

[C]

FIGURE 29.6

Schematic diagram of a lake, illustrating zonal regions.

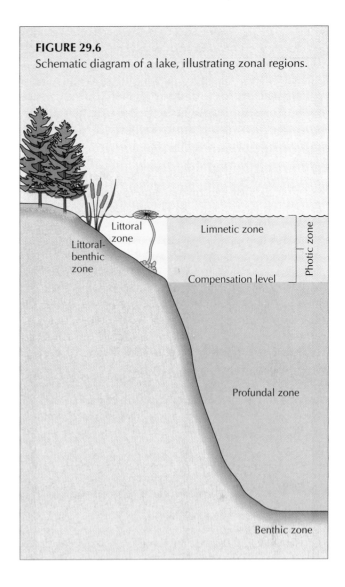

FIGURE 29.7

Occurrence of "blooms" or phytoplankton "pulses" in northern temperate lakes in spring and autumn. The combination of conditions—nutrient concentration, light, and temperature—accounts for this phenomenon. (*Courtesy of E. P. Odum, Fundamentals of Ecology, 3d ed., Saunders, Philadelphia, 1971.*)

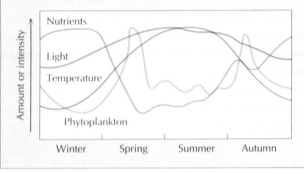

Some aquatic algae produce toxins which are lethal to fish and other animals. These toxins either are extracellular or are liberated from algal cells by bacterial decomposition of the algae in blooms. Certain marine algae (dinoflagellates belonging to the genera *Gymnodinium* and *Gonyaulax*) cause death of aquatic animals by producing a *neurotoxin*, or nerve poison. Neurotoxins are among the most potent toxins known. Certain toxins of some blooms are concentrated within the digestive glands or siphons of filter-feeding bivalve mollusks (clams, mussels, scallops, oysters, and others) and cause paralytic shellfish poisoning when ingested by humans. There have also been cases of livestock killed by drinking water containing algal blooms.

Lakes and ponds that are enriched with nutrients, particularly nitrogen and phosphorus, are likely to support excessive algal growth. When a lake or pond has been enriched with nutrients to the point where massive microbial growth occurs, it is said to be *eutrophic*. On the other hand, one that has low nutrient levels and corresponding poor conditions for microbial growth is described as *oligotrophic*. FIGURE 29.8 illustrates a profile of the bacterial population in a lake.

Streams and Rivers. Most of the nutrients in streams and rivers come from the surrounding terrestrial system. To a major extent, the aquatic microbial population reflects the terrestrial conditions, including the effects of domestic, agricultural, and industrial practices. The drastic environmental changes in streams and rivers created by rapidly expanding urbanization and by changes in the way land is farmed make it impossible to describe a characteristic microbial population.

Estuaries

Compared with ocean waters, estuaries are a more changeable environment because they receive water and materials from a variety of sources. Temperature, salinity, turbidity, nutrient load, and other conditions fluctuate widely over time. Some characteristics of Chesapeake Bay [FIGURE 29.9], one of the world's major estuarine systems, serve to illustrate the variations in an estuary:

1 The Chesapeake Bay serves as the receiving basin for nine major rivers, draining much of southern New York State, Pennsylvania, Maryland, and Virginia.
2 It has a shoreline of 4600 miles, which includes highly industrialized areas, residential areas, marinas, farmlands, and uninhabited marshlands.
3 The salinity varies from less than 1% in the tribu-

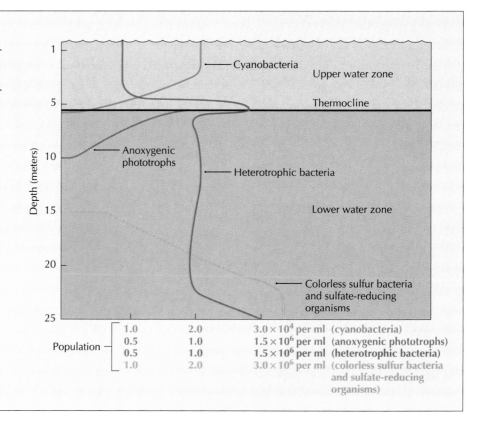

FIGURE 29.8
Vertical profile of bacterial populations in a lake. Cyanobacteria are abundant in the upper water zone. Sulfate-reducing bacteria are abundant near the bottom of the lower water zone. Maximal populations of heterotrophic bacteria occur just below the zone of maximal photosynthetic production and at the water-sediment interface.

taries to 3.5% at the mouth of the bay. It is estimated that an estuary system is filled approximately half by seawater and half by river water. Estuaries thus are subject to tidal as well as seasonal changes, both of which affect the salinity at various locations.

4 Directly or indirectly, the bay is affected by the activities of the millions of humans who reside within the region. Practices associated with agriculture, commerce, industry, transportation (motor vehicle exhaust), and recreation influence the condition of the bay.

From these observations it is apparent that the microbial population of the estuary is subject to considerable fluctuation.

Some microbial species are indigenous to specific ecological areas of the estuary, while others are transient, having been added from domestic, industrial, agricultural, or atmospheric sources. In areas receiving domestic wastes rich in organic nutrients, the predominant bacteria include coliforms (Gram-negative intestinal bacilli such as *Escherichia coli*); fecal streptococci (such as *Streptococcus faecalis*); and species of *Aeromonas, Bacillus, Proteus, Clostridium, Sphaerotilus, Beggiatoa, Thiothrix, Thiobacillus,* and many others. Intestinal viruses such as those that cause hepatitis type A or poliomyelitis are also likely to be found. In regions of the estuary that are nutritionally poor, budding and/or appendaged bacteria are found, such as species of *Hyphomicrobium, Caulobacter,* and *Gallionella.* Soil bacteria, including *Azotobacter, Nitrosomonas,* and *Nitrobacter* species, also may be present. Numerous fungi (*Ascomycetes, Phycomycetes,* and *Deuteromycetes*) occur in various regions of the estuary as well.

Oceans

Microorganisms inhabit all depths and all latitudes in oceans. They are part of the plankton and are in the sediment of the ocean floor. The great volume of the open sea provides an environment with more uniform conditions than those found in other natural waters. Because of the size and depth of the oceans, obtaining samples for study, including bottom sediments, presents significant technical problems. Specialized sampling devices and techniques have been developed for this purpose.

Marine Plankton. The phytoplankton population consists of numerous species of cyanobacteria, as well as algae (diatoms, dinoflagellates, coccolithophores, and chlamydomonads). This group of microorganisms is

FIGURE 29.9

The watershed of the Chesapeake Bay. Draining parts of six states from New York to Virginia, the Chesapeake watershed comprises a tangle of tributaries. Each stream and river funnels rain waters to the estuary from the Appalachian Mountains, the Piedmont, and the coastal plain. Domestic and industrial wastewaters, which are added to each of these streams and rivers, are carried into the bay. In addition, vast quantities of automobile and truck exhausts add pollution to the bay as well.

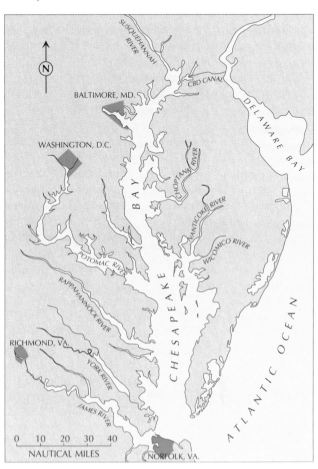

chiefly responsible for the conversion of radiant energy to chemical energy, the energy stored in chemical compounds that accumulate in the sea. The magnitude of this process is enormous: to support the growth of the potential world fish catch (approximately 50 million metric tons), a phytoplankton population equivalent to 50 billion metric tons is required.

Planktonic bacteria and algae, under certain environmental conditions, may grow into enormous populations in coastal areas and cause discoloration of the water. The characteristic color of the Red Sea is caused by heavy blooms of the cyanobacterium *Oscillatoria erythraea,* which contains the red pigment phycoerythrin. "Red tides" are likewise due to the explosive growth of certain planktonic species which may produce toxins that can be deadly for humans and fish. Brown, amber, or greenish-yellow discoloration of large areas of water occurs as the result of blooms of other microorganisms [FIGURE 29.10].

The bacterial population throughout the photic zone is closely related to the distribution of the phytoplanktonic algae. The algae provide organic compounds used by the bacteria; they also provide solid surfaces for bacterial attachment and aggregation. Most marine bacteria are moderately halophilic. The temperature of the marine environment is suitable for the growth of psychrophilic bacteria, and among the psychrophilic forms are luminous bacteria which can produce light in the presence of oxygen [FIGURE 29.11]. Some luminous bacteria exist in association with certain species of marine animals.

In general most marine bacteria are Gram-negative. It is thought that the Gram-negative cell wall with its outer membrane provides a structure better suited to life in nutritionally dilute aquatic environments than the Gram-positive cell wall, which lacks an outer membrane. For instance, important hydrolytic enzymes are retained in the Gram-negative periplasmic space, rather than being excreted and lost to the aquatic environment, as would be the case for Gram-positive bacteria. In addition, the lipopolysaccharide (LPS) of the outer membrane of Gram-negative bacteria protects against certain toxic molecules such as fatty acids and antibiotics, and it may serve to bind important nutrients from the water. Bacteria common to marine waters include species of *Vibrio*, *Acinetobacter*, *Pseudomonas*, *Flavobacterium*, and *Alteromonas*. Bacteria in the surface region of the marine environment are often pigmented, a characteristic which may protect the microbes from lethal solar radiation.

Marine Fungi and Protozoa. In addition to the marine bacteria and algae, some fungi and protozoa are found in oceans. Mold spores and mycelium fragments float in seawater throughout the photic zone. Fungi (deuteromycetes, phycomycetes, and myxomycetes) have been isolated from marine environments. Marine protozoa include species of *Foraminifera* and *Radiolaria*, as well as many flagellated and ciliated species. They exist in large numbers in the region inhabited by the phytoplankton. These zooplanktonic animals feed upon phytoplanktonic organisms, various bacteria, or detritus. During the day, vertically migrating zooplankton live beneath the region of photic activity, avoiding the light. At night they migrate and graze on phytoplankton at the water surface. The bacterial population is distributed more or less uniformly throughout and below these layers, feeding on descending organic material and other nutrients.

FIGURE 29.10

Algal blooms and the discoloration of water. **[A]** Golden algal bloom following sewage spill off Oahu, Hawaii. **[B]** Blue-green algal bloom (*Trichodesmium* sp.) in the open ocean 80 km north of Oahu, Hawaii. **[C]** "Red-tide" caused by *Noctiluca scintillans* in Tampa Bay, Florida.

[A]

[B]

[C]

FIGURE 29.11

Bioluminescence, the chemical emission of light by microorganisms, is characteristic of many marine forms of life. This photograph was taken by the light of the luminous bacterium *Photobacterium phosphoreum*. This bacterium is found in seawater, on the surface and in the alimentary tract of some marine fishes, and in the luminous organs of some fish and cephalopods.

TABLE 29.1

Bacteria Isolated from Pacific Ocean Sediment, Grouped into Physiological Types

Bacteria per gram of sediment (wet basis)	Sample 8160 at 32°51.2′ N, 117°28.3′ W, and depth of 780 m
Total aerobes, plate count	930,000
Total anaerobes, oval-tube count	190,000
Ammonification:	
Peptone → NH_4	100,000
Nutrose → NH_4	10,000
Urea fermentation, urea → NH_4	100
Proteolysis:	
Gelatin liquefaction	100,000
Peptone → H_2S	10,000
Denitrification, NO_3 → N_2	100
Nitrate reduction, NO_3 → NO_2	100,000
Nitrogen fixation	0
Nitrification, NH_4 → NO_2	0
Sulfate reduction, SO_4 → H_2S	1,000
Dextrose fermentation	10,000
Xylose fermentation	10,000
Starch hydrolysis	10,000
Cellulose decomposition	1,000
Fat hydrolysis (lipoclastic)	1,000
Chitin digestion	100

SOURCE: C. E. Zobell, *J. Sediment Petrol.* 8:10, 1938.

The area between these upper strata and the area just above the sea floor is relatively barren, a vast microbiological oceanic desert region. However, the bottom of the sea, the benthic region, is populated by a large variety of microorganisms.

The Benthic Population. Offshore sediments are inhabited by bacteria and protozoa. Large numbers are present at the mud-water interface; the bacterial population may range from a few hundred to millions per milliliter of water. The counts in sediments may be as high as hundreds of millions of bacteria per gram. A variety of physiological types of bacteria occur, as shown in TABLE 29.1.

Microbial Deposits. Many of the algae and protozoa that inhabit the photic zone at the surface have calcium- or silica-containing cell walls. When these organisms die and gradually sink to the bottom of the ocean, their undissolved skeletons accumulate in enormous quantities. Diatoms, radiolaria, and silicoflagellates produce siliceous (silica-containing) skeletons, whereas foraminifera and coccolithophores produce calcareous (calcium-containing) skeletons. Vast beds of these materials, sometimes hundreds of meters thick, occur in various regions of the sea. Some of these areas may later become raised above the sea. For example, the chalk beds of England and France are chiefly the remains of foraminifera, while a large part of the deposits at Lompoc, California, consists of the remains of diatoms. Bacteria, particularly cyanobacteria, are also involved in the precipitation of calcium carbonate and subsequent limestone formation.

The deposition and transformation of iron and manganese in sediments and sulfur deposits, like those found in the Gulf Coast areas of Texas and Louisiana, are closely linked to microbial activity. Microorganisms also play the major role in formation of petroleum deposits from accumulated and buried organic materials.

ASK YOURSELF

1 What is the microbial flora of plankton?

2 Characterize the zones of a body of fresh water.

3 What is an estuary? Compare the microbial flora of a body of fresh water with that of an estuary.

4 What is the cause of "red tides"? What conditions favor their occurrence?

5 What is the practical significance of the vast quantities of calcium- and silica-containing cell walls of certain algae and protozoa?

THE ROLE OF AQUATIC MICROORGANISMS

Aquatic life includes interactions among microorganisms and between microorganisms and higher forms of life, both plant and animal. Species of microorganisms carry out biochemical changes that recycle elements and nutrients in the water in much the same manner as that described for soil. These microorganisms perform a major role in maintaining a flow of nutrients for marine life, and thus occupy a key position in the aquatic food chain.

Food Chains and Food Webs in Aquatic Environments

A *food chain* is a system of relationships among organisms that produce food, organisms that consume food, and organisms that decompose plant and animal tissues to nutrients for the synthesis of more food. Microorganisms play an essential role in each aspect of this system. The principal events in an aquatic food chain are:

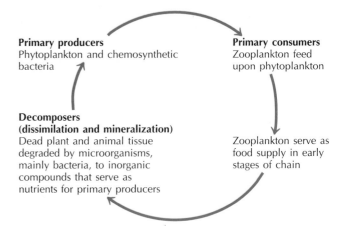

Primary producers
Phytoplankton and chemosynthetic bacteria

Primary consumers
Zooplankton feed upon phytoplankton

Zooplankton serve as food supply in early stages of chain

Decomposers (dissimilation and mineralization)
Dead plant and animal tissue degraded by microorganisms, mainly bacteria, to inorganic compounds that serve as nutrients for primary producers

However, in most environments the feeding relationships are in fact an interconnected complex resembling an interwoven web, that is, a *food web*. The role of microorganisms in the food web of a shallow estuary [FIGURE 29.12] differs somewhat from that in a food chain in ocean waters. In estuaries, significant amounts of organic nutrients are provided by vegetation and detritus, which are decomposed by microorganisms. In this manner the nutrients are converted to microbial protein,

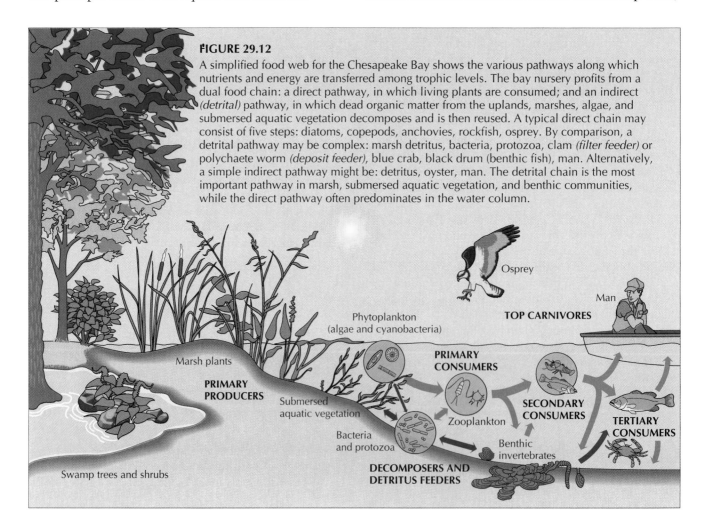

FIGURE 29.12

A simplified food web for the Chesapeake Bay shows the various pathways along which nutrients and energy are transferred among trophic levels. The bay nursery profits from a dual food chain: a direct pathway, in which living plants are consumed; and an indirect *(detrital)* pathway, in which dead organic matter from the uplands, marshes, algae, and submersed aquatic vegetation decomposes and is then reused. A typical direct chain may consist of five steps: diatoms, copepods, anchovies, rockfish, osprey. By comparison, a detrital pathway may be complex: marsh detritus, bacteria, protozoa, clam *(filter feeder)* or polychaete worm *(deposit feeder)*, blue crab, black drum (benthic fish), man. Alternatively, a simple indirect pathway might be: detritus, oyster, man. The detrital chain is the most important pathway in marsh, submersed aquatic vegetation, and benthic communities, while the direct pathway often predominates in the water column.

which serves as food for protozoa. Many higher animals in an estuarine environment are also direct consumers of vegetation and detritus: these include crustaceans, mollusks, insect larvae, nematodes, polychaetes, and a few fishes. Phytoplankton and benthic algae make only a small contribution to the estuary food supply, unlike their contribution in marine environments.

In ocean waters, primary production in the food chain is predominantly through photosynthesis by plankton and to a lesser extent through chemosynthetic bacteria.

A fascinating example of how microorganisms provide food for higher aquatic animals is found near hot water vents in the ocean floor. As described in Chapter 2, it was discovered in 1977 that a high density of microbial and animal life is present in areas immediately surrounding deep-sea hot springs, or **hydrothermal vents,** which occur along volcanic ridges 2600 meters below the ocean surface. These vents spew forth superheated water that contains hydrogen sulfide (H_2S). Water temperatures as high as 350°C have been recorded in some vents, but the water in the region surrounding the vents has an average temperature of 10 to 20°C. Many bacteria inhabit this region, not because of the warmth but because of the H_2S content of the water. These bacteria are autotrophs, and they obtain energy by oxidizing the H_2S. Much of this energy is used by the bacteria for CO_2 fixation and production of organic compounds.

Animal life also exists in abundance in the region near a thermal vent, but this animal life is completely dependent upon the organic substances produced by the sulfide-oxidizing bacteria. Many of the animal species are highly unusual, such as the giant tube worms up to a meter long and giant clams up to 30 centimeters long.

The Fertility of the Ocean

The term *fertility of the ocean* is used to express the capacity of an ocean for production of organic matter, also called the ocean's *productivity*. Fertility depends primarily upon the planktonic population. Marine plankton is referred to as the *pasture of the sea*, because fish, whales, and squid feed directly upon plankton or upon other animals which have fed upon plankton. A terrestrial environment produces 1 to 10 g of dry organic matter per square meter per day, compared with 0.5 g for the deep ocean areas. However, the oceanic area is so much larger than the productive land area that the total productivity of the ocean vastly exceeds that of the land.

The Antarctic Ocean is richer in life than any other major oceanic area. The large supply of nutrients in this region is caused by the mixing of the waters of the Atlantic, Pacific, and Indian oceans. This mixing action is brought about by the movement of the bottom current of

cold water that runs outward from the continental shelf of Antarctica. An abundance of nutrients in the upper layers results in a large phytoplankton crop. The red, shrimplike crustacean *Euphausia superba* (commonly called *krill*) feeds upon phytoplankton; in turn, the krill serves as food for fish, penguins, seabirds, seals, and whales. The krill is the key organism in the food chain in this environment—the link between photosynthetic planktonic life and the higher forms of life. The sequence of organisms in the food chain is shown in FIGURE 29.13. Analysis of planktonic populations is being greatly enhanced by new technology. Advances in computer hardware and software combined with fluorescent microscopic techniques have resulted in the development of image analysis systems of fluorescently stained specimens [FIGURE 29.14]. Automated equipment for color image–analyzed fluorescence microscopy is contributing significantly to a better understanding of plankton ecology.

Although coastal and estuarine regions provide a less stable physical environment than oceans, their fertility exceeds that of the open sea because of the large

FIGURE 29.13
Ecological pyramid showing various trophic levels. The higher the step in the pyramid, the smaller the number of individuals and the larger their size. In some environments, large animals circumvent some of the levels in the food chain. For example, humans take from all levels below them, including that of the producers.

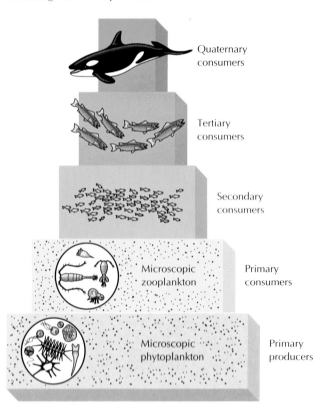

Quaternary consumers

Tertiary consumers

Secondary consumers

Microscopic zooplankton

Primary consumers

Microscopic phytoplankton

Primary producers

FIGURE 29.14
Examples of the use of color fluorescence to classify cell types from natural plankton samples. **[A]** Bacteria. **[B]** Photosynthetic cyanobacteria (*Synechococcus*). **[C]** Heterotrophic flagellates. **[D]** Heterotrophic ciliate. The color fluorescence is produced by fluorescing stains (DAPI in **[A]**, and proflavine in **[C]** and **[D]**) or autofluorescing plant pigments **[B]**. The blue/purple spots in **[C]** and **[D]** are 0.5 μm latex beads that have been added to trace feeding behavior. Some have been ingested and some (in **[C]**) are free in the water.

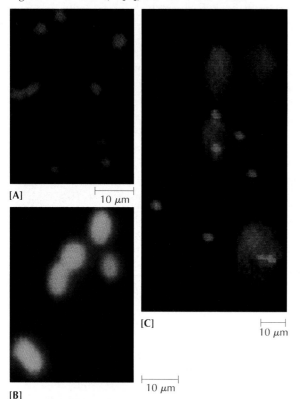

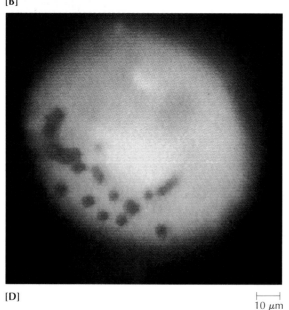

amounts of nutrients available from surrounding land areas.

Mixing Phenomena. Microbial populations in oceans are also affected by the flow of nutrients caused by currents. A phenomenon called *upwelling* occurs in an ocean when water rises from the bottom region to the surface region, usually as the result of a change of direction of offshore currents or winds. In this process the bottom water carries with it a rich supply of nutrients to the surface region. Upwelling occurs off the coasts of California and Peru and is responsible for the high productivity of these regions.

Gyres are large, spiraling surface currents in the ocean that tend to collect and retain nutrients, wastes, and microorganisms. Gyres have been appreciated only in recent years as a result of observations made possible by satellite imagery.

ASK YOURSELF

1 What is the role of primary producers and decomposers in an aquatic food chain?

2 What contributes to the fertility of the ocean?

DRINKING WATER

The drinking water of most communities and municipalities comes from surface sources—rivers, streams, and lakes. Such natural water supplies, particularly streams and rivers, are likely to be polluted with domestic, agricultural, and industrial wastes. Many city dwellers are not aware that the water coming from their faucets has been used previously, perhaps several times. As part of the hydrologic cycle, the reuse of water has traditionally been a natural process, but increasing pressures on our water supply are forcing new approaches to recycling water. The growth in population, the need for vast quantities of water by industry, and the expanded requirements of agricultural irrigation place new demands upon available water resources.

These modern-day factors have added a new dimension to water reuse, making it necessary to "speed up" the natural processes of water recycling and to ensure a safe water supply. For example, southern California has recently implemented rationing of water. Accordingly, there is a growing interest in developing acceptable methods for making "used" water safe and suitable for reuse more quickly. Comprehensive federal legislation has also been developed to enforce stringent regulations, designed to reduce water pollution and improve water quality.

Pollution

Water can be perfectly clear, odorless, and tasteless and yet be unsafe to drink. Contaminants that pollute water are classified into three categories: chemical, physical, and biological. Our discussion will focus on the biological pollutants, namely, microorganisms.

Water can endanger health and life if it contains pathogenic microorganisms (Chapter 25). The pathogens most frequently transmitted through water are those which cause infections of the intestinal tract. Examples are the causative agents of typhoid and paratyphoid fevers, shigellosis, cholera, campylobacteriosis, viral enteritis, and amoebiasis. These microorganisms are present in the feces or urine of an infected person and, when discharged, may enter a body of water that ultimately serves as a source of drinking water.

In order to prevent transmission of these pathogens, there must be (1) water-purification methods that provide safe drinking water, (2) treatment facilities for wastewater prior to its disposal or reuse, and (3) procedures whereby water can be examined to determine its microbiological quality.

Water Purification

Water that is safe to drink is free of disease-producing microorganisms and chemical substances harmful to health, and is called *potable* water. Nonpotable water, on the other hand, must be purified before it can be used for human consumption. Purification methods vary, depending on the source of water and the amount of water needed.

Single-Dwelling Water Supply. Underground sources—wells and springs—provide most of the water for individual homes in rural areas. Surface water should not be used for drinking purposes unless it is first treated (or boiled) to destroy any pathogenic microorganisms, since it will likely be polluted. Water from wells and springs is filtered as it penetrates through the layers of soil; this process removes suspended particles, including microorganisms. It is of prime importance that, when choosing a well site, contamination from pit privies, cesspools, septic tanks, and barnyards be avoided [FIGURE 29.15]. Water from home water supplies should be submitted for laboratory examination periodically for assurance of potability.

Municipal Water Supplies. The principal methods used in a municipal water-purification plant to produce potable water are *sedimentation, filtration,* and *chlorination* [FIGURE 29.16]. Sedimentation occurs in large reservoirs, where the water remains for a holding period; large particulate matter settles to the bottom. Sedimentation is enhanced by the addition of alum (aluminum sulfate), which produces a sticky, fluffy precipitate at the surface. Many microorganisms and finely suspended particulate material are removed as this precipitate descends through the water into settling beds, a process which removes 99 percent of the microorganisms. The water then passes through large sand filter beds for further removal of particulate matter. Subsequently, the water is chlorinated to kill any remaining microorgan-

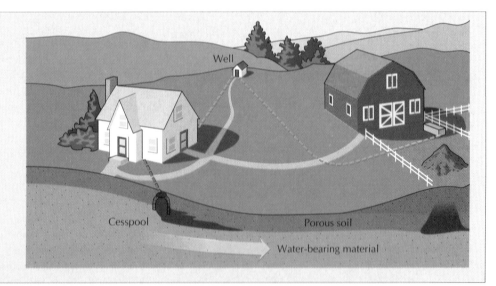

FIGURE 29.15
A farmstead showing a well properly located to avoid contamination. The arrow indicates the direction in which the groundwater moves.

Well

Cesspool

Porous soil

Water-bearing material

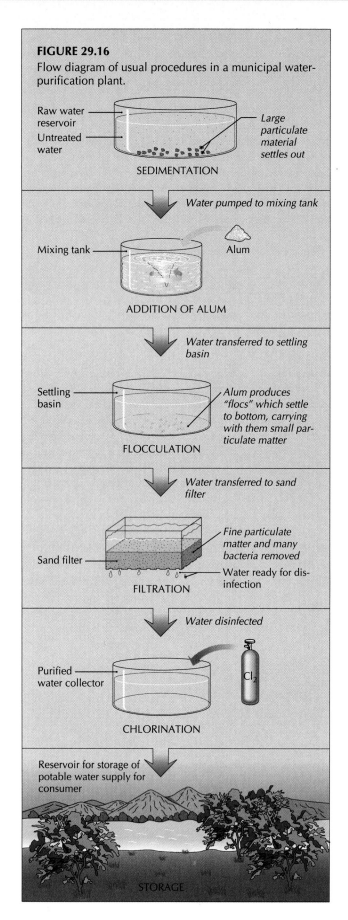

FIGURE 29.16

Flow diagram of usual procedures in a municipal water-purification plant.

Raw water reservoir

Untreated water

Large particulate material settles out

SEDIMENTATION

Water pumped to mixing tank

Mixing tank

Alum

ADDITION OF ALUM

Water transferred to settling basin

Settling basin

Alum produces "flocs" which settle to bottom, carrying with them small particulate matter

FLOCCULATION

Water transferred to sand filter

Sand filter

Fine particulate matter and many bacteria removed

Water ready for disinfection

FILTRATION

Water disinfected

Purified water collector

Cl₂

CHLORINATION

Reservoir for storage of potable water supply for consumer

STORAGE

isms and to ensure its potability. The chlorine dosage must be sufficient to leave a residue of 0.2 to 1.0 mg free chlorine per liter of water.

The purification process may include additional procedures, such as removing minerals that cause the water to be hard, adjusting the pH if the water is too acid or alkaline, removing undesirable colors or tastes, and adding fluoride for the prevention of dental caries.

Microorganisms As Indicators of Water Quality

The routine microbiological examination of water to determine its potability is not and should not be based on the isolation and identification of pathogenic microorganisms, for the following reasons:

1 Pathogens are likely to enter a water supply sporadically, and since they may not survive for long periods of time, they could be missed in a sample submitted to the laboratory.
2 If they are present in very small numbers, pathogens are likely to escape detection by laboratory procedures.
3 It takes 24 h or longer to obtain results from a routine laboratory examination for pathogenic microorganisms. By the time pathogens are found, many people would have consumed the water and would be exposed to these pathogenic microbes before action could be taken to correct the situation.

For these reasons, microbiologists have developed water testing procedures that do not rely on the isolation and identification of pathogens. Instead, tests are based upon finding a microorganism whose presence indicates the possibility of the presence of pathogenic microorganisms. The indicator organism serves as an "alarm" system.

Indicator Microorganisms. The term *indicator microorganism* refers to a kind of microorganism whose presence in water is evidence that the water is polluted with fecal material from humans or other warmblooded animals. This kind of pollution means that any pathogenic microorganisms that occur in the intestinal tract of these animals may also be present. Some of the important characteristics of an indicator organism are:

1 It is present in polluted water and absent from unpolluted (potable) water.
2 It is present in water when pathogens are present.
3 The quantity of indicator organism correlates with the amount of pollution.
4 It survives better and longer than the pathogens.
5 It has uniform and stable properties.

6 It is generally harmless to humans and other animals.
7 It is present in greater numbers than those of pathogens (making detection relatively easy).
8 It is easily detected by standard laboratory techniques.

Escherichia coli most closely satisfies the requirements of an ideal indicator of pollution and is the organism used in the United States. Other bacteria have been suggested and sometimes used as pollution indicators. These include *Streptococcus faecalis* and *Clostridium perfringens*; both are normal inhabitants of the large intestine of humans and other animals. There also is considerable interest in the development of a routine procedure for the detection of a virus as an indicator of pollution.

Like the coliform bacteria, enteric viruses can be carried by human wastes into water. Analysis of a water sample for presence of viruses requires more elaborate procedures than those used for isolation of bacteria. Although considerable research is under way, no "standard method" to detect viruses in water has been adopted.

***Escherichia coli* and Other Coliform Bacteria.** The coliform bacteria as a group are characterized as Gram-negative non-spore-forming facultative rod-shaped bacteria that ferment lactose with production of acid and gas within 48 h at 35°C. *E. coli* is a normal inhabitant of the intestinal tract of humans and other warmblooded animals and is thus regarded as a *fecal type* of coliform. Other members of the coliform group, for example, *Enterobacter aerogenes*, are widely distributed in nature and found in soil, water, grain, and also the intestinal tract of humans and other animals and are regarded as *nonfecal* coliforms. These species bear a very close resemblance to each other in their morphological and cultural characteristics. Consequently, it is necessary to use biochemical tests such as the following four to differentiate these species:

1 Ability to produce indole from tryptophan. *E. coli* does, and *Ent. aerogenes* does not.
2 Amount of acidity produced in a special glucose-broth medium and detected by the pH indicator methyl red. Both organisms produce acid from glucose. However, *E. coli* produces a lower pH, which turns the indicator red, whereas *Ent. aerogenes* cultures do not produce as large an amount of acid and thus do not produce the color change.
3 Ability to produce the compound acetylmethylcarbinol in a glucose-peptone medium. This chemical is detected by the Voges-Proskauer test procedure. *E. coli* does not produce acetylmethylcarbinol, but *Ent. aerogenes* does.

4 Utilization of sodium citrate. *Ent. aerogenes* is capable of utilizing sodium citrate as its sole source of carbon; it will grow in a chemically defined medium in which sodium citrate is the only carbon compound. *E. coli* does not grow under the same circumstances.

For convenience, these tests collectively are designated as the *IMViC reactions* (I = indole, M = methyl red, Vi = Voges-Proskauer reaction, and C = citrate). The reactions for a typical strain of each species are:

| Organism | TEST | | | |
	Indole	Methyl red	Voges-Proskauer	Citrate
Escherichia coli	+	+	−	−
Enterobacter aerogenes	−	−	+	+

The coliforms have several characteristics in common with species of the genera *Salmonella* and *Shigella*, all of which are pathogenic. However, a major distinctive biochemical difference is that the coliforms ferment lactose with the production of acid and gas; *Salmonella* and *Shigella* do not ferment lactose. Hence the fermentation of lactose is the key reaction in the laboratory procedure for determining the potability of water [FIGURE 29.17].

Bacteriological Examination of Water for Potability

Methods of examining water bacteriologically are contained in the book *Standard Methods for the Examination of Water and Wastewater* (prepared and published jointly by the American Public Health Association, the American Water Works Association, and the Federation of Sewage and Industrial Wastes Associations) and also in publications of the U.S. Environmental Protection Agency. The methods are "standard," and procedures must be followed precisely if the results of the test are to have official significance. It is essential that strict attention be given to the following details when water samples are submitted for bacteriological analysis:

1 The sample must be collected in a sterile bottle.
2 The sample must be representative of the supply from which it is taken.
3 Contamination of the sample must be avoided during and after sampling.
4 The sample should be tested as promptly as possible after collection.
5 If there is to be a delay in examination, the sample should be stored at a temperature between 0 and 10°C.

FIGURE 29.17
General scheme of laboratory testing used for the detection of members of coliform bacteria in water.

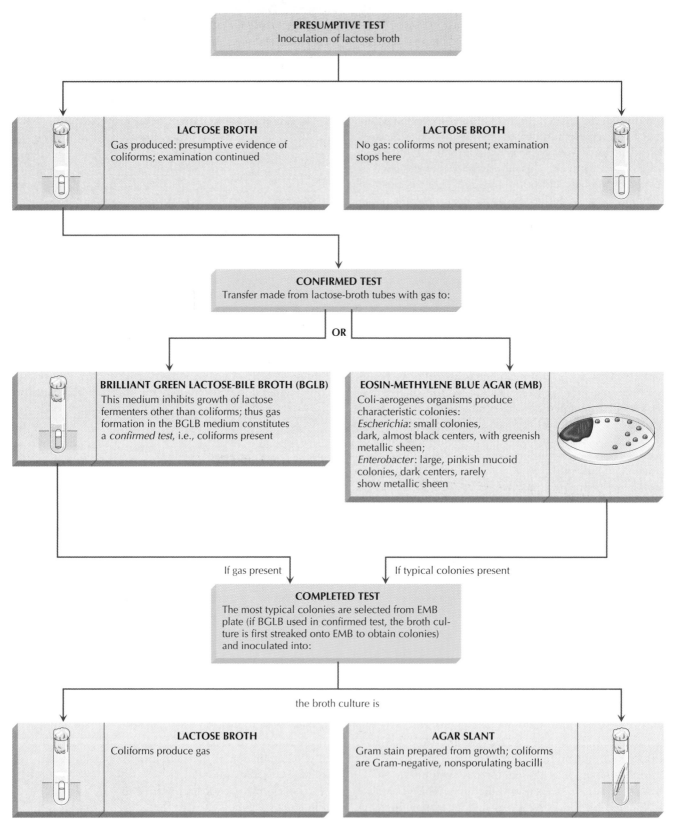

Fermentation of lactose broth and demonstration of Gram-negative, nonsporulating bacilli constitute a positive completed test demonstrating that some member of the coliform group is in the volume of sample examined.

The routine bacteriological procedures consist of (1) a standard plate count to determine the number of bacteria present, and (2) tests to reveal the presence or absence of coliform bacteria.

Standard Plate Count. Usually 1.0- and 0.1-ml quantities of the water sample are plated on an agar medium and incubated for 24 h, after which the colonies are counted. When using the standard plate count to test water, there are no particular numbers of bacteria that are officially acceptable. This is because water with a few pathogenic bacteria obviously is more dangerous than water containing many nonpathogenic bacteria. Nevertheless, water of good quality has a low total bacterial count, fewer than 100 per ml. Plate counts also are useful in determining the efficiency of the various procedures for removing or destroying organisms (sedimentation, filtration, and chlorination). A standard plate count can be made before and after a specific treatment to measure the reduction of the microbial population.

Membrane-Filter Technique. The membrane-filter technique for the bacteriological examination of water [FIGURE 29.18] consists of the following steps:

1 A sterile filter disk is placed in a filtration unit.
2 A measured volume of water is drawn through this filter disk; the bacteria are retained on the surface of the membrane-filter disk.
3 The filter disk is removed and placed upon an absorbent pad that has previously been saturated with an appropriate culture medium. Special Petri dishes that will hold both the absorbent pad and the filtration disk are used for incubation.
4 During incubation, colonies develop on the filter disk wherever bacteria were entrapped.

This technique has several desirable features. A large volume of water sample can be examined; theoretically almost any volume of water could be filtered through the disk. All of the microorganisms from the sample are retained on the disk. Results can be obtained more rapidly than by inoculating a series of tubes of lactose broth. By using selective and differential media, certain bacterial types such as coliforms can be identified.

Nuisance Bacteria in Water Systems

Certain bacteria are considered *nuisance bacteria* in water systems because they cause changes in odor, color, and taste. Some may form precipitates of insoluble compounds within pipes that reduce the rate of water flow. Algae may also be responsible for the development of odors, discoloration, and other objectionable charac-

teristics. The following are examples of nuisance microorganisms and the undesirable conditions they cause:

Slime-forming bacteria: Produce gummy or slimy conditions.
Iron bacteria: Transform soluble iron compounds to insoluble compounds. Deposition of insoluble iron compounds reduces the flow of water through pipes.
Sulfur bacteria: Produce sulfuric acid and hydrogen sulfide, which can make water very acidic and impart an obnoxious odor. Sulfuric acid formation in concrete sewer pipes can damage the structural quality of pipes [FIGURE 29.19].
Algae: Produce turbidity, discoloration, and unpleasant odor and taste.

ASK YOURSELF

1 What are the major steps in the purification of water for a municipality?

2 Why is *E. coli* used as an indicator of pollution rather than an enteric pathogen?

3 What are the advantages of the membrane-filter technique over the standard plate count–lactose broth inoculation procedure for determining the potability of water?

SWIMMING POOLS

Water in swimming places, particularly in public swimming pools, may be a health hazard. Swimming pools and surrounding areas may transmit infections of the eyes, nose, throat, and intestinal tract; they may also spread athlete's foot, impetigo, and other skin infections. Thus it is imperative that strict attention be given to the sanitary quality of the water. There must be surveillance of the disinfection process to ensure that the proper level of disinfectant is maintained. Chlorine is used widely as a disinfectant for swimming pool water.

ASK YOURSELF

1 What are the potential health hazards of swimming pool water?

2 What measures are employed to minimize the possibility of infection from swimming pool water?

FIGURE 29.18

Membrane filter technique. **[A]** A sterile absorbent pad is aseptically saturated with appropriate sterile culture medium in a Petri dish prior to collection of bacteria from a water sample. **[B]** A sterile filter disk is placed in a filtration unit, **[C]** a sample vessel is attached and **[D]** a measured volume of water is drawn through the filter into a collection vessel. **[E]** Filter disk retaining bacteria from the water sample is placed on the saturated pad. **[F]** Filter and pad are incubated prior to examination for bacteria. **[G]** Colonies of *Escherichia coli* on a membrane filter disk placed on a pad saturated with EMB medium.

[C]

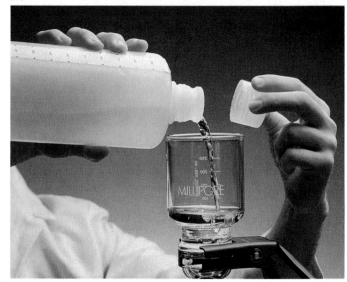

[D]

[A]

[B]

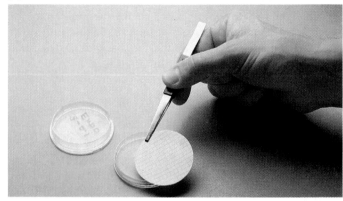

[E]

[F]

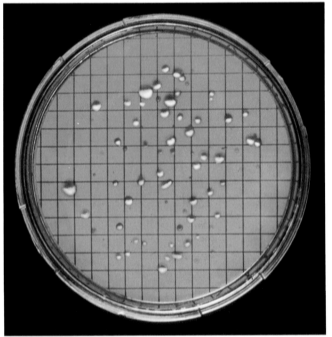

[G]

FIGURE 29.19
Crown corrosion in section of concrete sewer pipe. Anaerobic chemoheterotrophs produce H_2S, which is absorbed in condensate on the walls above the water line. Aerobic chemolithotrophs oxidize the reduced sulfur to SO_4^{2-}, forming H_2SO_4, which attacks and erodes the concrete, often to the point of structural failure.

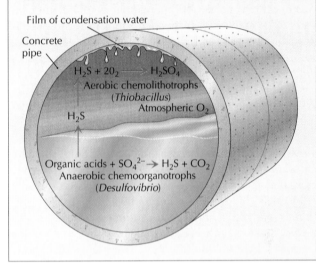

Film of condensation water

Concrete pipe

$H_2S + 2O_2 \longrightarrow H_2SO_4$
Aerobic chemolithotrophs
(*Thiobacillus*)
Atmospheric O_2

H_2S

Organic acids + $SO_4^{2-} \rightarrow H_2S + CO_2$
Anaerobic chemoorganotrophs
(*Desulfovibrio*)

WASTEWATER

Wastewater, or *sewage*, is defined as the used water supply of a community and consists of:

1 Domestic waterborne wastes, including human excrement and wash waters (everything that goes down the drains of a home and city and into its sewage system)
2 Industrial waterborne wastes such as acids, oils, greases, and animal and vegetable matter discharged by factories
3 Ground, surface, and atmospheric waters that enter the wastewater system

The wastewater of a city is collected by systems that carry the used water to locations for treatment and disposal. There are three kinds of wastewater systems: (1) *sanitary sewers*, which carry domestic and industrial sewage; (2) *storm sewers*, which are designed to carry off surface and rain water; and (3) *combined sewers*, which carry the wastewater from both sanitary and storm sewers.

Characteristics of Wastewater

Wastewaters exhibit a great diversity in physical, chemical, and microbiological characteristics. It is important to understand these factors when designing treatment plants to process wastewater.

Physical and Chemical Characteristics of Wastewater. Wastewater consists of approximately 99.9 percent water. The amount of suspended solids in wastewater is so small that it is expressed in parts per million (ppm); the solid content of wastewater ranges from a few ppm to 100 ppm. This amount of solids appears small; however, the tremendous volume of wastewater processed daily by a major municipal plant is several hundred million gallons and contains tons of solids. The chemical constituents, although present in low concentrations, are extremely important and vary in kind and amount from one community to the next, as well as from hour to hour. Inorganic chemicals initially present in the water supply will likewise be present in the wastewater. Organic compounds are added by human excrement and other domestic wastes. Both organic and inorganic compounds are added by industrial wastes. For example, slaughterhouses, sugar factories, paper mills, and creameries add organic substances; chemical and metal industries contribute acids and salts of metals and other inorganic chemical wastes.

Modern technology has changed wastewater characteristics. The use of household garbage-disposal units has increased the total organic load in wastewater. Synthetic detergents, which have largely displaced soaps, can adversely affect the microbial population needed for effective wastewater treatment.

Microbiological Characteristics. Fungi, protozoa, algae, bacteria, and viruses are present in wastewater. Untreated wastewater may contain millions of bacteria per milliliter, including the coliforms, streptococci, anaerobic spore-forming bacilli, the *Proteus* group, and other types originating in the intestinal tract of humans. Additional microorganisms are contributed from ground, surface, or atmospheric waters or from industrial wastes.

Moreover, the effectiveness of the treatment process is dependent upon the biochemical changes carried out by microorganisms [TABLE 29.2]. The predominant physiological types of bacteria involved may shift during the various stages of wastewater treatment. Conditions can range from highly aerobic to strictly anaerobic.

Biochemical Oxygen Demand. The *biochemical oxygen demand (BOD)* is the amount of dissolved oxygen required by microorganisms for the aerobic degradation of organic matter present in wastewater. One of the primary reasons for treating wastewater prior to its being returned to a stream or lake is to reduce the drain on the

---

TABLE 29.2
Generalized Scheme of Microbial Degradation of the Organic Constituents in Sewage

		REPRESENTATIVE END PRODUCTS	
Substrates	+ Enzymes of microorganisms →	Anaerobic conditions	Aerobic conditions
Proteins and other organic nitrogen compounds		Amino acids Ammonia Nitrogen Hydrogen sulfide Methane Carbon dioxide Hydrogen Alcohols Organic acids Indole	Amino acids Ammonia → nitrites → nitrates Hydrogen sulfide → sulfuric acid Alcohols Organic acids $\Big\} \to CO_2 + H_2O$
Carbohydrates		Carbon dioxide Hydrogen Alcohols Fatty acids Neutral compounds	Alcohols Fatty acids $\Big\} \to CO_2 + H_2O$
Fats and related substances		Fatty acids + glycerol Carbon dioxide Hydrogen Alcohols Short-chain fatty acids	Alcohols Lower fatty acids $\Big\} \to CO_2 + H_2O$

dissolved oxygen supply in the receiving body of water. The magnitude of the BOD is an indication of the amount of organic material in the sewage; the more oxidizable organic material present, the higher the BOD. The "strength" of wastewater is expressed in terms of BOD level. High values mean that a high level of organic material is present, whereas low values mean that little oxidizable material is present.

The life of any body of water depends to a large extent upon its ability to maintain a certain amount of dissolved oxygen, which is needed to maintain aquatic life. For example, without dissolved oxygen, fish suffocate and normal aquatic organisms are destroyed.

Wastewater Treatment Processes

Untreated wastewater cannot be disposed of without serious objectionable consequences. Disposal of inadequately treated wastewater may produce one or more of the following undesirable situations:

1 Greater possibility for dissemination of pathogenic microorganisms
2 Increased danger in using natural bodies of water for drinking supplies
3 Contamination of oysters and other shellfish by the pollution, making them unsafe for human consumption
4 Large losses in the waterfowl population because of pollution of their feeding grounds
5 Increased danger in swimming and diminished value of the water for other recreational purposes
6 Depletion of oxygen supply of the water by unstable organic matter in sewage, killing aquatic life
7 Creation of objectionable conditions such as offensive odors and accumulation of debris, thereby decreasing property values and recreational uses

Wastewater treatment processes are many and varied, but they may be divided into those applicable to a single dwelling or single-unit structure, and those used by a community or municipality.

Single Dwelling or Single-Unit Structures. Treatment and disposal of wastewater from individual dwellings or other single-unit structures, such as motels or shopping centers, can be accomplished by an anaerobic digestion or aerobic digestion tank. The **septic tank** is an anaerobic digestion tank commonly employed for treatment of a limited amount of wastewater [FIGURE 29.20]. A septic tank accomplishes two objectives: sedimentation of solid materials, and biological degradation of these solids. The material which accumulates at the bottom of the tanks is called **sludge.** As sewage enters the tank, sedimentation occurs in the lower portion, permitting a liquid with fewer suspended solids to be discharged. The sedimented solids are continually degraded by anaerobic

bacteria; the end products are organic compounds, have high BOD, and are odorous. The effluent from the septic tank is distributed under the soil surface through a disposal field, as shown in FIGURE 29.20. Further microbial degradation—largely aerobic oxidation of the organic material in the effluent—takes place as the liquid effluent seeps through the drainage field. This kind of treatment cannot guarantee elimination of all pathogens. Consequently, it is imperative that drainage from the system be prevented from seeping into the drinking water supply.

Aerobic wastewater treatment systems are also available commercially for small-unit situations. These tanks are designed with compartments and equipment to reduce incoming solids to small particle size, an aeration

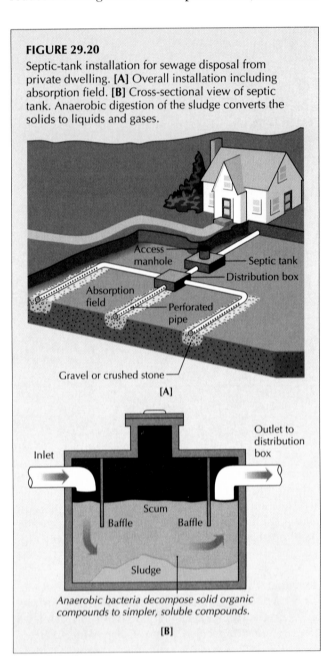

FIGURE 29.20
Septic-tank installation for sewage disposal from private dwelling. [A] Overall installation including absorption field. [B] Cross-sectional view of septic tank. Anaerobic digestion of the sludge converts the solids to liquids and gases.

Anaerobic bacteria decompose solid organic compounds to simpler, soluble compounds.

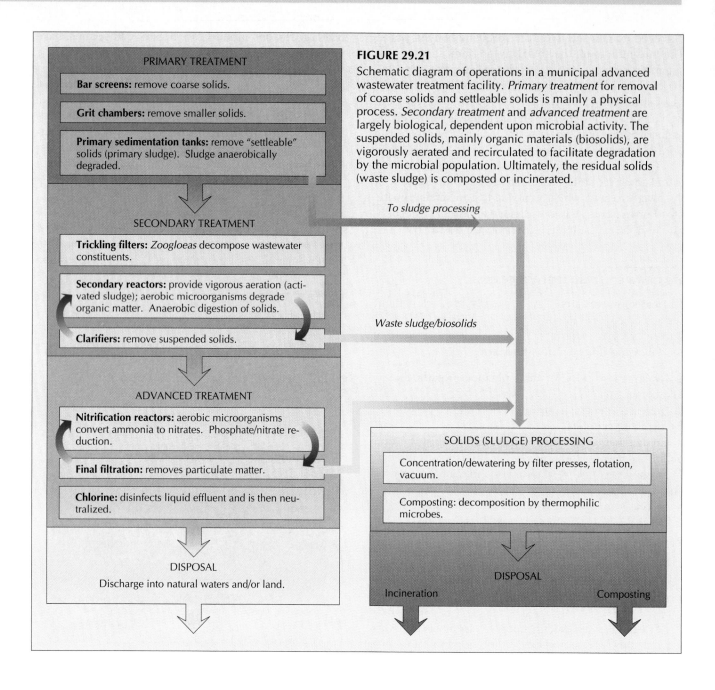

FIGURE 29.21

Schematic diagram of operations in a municipal advanced wastewater treatment facility. *Primary treatment* for removal of coarse solids and settleable solids is mainly a physical process. *Secondary treatment* and *advanced treatment* are largely biological, dependent upon microbial activity. The suspended solids, mainly organic materials (biosolids), are vigorously aerated and recirculated to facilitate degradation by the microbial population. Ultimately, the residual solids (waste sludge) is composted or incinerated.

chamber, and an effluent settling chamber. Oxygen is pumped into the aeration chamber to allow for continuous oxidation and aerobic decomposition of wastewater solids. These units are especially useful in locations where percolation through soil is poor, such as wetlands or soil with many stones and rocks.

Municipal Facilities. Municipal wastewater treatment plants carry out a series of treatment processes [FIGURE 29.21; DISCOVER 29.2]. The requirements for each level of treatment as specified in the Clean Water Act are summarized in TABLE 29.3 and are as follows:

1 Primary treatment—physical removal of coarse solids.
(a) *Screening* removes the largest solids such as boxes, tires, bottles, and cans. Material may be incinerated, ground up, or used for landfill.
(b) *Grit chambers* remove smaller solids, such as pebbles.
(c) *Sedimentation* (primary settling) removes smaller particulate material, such as fecal matter and paper. This particulate material (sludge or **biosolids**) is often treated biologically through anaerobic degradation in a sludge digester.

2 Secondary (biological) treatment—decomposition of

29.2 USING RECLAIMED MUNICIPAL WASTEWATER FOR IRRIGATION

Land application of municipal wastewater is a well-established practice in many arid and semiarid regions of the world. In some regions, 70 to 85 percent of such water is used for agricultural and landscape irrigation. As demand for water increases in the United States, irrigation with reclaimed municipal wastewater has become a logical and important component of total water resource planning and development.

In California, about 220,000 acre-feet of municipal wastewater from 240 cities and towns is used each year, principally for agricultural and landscape irrigation. In addition, about 610,000 acre-feet per year of treated wastewater is incidentally reused after it is discharged and enters surface or ground waters. Over half of the intentionally reclaimed municipal wastewater (57 percent) is used to irrigate fodder, fiber, and seed crops, a use not requiring a high degree of treatment. About 7 percent is used to irrigate orchard, vine, and other food crops. Irrigation of golf courses and landscape areas makes use of about 14 percent of reclaimed wastewater each year, and these uses are increasing.

There are several reasons for the growing use of reclaimed municipal wastewater, including: (1) the lack of fresh water at a competitive price; (2) the potential use of plant nutrients in reclaimed municipal wastewater; (3) the availability of high-quality effluents; (4) a need to establish comprehensive water resource planning, including water conservation and reuse; and (5) avoidance of costly compliance with more stringent water pollution control requirements, including a requirement for advanced wastewater treatment facilities for municipalities.

Although irrigation with municipal wastewater is in itself an effective form of wastewater treatment, some additional treatment must be made before such water can be used for agricultural or landscape irrigation. The degree of treatment is an important factor in the planning, design, and management of wastewater irrigation systems. Preapplication treatment is necessary to protect public health, to prevent nuisance conditions during application and storage, and to prevent damage to crops, soils, and groundwater.

From *California Agriculture*, March–April 1987, Division of Agriculture and Natural Resources, Oakland, Calif.

---

organic matter and reduction of the BOD. One or more of the following methods are used:

(a) *Trickling filters* spray wastewater (thus aerating it) over rock beds. Each rock is coated with a slimy mass of bacteria called *zoogloeas* that decompose the constituents of wastewater as it trickles over the rocks [FIGURES 29.22 and 29.23].

(b) The *activated-sludge* process vigorously aerates wastewater, resulting in the formation of particles teeming with aerobic microbial decomposers. This is accomplished in aeration tanks and is followed by further sedimentation for removal of biosolids.

(c) *Oxidation ponds (lagoons)* are shallow (2- to 4-ft-deep) ponds, where algae, such as species of *Chlorella*, consume wastewater nutrients and produce oxygen for aerobic decomposition.

(d) *Sludge digestion* decomposes solids accumulated during primary treatment and sometimes after secondary treatment. Anaerobes digest sludge in deep tanks, yielding methane (which may be used as heating fuel), carbon dioxide, and smaller amounts of nitrogen and hydrogen. Anaerobic wastewater degradation is a slow process.

3 Tertiary (advanced) wastewater treatment removes additional pollutants remaining after secondary treatment. A wastewater of high quality can be produced that is suitable for many reuses. The advanced treatment may consist of one or more of the following:

(a) *Chemical flocculation* removes much of the remaining particulate matter.

TABLE 29.3
Definitions of Municipal Treatment Levels

Treatment level	Treatment requirements*
Primary	Approximately 30% removal of BOD and 60% removal of TSS
Secondary	Removal of both BOD and TSS to levels of 25–30 mg/liter, but not less than 85% removal; pH between 6.0 and 9.0
Tertiary (advanced)	Removal of both BOD and TSS to levels less than 9 mg/liter, or removal of over 95% of BOD and TSS; additional requirements for removal of nutrients (e.g., nitrates, phosphates) on site-specific basis

Abbreviations: BOD = biological oxygen demand; TSS = total suspended solids.
*Treatment levels required by the Clean Water Act.

(b) *Final filtration* removes solids which are dried and incinerated, or used as landfill or fertilizer.

(c) Removal or reduction of phosphates and nitrates.

(d) *Chlorination* of the liquid effluent to kill microorganisms, some of which may be pathogenic. The final effluent should be dechlorinated before being discharged into a body of water, because chlorine is detrimental to aquatic life.

FIGURE 29.22
Distribution of liquid sewage from a rotary distributor onto the stones of a trickling filter. The stones are coated with a microbial growth. As the liquid effluent passes through this unit, the microorganisms growing on the stones' surfaces metabolize (oxidize) many of the organic compounds present in the effluent. The liquid effluent is collected at the bottom of the filter bed and piped to the next treatment process.

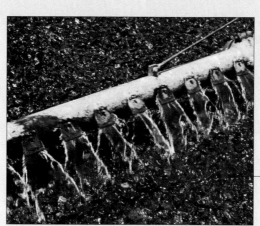
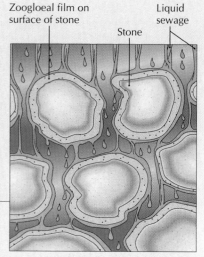

Zoogloeal film on surface of stone

Stone

Liquid sewage

FIGURE 29.23
Branched and amorphous zoogloeas collected from the surface of trickling filters receiving primarily domestic wastewaters. [A] Natural branched trickling-filter zoogloea. [B] Portion of specimen shown in part [A] illustrating morphological similarity of bacterial cells and their concentration at anterior points of zoogloeal branches. [C] Natural amorphous trickling-filter zoogloea. [D] Portion of specimen shown in part [C] illustrating presence of morphologically different bacteria. (All specimens treated with 10% skim milk to accentuate zoogloealmatrix. Phase-contrast microscopy.)

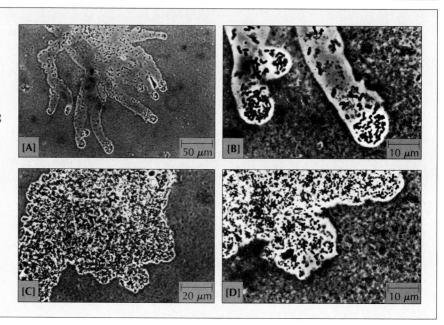

Economics of Wastewater Treatment

The average cost of treating wastewater in the United States is measured in cents per thousand gallons. However, when more advanced wastewater treatment processes are employed, the cost increases dramatically. By using the most modern and sophisticated wastewater treatment technology, it is possible to produce an effluent that is potable. The cost of these processes is very high, but some countries in the world have no alternative because of the scarcity of raw water. In a cost-benefit assessment, a judgment needs to be made based on the level of reused-water quality desired and the availability of alternative sources of water. The increasing demand for water, together with the demand for a clean environment, ensures an increase in the cost of this commodity, a commodity that was once viewed as free and of unlimited quantity.

ASK YOURSELF

1 What are the likely ingredients of wastewater?

2 Outline the steps used in a modern wastewater treatment plant, and describe the role performed by microorganisms in each step of the process.

3 What is BOD in terms of wastewater treatment? Assume that the effluent of a wastewater treatment plant has a high BOD. What does this indicate?

SUMMARY

1 The earth's supply of water undergoes continuous recycling; the various stages constitute the hydrologic cycle.

2 Natural bodies of surface waters can be categorized as fresh, estuary, and ocean. They vary considerably in physical characteristics, which affect the microorganisms present. Microorganisms in fresh water are very much influenced by agricultural practices, industrial activities, and urban development. The environmental conditions in estuaries range from fresh water to ocean water at the connection to the sea. Hence, the microbial flora is extremely diverse. The surface region of ocean water, as well as the water at all depths, also has a characteristic array of microbes.

3 Microorganisms in natural waters are distributed in broad "zones" or layers—from the surface region to the benthic zone. Those found in the surface region are mainly cyanobacteria, algae, and protozoa; together they are called *plankton*. Populations of cyanobacteria and algae are called *phytoplankton*; those made up of protozoa are called *zooplankton*. The benthic sediment contains large numbers of bacteria, many of which are facultative or anaerobic.

4 Microorganisms provide vital connections in the aquatic food web. For example, the zooplankton feed upon the phytoplankton. Photosynthetic plankton are primary producers of food for the food chains in the ocean. They convert the radiant energy of the sun into chemical energy (chemical compounds) via photosynthesis. Other microorganisms (chemosynthetic types) also act as primary producers by transforming inorganic chemicals into organic compounds through chemosynthesis.

5 Drinking water for communities is obtained from surface sources such as rivers or lakes. This "raw water" is likely to be polluted. In order to provide safe (potable) drinking water for a community it must first be treated. The major steps in a municipal water purification plant are sedimentation, filtration, and chlorination.

6 The standard laboratory procedure used to assess the potability of water is to determine whether *Escherichia coli* is present or absent. *Escherichia coli* is used as the indicator of pollution because it is a normal inhabitant of the intestinal tract of humans. If present in water, it indicates that the water is contaminated with fecal material and thus polluted and nonpotable.

7 Other microorganisms may be present in water that need to be differentiated from *E. coli*. These include other coliform bacteria closely related to *E. coli*; differentiation is based on biochemical tests. Viruses also gain entrance into raw water supplies through fecal pollution. Laboratory procedures for the isolation and identification of viruses are much more complicated than those for bacteria.

8 Water in swimming pools needs to be disinfected and monitored, so as to prevent transmission of numerous diseases.

9 Wastewater, or sewage, is the used water supply of a community. It contains domestic wastes, industrial wastes, and runoff from streets, lawns, and other surfaces. Sewage is approximately 99.9 percent water.

10 The treatment of wastewater aims to accomplish two objectives: (1) eliminate pathogenic microorganisms, and (2) reduce the amount of solids and oxidizable material in the final effluent. All wastewater treatment is dependent upon the biochemical activities of microorganisms, particularly bacteria that degrade complex organic substances.

11 A modern municipal wastewater treatment plant performs primary, secondary, and tertiary (advanced) treatment. The liquid effluent is chlorinated prior to final discharge into a body of water or onto land.

KEY TERMS

barophilic organisms
benthic zone
benthos
biochemical oxygen demand (BOD)
biosolids
detritus
epibacteria
eutrophic
food chain
gyres
hydrologic cycle
hydrothermal vents
indicator microorganism
limnetic zone
limnology
littoral zone
oligotrophic
photic zone
phytoplankton
plankton
potable
primary producers
profundal zone
septic tank
sewage
sludge
upwelling
wastewater
zoogloeas
zooplankton

R E V I E W   G U I D E

NATURAL WATERS

1 The earth's moisture, in terms of its location in the hydrologic cycle, can be classified as _____ water, _____ water, or _____.

2 Which of the following natural waters is an estuary? **(a)** pond; **(b)** lake; **(c)** bay; **(d)** ocean; **(e)** sea.

3 The study of the microbiology of natural waters is called _____ microbiology.

4 Subsurface water usually has a negligible microbial content. This is due to the process of _____.

THE AQUATIC ENVIRONMENT

5 The temperature of natural waters shows considerable variation. Match each temperature shown on the left with the corresponding natural water on the right.

_____ 0°C
_____ 80°C or above
_____ 5°C
_____ 0–75°C
_____ 30–40°C

(a) Surface water, polar regions
(b) Geothermal vents
(c) Surface water, equatorial
(d) Lake (East Coast)
(e) Most of the marine environment

6 Microorganisms that are isolated from ocean trenches and which require elevated atmospheric pressure for growth are described as _____.

7 The region of a natural water wherein photosynthesis occurs is called the _____ zone.

8 In terms of salinity, the range of dissolved salts in an estuary is between _____ percent and _____ percent.

9 Bacteria which attach themselves to solid surfaces and grow in the marine environment are called _____.

10 The pH of the marine environment ranges between pH _____ and pH _____.

DISTRIBUTION OF MICROORGANISMS IN THE AQUATIC ENVIRONMENT

11 Match each term on the left with the most appropriate description on the right.

_____ benthic
_____ blooms
_____ phytoplankton
_____ zooplankton
_____ littoral zone

(a) Inhabitants of the bottom region of an aquatic system
(b) Explosive growth of algae
(c) The region along the shoreline of a lake
(d) The mass of algae floating and drifting in the surface of a natural water
(e) Protozoa and other animal-like microorganisms appearing in the surface region of water

12 Lakes or ponds enriched with phosphates and nitrates result in excessive growth of algae. This is called _____.

13 A microbiological analysis is made of two aquatic samples, one from a limnetic zone, the other from a benthic zone. Which sample is likely to have the most anaerobic species?

14 A semienclosed coastal body of water that has a free connection with the open sea is called a(n) _____.

15 The salinity of Chesapeake Bay ranges from less than 1% to _____ % NaCl.

16 Bacteria of the genera *Hyphomicrobium* and *Caulobacter* would be found in regions of an estuary that have _____ levels of organic nutrients.

17 Enormous populations of cyanobacteria or algae, which may produce toxins lethal to aquatic animals, are referred to as _____.

18 The phytoplankton provides not only organic nutrients that can be used by non-photosynthetic bacteria but also _____ for the growth of many of these bacteria.

19 Some luminescent marine bacteria live in symbiosis with _____.

20 Most marine bacteria are Gram-_____.

21 The periplasmic space of Gram-negative bacteria retains important _____ enzymes which, without the cell wall, would be lost to the aquatic environment.

22 Marine bacteria in the surface region of the sea are often _____, which may help to protect them against the lethal portion of solar radiation.

23 Many zooplanktonic organisms graze on the phytoplankton at night but sink below the photic zone during the day in order to _____.

24 The region between the upper strata of the sea and the sea floor has relatively _____ numbers of microorganisms.

25 Marine sediments may have microbial populations as high as _____ per gram.

26 Microorganisms that occur in the mud and ooze at the bottom of a lake reside in which zone? **(a)** profundal; **(b)** benthic; **(c)** littoral; **(d)** limnetic; **(e)** photic.

27 A massive growth of algae is associated with: **(a)** eutrophication; **(b)** detritus; **(c)** a geothermal vent; **(d)** an oligotrophic condition; **(e)** the benthos.

28 The chalk beds of England were formed by an accumulation of the skeletal remains of _____.

THE ROLE OF AQUATIC MICROORGANISMS

29 _____ and _____ play a key role in the food chain because they are the primary producers.

30 In a shallow estuary, _____ and _____ convert organic vegetation into microbial protein, and protozoa in turn feed upon this.

31 Crustaceans, mollusks, insect larvae, nematodes, polychaetes, and a few fish can derive their energy from fragments of vascular plant matter in water; these organisms are called _____ consumers.

32 In terms of organic matter produced per square meter, terrestrial productivity is greater than that of the oceans; however, this difference is inconsequential because of

_____ .

33 Bacterial dissimilation of organic materials to carbon dioxide, water, and various

inorganic salts is a process called _____ .

34 The Antarctic Ocean is richer in life than other oceanic areas because of

_____ .

35 The small, red, shrimplike crustaceans that belong to the species *Euphausia*

superba are referred to by the common name _____ .

36 In the food chain in the ocean, the _____ in the upper layers is consumed by krill, which in turn is consumed by fish, penguins, seabirds, seals, and whales.

37 Which of the following is referred to as the "pasture of the sea"? **(a)** seaweed; **(b)** krill; **(c)** fish and other seafood; **(d)** plankton; **(e)** an estuary.

38 In the ocean, spiraling surface currents that concentrate nutrients, wastes, and microorganisms are called: **(a)** geothermal vents; **(b)** gyres; **(c)** foraminifera; **(d)** red tides; **(e)** photic zones.

39 Among the major factors limiting planktonic growth in the sea are nitrogen, phos-

phorus, trace elements, and _____ .

40 Microorganisms called "decomposers" in the food chain accomplish

_____ and _____ of organic compounds.

41 What is the most complex compound in the carbon cycle?

_____ The simplest? _____

42 Bacteria in ocean hydrothermal vents produce nutrients for other organisms

through _____ reactions.

43 Primary production of nutrients in the food chain is through

_____ and _____ .

44 Krill is a: **(a)** diatom; **(b)** flagellate; **(c)** fungus; **(d)** bacterium; **(e)** small crustacean.

DRINKING WATER   **45** Water that is safe to drink is called _____ water.

46 Potable water not only should be free of disease-producing microorganisms but

also should be free of _____ injurious to health.

47 Water from wells and springs is termed _____ water, whereas water from lakes and streams is termed _____ water.

48 Water undergoes _____ as it penetrates soil, thereby becoming partially free of microorganisms.

49 Groundwater for drinking should be located at a safe distance from possible sources of contamination such as barnyards, pit privies, cesspools, and

_____ tanks.

50 The main operations used by municipal water-purification plants to purify drinking water are (1) sedimentation, (2) _____, and (3)

_____ .

51 In sedimentation treatment of drinking water sources, a chemical called

_____ helps to produce a sticky flocculent precipitate.

52 Disinfection of water sources to be used for drinking is usually accomplished by means of _____ .

53 Fluoride is often added to municipal water supplies to help control

_____ .

54 The term _indicator microorganism,_ with reference to microbiological examination of water, refers to a kind of microorganism whose presence in water is evidence that

the water is polluted with _____ from humans or other warmblooded animals.

55 For bacteriological evidence of pollution, intestinal pathogens such as _Salmonella_ spp. are not usually sought, partly because (1) they have a(n)

_____ occurrence and often do not survive long in water,

and (2) they are usually present in _____ numbers.

56 If coliforms are present in the water, then _____ might also be present, and the water is potentially dangerous to drink.

57 The differentiation of _E. coli_ from _Ent. aerogenes_ is achieved by four biochemical

tests; these tests are called the _____ tests.

58 In the IMViC tests, _E. coli_ _____ indole from the amino

acid tryptophan and _____ acetylmethylcarbinol from glucose.

59 Which three of the following genera belong to the coliform group of bacteria? **(a)** _Klebsiella;_ **(b)** _Shigella;_ **(c)** _Salmonella;_ **(d)** _Escherichia;_ **(e)** _Enterobacter._

60 Which one of the following characteristics can be used to distinguish between fecal coliforms and _Salmonella_?

(a) Gram reaction

(b) fermentation of glucose

(c) sporulation

(d) fermentation of lactose

(e) temperature requirement for growth

61 A low standard plate count for a water sample is expected of water of good quality; however, it does not necessarily indicate that the water is

_____ .

62 In the presumptive test for coliforms in water, _____ is inoculated with the water sample, and after incubation a positive test is indicated by the production of _____.

63 In the confirmed test, transfer is made from positive presumptive test tubes to either _____ broth or _____ agar.

64 On EMB agar, colonies of *E. coli* are small, with dark, almost black centers, and have a(n) _____ sheen.

65 One advantage of the _____ method for bacteriological analysis of water is that large volumes of water can be tested.

66 Pipes can be corroded by the _____ acid produced by the genus *Thiobacillus* from the oxidation of _____.

67 The viruses most commonly found in sewage are _____ viruses such as polioviruses, coxsackieviruses, and echoviruses.

SWIMMING POOLS

68 A skin infection likely to be transmitted in swimming pool areas, particularly if not properly disinfected, is _____.

69 The chemical commonly used to disinfect swimming pools is

_____.

WASTEWATER

70 Wastewater consists of _____ waterborne wastes, _____ waterborne wastes, and groundwater, surface water, and rain water that enter a sewerage system.

71 Sanitary sewers carry _____ wastewater, whereas storm sewers carry off _____.

72 The amount of solids in sewage is approximately _____ percent.

73 The amount of oxygen used in microbial respiration for oxidation of the organic substances present in sewage is called the _____.

74 The more organic matter present in sewage, the _____ the BOD value.

75 Effluent from a sewage plant should have a _____ BOD value.

76 In the lower portion of a septic tank, solids undergo degradation and solubilization by _____ bacteria.

77 The effluent from a septic tank is discharged into a(n) _____; the latter must not be close to a source of drinking water, because the effluent _____.

78 In municipal treatment processes, sewage is subjected to screening, grinding, and removal of grit; it is then subjected to _____ to deposit (sediment) particulate solids.

79 In secondary treatment of sewage, soluble organic substances in the liquid portion of the sewage are oxidized by _____ microorganisms to decrease the _____ .

80 The rocks of a trickling filter are coated with a mass of aerobic microorganisms called _____ .

81 In the _____ method of secondary treatment of sewage, the sewage is vigorously aerated, and *floc* is produced, which consists of aggregates of the suspended and colloidal matter of sewage plus aerobic microorganisms.

82 Oxidation ponds are _____ ponds designed to allow the growth of _____ on the effluent from primary sewage treatment.

83 In the final treatment of a low-BOD effluent into a stream, the effluent is disinfected, usually by addition of _____ .

84 Anaerobic digesters may produce _____ , which can be used as fuel.

85 Which of the following is an aerobic sewage-treatment process? **(a)** trickling filter; **(b)** sludge digester; **(c)** septic tank; **(d)** a lagoon; **(e)** composting.

86 The higher the BOD of a sewage plant effluent: **(a)** the higher the concentration of dissolved oxygen in the effluent; **(b)** the lower the concentration of organic matter in the effluent; **(c)** the higher the quality of the effluent; **(d)** the more likely it is that the effluent will destroy aquatic life in the receiving body of water; **(e)** the lesser the effect on residual oxygen.

87 "If air is forced into the system, particles of suspended matter flocculate into small gelatinous masses, swarming with aerobic microscopic life and capable of oxidizing organic matter readily." This is a description of: **(a)** a trickling filter; **(b)** the intermittent sand filter; **(c)** an anaerobic digester; **(d)** composting; **(e)** activated sludge.

88 The major purpose of primary sewage treatment is to: **(a)** reduce the BOD; **(b)** remove many of the suspended and floating particles; **(c)** remove pathogens; **(d)** raise the BOD; **(e)** oxidize the organic constituents.

89 Combined sewers have the input from both: **(a)** domestic and industrial sewers; **(b)** human excrement and industrial wastes; **(c)** sanitary and storm sewers; **(d)** surface water and groundwater; **(e)** single-dwelling units and municipalities.

90 Which of the following occurs during final treatment of the effluent from a sewage-treatment plant? **(a)** anaerobic digestion; **(b)** reverse osmosis; **(c)** removal of grit; **(d)** drying and incineration; **(e)** chlorination.

91 The rocks of a trickling filter are coated with: **(a)** *E. coli*; **(b)** sedimented sludge; **(c)** a bulking agent; **(d)** a zoogloeal film; **(e)** *Methanobacterium* spp.

REVIEW QUESTIONS

1 What is plankton? Phytoplankton? Zooplankton? Name some organisms that belong to each category.

2 What is meant by the term *upwelling*? What effect does upwelling have on productivity of an ocean area? What is a gyre?

3 Describe several types of biochemical changes brought about by microorganisms in marine environments. What occurs during the process of mineralization?

4 What contributes to the fertility of the ocean? What does the term *pasture of the sea* refer to?

5 What is referred to by the term *primary producers*? Describe a food web.

6 Compare and contrast the fertility of the oceans and inland lakes and rivers.

7 Why is *Escherichia coli* considered an indicator of pollution? What are coliforms?

8 Why isn't the routine bacteriological examination of water directed toward isolation and identification of specific pathogens?

9 Outline the process by which a municipality produces potable water. How is the microbial population of the raw water affected at each step?

10 Describe how selective and differential media facilitate the bacteriological analysis of water samples.

11 What advantages does the membrane-filter technique offer for microbiological analysis of water?

12 Where are septic tanks used? Describe the microbiological activities that take place in a septic tank.

13 Outline the process of wastewater treatment which is followed in most large cities. Describe the biochemical transformation brought about by bacteria.

DISCUSSION QUESTIONS

1 Compare aquatic environments of lakes, estuaries, and oceans in terms of the fluctuations that may occur in the microbial flora.

2 Why are epibacteria particularly suited for growth in aquatic environments?

3 Distinguish between a food web and a food chain and give an illustration of each.

4 Assume that an industrial plant adds large quantities of a waste acid into a municipal sewerage system. What might be the effect on the microbiological processes of the various stages of sewage treatment?

5 Compare the advantages with the disadvantages of disposing of sludge on farmland.

6 In terms of soil characteristics, what are some conditions that would adversely affect the successful operation of a septic tank system for an individual home?

7 Speculate upon the microbial interaction possibilities as they might occur in the zoogloeal films of a sewage trickling filter.

8 What are the characteristics of an "ideal" microorganism which can be used as an indicator of pollution?

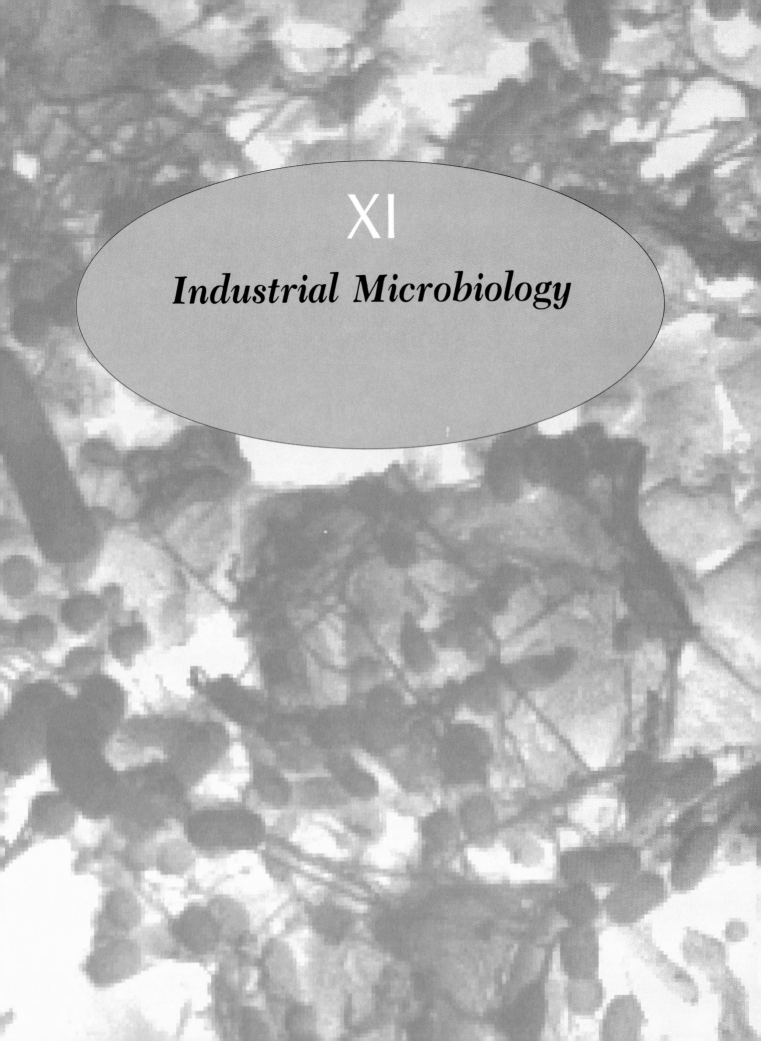

XI
Industrial Microbiology

Microbiology of Food

OBJECTIVES

After reading this chapter you should be able to

1 Account for the significance of microorganisms in food.

2 Describe procedures used to count and identify the microorganisms found in foods.

3 Characterize the microorganisms normally present in several kinds of fresh foods.

4 Outline the general principles that serve as the basis for food preservation.

5 Discuss the types of spoilage that may occur in fresh and canned foods and identify the responsible microorganisms.

6 Describe the role of microorganisms in the production of fermented vegetables, fermented milks, and cheeses.

7 Assess the significance of microbiology as related to the food service industry.

8 Describe "single-cell protein" and evaluate its potential as a source of food.

OVERVIEW

Microorganisms are intimately associated with the availability, the abundance, and the quality of food for human consumption. Food items are easily contaminated with microorganisms in nature, during handling, and in processing. After it is contaminated, food serves as a medium for the growth of the microorganisms. If they are allowed to grow, these microorganisms can change the physical and chemical characteristics of the food and may cause spoilage. Microorganisms in food may also be responsible for food poisoning and foodborne infections, as was explained in Chapter 25. Accordingly, much attention has been directed to developing methods for the preservation of food.

Other microorganisms are used to prepare certain foods. Many foods, such as cheese, yogurt, and pickles, are products of microbial fermentation. Moreover, large crops of some microbial cells, produced commercially, are used as food or feed supplements in some countries.

In this chapter you will learn about food spoilage by microorganisms and how this spoilage can be prevented, and also about the role of microorganisms in preparing various kinds of foods.

SIGNIFICANCE OF MICROORGANISMS IN FOOD

Microorganisms inhabit nearly every niche on earth, and our food supply is no exception. The quantity and quality of food you eat is affected by microbes of many kinds. Some decompose foods, causing spoilage; others are used to manufacture certain foods such as cheeses and soy sauce. Economically, microorganisms have a significant influence on both the food manufacturing industry and the food service industry. Their effects—both beneficial and detrimental—can be summarized as follows:

1 The numbers and kinds of microorganisms present in food reflect the quality and safety of that food.
2 Some may cause food spoilage.
3 Some must be kept out, removed, inhibited, or killed to prevent spoilage of food.
4 Some can cause food poisoning or foodborne infections as described in Chapter 25.
5 Some can produce certain food products by fermentation.
6 Some can be produced in large quantities as a food or feed supplement.
7 Contaminating microorganisms create special problems for the food service industry as more "ready-to-serve" and "fast-food" products become available.

ASK YOURSELF

1 What is the relationship between microorganisms and the quality of a food product?

2 Cite examples of microbial activities that are undesirable for the food industry.

3 Cite examples of microbial activities that are useful to the food industry.

FOOD AS A MEDIUM FOR GROWTH OF MICROORGANISMS

The contamination of food by microorganisms poses a problem that is different from microbial contamination of other kinds of materials. The food itself serves as a culture medium for microorganisms. Stated another way, contamination of food is comparable to the inoculation of a culture medium such as nutrient broth or agar. Numerous species of bacteria, yeasts, and molds can contaminate food, but the extent to which they grow is influenced by the chemical and physical properties of the food, the environmental conditions under which the food is stored, and the characteristics of the contaminating microorganisms.

The conditions that favor microbial growth are the same as those described for the cultivation of microorganisms in Part II of this book. Some items of food, such as milk, are excellent culture media. In fact, skim milk is used widely for the cultivation of many microorganisms, particularly bacteria. Other food items, such as flour, sugar, and cereals, are poor growth media for microbes, primarily because of their low moisture content.

ASK YOURSELF

Compare the likely events following microbial contamination of food to those following microbial contamination of water.

MICROBIOLOGICAL EXAMINATION OF FOODS

Standards and regulations have been developed to ensure that food received by the consumer is healthful, safe, and of the quality claimed on the label. A variety of agencies cooperate to define these standards and regulations. Some agencies operate at an international level—for example, agencies of the United Nations such as the Food and Agricultural Organization (FAO), the World Health Organization (WHO), and the International Children's Emergency Fund (UNICEF). In the United States several federal agencies have authority over foods shipped interstate or foods produced in, or shipped to, territories. The Food and Drug Administration (FDA) of the Department of Health and Human Services has developed specific microbiological criteria for foods. The surveillance of food at the state level is done by departments of health, agriculture, or sanitary engineering. Because of the numerous agencies and regulations involved, it is necessary for laboratory analyses of food to be standardized. To ensure this uniformity, individuals from the appropriate agencies and professional societies have published a book entitled *Compendium of Methods for the Microbiological Examination of Foods*. This volume describes, in great detail, how the microbiological examination of foods is to be performed. A similar publication is available for the microbiological examination of milk and milk products entitled *Standard Methods for the Examination of Dairy Products.*

Results from the microbiological examination of foods provide information on the quality of the raw food, the cleanliness of the conditions under which the food was processed, and the effectiveness of the method of preservation. In the case of spoiled foods, it is possible to identify the microorganism responsible for the spoilage and its source, as well as the conditions which permitted the spoilage to occur. Then corrective measures can be instituted to prevent spoilage in the future.

Microbiological food examination takes advantage of special microscopic techniques and cultural procedures. The particular procedure used is determined by the type of food product being examined and the specific purpose of the examination. It also may depend on the kind of microorganisms thought to be present, such as the wide variety of microorganisms looked for in food suspected of causing foodborne illness [TABLE 30.1]. FIGURE 30.1 illustrates a general scheme used to investigate microbiological contamination of foods.

Microscopic Techniques

Unless a food specimen is grossly contaminated, stained smears from the specimen are not likely to provide useful information. However, standard microscopic techniques are used for the examination of some food products. The Gram stain technique or a methylene blue stain of a standard fixed smear is normally used for this purpose, but other procedures are available. For example, a procedure known as the **Breed smear** is used to make a direct microscopic count of microorganisms in milk. In this procedure a measured amount of milk is spread over a calibrated area on a glass slide. The dry film of milk is stained with methylene blue, and a microscopic count is made of the microorganisms or clusters of microorganisms seen in several "fields" through the microscope. The total number of microorganisms per milliliter of milk can be calculated.

Another technique is the **Howard mold-counting slide,** which has a chamber that holds a measured amount of specimen. As its name suggests, it is used to enumerate mold fragments in food products such as

FIGURE 30.1

Generalized scheme for microbiological examination of foods.

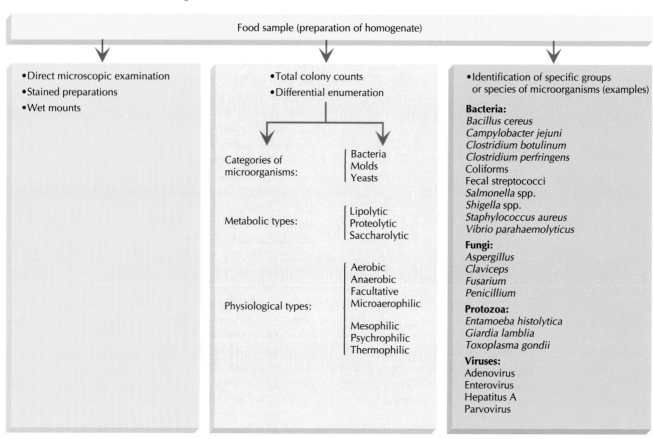

Guide for Tests to Perform the Examination of Foods Alleged, Suspected, or Epidemiologically Incriminated As Vehicles of Foodborne Illness

Food	Organism or toxin
Canned foods	*Clostridium botulinum* and its neurotoxin
Cereals, rice, foods containing cornstarch	*Bacillus cereus*, mycotoxins
Cream-filled baked goods	*Staphylococcus aureus* and its enterotoxin *Salmonella*
Confectionery products	*Salmonella*
Egg and egg products	*Salmonella*
Molluscan shellfish	*Vibrio parahaemolyticus* Shellfish toxin (saxitoxin) *Vibrio cholerae* Hepatitis A virus (epidemiological implication only)
Raw fruits and vegetables	Parasitic protozoa *Shigella*
Mixed vegetables, meat, poultry, fish, salads	*Staphylococcus aureus* and its enterotoxin *Salmonella* β-hemolytic streptococci *Shigella* Enteropathogenic *Escherichia coli*
Meat and poultry, and mixed foods containing meat and poultry	*Salmonella* *Clostridium perfringens* *Staphylococcus aureus* and its enterotoxin
Ham	*Staphylococcus aureus* and its enterotoxin
Fermented meats	*Staphylococcus aureus* and its enterotoxin
Fish	*Vibrio parahaemolyticus* Histamine (from *Proteus* spp.) Fish poisons
Crustaceans	*Vibrio parahaemolyticus* Fish poisons
Cheese	*Staphylococcus aureus* and its enterotoxin *Brucella* spp. Enteropathogenic *Escherichia coli*
Dry milk	*Salmonella* *Staphylococcus aureus* and its enterotoxin

SOURCE: M. L. Speck, ed., *Compendium of Methods for the Microbiological Examination of Foods*, 2d ed., American Public Health Association, Washington, D.C., 1984.

fruits, juices, and vegetables. When the mold counts obtained by this procedure exceed certain limits, the product is of poor quality or has been processed in an unsanitary manner.

Protozoa can also be identified and counted by direct microscopic examination. Since protozoa are likely to be present in only relatively small numbers, it is frequently necessary to use a procedure such as centrifugation or filtration that will concentrate these organisms in the food sample prior to microscopic examination.

Culture Techniques

Cultivation techniques described in earlier chapters of this book can be used, sometimes with modifications, to examine foods. For example, plate culture techniques are used to determine a specimen's total microbial population or to count some particular group of microorganisms. The term *total* needs qualification; the microorganisms enumerated by any culture technique are only that portion of the total population which will grow into visible colonies under the specific conditions provided. These conditions include the nutritional quality of the medium, the incubation temperature and time, and the type of gaseous atmosphere.

Another culture technique used is the standard plate count (SPC) for counting bacteria in milk. Details of this procedure are provided in *Standard Methods for the Examination of Dairy Products*. It is essential that the procedure be carried out precisely as specified in this publication. Other procedures, including use of selective and differential media, are available for the isolation and enumeration of particular physiological or biochemical types of microorganisms.

The cultivation of viruses from food specimens requires the use of tissue-culture techniques (Chapter 16). Prior concentration of the virus suspected in the food specimen may be necessary.

The traditional microscopic and culture techniques have been supplemented by more specific and more rapid methods based on newer concepts of molecular biology and immunology, such as DNA probes and monoclonal antibodies. These and other tests were described earlier.

ASK YOURSELF

1 What agencies define standards and regulations for the microbiological quality of foods?

2 Describe the major laboratory procedures used for the microbiological examination of food.

MICROORGANISMS IN FRESH FOODS

The inner tissues of healthy plants and animals are free of microorganisms, and therefore are sterile. However, surfaces of raw vegetables and meats are usually contaminated with a variety of microorganisms. The magnitude of this contamination is related to one or more of the following conditions: the microbial population of the environment from which the food was taken, the quality of the raw product, the method of handling, and the time and conditions of storage. If properly handled and prepared, raw foods should contain low numbers of microorganisms. Various raw foods—such as meats, poultry, and eggs—provide different conditions for microbial growth and thus differ in their microbial populations.

Meats

The carcass of a healthy animal slaughtered for meat and held in a refrigerated room is likely to have only a low level of surface microbial contamination (the inner tissues are sterile). Microbial counts of 100 to 100,000 per gram have been reported for the surfaces of beef carcasses. Fresh meat cut from the chilled carcass will be contaminated on its surface with microorganisms from the environment and the saws or knives used to cut the meat. Each new cut exposes a new surface, with the potential of adding more microorganisms to the exposed

tissue. Chopping or grinding meat into hamburger provides the greatest number of new surfaces and allows a high potential contamination. Microbial counts on hamburger may reach 5,000,000 to 10,000,000 per gram of sample.

Some of the more common types of bacteria occurring on fresh meats are pseudomonads, staphylococci, micrococci, enterococci, and coliforms. The low temperature at which fresh meats are held favors the growth of psychrophilic microorganisms. Species of microorganisms frequently isolated from meats and meat products are shown in TABLE 30.2.

To improve the microbiological quality of meats, particularly ground beef, cold cuts, and frankfurters, many states have proposed microbiological standards for these products at the time of purchase.

Poultry

Freshly dressed poultry has a bacterial flora on the surface that originates from bacteria normally present on the live birds and from organisms introduced during killing, defeathering, and evisceration. Under good sanitary conditions the bacterial count is from 100 to 1000 bacteria per square centimeter of skin surface, whereas less sanitary conditions may increase the count 100-fold or more. Bacteria, yeasts, and molds have been isolated from the surfaces of processed poultry. Among these are members of the bacterial genera *Pseudomonas*, *Acinetobacter*, *Escherichia*, *Flavobacterium*, and *Sal-*

TABLE 30.2
Frequently Isolated Microorganisms from Meats

Product	Microorganisms isolated

Fresh and refrigerated meat	Bacteria
	    Acinetobacter, Moraxella, Pseudomonas, Aeromonas, Alcaligenes, and *Micrococcus*
	Molds
	    Cladosporium, Geotrichum, Sporotrichum, Mucor, and *Thamnidium*
	Yeasts
	    Candida, Torulopsis, Debaryomyces, and *Rhodotorula*

Processed and cured meats	Bacteria
	    Lactobacillus and other lactic acid bacteria, *Acinetobacter, Bacillus, Micrococcus, Serratia,* and *Staphylococcus*
	Molds
	    Aspergillus, Penicillium, Rhizopus, and *Thamnidium*
	Yeasts
	    Debaryomyces, Torula, Torulopsis, Trichosporon, and *Candida*

SOURCE: W. C. Frazier and D. C. Westhoff, *Food Microbiology*, 4th ed., McGraw-Hill, New York, 1988.

monella; the yeasts *Trichosporon, Torulopsis, Candida,* and *Rhodotorula;* and the molds *Penicillium, Alternaria,* and *Aspergillus.* From a public health standpoint, *Salmonella* contamination, as discussed in Chapter 25, is of considerable significance.

Eggs

The inside of a freshly laid egg is usually free of microorganisms. Both the eggshell and a thin protein membrane just beneath the shell retard penetration of microorganisms into the egg's interior. In addition, egg white contains substances such as the protein lysozyme which are antibacterial. Cracks in the shell, however, will result in contamination and spoilage.

Some examples of bacterial spoilage of eggs are:

Green rots: Caused by green-pigmented *Pseudomonas* species that can grow at 0°C.
Colorless rots: Caused by species of *Pseudomonas, Acinetobacter, Alcaligenes,* and coliforms. Various kinds of odors may develop.
Black rots: Caused by *Proteus* species which turn eggs black. Usually indicative of storage at temperatures above recommended level.

Bacteria of the genus *Salmonella* have periodically been a major problem, causing food poisoning from contaminated egg products (Chapter 25). The salmonellas may come from a variety of sources: contaminated eggs, meat scraps and fish meal in poultry feed, contaminated poultry flocks, wild birds, or soil and water. Control measures developed by industry, new federal and local regulations, and identification of sources of contamination have contributed to better control of these bacteria.

Fruits and Vegetables

Microbial invasion of plant tissue by bacteria, fungi, and viruses can occur during various stages of fruit and vegetable development. The more the tissues are invaded, the greater the likelihood of spoilage. A second factor contributing to microbial contamination of fruits and vegetables is the type of postharvest handling used. Mechanical handling is likely to produce breaks in the tissue, allowing microorganisms to enter. The pH of fruits is relatively low, ranging from 2.3 for lemons to 5.0 for bananas. This acidity restricts bacterial growth but does not retard fungal growth. The pH range for vegetables is slightly higher (pH 5.0 to 7.0), making vegetables more susceptible than fruits to attack by bacteria.

Shellfish and Finfish

Microorganisms found in freshly harvested shellfish and finfish reflect the microbial quality of the waters from which they are harvested. If the water is sewage-polluted, the seafood is potentially capable of transmitting pathogenic microorganisms. The marine bacterium *Vibrio parahaemolyticus* has been responsible for a number of gastroenteritis epidemics in the United States due to consumption of raw or inadequately cooked seafood. This bacterium occurs widely in the Atlantic, Pacific, and Gulf Coast waters; it has been isolated from seafood samples that include fish, shellfish, and crustaceans. Shellfish that grow in contaminated water can also concentrate viruses in their tissues and may be sources of hepatitis infection. For example, raw oysters and clams from polluted waters have caused numerous epidemics of hepatitis in various parts of the world.

The increased popularity of seafood in American diets has raised a question about the microbiological quality of seafoods. This is particularly true for molluscan shellfish (mussels, scallops, clams, and oysters), which may be eaten either raw or partially cooked. Because of this concern, the Food and Drug Administration has increased its surveillance of seafood by establishing the Office of Seafood within the agency's Center for Food Safety and Applied Nutrition. This new FDA unit will enforce regulations and conduct research of seafood quality.

A new kind of seafood product (surimi) used extensively for centuries in Japan is now available in the United States. Because of the way in which surimi is prepared, there is great potential for microbial contamination. Fish flesh is mechanically deboned and then washed with water until it becomes colorless and odorless. After addition of selected ingredients, the fish flesh is extruded in shapes to resemble seafood such as crab legs, lobster tails, scallop, or shrimp. The extensive handling involved in preparation of surimi and surimi-based products requires adherence to good sanitary practices.

Milk

When milk is drawn from the udder of a healthy cow, it becomes contaminated by microorganisms that have entered the teat canal from the outside. The number of microorganisms present in freshly drawn milk ranges between several hundred and several thousand per milliliter. These counts vary among cows and are highest in milk taken during the initial stages of milking. From the time the milk leaves the cow's udder until it is dispensed into retail containers, everything with which it comes into contact is a potential source of added contamination.

This includes the milking equipment, the personnel, and the air in the environment. Disregard of sanitary practices results in heavily contaminated milk that spoils rapidly. However, milking done under sanitary conditions with strict attention to sanitary practices will produce milk with a low bacterial count and good keeping quality.

Milk has been described as the "most nearly perfect food." Its microbiology has been studied more systematically and thoroughly than that of any other food. This is because of the worldwide consumption of milk, its great susceptibility to microbial spoilage, its potential as a carrier of pathogens, and the fact that it is an excellent medium for growth of microorganisms.

ASK YOURSELF

1 What is likely to be the microbial flora of the inner tissues of healthy plants and animals?

2 What is the source of microorganisms in milk? In shellfish? In eggs?

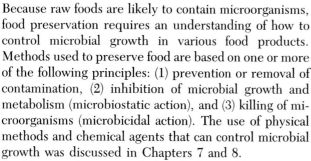

GENERAL PRINCIPLES OF FOOD PRESERVATION

Because raw foods are likely to contain microorganisms, food preservation requires an understanding of how to control microbial growth in various food products. Methods used to preserve food are based on one or more of the following principles: (1) prevention or removal of contamination, (2) inhibition of microbial growth and metabolism (microbiostatic action), and (3) killing of microorganisms (microbicidal action). The use of physical methods and chemical agents that can control microbial growth was discussed in Chapters 7 and 8.

Humans have grappled with the problem of food preservation for centuries. Ancient Egyptians and Romans were aware of the preservative effects of salting, drying, and smoking. The first example of preservation by salt may have been the burial of food along the seashore, where the salt of the seawater could cure, or preserve, the food. Native Americans placed strips of fresh bison and venison at the top of a tepee or over a campfire, where the meat was preserved by drying and smoking. Dried salt cod was a common food for colonial Americans. Perishable foods were often stored in caves and springs—the low temperatures helped to inhibit spoilage.

Modern food preservation is often an elaborate refinement of these primitive methods. Today we associate food preservation with refrigeration, freezing, dehydration, and canning. Highly efficient equipment and processes have been developed during the last several decades. The various practices used for food preservation include:

1 Aseptic handling and processing
2 High temperatures
  (a) Boiling
  (b) Steam under pressure
  (c) Pasteurization
  (d) Sterilization
3 Low temperatures
  (a) Refrigeration
  (b) Freezing
4 Dehydration
5 High osmotic pressure
  (a) In concentrated sugar
  (b) With salt brine
6 Chemical additives
  (a) Organic acids
  (b) Substances developed during processing (smoking)
  (c) Substances contributed by microbial fermentation (acids)
7 Radiation
  (a) Ultraviolet light
  (b) Ionizing radiation

Aseptic Handling and Processing

Many food items are handled a great deal before being processed by some preservation method. Each step in preparing a food for preservation is a potential source of contamination. The extent of contamination will depend upon the initial microbiological quality of the product and the level of aseptic precautions used during handling. Use of aseptic techniques is particularly important in preparing the highly perishable foods such as fish, oysters, and crabmeat, each of which requires considerable handling by individuals.

Aseptic processing is a relatively new development in the food industry. The food item is first sterilized then dispensed into previously sterilized containers and sealed under aseptic conditions [FIGURE 30.2]. This process uses plastic, paper, or tin containers and the resulting packaged item of food offers both economic and user advantages. The product, because it is sterile, can be stored at room temperatures, eliminating the need for refrigeration space. Food items preserved in this manner are becoming more available.

FIGURE 30.2

Diagrammatic representation of a hypothetical, aseptic food packaging process. In this particular example, two components are sterilized separately and then mixed in a sterile chamber. The resulting product is distributed into sterile containers and sealed in the same sterile environment before being packaged for final shipment.

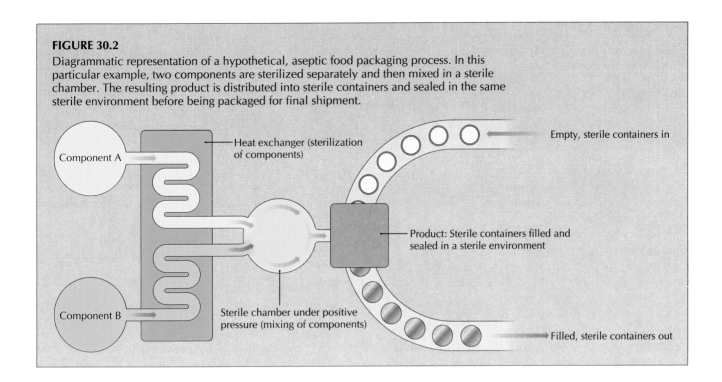

Component A

Heat exchanger (sterilization of components)

Empty, sterile containers in

Component B

Product: Sterile containers filled and sealed in a sterile environment

Sterile chamber under positive pressure (mixing of components)

Filled, sterile containers out

High Temperatures

High temperature is one of the safest and most reliable methods of food preservation. Heat is often used to destroy microorganisms in food products already packaged in cans, jars, or other types of containers that prevent entry of additional microorganisms. Although dry heat can prevent microbial growth, steam under pressure is even more effective. Used in pressure cookers and autoclaves, pressurized steam kills all spores and vegetative cells. Knowledge of the heat resistance of different species of microorganisms, particularly spore formers, is especially important in the preservation of food by high temperatures. Special laboratory equipment has been designed to determine their heat resistance. In addition, one must consider the rate at which heat penetrates through foods of different consistencies, for example, applesauce versus apple juice, as well as the size and shape of the containers in which the foods are packed. Killing microorganisms by heat involves a time-temperature relationship (discussed in Chapter 7), and considerable research has been done to determine the thermal death times of bacteria likely to cause food spoilage. This information makes it possible to establish satisfactory heat-processing conditions. It also accounts for the highly successful results achieved by the food canning industry.

Canning. Canning has been the basic method of food preservation for more than 180 years. Nicolas Appert

(1750–1841) is regarded as the father of canning. Appert, inspired by the French government's offer of a cash prize for a method to conserve food for transport, began a long series of experiments. He placed foods into glass containers, which were then sealed with corks and reinforced with wire and sealing wax. He then put the containers in boiling water for varying time periods. Appert's results, which won him the prize of 12,000 francs, were published in 1811 under the title: "The Art of Preserving All Kinds of Animal and Vegetable Substances for Several Years." In the same year Peter Durand was granted an English patent for using tin containers for food preparation.

Temperatures used for canning foods range from 100°C for high-acid foods to 121°C for low-acid foods. The canning process does not guarantee a sterile product, because spores of some bacterial species may survive these temperatures. The most important organism to be eliminated in canned foods is the spore-forming anaerobe *Clostridium botulinum*, which is capable of producing a very potent lethal toxin (Chapter 25).

Pasteurization of Milk. The Milk Ordinance and Code of the U.S. Public Health Service defines pasteurization as follows: "The terms pasteurization, pasteurized, and similar terms shall mean the process of heating every particle of milk or milk product to at least 145°F (62.8°C), and holding it continuously at or above this temperature for at least 30 minutes, or to at least 161°F (71.7°C), and holding it continuously at or above this temperature for at least 15 seconds, in equipment which is properly operated and approved by the health authority."

The original time-temperature relationships for pasteurization were determined with *Mycobacterium tuberculosis*, because this species was regarded as the most heat-resistant pathogen likely to occur in milk [FIGURE 30.3]. This organism is destroyed when exposed to a temperature of 140°F (60°C) for 10 min. To be safe, the pasteurization temperature was set at 143°F (61.6°C) for 30 min. Microbiologists later discovered that *Coxiella burnetii*, the causative agent of Q fever transmitted by milk, can survive in milk heated to 143°F for 30 min. This observation resulted in the present time and temperature for pasteurization.

Commercial pasteurization of milk is performed by one of two methods: (1) the low-temperature holding (LTH) method, or vat pasteurization, which holds the milk at 145°F (62.8°C) for 30 min; or (2) the high-temperature short-time (HTST) method, which exposes the milk to a temperature of 161°F (71.7°C) for 15 s. In either method of pasteurization, it is essential that the equipment be designed and operated so that all of the

milk is heated to the required temperature and held for the specified time. Precautions must be taken to prevent recontamination after pasteurization. The finished product should be stored at low temperatures to retard growth of microorganisms that survive pasteurization.

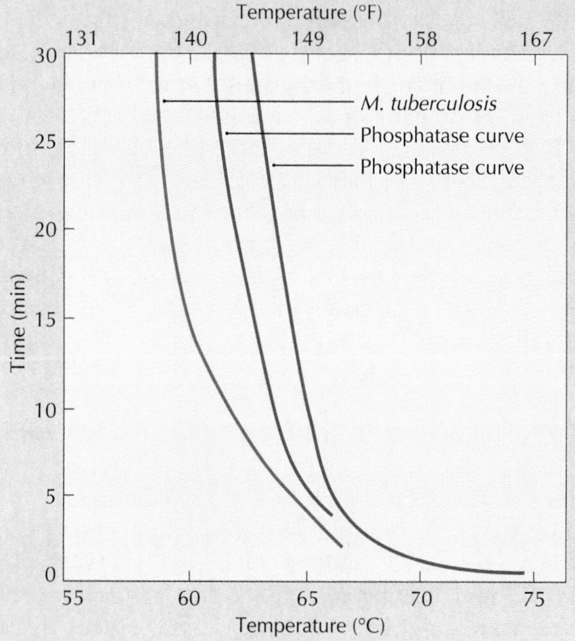

To determine whether a particular batch of milk has been pasteurized, one can perform a *phosphatase test.* Phosphatase is an enzyme present in raw (unheated) milk and body tissues that is destroyed by adequate pasteurization [FIGURE 30.3]. By testing for the absence of this enzyme, you can determine whether milk has been properly pasteurized. Milk is added to a substrate upon which the enzyme will act. The principle of the test is illustrated by the following reaction:

$$\text{Disodium phenyl phosphate} \xrightarrow[\text{(enzyme in raw milk)}]{\text{phosphatase}} \text{phenol + phosphate}$$

(Substrate)   (End products)

The amount of phenol liberated can be conveniently estimated by the addition of a reagent which turns blue in the presence of phenol. Color standards are used to interpret the results of this test. This is a very simple testing procedure, yet it provides valuable information about the heat treatment milk has received.

Pasteurization of Other Foods. Pasteurization is also used for the preservation of liquid egg products such as whole eggs and egg whites, to eliminate *Salmonella* and to reduce the total microbial population. The proper time-temperature relationship is critical because the temperature required to kill *Salmonella* is close to the temperature that denatures egg white protein. This situation makes pasteurization of eggs rather complicated. For example, in one process the egg whites are acidified with lactic acid to pH 6.8 to 7.3 and ammonium sulfate is added to prevent heat damage to egg white protein. The treated egg whites are then pasteurized at 140°F (60°C) for 3.5 min.

Crabmeat is another food item that is available raw or pasteurized. Considerable research was required to develop the appropriate time-temperature relationships that would reduce the microbial population to the desired level and still retain the quality of the crabmeat. Successful pasteurization has greatly extended the availability and the distribution of this highly perishable seafood product.

Sterilization. Commercial milk-sterilization techniques have been developed which expose milk to ultrahigh temperatures for very short periods of time—300°F (148.9°C) for 1 to 2 s. This sterilization process eliminates the chance that the milk will develop any traces of cooked flavor. The final product is comparable in flavor and nutritional quality to pasteurized milk. However,

FIGURE 30.3

Time-temperature curve for the killing of *Mycobacterium tuberculosis* compared with the time and temperature required for the inactivation of the enzyme phosphatase. The two phosphatase curves are plotted from different experimental data. (*Courtesy of McGraw-Hill Encyclopedia of Science and Technology, vol. 8, p. 502. Copyright 1971 by McGraw-Hill Book Company.*)

30.1 MICROWAVE OVENS

Microwave ovens are in wide use in kitchens and restaurants. How do they work for the preparation of foods? What is their antimicrobial effectiveness?

Microwaves are high-frequency electromagnetic waves somewhat like radio waves but considerably shorter. When food is placed in the microwave oven and the current turned on, the food absorbs the energy of the microwaves, causing the molecules of food substance to vibrate. The friction among the vibrat- ing molecules produces heat just like the heat generated by rubbing two pieces of metal together. The amount of heat pro- duced, that is, the temperature level, is dependent upon the power level at which the oven is operated. It is the heat produced in the food that imparts anti- microbial activity, not the microwaves per se. If the temperature of the food is brought to a high enough level, microor- ganisms will be killed. Some ovens are equipped with temperature probes that monitor the foods' internal temperature. Temperatures high enough and/or suffi- ciently long-lasting to be microbicidal can be achieved.

Microwaves do not penetrate met- als, and hence metal containers are not satisfactory for use. Glass, pottery, paper, and plastic are transparent to microwaves, and containers made of these materials are used.

---

the sterile milk does not require refrigeration and can be stored indefinitely. This product is becoming more pop- ular in grocery markets.

Microwave Ovens. The cooking or processing of food using the microwave oven is dependent upon the heat generated by microwave radiations. Microwaves do not act upon, or kill, microorganisms directly [DISCOVER 30.1].

how low the temperature, cannot be relied upon to kill all microorganisms. The numbers and types of viable and nonviable microorganisms present in frozen foods reflect the degree of contamination of the raw product and sani- tation in the processing plant, and the speed and care with which the produce was processed. The microbial count of most frozen foods decreases during storage [TABLE 30.3], but many organisms, including some pathogens, survive for long periods of time at −9 and −17°C.

Low Temperatures

Temperatures approaching 0°C and below retard growth and metabolic activities of microorganisms. Modern re- frigeration and freezing equipment have made it possi- ble to transport perishable foods and store them for long periods of time. Refrigerated trucks, railway cars, and ship vaults, as well as the home refrigerator and freezer, have improved the quality of the human diet and in- creased the variety of foods available. Frozen-food pro- duction in the United States almost tripled from 11 bil- lion pounds in 1965 to 29 billion in 1990 and continues to grow. Much of this increase will be in prepared frozen foods (foods ready to serve upon heating). The National Frozen Food Association, Inc., reported sales of approx- imately 7 billion pounds of prepared frozen foods in 1990. The growth and importance of this segment of the food industry places greater emphasis on the study of how microorganisms survive and grow at low tempera- tures.

Before freezing, fresh produce is steamed (blanched) to inactivate enzymes that would alter quality of the product even at low temperatures. Quick-freeze methods (using temperatures of −32°C or lower) are considered most satisfactory; smaller crystals of ice are formed, and cell structures in the food are not disrupted. It should be emphasized that freezing foods, no matter

Dehydration

Dried foods have been used for centuries, and they are more common worldwide than frozen foods. The re- moval of water by drying in the sun or applying heat causes dehydration. The preservation effect of dehydra- tion is due mainly to inhibition of microbial growth; the microorganisms are not necessarily killed (Chapter 7). Growth of all microorganisms can be prevented by re- ducing the moisture content of their environment below a critical level. This critical level is determined by char- acteristics of the particular organism and the capacity of the food item to bind water so that it is not available as free moisture. You will recall from Chapter 7 that lyophi- lized cultures of microorganisms survive for years.

High Osmotic Pressure

Water is withdrawn from microbial cells when they are placed in solutions containing large amounts of dissolved substances such as sugar or salt (Chapter 7). As a result of this water loss, microbial metabolism is halted. The anti- microbial effects of this water loss are similar in principle to metabolic inhibition by dehydration. Like dehydra- tion, high osmotic pressure may inhibit microbial

TABLE 30.3
Bacterial Counts in Frozen Foods after 12 Months' Frozen Storage and after Thawing 24 h at 70°F

Product	BACTERIA PER GRAM Frozen	BACTERIA PER GRAM After thawing
Beef stew	390	1,400,000
Beefsteak	390	1,400,000
Carrots, scalded	3,000	5,800,000
Eggs (canned)	190,000	70,000,000
Green beans, scalded	1,000	40,000,000
Haddock	38,000	770,000
Oysters	22,000	320,000,000
Peaches, with sugar 3:1	60	700
Peas, scalded	1,000	24,000,000
Pork chops	1,300	8,700,000
Raspberries, with sugar 3:1	3,000	8,000
Sour cherries, with sugar 3:1	0	20
Strawberries, with sugar 2:1	200	2,000
Sweet corn, scalded	1,500	60,000,000

SOURCE: G. J. Mountney and W. A. Gould, *Practical Food Microbiology and Technology*, 3d ed., Van Nostrand Reinhold, New York, 1988.

growth, but it cannot be relied upon to kill microorganisms. Yeasts and molds are relatively resistant to high osmotic pressure. For instance, jellies and jams are rarely affected by bacterial action, because of their high sugar content, but it is not uncommon to find mold growth on their surface if exposed to air. Condensed milk is preserved in part by its increased concentration of lactose (milk sugar) and supplemental sucrose (cane sugar), which also draws out water from microbial cells. Similar results are obtained by preserving meats and other foods in salt brines.

Chemical Additives

The addition of chemicals to preserve foods is controlled by provisions of the United States Food, Drug, and Cosmetic Act. In 1906, Congress passed the U.S. Pure Food and Drug Act; the new Food, Drug, and Cosmetic Act became law in 1939, and has been amended periodically since that date. According to this act, a food is adulterated if any poisonous or deleterious substance has been added which may make the food injurious to health. Only a few chemicals are legally acceptable for food preservation. Among the most effective are benzoic, sorbic, acetic, lactic, and propionic acids, all of which are organic acids. Sorbic and propionic acids are used to inhibit mold growth in bread, for example. Other common chemical additives are the nitrates and nitrites added to meats to preserve color; they are also inhibitory to some anaerobic bacteria. The use of nitrates and nitrites has been the subject of considerable controversy because of their possible roles as mutagenic or carcinogenic agents.

Sometimes chemical preservatives are not added to foods, but are produced *during* the preservation process. Foods prepared by fermentation processes, such as sauerkraut, pickles, and silage for animals, are preserved mainly by acetic, lactic, and propionic acids produced by the fermenting microorganisms. Smoking generates cresols and other antibacterial compounds that penetrate and preserve the meat.

Radiation

Compared with other preservation methods, the use of radiation is a relatively recent development in food preservation [DISCOVER 30.2]. There are various types of radiation; nonionizing and ionizing radiation have been used to control microorganisms in food.

Ultraviolet light—which is a type of nonionizing radiation—of sufficient intensity and time of exposure is microbicidal, but ultraviolet light has very limited penetration power. Thus, ultraviolet irradiation is limited to control of microorganisms on surfaces. Ultraviolet light is used in the food industry for such things as sanitizing equipment in meat-processing plants and controlling microbial growth on bakery products.

Ionizing radiations are also lethal to microorganisms. The fact that they are microbicidal at room temperature and have great penetrating ability makes them attractive for killing microorganisms in foods. Electron beams (beta and cathode rays) and gamma rays are being studied extensively for use in the food industry. Canned and packaged foods can be sterilized by an appropriate radiation dosage. This "cold sterilization" raises the temperature of the product only a few degrees, avoiding the deterioration of quality which might be caused by heat sterilization. *Radiation pasteurization* is a term describing the killing of over 98 percent (not 100 percent) of the organisms by doses of an ionizing radiation that are lower than those doses required for sterilization.

The resistance of microorganisms to ionizing radiation does not correspond to their thermal resistance. *Clostridium botulinum* appears to be the most radiation-resistant organism of importance to the food industry. FIGURE 30.4 illustrates the lethal effect of gamma radiation on spores of *C. botulinum*. Note that the survival of spores is influenced by the material in which they are suspended. Time is not a factor; it is the dose or intensity of the irradiation that is important. Therefore, the radiation death *dose*, rather than radiation death time, is determined before preserving foods with radiation.

30.2 PRESERVING FOOD WITH IONIZING IRRADIATION

Using irradiation to preserve foods is an effective and desirable method, according to an abundance of scientific evidence. International groups of scientists have studied this process extensively and have concluded that irradiation at recommended dosages is not hazardous. There is no residual radioactivity left in the processed food, nor does irradiation adversely affect the food's nutritional quality. There are also several advantages of using irradiation to kill the pathogenic and nonpathogenic microorganisms found on and in foods. Foods can be exposed to irradiation *after* packaging, and foods such as vegetables and fruits maintain their freshness for prolonged periods of time when irradiated.

In terms of cost, irradiation is comparable to conventional methods of food preservation, and it often prolongs the shelf life of food beyond that possible with other methods.

Some countries use the method in a limited manner, while others (30 or more countries) have approved irradiation processing of several foods. That this method of food preservation is not used on a major scale results, in part, from the assumption that the public is reluctant to buy irradiated foods. This public attitude has been reinforced by those opposed to the use of radioactive substances.

However, a large number of market tests in recent years indicate that the consumer will indeed buy irradiated foods. Some examples of irradiated foods sold during these successful tests are: Hawaiian papaya (California, 1987), apples (Missouri, 1988), potatoes and onions (Poland, 1987–1988), strawberries (France, 1987), sausage (Thailand, 1989), poultry (Israel, 1989), and fish (Bangladesh, 1988). There is general consensus among scientists, government officials, and food producers that the consumer is poorly informed about the advantages to be gained by preserving foods by irradiation. This lack of understanding means that an aggressive education campaign will be necessary to convince consumers of the safety of irradiation for food preservation.

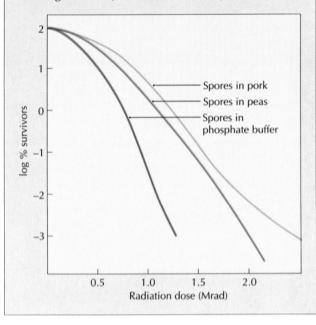

FIGURE 30.4
Gamma radiation kills spores of *Clostridium botulinum* in frozen foods. Curves show the effect on spores in pork, peas, and phosphate buffer. (*Courtesy of C. B. Denny, C. W. Bohrer, W. E. Perkins, and C. T. Townsend, "Destruction of Clostridium botulinum by Ionizing Radiation," Food Res. 24:44-50, 1959.*)

Sterilization with ionizing radiation presents an entirely new approach to food preservation that could bring about a radical change in industrial methods of food processing. However, despite the extensive research and documentation on the safety and effectiveness of ionizing radiation, this method has had limited acceptance in the United States. This is due to both economic factors and lingering uncertainties about the effect of the radiation on the food material. In addition, the United States already has well-developed systems for food preservation. This is not the case for many other countries. The World Health Organization has approved irradiation of poultry at a specified level, as has Canada for controlling salmonellas. In July 1983, the U.S. Food and Drug Administration approved the use of ionizing radiation for sterilizing certain spices and vegetable seasonings. Additional applications are being considered for approval. TABLE 30.4 lists several applications of food irradiation. The effect of irradiation on strawberries is shown in FIGURE 30.5.

ASK YOURSELF

1 What are the major practices used for the preservation of foods, and what is an example of food preserved by each?

2 What are some of the factors to be considered in selecting the method of preservation for an item of food produced commercially?

TABLE 30.4
Applications of Food Irradiation

Type of food	Radiation dose in kiloGrays*	Effect of treatment
Meat, poultry, fish, shellfish, some vegetables, baked goods, prepared foods	20–70	Sterilization. Treated product can be stored at room temperature without spoilage. Treated product is safe for hospital patients who require sterile diets.
Spices and other seasonings	8–30	Reduces number of microorganisms and insects.
Meat, poultry, fish	1–10	Delays spoilage by reducing the number of microorganisms in the fresh, refrigerated product. Kills some types of food poisoning bacteria.
Strawberries and some other fruits	1–4	Extends shelf life by delaying mold growth.
Grain, fruit, vegetables, and other foods subject to insect infestation	0.1–1	Kills insects or prevents them from reproducing. Could partially replace fumigants used for this purpose.
Bananas, avocados, mangoes, papayas, guavas, and certain other noncitrus fruits	0.25–0.35	Delays ripening.
Potatoes, onions, garlic	0.05–0.15	Inhibits sprouting.
Pork	0.08–0.15	Inactivates *Trichinella spiralis*.
Grain, dehydrated vegetables, other foods	Various doses	Desirable physical and chemical changes.

*Gray is a term used to express the dosage of ionizing radiations; 1 Gray is equivalent to 100 rads.
SOURCE: *Irradiated Foods*, American Council on Science and Health, Summit, N.J., 1985.

[A]

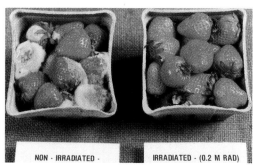

NON - IRRADIATED -   IRRADIATED - (0.2 M RAD)

[B]

FIGURE 30.5
Irradiation of fresh strawberries. **[A]** Tote boxes filled with strawberries on the irradiator warehouse conveyor about to enter the irradiator maze for exposure to gamma radiation. **[B]** Strawberries irradiated (0.2 Mrad) and stored for 15 days at 38°F (4°C) compared with nonirradiated strawberries stored for the same time and under the same conditions. Note that the nonirradiated strawberries are covered with mold growth.

MICROBIAL SPOILAGE OF FOODS

Considering the variety of foods and the methods by which each is handled during processing, it is apparent that practically all kinds of microorganisms are potential contaminants. The type of food, the processing method, and the storage method may encourage contamination by certain groups of microorganisms over others. Yet most foodstuffs serve as good growth media for many different microorganisms. Given a chance to grow, the organisms will produce changes in appearance, flavor, odor, and other qualities of food. These degradation processes may be described using the following reactions:

Putrefaction:

Protein foods + proteolytic microorganisms →
  amino acids + amines + ammonia + hydrogen sulfide

Fermentation:

Carbohydrate foods + saccharolytic microorganisms →
  acids + alcohols + gases

Rancidity:

Fatty foods + lipolytic microorganisms →
  fatty acids + glycerol

The changes that microbes cause in foods are not limited to the results of degradation; they may also be caused by products of microbial synthesis. For instance, some microorganisms discolor foods as a result of pigment production, and microorganisms capable of synthesizing polysaccharides may form slimes in or on foods.

Spoilage may occur in fresh foods [TABLE 30.5] and in canned foods [FIGURE 30.6]. As mentioned previously, milk is an excellent growth medium for bacteria; TABLE 30.6 summarizes the types of microorganisms that cause problems in milk.

TABLE 30.5

Types of Food Spoilage (Other Than Canned Foods) with Some Examples of Causative Organisms

Food	Type of spoilage	Some microorganisms involved
Bread	Moldy	Rhizopus nigricans Penicillium Aspergillus niger
	Ropy	Bacillus subtilis
Maple sap and syrup	Ropy	Enterobacter aerogenes
	Yeasty	Saccharomyces Zygosaccharomyces
	Pink	Micrococcus roseus
	Moldy	Aspergillus Penicillium
Fresh fruits and vegetables	Soft rot	Rhizopus Erwinia
	Gray mold rot	Botrytis
	Black mold rot	A. niger
Pickles, sauerkraut	Film yeasts, pink yeasts	Rhodotorula
Fresh meat	Putrefaction	Alcaligenes Clostridium Proteus vulgaris Pseudomonas fluorescens
Cured meat	Moldy	Aspergillus Rhizopus Penicillium
	Souring	Pseudomonas Micrococcus
	Greening, slime	Lactobacillus Leuconostoc
Fish	Discoloration Putrefaction	Pseudomonas Alcaligenes Flavobacterium
Eggs	Green rot	P. fluorescens
	Colorless rots	Pseudomonas Alcaligenes
	Black rots	Proteus
Concentrated orange juice	"Off" flavor	Lactobacillus Leuconostoc Acetobacter
Poultry	Slime, odor	Pseudomonas Alcaligenes

ASK YOURSELF

1 Describe several types of food spoilage, and identify the microorganisms responsible in each case.

2 Describe types of microbial spoilage of milk in terms of the several "substrates" contained in milk.

THE FOOD SERVICE INDUSTRY

Changes in the lifestyle of people in developed countries have resulted in a dramatic change in eating habits. An increasingly larger percentage of the population desires ready-to-cook meals which are precooked, frozen,

TABLE 30.6
Biochemical Types of Microorganisms That May Occur in Milk, Their Source, and the Changes They Produce

Biochemical types	Representative microorganisms	Source of microorganisms	Substrate acted upon and end products	Additional remarks
Acid producers	Streptococci	Dairy utensils, silage, plants	Lactose fermented to lactic acid or lactic acid and other products such as acetic acid, ethyl alcohol, and carbon dioxide.	Acid producers that produce only lactic acid are referred to as *homofermentative* types; those which produce a variety of products are called *heterofermentative* types.
	Lactobacilli	Feeds, silage, manure	Lactose is fermented to lactic acid and other products. Some species of lactobacilli are homofermentative; others are heterofermentative.	
	Microbacteria	Manure, dairy utensils, and dairy products	Lactose fermented to lactic acid and other end products; do not produce as much acid as the streptococci or lactobacilli.	Some of these bacteria can survive exposure to very high temperatures, e.g., 80–85°C for 10 min.
	Coliforms	Manure, polluted water, soil, and plants	Lactose fermented to a mixture of end products, e.g., acids, gases, and neutral products.	The number of coliform bacteria present in milk is an indicator of its sanitary quality.
	Micrococci	Ducts of cow's mammary glands, dairy utensils	Small amounts of acid produced from lactose (weakly fermentative); micrococci are also weakly proteolytic.	Moderately heat resistant; some strains capable of surviving 63°C for 30 min.
Gas producers	Coliforms *Clostridium butyricum* *Torula cremoris*	Soil, manure, water, feed	Lactose fermented with accumulation of gas; the gas may be a mixture of carbon dioxide and hydrogen, or only carbon dioxide in the case of yeast fermentation.	Bulk containers of milk may have their lids lifted by gas pressure in instances where contamination with gas producers is unusually high.
Ropy or stringy fermentation	*Alcaligenes viscolactis* *Enterobacter aerogenes* *Streptococcus cremoris*	Soil, water, plants, feed	Organisms synthesize a viscous polysaccharide material that forms a slime layer or capsule on the cells.	Milk favors the formation of capsular material; sterile skim milk is frequently used as the culture medium when capsule formation is sought.
Proteolytic	*Bacillus* spp. *Pseudomonas* spp. *Proteus* spp. *Streptococcus liquefaciens*	Soil, water, utensils	Proteolytic organisms degrade the casein to peptides which may be further dissimilated to amino acids; proteolysis may be preceded by coagulation of the casein by the enzyme rennin.	End products of proteolysis may impart abnormal flavor or odor to the milk; *Pseudomonas* spp. may produce coloration of milk.
Lipolytic	*Pseudomonas fluorescens* *Achromobacter lipolyticum* *Candida lipolytica* *Penicillium* spp.	Soil, water, utensils	Lipolytic microorganisms hydrolyze milk fat to glycerol and fatty acids.	Some fatty acids impart rancid odor and taste to milk.

FIGURE 30.6
Characteristics of spoiled canned food.

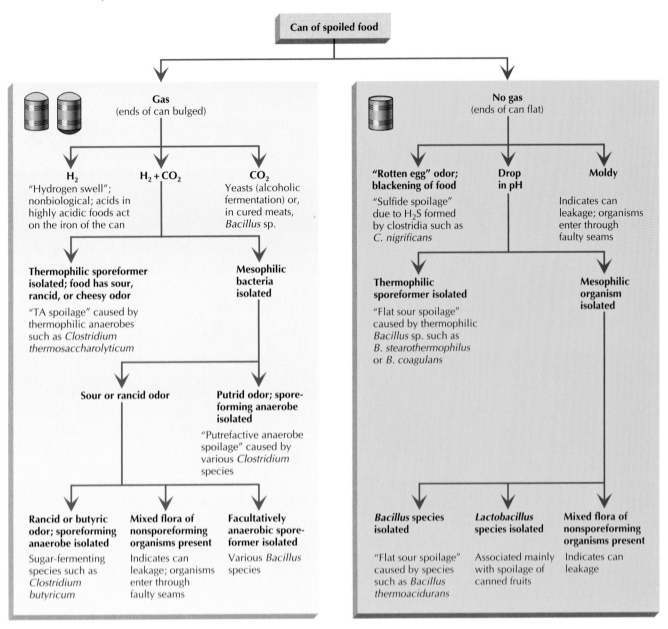

heated in the microwave oven, and ready for the dining room table! Many of these ready-to-eat refrigerated products are marketed with a shelf life of several weeks. This could result in serious problems, since some pathogenic microorganisms are capable of growing, albeit slowly, at refrigeration temperatures. Many institutions such as schools, hospitals, and the airline industry employ a food service system to supply meals. This ready-to-serve industry involves the handling of large quantities of food ingredients and food storage (both at refrigerated temperatures and high temperatures) for various time periods [FIGURES 30.7 and 30.8]. The threat of mi-

crobial contamination and microbial growth necessitates that rigid control measures be used during preparation, holding, and delivery of ready-to-serve meals.

ASK YOURSELF

What problems, microbiologically speaking, are associated with the increase in availability of precooked and ready-to-serve meals?

FIGURE 30.7

Schematic flow diagram of a Food Service Commissary System. The time and temperature that exists between each stage of this system—from food preparation to delivery to the consumer—will significantly effect the microbiological quality of the food.

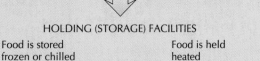

FOOD SERVICE COMMISSARY FACILITY

Preparation and packaging of "ready-to-serve" food products (billions of pounds prepared annually)

HOLDING (STORAGE) FACILITIES

Food is stored frozen or chilled

Food is held heated

CONSUMER EXAMPLES

Food delivered to hotels, airlines, supermarkets, etc. (food thawed, heated and served)

Food delivered to institutions, such as schools, hospitals, nursing homes, etc.

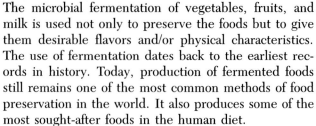

FOODS PRODUCED BY MICROORGANISMS

The microbial fermentation of vegetables, fruits, and milk is used not only to preserve the foods but to give them desirable flavors and/or physical characteristics. The use of fermentation dates back to the earliest records in history. Today, production of fermented foods still remains one of the most common methods of food preservation in the world. It also produces some of the most sought-after foods in the human diet.

In some cases, fermentation of a food material is accomplished by taking advantage of the microorganisms that occur naturally on the food. In other instances, particularly in the production of cheeses and fermented milks, cultures of specific microorganisms (*starter cultures*) are deliberately added to the food to initiate the fermentation.

FIGURE 30.8

Salmonellas and staphylococci multiply rapidly in chicken à la king and ham salad incubated at room temperature. Curves also show growth at other temperatures. *(Courtesy of R. Angelotti, M. J. Foter, and K. H. Lewis, "Time-Temperature Effects on Salmonellae and Staphylococci in Foods," Am. J. Public Health 51:76–88, 1961.)*

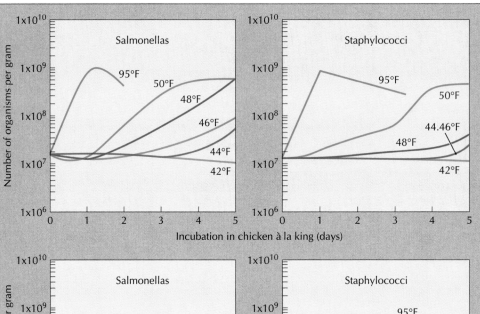

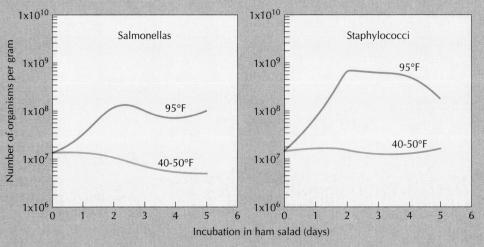

Fermented Vegetables

The fermentation of vegetables, such as cucumbers, cabbage, and olives, occurs in a series of stages:

1 Initiation stage. At first, many of the aerobic, facultative, and anaerobic microorganisms present on the vegetables begin to grow. Then the production of lactic acid by streptococci and lactobacilli lowers the pH and inhibits further growth of undesirable Gram-negative and spore-forming bacteria. It is important that the lactic acid be produced quickly to stop the growth of the undesirable bacteria.
2 Primary fermentation stage. Lactic acid bacteria and fermentative yeasts predominate during this stage. Fermentation continues until all fermentable carbohydrate is used or until the pH becomes sufficiently low that bacterial growth is inhibited.
3 Secondary fermentation. Fermentative yeasts, which are acid-tolerant, utilize any residual fermentable carbohydrate.
4 Postfermentation stage. Microbial growth, particularly molds and oxidative yeasts, may occur on the surface of the fermented product.

Large commercial facilities utilize these stages of fermentation to produce retail foods such as dill pickles [FIGURE 30.9]. Some examples of fermented vegetable products and the microorganisms involved are shown in TABLE 30.7.

Fermented Dairy Products

The dairy industry produces a large variety of fermented milks and cheeses. Microorganisms play the key role in producing a product with a desirable flavor, aroma, and physical appearance.

TABLE 30.7
Some Examples of Fermented Food Products

Fermented food	Starting product	Microorganisms involved
Sauerkraut	Shredded cabbage	Early stage: *Enterobacter cloacae* *Erwinia herbicola* Intermediate stage: *Leuconostoc mesenteroides* Final stage: *Lactobacillus plantarum*
Pickles	Cucumbers	Early fermentation: *L. mesenteroides* *Streptococcus faecalis* *Pediococcus cerevisiae* Later fermentation: *Lactobacillus brevis* *L. plantarum*
Green olives	Olives	Early stage: *L. mesenteroides* Intermediate stage: *L. plantarum* *L. brevis* Final stage: *L. plantarum*

Fermented Milks. Fermented foods made from milk, such as sour cream and yogurt, are mainstays in the human diet [TABLE 30.8]. Lactic acid bacteria are the most commonly used starter cultures for the preparation of these foods [FIGURE 30.10]. The production process begins with the addition of an active starter culture to pasteurized milk, followed by incubation at a temperature favorable for the growth of the starter culture microorganisms. The principal product of the fermentation

FIGURE 30.9

[A] Typical yard of wooden tanks (600–1000 bushel capacity) for fermentation and storage of brined cucumbers. Note the tall, white tank in the background, which is for storage of liquid nitrogen. Nitrogen gas is piped to each brine tank for use in purging of dissolved CO_2 from fermenting brines to prevent bloater damage in the cucumbers. [B] Surface of a cucumber brine tank being nitrogen-purged with a side-arm purger. Nitrogen gas purges dissolved CO_2 from the brine and also serves to circulate the brine. The white frothing is caused by the purging action.

 [A]

 [B]

is lactic acid, along with lesser amounts of flavoring substances such as the buttery-flavored compound diacetyl.

Production of Cheese. Although several hundred varieties of cheese are made, with few exceptions most of them start with cow's milk; a few are made from goat's milk. Bacteria convert the *curd* (the casein in milk) into the desired cheese. For the manufacture of some cheeses it is necessary to inoculate the curd with particular kinds of microorganisms in order to bring about the proper changes in the curd [TABLE 30.9]. In other instances, the conditions of incubation—particularly temperature and the addition of salt—favor the development of desired microorganisms.

The manufacture of cheese includes the following steps:

1 The curd is separated from the *whey* (the liquid portion of curdled milk). Precipitation of the casein is caused by the addition of the enzyme *rennin* to the milk or by the lactic acid produced when milk undergoes lactic acid fermentation.
2 Adjustments are made to the curd, such as adding salt, removing a specific amount of moisture, inoculating with a particular microorganism if required, and shaping the curd into a desired size and form.
3 The curd is incubated under conditions which favor the growth of the desired microorganisms.

T A B L E 30.8
Some Characteristics of Fermented Milks

Fermented product	Principal microorganisms responsible for fermentation	General remarks
Cultured buttermilk	A mixture of lactic streptococci (*Streptococcus lactis* or *S. cremoris*) with aroma-producing bacteria (*Leuconostoc citrovorum* or *L. dextranicum*)	The function of the lactic acid streptococci is to produce lactic acid, which gives the sour taste, and to curdle the milk; the function of the leuconostocs is to produce volatile and neutral products that impart a characteristic desirable odor; the starter culture must contain vigorously growing bacteria; incubation is performed at 21°C.
Cultured sour cream	Same as used for cultured buttermilk, i.e., streptococci and leuconostocs	Not strictly a fermented milk, but manufacture resembles that of cultured buttermilk. Cream is inoculated and incubated until the desired acidity develops; flavor and aroma compounds are also contributed by the starter culture.
Bulgarian milk	*Lactobacillus bulgaricus*	Incubation of inoculated milk at 37°C, but otherwise similar to cultured buttermilk; product differs from commercial buttermilk in having higher acidity and lacking aroma.
Acidophilus milk	*L. acidophilus*	Milk for propagation of *L. acidophilus* and the bulk milk to be fermented are sterilized, since this organism is easily overgrown by contaminating bacteria. Incubation is at 37°C; acidity allowed to develop to 0.6 to 0.7%.
Yogurt	*Streptococcus thermophilus* *L. bulgaricus*	Made from milk in which solids are concentrated by evaporation of some water and addition of skim milk solids; product has consistency resembling custard.
Kefir	*S. lactis* *L. bulgaricus* Lactose-fermenting yeasts	A mixed lactic acid and alcoholic fermentation; bacteria produce acid (0.6 to 1.0% lactic acid), and yeasts produce alcohol (0.5 to 1.0% ethanol); the organisms conglomerate to form small granules called kefir grains; the granules are used as the starter culture. In the Balkans, the fermentation is carried out in leather bags made of goatskin; the fermentation process may be continuous by adding fresh milk as the fermented product is removed. Kefir is made from cow, goat, or sheep milk.
Kumiss	Similar to those found in kefir grains	A mixed acid-alcoholic fermentation product made from mares' milk in some parts of Russia.

FIGURE 30.10

Some important species of bacteria for the dairy industry. **[A]** *Streptococcus lactis*, a lactic acid-producing species common in many dairy fermentations. **[B]** *Streptococcus cremoris*, one of the species in butter cultures. **[C]** *Lactobacillus bulgaricus* is important in several fermented milk products. (Debris in the center is coagulated milk protein.) **[D]** Photomicrograph of yogurt illustrating microbial flora *Streptococcus thermophilus* and *Lactobacillus bulgaricus*.

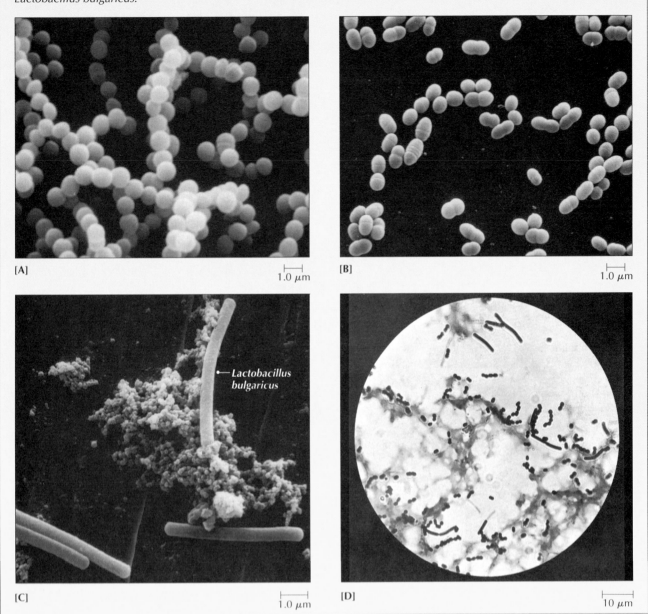

[A]   1.0 μm

[B]   1.0 μm

[C]   *Lactobacillus bulgaricus*   1.0 μm

[D]   10 μm

The hundreds of different cheeses can be classified in several ways. *Unripened cheeses* consist of curd which has not been fermented by microorganisms, such as cottage cheese and cream cheese. *Ripened cheeses* result from the growth of bacteria or molds in or on the curd during a prescribed incubation period. Ripened cheeses may be classified as *hard, semisoft,* or *soft,* reflecting the extent to which the solid casein has been metabolized by the ripening microorganisms. Some examples of unripened and ripened cheeses are shown in TABLE 30.9.

Microbial Cells As Food—Single-Cell Protein (SCP)

Cells of bacteria, yeasts, and algae produced in massive quantities can be used as food for animals as well as hu-

TABLE 30.9
Some Examples of Cheese Varieties with Starter Cultures and Associated Microorganisms and Their Function

Cheese type	Name of cheese	Ripened or unripened	Starter species	Starter function	Associated microbial flora	Function of associated microbial flora
High moisture (80%), soft	Cottage Cream Neufchatel	Unripened	*Streptococcus lactis* *S. cremoris* *Leuconostoc cremoris*	Production of acid and flavor	*S. lactis* subsp. *diacetylactis* in cottage cheese cream dressing	Production of flavor Increased shelf life
Semisoft, moisture 50%	Limburger	Ripened interior and surface	*S. lactis* *S. cremoris*	Production of acid and some flavor	*Brevibacterium linens* *Micrococcus* spp. Yeasts	Extensive surface curing Production of flavor
Hard, moisture 39%	Swiss cheese varieties	Ripened interior only	*S. lactis* *S. cremoris* *S. thermophilus* *Lactobacillus helveticus* *L. bulgaricus*	Production of acid and some flavor	*Propionibacterium freudenreichii* and *P. freudenreichii* subsp. *shermanii*	Formation of eyes and characteristic flavor

mans. They are attractive as food sources because they can be grown on industrial wastes or by-products and yield a large cell crop that is rich in protein (called *single-cell protein*). Some of the benefits of using single-cell protein as a food substitute or supplement are:

1 Microorganisms grow very rapidly and produce a high yield. A 1000-lb steer gains 1 lb of protein in one day; in contrast, 1000 lb of yeast would produce several tons of protein in one day! Algae grown in ponds can produce 20 tons (dry weight) of protein per acre per year—a yield 10 to 15 times higher than that of soybeans and 25 to 50 times higher than that of corn.
2 The protein content of microbial cells is very high. Dried cells of *Pseudomonas* species grown on petroleum products have 69 percent protein; yeast cells have a protein content between 40 and 50 percent; for algae, the range is from 20 to 40 percent. For comparison, meat is approximately 20 percent protein, while soybeans are approximately 35 percent protein.
3 The proteins of selected microorganisms contain all the essential amino acids.
4 Some microorganisms, particularly yeasts, have a high vitamin content.
5 The growth medium for SCP microorganisms may contain industrial wastes or by-products, such as hydrocarbons from oil refineries, spent sulfite liquid from the pulp and paper industry, beet molasses, and wood hydrolysates. Bacterial cells grown on hydrocarbon wastes from the petroleum industry are used as a source of protein in France, Japan, Taiwan, and

India. Yeast-cell crops harvested from the vats used to produce alcoholic beverages have been used as a food supplement for generations.

Despite the very attractive features of single-cell protein as a nutrient for humans, there are problems which limit its use on a global scale. For example, individual tastes and customs make microorganisms unattractive as a food substance to many persons. Moreover, the high nucleic acid content of some microbial cells can produce intestinal disturbances in humans. There needs to be assurance that the amino acid content of the microbial protein provides all of the essential amino acids. Otherwise supplements are required.

ASK YOURSELF

1 Describe the process by which a fermented vegetable product, such as sauerkraut, is made, with particular attention to microbiological events.

2 What is the role of microorganisms in the manufacture of a ripened cheese?

3 In terms of changes in the substrate acted upon by microorganisms, what is the difference between a hard and a soft cheese?

4 What are the attractive features of SCP as a feed or a food supplement?

SUMMARY

1 Microorganisms are closely tied to the quality and safety of a food. The numbers and kinds of microorganisms present in food reflect the sanitary conditions under which it was produced, as well as the present condition of the food. Some microorganisms can cause foodborne diseases, others are used to prepare foods, particularly fermented foods.

2 Food is particularly susceptible to microbial contamination and it can serve as a growth medium for the contaminating microorganisms.

3 International, federal, state and county agencies routinely inspect and regulate food production. Standard procedures have been developed for the microscopic and cultural examination of foods.

4 In their natural condition, foods vary considerably in their normal microbial content. For example, meat tissue from a healthy animal is essentially free of microorganisms. The surface of fresh vegetables has microorganisms that reflect the environment in which they were grown and the conditions under which they were harvested.

5 A variety of methods are available for reducing or eliminating microorganisms from food. Attention to aseptic handling during harvesting and marketing reduces the initial level of contamination. High temperatures, low temperatures, dehydration, chemical additives, and radiation are the principal means of preserving foods. The method of choice depends upon the nature of the food item as well as the practical level of preservation being sought.

6 All foods are susceptible to spoilage by microorganisms, some more than others. The nature of the spoilage depends upon the major chemical constituent of the food (carbohydrate, fat, protein) and the characteristics of the contaminating microorganisms.

7 Microorganisms are used to produce a large variety of foods, particularly fermented products such as pickles, fermented milks, and cheeses.

8 The expanding food service industry, including fast-food services, creates special microbiological problems for the industry and the public.

9 Massive "crops" of microbial cells (single-cell protein) are produced for animal feeds and human food supplement, but have not been accepted worldwide as a food alternative.

KEY TERMS

aseptic processing
Breed smear
Howard mold-counting slide
phosphatase test
radiation pasteurization
ripened cheese
single-cell protein
starter culture
unripened cheese

REVIEW GUIDE

SIGNIFICANCE OF
MICROORGANISMS
IN FOOD

1 Microorganisms are important in foods because: **(a)** they cause food spoilage; **(b)** they may cause food poisoning; **(c)** they may cause food infections; **(d)** they are used to make food products; **(e)** all of the above.

2 Massive quantities of microbial cells may be used as a(n) _____.

3 Both the total number and the kinds of microorganisms present in food reflect the _____ of a food product.

FOOD AS A MEDIUM
FOR GROWTH OF
MICROORGANISMS

4 A food item may serve as a(n) _____ for growth of microorganisms.

5 The major groups of microorganisms that can contaminate and cause spoilage of food are _____ and _____.

6 Milk is an excellent _____ for the cultivation of microorganisms.

7 In terms of microbial growth, the contamination of food is comparable to _____ of a microbiological medium.

MICROBIOLOGICAL
EXAMINATION OF
FOODS

8 Three United Nations agencies that are engaged with the microbiological surveillance of foods are the _____, _____, and _____.

9 In the United States, microbiological examination of food that is shipped from one state to another is under the surveillance of the _____.

10 The *Breed smear* procedure is a microscopic technique for counting bacteria in _____.

11 Which of the following abbreviations refers to a cultural technique for determining microorganisms in food? **(a)** FDA; **(b)** SPC; **(c)** FAO; **(d)** WHO; **(e)** IMC.

*In questions 12 and 13, indicate whether the statement is true (*T*) or false (*F*). Explain.*

12 A plate culture technique will reveal the total viable microorganisms of a food sample. _____

_____

_____

13 Enumeration of viruses in a food sample can be performed in the same manner as is done for bacteria. _____

_____

_____

14 Which one or more of the following groups or genera of bacteria is or are unlikely to be sought in the microbiological examination of a food sample? **(a)** *Clostridium* spp.; **(b)** fecal streptococci; **(c)** *Nitrobacter* spp.; **(d)** coliforms; **(e)** *Salmonella* spp.

MICROORGANISMS
IN FRESH FOODS

15 From a microbiological standpoint healthy meat tissue is essentially _____ of microorganisms.

16 Hamburger is more likely to have a larger population of bacteria than a comparable amount of steak because _____.

17 The surface of freshly dressed, eviscerated poultry which has been processed under good sanitary conditions has a bacterial count of _____ to _____ bacteria per square centimeter.

18 The interior of a freshly laid egg usually contains _____ microorganisms.

19 Microorganisms may penetrate the shell of an egg if the thin _____ coat underlying the shell deteriorates.

20 The low pH of fruits inhibits the growth of _____ but not _____.

21 Contamination of shellfish by pathogenic microorganisms is likely to occur in _____ waters.

22 *Vibrio parahaemolyticus* causes a type of gastroenteritis which can be contracted by consumption of raw or inadequately cooked _____.

23 In milk, *Streptococcus lactis* is homofermentative; that is, the sole or major product of sugar fermentation is _____.

24 In milk, a high number of coliforms indicates _____.

GENERAL PRINCIPLES OF FOOD PRESERVATION

25 Canning is a food preservation technique first devised by _____ in 1810.

26 The organism that is the most important to eliminate from canned foods is _____.

27 Low-acid foods require a _____ temperature than do high-acid foods during canning.

28 In the _____ pasteurization method, every particle of milk is heated at 62.8°C for 30 min, whereas in the _____ method, the milk is heated at 71.7°C for 15 s.

29 The pasteurization temperature in the LTH method was raised 2°F, from 143 to 145°F, in order to kill the causative agent of _____.

30 Although pasteurization accomplishes disinfection of milk, it does not _____ milk, and thus pasteurized milk must be stored under refrigeration.

31 Phosphatase is present in _____ milk but not in _____ milk.

32 Milk exposed to ultrahigh temperatures for 1 to 2 s and packaged into sterile containers does not require subsequent _____ during storage.

33 Before freezing, fresh produce is _____ to inactivate enzymes.

34 Is freezing generally a bactericidal process? ____

35 Which of the following methods of food preservation is microbicidal in action? **(a)** dehydration to produce "dry" milk; **(b)** freezing; **(c)** aseptic technical procedures; **(d)** irradiation with gamma rays; **(e)** drying of fruit.

36 Which of the following methods of food preservation is most likely to be microbiostatic in action? **(a)** pasteurization; **(b)** canning; **(c)** freezing; **(d)** gamma radiation; **(e)** ultraviolet light treatment.

37 Which one of the following genera is most likely to contain organisms capable of surviving high temperatures? **(a)** *Clostridium;* **(b)** *Pseudomonas;* **(c)** *Penicillium;* **(d)** *Torula;* **(e)** *Coxiella.*

38 The process of milk pasteurization: **(a)** kills *Clostridium botulinum* spores; **(b)** was invented by Koch; **(c)** kills *Coxiella burnetii;* **(d)** results in destruction of all microorganisms; **(e)** kills *Bacillus subtilis* spores.

MICROBIAL SPOILAGE OF FOODS

39 Putrefaction is the result of the breakdown of _____, fermentation is the result of the breakdown of _____, and rancidity is the result of the breakdown of _____.

40 Microbial spoilage of bread, particularly when bread becomes old, is caused by _____.

41 Spoilage of milk may include any of the following undesirable changes: acidity, gas, ropiness or stringiness, _____, or _____.

42 Spoilage of canned foods is due mainly to _____ bacteria, since such bacteria are the ones most likely to survive the heat treatment used in the canning process.

43 In canned foods having a pH of 4.6, *Bacillus stearothermophilus* causes a type of spoilage called _____, whereas *Clostridium thermosaccharolyticum* causes a type of spoilage called _____.

44 TA spoilage of canned foods is indicated by development of a sour, cheesy, or butyric odor and a(n) _____.

45 A can of corn bursts owing to gas production, and the corn has a putrid odor and shows partial digestion. This type of spoilage is called _____.

46 A can of fruit juice bursts owing to gas production, and the juice has a rancid odor. This type of spoilage is called _____ spoilage.

47 Match each organism on the left with the phenomenon on the right with which it best corresponds. (The items in both columns refer to microbiology of canned-food spoilage.)

_____ *Bacillus thermoacidurans*
_____ *Clostridium sporogenes*
_____ *Bacillus stearothermophilus*
_____ *Penicillium* spp.
_____ *Clostridium nigrificans*

(a) Flat sour spoilage of corn
(b) Sulfide spoilage
(c) Flat sour spoilage of tomato juice
(d) Putrefactive anaerobe spoilage
(e) Surface growth and musty odor

THE FOOD SERVICE INDUSTRY

48 The growing demand for packaged, ready-to-serve meals, from a microbiological standpoint, requires rigid control measures both in the

_____ of and the _____ of the meals.

FOODS PRODUCED BY MICROORGANISMS

49 In the manufacture of fermented dairy products, milk is inoculated with a

_____ culture to produce a desired type of fermentation.

50 In starter cultures for cultured buttermilk, the function of _Streptococcus lactis_ is to produce _____, which gives the sour taste and curdles the milk, whereas the function of _Leuconostoc dextranicum_ is to produce

_____, which impart a desirable

_____.

51 The starter culture for yogurt contains two species of bacteria:

_____ and _____.

52 The starter cultures for kefir and kumiss contain lactose-fermenting

_____, which produce ethyl alcohol.

53 In the production of cheese, both the starter culture and the enzyme

_____ are used to curdle the milk.

54 In cheesemaking, the watery fluid which separates out during draining of the cut

pieces of curd is called _____.

55 The bacterium used to make acidophilus milk is _____.

56 The starting material for the manufacture of sauerkraut is

_____, and that for the manufacture of pickles is

_____.

57 The microorganisms that predominate in the primary stages of the fermentation of

olives are _____ and _____.

58 In the initial stages of the fermentation of a vegetable like cabbage, many of the microorganisms already present on the vegetable start growing; but they are soon in-

hibited by the _____ produced by

_____ and _____.

59 Some advantages of using microorganisms as food sources are as follows: (1) mi-

crobial proteins contain all the essential _____; (2) some

microorganisms, particularly _____, have a high vitamin

content; (3) _____ can be used as the growth medium.

60 Bacteria, yeasts, and _____ have all been proposed as sources of single-cell protein.

REVIEW QUESTIONS

1 Identify the various ways that microorganisms may be of significance to foods.

2 Outline a procedure by which you could determine the amount of mold contamination in fresh tomatoes delivered to a cannery. What do high mold counts indicate about the quality of the product?

3 Outline a procedure for the isolation of coliforms from hamburger; of thermophilic anaerobes from a can of spoiled beans.

4 What are the potential changes in the microbial content of each of the following foods from its natural source to the time it reaches the consumer:
(a) hamburger; **(b)** oysters; **(c)** milk; **(d)** canned peas?

5 Compare the antimicrobial action of the following methods of food preservation: canning, refrigeration, dehydration, and increased osmotic pressure.

6 Compare the types of microorganisms that might be involved in the spoilage of refrigerated foods with those which may cause spoilage of canned foods.

7 What are the attractive features of food preservation through use of radiation, such as irradiation with gamma rays?

8 What is a "starter culture," and how is it used?

9 Describe the role of microorganisms in the production of dill pickles.

10 Describe the use of microorganisms in producing single-cell protein and the desirable and undesirable features of the product.

DISCUSSION QUESTIONS

1 A sample of raw milk is found to have a very high bacterial count. Describe several conditions which might be responsible for this.

2 In terms of the mechanism of inhibition of microorganisms, what is the similarity between preservation by dehydration and preservation by using salts or sugars, that is, high osmotic pressure?

3 Why is milk regarded as the most nearly perfect food? Why is it an excellent culture medium?

4 The tissue of a hind quarter of beef is likely to be free of microorganisms. Ground beef prepared from this same hind quarter might have a high bacterial count. How can this be explained?

5 What are the special concerns, in terms of microbiological contamination, associated with seafood products like raw oysters and crabmeat?

6 Many large food stores provide a food bar with ready-to-eat foods such as salads and soups. What special precautions need to be implemented to maintain satisfactory control of microorganisms?

7 Some investigators have suggested that *salmonella* contamination of poultry could be controlled by gamma irradiation of the product. What problems are associated with this suggestion? Are these problems real or merely perceived?

8 In terms of microbial activity in the manufacture of cheese, explain the essential difference between a hard and a soft ripened cheese.

Biotechnology: The Industrial Applications of Microbiology

OBJECTIVES

After reading this chapter you should be able to

1 Understand why microorganisms have many industrial applications.

2 Distinguish between present-day "biotechnology" and traditional industrial microbiology.

3 Identify the major categories of industrial products and processes.

4 Describe the industrial production of at least three substances that result from microbial dissimilation reactions.

5 Describe the industrial production of at least three substances that result from microbial synthesis.

6 Identify at least three pharmaceutical products that are produced by genetically engineered microorganisms.

7 Give two examples of microorganisms used as bioinsecticides and discuss the advantage of bioinsecticides over chemical insecticides.

8 Describe how microorganisms enhance recovery of metals from low-grade ores.

9 Describe the role of microorganisms in the petroleum industry.

10 Discuss different kinds of microbial deterioration of materials and methods available to prevent this deterioration.

OVERVIEW

Throughout this book you have learned that microbiology encompasses the many characteristics of microorganisms—including their growth and metabolism, their importance in disease and immune responses, and their role in recycling materials on a global scale. They are also key elements in commercial processes described earlier, such as food production and genetic engineering research. This chapter focuses on the industrial applications of microorganisms—both naturally occurring microorganisms and genetically engineered microorganisms (described in Chapter 14). The industrial use of microorganisms is one aspect of *biotechnology*.

Defined most simply, biotechnology is the application of technology to living systems. Any technique in which a living organism is used to produce a useful product or a desirable chemical change is an example of biotechnology. Today, however, biotechnology has been dramatically expanded by exploiting recombinant DNA technology to "engineer" microbes that produce valuable new products.

Whether altered genetically or not, microorganisms are used commercially because they are able to transform materials into new, more valuable substances or because they can transform pollutant wastes into harmless and sometimes useful substances. For instance, the microbial breakdown, or dissimilation, of a nutrient may result in a useful product, such as the alcohol produced from sugar fermentation or the antibiotics synthesized by microorganisms. As you learned in the chapters on microorganisms and disease, microbial cells or their products are used to make vaccines. Some microorganisms are also used as biological insecticides. Bacteria are able to increase the recovery of metals from low-grade ores; pumping oil from underground reservoirs is made easier when certain bacteria are injected into the drilling pipeline.

Microorganisms may also cause undesirable changes that damage industrial and domestic products. For instance, textiles, painted surfaces, and paper can deteriorate because of the growth and metabolic activities of various microorganisms. Commercial processes have been developed to minimize or prevent the economic losses due to such deterioration.

INDUSTRIAL MICROBIOLOGICAL PRODUCTS AND PROCESSES

There are thousands of commercially important products made by manipulating microorganisms, from basic foods described in Chapter 30 to still-experimental AIDS vaccines and anticancer therapeutic agents. These commercial products may be placed into several groups: (1) the microbial cells themselves, which may be used as food supplements or as immunizing agents to prevent disease; (2) large molecules, such as enzymes, that are synthesized by microorganisms; (3) primary metabolic products formed by microorganisms that are essential for cell growth, such as vitamins; and (4) secondary metabolic products, such as antibiotics, which are not required for cell growth.

The various industrial processes used to produce these microbial products can be divided into the following categories, based on the intended use of the final products:

1 *Production of pharmaceutical chemicals.* Most prominent in this category are antibiotics and steroid drugs. Other useful pharmaceutical products such as insulin and interferon are now being produced by genetically engineered bacteria, and many other new products are becoming available through genetic engineering.

2 *Production of commercially valuable chemicals.* This category includes solvents and enzymes, as well as various compounds used as starting materials for the industrial synthesis of other substances.

3 *Production of food supplements.* The mass production of yeasts, bacteria, and algae from inexpensive media containing inorganic nitrogen salts and other readily available nutrients can provide a good source of protein and other substances that are useful as food supplements for humans and animals. (Some of these supplements are described in Chapter 30.)

4 *Production of alcoholic beverages.* Brewing of beer, wine making, and the production of other alcoholic beverages constitute some of the oldest large-scale biotechnology processes.

5 *Production of vaccines (immunizing antigens).* Whole microbial cells, their parts, or their products are produced in large quantities and used for the production of vaccines.

6 *Production of microorganisms for use as insecticides (biocides).* The control of plant damage by insects can, in some cases, be accomplished by application of microorganisms known to act as insecticides. This is especially true for certain species of the genus *Bacillus* (*B. larvae*, *B. popilliae*, and *B. thuringiensis*). These species produce a crystalline protein which is lethal to lepidopteran (moths, butterflies, skippers) larvae such as the cabbage worm, gypsy moth, and tent caterpillar.

7 *Applications in mining and in the petroleum industry.* Numerous microbiological procedures are used to enhance the recovery of metals from low-grade ores and to improve recovery of oil from wells.

FIGURE 31.1

The essential features of an industrial microbiological process.

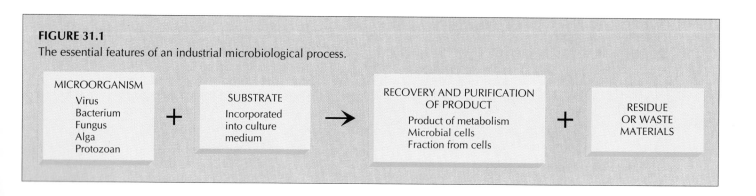

FIGURE 31.1 illustrates the essential components of an industrial microbial process.

Another dimension of industrial microbiology relates to microbes' ability to decompose or deteriorate materials, and the need to prevent this deterioration if materials are to be preserved. Leather, textiles, wood, paper, metals, and even electrical circuit boards and optical equipment are subject to damage caused by the growth and metabolism of microorganisms. There are specialized industries that develop chemicals and treatment processes to minimize or prevent harmful microbial effects on materials. A positive aspect of microbial deterioration is the degradation of pollutants that may accumulate in the environment. Commercial processes, called *bioremediation*, have been developed that use massive numbers of microorganisms known to decompose pollutants such as PCBs.

Industrial microbiological processes may be improved or even created by using genetically altered microorganisms which have been tailor-made to optimize production of a desired substance or to degrade toxic compounds. As you learned in Chapter 14, the techniques of molecular biology have made it possible to transfer specific genes from one cell to another cell. This aspect of biotechnology has revolutionized industrial microbiology. Not only is it possible to transfer genes from one microorganism to another microorganism, but it is also possible to transfer genes from plant or animal cells into a bacterium or yeast. These techniques have made the potential for microbial production of useful compounds almost limitless. The commercial promise of genetic engineering has spawned hundreds of "biotech" companies, which are already producing several important pharmaceutical products such as insulin. A large number of other products are presently in various stages of development. The final years of the twentieth century will likely see major advances in medicine and other areas due to biotechnology.

The effects of advanced biotechnology will eventually be felt throughout the world. Agriculture and food products, waste management and environmental quality, raw materials for the chemical industry, new pharmaceutical products, and the control of infectious diseases are all areas in which new discoveries will occur.

ASK YOURSELF

1 Name the major categories of industrial microbiological products.

2 Describe the essential components of an industrial microbiological process.

PRODUCTS OF MICROBIAL DISSIMILATION

Some commercially valuable products result from the breakdown of substrates by microorganisms. However, such dissimilation processes must occur on a large production scale to be useful; this "scale-up" depends upon the characteristics of the microorganism, the substrate, the culture medium, and the dissimilation product.

The microorganism used in industrial dissimilation processes must be able to convert a high proportion of the substrate to the desired product. Moreover, it must have stable characteristics, it must grow rapidly and vigorously, and it should not be pathogenic.

The culture medium, including the substrate from which the organism makes the product, must be inexpensive and available in large quantities. Sometimes it is possible to use nutrient-containing wastes as the culture medium, such as whey from the dairy industry or the waste liquids made in cooking wood during paper manufacturing.

There also must be some efficient, mass-scale method of recovering and purifying the end product formed by the metabolic activities of the microorganism. This product is present in a complex mixture of microbial cells, unused components of the culture medium, and products other than those being sought. Moreover, the product may be contained in a very large volume of culture, because industrial fermentations are performed in large tanks; capacities of 50,000 gallons are not unusual.

Some examples of industrial products from microbial dissimilation of a substrate are vinegar, lactic acid, alcohol, and alcohol-containing beverages.

Alcohol and Alcoholic Beverages

Ethanol (ethyl alcohol) is a common solvent and raw material used in the laboratory and in the chemical industry. It is produced by yeasts using any fermentable carbohydrate as a substrate. If polysaccharides such as cornstarch are used as the raw material, they must first be hydrolyzed to simple fermentable sugars. The hydrolysis can be accomplished with enzymes from barley malt or molds, or by heating the material in the presence of an acid. Corn, molasses, sugar beets, potatoes, and grapes are some of the common raw materials used for alcoholic fermentation.

Selected strains of the yeast *Saccharomyces cerevisiae* are usually used for ethanol production, although other yeast species also are employed. The yeast strain selected must grow well, produce a large yield of etha-

TABLE 31.1

The Role of Yeasts in the Production of Alcoholic Beverages

Product	Microorganism	Method of preparation	Factors influencing reaction	Function of yeast
Beer	*Saccharomyces cerevisiae* or *S. carlsbergensis*	Barley malt and starch adjuncts mixed with warm water; after enzymic starch conversion, wort is filtered, then boiled with hops, and finally fermented with yeast.	Aerobic in early stages, but quickly becomes anaerobic; temp. 8–12°C; pH at start 5.0–5.4, at end 4.0–4.8; primary fermentation lasts 5–9 days.	Converts sugar into alcohol and carbon dioxide; produces changes in proteins and other minor constituents which modify flavor.
Rum	*S. cerevisiae* or other yeasts	Blackstrap molasses containing 12–14% fermentable sugar; ammonium sulfate and occasionally phosphates may be added as nutrients; distilled after fermentation.	Optimum pH 4.0–4.7; initial temp. 21°C rising to final temp. of 35.5°C; fermentation lasts 3–7 days.	Sugar converted to alcohol, which is then removed by distillation.
Whiskey, Scotch	*S. cerevisiae* (generally a top yeast)	Grain mash cooked, saccharified with peated malt, and fermented; batch-distilled and distillate aged in oak casks at least 3 years; then blended with grain whiskey.	Optimum pH 4.0–5.0; initial temp. 26°C; fermentation completed in 72 h.	Produces alcohol and congeneric substances (acids, esters, various alcohols) which, with the peated malt, give characteristic Scotch flavor.
Whiskey, bourbon	*S. cerevisiae*	Grain mash consisting of corn (at least 51%) generally with rye; cooked and saccharified with malt and fermented; distillate, between 110 and 130 proof, matured in charred oak barrels.	Same as for Scotch.	Same as for Scotch, but flavor is characteristic of bourbon.
Wine	*S. ellipsoideus*, various strains	Grape must with sugar concentration up to 22%; balling is sulfited to reduce rate of fermentation; allowed to ferment with special strain of yeast, or with yeast naturally present on the grape; primary fermentation succeeded by a period of storage for maturation.	Aerobic in early stages, but mainly anaerobic later; temp. below 29.4°C, but varies according to local conditions, yeast strain, and type of wine; fermentation lasts 7–11 days.	Converts sugar into alcohol and also produces changes in minor constituents which modify flavor and bouquet; amount of alcohol varies according to type of wine.

SOURCE: From W. S. Spector, ed., *Handbook of Biological Data*, Saunders, Philadelphia, 1956.

nol, and have a high tolerance for ethanol. Microbiologists have spent a great deal of time selecting and improving yeast strains with these characteristics in mind. The yeast causes the following biochemical change to occur in the substrate:

$$C_6H_{12}O_6 \xrightarrow{\text{yeast enzymes}} 2CH_3CH_2OH + 2CO_2$$

Glucose (fermentable carbohydrate)   Ethanol   Carbon dioxide

Ethanol is a component of alcoholic beverages, and microorganisms are needed to produce such products as wine and beer. Depending on the particular beverage desired, the starting raw material, and the species of yeast, the factors that influence the biochemical reaction will vary. TABLE 31.1 summarizes some characteristics of the fermentation processes that produce beer, rum, whiskey, and wine.

Vinegar

The word *vinegar* is derived from the French *vinaigre*, meaning "sour wine." This is appropriate because vinegar is prepared by converting the ethanol in a "wine" to acetic acid.

Fermentation of a carbohydrate to produce ethanol is the first step in vinegar production. Differences among the various kinds of vinegars are associated mainly with the kind of carbohydrate-containing material used (for example, a fruit juice, a sugar-containing syrup, or a hydrolyzed starchy material). A yeast fermentation is used initially for production of the alcohol from the substrate. The solution's alcohol concentration is then adjusted to between 10 and 13%, and acetic acid–producing bacteria (genus *Acetobacter*) are added.

Many types of equipment have been designed for industrial production of vinegar. The essential features of one process, the Frings method, are shown in FIGURE 31.2. In this process, the alcohol solution is acidified by addition of some acetic acid (because acetobacters prefer acidic conditions), as well as special nutrients for acetobacters. The alcohol solution is poured into a trough at the top of the chamber and allowed to trickle down over beechwood shavings previously inoculated with the bacteria. As the alcohol passes over the shavings, the acetobacters oxidize some of the alcohol to acetic acid:

$$2CH_3CH_2OH + 2O_2 \longrightarrow 2CH_3COOH + 2H_2O$$

Ethanol | Acetic acid

The solution is collected at the bottom of the unit and may be recirculated over the shavings to allow more oxidation of alcohol, until vinegar of the desired strength is produced.

Note that this is an aerobic process—an abundant supply of air must be available throughout the chamber. Moreover, the temperature must be maintained between 15 and 34°C, the optimum range for *Acetobacter* growth and metabolism. The Frings vinegar generator is equipped with various accessories that permit control of these factors. Temperatures below or above 15 to 34°C not only are unfavorable for the acetobacters, but they also permit the growth of other microorganisms which produce undesirable end products.

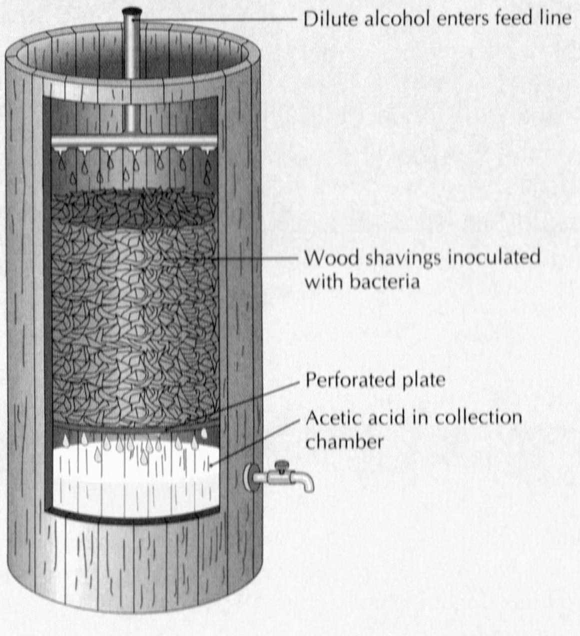

Lactic Acid

Lactic acid is a valuable industrial product because its derivatives have a variety of uses. For instance, calcium lactate is used in the treatment of calcium deficiency, and iron lactate is used in the treatment of anemia. Butyl lactate is a solvent in lacquers, and sodium lactate is used as a plasticizer and moisturizer.

Several carbohydrate substances—such as cornstarch, potato starch, molasses, and dairy whey—can be used for the production of lactic acid. Any starch used must first be hydrolyzed to glucose by treatment with acids or enzymes. The choice of carbohydrate material depends upon its availability, the treatment required prior to fermentation, and the cost.

A waste product, whey, from the manufacture of dairy products (cheese and butter) is commonly used to produce lactic acid because it is an inexpensive and efficient growth medium for various bacteria. It is a watery solution of milk sugar (lactose), nitrogenous substances such as vitamins, and various salts. Because the disposal of untreated whey can cause pollution, its use to produce lactic acid provides the added benefit of reducing sources of pollution. Microorganisms used to make lactic acid from whey must grow well in the whey medium and ferment most or all of the lactose to lactic acid:

$$C_{12}H_{22}O_{11} + H_2O \xrightarrow{\text{enzyme (lactase)}}$$

Lactose

$$2C_6H_{12}O_6 \xrightarrow{\text{system of enzymes}} 4CH_3CHOHCOOH$$

Glucose + galactose | Lactic acid

FIGURE 31.2

Frings vinegar generator. A dilute solution of alcohol percolates through wood shavings that are covered with a growth of acetobacters. The bacteria oxidize the alcohol to acetic acid.

- Dilute alcohol enters feed line
- Wood shavings inoculated with bacteria
- Perforated plate
- Acetic acid in collection chamber

Lactobacilli are suitable for this purpose, especially *Lactobacillus bulgaricus*.

When used as the inoculum for a fermentation tank, *L. bulgaricus* is cultured serially in increasingly larger volumes of sterile skim milk, pasteurized skim milk, and finally whey. (Milk is used initially to obtain a larger inoculum because it is a better medium than whey.) The whey culture is added to the fermentation tank in a volume equivalent to 5 to 10 percent of the total volume to be fermented. The incubation temperature is 43°C, high enough to inhibit the growth of many extraneous microorganisms without inhibiting *L. bulgaricus*. During the fermentation a slurry of lime, $Ca(OH)_2$, is added periodically to neutralize the acidity and form calcium lactate. Otherwise the accumulation of lactic acid would retard fermentation. The fermentation is complete after approximately two days, and the material in the tank is boiled to coagulate the microbial protein. The protein is trapped on a filter and processed for use as an animal feed supplement. The filtrate, which contains the soluble calcium lactate, is concentrated by using a vacuum to remove the water; additional treatments purify the compound. The process is shown in FIGURE 31.3.

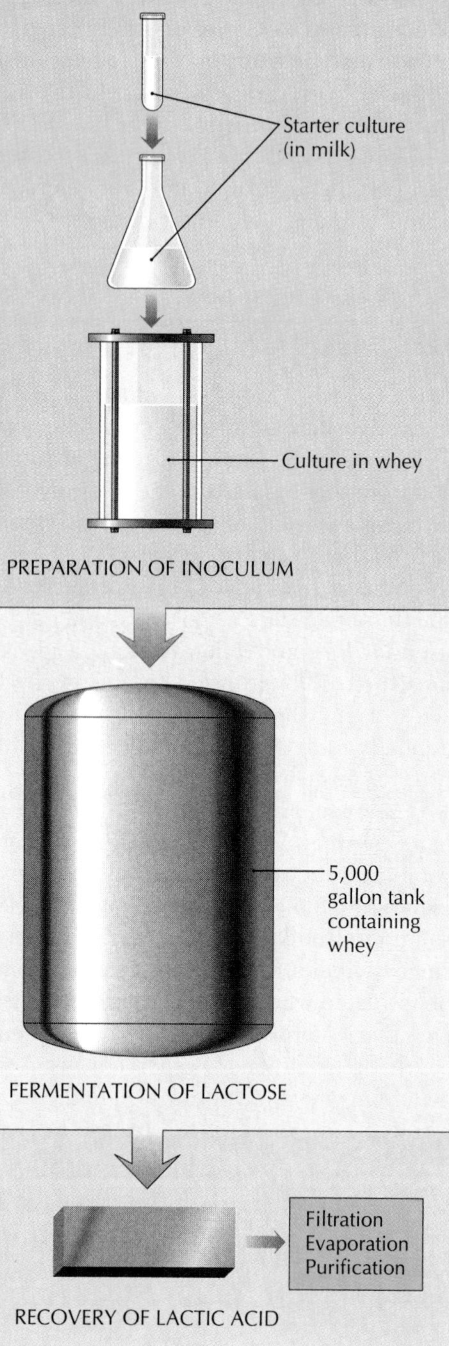

Other Products of Microbial Dissimilation

Many other industrial products are made by microbial dissimilation and are used for various purposes. Some of these products and the microorganisms used to make them are listed in TABLE 31.2.

FIGURE 31.3
Lactic acid production from whey by *Lactobacillus bulgaricus*.

Starter culture (in milk)

Culture in whey

PREPARATION OF INOCULUM

5,000 gallon tank containing whey

FERMENTATION OF LACTOSE

Filtration
Evaporation
Purification

RECOVERY OF LACTIC ACID

ASK YOURSELF

1 Write the general equations which identify the substrates and end products of microbial dissimilation.

2 Name several microorganisms that produce industrial products by dissimilation of the substrate. Identify the product in each instance.

3 Sketch a general scheme illustrating the sequence of events in the production of microbiological dissimilation products.

PRODUCTS OF MICROBIAL SYNTHESIS

Many industrial products are made through the biosynthetic activities of microorganisms. Examples of such products include antibiotics, enzymes, peptides, and amino acids.

T A B L E 31.2
Some Industrial Products Made by Microbial Dissimilation

Product	Microorganism	Uses
	BACTERIA	
Acetone and butanol	*Clostridium acetobutylicum* and other clostridia	Solvents; chemical manufacturing
2,3-Butanediol	*Bacillus polymyxa; Enterobacter aerogenes*	Solvent; moisturizer; chemical intermediate
2-Ketogluconic acid	*Pseudomonas* spp.	Intermediate for manufacture of isoascorbic acid (isovitamin C)
Sorbose	*Gluconobacter oxydans*	Manufacture of ascorbic acid (vitamin C)
	MOLDS	
Citric acid	*Aspergillus niger*	Foods and beverages; cosmetics; leather manufacture
Gluconic acid	*Aspergillus niger*	Foods; cleaning compounds
Itaconic acid	*Aspergillus terreus*	Manufacture of acrylic resins
Fumaric acid	*Rhizopus nigricans*	Manufacture of alkyd resins and wetting agents

Penicillin

In 1941 there was no antibiotic industry, but 10 years later the net worldwide sales of antibiotics were $344 million per year, and antibiotics had revolutionized the practice of medicine. The United States International Trade Commission recently reported that antibiotic production in the United States for 1990 was valued at approximately one-half billion dollars. How did this industry develop so dramatically in such a brief period? The answer begins with the history of penicillin [see DISCOVER 21.1].

Although discovered by the Englishman Alexander Fleming in 1927, penicillin was not widely recognized as useful at the time. However, when World War II created an urgent need for large amounts of a drug that could be used to treat and/or prevent infections in wounded soldiers, researchers worked to develop penicillin into an economically feasible drug. The transformation of Fleming's laboratory observations into a large-scale production process occurred when researchers discovered how to increase the yield of penicillin per milliliter of culture liquid by approximately 1000 times. Factors responsible for this achievement, which paved the way for successful manufacture of many other antibiotics, were the following:

1 Improvements in the composition of the culture medium.

2 Isolation of a better penicillin-producing species, *Penicillium chrysogenum.*
3 Development of the *submerged culture technique.* Initially, penicillin was produced by growing the mold on a shallow layer of medium, in small containers. This was necessary to provide an abundance of oxygen, required for growth of the mold [FIGURE 31.4A]. In the submerged culture technique, sterile air was forced through the medium, and this allowed the mold to grow abundantly through large volumes (thousands of gallons) of the medium [FIGURE 31.4B].
4 Selection of mutant strains of *P. chrysogenum.* The normal mutation rate of the mold was increased by the use of x-rays and ultraviolet light. Among the various mutants were some that had a greatly enhanced ability to synthesize penicillin.
5 Addition to the medium of chemical building blocks for penicillin. These precursors could be used directly by the mold for the synthesis of penicillin, resulting in higher yields.
6 Refinements in the methods used to recover the penicillin from the fermentation mixture.

FIGURE 31.5 shows the biochemical changes that occur during the fermentation process. Note the changes in pH, mold growth, and amount of penicillin produced as the time of incubation increases. The major steps in modern commercial production of penicillin are shown in FIGURE 31.6.

FIGURE 31.4

Penicillin production. In the early years of penicillin production, the fungus was grown in small, flat containers that contained a small volume of medium. This allowed for maximum surface area exposure, which provided maximum aeration for fungus growth.

[A] At the Sir William Dunn School of Pathology, Oxford, England, the penicillin for the first small clinical trial was produced in rectangular ceramic vessels with a sidearm for inoculation. **[B]** Tops of large fermentation tanks used today for antibiotic production.

[A]

[B]

FIGURE 31.5

Biochemical changes that occur in the fermenter during production of penicillin by *Penicillium chryso-genum*. (*Courtesy of R. Donovick, Appl. Microbiol. 8:117, 1960.*)

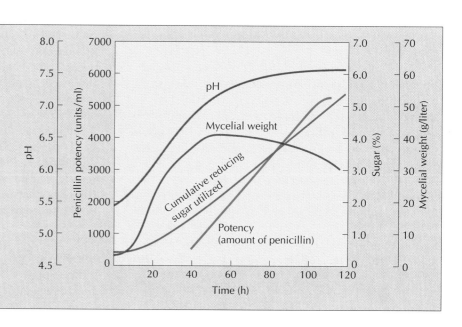

FIGURE 31.6

Manufacture of penicillin shown schematically. **[A]** A medium of corn-steep liquor, lactose, salts, and other ingredients is mixed, sterilized, cooled, and pumped into the fermenter. **[B]** The mold *Penicillium chrysogenum* is transferred from slant cultures to bran, and spore suspensions from bran are transferred to a sterile vessel with medium, which in turn is used to inoculate the seed tank. **[C]** The fermenter is inoculated from the seed tank; sterile air is forced through the fermenter during incubation. **[D]** After the maximum yield of penicillin is produced, the mold mycelia is removed by filtration and the penicillin is recovered in pure form by a series of manipulations which include precipitation, redissolving, and filtration.

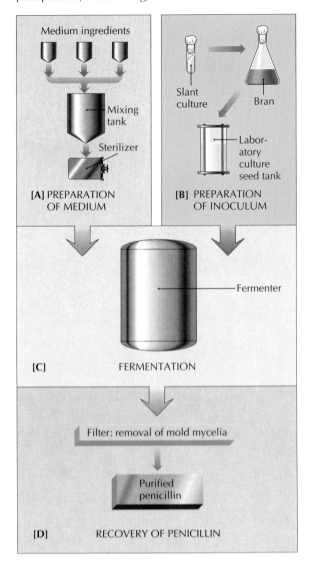

The production of most other antibiotics follows a similar plan. The major differences relate to the organism used, the composition of the medium, and the method of extracting the antibiotic from the fermentation mixture. Some manufacturers employ the same fermentation equipment for the production of more than one antibiotic. Some antibiotics are produced industrially by chemical synthesis when and if the chemical approach becomes more economical and more efficient than the biological process.

Enzymes

Many fungi and bacteria synthesize and secrete industrially useful enzymes into the surrounding medium. For instance, molds such as *Aspergillus, Penicillium, Mucor,* and *Rhizopus* secrete enzymes that are useful in the processing of a variety of materials. These enzymes include *amylase, invertase, protease,* and *pectinase.*

Amylase catalyzes the hydrolysis of starch to dextrin and sugars. It is used in preparing adhesives and sizings (substances that impart characteristics such as weight or luster to textiles and paper), clarifying fruit juices, manufacturing pharmaceutical products, and for other purposes. Invertase catalyzes the hydrolysis of the disaccharide sucrose to the monosaccharides glucose and fructose. It is used widely in making cream-filled candy and producing syrups that do not crystallize.

The term *protease* refers to a mixture of enzymes that break down proteins. One use of protease is the bating of leather, a treatment that imparts a finer texture and grain. For centuries—long before the role of enzymes was understood—hides were soaked in suspensions of dog or chicken manure. The manure contained the bacteria which produced the proteolytic enzymes. Today, standardized protease solutions have replaced the dung concoctions. Protease is also used in manufacturing liquid glue, degumming silks, and clarifying beer protein haze, and as a component of laundry detergent.

Pectinase catalyzes the hydrolysis of pectins, which are complex plant polysaccharides. Pectinase is used in the clarification of fruit juices and in the retting of flax for the manufacture of linen. (*Retting* refers to the process of loosening the cloth fibers from the woody stems of flax.) TABLE 31.3 contains examples and uses of enzymes produced commercially by microorganisms.

Immobilized Enzyme Technology. The commercial uses of microbial enzymes expanded greatly following the development of **immobilized enzyme technology,** in which an enzyme is bound (immobilized) on a solid material such as paper, wood chips, ceramic and glass beads, or ion-exchange resins. When a solution of the

TABLE 31.3

Examples of Microbial Enzymes Produced Industrially and Their Applications

Enzyme	Microbial source	Applications	Reactions
	BACTERIA		
Streptokinase	*Streptococcus* spp.	Treatment of patients following heart attacks	Activates blood plasminogen to plasmin, an enzyme that dissolves the fibrin of blood clots
Glucose isomerase	*Streptomyces* spp.; *Bacillus* spp.	Production of high-fructose syrups	Converts glucose to fructose
DNA polymerase	*Thermus aquaticus*	Polymerase chain reaction (PCR)	Mediates the formation of base pairs between free nucleotides and the linked DNA nucleotides
	MOLDS		
Lipase	*Rhizopus* spp.	Flavor improvement used in food processing; improvement of the cleaning action of detergents	Hydrolyzes lipids to glycerol and fatty acids
Cellulase	*Trichoderma reesii*	Digestive aid	Hydrolyzes cellulose to cellobiose
Glucose oxidase	*Aspergillus* spp.; *Penicillium* spp.	Removes glucose from eggs prior to drying; removes oxygen from canned foods, soft drinks, and beer; also used for manufacture of test papers for diabetes control	Oxidizes glucose to gluconic acid

substrate for the enzyme is passed through the material, the immobilized enzyme catalyzes the conversion of the substrate to a commercially desirable product. The advantages of this technology are: (1) the enzyme can be continually reused, since it remains on the solid material; and (2) the end product of the chemical reaction can be more conveniently recovered and purified because it does not contain the enzyme [FIGURE 31.7].

The technique can be adapted so that whole bacterial cells are immobilized in a matrix. Microbiologists have modified this procedure to degrade toxic compounds in soil and water.

Amino Acids

Many microorganisms can synthesize amino acids from inorganic nitrogen compounds such as ammonium sulfate. In some instances the amount of an amino acid synthesized can exceed the cell's need for that amino acid. The excess amino acid may be excreted into the culture medium. For example, glutamic acid, lysine, and tryptophan are produced industrially by microorganisms that produce an excess of these amino acids. One advantage of this process over chemical synthesis is that the microorganisms produce only the biologically active forms of the amino acids (the L isomers; see Chapter 1).

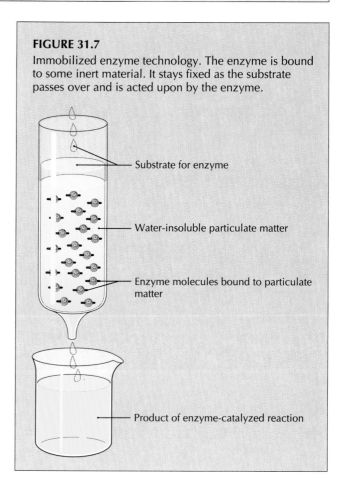

FIGURE 31.7

Immobilized enzyme technology. The enzyme is bound to some inert material. It stays fixed as the substrate passes over and is acted upon by the enzyme.

Substrate for enzyme

Water-insoluble particulate matter

Enzyme molecules bound to particulate matter

Product of enzyme-catalyzed reaction

L-Glutamic Acid Production. Glutamic acid is used as a condiment and flavor-enhancing agent, in the form of monosodium glutamate (MSG). About 300,000 tons of MSG is produced annually. *Corynebacterium glutamicum* is used for the industrial production of glutamic acid. The culture medium usually consists of a carbohydrate, peptone, inorganic salts, and the vitamin biotin. If the biotin is supplied at lower than optimal levels for growth, the synthesis of the cell-membrane structure is impaired, causing the cells to become "leaky" and enhancing the excretion of glutamic acid. The bacteria first make α-ketoglutaric acid, an intermediate in the citric acid cycle (Chapter 11), and then convert this compound to L-glutamic acid by the enzyme glutamic acid dehydrogenase:

$$
\begin{array}{l}
\text{COOH} \\
|\\
\text{C}=\text{O} \\
|\\
\text{CH}_2 \qquad + \text{NH}_3 + \text{NADH}_2 \xrightarrow{\text{glutamic acid dehydrogenase}} \\
|\\
\text{CH}_2 \\
|\\
\text{COOH}
\end{array}
$$

α-Ketoglutaric acid

$$
\begin{array}{l}
\text{COOH} \\
|\\
\text{HCNH}_2 \\
|\\
\text{CH}_2 \qquad + \text{NAD}^+ + \text{H}_2\text{O} \\
|\\
\text{CH}_2 \\
|\\
\text{COOH}
\end{array}
$$

L-Glutamic acid

The procedure normally uses a mutant strain of *C. glutamicum* that contains a high level of the enzyme glutamic acid dehydrogenase. This ensures a large yield of glutamic acid.

L-Lysine Production. L-Lysine is valuable as a supplement to plant proteins used as foods, because plant proteins are deficient in this amino acid. A mutant strain of *C. glutamicum* is also used in the commercial production of this amino acid. The biosynthetic pathway of the mutant is altered, favoring the production of large amounts of lysine. The final reaction in the sequence is the decarboxylation of diaminopimelic acid:

$$
\begin{array}{l}
\text{COOH} \\
|\\
\text{HCNH}_2 \\
|\\
\text{CH}_2 \\
|\\
\text{CH}_2 \xrightarrow{\text{DAP decarboxylase}} \\
|\\
\text{CH}_2 \\
|\\
\text{HCNH}_2 \\
|\\
\text{COOH}
\end{array}
\qquad
\begin{array}{l}
\text{H} \\
|\\
\text{HCNH}_2 \\
|\\
\text{CH}_2 \\
|\\
\text{CH}_2 \qquad + \quad \text{CO}_2 \\
|\\
\text{CH}_2 \\
|\\
\text{HCNH}_2 \\
|\\
\text{COOH}
\end{array}
$$

Diaminopimelic acid (DAP)   L-Lysine   Carbon dioxide

Other Products of Microbial Synthesis

Another product of microbial synthesis is bacterial cellulose. A technique has recently been developed whereby bacteria of the genus *Acetobacter* have been adapted for commercial production of a new type of cellulose [DISCOVER 31.1].

TABLE 31.4 lists examples of other compounds, such as vitamins and food stabilizers, that are produced industrially by microbial biosynthesis.

ASK YOURSELF

1 Penicillin, when originally discovered, was produced in extremely small quantities in a culture medium. Later the production of penicillin by *Penicillium* sp. was greatly increased. Explain how this came about.

2 Describe the process of immobilized enzyme technology. What advantages does this technique provide?

3 Describe the essential features of monosodium glutamate production: the substrate, the microorganisms, and the general chemical reaction.

PHARMACEUTICALS FROM GENETICALLY ENGINEERED CELLS

One of the fastest-growing applications of industrial biotechnology is in pharmaceuticals—the production of therapeutic drugs to treat diseases. In Chapter 14 you learned how the genetic material of a microorganism can be changed to give the organism new biochemical capabilities, including the production of new substances. For instance, it is now possible to produce human insulin by using a genetically engineered strain of *Escherichia coli*. Human insulin was the first therapeutic product to be made commercially by a genetically engineered bacterium (Chapter 14); it was approved for treatment of diabetes in 1982.

Human growth hormone is another pharmaceutical product made more efficiently by a genetically engineered bacterium. Previously, the hormone could be obtained only in extremely small quantities by extracting it from the pituitary glands of animals. The genetically engineered product became available in 1985 and is being used to treat children with pituitary dwarfism and other conditions related to growth hormone deficiency.

TABLE 31.4
Some Industrial Products of Microbial Synthesis Other Than Antibiotics and Enzymes

Product	Microorganism	Uses
	BACTERIA	
Dextran	*Leuconostoc mesenteroides*	Stabilizer in food products; blood plasma substitute.
Xanthan gum	*Xanthomonas campestris*	Stabilizer and emulsifying agent in foods.
β-Carotene	*Blakeslea trispora*	Yellow coloring for foods.
Vitamin B_{12}	*Streptomyces olivaceus; Propionibacterium freudenreichii*	Treatment of pernicious anemia; food and animal feed supplementation.
5'-Inosinic acid and 5'-guanylic acid	*Corynebacterium glutamicum*	The salts of these compounds are used as flavor intensifiers in foods.
	MOLDS	
Riboflavin	*Eremothecium ashbyi*	Vitamin supplement.
Gibberellic acid	*Fusarium moniliforme*	Promotes growth of plants, especially seedlings.

The production of *interferons* has also been greatly enhanced through biotechnology. The interferons are a class of proteins produced by animal cells infected with a virus (Chapter 18). Their activities include the protection of other cells against the same virus or other viruses, inhibition of cell division, modulation of the immune system, and activation of macrophages. Until the era of genetic engineering, human interferons could not even be tested for potential clinical value, because they were available only in extremely minute quantities extracted from cultured human cells. However, most of the genes for human interferons have now been cloned in bacteria, yeasts, or mammalian cells. Tests with α-interferon indicate that this substance reduces the duration of viral infections, decreases the incidence of attacks of multiple sclerosis, and may possibly have antitumor activity.

Tissue plasminogen activator (TPA) is the product of genetically engineered mammalian cells and has recently been approved for treatment of heart attacks. This enzyme can dissolve blood clots at the site of their formation. An enzyme produced by streptococci called *streptokinase* is also used to dissolve blood clots.

Other pharmaceutical products from genetically engineered cells are now being evaluated for therapeutic effectiveness. One of these is *interleukin-2*, which promotes activation and multiplication of leucocytes and enhances the host's ability to resist infection (Chapter 18). Another product is human renin, an enzyme pro-

duced in the kidney that facilitates production of angiotensin II. Angiotensin II has a marked ability to elevate blood pressure and heart rate. Now that adequate amounts of pure renin are available, it is possible to conduct more definitive research on the mechanism of renin action for a more effective treatment of hypertension.

Advances in our understanding of disease processes at the molecular level have resulted in the development of more precise therapeutic agents through new biotechnology—and there is good reason to believe this is only the beginning. During the 1980s several new biopharmaceutical products became available to the public. In addition to those already mentioned, biotechnology produced such products as a monoclonal antibody that prevents kidney transplant rejection, and erythropoietin, a hormone that stimulates the production of red blood cells and hemoglobin.

Although only a limited number of these biopharmaceuticals have been approved by the U.S. Food and Drug Administration (FDA) for human therapy, those that have been approved have caused dramatic results in patients [TABLE 31.5]. Many more are "waiting in the wings," ready to be approved. Approximately 15,000 biotechnology patent applications were pending in 1989 alone. The process from discovery of a new therapeutic agent to final FDA approval for human use is long and costly. Moving a single drug through this procedure may take several years and cost millions of dollars.

TABLE 31.5
Approved Biotechnology Drugs/Vaccines

Product name	Indication (applications)	U.S. approval
Epogen (tm)–Epoetin Alfa	Dialysis anemia	June 1989
Neupogen: granulocyte colony stimulating factor	Chemotherapy effects	February 1991
Humatrope (R)–Somatotropin	Human growth hormone deficiency in children	March 1987
Humulin (R): human insulin	Diabetes	October 1982
Actimmune: interferon gamma 1-b	Infection/chronic granulomatous disease	December 1990
Activase (R)–Alteplase	Acute myocardial infarction	November 1987
Protropin (R)–Somatrem for injection	Human growth hormone deficiency in children	October 1985
Roferon (R)-A: interferon alfa-2a	Hairy cell leukemia	June 1986
	AIDS-related Kaposi's sarcoma	November 1988
Leukine: granulocyte macrophage colony stimulating factor	Infection related to bone marrow transplant	March 1991
Recombivax HB (R): hepatitis B vaccine	Hepatitis B prevention	July 1986
Orthoclone OKT(R)3–Muromonab CD3	Kidney transplant rejection	June 1986
Procrit–Erythropoietin	AIDS-related anemia	December 1990
HlbTiter (tm): haemophilus B conjugate vaccine	Haemophilus influenza type B	December 1988
Intron (R) A: Interferon-alpha2b	Hairy cell leukemia	June 1986
	Genital warts	June 1988
	AIDS-related Kaposi's sarcoma	November 1988
	Hepatitis C	February 1991
Energix-B: hepatitis B vaccine	Hepatitis B	September 1989

SOURCE: Office of Technology Assessment, 1991; adapted from Pharmaceutical Manufacturers Association—Biotechnology Medicines in Development, 1990 Annual Survey.

ASK YOURSELF

1 Describe the general procedure for genetically engineering a bacterium to produce a new product. (Consult Chapter 14.)

2 The ability to genetically engineer microorganisms has great potential in terms of producing new and novel therapeutic substances. Why is this so?

MICROBIAL CELLS AND PRODUCTS FOR IMMUNIZATION

Control of infectious diseases through active immunization requires the production, on a commercial scale, of a variety of microbial antigens for use as vaccines. TABLE 31.6 gives examples of several kinds of immunizing antigens used as vaccines. New vaccines are emerging from genetic engineering techniques; two examples are the recently developed vaccines against type B hepatitis in humans and foot-and-mouth disease in cattle (Chapter 14). Development of effective immunizing antigens, together with the stringent test requirements to ensure their safe use, constitutes major programs in many large pharmaceutical companies.

Various antibody preparations used for passive immunization are also produced commercially, such as antitoxins against tetanus and botulism toxins and immune globulin against rabies. Most antibodies are produced by immunizing animals with appropriate antigens; however, monoclonal antibodies are produced by hybridoma cells propagated in tissue cultures or in animals (Chapter 20).

The total doses of several widely used immunizing agents distributed in the United States during January through December 1989 are listed in TABLE 31.7.

TABLE 31.7

Biologics Products Surveillance Summary for January–December 1989

Product description	Net number of doses sold or distributed this period
Influenza vaccine, trivalent	23,589,391
Diphtheria toxoid and tetanus toxoid (pediatric)	1,261,385
Diphtheria and tetanus toxoids with pertussis vaccine	21,944,643
Tetanus and diphtheria toxoid (adult)	10,024,973
Diphtheria toxoid	190
Tetanus toxoid	4,946,154
Pertussis vaccine	6,690
Poliomyelitis vaccine, inactivated	292,410
Poliomyelitis vaccine, live, oral, trivalent	18,795,970
Measles virus vaccine, live, attenuated	347,175
Rubella virus vaccine, live	168,327
Mumps virus vaccine, live	17,070
Mumps/rubella virus vaccine, live	16,488
Measles/mumps/rubella virus vaccine, live	6,594,516
Measles/rubella virus vaccine, live	955,759
Haemophilus B	3,168,261
Pneumococcal vaccine	1,105,285
Immune serum globulin, human	67,700
Tetanus immune globulin, human	360,220
Hepatitis B	1,729,804

SOURCE: Centers for Disease Control, U.S. Department of Health and Human Services, Public Health Services.

TABLE 31.6

Some Examples of Commercially Produced Microbial Products Used in Vaccines for Active Immunization

Disease	Nature of immunizing agent
Tuberculosis	Live attenuated cells of *Mycobacterium bovis*
Measles (rubeola)	Live attenuated virus of rubeola virus
Poliomyelitis	Live attenuated strains of poliovirus
Rabies	Killed rabies virus
Whooping cough (pertussis)	Killed cells of *Bordetella pertussis*
Typhoid fever	Killed cells of *Salmonella typhi*
Diphtheria	Toxoid prepared from the exotoxin of *Corynebacterium diphtheriae*
Tetanus	Toxoid prepared from the exotoxin of *Clostridium tetani*
Meningococcal meningitis	Capsular polysaccharides from *Neisseria meningitidis*
Pneumococcal pneumonia	Capsular polysaccharides from *Streptococcus pneumoniae*

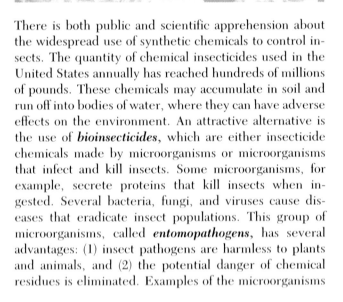

31.1 BACTERIAL PRODUCTION OF CELLULOSE

Collaborative research by scientists from a major timber company and a leading biotechnology company has resulted in the commercial production of cellulose by bacteria. This bacterial cellulose is made by selected strains of the genus *Acetobacter*. New strains are capable of growing in large fermenters (50,000-gallon tanks) with aeration and agitation. This was a major achievement, since the growth of *Acetobacter* and its cellulose production are normally suppressed by agitation during incubation.

The bacterial cellulose has several physical characteristics that differ from those of plant cellulose. For example, the bacterial cellulose (called *Cellulon*) has narrower fibers (0.1 μm wide) than those of softwood pulp, which are about 30 μm wide. The bacteria-produced fibers form an intricate meshwork. These characteristics make the bacterial cellulose particularly attractive for the binding, thickening, and coating processes that are used in the manufacture of a wide variety of products, including paper, foods, and cosmetics. This source of cellulose is very attractive when compared with the usual sources, plants and trees.

ASK YOURSELF

1 Describe the characteristics of the antigen for different types of vaccine preparations.

2 What is the nature of the material used for passive immunization?

3 How has genetic engineering changed the process of developing antigens—for example, the antigen for immunization against foot-and-mouth disease? (Consult Chapter 14.)

MICROORGANISMS FOR INSECT CONTROL

There is both public and scientific apprehension about the widespread use of synthetic chemicals to control insects. The quantity of chemical insecticides used in the United States annually has reached hundreds of millions of pounds. These chemicals may accumulate in soil and run off into bodies of water, where they can have adverse effects on the environment. An attractive alternative is the use of **bioinsecticides,** which are either insecticide chemicals made by microorganisms or microorganisms that infect and kill insects. Some microorganisms, for example, secrete proteins that kill insects when ingested. Several bacteria, fungi, and viruses cause diseases that eradicate insect populations. This group of microorganisms, called **entomopathogens,** has several advantages: (1) insect pathogens are harmless to plants and animals, and (2) the potential danger of chemical residues is eliminated. Examples of the microorganisms now being used to destroy insects are *Bacillus thuringiensis*, *B. popilliae*, and *B. lentimorbus*.

Bacillus thuringiensis is an endospore-forming bacillus that is pathogenic for many insect larvae, such as the gypsy moth, cabbage worm, and tent caterpillar. The bacillus produces a protein crystal called a *parasporal body* within the cell. This protein is toxic to insect larvae, and when it is ingested it dissolves and causes destruction of the surface tissue of the larval gut, causing death of the insect. The toxin is harmless to higher animals and humans. The commercial product made from *B. thuringiensis* consists of a mixture of the protein toxin and the bacterial endospores. It is applied as a dust or spray to field crops, trees, ornamental plants, and home vegetable gardens [see DISCOVER 9.2].

Bacillus popilliae and *B. lentimorbus* are used widely to kill larvae of the Japanese beetle. The bacteria cause an infection called *milky disease*, so named because the blood of the infected larvae becomes filled with bacteria and endospores and has a milky appearance. The commercial product is a mixture of the endospores and larval material and is applied into shallow trenches in the soil. As infected larvae die they liberate more spores into the soil; the spores can survive for years to perpetuate the infection. The use of *B. popilliae* and *B. lentimorbus* has resulted in the virtual elimination of Japanese beetles from previously infected areas.

Microbial insecticides continue to be improved through genetic engineering. For instance, researchers have been successful in transferring the gene for the protein toxin of *B. thuringiensis* to other species of bacteria that inhabit soil. This may lead to an insect-control procedure in which seeds are dusted with genetically engineered bacteria before planting. The gene for synthesis of the *B. thuringiensis* toxin has been transferred to some plants.

ASK YOURSELF

1 How are entomopathogens used in practical situations for the control of insects?

2 In terms of the environment, what advantages does the use of entomopathogens offer over that of synthetic chemical insecticides?

MICROORGANISMS AND THE RECOVERY OF RAW MATERIALS

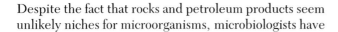

Despite the fact that rocks and petroleum products seem unlikely niches for microorganisms, microbiologists have learned that microorganisms can be invaluable in both the mining industry and the petroleum industry. The research in these areas is on the rise, prompted by the increasingly difficult task of extracting minerals from the earth and discovering new reservoirs of oil.

Microbiology and Mining

The extraction of various metals from ores has become a problem for the mining industry because the richer mineral deposits are becoming depleted. This has made it necessary to process lower-quality ores and to find techniques for more efficient extraction of metal in the ores. Another problem is the environmental issue. Smelting, the traditional method of processing ores, is a major source of air pollution and is under attack by the U.S. Environmental Protection Agency and the general public.

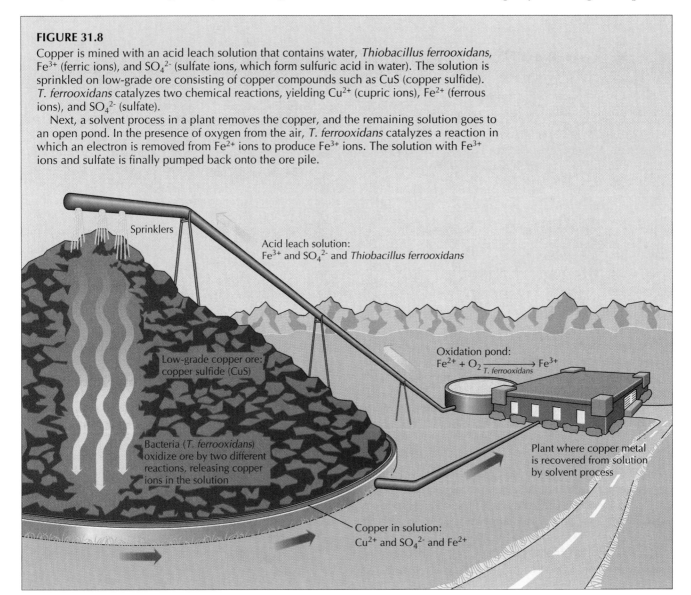

FIGURE 31.8

Copper is mined with an acid leach solution that contains water, *Thiobacillus ferrooxidans*, Fe^{3+} (ferric ions), and SO_4^{2-} (sulfate ions, which form sulfuric acid in water). The solution is sprinkled on low-grade ore consisting of copper compounds such as CuS (copper sulfide). *T. ferrooxidans* catalyzes two chemical reactions, yielding Cu^{2+} (cupric ions), Fe^{2+} (ferrous ions), and SO_4^{2-} (sulfate).

Next, a solvent process in a plant removes the copper, and the remaining solution goes to an open pond. In the presence of oxygen from the air, *T. ferrooxidans* catalyzes a reaction in which an electron is removed from Fe^{2+} ions to produce Fe^{3+} ions. The solution with Fe^{3+} ions and sulfate is finally pumped back onto the ore pile.

Sprinklers

Acid leach solution:
Fe^{3+} and SO_4^{2-} and *Thiobacillus ferrooxidans*

Low-grade copper ore: copper sulfide (CuS)

Bacteria (*T. ferrooxidans*) oxidize ore by two different reactions, releasing copper ions in the solution

Oxidation pond:
$Fe^{2+} + O_2 \xrightarrow{T.\ ferrooxidans} Fe^{3+}$

Plant where copper metal is recovered from solution by solvent process

Copper in solution:
Cu^{2+} and SO_4^{2-} and Fe^{2+}

31.2 A MICROBIAL SOLUTION TO THE ACID RAIN DILEMMA

Acid rain is one of the major environmental problems of the industrialized regions of the world. Oxides of sulfur and nitrogen are the principal sources of acid in the atmosphere; coal-burning power plants and factories emit sulfur dioxide, while trucks, automobiles, and fossil-fuel power plants are the main sources of nitrogen oxides. The amounts released are staggering—millions of tons per year! These oxides are widely distributed by air movements, and so the harmful effects can be found at great distances from the source of pollution.

In Canada, the United States, and northern Europe, vast areas of forest lands have been damaged by acid rain. The aquatic life in thousands of lakes and miles of streams has also suffered. Many lakes are already "dead," with their plants and animals wiped out by the pollution.

The removal of sulfur from coal prior to its combustion would help solve the problem of sulfur dioxide in the atmosphere. Engineering technology has not been able to provide an economically feasible way to do this. However, microorganisms may be used to produce sulfur-free coal. Sulfur in coal occurs in both inorganic and organic forms. Bacteria such as *Thiobacillus ferrooxidans*, *T. thiooxidans*, and *Sulfolobus acidocaldarius* can oxidize sulfides (inorganic sulfur) to sulfates, which can be drained from the coal. Recently, scientists at the Institute of Gas Technology have isolated and developed strains of bacteria that can remove sulfur from organic compounds. This research may lead to a cost-efficient method to desulfurize coal. If accomplished, this may help solve the acid rain dilemma, as well as make coal a more attractive source of energy.

Microorganisms are capable of improving both these situations. For example, the autotrophic bacteria *Thiobacillus thiooxidans* and *T. ferrooxidans*, when grown in the presence of metal ores such as iron, copper, and zinc, produce acids and cause oxidation of the ore with subsequent precipitation of the metal. This process, called **leaching**, improves the recovery of metal from an ore and does not cause pollution of the atmosphere.

Examples of bacterial leaching processes applied to low-grade ore are shown in FIGURES 31.8, 31.9, and 31.10.

Sulfurous emissions from the burning of coal is both a major problem and a major constraint on the increased use of coal. These emissions come from the sulfur found in coal and are linked with the acid rain phenomenon. Unfortunately, there is an insufficient quantity of low- or nonsulfur-containing coal to meet the energy needs of large industrial operations, such as coal-burning steam generation plants used to produce electricity. How can sulfur-containing coal be desulfurized in an economical manner? Microorganisms offer a possible solution. There are species of bacteria that can degrade the sulfur compounds in coal to water-extractable compounds [DISCOVER 31.2].

Petroleum Microbiology

Microorganisms are associated with petroleum in its formation, its recovery by drilling, its decomposition, and its utilization. It is only in the last few decades that significant attention has been directed to research in this field. Petroleum microbiology requires interdisciplinary cooperation; the microbiologist needs to work closely with chemists, engineers, physicists, and representatives from other fields of study. The relation of microorganisms to petroleum can be summarized as follows.

Petroleum Formation. Much of the sedimentary material in marine environments consists of dead microbial cells. Biochemical changes in this sedimentary deposit are made by a variety of microorganisms, and these changes are associated with the formation of petroleum.

Petroleum Exploration. Soil in the region of a petroleum reservoir may contain vapors of hydrocarbon compounds such as methane and ethane. These compounds can be detected by using microorganisms that use hydrocarbons as their source of carbon for growth. The cultures are incorporated in a test system that contains all nutrients for growth, with the exception of a carbon source. Growth of the microbes indicates that hydrocarbon vapors are probably present in the soil. Alternatively, if a large number of hydrocarbon-oxidizing microorganisms are isolated from soil, this suggests that their presence is due to continued release of hydrocarbon vapors from a petroleum deposit.

Petroleum Recovery. When an oil well is drilled, the initial recovery of the oil is made possible by the pressure within the rock formation. Later, as the pressure decreases and the oil flow lessens, additional wells are drilled and water or steam is injected to force the oil to the surface. Microbial activity has been suggested as a potential means of enhancing the recovery of oil trapped in the rock. For example, bacteria injected into the oil deposit can produce acids that dissolve the rock formation; this would release the oil and increase the pressure. Microorganisms can also decrease the viscosity of the oil, which would improve the rate of flow to the surface.

FIGURE 31.9

Thiobacillus ferrooxidans growing on iron pyrite (FeS$_2$) as seen through epifluorescence/phase-contrast microscopy. *T. ferrooxidans* is used for the leaching of metals from low-grade ores and the leaching of iron pyrite from coal. Shown here is the increased attachment during leaching in a shake flask culture. **[A]** Iron pyrite particles after inoculation. **[B]** Cell attachment at an intermediate point of incubation. **[C]** Cell attachment after further incubation and increased leaching.

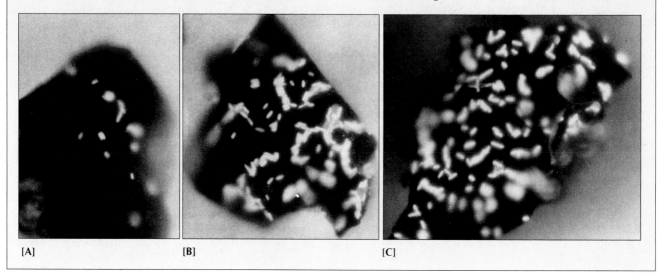

[A] [B] [C]

FIGURE 31.10

An aerial view of the leach dump used for recovery of copper from low-grade ore and mine waste. Ponds are visible on the surface of the dump in which oxidation of ferrous iron is occurring. The green coloration is the most recently applied leach solution, and the red coloration is either solution with oxidized iron or the surface of the dump after the solution has percolated into the dump. The surface of the dump contains (and maintains) a large population of *Thiobacillus ferrooxidans*. *Leptospirillum*-like bacteria and moderately thermophilic iron-oxidizing bacteria also occur in the copper leaching dumps.

FIGURE 31.11

[A] Corroded cast iron pipes from a tidal marsh. Corrosion is due primarily to activities of sulfate-reducing bacteria. [B] *Desulfovibrio* sp. growing on an iron salts–agar medium. The colonies appear black because of iron sulfide formation. *Desulfovibrio* spp. occur widely in fresh, polluted, marine, and brackish waters.

[A]

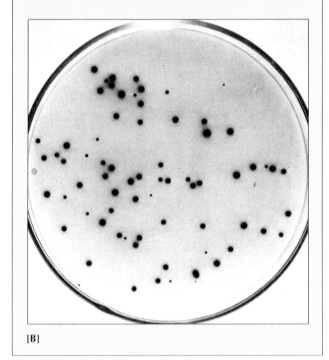

[B]

On the other hand, bacteria can cause serious setbacks in the recovery of oil. Corrosion of iron pipes by *Desulfovibrio* bacteria is a major problem in the oil industry [FIGURE 31.11]. Also, contamination of drilling fluids by various bacterial species can have costly results, because they change the physical characteristics of the fluids.

Oil Spills. The international transportation of oil in supertankers occasionally results in accidents that create huge oil spills. These oil spills are a major threat to the environment. One approach to cleaning up the oil from a spill is to inoculate the spill area with a microorganism that can degrade the oil. For example, a genetically engineered strain of *Pseudomonas putida* has been developed that has the ability to metabolize the four hydrocarbons in crude petroleum: camphor, octane, xylene, and naphthalene. This bacterial strain made legal history in microbiology by being the first genetically engineered microorganism ever patented [see DISCOVER 13.2].

ASK YOURSELF

1 Describe the role of microorganisms in the leaching of an ore.

2 Describe several processes relating to the petroleum industry where microorganisms perform a significant function.

MICROBIAL DETERIORATION OF MATERIALS

Paper, textiles, wood, rubber, and metals all deteriorate over time. Deterioration of such materials from all causes represents a loss to industry of several billion dollars annually. Microorganisms are responsible for a significant amount of this destruction, and virtually no material is totally resistant to microbial deterioration. For instance, metal equipment used in marine environments and the metal walls of fuel storage tanks on dry land are susceptible to microbial corrosion. Even the glass lenses of optical equipment can be etched by products of microbial growth on their surfaces. The deterioration of paper products, textiles and cordage, and painted surfaces is of importance, especially in tropical environments favorable to growth of microorganisms, particularly fungi.

Paper Products

The manufacture of paper involves two major operations: (1) the physical or chemical treatment of cellulose-containing material such as wood, cotton, or linen rags in order to separate and purify the cellulose fibers; and (2) after further refinement, processing of the fibrous pulp to redeposit the fibers in the form of a sheet. Microorganisms can cause problems by forming slime in the paper pulp, which leads to objectionable spots on the finished paper sheets. Bacteria, yeasts, molds, algae, and protozoa have all been isolated from pulp slimes, but bacteria are the most important.

Finished paper is also subject to microbial attack, because cellulose, the major constituent of paper, is susceptible to degradation by many species of fungi and bacteria. These organisms can weaken fibers, causing holes and even complete destruction of the paper. Other components of paper, such as glue or casein, may also serve as substrates for microbes, and the paper may be stained or discolored by the products of microbial metabolism.

Textiles and Cordage

Many textiles are made from natural fibers such as cotton, wool, linen, and silk, all of which can be attacked by microorganisms. The same is true of cordage. The annual losses due to microbial attack on fabric and rope in the United States run into millions of dollars. Microbial degradation of fabric causes enormous problems for troops serving in tropical climates.

Molds are the principal organisms responsible for this damage. Many cellulose-degrading fungi inhabit the soil and can readily contaminate textiles. The fungus *Myrothecium verrucaria* is especially notorious for its ability to degrade cellulose, and researchers often make use of this organism in studying cellulose decomposition. Mold growth is favored by high humidity, moderate temperatures, and diminished light, and when this combination of conditions prevails deterioration is greatly enhanced. For example, a lightweight canvas, when exposed to fungi under ideal conditions for mold growth, can lose significant strength after a few weeks. FIGURE 31.12 illustrates microbial deterioration of fabric by microorganisms.

Painted Surfaces

Unless paint contains an effective fungicidal ingredient, mold spotting or mildew may appear on painted surfaces. These discolorations are caused by metabolic products of molds growing on the organic constituents of the paint. Many species of molds have been isolated from mildewed or "moldy" painted surfaces, including species of *Aspergillus*, *Penicillium*, *Cladosporium*, *Pullularia*, and *Alternaria*. *Pullularia* species appear to be the most common cause of mildewed paint. The effectiveness of incorporating an antifungal agent in paint is shown in FIGURE 31.13.

FIGURE 31.12
Deterioration of fabric by fungi. Fabric treated with fungicide—no deterioration (left). Untreated fabric (right). Note discoloration due to growth of fungus. The fibers become weakened and break.

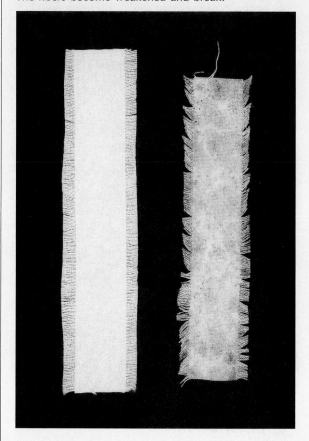

More efficient methods of preservation are continually being developed to minimize the microbial deterioration of materials. Some control measures include the incorporation of microbicidal agents into the material, use of packaging that protects material from contamination, and storage under conditions that inhibit microbial growth.

ASK YOURSELF

Describe a type of microbial deterioration of materials such as paper, textiles, fuel, and metals. Characterize the microorganisms responsible in each example.

FIGURE 31.13

Agar-plate test demonstrates the effectiveness of an antifungal agent incorporated into paint. In the plate on the left is paint containing an antifungal agent. The plate on the right contains untreated paint overgrown with test fungus.

BIOREMEDIATION

Bioremediation is the technology of using biological agents, particularly microorganisms, to remove toxic pollutants from the environment, particularly from soil and water. The pollutants are decomposed to nontoxic substances through microbial metabolism.

Either microorganisms indigenous to the environment or custom-made cultures (some with genetically engineered species) are used for bioremediation. For example, in the cleanup of crude oil following the Valdez oil spill in Alaska, microbe-enhancing fertilizers were applied to 79 miles of shoreline to promote the growth and metabolic activity of hydrocarbon-degrading bacte-

ria already present. In other instances microbes are being genetically engineered to decompose specific toxic pollutants. A specific example of bioremediation is discussed in DISCOVER 31.3.

ASK YOURSELF

1 Define *bioremediation*. What are the attractive features of this process from an environmental point of view?

2 Describe a specific bioremediation process.

31.3 BIOREMEDIATION: THE BIODEGRADATION OF POLLUTANTS

Researchers are vigorously pursuing the isolation and the identification of bacteria that have the ability to degrade toxic chemicals, in order to "harness" these organisms in a manner that they will "clean-up" the pollutants that find their way into soil and streams.

Investigators at the Monsanto Company have targeted Roundup™ (glyphosate, or N-phosphonomethyl-glycine)—the world's most widely used herbicide. Although the biodegradation of glyphosate in nature was already known to occur, it was only recently that Monsanto researchers isolated and characterized bacteria that degrade the chemical, namely, *Agrobacterium*

radiobacter, *Achromobacter* sp., and *Flavobacterium* sp.

With this knowledge the researchers utilized these organisms to remove glyphosate from industrial waste streams by using immobilized bacteria technology. In this technique large numbers of the bacteria are mixed with diatomaceous earth; the bacterial cells are distributed throughout the particles of diatomaceous earth, which serve as an inert support system to form a fixed-bed reactor system, as shown below. The reactors are aerated, maintained at pH 7.0–8.0 and 25°C, and supplemented with a nitrogen source (NH_4NO_3). Then liquid waste containing glyphosate is passed

through the reactor as shown schematically. Degradation of glyphosate to non-toxic intermediates was greater than 96 percent after 21 days of operation.

Pilot field tests have produced results that demonstrate immobilized bacteria technology as a cost-effective alternative for the removal of low levels of glyphosate from high-volume industrial waste streams.

Monsanto is investigating the use of fluidized bed reactors (the bacteria are immobilized on beads to prevent "clogging") to process raw industrial waste water for removal of pollutants.

Courtesy of L. E. Hallas, Monsanto Agricultural Co.

Bioremediation. Special strains of bacteria, selected from natural sources or genetically engineered, have the capacity to metabolize specific chemical pollutants. The bacterial cells can be packed into beds or columns containing an inorganic matrix which holds them in position. The fluid containing the chemical pollutant is passed through this immobilized column of cells and the chemical is degraded by the microbial population.

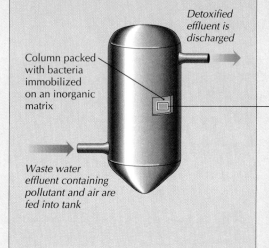

Detoxified effluent is discharged

Column packed with bacteria immobilized on an inorganic matrix

Waste water effluent containing pollutant and air are fed into tank

Electron micrograph of immobilized bacteria.

SUMMARY

1 Microorganisms are capable of producing a great variety of substances that have commercial value. Many industrial processes are based on microorganisms as the source of some desirable substance or biochemical change. All major groups of microorganisms—bacteria, fungi, viruses, algae, and protozoa—have industrial applications.

2 Biotechnology is the application of technology to living systems. Modern biotechnology includes manipulations of microorganisms and other cells at the genetic level to convert them to agents that are useful for industrial applications.

3 Products from the microbial dissimilation of a substrate include alcohol from the fermentation of glucose by yeasts, vinegar from the oxidation of alcohol by acetobacters, and lactic acid from the fermentation of milk sugar by lactobacilli.

4 Products resulting from the synthetic ability of microorganisms include penicillin and other antibiotics, amino acids, proteins, and cellulose.

5 Genetically engineered microorganisms or genetically engineered plant and animal cells hold great promise for producing therapeutic drugs. Current biotechnology places emphasis on transferring a gene into a microorganism, or some other organism, so that the recipient organism acquires the ability to synthesize an important new product, such as insulin, interferon, or tissue plasminogen activator.

6 Large quantities of microbial cells, or the parts or products of microbial cells, are produced commercially for preparation of vaccines.

7 Entomopathogens, microorganisms that are pathogenic for insects, have been used as microbial insecticides. They have advantages over chemical insecticides because they are usually harmless to plants, animals, and humans and do not leave toxic chemical residues. *Bacillus thuringiensis, B. popilliae,* and *B. lentimorbus* are examples of entomopathogens used in commercial insecticides.

8 Some microorganisms are useful for the recovery of natural resources. In the recovery of iron and copper from low-grade ores, the ore is exposed to certain species of bacteria which produce acids; the acids solubilize the metal and enable it to be concentrated more conveniently. Microorganisms also are used for exploration of petroleum reserves and to enhance the recovery of oil from wells.

9 Microorganisms cause deterioration of material such as wood, textiles, leather, paints, and metal pipes. Industries are continually engaged in developing new treatment processes and antimicrobial agents to minimize such deterioration.

KEY TERMS

bioinsecticides
bioremediation
biotechnology
entomopathogens
immobilized enzyme technology
leaching
submerged culture technique

1 A general equation which illustrates the components of an industrial microbiological process may be written as:

Microorganism + _____ →

product + residue or waste material

2 Secondary metabolic products are defined as: **(a)** compounds such as vitamins that are essential for cell growth; **(b)** microbial cells that are used for vaccines; **(c)** compounds such as antibiotics that are not required for cell growth; **(d)** products having only minor industrial importance; **(e)** food supplements consisting of yeasts, bacteria, or algae.

3 The term *biotechnology* as now used in industrial microbiology usually refers to the

_____ engineering of microorganisms or other cells.

4 In practical industrial microbiological processes, the microorganism must be stable, grow rapidly and vigorously, be nonpathogenic, and: **(a)** grow aerobically; **(b)** produce a high yield of the product; **(c)** mutate rapidly; **(d)** be biodegradable; **(e)** self-destruct.

5 In practical industrial microbiological processes, the medium must be readily available in large quantities and must also be _____.

6 In practical industrial microbiological processes, there must be an efficient and economical mass-scale method available for _____ and

_____ of the end product.

7 The yeasts that are used for production of ethyl alcohol belong to the genus

_____.

8 If the starting material for alcohol production is starch, the starch must first be hydrolyzed to _____.

9 The yeast strain used for alcohol production must not only produce a high yield of alcohol but must also have: **(a)** the ability to oxidize the alcohol; **(b)** the ability to convert the alcohol to starch; **(c)** the ability to kill contaminating microorganisms; **(d)** a high tolerance to alcohol; **(e)** the ability to hydrolyze starch.

10 Vinegar production involves which two of the following general biochemical changes? **(a)** fermentation of glucose to ethanol by yeasts; **(b)** oxidation of ethanol to acetic acid by acetobacters; **(c)** fermentation of a carbohydrate to ethanol by acetobacters; **(d)** breakdown of proteins to amino acids by yeasts; **(e)** oxidation of acetic acid to ethanol by acetobacters.

11 The method for vinegar production in which alcohol solution percolates through wood shavings that are covered with acetic acid bacteria is called the

_____ method.

12 Which *two* of the following conditions are satisfactory for optimum production of vinegar; **(a)** aerobic conditions; **(b)** restricted air supply; **(c)** high temperature, above 35°C; **(d)** anaerobic conditions; **(e)** an alcohol concentration between 10 and 13%.

13 Whey is a waste product in the manufacture of certain dairy products such as

_____.

14 In the commercial production of lactic acid, bacteria belonging to the genus

_____ ferment the sugar lactose, which is present in whey.

15 The first step in the fermentation of lactose is the cleavage of the disaccharide to two monosaccharides called: **(a)** glucose and galactose; **(b)** fructose and sucrose; **(c)** maltose and glucose; **(d)** galactose and maltose; **(e)** glucose and starch.

16 In the production of lactic acid, lime is added periodically to the fermentation tank to: **(a)** kill the lactobacilli; **(b)** convert calcium lactate to lactic acid; **(c)** increase the pH; **(d)** absorb the whey; **(e)** coagulate the protein.

17 In the production of lactic acid, the final tank material is boiled to

_____ , and the latter is used as an animal feed supplement.

18 Iron lactate is used: **(a)** as a plasticizer and moisturizer; **(b)** as a solvent in lacquers; **(c)** as an antibiotic; **(d)** to treat anemia; **(e)** to prevent iron pipes from rusting.

PRODUCTS OF
MICROBIAL
SYNTHESIS

19 The first antibiotic to be produced industrially was

_____ .

20 Although Fleming found that _Penicillium notatum_ produced penicillin, the species subsequently used for manufacture of the antibiotic was _Penicillium_

_____ , because it gave a much higher yield.

21 One factor leading to increased yields of penicillin was the use of

_____ strains of the mold; these strains produced higher yields of penicillin than the wild-type strain.

22 In the submerged culture technique for penicillin production: **(a)** the mold is grown in shallow pans; **(b)** the mold is grown at the bottom of the tank; **(c)** the mold is immobilized on a solid material such as ceramic beads, which sink to the bottom of the tank; **(d)** sterile air is forced through the culture; **(e)** anaerobic organisms predominate.

23 In leather processing, hides are treated with enzymes called

_____ to provide a finer texture and grain.

24 Amylase hydrolyzes _____ to dextrins and sugars,

whereas invertase hydrolyzes _____ to glucose and fructose.

25 An enzyme called _____ is used to hydrolyze pectins in the retting of flax for the manufacture of linen.

26 The conversion of a substrate to a product by continuously passing a solution of the substrate through particulate matter to which an enzyme has been bound is called

_____ enzyme technology.

27 In the microbial production of an amino acid, which form of the amino acid is synthesized? **(a)** the M stereoisomer; **(b)** the D stereoisomer; **(c)** the L stereoisomer; **(d)** a mixture of the L and D forms; **(e)** a mixture of the M and T forms.

28 Lysine is made by removing CO_2 from a seven-carbon amino acid produced by _E. coli_. This amino acid is called: **(a)** guanine; **(b)** proline; **(c)** diaminopimelic acid; **(d)** glutamic acid; **(e)** α-ketoglutaric acid.

29 Glutamic acid is made by a reaction in which the substrates are NH_3, $NADH_2$, and _____.

30 Industrial production of glutamic acid uses species of which genus? **(a)** *Corynebacterium*; **(b)** *Pseudomonas*; **(c)** *Escherichia*; **(d)** *Acetobacter*; **(e)** *Clostridium*.

31 The enzyme DAP decarboxylase converts diaminopimelic acid to: **(a)** ethanol; **(b)** acetic acid; **(c)** glutamic acid; **(d)** lactic acid; **(e)** lysine.

32 Glutamic acid is in demand as a(n): **(a)** vitamin supplement; **(b)** supplement to products made with cereal grains; **(c)** flavor-enhancing agent; **(d)** intermediate for manufacture of tartaric acid; **(e)** stabilizer in food products.

PHARMACEUTICALS FROM GENETICALLY ENGINEERED CELLS

33 Human insulin can be produced commercially by a genetically engineered form of the bacterium (genus, species) _____.

34 The proteins which protect host cells from some virus infections, and which are now produced by genetically engineered bacteria, are called

_____.

35 _____ activator is an enzyme which can dissolve blood clots at the site of their formation.

36 Many of the new pharmaceutical products now available through biotechnology were formerly available only from mammalian cells in

_____ quantities.

MICROBIAL CELLS AND PRODUCTS FOR IMMUNIZATION

37 Which *two* of the following vaccines are products of genetic engineering? **(a)** diphtheria vaccine; **(b)** hepatitis B vaccine; **(c)** foot-and-mouth disease vaccine; **(d)** influenza vaccine; **(e)** tetanus vaccine.

38 Monoclonal antibodies are not produced by immunizing animals; instead they are produced by _____ that are propagated in tissue cultures or in animals.

MICROORGANISMS FOR INSECT CONTROL

39 Which *two* of the following are used as bioinsecticides? **(a)** *Bacillus thuringiensis*; **(b)** *Myrothecium verrucaria*; **(c)** *Saccharomyces cerevisiae*; **(d)** *Penicillium chrysogenum*; **(e)** *Bacillus popilliae*

40 The parasporal crystalline protein produced by (genus, species)

_____ is toxic to larvae.

41 *Bacillus popilliae* and *Bacillus lentimorbus* cause _____

disease in the larvae of _____ beetles.

42 Which of the following pertain to bioinsecticides? **(a)** They produce less damage to the environment; **(b)** they are harmless for plants, animals, and humans; **(c)** they do not leave long-lasting chemical residues toxic to plants, animals, and humans; **(d)** once applied, bacterial spores such as those causing milky disease can persist in the soil for a long time; **(e)** all of the above.

MICROORGANISMS AND THE RECOVERY OF RAW MATERIALS

43 The soil above petroleum deposits may contain vapors of hydrocarbon compounds that can be used as carbon sources by certain microorganisms. These hydrocarbon compounds are: **(a)** ammonia and nitrogen; **(b)** acetic acid and lactic acid; **(c)** methane and ethane; **(d)** glucose and fructose; **(e)** ethanol and butanol.

44 The occurrence of petroleum deposits in a particular area would be suggested by the finding of large numbers of _____-oxidizing bacteria in the soil.

45 Bacteria injected into an oil deposit may produce _____ that dissolve rock formation, thereby releasing the oil.

46 A strain of bacteria has been genetically engineered to be capable of using the four hydrocarbons present in crude petroleum. This strain is the first genetically engineered strain to receive a patent. The strain belongs to the species: **(a)** *Escherichia coli;* **(b)** *Pseudomonas putida;* **(c)** *Bacillus subtilis;* **(d)** *Nitrosomonas europaea;* **(e)** *Agrobacterium tumefaciens.*

47 The process which uses *Thiobacillus* spp. to produce acid that solubilizes the metal content of low-grade copper ores is called: **(a)** acidification; **(b)** thiol production; **(c)** calcification; **(d)** immobilized bacteria technology; **(e)** leaching.

MICROBIAL DETERIORATION OF MATERIALS

48 In paper manufacturing, _____-producing bacteria are the most important single group of bacteria to cause undesirable effects in the paper pulp.

49 The growth of _____-decomposing bacteria can cause weakening of fibers, holes, and even complete destruction of a paper product.

50 Deterioration of cellulose-containing textiles such as canvas can be caused by various microorganisms, but one mold is especially notorious for its ability to degrade cellulose. This mold is: **(a)** *Penicillium notatum;* **(b)** *Thiobacillus thiooxidans;* **(c)** *Myrothecium verrucaria;* **(d)** *Saprolegnia parasitica;* **(e)** *Alternaria tenuis.*

51 In deterioration of cellulosic textiles and cordage, mold growth is favored by which *two* of the following conditions? **(a)** High humidity; **(b)** strong illumination; **(c)** low temperatures; **(d)** moderate temperatures; **(e)** high temperatures.

52 Paint films should contain an effective _____ to prevent deterioration by growth of molds.

BIOREMEDIATION

53 Enter **T** if true and **F** if false: Bioremediation is accomplished only with genetically engineered bacteria. ____ Explain your answer:

_____

_____

54 One of the procedures used to clean up the contaminated shoreline following the Valdez oil spill in Alaska was the application of _____ along the shoreline.

REVIEW QUESTIONS

1 What are the major categories of products manufactured by industrial microbiological processes, i.e., biotechnology?

2 What are some of the prerequisites which must be met before it is feasible to develop a commercial microbiological process?

3 Describe the basic principles involved in (1) the Frings method of producing vinegar; (2) immobilized enzyme technology; (3) the submerged culture technique; (4) production of human insulin by *Escherichia coli*.

4 How might immobilized enzyme technology be applied to the production of L-lysine? What advantage does this technique have over merely mixing the substrate with the enzyme to produce the end product?

5 Is the Frings method for vinegar production an example of the use of immobilized bacterial cell technique? Explain.

6 What developments contributed to the increase in yield of penicillin over that originally obtainable?

7 What are bioinsecticides? Give examples.

8 Describe the various ways in which microorganisms are involved in the petroleum industry.

9 In paper manufacturing, how might microorganisms cause defects in the quality of the paper product?

10 Why is the deterioration of textiles and fabrics of particular concern in tropical climates?

11 What is the role of microorganisms in bioremediation?

DISCUSSION QUESTIONS

1 A microorganism is discovered which produces a valuable chemical substance but in extremely small amounts. Describe some experimental procedures that might be used to increase the yield of this chemical.

2 How have modern knowledge and techniques in bacterial genetics changed biotechnology?

3 In the submerged culture technique, the desired product of microbial metabolism, e.g., a vitamin, must be recovered (extracted) from the medium. Assuming that one could develop an immobilized cell system to produce the same vitamin, what advantages would this have in terms of recovering the vitamin?

4 Describe several situations wherein deterioration of materials by microorganisms is of industrial significance. How can this kind of deterioration be controlled?

5 Compare advantages and disadvantages of insect control by chemicals and by microorganisms.

6 Describe the role of microorganisms in the recycling process which occurs in landfills.

7 Outline an experimental procedure (including the use of the enrichment culture technique) designed to isolate a microorganism that can decompose a chemical herbicide, which we will call compound X.

Appendixes

Further Reading

Credits

Glossary

Indexes

Answers to the Review Guides

CHAPTER 1
1 b; **2** a; **3** number; **4** c; **5** ion; **6** compounds; **7** a; **8** a, e, c, b, d; **9** d; **10** water molecules; **11** sodium; acetate; **12** c and d; **13** hydrophobic; **14** d, c, a, b, e; **15** 5; w/w; **16** 5; w/v; **17** b; **18** e, a, c, b, d; **19** d and e; **20** 100; **21** acid; **22** b; **23** d, b, e, c, a, f; **24** a; **25** c; **26** optical isomers, or D and L isomers; **27** asymmetric; **28** monosaccharides; **29** c; **30** glycerol; fatty acid; **31** b; **32** e, g, a, f, c, d, b; **33** adenine; guanine; **34** d; **35** uracil; ribose; **36** backward reaction, or reverse reaction **37** e, d, f, b, a, c; **38** substrate; **39** b

CHAPTER 2
1 Robert Hooke; **2** structural; **3** protoplasm; **4** proteins; nucleic; **5** nucleus; nucleoid; **6** living organisms; **7** c; **8** species; **9** kingdom; **10** species; **11** binomial **12** c, d, a, b, e; **13** plant; animal; **14** Protista; **15** photosynthesis; absorption; ingestion; **16** Monera; Protista; **17** procaryotes; **18** nucleotide; *r*RNA, or ribosomal RNA; **19** (a) Monera; (b) Protista; (c) Fungi; (d) Fungi; (e) Protista; **20** d; **21** mitochondria; chloroplasts; **22** animal; **23** cilia; flagella; **24** chlorophyll; cell wall; **25** molds; hyphae; **26** yeast; **27** eubacteria; archaeobacteria; **28** spheres; rods; spirals; **29** archaeobacteria; **30** living or host cell; **31** d, b, e, c, a; **32** (a) T; (b) T; (c) T; (d) F; (e) T; **33** 50; **34** It contains billions of different species. **35** ubiquitous; **36** F; **37** recycling; **38** basic; applied; **39** c, d, e; **40** T; Many biological reactions carried out by higher forms of life, including humans, are identical to those performed by microorganisms and microorganisms are very convenient for carrying out laboratory experiments at the molecular level.

CHAPTER 3
1 mixed; **2** pure culture; **3** pure; **4** inoculum; **5** colony; **6** streak-plate; spread-plate; **7** stock culture; **8** lyophilization; **9** e; **10** F; **11** resolving; **12** (a) low-power; (b) high-power; (c) oil-immersion; **13** 10; **14** wavelength of light (or electron beam); numerical aperture of objective lens; **15** 2000; **16** oil-immersion; **17** b; **18** c; **19** b; **20** e; **21** living; **22** transmission (TEM); scanning (SEM); **23** T **24** T **25** F **26** viable or living; **27** smear; **28** simple; **29** differential; **30** violet; red; **31** red; **32** differential; **33** alcohol; **34** bright-field; **35** d; **36** c, a, d, e, b; **37** F; **38** metabolism; **39** pathogenic; nonpathogenic; **40** antigenic; **41** genetic; **42** (c); **43** substrates or biochemicals; **44** optical scanning

CHAPTER 4
1 disintegrate; **2** pathogenic; **3** 0.5; 1.0; **4** spirilla; **5** spherical; **6** pear-shaped; disk-shaped; **7** a; **8** streptococci; **9** rosette; **10** c; **11** two; **12** flagellin;

13 lophotrichous; **14** periplasmic; **15** three-dimensional random walk; **16** tumble; **17** adhere; **18** sex; **19** capsule; **20** protoplasts; **21** thinner; **22** murein; **23** *N*-acetylglucosamine; *N*-acetylmuramic acid; **24** peptidoglycan; **25** teichoic; **26** Gram-negative; **27** lipopolysaccharide; **28** periplasmic; **29** endotoxin; **30** lipid A; core polysaccharide; **31** porins; **32** mesosomes; **33** poly-β-hydroxybutyrate; **34** nucleoid; **35** c, b, a; **36** survival; **37** refractile; **38** one; **39** heat; **40** *Azotobacter*; **41** b, c, a; **42** seaweeds; mushrooms; **43** filamentous; **44** dimorphism; **45** cell walls; particulate food; **46** photosynthetic; **47** d, a, c, b, e; **48** c, a, d, e, g, f, b; **49** protozoa; **50** blue-green; black; **51** sexual; **52** protective; reproductive

CHAPTER 5
1 inorganic; organic; **2** dissolved; **3** media; **4** a; **5** synthesis; **6** carbon; nitrogen; **7** b; **8** autotrophs; **9** d; **10** T; **11** amino acids; **12** cystine; cysteine; **13** nucleic acids; **14** activate; **15** chemotrophs; radiant or light; **16** chemoautotrophs; **17** photoautotrophs; **18** F; Under anaerobic conditions, *Rhodospirillum rubrum* depends on light as its energy source and lives as a photoheterotroph. **19** d; **20** peptone; **21** vitamins; **22** 40; **23** sugar; pH; **24** Sabouraud's; **25** c; **26** anaerobic; **27** autoclaving; **28** selective; **29** differential; **30** enrichment; **31** tissue cultures; animal cells; **32** selective; **33** explants; **34** primary; **35** transformed; **36** insects; vectors; **37** callus; **38** growth regulators

CHAPTER 6
1 media; **2** growth; **3** chromosomes; **4** b; **5** growth rate; **6** a; **7** cardinal; **8** psychrophiles; mesophiles; thermophiles; **9** 15; 20; **10** c; **11** 37; **12** carbon dioxide; **13** oxygen; **14** superoxide; **15** superoxide dismutase; **16** a; **17** 7.5; **18** lower; **19** buffer; **20** solutes; **21** isotonic; **22** loss; **23** asexual; **24** mitosis; **25** prophase; metaphase; anaphase; telophase; **26** mitotic spindle; **27** chromosomes; **28** fertilization; **29** meiosis; **30** alternation of generations; **31** d; **32** e; **33** T; **34** T; **35** F; In sexual reproduction, a new individual is formed by the fusion of two different sex cells called gametes. **36** T; **37** interphase; mitosis; **38** growth$_1$ (G$_1$); DNA synthesis (S); growth$_2$ (G$_2$); **39** karyokinesis; **40** binary fission; **41** b, c, d, a; **42** generation time; **43** growth rate; generations; **44** balanced growth; **45** death or decline; **46** a; **47** chemostat; **48** synchrony; **49** closed; **50** logarithmic

CHAPTER 7
1 antimicrobial; **2** -cidal; -static; **3** reproduce; **4** instantly; **5** 10; **6** proportional; **7** straight; **8** death; **9** more; **10** increase; **11** cytoplasmic membrane; **12** coagulating or

denaturing; oxidation; **13** spores; **14** shortest; **15** decimal reduction; **16** autoclave; **17** endospore; **18** *Pseudomonas* sp.; **19** disinfection; **20** 121; 15; **21** 160; 120; **22** sterilization; **23** b; **24** 0°C; **25** −196°C; **26** not kill; **27** 0.001; **28** ionizing; **29** gamma; x-; **30** UV radiation; **31** 265; **32** penetrating; **33** DNA; **34** dimers; **35** e, b, a, c, d; **36** (a) uniformity of pore size; (b) known pore size; (c) rapidity of filtration; (d) smaller amount of material retained on filter; **37** high-efficiency particulate air; **38** lyophilization; **39** a; **40** desiccation (dehydration)

CHAPTER 8

1 sterilization; **2** antiseptic; **3** disinfectant; **4** c; **5** d; **6** a; The microbial population is reduced to safe limits. Cleansing occurs during the process. **7** a,b,c; **8** U.S. Food and Drug Administration (FDA); Environmental Protection Agency (EPA); **9** any of the following: antimicrobial activity; solubility; stability; lack of toxicity; homogeneity; minimum inactivation by extraneous material; activity at ordinary temperatures; ability to penetrate; noncorrosiveness and removability; deodorizing ability; detergent ability; availability and low cost; **10** broad; **11** phenol; **12** phenol; **13** greater; **14** cell membrane; **15** 70, 90; **16** toxic; **17** halogens; **18** HClO; HCl; **19** carriers and solubilizing agents; **20** 0.5 to 1; **21** sulfhydryl; **22** algicide; **23** silver nitrate; **24** cationic; anionic; **25** cationic; anionic; **26** greater or higher; **27** a, b, d, c, e; **28** a clear zone (no growth) around the disk; **29** bacteriostatic; bactericidal; **30** 2; **31** antimicrobial activity; penetrating power; **32** carbon dioxide; Freon; **33** alkylation; **34** penetrating; **35** formalin (formaldehyde); glutaraldehyde

CHAPTER 9

1 b; **2** eubacteria; archaeobacteria; **3** c; **4** Gram-negative; Gram-positive; cell wall; **5** membrane; peptidoglycan; **6** a, d, e; **7** d; **8** a; **9** dark-field microscopy; **10** rigid; periplasmic; **11** h, c, e, g, b, d, a, f; **12** c, e, h, a, d, b, f, g; **13** anoxygenic; **14** bacteriochlorophyll; **15** carotenoids; **16** c; **17** oxygen; **18** chlorophyll a; phycobilins; **19** heterocysts; **20** c, b, a, d; **21** nitrite; nitrate; **22** d; **23** thicker; membrane; **24** d; **25** e; **26** *lactis*; **27** *Sporosarcina*; **28** *Bacillus popilliae*; **29** *Clostridium*; *Desulfotomaculum*; **30** c, g, b, i, d, e, h, a, f, j; **31** c; **32** penicillin; **33** blood serum; **34** d; **35** b and c; **36** b and c; **37** NaCl; **38** bacteriorhodopsin; **39** c; **40** aerobic; anaerobic

CHAPTER 10

1 perfect; **2** fruiting bodies; **3** cellular **4** flagellated; **5** fish; **6** Plasmodiophoromycetes; **7** ascospores; basidiospores; **8** d; **9** b; **10** e; **11** a; **12** T; **13** T; **14** F; *Chlamydomonas* is a unicellular motile green alga while *Chlorella* is a unicellular nonmotile green alga. **15** nonmotile; **16** silica; **17** phagotrophically; **18** valves; **19** bioluminescence; **20** d; **21** e; **22** b, a, d, c, f, e; **23** *Entamoeba histolytica*; **24** radiolarians; foraminiferans; **25** toxoplasmosis; **26** definitive; **27** *Balantidium coli*

CHAPTER 11

1 breakdown; energy; **2** b; **3** c; **4** chemical; **5** b; **6** d, b, c, a; **7** adenine; ribose; phosphate; **8** phosphorylation; **9** f, a, c, d, b, e; **10** a; **11** ferrous; hydrogen atom; **12** electron donor; terminal electron acceptor; **13** hydrogen; protonmotive; ATP; **14** c; **15** e; **16** photosystem I, or PS I; photosystem II, or PS II; PS II;

17 II; I; protonmotive; ATP; **18** amino; monosaccharides; glycerol; fatty; **19** pyruvic acid; **20** b; **21** c; **22** NADH; NAD; **23** a; **24** d; **25** c, b, a; **26** respiration; **27** an unlimited supply of nutrients

CHAPTER 12

1 greater; **2** energization; **3** hydrogen; ammonia; **4** reductive amination; **5** d; **6** first; **7** c; **8** DNA; **9** deoxyribose; **10** c; **11** AMP; GMP; dAMP; dGMP; **12** CMP; UMP; dCMP; dTMP; **13** d; **14** DNA; **15** ATP; electron; **16** e; **17** c; **18** d; **19** b; **20** c; **21** a; **22** c; **23** b; **24** e; **25** simple; facilitated; **26** c; **27** the protonmotive force; **28** ATP

CHAPTER 13

1 e; **2** b; **3** linear; 10; **4** c; **5** d; **6** d; **7** b; **8** e, b, h, i, d, c, f, g, a; **9** d; **10** e; **11** d; **12** environment; **13** mutant; wild type; **14** c, a, b, d; **15** mutagen; **16** c; **17** protooncogenes; **18** a, b, c, e, d; **19** d; **20** crossing-over; **21** b; **22** a; **23** incompatibility; **24** "cured"; **25** d; **26** inducible; constitutive; **27** cannot; operator; cannot; **28** b; **29** can; operator; can

CHAPTER 14

1 gene; **2** e; **3** pilot; industrial or commercial; **4** donor organism; **5** c; **6** e; **7** c; **8** d; **9** c; **10** e; **11** c, b, a, e, d; **12** buoyant density; **13** methyl groups; **14** ribosomal RNA (*r*RNA); **15** recipient bacterial cell; **16** c, a, d, b; **17** start; stop; **18** c; **19** warmed, or heat-shocked; **20** b; **21** a; **22** independently; **23** the product of a cloned gene; **24** d, e, b, a, c; **25** the gene to be cloned; **26** e; **27** degraded or destroyed; aggregates; **28** b; **29** secreted; positive; negative; **30** d; **31** d; **32** c; **33** any progress in research and industrial development of the beneficial aspects of genetic engineering

CHAPTER 15

1 protein; energy; **2** bacteriophages; phages; **3** receptors; **4** 20; 300; **5** nucleic acid; capsid; **6** icosahedral; helical; **7** protomers; capsomeres; **8** RNA; DNA; **9** b; c; **10** *m*RNA; **11** reverse transcriptase; **12** Twort-d'Hérelle; **13** "bacteria eater"; **14** nucleic acid; protein; **15** RNA; **16** filamentous; **17** b, a, d, e, c; **18** F; The common names of bacteriophages do not follow any rules of nomenclature and are simply code symbols. **19** F; More than 95 percent of the known viruses infecting eubacteria belong to one of the three families of long-tailed phages. **20** T; **21** d; **22** David Baltimore; **23** d; **24** d; **25** d; **26** dsDNA; **27** receptor sites; **28** core; **29** contracts; **30** replicate; transcribe; **31** b, d, a, e, c; **32** T; **33** F; In the usual type of lysogeny, the prophage is the phage genome integrated into the bacterial chromosomes. **34** F; Phage Mu has no site specificity for insertion and is able to insert multiple copies of its DNA into a single host chromosome. **35** tadpole; **36** nucleic acid; capsid.; **37** envelope; spikes; **38** naked; **39** symmetrical; **40** c; **41** b, a, d, c; **42** b, f, a, d, c, e; **43** receptor; **44** spikes; **45** fusion; **46** insect feeding; **47** nucleic acid replication; **48** F; The process of viral assembly does not appear to involve special biosynthetic enzymes but rather occurs spontaneously. **49** F; The average yield of plant and animal virions ranges from several thousand to about 1 million per cell, compared with the yield of several hundred phages from a bacterial cell.

CHAPTER 16
1 b; **2** habitat; **3** bacteria; **4** c; **5** c; **6** embryonated chicken eggs; **7** chorioallantoic membrane; amniotic; **8** cytopathic effect; **9** c; **10** 10; **11** protoplasts; **12** tobacco mosaic; **13** b; d; **14** untranslated; **15** protein coat; **16** d; **17** protein; **18** neurological; **19** b, c, d, a; **20** b; **21** c; **22** a; **23** T; **24** T; **25** F; **26** F; **27** T; **28** T

CHAPTER 17
1 c; **2** c; **3** opportunistic pathogen; **4** resident; transient; **5** b and c; **6** c, d, b, e, a, f; **7** receptor; **8** K; **9** positive; negative; **10** cause disease; **11** echoviruses; disease; **12** a, c, d; **13** moist; **14** d; **15** c, d, b, e, a; **16** mucus; **17** flushing action of the saliva; **18** teeth; sucrose; **19** b; **20** 10; **21** ileum; **22** b; **23** c; **24** *Entamoeba histolytica*; **25** d; **26** *Candida albicans*

CHAPTER 18
1 c, d, a, b; **2** endotoxin; **3** exotoxin; **4** antitoxins; **5** heatstable; toxoids; less; **6** amebocytes; **7** β; **8** a, b; **9** body temperature; **10** e; **11** d, c, a, b; **12** follicles; sweat; sebaceous; **13** destroy; remove; limit; **14** a, d; **15** granulocytes; agranulocytes; **16** neutrophils; macrophages; **17** d, e; **18** (a) T; (b) F; (c) T; **19** less; **20** b; c; d; **21** (a) T; (b) F; The early steps of the complement cascade stimulate the inflammatory response. **22** C3a; C3b; **23** classical; **24** c; **25** All are true.; **26** c, d, and e

CHAPTER 19
1 antibodies; **2** cellular immunity; **3** discrimination, specificity; **4** lymphocytes; **5** F; T and B lymphocytes can be distinguished on the basis of distinct membrane glycoproteins. **6** organs; tissues; **7** thymus; **8** humoral antibodies; **9** d, b, a, c; **10** active; active; passive; passive; **11** artificial; natural; artificial; natural; **12** four; **13** bivalent; **14** Fc; **15** IgM; **16** IgG; **17** IgA; **18** IgE; **19** immunogenicity; **20** epitope; **21** immunogenicity; **22** toxoid; **23** no; **24** T; **25** a, c, d; **26** cytolytic; **27** III; **28** T; **29** cytolytic; **30** histocompatibility; **31** c, d; **32** ABO; Rh; **33** viral antigens; **34** fetal; neonatal; **35** immunotherapy; **36** monoclonal; **37** T cells; cell-mediated; **38** B-cell; **39** NK; **40** T cell

CHAPTER 20
1 serology; **2** serum; **3** equivalence; **4** lattices; **5** fluid; **6** c; **7** electrophoresis; **8** immunoelectrophoresis; **9** soluble; particulate; **10** *Proteus*; **11** neutralizing; **12** hemolysis; **13** competitive; **14** enzyme-linked immunosorbent assay; **15** c; **16** b; d; **17** hybridomas; **18** myeloma; **19** c; d; **20** T; **21** e; b; f; a; d; c; **22** cell-mediated; **23** macrophages; **24** lymphoblasts; DNA; **25** thymidine; **26** lyse (destroy); **27** chromium

CHAPTER 21
1 e; **2** b; **3** penicillin; **4** mold; **5** microorganisms; **6** broad-spectrum; **7** e; **8** b and e; **9** e; **10** antimicrobial; **11** toxic; **12** *Streptomyces*; **13** a, b, and e; **14** c; **15** b; **16** 6-aminopenicillanic; **17** semisynthetic; **18** β-lactamases; methicillin; **19** d; **20** aminoglycosides; **21** c, d, a, b, b, d; nystatin and amphotericin B; **22** b; **23** cell-wall; **24** d; **25** b; **26** e, a, b, d, c, f; **27** b; **28** c; **29** *Escherichia coli*; **30** e; **31** tetrahydrofolic; **32** *para*-aminobenzoic acid, or PABA; **33** folic; **34** nitro, or —NO₂; **35** pyridoxine (vitamin B₆); nicotinamide; **36** tuberculosis; **37** DNA

gyrase; **38** DNA; RNA; **39** thymidine; AIDS; **40** influenza type A; genital herpes; **41** a and b; **42** less; active; inactive; **43** standard; **44** minimum inhibitory concentration, or MIC; **45** A; **46** MIC; **47** d; **48** to stimulate or enhance growth; **49** resistant; **50** streptomycin, erythromycin, and nystatin

CHAPTER 22
1 d; **2** d; **3** b, d, e; **4** c; **5** b; **6** occurrence; distribution; **7** a source of pathogenic microorganisms; a route of transmission; a susceptible host; **8** c; **9** c; **10** e; **11** e; **12** c; **13** hands; patient; **14** c; **15** d; **16** e; **17** surveillance; **18** infection-control officer; **19** d; **20** infection-control; **21** microbiology; **22** d; **23** ICO, or infection-control officer; **24** e

CHAPTER 23
1 venereal; **2** b, c, e; **3** e; **4** d; **5** c; **6** conjunctivitis; **7** c; **8** urethra; cervix; **9** b; **10** ectopic pregnancy; **11** antibiotics; **12** penicillin **13** less; **14** c; **15** c, d, a, b; **16** dark-field; **17** b; **18** a and c; **19** million; **20** a and d; **21** conjunctivitis; pneumonia; **22** b; **23** b, c, a; **24** a; **25** human immunodeficiency virus; **26** c and g; **27** T4; **28** RNA; **29** host-cell DNA; **30** c and d; **31** d, e, a, g, c, f, b; **32** c; **33** c; **34** e; **35** DNA; reverse transcriptase; **36** HSV-2; HSV-1; **37** c, d; **38** nerves; recurrent; **39** c and e; **40** b; **41** surface antigen; **42** b; **43** b; **44** c; **45** out of; **46** public education; **47** a

CHAPTER 24
1 d; **2** a and d; **3** infectious dust; **4** g, b, f, c, h, d, a, e, i; **5** positive; β; A; **6** d and e; **7** b; **8** b and c; **9** infection; are not; **10** b and e; **11** c; **12** antibodies; **13** d; **14** drinking contaminated raw milk; **15** *Mycobacterium leprae*; **16** c, b, d, e, a, f; **17** cell-mediated; **18** reactivation; **19** negative; cysteine; **20** d; **21** d, b, c, g, e, f, a; **22** rhino; corona; **23** c; **24** d; **25** b; **26** A; **27** c; **28** hemagglutinin; neuraminidase; **29** a; **30** amantadine; **31** f; b; e; c; d; a; **32** b; **33** cell-mediated; **34** yeast; mold; **35** tuberculosis; tubercles; **36** disseminated; immune; **37** b; **38** amphotericin B; **39** a; c; d; b

CHAPTER 25
1 water; **2** c; e; b; a; d; **3** adenylate cyclase; **4** enterotoxin; **5** c and e; **6** refrigerate; **7** infant; **8** b and d; **9** normal intestinal flora; **10** the body, or, more specifically, the intestinal tract; **11** b; **12** *cereus*; **13** c; **14** b; **15** d, e, b, c, a; **16** animals; **17** c and e; **18** serotypes; **19** urinary; **20** d; **21** c; **22** d; **23** b; **24** antibiotics; **25** d; **26** f, a, d, b, e, c; **27** mass immunization; **28** icosahedral; single; RNA; **29** c; **30** c and e; **31** rota; **32** b; **33** Norwalk; **34** isolated; **35** liver **36** e, b, c, d, a; **37** c; **38** e, b, d, c, a; **39** intestine; **40** cysticercosis; **41** pork; **42** d; **43** b; **44** penetration; **45** e; **46** laboratory tests; **47** contamination of water supplies

CHAPTER 26
1 mechanical; biological; **2** eggs; **3** c, f, b, e, d, a; **4** d, c, e, b, a; **5** eastern; summer; **6** b; **7** e; **8** spirochete; ticks; **9** a; **10** c; **11** interleukin-1; **12** *Rickettsia prowazekii*; lice; **13** lice; ticks; **14** yellow fever; **15** Walter Reed; **16** urban cycle: a and e; sylvatic cycle: b, c, and d; **17** kidney; liver; stomach bleeding; **18** live attenuated virus; **19** ticks; **20** *Plasmodium*; **21** b; **22** d; **23** b, f, d, c, e, a; **24** c;

25 *Trypanosoma; Leishmania;* **26** c, a, d, b; **27** tropical and subtropical; **28** e; **29** c; **30** microfilarias; **31** larvae; **32** lymph; blood circulatory; **33** elephantiasis

CHAPTER 27

1 skin; **2** b; **3** large aerosol droplets; **4** c; **5** a, c, and d; **6** endospore; **7** inhibitory chemical; **8** c; **9** c, a, d, b, e; **10** d; **11** d, b, c, e, a; **12** abscess; **13** blood circulation; **14** tampons; **15** arthropods; **16** c; **17** b, e, d, c, a; **18** Louis Pasteur; **19** c; **20** central nervous; **21** d; **22** c; a; e; d; b; **23** hookworms; **24** c; **25** anemia; **26** b, c and d; **27** *mansoni; japonicum; haematobium;* **28** a and c; **29** c; **30** d; **31** e; **32** moisture; **33** keratin; **34** b; **35** actinomycetes

CHAPTER 28

1 biology; geology; **2** horizons; **3** moisture; texture; nutrients; **4** (a) microscopic examination; (b) agar-plate culture; (c) enrichment culture; **5** b, c, e; **6** b; **7** e, b, d, c, a; **8** nitrogen; **9** light; **10** plant roots; **11** greater; **12** symbiosis; **13** c, e, a, b, d; **14** a, b, d; **15** commensalism; **16** antagonism; **17** antibiotics; **18** destroy, dissolve, or lyse; **19** parasitism; **20** *Bdellovibrio;* **21** parasites; **22** closed; recycling; **23** mineralization; **24** proteinases; peptidases; **25** pyruvic acid; ammonia; **26** nitrification; **27** nitrite; nitrite; **28** *Nitroso-; Nitro-;* **29** nitrification; nitrate; **30** denitrification; **31** loss of nitrogen from the soil; **32** deficient, or absent; **33** nitrogen fixation; **34** nitrogenase; **35** oxygen; **36** nitrogenase; **37** cyanobacteria; green; purple; **38** *Clostridium pasteurianum;* **39** *Azotobacter,* or *Beijerinckia,* or *Derxia;* **40** *Rhizobium;* **41** root hairs; nodules; **42** mutualism; **43** rice paddies; **44** *Frankia;* **45** b, c; **46** b, c, e, d, a; **47** anoxygenic (green-purple); **48** CH_2O; **49** oxaloacetic acid; **50** bacteria; fungi; **51** cellulose; **52** cellulase; glucose; **53** cellulose, lignin, hemicellulose; **54** e; **55** CO_2; H_2O; **56** H_2SO_4; **57** cysteine, or cystine, or methionine; **58** hydrogen sulfide; **59** hydrogen sulfide; **60** a, d, e; **61** microorganisms; **62** degradation or detoxification; **63** *Bacillus thuringiensis;* **64** *B. popillae; B. lentimorbus;* **65** a; **66** *Cladosporium;* **67** soil; surface water; **68** c

CHAPTER 29

1 atmospheric; surface; groundwater; **2** c; **3** aquatic; **4** filtration; **5** a, b, e, d, c; **6** barophilic; **7** photic; **8** 0, 3.5; **9** epibacteria; **10** 7.5, 8.5; **11** a, b, d, e, c; **12** eutrophication; **13** benthic zone; **14** estuary; **15** 3.5; **16** low; **17** blooms; **18** surfaces; **19** marine animals or fish; **20** negative; **21** hydrolytic; **22** pigmented; **23** avoid light; **24** low; **25** hundreds of millions; **26** b; **27** a; **28** foraminifera **29** algae; cyanobacteria; **30** bacteria; fungi; **31** detritus; **32** the greater area of the ocean; **33** mineralization; **34** mixing of waters from other oceans; **35** krill; **36** phytoplankton crop; **37** d; **38** b; **39** radiant energy; **40** dissimilation; mineralization; **41** cellulose; carbon dioxide; **42** chemosynthesis; **43** photosynthesis; chemosynthesis; **44** e; **45** potable; **46** chemicals; **47** ground; surface; **48** filtration; **49** septic; **50** filtration; chlorination; **51** alum; **52** chlorination; **53** dental caries; **54** fecal material; **55** sporadic; low; **56** pathogenic

microorganisms; **57** IMViC; **58** produces; does not produce; **59** a; d; e; **60** d; **61** potable; **62** lactose broth; gas; **63** brilliant green lactose-bile; eosin-methylene blue; **64** greenish metallic; **65** membrane-filter; **66** sulfuric; sulfur; **67** enteric or intestinal; **68** athlete's foot; **69** chlorine; **70** domestic; industrial; **71** domestic and industrial; surface water and rainwater; **72** 0.1; **73** biochemical oxygen demand, or BOD; **74** higher; **75** low; **76** anaerobic; **77** disposal field; may contain pathogenic microorganisms; **78** primary settling, or sedimentation; **79** aerobic; BOD; **80** zoogloea; **81** activated-sludge; **82** shallow; algae; **83** chlorine; **84** methane; **85** a; **86** d; **87** e; **88** b; **89** c; **90** e; **91** d

CHAPTER 30

1 e; **2** animal feed or food; **3** quality; **4** medium; **5** bacteria; fungi; **6** medium; **7** inoculation; **8** Food and Agriculture Organization (FAO); World Health Organization (WHO); International Children's Emergency Fund; (UNICEF); **9** Food and Drug Administration (FDA); **10** milk; **11** b; **12** F (only those microorganisms will grow into colonies whose nutritional requirements and physical conditions for growth are satisfied); **13** F (viruses require use of tissue-culture techniques); **14** c; **15** free; **16** grinding of a solid piece of meat to prepare hamburger exposes more "surfaces" to contamination; **17** 100; 1000; **18** no; **19** protein; **20** bacteria; fungi; **21** polluted; **22** seafood; **23** lactic acid; **24** poor sanitary quality or fecal contamination; **25** Appert; **26** *Clostridium botulinum;* **27** higher; **28** LTH; HTST; **29** Q fever; **30** sterilize; **31** raw; pasteurized; **32** refrigeration; **33** blanched or steamed; **34** no; **35** d; **36** c; **37** a; **38** c; **39** proteins; carbohydrates; fats; **40** molds; **41** putrefaction (proteolysis); rancidity (lipolysis); **42** endospore-forming; **43** flat sour; TA, or thermophilic anaerobe; **44** swelling or bursting of the can; **45** putrefaction; **46** butyric anaerobe; **47** c, d, a, e, b; **48** preparation; holding or storage; **49** starter; **50** lactic acid; volatile and neutral products; aroma; **51** *Streptococcus thermophilus; Lactobacillus bulgaricus;* **52** yeasts; **53** rennin; **54** whey; **55** *Lactobacillus acidophilus;* **56** shredded cabbage; cucumbers; **57** lactic acid bacteria; fermentative yeast; **58** lactic acid; streptococci; lactobacilli; **59** amino acids; yeasts; industrial wastes or by-products; **60** algae

CHAPTER 31

1 substrate; **2** c; **3** genetic; **4** b; **5** inexpensive; **6** recovery; purification; **7** *Saccharomyces;* **8** simple sugars, or glucose; **9** d; **10** a and b; **11** Frings; **12** a and e; **13** cheese; **14** *Lactobacillus;* **15** a; **16** c; **17** coagulate the protein; **18** d; **19** penicillin; **20** *chrysogenum;* **21** mutant; **22** d; **23** proteases; **24** starch; sucrose; **25** pectinase; **26** immobilized; **27** c; **28** c; **29** α-ketoglutaric acid; **30** a; **31** e; **32** c; **33** *Escherichia coli;* **34** interferons; **35** tissue plasminogen; **36** very small; **37** b and c; **38** hybridomas; **39** a and e; **40** *Bacillus thuringiensis;* **41** milky; Japanese; **42** e; **43** c; **44** hydrocarbon; **45** acids; **46** b; **47** e; **48** slime; **49** cellulose; **50** c; **51** a and e; **52** fungicide; **53** F; both naturally occurring microorganisms and genetically engineered microbes can be used; **54** fertilizer to enhance microbial growth

B

Differentiating Bacterial Species by Biochemical Tests

	Escherichia coli	Typical Salmonella	Salmonella typhi	Citrobacter freundii	Klebsiella pneumoniae	Enterobacter cloacae	Enterobacter aerogenes	Hafnia alvei	Serratia marcescens	Serratia liquefaciens	Proteus vulgaris	Proteus mirabilis	Providencia alcalifaciens	Yersinia enterocolitica
Indole	+	−	−	−	−	−	−	−	−	−	+	−	+	V
Methyl red	+	+	+	+	V	−	−	V	V	V	+	+	+	+
Voges-Proskauer	−	−	−	−	+	+	+	V	+	V	−	V	−	V
Simmons' citrate	−	V	−	+	+	+	+	V	+	+	V	(V)	+	−
Hydrogen sulfide (TSI)	−	+	+^{W}	+	−	−	−	−	−	−	+	+	−	−
Urea	−	−	−	V^W	+	V^W	−	−	V^W	V^W	+	V	+	+
KCN	−	−	−	+	+	+	+	+	+	+	+	+	+	−
Motility	V	+	+	+	−	+	+	+	+	+	+	+	+	−37C +22C
Gelatin (22°C)	−	−	−	−	−	V	V	−	(V)	+	+	+	−	−
Lysine decarboxylase	V	+	+	−	+	−	+	+	+	(V)	−	−	−	
Arginine dihydrolase	V	(V)	−	V	−	+	−	V	−	−	−	−	−	
Ornithine decarboxylase	V	+	−	V	−	+	+	+	+	+	−	+	−	+
Phenylalanine deaminase	−	−	−	−	−	−	−	−	−	−	+	+	+	−
Malonate	−	−	−	V	+	V	V	V	−	−	−	−	−	−
Gas from D-glucose	+	+	−	+	+	+	+	+	V	V	V	+	V	−
Lactose	+	−	−	(V)	+	(V)	+	V	−	V	−	−	−	−
Sucrose	V	−	−	V	+	+	+	V	+	+	+	V	V	+
D-Mannitol	+	+	+	+	+	+	+	+	+	+	−	−	−	+
Dulcitol	V	V*	−	V	V	V	−	−	−	−	−	−	−	−
Salicin	V	−	−	V	+	(V)	+	V	+	V	V	V	−	V
Adonitol	−	−	−	−	V	V	+	−	V	V	−	−	+	−
Meso-inositol	−	V	−	−	+	V	+	−	V	(V)	−	−	−	(V)
D-Sorbitol	V	+	+	+	+	+	+	−	+	+	−	−	−	+
L-Arabinose	+	+*	−	+	+	+	+	+	−	+	−	−	−	+
Raffinose	V	−	−	V	+	(+)	+	−	−	+	−	−	−	−
L-Rhamnose	V	+	−	+	+	+	+	+	−	V	−	−	−	−

+ = 90% or more positive within 48 h
− = less than 10% positive within 48 h
V = 10 to 89.9% positive within 48 h

(+) = 90% or more positive between 3 and 7 days
(V) = more than 50% positive within 48 h, and more than 90% positive in 3 to 7 days
w = weak reaction

*A few serotypes including S. choleraesuis, S. paratyphi A, and S. pullorum do not ferment dulcitol within 48 h. S. choleraesuis does not ferment arabinose.

NOTE: This chart is designed to be a brief guide to the reactions of the more clinically important species of Enterobacteriaceae. Only 25 of the 60 or more tests used to distinguish between species are listed. Specific biotypes (H$_2$S$^+$ E. coli, lactose$^+$ and raffinose$^+$ Y. enterocolitica, etc.), fastidious strains, and atypical strains are not addressed. For a more sophisticated treatment of these and other species of Enterobacteriaceae, the reader should consult specialty publications that give the above information and percentages.

SOURCE: Modified from Enteric Section and Bacteriology Training Branch, Centers for Disease Control, Atlanta.

C
Use of Exponential Notation and Logarithms in Microbiology

Microbiologists frequently use scientific notation to express numbers. An important element of scientific notation is that of exponential notation. For example, exponential notation is used to denote the large number of cells in a population (culture) of microorganisms. Instead of saying that there are 10 million, or 10,000,000, cells in a culture, we can say that there are 1×10^7 or simply 10^7 cells. The number 1 is the coefficient and the number 7 is an *exponent* and the number of cells is expressed in *exponential notation*, that is, as a power of a number such as 10, or specifically as 10^7, where 7 is the power or exponent of the base number 10. When a number is multiplied by itself one or more times, it is raised to a power (exponent). If it is multiplied by itself once, it is squared, or raised to the second power. If it is multiplied by itself twice, it is cubed, or raised to the third power. If it is multiplied by itself thrice, it is raised to the fourth power, and so on. Thus 10^7 is multiplying 10 by itself 6 times. The power to which a base number is raised is written alongside the upper right-hand corner of the number; in this case, 10 is raised to the power 7. Remember, however, that any other base number can also be multiplied by itself; for example, $2 \times 2 \times 2 \times 2 = 2^4$ or 16. But only 10 serves as the base number for *scientific notation*, which combines exponential notation with nonwhole number coefficients in a system that allows one to express complicated numbers of very large or small magnitude in a relatively simple manner.

Numbers need not be rounded off as neatly as 10,000,000 as in the first example. Consider the number 5,450,000,000. It can be expressed in scientific notation as 5.45×10^9. In this case, 5.45 becomes the *coefficient*, a quantity, or number, placed before and multiplying another quantity that is expressed in exponential notation with a base number of 10 (i.e., 10^9). The coefficient is determined by placing a decimal point in the number so that only one nonzero digit is to the left of it; the exponent is determined by counting the number of places (numbers) in the original number to the right of that nonzero digit. This is how 5.45×10^9 is obtained from 5,450,000,000.

Microbiologists sometimes also work with small numbers. For example, in working with mutation rates, it might be noted that a mutation occurs once in 1 million cell divisions. The rate of mutation may be described as 1/1,000,000 or 0.000001 times the number of divisions. The coefficient again is obtained by placing a decimal point in the number so that there is only one nonzero digit to the left of it. Next, counting the number of places that the decimal point has been moved to the right will yield the exponent, which becomes a negative value. Thus the number 0.000001 becomes 1×10^{-6}. (Upon multiplying $1 \times$ 10^{-6}, which is multiplying 10^{-1} by itself 5 times, one gets $1/10^6$, or 1/1,000,000, or 0.000001.)

To multiply numbers written in scientific notation, you simply *add* the exponents. For instance, the rate at which mutations occur in two separate genes is the product of the rates for the individual genes. If gene A mutates at a rate of 10^{-5} and gene B mutates at a rate of 10^{-6}, the rate of formation of a mutant containing mutations in both gene A and gene B becomes $10^{-5} \times 10^{-6} = 10^{-11}$. The coefficients, if present, are simply *multiplied*; for example, $(2 \times 10^6) \times (3 \times 10^{-3}) = (2 \times 3) \times 10^{+6-3} = 6 \times 10^3$.

To divide numbers in scientific notation, you simply *divide* the coefficients and *subtract* the exponents. For instance, divide (8×10^4) by (2×10^3). Solve this by $(8/2) \times 10^{4-3} = 4 \times 10^1 = 4 \times 10$.

A *logarithm (log)* is the power to which a base number is raised to produce a given number. We are most familiar with logarithms to the base 10, denoted as log_{10}. Microbiologists frequently work with log_{10} because cell numbers in a microbial culture are expressed as multiples of powers of 10, for example, in thousands or millions of cells. The first step in determining the log_{10} of any number is to write it in exponential notation. If the coefficient is exactly 1, the log_{10} is simply equal to the exponent. In the example of 1×10^7, log_{10} is written as 7. If the coefficient is not 1, a calculator (or a log table) may be employed to determine the logarithm. For example, to determine the logarithm to the base 10 (log_{10}) of 3.2×10^7, use a calculator to determine log_{10} of 3.2. The value is 0.5051. Therefore, log_{10} 3.2×10^7 becomes 7.5051. Values like this over the incubation period of a culture may be plotted to obtain a growth curve: the log values of cell numbers may be plotted on the ordinate (y axis) and the time in minutes or hours on the abscissa (x axis). This is called a semilogarithmic plot, since only the values on the ordinate are in log values. Such a plot, using logarithms of cell numbers to any base number (e.g., log_{10}) against time, always gives a straight line *when growth is exponential*, and for this reason exponential growth is also termed *logarithmic growth*.

Although cell numbers are usually plotted in log_{10}, plotting in log_2 has the advantage that each unit of the ordinate corresponds to one doubling (twofold increase), or one generation (since bacteria divide by binary fission). Such a plot facilitates reading the number of generations in an interval of time or the generation time directly from the graph. Values of log_2 may be obtained from the relationship $log_2 X = 3.3219 \, log_{10} X$. Thus if $X = 3000$, $log_2 3000 = 3.3219 \times 3.48 = 11.56$.

D

Restriction Endonucleases

Restriction endonucleases are important tools for genetic engineering (see Chapter 14), and over 200 different restriction endonucleases have been isolated. The ones that cut DNA in a staggered fashion (producing sticky ends) have, in general, been more useful than those that produce blunt ends. This is because the two blunt ends of a DNA molecule are often merely rejoined by DNA ligase to form a useless, nonrecombinant DNA circle. However, this problem can be overcome by various technical manipulations, such as using a high concentration of one DNA fragment in the mixture of fragments, adding a *linker* (short DNA segment containing a restriction site) to the blunt ends of the molecule and then using an endonuclease to cut the linker in a staggered fashion, or by adding artificial *homopolymer* tails (such as -A-A-A-A and -T-T-T-T) to the blunt ends of the molecule.

The name of each restriction endonuclease is written in the following fashion. The first three letters, in italics, indicate the name of the bacterium from which the enzyme was isolated (e.g., *Alu* refers to *Arthrobacter luteus; Bal* refers to *Brevibacterium albidum*). A subsequent nonitalicized letter or number, if present, indicates the particular strain of the bacterial species (e.g., *Sau*[96] refers to strain no. 96 of *Staphylococcus aureus; EcoR* refers to strain R of *Escherichia coli*). Finally, a roman numeral indicates the particular kind of endonuclease of the several kinds present in the particular bacterial species or strain (e.g., *Sst* I and *Sst* II refer to two different restriction endonucleases isolated from *Streptomyces stanford*).

The following table gives some examples of restriction endonucleases, their cleavage sites, and their sources.

Restriction endonuclease	DNA cleavage site	Type of cut	Bacterial source
ENZYMES WITH 4 BASE-PAIR RECOGNITION SEQUENCES			
Alu I	5′ –A–G↓C–T– 3′ 3′ –T–C↑G–A– 5′	Blunt	*Arthrobacter luteus*
Dpn I	5′ –G–m⁶A↓T–C– 3′ 3′ –C–T↑m⁶A–G– 5′	Blunt	*Streptococcus pneumoniae*
Hha I	5′ –G–C–G↓C– 3′ 3′ –C↑G–C–G– 5′	Staggered (3′ overhang)	*Haemophilus haemolyticus*
Mbo I	5′ ↓G–A–T–C– 3′ 3′ –C–T–A–G↑ 5′	Staggered (5′ overhang)	*Moraxella bovis*
*Bsa*J I	5′ –C↓C–N–N–G–G– 3′ 3′ –G–G–N–N–C↑C– 5′	Staggered (5′ overhang)	*Bacillus stearothermophilus*
*Sau*96 I	5′ –G↓G–N–C–C– 3′ 3′ –C–C–N–G↑G– 5′	Staggered (5′ overhang)	*Staphylococcus aureus*
ENZYMES WITH 5 BASE-PAIR RECOGNITION SEQUENCES			
Ava II	5′ –G↓G–W–C–C– 3′ 3′ –C–C–W–G↑G– 5′	Staggered (5′ overhang)	*Anabaena variabilis*
*Bst*N I	5′ –C–C↓W–G–G– 3′ 3′ –G–G–W↑C–C– 5′	Staggered (5′ overhang)	*Bacillus stearothermophilus*

Restriction endonuclease	DNA cleavage site	Type of cut	Bacterial source
Alw I	5' –G–G–A–T–C–N–N–N–N↓N–N– 3' 3' –C–C–T–A–G–N–N–N–N–N↑N– 5'	Staggered (5' overhang)	*Acinetobacter lwoffii*

ENZYMES WITH 6 BASE-PAIR RECOGNITION SEQUENCES

Bal I	5' –T–G–G↓C–C–A– 3' 3' –A–C–C↑G–G–T– 5'	Blunt	*Brevibacterium albidum*
EcoR I	5' –G↓A–A–T–T–C– 3' 3' –C–T–T–A–A↑G– 5'	Staggered (5' overhang)	*Escherichia coli*
Kpn I	5' –G–G–T–A–C↓C– 3' 3' –C↑C–A–T–G–G– 5'	Staggered (3' overhang)	*Klebsiella pneumoniae*
Sst I	5' –G–A–G–C–T↓C– 3' 3' –C↑T–C–G–A–G– 5'	Staggered (3' overhang)	*Streptomyces stanford*
Sst II	5' –C–C–G–C↓G–G– 3' 3' –G–G↑C–G–C–C– 5'	Staggered (3' overhang)	*Streptomyces stanford*
Sty I	5' –C↓C–W–W–G–G– 3' 3' –G–G–W–W–C↑C– 5'	Staggered (5' overhang)	*Salmonella typhi*
BstE II	5' –G↓G–T–N–A–C–C– 3' 3' –C–C–A–N–T–G↑G– 5'	Staggered (5' overhang)	*Bacillus stearothermophilus*
Bgl I	5' –G–C–C–N–N–N–N↓N–G–G–C– 3' 3' –C–G–G–N↑N–N–N–N–C–C–G– 5'	Staggered (3' overhang)	*Bacillus globigii*

ENZYMES WITH 7 BASE-PAIR RECOGNITION SEQUENCES

PpuM I	5' –R–G↓G–W–C–C–Y– 3' 3' –Y–C–C–W–G↑G–R– 5'	Staggered (5' overhang)	*Pseudomonas putida*
Rsr II	5' –C–G↓G–W–C–C–G– 3' 3' –G–C–C–W–G↑G–C– 5'	Staggered (5' overhang)	*Rhodopseudomonas sphaeroides*

ENZYMES WITH 8 BASE-PAIR RECOGNITION SEQUENCES

Not I	5' –G–C↓G–G–C–C–G–C– 3' 3' –C–G–C–C–G–G↑C–G– 5'	Staggered (5' overhang)	*Nocardia otitidis-caviarum*
Pac I	5' –T–T–A–A–T↓T–A–A– 3' 3' –A–A–T↑T–A–A–T–T– 5'	Staggered (3' overhang)	*Pseudomonas alcaligenes*
SgrA I	5' –C–R↓C–C–G–G–Y–G– 3' 3' –G–Y–G–G–C–C↑R–C– 5'	Staggered (5' overhang)	*Streptomyces griseus*
Sfi I	5' –G–G–C–C–N–N–N–N↓N–G–G–C–C– 3' 3' –C–C–G–G–N↑N–N–N–N–C–C–G–G– 5'	Staggered (3' overhang)	*Streptomyces fimbriatus*

SYMBOLS: A, adenine; T, thymine, C, cytosine; G, guanine; R, guanine or adenine; Y, cytosine or thymine; W, adenine or thymine; N, any base (adenine, cytosine, guanine, or thymine); m⁶A, 6-methyladenine.

SOURCES: New England Biolabs Inc. 1990 to 1991 catalog, Beverly, Mass.; Boehringer Mannheim Biochemicals, 1990 catalog, Indianapolis, Ind.; J. Sambrook, E. F. Fritsch, and T. Maniatis, *Molecular Cloning: A Laboratory Manual,* Cold Spring Harbor Laboratory Press, Cold Spring Harbor, N.Y., 1989.

Further Reading

PROLOGUE
DISCOVERING THE MICROBIAL WORLD

Brock, T., ed.: *Milestones in Microbiology*, Prentice-Hall, Englewood Cliffs, N.J., 1961. *A compilation of historically important papers that are useful supplementary material. Reading these papers will give an insight into how current theories have developed out of the past and will help develop an understanding of experimental design.*

Bulloch, W.: *The History of Bacteriology.* Oxford University Press, London, 1938. *The most complete and authoritative history of the development of bacteriology. This volume includes an extensive bibliography and a long list of biographical entries on some of the early workers in bacteriology.*

Clark, P. F.: *Pioneer Microbiologists of America*, University of Wisconsin Press, Madison, 1961. *The people who have made microbiology a science in the United States. The author's entertaining style makes this an enjoyable as well as informative book, and his acquaintance with many of those he writes about adds a personal touch.*

Dobell, C.: *Antony van Leeuwenhoek and His "Little Animals,"* Dover, New York, 1960. *A collection of the writings of the founder of microbiology, with a historical background to set the environment in which he lived.*

Doetsch, Raymond N.: *Microbiology: Historical Contributions from 1776 to 1908*, Rutgers University Press, New Brunswick, N.J., 1960. *Illustrates, in the field of general microbiology, how science has been and is concerned with ideas as they arise from the conditions of time and circumstance.*

Dowling, H. F.: *Fighting Infection: Conquests of the Twentieth Century*, Harvard University Press, Cambridge, Mass., 1977. *One of the great success stories of the twentieth century is retold in this interesting history of the diagnosis, prevention, and treatment of infectious diseases.*

Dubos, René J.: *Louis Pasteur: Free Lance of Science*, Little, Brown, Boston, 1950. *An interesting account of the life and contributions of Louis Pasteur, written in a pleasing style.*

Lechevalier, H., and M. Solotorovsky: *Three Centuries of Microbiology*, McGraw-Hill, New York, 1965. *A definitive history of microbiology, covering the important discoveries and theories from the period of the invention of the microscope to our own time.*

Turner, G. L'E.: *God Bless the Microscope*, Royal Microscopical Society, Oxford, England, 1989. *A history of the Royal Microscopical Society published on the occasion of the society's 150th anniversary.*

Van Iterson, G., L. Den Dooren de Jong, A. J. Kluyver, C. B. Van Neil, and T. D. Brock: *Martinus Beijerinck: His Life and Work*, Science Tech Publishers, Madison, Wis., 1984. *Beijerinck's contributions to the founding of general microbiology were numerous and highly significant. This biography provides an excellent story of his life and professional accomplishments.*

PART I
AN OVERVIEW OF MICROBIOLOGY

Alexopoulos, C. J., and C. W. Mims: *Introductory Mycology*, 3d ed., Wiley, New York, 1979. *A classic text widely used in introductory mycology courses. The study of fungi is approached from the standpoint of taxonomy and morphology. A useful reference text.*

Boatman, E. S., M. W. Burns, R. J. Walter, and J. S. Foster: "Today's Microscopy: Recent Developments in Light and Acoustic Microscopy for Biologists," *Bioscience* 37:384–394, 1987. *As the title implies, this article reviews recent developments in microscopic technology.*

Bold, H. C., and M. J. Wynne: *Introduction to the Algae: Structure and Reproduction*, 2d ed., Prentice-Hall, Englewood Cliffs, N.J., 1985. *A comprehensive and well-referenced textbook written for the teaching of general phycology. Well illustrated with both photomicrographs and electron micrographs.*

Delauney, A., and H. Erni, eds.: *The World of Microbes*, vol. 4 of *Encyclopedia of the Life Sciences*, Doubleday, Garden City, N.Y., 1965. *A beautifully illustrated and well-summarized account of microbes in relation to human beings. It is an inspiring introductory book for the new student.*

Farmer, J. N.: *The Protozoa: Introduction to Protozoology*, Mosby, St. Louis, 1980. *This textbook is organized for the beginning student; it was written with the student in mind and not as a reference text. Profusely illustrated with photographs and line drawings.*

Frederick, J. F., ed.: *Origins and Evolution of Eukaryotic Intracellular Organelles*, vol. 361 in *Annals of the New York Academy of Sciences*, New York, 1981. *A series of essays on evolution, particularly with respect to procaryotic cells and the individual organelles of eucaryotic cells.*

Heden, C. G.: "Microbiology in World Affairs," *Impact of Science on Society* 17:187, 1967, UNESCO. *An essay on the potential of the science of microbiology to contribute to the improvement of human welfare both on a global basis and in underdeveloped countries.*

Isenberg, H. D., ed.: *Clinical Microbiology Procedures Handbook*, American Society for Microbiology, Washington, D.C., 1992. *A comprehensive (two-volume) compilation of microbiological laboratory procedures that includes techniques for the cultivation of bacteria, fungi, viruses, and parasites. These volumes also provide a good overview of the variety of techniques used in microbiology.*

Leadbetter, E. R., and J. S. Poindexter, eds.: *Bacteria in Nature*, vol. 1: *Bacterial Activities in Perspective*, Plenum, New York, 1985. *A series of essays describing the role of bacteria in several different natural environments.*

Postlethwait, J. H., and J. L. Hopson: *The Nature of Life*, McGraw-Hill, New York, 1989. *An outstanding textbook of modern biology that aims to help students master basic concepts through motivation and clear explanation. Beautifully illustrated in full color so that it inspires students to read.*

Taylor, D. L., M. Nederlof, F. Lanni, and A. S. Waggoner: "The New Vision of Light Microscopy," *American Scientist* 80:322, July–August 1992. *An article on how lasers, video cameras, and digital image analysis combine with the most venerable instrument of the life sciences to create new ways of seeing events in the living cell.*

Vander, A. J., J. H. Sherman, and D. S. Luciano: *Human Physiology: The Mechanisms of Body Function*, 5th ed., McGraw-Hill, New York, 1990. *Chapter 2 of this textbook provides an excellent general introduction to the nature of atoms, molecules, and biologically important compounds.*

Woese, C. R.: *The Origin of Life*, Carolina Biological Supply Co., Burlington, N.C., 1984. *In the 31 pages of this pamphlet, Woese summarizes recent evidence regarding the origin of living organisms, cellular forms, macromolecules, and cellular metabolism.*

PART II
NUTRITION AND CULTIVATION OF MICROORGANISMS

American Type Culture Collection: *Media Handbook*, Rockville, Md., 1984. *A compendium of the compositions of microbiological media used for the maintenance and propagation of microbes in the American Type Culture Collection. An extremely useful reference manual for the media laboratory.*

Anderson, O. R.: *Comparative Protozoology*, Springer-Verlag, New York, 1988. *This scholarly and comprehensive text compares the flagellates, ciliates, and amoebas. It is an especially good text for microbial ecologists, since it discusses the habitats and symbiotic relationships in great detail.*

Berry, D. R., ed.: *Physiology of the Industrial Fungi*, Blackwell Scientific Publications, Palo Alto, Calif., 1988. *A good reference book on the physiology of fungi involved in the production of fermentation products. Section A covers the physiology of fungal growth, with special reference to carbon, nitrogen, and micronutrient nutrition and metabolism.*

Difco Laboratories: *Difco Manual*, 10th ed., Detroit, Mich., 1984. *An exhaustive compilation of dehydrated culture media and reagents used in microbiology. The composition and preparation of each product is preceded by a statement of intended use, a brief history, and principles.*

Gerhardt, P., editor-in-chief: *Methods for General and Molecular Bacteriology*, American Society for Microbiology,

Washington, D.C., 1993. *This new volume is an updated version of its predecessor,* Manual of Methods for General Bacteriology *published in 1981. The contents have been broadened to include techniques in molecular biology.*

Neidhardt, F. C., J. L. Ingraham, and M. Schaechter: *Physiology of the Bacterial Cell: A Molecular Approach*, Sinauer Associates, Inc., Sunderland, Mass., 1990. *A text designed to introduce college and graduate students to the physiological properties of bacteria.*

Power, D. A., and P. J. McCuen: *Manual of BBL Products and Laboratory Procedures*, 6th ed., Becton-Dickinson Microbiology Systems, Cockeysville, Md., 1988. *A manual intended to serve as a valuable technical resource for information regarding specific products and procedures. It provides the laboratory worker with specific methods for performing a wide variety of microbiological procedures in which the company's products can be utilized.*

Sze, P.: *A Biology of the Algae*, Wm. C. Brown, Dubuque, Iowa, 1986. *A comprehensive text on the morphology, evolutionary patterns, and ecological importance of the algae.*

PART III
CONTROL OF MICROORGANISMS

Balows, A., W. J. Hausler, Jr., K. L. Herrmann, H. D. Isenberg, and H. J. Shadomy, eds.: *Manual of Clinical Microbiology*, 5th ed., American Society for Microbiology, Washington, D.C., 1991. *Section III of this manual covers procedures for control of infections, sterilization, disinfection, and antisepsis.*

Block, S. S., ed.: *Disinfection, Sterilization, and Preservation*, 4th ed., Lea & Febiger, Baltimore, 1991. *A comprehensive coverage of the subject of killing and inhibiting microorganisms.*

Hugo, W. B., and A. D. Russell: *Pharmaceutical Microbiology*, 4th ed., Blackwell Scientific Publications, Oxford, England, 1987. *Part II of this volume provides comprehensive coverage of antimicrobial agents including information on major groups, mechanism of antimicrobial action, methods for assay of potency, and the development of resistance.*

Perkins, J. J.: *Principles and Methods of Sterilization in Health Sciences*, 2d ed., Charles C Thomas, Springfield, Ill., 1983. *A good coverage of fundamentals of sterilization and control of microorganisms.*

PART IV
MAJOR GROUPS OF MICROORGANISMS

Anderson, O. R.: *Comparative Protozoology*, Springer-Verlag, New York, 1988. *This text contains 20 chapters covering a wide range of topics. Section I contains nine chapters on morphology and ecology and includes a chapter on human parasitic protozoa. Section II has five chapters on fine structure. Section III contains six chapters covering basic physiology and biochemistry. An especially good text for microbial ecologists, and one of the most comprehensive texts available to date on protozoology.*

Balows, A., H. G. Trüper, M. Dworkin, W. Harder, and K.-H. Schleifer, eds.: *The Prokaryotes: A Handbook on the Biology of Bacteria: Ecophysiology, Isolation, Identification, Applications*, 2d ed., Springer-Verlag, New York, 1992. *Al-*

though not primarily concerned with classification, the four volumes of this monumental reference work provide a wealth of descriptive information and illustrations concerning the various genera of bacteria.

Krieg, N. R.: "Bacterial Classification: An Overview," *Can. J. Microbiol.* 34:536–540, 1988. *This article is a brief introduction to the approaches that have been used in bacterial classification, including the use of rRNA analysis.*

Krieg, N. R. and J. G. Holt, eds., vol. 1; P. H. A. Sneath et al., eds., vol. 2; J. T. Staley et al., eds., vol. 3; S. T. Williams and J. G. Holt, eds., vol. 4: *Bergey's Manual of Systematic Bacteriology,* Williams & Wilkins, Baltimore, 1984–1989. *The four volumes of this international reference work provide the most widely accepted classification of bacteria together with detailed descriptions of all established genera and species.*

Margulis, L., J. O. Corliss, M. Melkonian, and D. J. Chapman, eds.: *Handbook of Protoctista,* Jones & Bartlett, Boston, 1990. *A major, comprehensive volume on eucaryotic microorganisms (the single-celled protists and their multicellular descendants). This volume on Protoctista is somewhat comparable to* Bergey's Manual *for bacteria.*

Sleigh, M. A.: *Protozoa and Other Protists,* Cambridge University Press, New York, 1989. *The author provides a current view of the position of Protista among eucaryotic organisms and relationships among the members of this diverse taxonomic group.*

Sze, P.: *A Biology of the Algae,* Wm. C. Brown, Dubuque, Iowa, 1986. *An introduction to the algae. The text gives a good overview of the algae and serves as a primary textbook for a course in phycology. Chapter 1 is an introduction to the algae. Chapters 2 through 6 survey the different groups of algae. Chapters 7 through 9 discuss different ecological communities of algae. Well illustrated.*

Webster, J.: *Introduction to Fungi,* Cambridge University Press, New York, 1980. *In addition to emphasizing important morphological details with excellent illustrations, this text also considers the economic and ecological importance of fungi.*

PART V
MICROBIAL METABOLISM

Dawes, I. W., and I. W. Sutherland: *Microbial Physiology,* 2d ed., Blackwell Scientific Publications, Oxford, England, 1992. *This concise book covers microbial chemical cytology, nutrient transport, energy production, biosynthesis, metabolic regulation, and microbial growth.*

Gottschalk, G.: *Bacterial Metabolism,* 2d ed., Springer-Verlag, New York, 1986. *The 359 pages of this text provide a comprehensive and detailed coverage of the energy-yielding and energy-utilizing mechanisms of bacteria.*

Harold, F. M.: "The 1978 Nobel Prize in Chemistry," *Science* 202:1174–1176, 1978. *This brief article provides a fascinating description of the discovery of the protonmotive force by the biochemist Peter Mitchell.*

Moat, A., and J. W. Foster: *Microbial Physiology,* 2d ed., Wiley-Interscience, New York, 1988. *Chapter 1 not only provides an introduction to microbial physiology but also describes many of the various biosynthetic reactions of microorganisms and relates them to the structures of the cell.*

Other chapters deal with carbohydrate metabolism and energy production, nitrogen metabolism, cell lipids, nucleotides, DNA, RNA, amino acids, and protein synthesis.

PART VI
MICROBIAL GENETICS

Baum, R. M.: "Biotech Industry Moving Pharmaceutical Products to Market," *Chem. Eng. News,* July 20, 1987, 11–32, and "Agricultural Biotechnology Advances toward Commercialization," *Chem. Eng. News,* August 10, 1987, 9–14. *These two articles provide an excellent summary of the health care and agricultural applications of genetic engineering. Particular emphasis is given to the scientific, economic, and legal problems associated with various genetically engineered products.*

Cohen, S. N., A. C. Y. Chang, H. W. Boyer, and R. B. Helling: "Construction of Biologically Functional Bacterial Plasmids in Vitro," *Proc. Nat. Acad. Sci. U.S.A.* 70:3240–3244, 1973. *The classic paper that described the construction of recombinant plasmids by use of the restriction endonuclease technique.*

Freifelder, D.: *Essentials of Molecular Biology,* Jones & Bartlett, Boston, 1985. *Chapter 13 of this book gives a description of the principles and applications of genetic engineering in clear, understandable fashion.*

Hershberger, C. L., S. W. Queener, and G. Hegeman: *Genetics and Molecular Biology of Industrial Microorganisms,* American Society for Microbiology, Washington, D.C., 1989. *This volume brings together the work of leading researchers in the field of recombinant DNA technology.*

Klug, W. S., and M. R. Cummings: *Concepts of Genetics,* 2d ed., Merrill, Columbus, Ohio, 1986. *Chapter 20 of this textbook gives a succinct discussion of genetic engineering and its risks and benefits.*

Postlethwait, J. H., and J. L. Hopson: *The Nature of Life,* McGraw-Hill, New York, 1989. *Chapters 9 and 10 of this modern textbook of biology describe the processes of DNA replication and protein synthesis.*

PART VII
VIRUSES

Ackermann, H.-W., and M. S. DuBow: *Viruses of Prokaryotes,* vols. I and II, CRC Press, Boca Raton, Fla., 1987. *These two volumes give a general view of bacteriophages and discuss them comparatively. There has not been a comprehensive work on bacteriophages since Adams'* Bacteriophages *in 1959 and Tikhonenko's* Ultrastructure of Bacterial Viruses *in 1968 in Russian (translated into English in 1970). Volume I includes eight chapters on general subjects, e.g., history, taxonomy, occurrence and frequency, physiology, lytic cycle, and lysogeny. Volume II is concerned with phage systematics and identification. An excellent work for learning and reference.*

Dimmock, N. J., and S. B. Primrose: *Introduction to Modern Virology,* 3d ed., Blackwell Scientific Publications, Oxford, England, 1987. *A paperback textbook on virology that treats bacterial, plant, and animal viruses as like entities. Emphasis is on the biochemical and genetic aspects of virology.*

Doane, F. W., and N. Anderson: *Electron Microscopy in Diagnostic Virology: A Practical Guide and Atlas,* Cambridge University Press, Cambridge, 1987. *A practical compendium of successful procedures as well as an identification aid based on ultrastructure for virologists, pathologists, and technologists in human and veterinary medicine.*

Dulbecco, R., and H. S. Ginsberg: *Virology,* 2d ed., Lippincott, Philadelphia, 1988. *A paperback text that is also pubished as a section of* Microbiology, *4th ed., by Davis, Dulbecco, Eisen, and Ginsberg. The text discusses both the biological and the pathogenic properties of viruses.*

Fields, B. N., D. M. Knipe, R. M. Chanock, J. L. Melnick, B. Roizman, and R. E. Shope, eds.: *Fundamental Virology,* Raven Press, New York, 1986. *There are a total of 40 contributors to this text, which is designed for graduate and upper-level undergraduate students as well as researchers whose primary interest is in the basic aspects of virology. The introductory chapters cover the basic concepts of virology. Later chapters cover the biochemistry, molecular biology, and cellular aspects of the replication of different groups of viruses.*

Matthews, R. E. F.: "Viral Taxonomy for the Nonvirologist," *Ann. Rev. Microbiol.* 39:451–474, 1985. Annual Reviews, Inc., Palo Alto, Calif. *The article provides a historical consideration of viral taxonomy and gives the reader an account of the present state of viral taxonomy.*

PART VIII
MICROORGANISMS AND DISEASE: RESISTANCE TO INFECTION

Benjamini, E., and S. Leskowitz: *Immunology: A Short Course,* 2d ed., Wiley-Liss, New York, 1991. *A text that presents the essentials of immunology in a form easily assimilated by the student.*

Conte, J. E., Jr., and S. L. Barriere: *Manual of Antibiotics and Infectious Diseases,* 7th ed., Lea & Febiger, Baltimore, 1992. *Current information on antibiotics: therapy and susceptibilities, prophylactic antibiotics, immunobiologic agents, and antiparasitic drugs.*

Golub, E. S.: *Immunology: A Synthesis,* 2d ed., Sinauer Associates, Inc., Sunderland, Mass., 1991. *In this text the author has successfully conveyed to the nonimmunologist the logic and the order of the immune system. The text is well organized, well illustrated, and replete with adequate data for a student to understand the reasoning behind a conclusion. Highly recommended as an introduction to the science of immunology.*

Kimball, J. W.: *Introduction to Immunology,* 3d ed., Macmillan, New York, 1990. *A textbook on immunology written for the student who is familiar with terminology and concepts acquired in a basic biology course. Cell-mediated immune responses are emphasized as much as humoral immunity. The material is developed from fundamentals right up to the frontier of research in each topic.*

Kuby, J.: *Immunology,* Freeman, New York, 1992. *A comprehensive and richly illustrated introduction to immunology at the molecular and cellular levels.*

Mims, C. E.: *The Pathogenesis of Infectious Disease,* 3d ed., Academic, New York, 1987. *A volume on the principles of microbial infection and pathogenicity. It is a unifying book on the many aspects of the host-microbe interaction.*

Paul, W. E.: *Immunology: Recognition and Response,* Free-
man, New York, 1991. *This is a collection of papers (12) from* Scientific American *which describe and illustrate the major aspects of the human defense against infectious agents.*

Pratt, W. B., and R. Fekety: *The Antimicrobial Drugs,* Oxford University Press, New York, 1986. *An excellent reference for detailed information on specific antibiotics.*

Rose, N. R., ed.: *Manual of Clinical Laboratory Immunology,* 4th ed., American Society for Microbiology, Washington, D.C., 1992. *Best available guide to immunologic methods and their applications. Contains authoritative information on the best methods available for conducting specific immunologic tests, and laboratory techniques used in clinical diagnostic laboratories and in research in immunology. More than 240 contributing authors.*

Sherris, J. C., ed.: *Medical Microbiology,* 2d ed., Elsevier Science Publishing, New York, 1990. *Chapter 9, entitled "Normal Microbial Flora," and Chap. 13, "Antimicrobics and Chemotherapy of Bacterial and Viral Infections," are particularly appropriate for Part VIII of this book.*

Vander, A. J., J. H. Sherman, and D. S. Luciano: *Human Physiology: The Mechanisms of Body Function,* 5th ed., McGraw-Hill, New York, 1990. *A lucidly written and beautifully illustrated text on the principles and facts of human physiology. A recommended, relevant chapter for further reading is Chap. 19, "Defense Mechanisms of the Body."*

PART IX
MICROORGANISMS AND DISEASE: MICROBIAL DISEASES

American Academy of Arts and Sciences: *Living with AIDS: Part II,* Daedalus, 1989 (published as vol. 118, no. 3, of the Proceedings of the Academy). *This paperback volume provides a comprehensive treatment of the global, social, political, legal, psychological, educational, and public health aspects of AIDS. The topics are presented by a panel of distinguished authorities in clear, easily understandable language. A copy can be obtained for $6.00 from the Daedalus Business Office, P.O. Box 515, Canton, MA 02021.*

Baron, E. J., and S. M. Finegold: *Bailey and Scott's Diagnostic Microbiology,* 8th ed., Mosby, St. Louis, 1990. *Replete with many full-color illustrations, this excellent reference book is designed for the clinical microbiology laboratory and describes the identifying features and laboratory diagnosis of the medically important bacteria, fungi, protozoa, and helminths.*

Cherfas, J.: "Malarial Vaccines: The Failed Promise," *Science* 247:402–403, 1990. *A brief discussion of the various approaches to developing an effective vaccine against malaria and the difficulties that have been encountered so far.*

Coppel, R. L.: "Prospects for a Malaria Vaccine," *Microbiol. Sci.* 3:292–295, 1986. *A succinct summary of advances being made toward development of a malaria vaccine using recombinant DNA technology.*

Gallo, R. C., and L. Montagnier: "AIDS in 1988," *Scientific American,* October 1988. *In this article, the two researchers who discovered HIV recount the discovery and offer prospects for a vaccine, for therapy, and for controlling the epidemic. Nine other articles in the same issue deal with the origins of HIV, the molecular biology of HIV, the epidemiol-*

ogy of AIDS, AIDS therapies, AIDS vaccines, the social dimensions of AIDS, and related topics.

Garner, J. S., and M. S. Favero: "Guideline for Handwashing and Hospital Environmental Control," U.S. Department of Health and Human Services, Centers for Disease Control, Atlanta, 1985. *This is one of a series of guidelines included in a manual entitled* Guidelines for Prevention and Control of Nosocomial Infections. *The series consolidates the various CDC recommendations and is especially helpful for hospital personnel and those responsible for infection control and surveillance.*

Habicht, G. S., G. Beck, and J. L. Benach: "Lyme Disease," *Scientific American*, July 1987. *A fascinating account of the discovery of the causative agent of Lyme disease and its tick vector.*

Joklik, W. K., H. P. Willett, D. B. Amos, and C. M. Wilfert: *Zinsser Microbiology*, 20th ed., Appleton & Lange, East Norwalk, Conn., 1992. *This well-organized textbook of medical microbiology provides excellent coverage of the important bacterial, viral, and fungal agents of human disease.*

Koop, C. E.: *Surgeon General's Report on Acquired Immune Deficiency Syndrome*, U.S. Department of Health and Human Services, U.S. Public Health Service, Washington, D.C., 1987. *Possibly the most important document of the decade for public education about AIDS, this 36-page pamphlet was prepared by the surgeon general of the United States to provide clear, concise information about the current AIDS epidemic and the measures that must be taken to stop its spread. A free copy can be obtained by writing the National Institutes of Health, National Institute of Allergy and Infectious Diseases, Building 31, Room 7A32, 9000 Rockville Pike, Bethesda, MD 20892. Additional copies may be purchased from the Superintendent of Documents, Government Printing Office, Washington, D.C. 20402-9325.*

Mandell, G. L., R. G. Douglas, Jr., and J. E. Bennett, eds.: *Principles and Practice of Infectious Diseases*, 3d ed., Wiley, New York, 1990. *A comprehensive reference that describes the pathogenesis, clinical signs and symptoms, treatment, and prevention of microbially caused diseases.*

Virginia Polytechnic Institute and State University: *AIDS: The Modern Plague*, Proc. 2d Ann. President's Symp., Virginia Polytechnic Institute and State University, Blacksburg, 1991. *This publication contains papers presented in March 1991 by eminent researchers and public health authorities. Among the titles included are* "The First Ten Years of Human Retroviruses," "The Worldwide AIDS Epidemic: A Crisis in Public Health," "AIDS and Public Health Policy," "Public Policy and Public Health," *and* "AIDS in the Future: Some Epidemiological and Evolutionary Consequences." *Copies of this publication are available for $10.00 from the Publications Department, Virginia Polytechnic Institute and State University, Blacksburg, VA 24061.*

Wenzel, R. P., ed.: *Prevention and Control of Nosocomial Infections*, Williams & Wilkins, Baltimore, 1987. *Written by practicing experts, this book provides state-of-the-art information on the causes, prevention, and implications of nosocomial infections.*

White, D. O., and F. Fenner: *Medical Virology*, 3d ed., Academic, New York, 1986. *Part II of this clearly written textbook provides detailed discussions of the transmission, clinical features, diagnosis, and control of viral infections.*

PART X
MICROBIAL ECOLOGY

Atlas, R. M., and R. Bartha: *Microbial Ecology: Fundamentals and Applications*, 2d ed., Benjamin-Cummings, Menlo Park, Calif., 1987. *A good general coverage of microorganisms in nature, including soil, and the biochemical changes they bring about.*

Campbell, R.: *Microbial Ecology*, 2d ed., Blackwell Scientific Publications, Oxford, England, 1983. *A concise coverage of microorganisms in soil, water, and air and their role in bringing about chemical changes.*

Clesceri, L. S., A. E. Greenberg, and R. R. Trussell: *Standard Methods for the Examination of Water and Wastewater*, 17th ed., American Public Health Association, American Water Works Association, and the Water Pollution Control Federation, Washington, D.C., 1989. *An extensive compendium of physical, chemical, and biological "standard methods" for the examination of water and wastewater. The laboratory procedures are presented in considerable detail.*

Leadbetter, E. R., and J. S. Poindexter, eds.: *Bacteria in Nature*, vol. I: *Bacterial Activities in Perspective*, Plenum, New York, 1985. *This volume contains chapters on biochemical activities of microorganisms in the environment including their role in soil.*

Levin, M. A., R. J. Seidler, and M. Rogul, eds.: *Microbial Ecology: Principles, Methods, and Applications*, McGraw-Hill, New York, 1992. *A comprehensive compilation of concepts and procedures used in the study of microbial ecology.*

Mitchell, R., ed.: *Environmental Microbiology*, Wiley-Liss, New York, 1992. *An in-depth examination of the role of microorganisms in water, soil, and the atmosphere and of methods for the control of pollution.*

Paul, E. A., and F. E. Clark: *Soil Microbiology and Biochemistry*, Academic, San Diego, 1989. *The theme of this book is to provide the student with an overview of the role of microorganisms in the biochemical processes, such as nutrient recycling, that occur in soil.*

Rheinheimer, G.: *Aquatic Microbiology*, 4th ed., Wiley, New York, 1991. *A good introductory book in aquatic microbiology; a survey of aquatic bacteria and fungi and their role in the life of lakes, rivers, and seas.*

Stolp, H.: *Microbial Ecology: Organisms, Habitats, Activities*, Cambridge University Press, Cambridge, 1988. *A small book (300 pages) which characterizes microorganisms as well as their activities in the environment. Each chapter includes an extensive list of references.*

Strickland, R. M.: *The Fertile Fjord: Plankton in Puget Sound*, Puget Sound Books, University of Washington Press, Seattle, 1983. *An excellent introductory discussion of plankton that provides descriptions of planktonic organisms and their form and function. Very well illustrated.*

Tunnicliffe, V.: "Hydrothermal-Vent Communities of the Deep Sea," *American Scientist* 80:336, July–August 1992. *An article on how nuclear and chemical energy at hot vents along mid-ocean ridges make possible exotic ecosystems that have evolved in near-total isolation.*

Water Pollution Control Federation: *Literature Review Issue, J. Water Pollution Control Fed.*, Washington, D.C.,

June 1992. *Each year the entire June issue of the journal of the Water Pollution Control Federation is devoted to the review of the current literature on topics such as wastewater treatment, industrial wastes, and water pollution.*

PART XI
INDUSTRIAL MICROBIOLOGY

Crueger, W., and A. Crueger: *Biotechnology: A Textbook of Industrial Microbiology*, 2d ed., Sinauer Associates, Inc., Sunderland, Mass., 1990. *This text provides the key principles and major processes of industrial microbiology. It is written for advanced undergraduate and graduate students.*

Demain, A. L., and N. A. Solomon, eds.: *Manual of Industrial Microbiology and Biotechnology*, American Society for Microbiology, Washington, D.C., 1986. *This volume brings together the biological and engineering methodology needed to develop industrial processes from the isolation of the culture to the isolation of the product.*

Frazier, W. C., and D. C. Westhoff: *Food Microbiology*, 4th ed., McGraw-Hill, New York, 1988. *One of the standard food microbiology textbooks that provides a general coverage of the subject.*

U.S. Congress, Office of Technology Assessment: "Biotechnology in a Global Economy," OTA-BA-494, Government Printing Office, Washington, D.C., 1991. *This report examines the impact of developments in biotechnology in several industries including pharmaceuticals, chemicals, agriculture, and waste management.*

Vanderzant, C., and D. Splittstoesser.: *Compendium of Methods for the Microbiological Examination of Foods*, American Public Health Association, Washington, D.C., 1992. *Detailed methods for the microbiological examination of foods compiled by an intersociety and interagency committee; it is very comprehensive. These methods represent what might be considered standard for the food industry.*

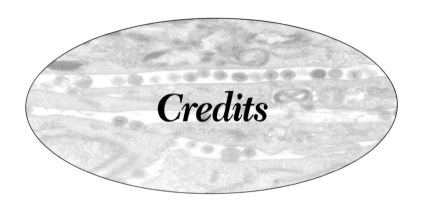

Credits

We are most grateful to the many individuals and organizations who kindly provided numerous photographs and drawings that have so greatly enhanced the quality of *Microbiology: Concepts and Applications.*

PROLOGUE P.1: Parke-Davis Division of Warner-Lambert Company. **P.2: [A]** From the collection of the Armed Forces Institute of Pathology, Washington, D.C.; **[B]** After C. E. Dobell, *Anthony van Leeuwenhoek and His "Little Animals,"* Russel and Russel, New York, 1932. **P.3:** The Wellcome Institute of the History of Medicine. Courtesy of the Wellcome Trustees. **P.5:** Parke-Davis Division of Warner-Lambert Company. **P.6:** Institut Pasteur, Paris. **P.8:** C. W. Hesseltine, Northern Regional Research Center, USDA. **P.9:** American Society for Microbiology Archives. **P.10:** The Bettmann Archive. **P.11:** American Society for Microbiology Archives. **P.12:** American Society for Microbiology Archives. **P.13:** Parke-Davis Division of Warner-Lambert Company. **P.14:** National Library of Medicine. **P.16:** Parke-Davis Division of Warner-Lambert Company. **P.17:** Dr. Robert I. Krasner, Professor of Biology, Providence College. **P.18:** René Dubos. **P.19: [A, B]** Waksman Institute of Microbiology, Rutgers University. **P.20:** American Society for Microbiology Archives. **P.21: [A]** George Beadle; **[B]** Edward L. Tatum; **[C]** Joshua Lederberg.

CHAPTER 2 2.1: [A, B] National Library of Medicine. **2.3: [A]** Dr. K. S. Kim/Peter Arnold; **[B]** W. L. Dentler, University of Kansas/Biological Photo Service. **2.6:** Redrawn after J. H. Postlethwait and J. L. Hopson, *The Nature of Life,* McGraw-Hill, New York, 1989. **2.8: [A]** J. R. Waaland/BPS; **[B]** Paul W. Johnson/BPS; **[C]** Eric Grave/Phototake. **2.9: [A]** E. Guehd/CNRI/Photo Researchers; **[B]** Stanley Flegler/Visuals Unlimited; **[C]** Merna Pelczar; **[D]** Photo Researchers. **2.10:** George Svihla, Argonne National Laboratory Annual Report, 1965. **2.11: [A]** Paul W. Johnson/BPS; **[B]** CNRI/Phototake; **[C]** Eric Grave/Phototake. **DISCOVER 2.1: [A]** Woods Hole Oceanographic Institution; **[B]** S. Frederick Grassle/WHOI; **[C]** Holger W. Jannasch/WHOI and the National Oceanic and Atmospheric Administration.

CHAPTER 3 3.1: Environmental Services Branch, National Institutes of Health. **3.2: [A, B]** Becton Dickinson Microbiology Systems, Baltimore, Md. **3.3: [A, B]** Becton Dickinson Microbiology Systems, Baltimore, Md.; **[C]** Liliane Therrien and E. C. S. Chan, McGill University. **DISCOVER 3.1:** American Type Culture Collection. **3.6: [A, B]** Nikon, Inc., Instrument Group. **3.7:** Carl Zeiss, Inc., Thornwood, N.Y. **3.8: [C]** E. C. S. Chan. **3.9:** Virginia Uy, Orion Welcome Diagnostics. **3.10: [A–C]** O. W. Richards, Research Department, American Optical Company. **3.11:** (top) Redrawn after J. H. Postlethwait and J. L. Hopson, *The Nature of Life,* McGraw-Hill, New York, 1989; (bottom) **[A]** Michael J. Pelczar, Jr.; **[B]** CNRI/Science Photo Library/Photo Researchers; **[C]** Jonathan Eisenback/CNRI/Phototake. **3.12:** Dr. V. Hari, Department of Biological Sciences, Wayne State University, Detroit, Michigan. **3.13:** DNA Plant Technology Corporation, Cinnaminson, N.J. **3.17: [B, C]** Biolog, Hayward, Ca. **TABLE 3.2:** (top to bottom) Centers for Disease Control, Atlanta, Ga.; Centers for Disease Control, Atlanta, Ga.; John D. Cunningham/Visuals Unlimited; G. W. Willis, MB/BPS; Dustman and Lukas/McGraw-Hill, Inc.; BPS; G. W. Willis, MD/BPS; BPS.

CHAPTER 4 4.1: [B] A. M. Siegelman/Visuals Unlimited. **4.2: [A]** Manfred Kage/Peter Arnold; **[B]** Fred Hossler/Visuals Unlimited; **[C]** E. C. S. Chan. **4.3:** Courtesy of E. C. S. Chan and *Can. J. Microbiol.* **4.4: [A, B]** David M. Phillips/Visuals Unlimited; **[C]** Liliane Therrien and E. C. S. Chan, McGill University; **[D]** Al Lamme/Phototake; **[E]** Leon J. LeBeau/BPS. **4.5: [A]** Liliane Therrien and E. C. S. Chan, McGill University; **[B]** V. B. D. Skerman; **[C]** Jack M. Bostrack/Visuals Unlimited. **4.6:** G. J. Hageage, Jr. **4.8: [A, B]** T. Iino, University of Tokyo. **4.9: [A–D]** Liliane Therrien and E. C. S. Chan, McGill University. **4.10: [A]** S.-L. Cheng, Anna Campana, and E. C. S. Chan, McGill Univerity. **DISCOVER 4.2:** E. C. S. Chan. **4.11:** Redrawn after diagrams courtesy of R. M. MacNab and M. K. Ornston, *J. Mol. Biol.* 112:1, 1977. **4.12:** J. W. Coulton, McGill University. **4.13:** C. Brinton, Jr., and Judith Camahan, University of Pittsburgh. **4.14:** Jack M. Bostrack/Visuals Unlimited. **4.15: [A]** J. W. Coulton, McGill University; **[B]** Russell Siboo, McGill University. **4.16:** Adapted from V. Braun and *J. Bacteriol.* 114:1264–1270, 1973. **4.17:** W. Baumeister, Max Planck Institut für Biochimie. **4.18:** A. Ryter and C. Frebel. **4.19: [A, B]** R. A. Macleod, Macdonald College of McGill University. **4.20:** J. W. Coulton, McGill University. **4.23:** J. W. Coulton, McGill University. **4.24:** Institut Pasteur, Department de Biologie Moléculaire. **4.25:** S. W. Watson. **4.27:** R. L. Gherna, American Type Culture Collection. **4.28:** G. Auling, M. Reh, C. M. Lee and H. G. Schlegel, *Int. J. Syst. Bacteriol.* 28:82, 1978. **4.29 [B]** E. C. S. Chan. **4.30:** Redrawn, with modifications, from L. E. Hawker and A. H. Linton, *Microorganisms: Function, Form and Environment,* 2d ed., University Park Press, Baltimore, 1979. **4.31: [A, B]** SAB photos LS 203 and 204. G. Knaysi, R. F. Baker, and J. Hillier, *J. Bacteriol.* 53:525, 1947. **4.32:** Y.-T. Tchan and P. B. New, from N. R. Krieg and J. G. Holt, eds., *Bergey's Manual of Systematic Bacteriology,* vol. 1, Williams & Wilkins, Baltimore, 1984. **4.33: [A]** David Scharf/Peter Arnold; **[B]** David M. Phillips/Visuals Unlimited; **[C]** Runk-Schenberger/Grant Heilman; **[D]** BPS. **4.34: [A, B]** E. C. S. Chan. **4.35: [A]** Manfred Kage/Peter Arnold. **DISCOVER 4.3:** Cabisco/Visuals Unlimited. **4.36: [A–E]** James L. van Etten, Lee A. Bulla, Jr., and Grant St. Julian, and the American Society for Microbiology. **4.37: [A, B]** Bob Lee and E. C. S. Chan, McGill University. **4.38: [A]** R. G. Kessel and C. Y. Shih, *Scanning Electron Microscopy in Biology,* Springer Verlag, Berlin, 1974. **4.39: [A]** Dennis Kunkel, University of Washington. **4.41:** Viqar Zaman, National University of Singapore. **4.42:** Viqar Zaman, National University of Singapore. **4.43: [A]** Peter R. Gardiner, International Laboratory for Research on Animal Diseases, Nairobi, Kenya, and the Society of Protozoologists; **[B]** Adapted from P. W. Davis and E. P. Solomon, *The World of Biology,* McGraw-Hill, New York, 1979. **4.44: [A]** K. Jean/Visuals Unlimited. **4.45: [A, B]** Nathalie Chaly, Carleton University, Ottawa, Canada. **4.52: [B]** Stanley F. Flegler, Pesticide Research Center, Michigan State University. **4.53: [B]** B. Kendrick, University of Waterloo. **4.54: [A]** Dustman and Lukas, Slides for *Microbiology,* unit 5, McGraw-Hill, New York; **[B]** L. Kapica and E. C. S. Chan, McGill University. **4.55:**

[B, C] Orson K. Miller, Jr., Virginia Polytechnic Institute and State University, Blacksburg; [D] H. E. Huizar, J. T. Ellzey, and W. L. Steffens, The University of Texas at El Paso.

CHAPTER 5 5.1: E. C. S. Chan. 5.2: E. C. S. Chan. 5.3: Liliane Therrien and E. C. S. Chan, McGill University. 5.4: Becton Dickinson Microbiology Systems. 5.5: [A, B] Becton Dickinson Microbiology Systems. 5.6: Liliane Therrien and E. C. S. Chan, McGill University. 5.7: Liliane Therrien and E. C. S. Chan, McGill University. 5.8: E. C. S. Chan. 5.10: E. C. S. Chan, J. de Vries, and R. F. Harvey, J. Clin. Microbiol. 9: 124–126, 1978. 5.11: [A, B] E. C. S. Chan. 5.12: Liliane Therrien and E. C. S. Chan, McGill University. 5.13: Liliane Therrien and E. C. S. Chan, McGill University. 5.14: E. C. S. Chan. 5.15: Michael G. Gabridge/Visuals Unlimited. 5.16: E. C. S. Chan.

CHAPTER 6 6.3: Cetus Corporation. 6.4: E. C. S. Chan. 6.5: The Germfree Laboratories, Inc. 6.6: [B] Becton Dickinson Microbiology Systems. 6.9: Adapted from J. H. Postlethwait and J. L. Hopson, The Nature of Life, McGraw-Hill, New York, 1989. 6.13: [A, B] I. D. J. Burdett and R. G. E. Murray, J. Bacteriol. 119:1039, 1974.

CHAPTER 7 7.6: [A] SIU/Visuals Unlimited. 7.10: Nordian International, Inc., Ontario, Canada. 7.11: [B] Bill Varie/AMGEN, Inc. 7.12: [B] Gelman Sciences, Inc.; [C] Pall/Visuals Unlimited. 7.14: [A, B] Centers for Disease Control, Atlanta, Ga. 7.15: Centers for Disease Control, Atlanta, Ga.

CHAPTER 8 8.1: National Library of Medicine. 8.4: E. C. S. Chan.

CHAPTER 9 9.1: R. Joseph and E. Canale-Parola. 9.2: J. Nowak, Documenta Microbiologica, Part 1, "Bakterien," Gustav Fischer Verlag, Jena, Germany, 1927. 9.3: N. R. Krieg. 9.4: N. R. Krieg, Bacteriol. Rev., 40:55, 1976. DISCOVER 9.1: D. L. Balkwill, D. Maratea, and R. P. Blakemore, J. Bacteriol. 141:1399, 1980. 9.6: [A] J. M. Larkin, P. M. Williams, and R. Taylor, Int. J. Syst. Bacteriol. 27:147, 1977. 9.7: Centers for Disease Control, Atlanta, Ga. 9.8: R. Unz, from N. J. Palleroni in M. P. Starr et al., eds., The Prokaryotes: A Handbook on Habitats, Isolation, and Identification of Bacteria, Springer-Verlag, 1981. 9.9: John D. Cunningham/Visuals Unlimited. 9.10 R. G. E. Murray, from Bergey's Manual of Determinative Bacteriology, 8th ed., Williams & Wilkins, Baltimore, 1974. 9.11: Manfred Kage/Peter Arnold. 9.12: [B] A. M. Siegelman/Visuals Unlimited. 9.15: N. J. Kramis and the Rocky Mountain Laboratory, U.S. Public Health Service. 9.16: [B] Centers for Disease Control,

Atlanta, Ga. 9.17: [A–C] N. Pfennig, J. Bacteriol. 99:597, 1969. 9.18: [A–D] George J. Schumacher, State University of New York at Binghamton. 9.19: After H. Reichenbach, from Martin Dworkin, "The Myxobacterales," in A. I. Laskin and H. A. Lechevalier, eds., Handbook of Microbiology, CRC Press, Boca Raton, Fla., 1974. 9.20: [A–E] P. L. Grilione and J. Pangborn and J. Bacteriol. 124:1558, 1975. 9.21: [A] H. F. Ridgeway, Jr., Scripps Institution of Oceanography; [B] Hans Reichenbach. 9.22: EPA/Visuals Unlimited. 9.23: [A] A. L. Houwink and W. van Iterson, Biochem. Biophys. Acta. 5:10, 1950. 9.24: Jean M. Schmidt, Arizona State University. 9.29: Centers for Disease Control, Atlanta, Ga. DISCOVER 9.2: David J. Vitale and George B. Chapman. 9.30: [B] Centers for Disease Control, Atlanta, Ga. 9.31: Mary P. Lechevalier. 9.32: Mary P. Lechevalier. 9.33: G. Biberfeld and P. Biberfeld, J. Bacteriol. 102:855, 1970.

CHAPTER 10 10.1: [B] All, Cabisco/Visuals Unlimited. 10.2: (clockwise from top) Ray Simons/Photo Researchers; Robert Knauft/Photo Researchers; Robert Knauft/Biology Media/Photo Researchers; Biophoto Associates/Photo Researchers. 10.3: [A] M. W. Miller, University of Maryland. 10.6: [A] M. F. Brown and H. G. Brotzman, University of Missouri. 10.7: [A, B] M. F. Brown and H. G. Brotzman, University of Missouri. 10.9: [A] I. Benda and Avi Publishing Co., Inc., [B] Dr. Teena Walker, National Research Council of Canada, Ottawa, Ontario. From L. C. Sowden and T. Walker, 1988, Can. J. Microbiol. 34:577–582, 1986. 10.10: [A] George Svihla and the Miscroscope and Crystal Front. 10.12: George Knaphus/Visuals Unlimited. 10.13: Patrick Lynch/Photo Researchers. 10.14: John D. Cunningham/Visuals Unlimited. 10.15: Dr. T. C. Sewall, University of Georgia, Athens, Ga. From C. W. Mims, E. A. Richardson, and W. E. Timberlake, Protoplasma 144:132–141, 1988. 10.16: [A, B] L. Kapica and E. C. S. Chan, McGill University. 10.17: [A–F] U.S. Department of Commerce. 10.20: Dennis D. Kunkel, University of Washington, 1985 Polaroid International Instant Photomicrography Competition. 10.21: [A, B] U.S. Department of Commerce. DISCOVER 10.1: The 1986 Polaroid International Instant Photomicrography Competition; photo by Carol Strong Weidman. 10.24: [A] U.S. Department of Commerce. DISCOVER 10.2: D. F. Bird and J. Kalff, McGill University. 10.25: [A] Biophoto Associates/Science Source/Photo Researchers. 10.27: Viqar Zaman, National University of Singapore. 10.28: [A] Viqar Zaman, National University of Singapore. 10.29: [A] John A. Kloetzel, University of Maryland, Baltimore.

CHAPTER 11 11.8: Norma J. Lang and J. Phycol. 1:127–134, 1965.

CHAPTER 13 13.1: By permission from J. D. Griffith, University of North Carolina. DISCOVER 13.1: Cetus Corporation. 13.8: [A] N. R. Krieg. 13.10: [A, B] N. R. Krieg. 13.19: Michiko Egel-Mitani.

CHAPTER 14 14.1: [A, B] Eli Lilly Co.

CHAPTER 15 15.3: Kendall O. Smith and Melvin D. Trousdale. 15.4: [A, B] H.-W. Ackermann, Laval University. 15.5: CNRI/Phototake. 15.6: Centers for Disease Control, Atlanta, Ga. 15.7: [A] Margaret Gommersall, McGill University; [B] K. B. Easterbrook, Dalhousie University. 15.9: A. K. Kleinschmidt, University of Ulm, Germany, in A. K. Kleinschmidt et al., Biochim. Biophys. Acta 61:857–864, 1962. 15.10: [A] H.-W. Ackermann, Laval University; [B] Runk-Schoenberger/Grant Heilman; [C] R. L. Wiseman, The Public Health Research Institute of the City of New York, Inc. 15.11: H.-W. Ackermann, Laval University. 15.12: From drawings by H.-W. Ackermann, Laval University. Reproduced from R. E. F. Matthews, "Classification and Nomenclature of Viruses," Intervirology 17:1–199, 1982. By permission from S. Karger, Basel, Switzerland. 15.13: H.-W. Ackermann, Laval University. 15.16: [A, B] S. Mizushima, Nagoya University. From H. Furukawa, T. Kuroiwa and S. Mizushima, "DNA Injection During Bacteriophage T4 Infection of Escherichia coli," J. Bacteriol. 154:938–945, 1983. 15.18: Lee D. Simon, The Waksman Institute, Rutgers University, New Brunswick, N.J. 15.20: J. W. Coulton, McGill University. 15.23: [A–D] M. K. Corbett, University of Maryland. 15.24: [A–C] Centers for Disease Control, Atlanta, Ga. 15.25: Reproduced from drawings by Mrs. J. Keeling in R. E. F. Matthews, "Classification and Nomenclature of Viruses," Intervirology 17:1–99, 1982. By permission from S. Karger AG, Basel, Switzerland. 15.26: Reproduced from drawings by Mrs. J. Keeling in R. E. F. Matthews, "Classification and Nomenclature of Viruses," Intervirology 17:1–99, 1982. By permission from S. Karger AG, Basel, Switzerland.

CHAPTER 16 16.1: Bruce Iverson/BSC. 16.3: Texas State Department of Health. 16.5: [A] W. Siegel, American Type Culture Collection; [B] W. Siegel. 16.7: E. C. S. Chan. 16.8: [A–E] M. K. Corbett, University of Maryland.

CHAPTER 17 17.1: David Schaus, Victoria Hospital, London, Ontario, Canada. 17.2: [B] Visuals Unlimited. 17.3: [A, B] Dr. W. Bowen. 17.5: Adapted from B. C. Block and J. Ducas, Man, Microbes, and Matter, McGraw-Hill, New York, 1975. 17.7: Stanley Flegler/Visuals Unlimited. 17.8: Anna Campana and E. C. S. Chan, McGill University. 17.9: David M. Phillips/

Visuals Unlimited. **17.10:** Manfred Kage/ Peter Arnold.

CHAPTER 18 18.1: Jack Bostrack/Visuals Unlimited. **18.2:** Liliane Therrien and E. C. S. Chan, McGill University. **18.6:** **[A, B]** Dorothea Zucker-Franklin, New York University Medical Center. **18.9:** Jacob Bastacky and Thomas L. Hayes, University of California at Berkeley. **18.11 [B]** David M. Phillips/Visuals Unlimited. **18.14:** **[A, B]** Jill A. Jenkins and D. D. Ourth, Memphis State University.

CHAPTER 19 19.1: After an original drawing by Malcolm Baines, McGill University. **19.2:** After an original drawing by Malcolm Baines, McGill University. **19.14: [A, B]** American Type Culture Collection.

CHAPTER 20 20.17: Liliane Therrien, Russell Siboo, and E. C. S. Chan, McGill University. **20.23:** E. C. S. Chan. DISCOVER **20.1:** Dr. A. Liepins/Science Photo Library/ Photo Researchers.

CHAPTER 21 21.1: Parke-Davis Division of Warner-Lambert Company. **21.2:** **[A]** The Bettmann Archive; **[B]** Robert Cruickshank. **21.3:** National Library of Medicine. **21.5: [A, B]** William Fenical, Scripps Institute of Oceanography. **21.10:** Roger D. Reid. **21.12:** The Research Corporation. **21.13: [A, B]** Department of Chemotherapy, Hoffmann-La Roche; **[C, D]** Department of Chemotherapy, Glaxo Group Research, Ltd. **21.21: [A–E]** Lilly Research Laboratories, Division of Eli Lilly and Company.

CHAPTER 22 22.1: [A] Parke-Davis Division of Warner-Lambert Company. **22.2: [A, B]** National Library of Medicine. **22.6: [A, B]** University of Maryland's Institute for Emergency Medical Services Systems. **22.8:** National Cancer Institute. **22.9:** Environmental Service Branch, National Institutes of Health, and Public Health Service.

CHAPTER 23 23.4: A. M. Siegelman/ Visuals Unlimited. **23.16:** Liliane Therrien and E. C. S. Chan, McGill University. **23.1; 23.3 [B]; 23.5 [A–F]; 23.7; 23.12 [B]; 23.15; 23.17 [B, C]; 23.20 [A–C]; 23.21; 23.22 [B]:** Centers for Disease Control, Atlanta, Ga.

CHAPTER 24 24.1: [A] Kent Wood/Photo Researchers; **[B]** Michael P. Gadomski/ Photo Researchers. **24.8:** Liliane Therrien and E. C. S. Chan, McGill University. **24.9:** N. R. Krieg. **24.10:** Dr. E. H. Cook/ Photo Researchers. **24.11: [A, C, D]** Centers for Disease Control, Atlanta, Ga.; **[B]** Randall C. Cultlip, *Infect. Immun.* 1:500, 1970. **24.12:** Frances Doane, University of Toronto. **24.4 [A, B]; 24.6; 24.7; 24.13; 24.14 [B]; 24.15 [A–F]; 24.16 [A–C]:** Centers for Disease Control, Atlanta, Ga.

CHAPTER 25 25.4: Orson K. Miller, Biology Dept., Virgina Polytechnic Institute. **25.6:** Adapted from a drawing by H. E. Marthedal in *Proc. Int. Symp. on Salmonella and Prospects for Control*, 1977. **25.7:** N. R. Krieg. **25.8: [A]** N. R. Krieg. **25.14: [A]** N. R. Krieg; **[B]** After an original drawing by N. R. Krieg. **25.2; 25.3 [A, B]; 25.5; 25.9 [A–E]; 25.11; 25.12; 25.13; 25.15 [A, B]; 25.16 [A–D]; 25.17:** Centers for Disease Control, Atlanta, Ga.

CHAPTER 26 26.1: U.S. Naval Biological Laboratory. **26.7:** E. C. Turner, Department of Entomology, Virginia Polytechnic Institute and State University, Blacksburg. **26.9:** Penelope J. Padgett, Department of Biology, Shippensburg University. **26.10:** Dr. Andrew Spielman, Department of Tropical Public Health, Harvard School of Medicine, Harvard University, Boston, and Centers for Disease Control, Atlanta, Ga. **26.19:** Fran Heyl Associates. **26.21:** Rhodes B. Holliman, Department of Biology, Virginia Polytechnic Institute and State University, Blacksburg. **26.22:** Rhodes B. Holliman, Department of Biology, Virginia Polytechnic Institute and State University, Blacksburg. **26.3; 26.6 [B]; 26.8 [A, B]; 26.12; 26.13; 26.14 [B]; 26.16; 26.17; 26.18; 26.20 [A]:** Centers for Disease Control, Atlanta, Ga.

CHAPTER 27 27.5: N. R. Krieg. **27.7: [A, B, D]** Centers for Disease Control, Atlanta, Ga.; **[C]** USDA, Bureau of Animal Industry; **[E]** Fred Marsik/Visuals Unlimited; **[F]** N. R. Krieg. **27.8: [B]** Tektoff-RM/Science Photo/Photo Researchers. **27.9:** J. Nowak, *Documenta Microbiologica*, Part 2, "Pilze und Protozoen," Gustav Fischer Verlag, Jena, Germany, 1930. **27.12:** Adapted from a diagram provided by courtesy of the Centers for Disease Control, Atlanta, Ga. **27.1; 27.3; 27.4 [A, B]; 27.6; 27.10 [A, B]; 27.11; 27.13; 27.14; 27.15; 27.16 [A, B]; 27.17 [A, B]; 27.18; 27.19; 27.20; 27.21:** Centers for Disease Control, Atlanta, Ga.

CHAPTER 28 28.2: Redrawn from T. Hattori, in R. W. Fairbridge and C. W. Finkl, Jr., eds., *The Encyclopedia of Soil Science*, Part 1, *Physics, Chemistry, Biology, Fertility, and Technology*, Dowden, Hutchinson and Ross, Inc., Stroudsburg, Pa. **28.3:** H. Boyd Woodruff. **28.5:** Redrawn from R. Campbell, 1983, based on data from J. F. Derbyshire and M. R. Greaves, *Can. Jour. Microb.* 13:1057, 1967, courtesy National Research Council, Canada. **28.6: [A, D]** K. M. Old, and *New Phytol.* 74:51, 1975. **28.7: [A, B]** Orson K. Miller, Biology Department, Virginia Polytechnic Institute and State University, Blacksburg. DISCOVER **28.1: [B, C]** Peter G. Hartel, *Appl. Environ. Microbiol.* 55:1291, May 1989. **28.8: [B]** General Biological Supply House. **28.9: [A, B]** Dennis D. Focht, Department of Soil and Environmental Sciences,

University of California, Riverside. **28.10: [A]** O'Driscoll/USDA; **[B]** Mirian Shilo, *J. Bacteriol.* 104:453, 1970. **28.12:** L. W. Erdman, USDA. **28.13:** Photomicrographs courtesy Frank B. Dazzo, Department of Microbiology, Michigan State University, East Lansing. **28.14: [A, B]** T. A. Lumpkin and Marcel Dekker, Inc., N.Y. DISCOVER **28.2: [A]** G. L. Leibee, University of Florida.

CHAPTER 29 29.2: K. O. Stetter. **29.4: [A, B]** W. A. Corpe, L. Matsuuchi, B. Armbruster and *Proc. 3d Int. Biodegradation Symp.*, 1976. **29.5: [A]** (*Noctiluca, Tintinnopsis*) Alexander J. Chester; (*Calanus, Euchaeta*) Charles H. Greene; (*Euphausia*) Mark D. Ohman; (*Brachionus*) Richard Kaiser; **[B]** (*Coscinodiscus*) National Marine Fisheries Service, NOAA, Micrograph by Michael Eng; (*Chaetoceros*) Beatrice C. Booth; (*Skeletonema*) B. Dumbauld; (*Navicula*) School of Oceanography, University of Washington; (*Gymnodinium, Gonyaulax*) Susan B. Stanton; (*Pyramimonas, Dichtyocha*) Beatrice C. Booth; **[C]** R. L. Irgens. **29.8:** Redrawn after G. Rheinheimer, *Aquatic Microbiology*, 3d ed., Wiley, New York, 1985. With permission of Dr. G. Rheinheimer, Institute für Meereskunde, Kiel. **29.10: [A]** E. H. Chave, HURL, University of Hawaii; **[B]** Dale Hebel, Department of Oceanography, University of Hawaii; **[C]** Florida Marine Research Institute, Florida, Department of Natural Resources. **29.11: [C]** F. H. Johnson, Princeton University. **29.12:** Redrawn from a drawing by Karen Teramura in C. P. White, *Chesapeake Bay, Nature of the Estuary: A Field Guide*, Tidewater Publishers, Centreville, Md., 1989. **29.13:** Adapted from *Patterns and Perspectives in Environmental Sciences*, National Science Board, 1972. **29.14:** M. E. Sieracki and L. K. Webb, Bigelow Laboratory for Ocean Sciences, West Boothbay Harbor, Maine. **29.15:** Redrawn after "Safe Water for the Farm," *Farmers' Bulletin*, no. 1978, U.S. Department of Agriculture, 1948. **29.18: [A–G]** Millipore Corporation. **29.19:** Redrawn after G. Tchobanoglous, *Wastewater Engineering: Collection and Pumping of Wastewater*, McGraw-Hill, New York, 1981. **29.20: [A]** Redrawn from Public Health Rep., Reprint 2361. **29.22:** R. E. McKinney, *Microbiology for Sanitary Engineers*, McGraw-Hill, New York, 1962. Used by permission. **29.23: [A–D]** R. F. Unz and N. C. Dondero, *Water Res.* 4:575, 1970.

CHAPTER 30 30.5: [A] NORDIAN International, Inc.; **[B]** Department of the Army. **30.6:** After W. C. Frazier and D. C. Westhoff, *Food Microbiology*, 4th ed., McGraw-Hill, New York, 1988. **30.9: [A, B]** H. P. Fleming, USDA. **30.10: [A–C]** E. A. Zottola, University of

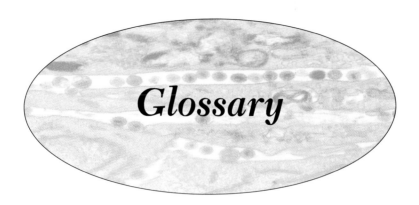

Glossary

ABIOGENESIS [ay·bye·o·JEN·uh·sis, ab·ee·o·JEN·uh·sis]. *See* **spontaneous generation.** (*Abio-* means nonliving; *genesis* means origin.)

ABIOTIC [ab·ee·OT·ik]. Pertaining to or characterized by the absence of living organisms.

ABSCESS [AB·sess]. A localized collection of pus in a cavity formed by tissue disintegration.

ACELLULAR SLIME MOLDS. True plasmodium—not cellular, but a mass of protoplasm with many nuclei.

ACERVULUS. An asexual fruiting body or reproductive structure in a fungus.

ACETYLENE REDUCTION TEST. A technique to measure nitrogenase activity.

ACID. A substance that ionizes in water and liberates a hydrogen ion.

ACID CURD. Milk protein coagulated by acid.

ACID DYE. A dye consisting of an acidic organic grouping of atoms (anion), which is the actively staining part, combined with a metal; the dye has affinity for cytoplasm.

ACID-FAST. Retaining the initial stain and difficult to decolorize with acid alcohol. A property of certain bacteria.

ACTINOMYCETES [ak·tin·o·MYE·seets]. Gram-positive bacteria that are characterized by the formation of branching filaments.

ACTIVATED-SLUDGE PROCESS. The use of biologically active sewage sludge to hasten the breakdown of organic matter in raw sewage during secondary treatment.

ACTIVE IMMUNITY. Specific resistance to disease acquired by individuals as a result of their own reactions to pathogenic microorganisms or to the products of such organisms.

ACTIVE TRANSPORT. The energy-requiring pumping of ions or other solutes across a cell membrane from a lower to a higher concentration.

ADAPTIVE ENZYME. An enzyme produced by an organism in response to the presence of the enzyme's substrate or a related substance. Also called *induced enzyme.*

ADENINE [AD·un·neen]. A purine component of nucleosides, nucleotides, and nucleic acids.

ADENOSINE [uh·DEN·o·seen]. A mononucleoside consisting of adenine and D-ribose, produced by the hydrolysis of adenosine monophosphate.

ADENOSINE DIPHOSPHATE (ADP). A compound consisting of adenosine and two phosphate groups.

ADENOSINE TRIPHOSPHATASE (ATPase). An enzyme that catalyzes the breakdown or synthesis of adenosine triphosphate (ATP).

ADENOSINE TRIPHOSPHATE (ATP). A compound consisting of adenosine and three phosphate groups.

ADENOVIRUSES. A group of icosahedral double-stranded DNA viruses.

ADJUVANT [AJ·oo·vunt]. A substance that when injected together with antigen increases antibody production.

AEROBE [AIR·obe]. An organism that can use oxygen as an electron acceptor at the terminus of an electron-transport chain, can grow at a level of O_2 equivalent to or higher than that present in an air atmosphere (21%), and has a strictly respiratory type of metabolism. *Compare* **anaerobe, microaerophile, facultative anaerobe.**

AEROBIC RESPIRATION. Respiration in which oxygen is the terminal electron acceptor for the electron-transport system. *Contrast with* **anaerobic respiration.**

AEROSOL. Atomized particles or droplets suspended in air.

AFLATOXIN [aff·luh·TAHK·sin]. The toxin produced by some strains of the fungus *Aspergillus flavus;* a carcinogen.

AGAR [AH·gar]. A dried polysaccharide extract of red algae (*Rhodophyceae*) used as a solidifying agent in microbiological media.

AGGLUTINATION [uh·gloo·tin·AY·shun]. The clumping of cells.

AGGLUTININ [uh·GLOO·tin·in]. An antibody capable of causing the clumping or agglutination of bacteria or other cells.

AKINETES. Thick-walled single-celled nonmotile asexual resting spores formed by the thickening of the parent cell wall; formed by some cyanobacteria.

ALGA, pl. **ALGAE** [AL·guh, AL·jee]. Any member of a heterogeneous group of eucaryotic, photosynthetic, and unicellular or multicellular organisms.

ALLELES [uh·LEELZ]. Two genes that are alternative occupants of the same chromosomal locus on a pair of homologous chromosomes.

ALLERGY. A type of antigen-antibody reaction marked by an exaggerated physiological response to a substance in sensitive individuals.

ALLOGRAFTS. Grafts (tissue) from genetically different members of the same species.

ALLOSTERIC ENZYMES [al·o·STEHR·ik, al·o·STEER·ik]. Regulatory enzymes with a binding or catalytic site for the substrate and a different site (the *allosteric site*) where a modulator acts.

ALPHA (α) HEMOLYSIS. Partial destruction of red blood cells on blood-agar medium, resulting in greenish zones around bacterial colonies.

ALTERNATE PATHWAY. A pathway of the complement system that does not depend on antibody for activation. *Compare* **classical pathway.**

ALVEOLI. Air sacs of the lung.

AMINO ACID [uh·MEEN·O]. An organic compound containing both amino (—NH$_2$) and carboxyl (—COOH) groups.

AMINOGLYCOSIDE ANTIBIOTICS. A class of antibiotics which disrupt the normal synthetic sequence of protein synthesis.

AMMONIFICATION [uh·mon·i·fi·KAY·shun, uh·mo·nif·i·KAY·shun). The decomposition of organic nitrogen compounds, e.g., proteins, by microorganisms, with the release of ammonia.

AMPHIPATHIC. Descriptive of compounds that contain polar or ionized groups at one end of the molecule and a nonpolar region at the other end.

AMPHITRICHOUS [am·FIT·rik·us]. Descriptive of a cell having a single flagellum at each end.

AMYLASE [AM·i·lase, AM·i·laze]. An enzyme that hydrolyzes starch.

ANABOLISM [uh·NAB·o·lizm]. The synthesis of cell constituents from simpler molecules, usually requiring energy. *Compare* **catabolism.**

ANAEROBE [AN·uh·robe]. An organism that does not use O$_2$ to obtain energy, that cannot grow under an air atmosphere, and for which O$_2$ is toxic. *Compare* **aerobe.**

ANAEROBIC RESPIRATION. Respiration in which a compound other than oxygen is the terminal electron acceptor for the electron-transport system. Terminal electron acceptors may include inorganic compounds such as fumarate or trimethylamine oxide. *Contrast with* **aerobic respiration.**

ANAMNESTIC RESPONSE [an·am·NESS·tik]. The heightened immunologic reaction to a second exposure to an antigen.

ANAPHYLATOXIN. A complement-derived peptide, C5a, that causes the release of histamine from mast cells.

ANAPHYLAXIS [an·uh·fi·LAK·sis]. Hypersensitivity in an animal following the parenteral injection of an antigen.

ANAPLASIA [an·uh·PLAY·zhuh]. Structural abnormality in a cell or cells.

ANIMALIA. The kingdom that includes animals that ingest food.

ANION. An ion with a negative charge.

ANIONIC DETERGENTS. Detergents whose wetting property is in the negatively charged portion of the molecule.

ANOXYGENIC. Not producing oxygen in the conversion of light energy into chemical energy.

ANTAGONISM. The killing, injury, or inhibition of growth of one species of microorganism by another when one organism adversely affects the environment of the other.

ANTHERIDIUM, pl. **ANTHERIDIA.** A male gametangium.

ANTHRAMYCIN. An antitumor antibiotic.

ANTIBACTERIAL. Descriptive of agents that kill or prevent growth of bacteria.

ANTIBIOSIS [an·tee·bye·O·sis]. An antagonistic association between two organisms in which one is adversely affected.

ANTIBIOTIC [an·tee·bye·OT·ik]. A substance of microbial origin that has antimicrobial activity in very small amounts.

ANTIBODY [AN·ti·bod·ee]. Any of a class of substances (proteins) produced by an animal in response to the introduction of an antigen.

ANTICODON [an·tee·KO·don]. A sequence of three nucleotides (in a *t*RNA) complementary to a codon triplet in *m*RNA.

ANTIFUNGAL. Descriptive of agents that kill or prevent growth of fungi.

ANTIGEN [AN·ti·jen]. A substance that when introduced into an animal body stimulates the production of specific substances (antibodies) that react or unite with the substance introduced (antigen).

ANTIGENIC DETERMINANT [an·ti·JEN·ik]. The part of an antigen molecule that, as the structural complement of certain chemical groupings on certain antibody molecules, determines the specificity of the antigen-antibody reaction.

ANTIGENICITY. Property of substances that can elicit an immune response.

ANTIMICROBIAL AGENT [an·tee·migh·KRO·bee·ul]. Any chemical or biologic agent that either destroys or inhibits the growth of microorganisms.

ANTIPROTOZOAN. Descriptive of agents that kill or prevent growth of protozoa.

ANTISEPSIS. Prevention of infection by inhibiting or destroying the causative agents of disease.

ANTISEPTIC. Acting against or opposing sepsis, putrefaction, or decay by either preventing or arresting the growth of microorganisms.

ANTISERUM [AN·tee·seer·um]. Blood serum that contains antibodies.

ANTITOXIN [an·tee·TAHK·sin]. An antibody capable of uniting with and neutralizing a specific toxin.

ANTIVIRAL. Descriptive of agents that kill or prevent growth of virus.

APERTURE. The magnitude of the angle subtended by the optical axis and the outermost rays still covered by the objective.

APLANOSPORE [ay·PLAN·o·spore]. A nonmotile spore; an abortive zoospore.

APOENZYME [ap·o·EN·zime]. The protein moiety (portion) of an enzyme.

APOPHYSIS [uh·PAH·fi·sis]. The base of the sporangium.

APOTHECIUM A sexual fruiting body in a fungus.

ARCHAEOBACTERIA. A major group of bacteria that includes the methanogens, the red extreme halophiles, and the thermoacidophiles, and which diverged from other bacteria at a very early stage in evolution. Also called *archaebacteria.*

ARTHROPOD [AHR·thro·pod]. An invertebrate with jointed legs, such as an insect or a crustacean.

ARTHROSPORE [AHR·thro·spore]. An asexual spore formed by the fragmentation of the mycelium.

ASCITIC FLUID [uh·SIT·ik]. Serous fluid that accumulates abnormally in the peritoneal cavity.

ASCOCARPS. Sexual fruiting bodies in which spores are produced.

ASCOMYCETES [ass·ko·migh·SEE·teez]. A class of fungi distinguished by the ascus.

ASCOSPORE [ASS·ko·spore]. A sexual spore, characteristic of the *Ascomycetes,* produced in a saclike structure (an ascus) after the union of the two nuclei.

ASCUS [ASS·kus]. A saclike structure, characteristic of the *Ascomycetes,* in which ascospores are produced.

ASEPSIS [ay·SEP·sis]. A condition in which harmful microorganisms are absent. Adjective: **aseptic** [ay·SEP·tik].

ASEPTIC PROCESSING. Procedure of sterilizing a food item and dispensing it into sterilized containers under aseptic conditions.

ASEPTIC TECHNIQUE. Precautionary measures taken to prevent contamination.

ASEXUAL REPRODUCTION. Production of new individuals by one parent organism or by one cell.

ASSAY [ASS·ay]. The qualitative or quantitative determination of the components of a material, such as a drug.

ASSIMILATION [uh·sim·i·LAY·shun]. The conversion of nutritive material into protoplasm.

ASSIMILATORY NITRATE REDUCTION. A process by which heterotrophic bacteria convert nitrate back to ammonia.

ASYMPTOMATIC [ay·sim·tuh·MAT·ik]. Exhibiting no symptoms.

ATOM. The individual structure which constitutes the basic unit of any chemical element.

ATOMIC NUMBER. The number of protons in the nucleus of a given atom.

ATOMIC WEIGHT. The sum of the weights of the neutrons and protons in the nucleus of a given atom.

ATP. *See* adenosine triphosphate.

ATTENUATION [uh·ten·yoo·AY·shun]. A weakening; a reduction in virulence.

AUTOCLAVE [AW·toe·klave]. An apparatus using pressurized steam for sterilization.

AUTOGENOUS VACCINE [aw·TOJ·uh·nus]. A vaccine prepared from bacteria isolated from the patient to be treated.

AUTOIMMUNE DISEASE [aw·toe·im·YOON]. A condition in which the body develops an immunologic reaction against its own tissues.

AUTOLYSINS [au·TOL·i·sins]. Enzymes present in a cell that catalyze the breakdown of cell structures.

AUTOLYSIS [aw·TOL·i·sis]. The disintegration of cells by the action of their own enzymes.

AUTOTROPH [AW·toe·trofe]. A microorganism that uses inorganic materials as a source of nutrients; carbon dioxide is the sole source of carbon. *Compare* **heterotroph.**

AUXOTROPHIC MUTANT [awk·so·TROE·fik]. An organism having a growth requirement of specific nutrients not necessary in the parental strain.

AVIRULENT. Descriptive of an organism that has lost the ability to cause disease.

AXENIC CULTURE [ay·ZEN·ik, ay·ZEE·nik]. A colony of a microorganism of a single species, e.g., a bacterium, a fungus, an alga, or a protozoan, growing in a medium free of other living organisms.

BACILLUS [buh·SIL·us], pl. **BACILLI** [buh·SIL·ligh]. Any rod-shaped bacterium.

BACTEREMIA [bak·tuh·REE·mee·uh]. A condition in which bacteria are present in the bloodstream.

BACTERIAL FILTER. A special type of filter through which bacterial cells cannot pass.

BACTERICIDE [bak·TEER·i·side]. An agent that destroys bacteria.

BACTERIOCHLOROPHYLL [bak·TEER·ee·o·KLOR·uh·fil]. A chlorophyll-like pigment possessed by anoxygenic photosynthetic bacteria.

BACTERIOCIN [bak·TEER·ee·o·sin]. *See* **bacteriocinogenic factor.**

BACTERIOCINOGENIC FACTOR [bak·TEER·ee·o·sin·o·JEN·ik]. A plasmid in some bacteria that determines the formation of bacteriocins, which are proteins that kill the same or closely related species of bacteria.

BACTERIOLYSIN [bak·TEER·ee·o·LYE·sin]. A substance that causes the disintegration of bacteria.

BACTERIOPHAGE [bak·TEER·ee·o·fayj]. A virus that infects bacteria and causes the lysis of bacterial cells.

BACTERIORHODOPSIN. A purple pigment that occurs in the cytoplasmic membrane of the group of archaeobacteria called the *red extreme halophiles;* similar to the rhodopsin that occurs in the retinal rods of higher vertebrates.

BACTERIOSTASIS [bak·TEER·ee·o·STAY·sis]. The inhibition of the growth and reproduction of bacteria without killing them.

BACTERIOSTATIC. Inhibiting the growth of bacteria without killing them.

BACTERIUM, pl. **BACTERIA** [bak·TEER·ee·um, bak·TEER·ee·uh]. Any of a group of diverse and ubiquitous procaryotic single-celled microorganisms.

BACTEROIDS. The morphological form of *Rhizobium* cells within the root nodules of legumes.

BAROPHILE. An organism that grows under conditions of high hydrostatic pressure.

BASAL BODY. The bottommost portion of a flagellum or cilium that anchors it to the cell.

BASE. A substance which when ionized releases a negatively charged ion that accepts a hydrogen ion.

BASIC DYE. A dye consisting of a basic organic grouping of atoms (cation), which is the actively staining part, combined with an acid, usually inorganic; the dye has affinity for nucleic acids.

BASIC MICROBIOLOGY. The study of the fundamental nature and properties of microorganisms.

BASIDIOCARP. Fruiting body that bears basidia, which produce basidiospores.

BASIDIOMYCETES [buh·SID·ee·o·mye·see·teez]. A class of fungi that form basidiospores.

BASIDIOSPORE [buh·SID·ee·o·spore]. A sexual spore produced following the union of two nuclei on a specialized clublike structure known as a *basidium.*

BASIDIUM [buh·SID·ee·um]. A club-shaped specialized structure of the *Basidiomycetes* on which are borne the exogenous basidiospores.

BCG VACCINE. Bacillus Calmette-Guérin vaccine; an attenuated strain of *Mycobacterium bovis* used to immunize against tuberculosis.

BENIGN TUMORS. Noncancerous tumors.

BENTHOS [BEN·thahss]. A collective term for the organisms living along the bottom of oceans and lakes.

BERGEY'S MANUAL OF SYSTEMATIC BACTERIOLOGY. An international reference work which classifies and describes bacteria.

BETA (β) HEMOLYSIS. Complete lysis of red blood cells on blood-agar medium by certain bacterial colonies, resulting in a sharply defined colorless, clear zone surrounding the colonies.

BETA (β-) LACTAM RING. Cyclic structure consisting of three carbon atoms and one nitrogen atom (a four-membered ring) present in some antibiotics.

BETA (β-) LACTAMASES. Enzymes that destroy the β-lactam ring in the core structure of antibiotics such as penicillins.

BINOMIAL NOMENCLATURE [bye·NO·mee·ul]. The scientific method of naming plants, animals, and microorganisms, so called because species names are binomial, i.e., consist of two terms.

BIOCHEMICAL OXYGEN DEMAND. A measure of the amount of oxygen consumed in biological processes that break down organic matter in water; a measure of the organic pollutant load. Abbreviation: BOD.

BIOCHEMISTRY. A branch of chemistry that deals specifically with chemistry in relation to life processes.

BIODEGRADABLE [bye·o·dee·GRADE·uh·bul]. Capable of being broken down by microorganisms.

BIOGENESIS [bye·o·JEN·uh·sis]. The production of living organisms only from other living organisms. *Compare* **spontaneous generation.**

BIOGEOCHEMICAL AGENTS [bye·o·jee·o·KEM·i·kul]. Microorganisms that mediate transformations of elements in global cycling.

BIOINSECTICIDES. Chemicals made by microorganisms (or microorganisms themselves) used to kill insects.

BIOLOGICAL VECTOR. A disease-transmitting arthropod in which a pathogen undergoes growth and development.

BIOLUMINESCENCE [bye·o·loo·min·ESS·unce]. The emission of light by living organisms.

BIOMASS [BYE·o·mass]. The mass of living matter present in a specified area.

BIPOLAR STAINING. Process in which cells stain deeply in areas at both ends.

BIOREMEDIATION. The use of naturally occurring or genetically engineered biological agents (microorganisms) to remove toxic pollutants from the environment.

BIOSOLIDS. Particulate organic solids in sewage; also called *sludge.*

BIOSPHERE [BYE·o·sfeer]. The zone of the earth that includes the lower atmosphere and the upper layers of soil and water.

BIOSYNTHETIC PROCESSES. The construction of chemical substances by cells from simple inorganic compounds.

BIOTECHNOLOGY. The combination of scientific and engineering principles that use biological agents to process materials into commercially valuable products.

BIOVAR. A subdivision of a species based upon physiological characteristics. Also called *biotype.*

BLASTOSPORE [BLASS·toe·spore]. A spore produced by a budding process along the hypha or by a single cell.

BLOOD PLASMA. The fluid portion of blood. Also called *plasma.*

BLOOD SERUM. The fluid expressed from clotted blood or clotted blood plasma.

BLOOM. A colored area on the surface of a body of water caused by heavy growth of plankton.

BOD. See **biochemical oxygen demand.**

BONE MARROW–DERIVED LYMPHOCYTES (B CELLS). One kind of cell capable of responding to antigens to produce antibodies.

BRAUN'S LIPOPROTEIN. A cell-wall lipoprotein which anchors the outer membrane of enteric Gram-negative bacteria to the peptidoglycan layer.

BRIGHT-FIELD MICROSCOPY. The use of a bright light source that illuminates the entire specimen field.

BROAD-SPECTRUM ANTIBIOTICS. Antimicrobial agents produced by microbes that are effective against many species of microorganisms.

BRONCHI. Branches of the trachea.

BREED SMEAR. A microscopic method of counting bacteria in a dried, stained film of milk.

BROWNIAN MOTION [BROWN·ee·un]. A peculiar dancing motion exhibited by finely divided particles and bacteria in suspension, due to bombardment by the molecules of the fluid.

BUBO. A swollen infected lymph node.

BUDDING. A form of asexual reproduction typical of yeast, in which a new cell is formed as an outgrowth from the parent cell.

BUFFER. A chemical mixture that causes a solution to resist change in pH.

BURST SIZE. The number of bacteriophages produced upon lysis of a bacterial cell.

CALCIUM CHLORIDE ($CaCl_2$) TRANSFORMATION. A method to insert DNA or plasmids into recipient bacteria.

CALLUS. A mass of unorganized plant cells when grown on agar.

CALORIE. A unit of heat; the amount of heat required to raise the temperature of 1 g of water by 1°C.

CAPSID. The protein coat of a virus.

CAPSOMERE [KAP·so·meer]. A morphologic subunit of a capsid as seen by electron microscopy.

CAPSULE. An envelope or slime layer surrounding the cell wall of certain microorganisms.

CARBON DIOXIDE (CO_2) FIXATION. The reduction of carbon dioxide (CO_2) to carbohydrate (CH_2O) by a cell.

CARCINOMAS. Solid tumors that grow from epithelial tissues.

CARDINAL TEMPERATURES. The minimum, optimum, and maximum growth temperatures of a microbial species.

CARDIOLIPIN. A lipid component of the cytoplasmic membrane of human and other mammalian cells.

CAROTENOID. A water-insoluble pigment, usually yellow, orange, or red, which consists of a long aliphatic polyene chain composed of isoprene units.

CARRIER. A person in apparently good health who harbors a pathogenic microorganism.

CARRIER PROTEINS. Special proteins that transport nutrients across the cytoplasmic membrane.

CATABOLISM [kuh·TAB·o·lizm]. The dissimilation, or breakdown, of complex organic molecules, releasing energy. A part of the total process of metabolism. *Compare* **anabolism.**

CATALASE [KAT·uh·lase, KAT·uh·laze]. An enzyme that catalyzes the breakdown of hydrogen peroxide to water and oxygen.

CATALYST [KAT·uh·list]. Any substance that accelerates a chemical reaction but remains unaltered in form and amount.

CATION. An ion with an overall positive charge.

CATIONIC DETERGENTS. Detergents having their cleaning property in the negatively charged portion of the molecule.

CAVITATION [kav·i·TAY·shun]. The use of high-frequency sound waves in liquid to produce small bubbles that collapse violently, disintegrating microbial cells.

CECUM. The distended intestinal pouch into which open the ileum, the colon, and the appendix.

CELL. The microscopic, functionally and structurally basic unit of all living organisms.

CELL-MEDIATED CYTOTOXICITY (CMC). The cytolytic reaction, specific with sensitized lymphocytes, cytotoxic only for target cells bearing the same epitopes as the stimulating cells.

CELLULAR SLIME MOLDS. The group of protozoanlike cells in the fungi.

CELLULASE [SEL·yoo·lase]. An extracellular enzyme that hydrolyzes cellulose to produce cellobiose.

CELLULOSE. A complex polysaccharide consisting of many glucose molecules; the characteristic structural material of plant cell walls.

CELL WALL. A rigid external covering of the cytoplasmic membrane.

CENTRIFUGE. An apparatus that uses centrifugal force to separate or remove particulate matter suspended in a liquid.

CENTRIOLES. Cylinders of protein microtubules found in eucaryotic cells that migrate to opposite sides of the cell during mitosis.

CENTROMERE. A ring of protein that joins duplicated chromosomes in the process of mitosis.

CERCARIAE. The infective forms of schistosomes (flatworms).

CESTODES. Tapeworms.

CHELATING AGENT. An organic compound in which atoms form more than one coordinate bond with metals, keeping them in solution.

CHEMICAL ENERGY. Energy contained in the chemical bonds of a compound.

CHEMICAL REACTION. The interaction of molecules, atoms, or ions resulting in the formation of one or more new substances.

CHEMICALLY DEFINED MEDIA. Media whose exact chemical composition is known.

CHEMIOSMOTIC THEORY. A theory which states that the energy liberated by the oxidation-reduction reactions of a respiratory chain can be conserved in the form of an electrochemical gradient of protons across the membrane; this gradient then is used to drive the synthesis of ATP.

CHEMISTRY. The science that deals with the composition, structure, and properties of substances and the transformations they undergo.

CHEMOAUTOTROPH [kee·mo·AW·toe·trofe]. An organism that obtains energy by oxidizing inorganic compounds. Carbon dioxide is the sole source of carbon.

CHEMOHETEROTROPH. An organism that uses chemical substances (organic) as sources of energy and organic compounds as the source of carbon.

CHEMOLITHOTROPH [kee·mo·LITH·o·trofe]. An organism that uses inorganic compounds as electron donors and relies on chemical compounds for energy.

CHEMOPROPHYLAXIS. The use of chemicals such as antibiotics to prevent disease.

CHEMORECEPTORS. Proteins located on the cytoplasmic membrane which sense gradients and are specific for various attractants and repellents.

CHEMOSTAT [KEE·mo·stat, KEM·o·stat]. A device for maintaining organisms in continuous culture; it regulates the growth rate of the organisms by regulating the concentration of an essential nutrient.

CHEMOTAXIS [kee·mo·TAK·sis]. The movement of an organism in response to a chemical stimulus.

CHEMOTHERAPEUTIC AGENTS. Chemicals used in treatment of diseases.

CHEMOTHERAPY [kee·mo·THEHR·uh·pee]. The treatment of a disease by the use of chemicals.

CHEMOTROPH [KEE·mo·trofe]. An organism that uses chemical compounds for energy. *Compare* **phototroph**.

CHITIN. A polymer of *N*-acetylglucosamine present in the covering layer of arthropods and in the cell walls of many fungi.

CHLAMYDOSPORE [KLAM·id·o·spore]. A thick-walled, resistant spore formed by the direct differentiation of the cells of the mycelium.

CHLORAMINES. Organic chlorine-containing compounds used as disinfectants.

CHLOROPHYLL [KLOR·uh·fil]. A light-trapping green pigment essential as an electron donor in photosynthesis and serving as an electron donor to drive the synthesis of ATP.

CHLOROPLAST [KLOR·o·plast]. A cell plastid (specialized organelle) in plants and algae that contains chlorophyll pigments and functions in photosynthesis.

CHROMATIN. Threads of combined DNA and protein.

CHROMATIN BODY. Bacterial nuclear material.

CHROMATOPHORE. A pigment-containing body; specifically applied to chlorophyll-bearing granules in bacteria.

CHROMOGENESIS. The production of pigments by microorganisms.

CHROMOSOME [KRO·muh·sohm]. A gene-containing filamentous structure in a cell nucleus; the number of chromosomes per cell nucleus is constant for each species.

CHRONIC CARRIERS. Persons recovered from typhoid fever or another disease who continue to excrete the pathogen.

CHYTRIDIOMYCETES. A class of fungi that produce zoospores, each of which possesses a single posterior whiplash flagellum.

CILIUM, pl. **CILIA** [SIL·ee·um, SIL·ee·uh]. On certain eucaryotic cells, a relatively short, hairlike appendage which is capable of a vibratory beating or lashing movement.

CISTRON [SISS·trahn]. The genetic unit that carries information for the synthesis of a single enzyme or protein molecule; determined by the cis-trans complementation test.

CITRIC ACID CYCLE. A cyclic sequence of biochemical reactions by which pyruvic acid is oxidized to carbon dioxide and water with the concomitant reduction of NAD to $NADH_2$ and FAD to $FADH_2$.

CLASSICAL PATHWAY. A pathway of the complement system that is activated by antibodies.

CLASSIFICATION. The systemic arrangement of units (e.g., organisms) into groups, and often further arrangement of those groups into larger groups.

CLONAL SELECTION THEORY OF IMMUNITY. A theory of antibody formation. Selected lymphocytes, whose receptors interact with a specific antigen, respond by undergoing mitosis and producing a clone of cells expressing the same receptor specificity and secreting the same type of antibodies.

CLONE [KLOHN]. A population of cells descended from a single cell.

CLONING VECTOR. A plasmid into which a fragment of foreign DNA has been inserted, and which serves as the vehicle by which the DNA fragment is placed into a recipient cell.

COAGULASE [ko·AG·yoo·lase, ko·AG·yoo·laze]. An enzyme, produced by pathogenic staphylococci, that causes the coagulation of blood plasma.

COCCUS [KOCK·us] pl. **COCCI** [KAHK·sigh]. A spherical bacterium.

CODON [KO·dahn]. A sequence of three nucleotide bases (in *m*RNA) that codes for an amino acid or the initiation or termination of a polypeptide chain.

COENOCYTIC [see·no·SIT·ik]. A term applied to a cell or an aseptate hypha containing numerous nuclei.

COENZYME [ko·EN·zime]. The nonprotein portion of an enzyme.

COFACTORS. Metal ions which function in combination with the enzyme protein and are regarded as coenzymes.

COLIPHAGE [KO·li·fayj]. A virus that infects *Escherichia coli*.

COLONY. A macroscopically visible growth of microorganisms on a solid culture medium.

COLONY-FORMING UNIT (CFU). The cell or aggregate of cells which gives rise to a single colony in the plate-culture technique.

COLOSTRUM. The first milk secreted by a mother after giving birth.

COLUMELLA. The dome-shaped apex of the sporangiophore in some phycomycetes.

COMMENSALISM [kuh·MEN·suh·lizm]. A relationship between members of different species living in proximity (the same cultural environment) in which one organism benefits from the association but the other is not affected.

COMMUNICABLE. Pertaining to a disease whose causative agent is readily transferred from one person to another.

COMPETITION. A form of symbiosis in which species compete for available nutrients.

COMPETITIVE INHIBITION. The inhibition of the action of an enzyme by a nonsubstrate molecule occupying the site on the enzyme that would otherwise be occupied by the substrate.

COMPLEMENT [KOM·pluh·ment]. A normal thermolabile protein constituent of blood serum that participates in antigen-antibody reactions.

COMPLEMENTARY BASE PAIR. A-T or G-C. In double-stranded DNA, adenine (A) on one DNA strand is linked by hydrogen bonds to thymine (T) on the other strand, or guanine (G) is linked to cytosine (C).

COMPLEMENTARY DNA (CDNA). DNA artificially produced by RNA-directed DNA polymerase.

COMPLEMENT FIXATION. The binding of complement to an antigen-antibody complex so that the complement is unavailable for a subsequent reaction.

COMPOUNDS. Substances composed of a single kind of molecule.

COMPROMISED HOST. A person already weakened by debilitating disease, malnutrition, or some other cause.

CONGENITAL INFECTION. A disease acquired by a fetus in the mother's womb.

CONIDIOPHORE [ko·NID·ee·o·fore]. A hypha which bears conidiospores.

CONIDIOSPORES [ko·NID·ee·o·spore]. Any asexual spores which are formed at the tip of a hypha and which are not enclosed within a sac (as distinguished from sporangiospores). Also called *conidia*.

CONIDIUM [ko·NID·ee·um], pl. **CONIDIA**. An asexual spore that may be one-celled or many-celled and may be of many sizes and shapes. Also called *conidiospore*.

CONJUGATION. A mating process characterized by the temporary fusion of the mating partners and the transfer of genes. Conjugation occurs particularly in unicellular organisms.

CONJUNCTIVA. The membrane covering the eyeball and lining the eyelids.

CONTAMINATION. The entry of undesirable organisms into some material or object.

CONTINUOUS CELL LINES. Transformed cell cultures which can be maintained indefinitely.

CONTINUOUS CULTURE. Culture in which continued growth is ensured by adding fresh sterile medium at the same rate that used cell-containing medium is removed (also known as an *open system*).

CORD FACTOR. A toxic mycolic acid derivative, trehalose dimycolate, which occurs in the cell walls of corynebacteria and mycobacteria.

COUNTERCURRENT IMMUNOELECTRO-PHORESIS. Technique to detect antigens and antibodies by forcing them toward each other in an electrical field.

COVALENT BOND. A linkage based on sharing a pair of electrons, represented in writing by a dash connecting two symbols for elements in a formula: e.g., H—O—H.

CRISTAE. Infoldings of the inner membrane of the mitochondrion increasing the surface area for respiratory activity.

CRUSTOSE. A flat, crustlike growth of lichens.

CULTURE. A population of microorganisms cultivated in a medium.

CURD. Coagulated milk casein.

CYANOBACTERIA. Oxygenic phototrophs, formerly called *blue-green algae*.

CYST. A thick-walled dormant form of an organism which is resistant to desiccation, e.g., the cysts formed by certain bacteria such as *Azotobacter* or by various protozoa.

CYSTICERCI. Dormant encysted forms of tapeworm.

CYTOCHROME [SIGH·toe·krome]. One of a group of iron porphyrins that serve as reversible oxidation-reduction carriers in respiration.

CYTOKINESIS. The division of the cytoplasm following nuclear division.

CYTOLYSIS. The dissolution or disintegration of a cell.

CYTOPATHIC EFFECT (CPE). The deterioration of tissue-culture cells caused by a virus.

CYTOPHARYNX. The region through which nutrients must pass to be enclosed in a food vacuole.

CYTOPLASM [SIGH·toe·plazm]. The living matter of a cell between the cell membrane and the nucleus.

CYTOPLASMIC MEMBRANE. A thin layer under the cell wall consisting mainly of phospholipids and proteins; it is responsible for the selective permeability properties of the cell. Also called *plasma membrane*.

CYTOSKELETON. A network of fibrils that helps maintain the shape of the cell.

CYTOSTOME. The opening through which food is ingested in ciliates.

DARK-FIELD MICROSCOPY. A type of microscopic examination in which the microscopic field is dark and any objects, such as organisms, are brightly illuminated.

DEAMINASE. An enzyme involved in the removal of an amino group from a molecule; ammonia is liberated.

DEAMINATION [dee·am·i·NAY·shun]. The removal of an amino group, especially from an amino acid.

DEATH PHASE. Decline in viable population until all microbial cells die in a closed system of microbial cultivation. Also called the *decline phase*.

DECARBOXYLASE. An enzyme that liberates carbon dioxide from the carboxyl group of a molecule, e.g., an amino acid.

DECARBOXYLATION [dee·kar·bock·si·LAY·shun]. The removal of a carboxyl group (—COOH).

DECIMAL REDUCTION TIME. The amount of time at a particular temperature sufficient to reduce a viable microbial population by 90 percent.

DEHYDRATION. The removal of water.

DEHYDROGENASE. An enzyme which oxidizes a substrate by removing hydrogen atoms from it.

DELAYED-HYPERSENSITIVITY LYMPHOCYTES (DHL). Sensitized T lymphocytes that produce lymphokines.

DEMINERALIZATION [dee·min·ur·ul·i·ZAY·shun]. The process by which acid produced by bacteria dissolves the calcium salts of tooth enamel.

DENATURE [dee·NAY·chur]. To modify, by physical or chemical action, the structure of an organic substance, especially a protein.

DENITRIFICATION [dee·nigh·tri·fi·KAY·shun]. The reduction of nitrates to nitrogen gas.

DENSITY GRADIENT CENTRIFUGATION. A technique in which a mixture of proteins or nucleic acids is centrifuged in a liquid whose density increases from top to bottom. Each substance in the mixture localizes at its own particular density level.

DENTAL PLAQUE [PLAK]. An aggregation of bacteria and organic material on the tooth surface.

DEOXYRIBONUCLEIC ACID [dee·AHK·see·rye·bo·new·KLEE·ik]. The carrier of genetic information; a type of nucleic acid occurring in cells, containing phosphoric acid, D-2-deoxyribose, adenine, guanine, cytosine, and thymine. Abbreviation: DNA.

DEOXYRIBONUCLEOTIDES. Nucleotides having the sugar deoxyribose as the pentose and used for biosynthesis of DNA.

DEOXYRIBOSE [dee·ahk·see·RYE·bose, dee·ahk·see·RYE·boze]. A five-carbon sugar having one oxygen atom fewer than the parent sugar, ribose; a component of DNA.

DERMATOMYCOSES. Infections of hair, nails, and skin by pathogenic fungi.

DERMATOPHYTES. Pathogenic fungi.

DERMATOTROPIC [dur·muh·toe·TROPE·ik]. Having a selective affinity for the skin.

DERMIS. The connective tissue layer under the epidermis.

DESMID. Any of several freshwater algae.

DESQUAMATION. The shedding of epithelial cells from the body surface.

DESULFURASE. An enzyme that removes sulfur from a compound.

DETERGENT. A synthetic cleaning material containing surface-active agents which do not precipitate in hard water.

DETRITUS. Particulate organic matter suspended in water.

DEUTEROMYCETES. A taxon of fungi that are not known to have a sexual stage in the life cycle.

DEXTRAN [DEKS·tran]. A polysaccharide (glucose polymer) produced by a wide range of microorganisms, sometimes in large amounts.

DIALYSIS [dye·AL·i·sis]. The separation of soluble substances from colloids by diffusion through a semipermeable membrane.

DIALYZE. To pass through a semipermeable membrane.

DIAMINOPIMELIC ACID (DAP). A seven-carbon diamino acid that occurs as a component of cell-wall peptidoglycan in some bacteria.

DIATOMITE. Silica-containing shells (cell walls) resulting from centuries of growth of diatoms.

DIATOMS. An aggregate of unicellular algae with cell walls composed of silica, a component of phytoplankton.

DIAUXIC GROWTH [dye·AWK·sik]. Growth in two separate phases due to the preferential use of one carbon source over another; a temporary lag occurs between the phases.

DIFFERENTIAL MEDIA. Culture media used to differentiate among kinds of microorganisms by differences in colonial appearance or by different changes in the medium.

DIFFERENTIAL STAIN. A procedure using a series of dye solutions or staining reagents to bring out differences in microbial cells.

DIMORPHIC [dye·MORE·fik]. Occurring in two forms.

DINOFLAGELLATES. Unicellular algae with two flagella, which produce a twirling motion.

DIPLOBACILLI [dip·lo·buh·SIL·eye]. Bacilli occurring in pairs.

DIPLOCOCCI [dip·lo·KAHK·sigh]. Cocci occurring in pairs.

DIPLOID [DIP·loyd]. Having chromosomes in pairs the members of which are homologous; having twice the haploid number.

DISACCHARIDE [dye·SAK·uh·ride]. A sugar composed of two monosaccharides.

DISINFECTANT. An agent that frees from infection by killing the vegetative cells of microorganisms.

DISINFECTION. Process using a chemical substance to destroy infectious microorganisms.

DISK-PLATE TECHNIQUE. A procedure to determine whether a microorganism is resistant or susceptible to various antibiotics.

DISSIMILATION [dis·sim·i·LAY·shun]. Chemical reactions that release energy by the breakdown of nutrients or chemical substances.

DNA. See deoxyribonucleic acid.

DNA-DEPENDENT RNA POLYMERASE. An enzyme that catalyzes the synthesis of RNA by using DNA as a template.

DNA LIGASE. An enzyme that can connect, or ligate, broken sugar-phosphate linkage in DNA.

DNA PROBE. A piece of single-stranded DNA, labeled in some manner (e.g., by means of a radioisotope), that is used to detect the presence of a complementary DNA sequence by binding specifically to it.

ECOLOGY. The study of the interrelationships that exist between organisms and their environment.

ECOSYSTEM. A functional system which includes the organisms of a natural community together with their environment.

ECTOTROPHIC. Said of root-fungus associations in which fungal parasites growing on the outside root surface obtain nourishment from the plant.

EDEMA [eh·DEE·muh]. The excessive accumulation of fluid in body tissue.

EFFLUENT [EFF·loo·unt]. The liquid waste of sewage and industrial processing.

ELECTROIMMUNOASSAY. A technique that combines immunoelectrophoresis assay and radial immunodiffusion.

ELECTROMAGNETIC RADIATION. Energy in the form of waves transmitted through space or through a material.

ELECTRON. An elementary particle (i.e., a component of an atom) that has one unit of negative electric charge and is about 1840 times lighter than a proton or neutron.

ELECTRON MICROSCOPE. An instrument that uses a beam of electrons controlled by a system of magnetic fields to produce magnification.

ELECTRON-TRANSPORT SYSTEM. An integrated series of sequential oxidation reactions in which energy is released incrementally. Also called *respiratory chain.*

ELECTROPHORESIS. An electrochemical process in which suspended particles with an electric charge migrate in a solution under the influence of an electric current.

ELEMENT. Substance consisting of one kind of atom as defined by atomic number.

ELEPHANTIASIS. A condition in which parts of the body are grossly swollen.

ELISA (ENZYME-LINKED IMMUNOSORBENT ASSAY). A serological diagnostic technique that uses an antibody chemically linked to an enzyme.

END-PRODUCT REPRESSION. Type of regulation of a biosynthetic pathway in which the end product of the pathway activates a repressor that inhibits gene transcription.

ENDEMIC [en·DEM·ik]. With reference to a disease, one that has a low incidence but which is constantly present in a particular geographic region.

ENDERGONIC [en·dur·GAHN·ik]. Describing or pertaining to a chemical reaction which requires the input of free energy in order to proceed.

ENDOCARDITIS. Inflammation of the membrane lining the heart and its valves.

ENDOENZYME [EN·doe·EN·zime]. An enzyme formed within the cell and not excreted into the medium. Also called *intracellular enzyme.*

ENDOFLAGELLA. *See* **periplasmic flagella.**

ENDOGENOUS [en·DAHJ·uh·nus]. Produced or originating from within.

ENDOLYSIN. An enzyme that lyses a phage-infected bacterial cell and releases mature phages.

ENDONUCLEASE. An enzyme that hydrolyzes bonds at sites within a molecule of nucleic acid (as opposed to an *exonuclease*, which hydrolyzes bonds only at the end of a nucleic acid molecule).

ENDOPHYTIC [en·doe·FIT·ik]. Describing or pertaining to algae that are not free-living but live in other organisms.

ENDOPLASMIC RETICULUM [en·doe·PLAZ·mik ree·TIK·yoo·lum]. An extensive array of internal membranes in a eucaryotic cell.

ENDOSPORE [EN·doe·spore]. A thick-walled spore formed in the bacterial cell. Very resistant to physical and chemical agents.

ENDOSYMBIONT. An organism that lives within the body of the host without a deleterious effect on the host.

ENDOTHERMIC [en·doe·THUR·mik]. Describing or pertaining to a chemical reaction in which energy is consumed overall.

ENDOTOXIN [en·doe·TAHK·sin]. A heat-stable toxin which consists of the "lipid A" portion of lipopolysaccharide; it is located in the outer membrane of Gram-negative bacteria and is liberated only when the bacteria disintegrate.

ENDOTROPHIC. Said of root-fungus associations in which fungal parasites growing within the plant root cells obtain nourishment from them.

ENRICHMENT MEDIA. Media used to grow species of microorganisms with special nutritional requirements that occur in low numbers in the inoculum sample.

ENTERIC [en·TEHR·ik]. Pertaining to the intestines.

ENTEROBACTERIACEAE. A family of genetically interrelated, Gram-negative facultative rod-shaped bacteria many of which inhabit the gastrointestinal tract.

ENTEROTOXIN. A protein toxin excreted from microbial cells that causes diarrhea when ingested.

ENTOMOPATHOGENS. A group of microorganisms that cause diseases in insects.

ENZYME [EN·zime]. An organic catalyst produced by an organism. See also **adaptive enzyme; endoenzyme; exoenzyme;** and **enzyme, constitutive.**

ENZYME, ADAPTIVE. *See* **adaptive enzyme.**

ENZYME, CONSTITUTIVE. An enzyme whose formation is not dependent upon the presence of a specific substrate.

ENZYME, INDUCIBLE. *See* **adaptive enzyme.**

ENZYME, INTRACELLULAR. *See* **endoenzyme.**

EPIBACTERIA. Bacteria that adhere to solid surfaces.

EPICELLULAR. On the surface of host cells.

EPIDEMIC [ep·i·DEM·ik]. With reference to a disease, one that displays a sudden increase in incidence in a particular geographic region.

EPIDEMIOLOGY [ep·i·dee·mee·AHL·uh·jee, ep·i·dem·ee·AHL·uh·jee]. The study of the occurrence and distribution of disease.

EPIDERMIS. The outer surface of the skin.

EPITOPES. Particular sites of the antigen surface with which antibodies will react specifically.

EQUIVALENCE ZONE. Zone of optimum concentration of antigen and antibody for complete precipitation.

ERGOT. A toxin resulting from infection of grain that, when eaten, causes abortion or death in humans and other animals.

ERYTHROCYTIC CYCLE (in malaria). Cycle of red blood cell invasion in malarial infection. When a *Plasmodium* merozoite infects a human red blood

cell, it develops into a trophozoite, which divides to produce more merozoites. As the blood cell disintegrates, the merozoites are released to attack more red blood cells. This produces more merozoites that attack more red blood cells, and so on.

ERYTHROGENIC TOXIN. A toxin produced by some strains of *Streptococcus pyogenes* that causes the skin rash of scarlet fever.

ESTERASE. One of a group of enzymes that catalyze the hydrolysis of esters.

ESTUARY. A semienclosed coastal body of water which opens to the sea.

ETIOLOGY [ee·tee·AHL·uh·jee]. The study of the cause of a disease.

EUBACTERIA. One of the two major groups of bacteria (the other being the archaeobacteria). Eubacteria have fundamental features that are considered to be typical of most bacteria.

EUCARYOTE [yoo·CARE·ee·ote]. A cell that possesses a definitive or true nucleus. *Compare* **procaryote.**

EUGLENOIDS. Algae with chlorophyll *a* and *b* that belong to the division *Euglenophyta.*

EUTROPHIC. Descriptive of a lake or pond enriched with nutrients resulting in massive microbial growth and causing depletion of oxygen.

EVAPOTRANSPIRATION. Evaporation from soil surfaces, lakes, and streams and by transpiration from plants into the atmosphere.

EXERGONIC [ek·sur·GAHN·ik]. Energy-yielding, as in a chemical reaction.

EXOENZYME [ek·so·EN·zime]. An enzyme secreted by a microorganism into the environment. Also called *extracellular enzyme.*

EXOGENOUS [ek·SAHJ·uh·nus]. Produced or originating from without.

EXONS. Regions that code for proteins in eucaryotic genes.

EXONUCLEASE [ek·so·NEW·klee·ase, ek·so·NEW·klee·aze]. An enzyme that hydrolyzes a nucleic acid, starting at one end.

EXOSPORE. A heat- and desiccation-resistant spore formed external to the vegetative cell by a budding process; e.g., the exospores of the methane-oxidizing genus *Methylosinus.*

EXOTHERMIC [ek·so·THUR·mik]. Describing a chemical reaction that gives off energy.

EXOTOXIN [ek·so·TAHK·sin]. A toxic protein excreted by a microorganism into the surrounding medium.

EXPLANTS. Small pieces of animal or plant cell tissue immersed in a sterile balanced-salt solution for growth in vitro.

EXPONENTIAL DEATH [ek·spuh·NEN·chul]. Pattern of death of microorganisms—death at a constant rate over a period of time.

EXPONENTIAL GROWTH PHASE. The period of culture growth when cells divide steadily at a constant rate. Also called *logarithmic phase* (commonly, *log phase*).

EXTRACHROMOSOMAL GENETIC ELEMENT [ek·struh·kro·muh·so·mul]. A genetic element, called a *plasmid*, that is capable of autonomous replication in the cytoplasm of the bacterial cell.

EXUDATE [EKS·yoo·date]. The more or less fluid material found in a lesion or inflamed tissue.

Fab. Either of the two antigen-binding fragments that result from the action of papain on the immunoglobulin monomer. The Fab fragments contain the specific antigen-binding sites of the antibody.

FACILITATED DIFFUSION A category of carrier-mediated transport across a cell membrane.

FACULTATIVE ANAEROBE [FAK·ul·TAY·tiv]. An organism which does not require O_2 for growth (but may use it if available), which grows well under both aerobic and anaerobic conditions, and for which oxygen is not toxic.

FASTIDIOUS ORGANISM [fass·TID·ee·us]. An organism that is difficult to isolate or cultivate on ordinary culture media because of its need for special nutritional factors.

F PLASMID. Fertility piece of double-stranded DNA (not a part of the bacterial chromosome) that replicates independently; formerly called *F factor.*

FC. The crystallizable fragment that results from the action of papain on an immunoglobulin monomer. It is identical for all antibodies of the same class and determines many of the physical properties of an antibody molecule.

FEEDBACK INHIBITION. A cellular control mechanism by which the end product of a series of metabolic reactions inhibits the further activity of an earlier enzyme of the sequence.

FERMENTATION. An energy-yielding process that does not involve an electron-transport chain and an exogenous terminal electron acceptor but instead relies on substrate-level phosphorylation and an endogenously generated electron acceptor (e.g., pyruvate from glycolysis, which can be reduced to lactate). *Contrast with* **respiration.**

FIBRIN. An insoluble protein formed during the clotting of blood.

FIBRINOLYSIN [figh·bri·NAHL·i·sin]. A substance, produced by hemolytic streptococci, that can liquefy clotted blood plasma or fibrin clots. Also called *streptokinase.*

FILAMENTOUS [fil·uh·MEN·tus]. Characterized by threadlike structures.

FILARIAS. A group of pathogenic nematodes.

FILTER, BACTERIOLOGICAL. A special type of filter through which bacterial cells cannot pass.

FIMBRIA, pl. **FIMBRIAE,** [FIM·bree·uh, FIM·bree·ee]. Surface appendages of certain Gram-negative bacteria, composed of protein subunits. They are shorter and thinner than flagella. Also called *pili.*

FISSION [FISH·un]. An asexual process by which some microorganisms reproduce; transverse cell division in bacteria.

FISSION, BINARY. A single nuclear division followed by the division of the cytoplasm to form two daughter cells of equal size.

FLAGELLATES [FLAJ·uh·luts, FLAJ·uh·laits]. Members of one of the subphyla of the phylum *Protozoa.*

FLAGELLIN. Molecules of protein constituting the distal end of a flagellar filament.

FLAGELLUM, pl. **FLAGELLA** [fluh·JEL·um, fluh·JEL·uh]. A thin, filamentous appendage on cells, responsible for swimming motility.

FLATWORMS. Helminths that are flat in cross section.

FLOC. An aggregate of the finely suspended and colloidal matter of sewage.

FLOCCULE. An adherent aggregate of microorganisms or other materials floating in or on a liquid.

FLORA [FLORE·uh]. In microbiology, the microorganisms present in a given environment, e.g., intestinal flora, the normal flora of soil.

FLUORESCENCE [floo·uh·RESS·unce]. The emission of light of a particular wavelength by a substance which has absorbed light of a shorter wavelength (for example, the emission of green light by molecules of fluorescein dye which have absorbed blue light).

FLUORESCENCE MICROSCOPY [migh·KRAHSS·kuh·pee]. Microscopy in which cells or their components are stained with a fluorescent dye and thus appear as glowing objects against a dark background.

FLUORESCENT TREPONEMAL ANTIBODY (FTA) TEST. A specific indirect fluorescent antibody test to diagnose syphilis.

FOLIOSE. Leaflike.

FOMITES [FO·mites]. Inanimate objects that carry viable pathogenic organisms.

FOOD POISONING. Stomach or intestinal disturbances due to food contaminated with certain microbial toxins.

FORMALIN [FOR·muh·lin]. A 37 to 40% aqueous solution of formaldehyde.

FORSSMAN ANTIGENS [FORCE·mun]. Heterophile antigens widely distributed in nature.

FRACTIONAL STERILIZATION. The sterilization of material by heating it to 100°C (212°F) on three successive days with incubation periods in between.

FREI TEST [fry]. A skin test to determine sensitivity to the agent that causes lymphogranuloma venereum.

FRUITING BODY. A specialized, spore-producing organ.

FRUSTULE. Cell wall of diatoms.

FRUTICOSE. Shrublike.

FULMINATING INFECTION. A sudden, severe, and rapidly progressing infectious disease.

FUNGICIDE [FUN·ji·side]. An agent that kills or destroys fungi.

FUNGISTATIC. An agent that inhibits the growth of fungi.

FUNGUS, pl. **FUNGI.** [FUN·jye, FUNG·gus]. Organisms that are eucaryotic and have cell walls but lack chlorophyll and absorb their food: molds and yeasts.

FUSIFORM [FYOO·zi·form]. Spindle-shaped, tapered at the ends.

GAMETANGIUM, pl. **GAMETANGIA.** Sex organelle of fungi.

GAMETE [GAM·eet, guh·MEET]. A reproductive cell that fuses with another reproductive cell to form a zygote, which then develops into a new individual; a sex cell.

GAMETOPHYTE. An organism in the haploid, gamete-producing stage of its life cycle.

GAMMA GLOBULIN. A fraction of serum globulin that is rich in antibodies.

GAS CHROMATOGRAPH. An instrument which allows the separation and identification of various volatile chemical compounds in a gaseous mixture by means of selective adsorption.

GASTROENTERITIS [gass·tro·en·tur·EYE·tis]. Inflammation of the mucosa of the stomach or intestine.

GELATIN. A protein obtained from skin, hair, bones, tendons, and similar tissues, used in culture media for the determination of a specific proteolytic activity of microorganisms or for the preparation of a peptone.

GELATINASE [juh·LAT·i·nase, juh·LAT·i·naze]. An exoenzyme that degrades gelatin.

GENE. A segment of DNA that contains the nucleotide sequence for making a particular protein.

GENERATION TIME. The time interval necessary for a cell to divide.

GENETIC CODE. The genetic information carried by messenger RNA as transcribed from DNA. The information is in terms of codons (nucleotide base triplets), each of which designates a particular amino acid to be added to a growing protein chain.

GENETIC ENGINEERING. The deliberate changing of the genetic makeup of living cells by transferring a fragment of DNA from the cells of one organism to the cells of a different organism so that the latter can produce new substances. *Also called* **recombinant DNA technology.**

GENOME [JEE·nohm]. A complete set of genetic material; i.e., a complete set of genes found in an individual organism or virus.

GENOTYPE [JEE·nuh·tipe, JEN·uh·tipe]. The particular set of genes present in an organism's cells; an organism's genetic constitution. *Compare* **phenotype.**

GENUS, pl. **GENERA** [JEE·nus, JEN·ur·uh]. A group of very closely related species.

GERM. A microbe, usually a pathogenic one.

GERM THEORY OF DISEASE. Belief that microbes cause some diseases.

GERMICIDE [JURM·i·side]. An agent capable of killing germs, usually pathogenic microorganisms.

GINGIVA [JIN·ji·vuh]. The mucous membrane and soft tissue surrounding a tooth. Adjective: **gingival** (**jin**·ji·vul).

GLIDING MOTILITY. A type of movement across surfaces that is exhibited by some bacteria (e.g., myxobacters) which are devoid of flagella.

GLOBULIN [GLAHB·yoo·lin]. A protein soluble in dilute solutions of neutral salts but insoluble in water. Antibodies are globulins.

GLUCAN. A polymer of glucose.

GLUCOSE [GLOO·kose]. A carbohydrate classified as a monosaccharide (hexose), used as an energy source by many microorganisms. Also called *dextrose* or *grape sugar.*

GLYCOCALYX. Layer of viscous material surrounding some bacteria (capsule or slime layer).

GLYCOGEN [GLYE·kuh·jen]. A carbohydrate of the polysaccharide group, stored by animals. It yields glucose on hydrolysis.

GLYCOLYSIS [glye·KAHL·i·sis]. Anaerobic dissimilation of glucose to pyruvic acid by a sequence of enzyme-catalyzed reactions. Also called the *Embden-Meyerhoff pathway.*

GLYOXYLATE CYCLE. A sequence of biochemical reactions by which acetate is converted to succinic acid (a bypass of the Krebs cycle).

GNOTOBIOTIC [no·toe·bye·AHT·ik]. Pertaining to higher organisms living in the absence of all demonstrable viable organisms other than those known to be introduced.

GOLGI COMPLEX [GOL·jee]. A membranous organelle in the endoplasmic reticulum of the eucaryotic cell.

GONIDIUM. An asexual reproductive cell arising in a special organ in eucaryotes.

GONOCOCCUS. Common name for the bacterium that causes gonorrhea.

GRAM STAIN. A differential stain by which bacteria are classed as Gram-positive or Gram-negative depending upon whether they retain or lose the primary stain (crystal violet) when subjected to treatment with a decolorizing agent.

GRANULES, METACHROMATIC. Intracellular granules of polyphosphate found in certain microorganisms; such granules stain a reddish-purple color when the cells are stained with dilute methylene blue.

GRANULOCYTES. One group of leucocytes that have numerous granules in their cytoplasm. Includes neutrophils, basophils, and eosinophils.

GRANUM, pl. **GRANA.** A stack of thylakoids containing chlorophyll and carotenoid pigments that function in photosynthesis in chloroplasts.

GROUNDWATER. All subsurface water, especially that occurring in the zone of saturation.

GROWTH CURVE. A graphic representation of the growth (population changes) of bacteria in a culture medium.

GROWTH RATE. The number of cell divisions per unit of time.

GUANINE [GWAH·neen]. A purine base, occurring naturally as a fundamental component of nucleic acids.

GUARNIERI BODIES. Cytoplasmic inclusion bodies found in the epidermal cells of smallpox and chicken pox patients.

GUMMAS. Tumorlike lesions that develop in patients with tertiary syphilis.

H ANTIGEN. A heat-labile protein antigen found in the flagella of certain bacteria.

HABITAT. The natural environment of an organism.

HALOBACTERIA. Gram-negative pigmented aerobic archeobacteria that require 17 to 32% salt for good growth.

HALOPHILE [HAL·o·file]. A microorganism whose growth is accelerated by or dependent on high salt concentrations.

HANGING-DROP TECHNIQUE. A technique in which microorganisms are observed suspended in a drop of fluid.

HAPLOID [HAP·loyd]. Having a single set of unpaired chromosomes in each nucleus; having the chromosome number characteristic of a mature gamete of the species. *Compare* **diploid.**

HAPTEN. A simple substance that reacts like an antigen in vitro by combining with antibody but cannot induce the formation of antibodies by itself.

HeLa CELLS [HEE·luh]. A pure cell line of human cancer cells used for the cultivation of viruses.

HELICAL. Shaped like a corkscrew, with one or more turns or twists.

HELIX [HEE·liks]. A coiled spiral form.

HELMINTHS. Parasitic worms.

HEMAGGLUTINATION [hee·muh·gloo·ti·NAY·shun]. The agglutination (clumping) of red blood cells.

HEMAGGLUTINATION INHIBITION TEST. A diagnostic technique based on the inhibition of agglutination of red blood cells.

HEMOGLOBIN [HEE·mo·glo·bin]. The constituent of red blood cells that gives them their color and carries oxygen.

HEMOLYSIN [hee·MAHL·i·sin]. A substance produced by microorganisms that lyses red blood cells, liberating hemoglobin. Also can refer to a type of antibody that acts in conjunction with complement to cause the lysis of red blood cells.

HEMOLYSIS [hee·MAHL·i·sis]. The process of dissolving red blood cells. *See* alpha (*α*) hemolysis; beta (*β*) hemolysis.

HEMOPOIETIC. Descriptive of stem cells in bone marrow that are the origin of erythrocytes and of leucocytes including lymphocytes.

HEMORRHAGIC. Showing evidence of hemorrhage (bleeding). The tissue becomes reddened by the accumulation of blood that has escaped from capillaries into the tissue.

HETERO-. A prefix meaning "different."

HETEROCYSTS. Thick-walled cells formed by certain cyanobacteria. Heterocysts lack photosystem II but can fix molecular nitrogen, unlike the vegetative cells.

HETEROGAMY [het·ur·OG·uh·mee]. The conjugation of unlike gametes.

HETEROLOGOUS [het·ur·AHL·uh·gus]. Different with respect to type or species.

HETEROPHILE ANTIBODY [HET·ur·o·file]. An antibody that reacts with microorganisms or cells that are unrelated to the antigen that stimulated production of the antibody. The agglutination of *Proteus* spp. cells by serum from typhus fever patients is an example.

HETEROPHILE ANTIGEN. An antigen that reacts with antibodies stimulated by unrelated species.

HETEROTHALLIC. Describing organisms in which one individual produces male gametes and another produces ova.

HETEROTROPH [HET·ur·o·trofe]. A microorganism that is unable to use carbon dioxide as its sole source of carbon and requires one or more organic compounds. *Compare* autotroph.

HIGH-ENERGY PHOSPHATE BOND. The bond between a phosphate group and another chemical entity when a large amount of energy was required to establish the bond. (Example: the bond that is formed when a phosphate group is linked to ADP to form ATP.)

HISTOCOMPATIBILITY DIFFERENCE. Property of grafts that are antigenically very dissimilar to the recipient's tissue and are usually rejected.

HISTOPLASMIN TEST. A skin test that detects individuals infected with *Histoplasma capsulatum*.

HOLDFAST. An adhesive base that attaches the thallus of certain microorganisms to a surface.

HOLOENZYME [ho·lo·EN·zime, hahl·o·EN·zime]. A fully active enzyme, containing an apoenzyme and a coenzyme.

HOMOGRAFT. A tissue graft with tissue from one species of organism to a recipient of the same species.

HOMOLOGOUS. The same with respect to type or species.

HOMOTHALLIC. Descriptive of plants which produce both male and female sex cells and can self-fertilize.

HOST. An organism harboring another organism as a parasite (or as an infectious agent).

HUMAN GROWTH HORMONE. A pituitary secretion essential for normal growth and metabolism. Available as a pharmaceutical product made by a genetically engineered bacterium, for persons having a deficiency.

HUMORAL IMMUNITY [HYOO·mur·ul]. Immunity arising from the formation of specific antibodies that circulate in the bloodstream in response to the introduction of an antigen.

HUMUS. Highly complex organic residual matter in soil; not readily degraded by microorganisms.

HYALURONIDASE [high·ul·yoo·RON·i·dase, high·ul·yoo·RON·i·daze]. An enzyme that catalyzes the breakdown of hyaluronic acid. Also called *spreading factor*.

HYBRIDIZATION. The act of producing hybrids, i.e., offspring from genetically dissimilar strains.

HYBRIDOMA. A hybrid cell resulting from the fusion of a myeloma cell with an antibody-producing B lymphocyte.

HYDROGEN BOND. A relatively weak chemical bond based on the linkage of a polar hydrogen atom and another polar atom that is electronegative.

HYDROLOGIC CYCLE [high·dro·LAHJ·ik]. The complete cycle through which water passes, from oceans, through the atmosphere, to the land, and back to the oceans.

HYDROLYSIS [high·DRAHL·i·sis]. The breaking of chemical bonds within molecules through the intervention of a water molecule.

HYDROPHOBIA. A term meaning "dread of water," used to describe rabies.

HYDROSTATIC PRESSURE. Pressure exerted on cells by the weight of the water column above them.

HYDROXYL RADICALS (OH·). Radicals produced from superoxide radicals that can destroy vital cell components.

HYPERBARIC OXYGEN. The use of pure oxygen under pressure to treat patients with gas gangrene.

HYPERPLASIA. Uncontrolled proliferation of cells.

HYPERSENSITIVITY. Extreme sensitivity to foreign antigens, e.g., allergens.

HYPERTONIC SOLUTION. A medium containing a higher concentration of solutes than that inside cells suspended in the solution.

HYPERTROPHY. An abnormal enlargement of the cells, organs or parts, e.g., fungi growing within plants.

HYPHA [HIGH·fuh], pl. **HYPHAE** [HIGH·fee]. One filament or thread of a mycelium.

HYPHOCHYTRIDIOMYCETES. Group of fungi that are motile by a single anterior flagellum.

HYPOCHLORITES. Chlorine-containing compounds used as disinfectants and sanitizing agents.

HYPOTONIC SOLUTION. A solution in which the molar concentration of solutes is lower than that within cells that are suspended in the solution.

ICOSAHEDRON [eye·kah·suh·HEE·drun, eye·ko·suh·HEE·drun]. A structure formed of 20 triangular faces and 12 corners; the geometrical shape of many virions.

IDU. An antiviral agent; 5-iodo-2'-deoxyuridine.

IMMUNE ANTIBODIES. Immunoglobulin factors that antigen induces the immune system to produce.

IMMUNE CELLS. Cells that antigen induces the immune system to produce.

IMMUNE SERUM. Blood serum that contains one or more specific antibodies.

IMMUNE SYSTEM. Cells and organs within a living animal that protect against specific diseases.

IMMUNITY. A natural or acquired resistance to a specific disease.

IMMUNIZATION. Any process that develops resistance (immunity) to a specific disease in a host.

IMMUNOELECTROPHORESIS. A technique which employs a combination of immunodiffusion and electrophoresis to identify various antigens.

IMMUNOGENICITY [im·yoo·no·jeh·NISS·i·tee]. The capacity to stimulate the formation of specific antibodies.

IMMUNOGLOBULIN (IG) [im·yoo·no·GLOB·yoo·lin]. Any of the serum proteins, such as gamma globulin, that possess antibody activity.

IMMUNOLOGY. The study of natural resistance and the immune system.

IMPERFECT FUNGI. Fungi that do not have a sexual cycle.

IMViC. A group of tests used to differentiate *Escherichia coli* from *Enterobacter aerogenes*.

IN SITU [in SIGH·too, in SIGH·tyoo]. In the original or natural location.

IN VITRO [in VEE·troe]. Literally, "in glass." Pertaining to biologic experiments performed in test tubes or other laboratory vessels. *Compare* **in vivo.**

IN VIVO [in VEE·voe]. Within the living organism; pertaining to the laboratory testing of agents within living organisms. *Compare* **in vitro.**

INACTIVATE. To destroy the activity of a substance; e.g., to heat blood serum to 56°C for 30 min to destroy complement.

INCINERATION. Destruction of microorganisms by burning to ashes.

INCLUSION BODIES. Discrete assemblies of virions and/or viral components that develop within virus-infected cells.

INCUBATION. In microbiology, the subjecting of cultures of microorganisms to conditions (especially temperatures) favorable to their growth.

INCUBATION PERIOD. The elapsed time between the exposure to an infection and the appearance of disease symptoms, or the time period during which microorganisms inoculated into a medium are allowed to grow.

INDICATOR. A substance that changes color as conditions change; e.g., pH indicators reflect changes in acidity or alkalinity.

INDICATOR MICROORGANISM. A kind of microorganism which, when present in water, is evidence of pollution of the water with fecal material.

INDUCED ENZYME. *See* **adaptive enzyme.**

INDUCTION. The stimulation of an increase in the rate of synthesis of an enzyme, generally by increasing the enzyme's substrate or a closely related compound.

INFECTION. A pathological condition due to the growth of microorganisms in a host.

INFECTION-CONTROL OFFICER (ICO). A person in a hospital who monitors surveillance and investigation of infections and supervises infection-control activities.

INFECTIOUS. Capable of producing disease in a susceptible host.

INFLAMMATION. A tissue reaction resulting from irritation by a foreign material and causing a migration of leucocytes and an increased flow of blood to the area, producing swelling, reddening, heat, pain, and tenderness.

INGESTION. The intake of food.

INHIBITION. In microbiology, the prevention of the growth or multiplication of microorganisms.

INOCULATION [in·ahk·yoo·LAY·shun]. The artificial introduction of microorganisms or other substances into the body or into a culture medium.

INOCULUM [in·AHK·yoo·lum]. The substance, containing microorganisms or other material, that is introduced in inoculation.

INORGANIC COMPOUNDS. Substances that contain no carbon. Carbon dioxide (CO_2) is considered inorganic and thus is an exception.

INTERCELLULAR. Between cells.

INTERFERON [in·tur·FEER·ahn]. An antiviral substance produced by animal tissue.

INTERLEUKIN. A lymphokine, i.e., a soluble protein mediator of an immune response, that is produced by T lymphocytes or macrophages in response to an immunogenic stimulus.

INTERLEUKIN-1 (IL-1). A macrophage-produced interleukin that causes immunogenically stimulated T lymphocytes to produce interleukin-2. Also called *lymphocyte activating factor (LAF).*

INTERLEUKIN-2 (IL-2). An interleukin produced by T lymphocytes in response to interleukin-1. It causes immunogenically stimulated T lymphocytes to multiply and also may cause them to produce gamma interferon (INF-γ). Also called *T-cell growth factor (TCGF).*

INTRACELLULAR [in·truh·SEL·yoo·lur]. Within a cell.

INTRONS. Regions that do not code for proteins in eucaryotic genes.

INVERTASE [in·VUR·tase, IN·vur·tase]. An enzyme that hydrolyzes sucrose to glucose and fructose.

IODOPHORES. Organic compounds of iodine used as skin disinfectants.

ION. An atom or a group of atoms which gains or loses electrons and acquires a net electric charge.

IONIC BOND. A strong chemical bond based on electrical attraction between an atom that has gained electrons and one that has lost electrons.

ISOANTIBODY [eye·so·AN·ti·bod·ee]. An antibody, found only in some members of a species, that acts upon cells or cell components of other members of the same species.

ISOANTIGEN. A tissue-specific antigen present in one individual of a species but not in another. Also called *alloantigen.*

ISOENZYME [eye·so·EN·zime]. Any one of a group of enzymes that differ in their amino acid sequence but possess identical (or nearly identical) catalytic properties. Also called *isozyme.*

ISOTONIC. Pertaining to a solution that has the same osmotic pressure as that within a cell suspended in the solution.

ISOTOPES Atoms with the same number of protons in their nuclei but differing in the number of neutrons.

KARYOGAMY. The fusion of gametic nuclei, as in fertilization.

KARYOPLASM. The material inside the nuclear membrane.

KARYOTYPE. The diploid appearance of the set of chromosomes.

KERATIN. A tough protein which is the main constituent of hair, nails, and the outer layer of the epidermis.

KOCH'S POSTULATES. Guidelines to prove that a disease is caused by a specific microorganism.

KREBS CYCLE. *See* **citric acid cycle.**

KRILL. A name applied to planktonic crustaceans.

LACHRYMAL FLUID. Tears.

LACTOSE. A carbohydrate (disaccharide) that is split into glucose and galactose on hydrolysis. Also called *milk sugar.* Abbreviation: lac.

LAG PHASE. The period of slow, orderly growth when a medium is first inoculated with a culture.

LAMINAR AIRFLOW [LAM·i·nur]. The flow of air currents in which streams do not intermingle; the air moves along parallel flow lines.

LANCEFIELD GROUPS. Groups of streptococci based on various kinds of cell-wall polysaccharides.

LAWN (BACTERIAL). A turbid layer of bacteria on an agar-plate culture; bacteriophage produces plaques (clear zones) in the lawn.

LEACHING. Process of using microorganisms to recover metal from an ore.

LECHITHIN. A phospholipid component of cell membranes (phosphatidylcholine).

LECITHINASE. An enzyme that catalyzes the breakdown of lecithin.

LEGHEMOGLOBIN. A hemoglobinlike oxygen-binding red pigment in the root nodules of legumes which protects the nitrogenase enzyme complex from being destroyed by excess oxygen.

LEUCOCIDIN. A substance that destroys host phagocytes.

LEUCOCYTE [LOO·ko·sight]. A type of white blood cell which is characterized by a beaded, elongated nucleus.

LEUCOCYTOSIS [loo·ko·sigh·TOE·sis]. An increase in the number of leucocytes that is caused by the body's response to an injury or infection.

LEUKEMIAS. Conditions in which abnormal numbers of white cells (leucocytes) are produced by the bone marrow.

LEUKOPENIA [koo·ko·PEE·nee·uh]. A decrease in the number of leucocytes.

LICHEN [LYE·kun]. A symbiotic, or mutualistic, association of an alga and a fungus.

LIGAND [LIG·und, LYE·gand]. A molecule that binds to a protein; e.g., one that binds to an enzyme and, through the role it plays in other processes, directly controls enzyme activity.

LIGHT MICROSCOPE. An instrument that magnifies an object by use of lenses to manipulate the light beam between the object and the eye.

LIMNETIC ZONE. The surface region of a body of water away from the shore.

LIMNOLOGY. The study of the physical, chemical, geological, and biological aspects of lakes and streams.

LIPASE [LYE·pase, LYE·paze]. An enzyme that catalyzes the hydrolysis of fats into glycerol and fatty acids.

LIPID. An organic compound that is soluble in nonpolar solvents but not in water. Examples: fats, phospholipids, sterols.

LIPID CARRIER. A large isoprenoid lipid phosphate molecule with ability to carry a peptidoglycan building unit across the cytoplasmic membrane to the cell wall.

LIPOLYTIC ENZYME [lip·o·LIT·ik]. An enzyme that hydrolyzes lipids.

LIPOPOLYSACCHARIDE. A complex molecular structure composed of sugars and fatty acids; occurs in the outer membrane of Gram-negative bacteria. Abbreviation: LPS.

LIPOPROTEIN. A molecule composed of both a protein and a lipid.

LIQUEFACTION [lik·wi·FAK·shun]. The transformation of a gas or solid (e.g., a gel) to a liquid.

LITER [LEE·tur]. A metric unit of volume containing 1000 ml, or 1000 cm^3; equivalent to 1.0567 quarts.

LITHOTROPH [LITH·o·trofe]. An organism which uses reduced inorganic compounds as electron donors.

LITMUS. A lichen extract used as an indicator for pH and oxidation or reduction.

LITTORAL ZONE. Area along the shore where light penetrates to the bottom of the water.

LOCKJAW. A symptom of tetanus consisting of violent contraction of neck and jaw muscles restricting opening the mouth.

LOCUS pl. **LOCI** [LOH·sigh]. In genetics, the site on a chromosome occupied by a gene, operon, a mutation, or an allele is said to occur at a particular gene locus; in some cases, identifiable by reference to a marker.

LOGARITHMIC PHASE [log·uh·RITH·mik]. Commonly called *log phase*. See **exponential growth phase.**

LOPHOTRICHOUS [lo·FAHT·ri·kus]. Having a polar tuft of flagella.

LUMEN. A hypha cavity filled by protoplasm. Also, a channel within a tubular organ, such as the lumen of the intestine.

LYMPH. A fluid containing white blood cells that resembles blood plasma, which is conveyed through lymphatic vessels to the blood stream.

LYMPH NODES. Ovoid structures of the lymphatic system which range in size from 1 mm to several mm and are widely distributed throughout the body. Also called *lymph glands.*

LYMPHOCYTOSIS [lim·fo·cye·TO·sis]. An abnormally high lymphocyte count in the blood.

LYMPHOKINES. Soluble proteins produced and secreted by sensitized T lymphocytes (a type of leucocyte).

LYMPHOMAS. Conditions in which abnormal numbers of lymphocytes are produced by the spleen and lymph nodes.

LYOPHILIZATION [lye·off·il·i·ZAY·shun]. The preservation of biological specimens by rapid freezing and rapid dehydration in a high vacuum.

LYSIN [LYE·sin]. An enzyme, antibody, or other substance capable of disrupting or disintengrating cells (lysis).

LYSIS [LYE·sis]. The disruption or disintegration of such cells as bacteria or erythrocytes, e.g., by the action of specific antibodies plus complement.

LYSOGENIC BACTERIA [lye·so·JEN·ik]. Bacteria that carry prophages.

LYSOGENY [lye·SAH·juh·nee]. The state of a bacterium that is carrying a bacteriophage (often as a prophage) to which it is not itself susceptible.

LYSOSOMES [LYE·so·sohms]. Membrane-enclosed granules which occur in the cytoplasm of animal cells and contain hydrolytic enzymes.

LYSOZYME [LYE·so·zime]. An enzyme that catalyzes the hydrolysis of bacterial cell wall peptidoglycan.

LYTIC CYCLE. The process of replication of a virulent (lytic) bacteriophage, the bursting of the host cell, and release of new phage that can infect other host cells.

LYTIC PHAGE [LIT·ik]. A virulent bacterial virus.

M PROTEINS. Antiphagocytic protein antigens located on the surface of the cell walls of streptococci.

MACROPHAGE. Any of the large mononuclear phagocytic cells which are found in tissues and which develop from blood monocytes.

MACROSCOPIC [mak·ro·SKAHP·ik]. Visible without the aid of a microscope.

MAGNETOSOMES. Magnetite inclusions within a cell that allow the cell to become oriented as a magnetic dipole.

MAGNETOTAXIS. A movement of organisms in response to a magnetic field.

MALIGNANT TUMORS. Cancerous growths.

MALTASE [MAWL·tase, MAWL·taze]. An enzyme catalyzes the hydrolysis of maltose, yielding glucose.

MALTOSE [MAWL·tose]. A carbohydrate (disaccharide) produced by the enzymatic hydrolysis of starch by diastase.

MARINE. Of or relating to oceanic and estuarine environments.

MATTER. The substance of which any physical object is composed.

MECHANICAL VECTOR. An arthropod that merely transmits pathogens that adhere to its mouthparts or legs.

MEDICAL ASEPSIS. Practices to keep personnel, patients, and environment as free as possible of infectious microorganisms.

MEDIUM, pl. MEDIA. A substance used to provide nutrients for the growth and multiplication of microorganisms.

MEIOSIS [mye·O·sis]. A process occurring during cell division at different points in the life cycles of different organisms, in which the chromosome number is reduced by half, thus compensating for the chromosome-doubling effect of fertilization. Compare **mitosis.**

MEMBRANE ATTACK UNIT. A unit formed by the classical and alternate complement pathways that generates the lytic complex which forms a channel across the cytoplasmic membrane of a cell.

MEMBRANE FILTER. A filter made from such polymeric materials as cellulose, polyethylene, or tetrafluoroethylene with pores of known, uniform diameter.

MENINGES. The membranes that cover the brain and the spinal cord.

MEROZOITES. Daughter cells of sporozoites that reproduce inside liver cells, as applied to malaria.

MESOPHILE [MEZ·o·file]. A bacterium growing best at the moderate temperature range 25 to 40°C.

MESOSOMES [MEZ·o·sohms]. Membrane invaginations in the form of convoluted tubules and vesicles.

MESSENGER RNA. The intermediary substance that passes information from the DNA in the nuclear region to the ribosomes in the cytoplasm. Abbreviation: *mRNA.*

METABOLIC PATHWAY [met·uh·BOL·ik]. A series of steps in the chemical transformation of organic molecules.

METABOLISM [meh·TAB·o·lizm]. The system of chemical changes by which the nutritional and functional activities of an organism are maintained.

METABOLITE [meh·TAB·uh·light]. Any chemical participating in metabolism; a nutrient.

METACHROMATIC GRANULE [met·uh·kro·MAT·ik]. *See* **granules, metachromatic.**

METAPHASE. A stage of mitosis or meiosis in which the chromosomes are arranged at the equatorial plane of the cell prior to their separation into the daughter cells.

METASTASIS [meh·TASS·tuh·sis]. The process of a malignant cell's detaching itself from a tumor and establishing a new tumor at another site within the host.

METAZOA [met·uh·ZOE·uh]. Animals whose bodies consist of many cells.

METHANOGENIC BACTERIA [meth·uh·no·JEN·ik]. Anaerobic archaeobacteria that produce methane; also called **methanogens.**

MICROAEROPHILE [migh·kro·AIR·o·file]. An organism that requires low levels of oxygen for growth but cannot tolerate the level of oxygen (21%) present in an air atmosphere.

MICROBE [MIGH·krobe]. Any microscopic organism; a microorganism. Adjective: **microbial** [migh·KRO·bee·ul].

MICROBICIDAL. Descriptive of agents that kill microorganisms.

MICROBIOLOGY [migh·kro·bye·AHL·uh·jee]. The study of organisms of microscopic size (microorganisms), including their culture, economic importance, and pathogenicity.

MICROBIOSTATIC. Descriptive of agents that inhibit microorganisms.

MICROFILARIAS. Small, threadlike forms of filaria worms produced by the female worm and discharged into the bloodstream.

MICROMANIPULATOR [migh·kro·muh·NIP·yoo·lay·tur]. A device for the manipulation of microscopic specimens under a microscope.

MICROMETER [MIGH·kro·mee·tur]. A unit of measurement: one millionth of a meter (10^{-6} m). Abbreviation: μm.

MICROORGANISM [migh·kro·OR·guh·nizm]. Any organism of microscopic dimensions.

MICROSCOPY. The use of microscopes in all their various forms.

MICROTOME [MIGH·kro·tohm]. An instrument for making thin sections of tissues or cells.

MICROTUBULES [migh·kro·TYOO·byoolz]. Very thin rods that occur within all types of eucaryotic microbial cells.

MIGRATION INHIBITORY FACTOR (MIF). A lymphokine released by sensitized T lymphocytes after they encounter the sensitizing antigen. It prevents macrophages from migrating away from the site where they meet the antigen. Also called *macrophage migration inhibition factor.*

MINERALIZATION. Breaking down organic compounds to inorganic compounds and their constituent elements.

MINICELL. A small daughter cell which arises from asymmetric septum formation during binary fission and which lacks DNA.

MINIMUM INHIBITORY CONCENTRATION (MIC). Lowest concentration of an agent able to completely prevent the growth of a microbe.

MIRACIDIA. Ciliated larvae of blood flukes.

MITOCHONDRION [migh·toe·KAHN·dree·un]. A cytoplasmic organelle in eucaryotic cells; the site of cell respiration.

MITOGENS. Substances that induce cells to enter mitosis.

MITOSIS [mye·TOE·sis]. A form of nuclear division characterized by complex chromosome movement and exact chromosome duplication. *Compare* **meiosis.**

MITOTIC SPINDLE. Structure of a system of microtubules existing during the metaphase stage of mitosis; attached to the centromeres as the centrioles separate.

MIXED CULTURE. Culture in which more than one species is growing.

MIXED LYMPHOCYTE REACTION (MLR). Mutual interaction which occurs when lymphocytes of two individuals are mixed and cultured.

MIXOTROPHS. Chemolithotrophic heterotrophs which obtain energy by utilizing inorganic electron donors but obtain most of their carbon from organic compounds.

MODIFICATION. A temporary change or variation in the characteristics of an organism.

MODULATOR. The regulatory metabolite that binds to the allosteric site of an enzyme and alters the maximum velocity. Also called *effector, modifier.*

MOIETY. A part of a molecule having a characteristic chemical property.

MOLD. A fungus characterized by a filamentous structure.

MOLE. The weight of a compound in grams equal to the numerical value of its molecular weight.

MOLECULAR WEIGHT. The sum of the atomic weights of all the atoms in a molecule of a compound.

MOLECULE. A combination of atoms that are linked together to form the smallest unit of a specific chemical substance.

MONERA. Name of the kingdom that includes the procaryotes in Whittaker's five-kingdom system of classification.

MONOCLONAL ANTIBODY. Antibody produced by a clone of genetically identical cells derived from a single antibody-producing cell called a *hybridoma.* The antibody is homogeneous and is specific for a single epitope.

MONONUCLEOTIDE [mah·no·NEW·klee·o·tide]. The basic building block of nucleic acids (DNA and RNA); consists of a purine or pyrimidine base, ribose or deoxyribose, and phosphate.

MONOSACCHARIDE [mah·no·SAK·uh·ride]. A simple sugar, such as a five-carbon or six-carbon sugar.

MONOTRICHOUS [mo·NOT·ri·kus]. Having a single polar flagellum.

MORDANT [MORE·dunt]. A substance that fixes dyes.

MORPHOGENESIS [more·fo·JEN·uh·sis]. The process by which cells are organized into tissue structures.

MORPHOLOGY [more·FAHL·uh·jee]. The branch of biological science that deals with the study of the structure and form of living organisms.

*m*RNA. *See* **messenger RNA.**

MUREIN. *See* **peptidoglycan.**

MURINE TOXIN. A protein substance produced by *Yersinia pestis* that contributes to its pathogenicity.

MUTAGEN [MYOO·tuh·jen]. A physical agent or chemical substance that causes mutation.

MUTANT [MYOO·tunt]. A cell or an organism carrying a mutated gene.

MUTATION [myoo·TAY·shun]. A stable change of a gene such that the changed condition is inherited by off-spring cells.

MUTUALISM. A symbiosis in which two or more organisms living together benefit each other.

MYCELIUM [mye·SEE·lee·um], pl. **MYCELIA.** A mass of threadlike filaments, branched or composing a network, that constitutes the vegetative structure of a fungus.

MYCOLIC ACIDS. High-molecular-weight α-branched β-hydroxy fatty acids which occur in the cell walls of corynebacteria, mycobacteria, and some nocardioform bacteria.

MYCOLOGY [mye·KAHL·uh·jee]. The study of fungi.

MYCOPHAGE [MYE·ko·fayj]. A fungal virus.

MYCOPLASMA [mye·ko·PLAZ·muh]. A member of a group of eubacteria characterized by the absence of a cell wall.

MYCORRHIZA. A symbiotic association of a fungus with the roots of a higher plant.

MYCOSIS [mye·KO·sis]. A disease caused by fungi.

MYCOTOXIN [mye·ko·TOK·sin]. Any toxic substance produced by fungi.

MYELOMA. Cancer due to the proliferation of an antibody-producing cell.

MYXAMOEBA [mik·suh·MEE·buh]. A nonflagellated amoeboid cell that occurs in the life cycle of acellular slime molds.

MYXOSPORE [MIK·so·spore]. A desiccation-resistant resting cell of myxobacteria. Also called a *microcyst.*

NAKED VIRION. A nonenveloped virus.

NANOMETER [NAN·o·mee·tur, NAY·no·mee·tur]. A unit of length equal to one-billionth of a meter, or 10^{-9} m. Abbreviation: nm.

NASOPHARYNX. The region of the respiratory tract above the soft palate.

NATURAL KILLER (NK) CELLS. Lymphocytes that kill undesirable cells such as tumor cells and virus-infected cells.

NATURAL PENICILLINS. Penicillins produced by microorganisms and not modified by chemists.

NEGRI BODIES [NEG·ree]. Minute pathological structures (inclusion bodies) found in certain brain cells of animals infected with rabies virus.

NEMATODES. Tapered roundworms, many of which are animal pathogens, some are plant pathogens, and some are saprophytes.

NEOPLASM [NEE·o·plazm]. An aberrant new growth of abnormal cells or tissue; a tumor.

NEURAMINIDASE. An enzyme that catalyzes the hydrolysis of polysaccharides containing sialic acid (a neuraminic acid derivative found in mucus) and thus degrades the protective mucus layers of mucous membranes.

NEUROTOXIN [nyoo·ro·TAHK·sin]. Any nerve poison, such as those produced by certain marine algae.

NEUTRALISM. A neutral interaction between two species in which there is no evident effect on either species.

NEUTRON. An elementary particle which carries no electric charge and is approximately the same weight as a proton.

NICOTINAMIDE ADENINE DINUCLEOTIDE (NAD). A coenzyme that functions in enzymatic systems concerned with oxidation-reduction reactions.

NICOTINAMIDE ADENINE DINUCLEOTIDE PHOSPHATE (NADP). A coenzyme similar to NAD but having an additional phosphate group.

NITRATE REDUCTION. The reduction of nitrates to nitrites or ammonia.

NITRIFICATION [nigh·trif·i·KAY·shun]. The overall process of oxidation of ammonia to nitrates.

NITROFURANS. Synthetic antimicrobial agents derived from furfural.

NITROGENASE. The enzyme system that converts atmospheric nitrogen gas to ammonia during nitrogen fixation.

NITROGEN FIXATION. The formation of ammonia from free atmospheric nitrogen.

NOMENCLATURE [NO·men·klay·chur]. Any system of scientific names, such as those employed in biological classification.

NONCOMPETITIVE INHIBITION. Inhibition of an enzyme other than by competition with substrate for an "active" site on the enzyme.

NONIONIC DETERGENTS. Detergents that do not ionize when dissolved in water.

NONPOLAR COMPOUNDS. Compounds that do not ionize and do not have polar groups; poorly soluble in water.

NONSEPTATE [non·SEP·tait]. Having no dividing walls; said of fungal hyphae.

NORMAL FLORA. Microorganisms which normally inhabit the healthy human body or other natural environments.

NOSOCOMIAL DISEASE [no·so·KO·mee·ul]. Describing or pertaining to disease acquired in the hospital.

NUCLEAR MEMBRANE. A double membrane envelope surrounding the nucleus of eucaryotic cells.

NUCLEIC ACID [new·KLEE·ik]. One of a class of molecules composed of joined nucleotides; the types are deoxyribonucleic acid (DNA) and ribonucleic acid (RNA).

NUCLEOCAPSID. The nucleic acid and capsid in a virion.

NUCLEOID. An indistinct area within a bacterial cell where the DNA is located. Also termed *chromatin body, nuclear equivalent,* or *bacterial chromosome.*

NUCLEOLUS. A structure within the cell nucleus made up of RNA and protein—the site of the synthesis of ribosomal RNA.

NUCLEOPROTEIN [ne·klee·o·PRO·teen]. A molecular complex composed of nucleic acid and protein.

NUCLEOSIDE. A pentose sugar linked to a purine or pyrimidine base.

NUCLEOTIDE [NEW·klee·o·tide]. The basic building block of nucleic acids (DNA and RNA); consists of a purine or pyrimidine base, ribose or deoxyribose, and phosphate.

NUCLEUS. The membrane-bounded organelle of a eucaryotic cell where the

DNA is located; hence, the organelle that controls cell function and inheritance. Contrast with the **nucleoid** of a procaryotic cell, which is not membrane-bounded.

NULL CELLS. Lymphocytes that lack the surface markers that characterize B and T lymphocytes, such as natural killer (NK) and antibody-dependent killer (K) lymphocytes.

NUMERICAL TAXONOMY. A method used in taxonomy to determine and numerically express the degree of similarity of every strain to every other strain in a particular group.

O ANTIGENS. Long polysaccharide chains of the lipopolysaccharide which extend from the outer membrane of Gram-negative bacterial cells into the surrounding medium.

OBJECTIVE. In a compound microscope, the system of lenses nearest the object being observed.

OCULAR MICROMETER [migh·KROM·uh·tur]. A glass disk etched with equidistant lines that fits into the eyepiece of a microscope.

OIDIUM, pl. OIDIA [oh·ID·ee·um, oh·ID·ee·uh]. A single-celled spore formed by the separation of hyphal cells.

OLIGODYNAMIC ACTION [ahl·i·go·dye·NAM·ik]. The lethal effect exerted on bacteria by small amounts of certain metals.

OLIGOTROPHIC. Condition of low nutrient levels and poor microbial growth.

ONCOGENES. Genes which can potentially induce the development of cancer in a cell in which they occur or into which they are introduced.

ONCOLOGY [on·KAHL·uh·jee]. The study of the causes, development, characteristics, and treatment of tumors.

ONE-STEP GROWTH CURVE. A procedure for the quantitative study of lytic bacteriophage replication.

OOCYST. Encysted form of fertilized egg, a zygote, that develops outside a mosquito's stomach lining.

OOGAMY. The union of an egg cell and a sperm cell.

OOGONIUM. In certain algae and fungi, the female sex organ that contains one or more eggs.

OOKINETE. The elongated mobile zygote of certain sporozoa, as that of a malarial parasite.

OOMYCETES. Group of fungi that are filamentous, consisting of a coenocytic mycelium.

OOSPORES. Spores formed after the fertilization of the eggs within the oogonium.

OPERATOR. Region of a DNA molecule to which a specific repressor protein can bind to inhibit transcription of an adjacent gene or set of genes.

OPERON. A functional genetic unit consisting of a promoter region, an operator region, and one or more adjacent structural genes. Example: the *lac* operon of *Escherichia coli*.

OPPORTUNISTIC MICROORGANISM. A microorganism that is not normally pathogenic but can cause disease if host defense mechanisms are decreased, as by a breach in the skin or mucous membranes, by some prior debilitating disease, or by therapy with immunosuppressive agents. Also called *opportunistic pathogen*.

OPSONIN [OP·suh·nin]. An antibody that renders microorganisms susceptible to ingestion by phagocytes.

OPTICAL ISOMERS (D and I isomers). Two forms of a compound each of which is the mirror image of the other.

OPTIMUM GROWTH TEMPERATURE. The temperature at which a species of microorganism grows most rapidly.

ORDER. In systematic biologic classification, a group of families.

ORGANELLE [or·guh·NEL]. A structure or body in a cell that performs a specific function.

ORGANIC COMPOUNDS. Substances that contain carbon (except for carbon dioxide, which is considered an inorganic compound).

ORGANOTROPH [or·GAN·uh·trofe]. An organism that uses organic compounds as a source of electrons.

OSMOSIS. The passage of a solvent (usually water) from one solution into another solution having a greater solute concentration, across a semipermeable membrane that separates the two solutions.

OSMOTIC PRESSURE. Pressure equivalent to that needed to prevent a solvent from passing across a semipermeable membrane during osmosis.

OVUM. An egg cell.

OXIDASE [OK·si·dase, OK·si·daze]. An enzyme that brings about oxidation.

OXIDASE TEST. A test for the presence of cytochrome *c*; in bacteria that respire with oxygen; colonies become purple when treated with tetramethyl-*p*-phenylenediamine.

OXIDATION. (1) The process of combining with oxygen. (2) The loss of electrons or hydrogen atoms.

OXIDATION-REDUCTION (O/R) SYSTEM. Pairs of substances, one the oxidized and the other the reduced form.

OXIDATIVE PHOSPHORYLATION. The utilization of energy liberated by oxidation reactions in a respiratory chain to make ATP from ADP.

PALISADE ARRANGEMENT. Cells lined side by side, as in the genus *Corynebacterium*.

PALMELLOID. A stage of some algae in which masses of daughter cells without flagella develop.

PANDEMIC [pan·DEM·ik]. A worldwide epidemic.

PAPAIN. A proteolytic enzyme found in the juice of the fruit and in the leaves of the papaya plant.

para-AMINOBENZOIC ACID (PABA). A natural biochemical compound whose core structure resembles that of sulfonamides.

PARAMECIUM [pehr·uh·MEE·see·um]. A protozoan ciliate having cilia over the entire cell.

PARASITE. An organism that lives in or on another organism and derives nourishment from it.

PARASITISM. An interaction in which one organism lives in or on another organism.

PARENTERAL [pur·REN·tur·ul]. By some route other than via the intestinal tract.

PASSIVE IMMUNITY. Immunity produced by receiving blood or serum containing antibodies.

PASTEURIZATION. The process of heating a liquid food or beverage to a controlled temperature to enhance the keeping quality and destroy harmful microorganisms.

PATHOGEN [PATH·uh·jen]. An organism capable of producing disease.

PELLICLE. A compound covering of membranes in protozoa; also, a film on the surface of fluid culture media due to the growth of microorganisms.

PENICILLIN. The generic name for a large group of antibiotic substances derived from several species of the mold *Penicillium*.

PENICILLINASES. Enzymes that can destroy penicillins.

PENTOSE. A sugar with five carbon atoms; e.g., ribose.

PEPSIN. A proteolytic enzyme from stomach tissues.

PEPTIDASE. An enzyme that catalyzes the liberation of individual amino acids from a peptide.

PEPTIDE. A compound consisting of two or several amino acids.

PEPTIDOGLYCAN [pep·ti·doe·GLYE·kan]. A large polymer that provides the rigid structure of the cell wall of eubacteria, composed of three kinds of building blocks: (1) acetylglucosamine, (2) acetylmuramic acid, and (3) a peptide consisting of four amino acids.

PEPTONE. A partially hydrolyzed protein.

PEPTONIZATION [PEP·tun·i·ZAY·shun]. The conversion of proteins into peptones; the solubilization of casein in milk curd by proteolytic enzymes.

PERFECT FUNGI. Fungi with both an asexual and a sexual life cycle.

PERIPHERAL LYMPHOID SYSTEM. A system within the human body including lymph nodes, spleen, adenoids, tonsils, and Peyer's patches.

PERIPHYTES [PEHR·i·fites]. Microorganisms that become attached to surfaces, grow and form microcolonies, and produce a film to which other organisms become attached and grow.

PERIPLASMIC FLAGELLA. Flagella of the type which is possessed by spirochetes; they are located between the protoplasmic cylinder and the outer sheath; also called *axial fibrils* or *endoflagella*.

PERIPLASMIC SPACE. The space between the cytoplasmic membrane and the outer membrane of Gram-negative bacteria.

PERIPLAST [PEHR·i·plast]. A surface membrane or pellicle of certain algae and bacteria.

PERISTALSIS. Progressive and rhythmic contractions of the intestines.

PERITHECIUM [pehr·i·THEECE·ee·um]. A spherical, cylindrical, or oval ascocarp that usually opens by a slit or pore at the top.

PERITRICHOUS [puh·RIT·ri·kus]. Having flagella on the entire surface of the cell.

PERMEABILITY. The extent to which molecules of various kinds can pass through cell membranes.

PERMEASE [PUR·me·ase]. Any of a group of enzymelike proteins which are located in the cytoplasmic membrane and mediate the passage of nutrients across the membrane.

PEROXIDASE. An enzyme which catalyzes the reaction of hydrogen peroxide with a reduced substrate, resulting in the formation of H_2O and oxidized substrate.

pH. A symbol for the degree of acidity or alkalinity of a solution; $pH = \log(1/[H^+])$, where $[H^+]$ represents the hydrogen ion concentration.

PHAGE [FAYJ]. *See* **bacteriophage.**

PHAGOCYTE [FAG·o·site]. A cell capable of ingesting microorganisms or other foreign particles.

PHAGOLYSOSOME. A digestive vacuole formed by fusing of lysosome and phagosome in phagocytes.

PHAGOSOME A fusion of pseudopodia surrounding a microbe during phagocytic ingestion to form a vacuole.

PHASE-CONTRAST MICROSCOPY. The use of a light microscope fitted with special objectives and condenser to show contrast between substances of different thickness and density.

PHENOL COEFFICIENT. The ratio between the greatest dilution of a test germicide capable of killing a test organism in 10 min but not in 5 min and the greatest dilution of phenol giving the same result.

PHENOTYPE [FEE·no·tipe]. That portion of the genetic potential of an organism which is actually expressed.

PHOSPHATASE [FAHSS·fuh·tase, FAHSS·fuh·taze]. An enzyme that splits phosphate from an organic molecule.

PHOSPHATASE TEST. A test to determine the efficiency of the pasteurization of milk. The test is based on the thermolability of the enzyme phosphatase.

PHOSPHOLIPID. An amphipathic compound consisting of a molecule of glycerol to which two long-chain fatty acids (or, in the case of archaeobacteria, two long-chain branched alcohols) and one phosphate group are linked. The major type of lipid in cell membranes.

PHOSPHORYLATION [fahss·fo·ri·LAY·shun]. The addition of a phosphate group to a compound.

PHOTIC ZONE. The layer in a body of water in which photosynthesis occurs.

PHOTOAUTOTROPH [fo·toe·AW·toe·trofe]. An organism that derives energy from light and uses carbon dioxide as its sole carbon source.

PHOTOHETEROTROPHS. Organisms that use light as a source of energy and organic compounds as a main source of carbon.

PHOTOLITHOTROPH. An organism which obtains energy from light and uses inorganic compounds as a source of electrons.

PHOTOLYSIS [fo·TOL·i·sis]. Light-generated breakdown of water.

PHOTOORGANOTROPH. An organism which obtains energy from light and uses organic compounds as a source of electrons.

PHOTOPHOSPHORYLATION. The utilization of light energy to drive the synthesis of ATP.

PHOTOREACTIVATION. The restoration to full viability by the immediate exposure to visible light of cells damaged by an exposure to lethal doses of ultraviolet light.

PHOTOSYNTHESIS [fo·toe·SIN·thuh·sis]. The process in which chlorophyll and the energy of light are used by plants and some microorganisms to synthesize carbohydrates from carbon dioxide.

PHOTOTAXIS. The movement of organisms in response to a change in light intensity.

PHOTOTROPH [FO·toe·trofe]. A bacterium capable of utilizing light energy for metabolism.

PHYCOBILINS. Water-soluble pigments, such as phycocyanin and phycoerythrin, which can transmit the energy of absorbed light to chlorophyll.

PHYCOBILISOMES. Granules on the surface of thylakoids, which contain phycobilin pigments.

PHYCOLOGY [fye·KAHL·uh·jee]. The study of algae.

PHYLOGENY [fye·LAHJ·uh·nee]. The evolutionary or ancestral history of organisms.

PHYLUM, pl. **PHYLA** [FYE·lum, FYE·luh]. A taxon consisting of a group of related classes.

PHYSIOLOGY. The study of the life processes of living things.

PHYTANOLS. Long-chain branched alcohols present in phospholipids of archeobacteria.

PHYTOFLAGELLATE [fye·toe·FLAJ·uh·lut, fye·toe·FLAJ·uh·lait]. A plantlike form of flagellate. *Compare* **zooflagellate.**

PHYTOPLANKTON [fye·toe·PLANK·tun]. A collective term for plants and plantlike organisms present in plankton. *Compare* **zooplankton.**

PILUS, pl. **PILI.** Any filamentous appendage other than flagella on certain Gram-negative bacteria.

PINOCYTOSIS. The uptake of fluids and soluble nutrients through small invaginations in the cell membrane that form intracellular vesicles.

PLANKTON [PLANK·tun]. A collective term for the passively floating or drifting flora and fauna of a body of water, consisting largely of microscopic organisms.

PLANTAE. Kingdom in which are found the photosynthetic eucaryotes: green plants and algae.

PLAQUE (DENTAL). Aggregation of bacteria and organic matter on the surface of teeth.

PLAQUES. Clear zones created by lysis of bacteria by phage on a lawn of bacteria.

PLASMA. *See* blood plasma.

PLASMA MEMBRANE. *See* cytoplasmic membrane.

PLASMALEMMA. The double-layered membrane surrounding the protoplasm in a hypha.

PLASMIDS. Double-stranded DNA molecules that are smaller than chromosomes and replicate independently.

PLASMIN. An enzyme that dissolves the fibrin of blood clots.

PLASMODIOPHOROMYCETES. A group of heterotrophic fungi that are obligate parasites.

PLASMODIUM, pl. **PLASMODIA.** A multinucleated mass of protoplasm bounded by a cytoplasmic membrane that is usually motile; variable in size and form.

PLASMOGAMY. The joining of two cells and the fusion of their protoplasts in the process of sexual reproduction.

PLASMOLYSIS [plaz·MAHL·i·sis]. The shrinkage of cell contents as a result of the withdrawal of water by osmosis.

PLASTID. A pigmented inclusion body found in algae.

PLEOMORPHISM [plee·o·MORE·fizm]. The existence of different morphological forms in the same species or strain of microorganism. Also called *polymorphism.*

POLAR. Located at one end or at both ends.

POLAR MOLECULES. Molecules with negatively and positively charged areas; usually water-soluble.

POLY-β-HYDROXYBUTYRATE. A chloroform-soluble polymer of β-hydroxybutyric acid; occurs in the form of intracellular granules within certain bacteria and can be stained by fat-soluble dyes. Abbreviation: PHB.

POLYENE ANTIBIOTICS. A chemical class of antibiotics that have large ring structures and increase cell permeability.

POLYMERASE CHAIN REACTION (PCR). A molecular biology technique by which an enormous number of copies of one or more genes can be made from very tiny initial quantities of DNA.

POLYMORPHISM. Morphologically different forms at different stages in the life cycle of an organism.

POLYPEPTIDE [pahl·ee·PEP·tide]. A molecule consisting of many joined amino acids.

POLYSACCHARIDE. A carbohydrate formed by the combination of many molecules of monosaccharides; examples of polysaccharides are starch, cellulose, and glycogen.

POLYSOME [PAHL·ee·sohm]. A complex of ribosomes bound together by a single *m*RNA molecule. Also called *polyribosome.*

PORINS. Channel-containing proteins that span the outer membrane of Gram-negative bacteria.

POTABLE [PO·tuh·bul]. Suitable for drinking.

POUR-PLATE METHOD. Procedure to obtain separate colonies by mixing inoculum in melted cooled agar medium and pouring the mixture into a sterile Petri dish.

PRECIPITIN [pree·SIP·i·tin]. An antibody causing the precipitation of a soluble homologous antigen.

PREDATION. An interaction in which one organism, the predator, feeds on and digests another organism, the prey.

PRIMARY CELL LINES. An animal cell culture derived from an explant; usually dies out after a few generations.

PRIMARY PRODUCERS. Phototrophic microorganisms that produce organic matter via photosynthesis.

PRIMARY TREATMENT. The first stage in wastewater treatment, in which floating or settleable solids are mechanically removed by screening and sedimentation.

PRIONS. Infectious agents devoid of nucleic acids; protein is their only detectable component.

PROCARYOTE [pro·CARE·ee·ote]. A type of cell in which the nuclear substance is not enclosed within a membrane; e.g., a bacterium or cyanobacterium. *Compare* **eucaryote.**

PROMOTER. The binding site for RNA polymerase; it is near the operator.

PROPHAGE. The viral DNA of a temperate phage which becomes incorporated into the host DNA.

PROPHASE. In mitosis, the stage during which the chromosomes condense into visible, threadlike structures, the centrioles migrate to opposite sides of the cell, the mitotic spindle begins to form, and the nuclear membrane begins to disintegrate. In meiosis there are two prophase stages; prophase I has five substages and occurs in the first meiotic division, and prophase II occurs during the second meiotic division. Crossing over between chromosomes can occur during prophase I.

PROPHYLAXIS [pro·fi·LAK·sis]. Preventive treatment for protection against disease.

PROSTHECA [pros·THEEK·uh]. A narrow, semirigid extension of a bacterial cell. *Contrast with* **stalk.**

PROTEIN. One of a class of complex organic nitrogenous compounds composed of an extremely large number of amino acids joined by peptide bonds.

PROTEINASE [PRO·teen·ase, PRO·teen·aze]. An enzyme that hydrolyzes proteins to polypeptides.

PROTEOLYSIS. The enzymatic breakdown of proteins.

PROTIST [PRO·tist]. Name used for unicellular microorganisms in the kingdom *Protista.*

PROTISTA. Name of a third kingdom which includes microorganisms having features of both animals and plants.

PROTOMERS. Viral proteins in viral capsids.

PROTON. An elementary particle which has one unit of positive electric charge ($+1$) and is 1840 times heavier than an electron.

PROTONMOTIVE FORCE. The force which results from an electrochemical gradient of protons across a membrane and which can be used to drive ATP synthesis and certain other energy-requiring processes of a living cell.

PROTOPLASM [PRO·toe·plazm]. The living substance of a cell. The term usually refers to the substance enclosed by the cytoplasmic membrane.

PROTOPLAST. A spherical cell resulting from the complete degradation of the wall of a Gram-positive bacterial cell; the outermost boundary is the cytoplasmic membrane.

PROTOTROPH [PRO·toe·trofe]. An organism that is nutritionally independent and able to synthesize all required growth factors from simple substances.

PROTOZOA [pro·tuh·zo·uh]. Eucaryotic microorganisms with animal characteristics such as ingestion of food.

PSEUDOPODIUM [syoo·doe·PO·dee·um], pl. PSEUDOPODIA. A temporary projection of the protoplast of an amoeboid cell in which cytoplasm flows during extension and withdrawal.

PSYCHROPHILES. Organisms that grow best at temperatures from 15 to 20°C.

PURE CULTURE. A culture containing only one species of organism.

PUS. A whitish, pasty mass consisting mainly of neutrophils and a thin fluid; formed in response to infections by certain pathogenic microorganisms such as staphylococci.

PUTREFACTION [pyoo·truh·FAK·shun]. The decomposition of proteins by microorganisms, producing disagreeable odors.

PYCNIDIUM. An asexual fruiting body in fungi.

PYOGENIC [pye·o·JEN·ik]. Forming pus.

PYRENOIDS. In chloroplasts, dense regions on which surface starch granules form.

PYROGEN. A chemical that affects the hypothalamus, which regulates body temperature.

QUATERNARY AMMONIUM COMPOUNDS. Most widely used detergents that belong to the cationic group, with a basic structure related to that of ammonium chloride.

QUELLUNG REACTION. The increase in the visibility of a bacterial capsule that results from the reaction between the capsular antigens and specific anticapsular serum.

RADIATION PASTEURIZATION. Procedure for killing microorganisms by means of ionizing radiation.

RADIOIMMUNOASSAYS (RIAS). An extremely sensitive serological technique that employs radioactively labelled antigen; assays using radioactive components.

RADIOISOTOPE [ray·dee·o·EYE·so·tope]. An isotope that exhibits radioactivity.

RDE. Receptor-destroying enzyme. An enzyme that destroys the specific receptor by which a virus can attach to a susceptible cell.

REAGIN. Antibodies against cardiolipin, such as occur in syphilitic patients. Also termed *Wassermann antibodies*. The term is sometimes used to refer to the IgE antibodies which are involved in immediate hypersensitivities.

RECOMBINANT [ree·KAHM·bi·nunt]. A cell or clone of cells resulting from recombination.

RECOMBINANT DNA TECHNOLOGY. The technique of transferring a fragment of DNA from one organism to another; also called genetic engineering.

RECOMBINANT PLASMID. A plasmid containing two different kinds of DNA molecules that have been joined, usually by artificial means, to form a single circular DNA molecule.

RECOMBINATION. A process that results in a new combination of genes on a DNA molecule. It may occur naturally through an exchange of genetic material between two homologous chromosomes, or it may occur by artificial means through genetic engineering.

REDUCTION. A chemical process involving the removal of oxygen, the addition of hydrogen atoms, or the gain of electrons.

REDUCTIVE AMINATION. The reaction whereby glutamic acid is made from ammonia and α-ketoglutaric acid.

REGULATOR GENE. A gene that codes for a repressor protein which controls transcription of a gene.

RENNET CURD. The result of the coagulation of milk by the action of the enzyme rennin. Referred to as *sweet curd*.

RENNIN. An enzyme that transforms the soluble casein of milk into insoluble paracasein. The enzyme is obtained from the gastric juice of a calf.

REPLICA PLATING. The replication of a pattern of colonies from one plate to another; a disk of sterile material (often velveteen) is pressed on the surface of the first plate, and the adhering bacteria are printed on the second.

RESERVOIRS OF INFECTION. Living organisms that harbor pathogens, and substances or objects carrying pathogenic microorganisms.

RESOLUTION. In microscopy, the smallest distance by which two objects can be separated and still be visualized as separate objects.

RESOLVING POWER. Ability to distinguish images of two close objects as separate, distinct objects.

RESPIRATION. An energy-yielding process in which electrons from an oxidizable substrate are transferred via a series of oxidation-reduction reactions to an exogenous terminal electron acceptor.

RESPIRATORY CHAIN. *See* **electron-transport system.**

RESTRICTION ENDONUCLEASE. An endonuclease (an enzyme) whose normal function in a cell is to destroy foreign DNA that might enter the cell; it recognizes certain sites in foreign double-stranded DNA molecules and makes a cut in the deoxyribose-phosphate backbone of the DNA. Restriction endonucleases are used extensively as tools in genetic engineering.

RETICULATE BODY. In the developmental cycle of chlamydias, a noninfectious intracellular form that develops from an elementary body, is larger than the elementary body, and has a less dense arrangement of nuclear material. Also termed *initial body*.

RETICULOENDOTHELIAL SYSTEM [ree·TIK·yoo·lo·en·doe·THEEL·ee·ul]. A system of cells in various organs and tissues, such as the spleen, liver, and bone marrow, that are important in resistance and immunity.

REVERSE TRANSCRIPTASE [tran·SKRIP·tase]. An enzyme for the synthesis of a DNA molecule using RNA as a template.

RHIZINES. Short twisted strands of hyphae which serve as anchors in an alga-fungus lichenlike relationship.

RHIZOID [RYE·zoyd]. A single-celled or multicellular hairlike structure having the appearance of a root.

RHIZOMYCELIUM. A system of branched hyphae that emerge from the posterior of the thallus to anchor it to the substrate.

RHIZOSPHERE [RYE·zo·sfeer]. The soil region subject to the influence of plant roots and characterized by a zone of increased microbiological activity.

RIBONUCLEIC ACID [rye·bo·new·KLEE·ik]. A nucleic acid occurring in the cytoplasm and the nucleolus, containing phosphoric acid, D-ribose, adenine, guanine, cytosine, and uracil. Abbreviation: RNA.

RIBONUCLEOTIDES. Nucleotides that contain the sugar ribose as the pentose and are used for synthesis of RNA.

RIBOSOMAL RNA [rye·bo·so·mul]. The RNA of the ribosomes, constituting about 90 percent of the total cellular RNA. Abbreviation: rRNA.

RIBOSOME [RYE·bo·sohm]. A cytoplasmic structural unit, made up of RNA and protein, that is the site of protein synthesis.

RICKETTSIAS [ri·KET·see·uhs]. Obligately parasitic bacteria of arthropods; many are pathogenic for humans and other mammals.

RINGWORM. Dermatomycosis that gives a ringlike appearance.

RNA. *See* ribonucleic acid.

RNA POLYMERASE [PAHL·im·ur·ase, pahl·IM·ur·ase]. An enzyme that synthesizes *m*RNA on a DNA template.

ROCKET IMMUNOELECTROPHORESIS. A serological technique in which antigen migrates by electrophoresis from a well into an agar gel containing specific antiserum, giving a rocketlike configuration to the antigen-antibody precipitate.

ROOT-NODULE BACTERIA. Bacteria belonging to the genus *Rhizobium*, family *Rhizobiaceae*, that live symbiotically in the nodules of roots of leguminous plants and fix atmospheric nitrogen.

RPR (RAPID PLASMA REAGIN) TEST. A macroscopic agglutination test for the detection of reagin (antibodies against cardiolipin); used as a preliminary screening test in the laboratory diagnosis of syphilis.

*r*RNA. *See* ribosomal RMS.

RUMEN. The first chamber of the ruminant stomach.

SABIN VACCINE. Polio vaccine containing live, attenuated strains of three serotypes of poliovirus.

SACCHAROLYTIC [sak·uh·ro·LIT·ik]. Capable of splitting sugar compounds.

SALK VACCINE. Polio vaccine consisting of three serotypes of killed poliovirus.

SALMONELLOSIS [sal·muh·nel·O·sis]. An infection by *Salmonella* spp. that affects the gastrointestinal tract.

SALVARSAN. First laboratory-synthesized chemical that could cure a disease without harming the patient.

SANITIZER. An agent that reduces to levels judged safe by public health authorities the microbial flora in materials or on such articles as eating utensils.

SAPROPHYTE [SAP·ro·fight]. An organism that lives on dead organic matter.

SARCINA. Cubical packet of eight spherical cells of bacteria.

SARCOMAS. Solid tumors that grow from connective tissues, cartilage, bone, muscle, and fat.

SCANNING ELECTRON MICROSCOPY (SEM). Technique that provides three-dimensional views of the cell surface.

SCHICK TEST. A skin test used to determine a person's susceptibility to diphtheria.

SCHISTOSOMES. Blood flukes (flatworms) of the genus *Schistosoma*.

SCHIZOGONY [skiz·OG·un·nee]. Asexual reproduction by multiple fission of a trophozoite (a vegetative protozoan).

SCHIZONT [SKIZ·ont]. A stage in the asexual life cycle of the malaria parasites.

SELECTIVE MEDIA. Media used to enhance growth of a particular kind of microorganism and/or suppress growth of other kinds.

SEMICONSERVATIVE REPLICATION. The replication of a complete DNA molecule in such a way that both the resultant double-stranded molecules contain one original and one new strand.

SEMISYNTHETIC PENICILLIN. The penicillin core (6-amino-pencillanic acid) plus various chemical side chains which chemists have added to create forms of penicillin not found in nature.

SEPSIS [SEP·sis]. Poisoning by the products of putrefaction; a severe toxic state resulting from an infection with pyogenic microorganisms.

SEPTATE. Possessing crosswalls.

SEPTICEMIA [sep·ti·SEE·mee·uh]. A systemic disease caused by the invasion and multiplication of pathogenic microorganisms in the bloodstream.

SEPTIC TANK. A unit using an anaerobic system for the treatment of a limited volume of sewage.

SEPTUM. A crosswall.

SERIAL DILUTION. Successive dilution of a specimen; e.g., a 1:10 dilution equals 1 ml of specimen plus 9 ml of diluent; a 1:100 dilution equals 1 ml of a 1:10 dilution plus 9 ml of diluent.

SEROLOGY. The study of in vitro interactions involving one or more of the constituents of serum.

SEROTYPE. *See* serovar.

SEROVAR. A subdivision of a species based on its antigenic composition. Also called *serotype*.

SERUM. *See* blood serum.

SEWERAGE SYSTEM. The system that collects and carries sewage from the source to the point of treatment and disposal.

SEXUAL REPRODUCTION. Reproduction in which two cells (gametes) fuse into one fertilized cell.

SHEATH. A hollow tubular structure surrounding a chain of cells or a trichome; also refers to the covering that surrounds the flagella of certain Gram-negative bacteria.

SHOTGUN CLONING. Treatment of total cellular DNA with endonuclease resulting in many random fragments with a few containing the desired genes.

SHUNT. An alternate pathway; a bypass.

SIMPLE DIFFUSION. The movement of solutes across a semipermeable membrane.

SIMPLE STAIN. The coloration of bacteria or other organisms by applying a single solution of a stain to a fixed film or smear.

SINGLE-CELL PROTEINS. Microorganisms cultivated on industrial wastes or by-products to yield a large cell crop rich in protein.

SLIME LAYER. A disorganized gelatinous covering attached to a cell wall.

SLUDGE. The semisolid part of sewage that has been sedimented or acted upon by bacteria.

SMEAR. A thin layer of material, e.g., a bacterial culture spread on a glass slide for microscopic examination. Also called a *film*.

SOLUTES. Substances dissolved in a solvent.

SOLVENT. A liquid, such as water, that has the ability to dissolve a great variety of substances.

SPECIES. The basic taxonomic group; in bacteriology, a species consists of a type strain together with all the other strains that are considered sufficiently similar to the type strain to warrant inclusion in the species.

SPECTROPHOTOMETER. An instrument that measures the transmission of light, permitting the accurate analysis of color or the accurate comparison of the luminous intensities of two sources of specific wavelengths.

SPERMATIUM, pl. SPERMATIA [spur·MA·she·əm, spur·MA·she·ə]. A special male structure in fungi.

SPHEROPLAST [SFEER·o·plast]. A Gram-negative bacterial cell with the peptidoglycan removed, leaving it devoid of rigidity.

SPIRILLUM [spye·RIL·um], pl. **SPIRILLA.** A rigid helical bacterium. A genus of helical bacteria is *Aquaspirillum*.

SPIROCHETE [SPYE·ro·keet]. A helical bacterium which is flexible and has periplasmic flagella.

SPONTANEOUS GENERATION. The origination of life from nonliving material. Also called *abiogenesis*. *Compare* **biogenesis.**

SPORANGIOLES. Walled vessels containing myxospores; occur in the fruiting bodies formed by certain myxobacters. Also termed *cysts.*

SPORANGIOPHORE [spo·RAN·jee·o·fore]. A specialized mycelial branch bearing a sporangium.

SPORANGIOSPORES. Asexual spores that develop within a sac (sporangium).

SPORANGIUM [spo·RAN·jee·um]. The mother cell, a saclike structure within which asexual spores are produced.

SPORE. A resistant body formed by certain microorganisms.

SPORICIDE [SPORE·i·side]. An agent that kills spores.

SPOROGENESIS [spore·o·JEN·uh·sis]. (1) Reproduction by means of spores. (2) The formation of spores.

SPOROPHORE [SPORE·o·fore]. A specialized mycelial branch upon which spores are produced.

SPOROZOITE [spore·uh·zo·ite]. A motile infective stage of certain sporozoans; it results from sexual reproduction and gives rise to an asexual cycle in a new host.

SPORULATION [spore·yoo·LAY·shun]. The process of spore formation.

SPREAD-PLATE METHOD. A procedure for separating cells and obtaining colonies by spreading inoculum on a sterile agar surface with a bent glass rod.

SPUTUM. Mucus coughed up by a patient.

STAGE MICROMETER [migh·KROM·uh·tur]. An instrument that functions as a ruler for the measurement of microorganisms under the microscope.

STALK. A nonliving ribbonlike or tubular appendage excreted by a bacterial cell. *Contrast with* **prostheca.**

STAPHYLOCOCCI [staff·i·lo·KAHK·sigh]. Spherical bacteria (cocci) occurring in irregular, grapelike clusters.

STARTER CULTURE. A known culture of microorganisms used to inoculate milk, pickles, and other food to produce the desired fermentation.

STATIONARY PHASE. The interval directly following a growth phase when the number of viable bacteria remains constant.

STEM CELLS. Formative cells in the bone marrow from which specialized cells, such as lymphocytes, arise.

STERILE. Free of living organisms.

STERILIZATION. The process of making sterile; the killing of all forms of life.

STEROID [STEER·oyd]. A complex chemical substance containing the tetracyclic carbon ring system of the sterols; steroids are often used as therapeutic agents.

STEROL. Any of the natural products derived from the steroid nucleus.

STICKY-ENDED DNA. Double-stranded DNA that has been cut in a staggered fashion by an endonuclease to yield complementary single-stranded ends that can join by hydrogen bonding.

STOCK CULTURES. Known species of microorganisms maintained in the laboratory for various tests and studies.

STRAIN. All the descendents of a pure culture; usually a succession of cultures derived from an initial colony.

STREAKED-PLATE METHOD. A procedure for separating cells on a sterile agar surface so that individual cells will grow into distinct, separate colonies.

STREPTOBACILLI [strep·toe·buh·SIL·eye]. Bacilli in chains.

STREPTOCOCCI [strep·toe·KAHK·sigh]. Cocci that divide in such a way that chains of cells are formed.

STREPTOKINASE [strep·toe·KIGH·nase]. *See* **fibrinolysin.**

STREPTOLYSIN O (SLO). A streptococcal hemolysin and leucocidin that is inactivated by oxygen.

STREPTOLYSIN S (SLS). A streptococcal hemolysin and leucocidin that is stable to oxygen.

STRICT ANAEROBES. Microorganisms that cannot tolerate oxygen.

STRUCTURAL GENE. A gene that codes for the amino acid sequence of a polypeptide chain.

SUBCLINICAL. Pertaining to an infection so minor that there are no detectable clinical signs or symptoms of the infection.

SUBCUTANEOUS [sub·kyoo·TAY·nee·us]. Beneath the skin.

SUBCUTANEOUS MYCOSES. Infections caused by fungi in tissue under the skin.

SUBSTRATE-LEVEL PHOSPHORYLATION. The process by which a phosphate group is removed from one chemical compound and added to ADP.

SUBTERMINAL. Situated near the end, but not at the extreme end, of a cell.

SULFONAMIDE [sul·FON·ə·mid]. A synthetic chemotherapeutic agent charac-

terized by the chemical group $-SO_2N\lessgtr$.

SUPERNATE. The liquid over a precipitate or sediment; the fluid remaining after the removal of suspended matter.

SUPEROXIDE DISMUTASE. An enzyme which catalyzes the dismutation of superoxide radicals to form O_2 and H_2O_2.

SUPEROXIDE RADICAL. The free radical (an anion) resulting from the addition of an electron to molecular oxygen: $O_2 + e^- \rightarrow O_2^-$.

SUPPURATION. The formation of pus.

SURFACE TENSION. The force acting on the surface of a liquid, tending to minimize the area of the surface.

SURFACTANT. A soluble compound that reduces the surface tension of liquids or reduces interfacial tension between two liquids or a liquid and a solid.

SURGICAL ASEPSIS. Procedures and conditions that prevent microbes from gaining access to wounds and tissues during surgery.

SWARM CELLS. Haploid cells with two flagella formed in the growth cycle of cellular slime molds.

SYMBIOSIS [sim·bee·o·sis]. The living together of two or more organisms; microbial association.

SYNCHRONOUS GROWTH [SING·kruh·nus]. Growth in a cell population in which all cells divide at the same time.

SYNERGISM. The ability of two or more organisms to bring about changes (usually chemical) that neither can accomplish alone.

SYNTHETIC CHEMOTHERAPEUTIC AGENT. A compound made by a chemist in the laboratory for therapeutic use.

SYNTHETIC MEDIUM. A medium composed of pure chemical compounds.

SYNTROPHISM. A type of mutualism involving an exchange of nutrients between two species.

SYSTEMATICS. The science of animal, plant, and microbial classification.

SYSTEMIC [sis·TEM·ik]. Relating to the entire organism instead of to a part.

TAXIS [TACK·sis]. The movement away from or toward a chemical or physical stimulus.

TAXON, pl. **TAXA** [TACK·sahn, TACK·suh]. A taxonomic group, such as a species, genus, or family, whose members share common characteristics.

TAXONOMY [tack·SAHN·uh·mee]. The classification (arrangement), nomenclature (naming), and identification of organisms.

TEICHOIC ACID [tei·KO·ik]. Polymers of ribitol phosphate or glycerol phosphate which occur in the walls of certain Gram-positive bacteria.

TEMPERATE BACTERIOPHAGE. A bacteriophage capable of integrating its DNA into the host genome, thus being transmitted through cell divisions without causing host lysis.

TERMINAL INFECTION. An infection with pathogenic microorganisms that terminates in the death of the host.

TETRACYCLINES. A chemical class of broad-spectrum antibiotics which inhibit protein synthesis.

TETRAD. Group of four coccoid microorganisms in the shape of a square.

TETRAHYDROFOLIC ACID (THFA). An oxygen-labile coenzyme composed of tetrahydropteridine, *p*-aminobenzoic acid, and glutamic acid; it acts as an intermediary carrier in the transfer of 1-carbon groups.

THALLOPHYTE [THAL·o·fite]. A plant having no true stem, roots, or leaves; the group includes the algae and fungi.

THALLOSPORE [THAL·o·spore]. A spore that develops by the budding of hyphal or vegetative cells.

THALLUS [THAL·us], pl. **THALLI.** A plant or microbial body lacking special tissue systems or organs; thalli may vary from a single cell to a complex, branching multicellular structure.

THERAPEUTIC. Pertaining to the treating or curing of a disease.

THERMAL DEATH TIME (TDT). The time necessary to kill microorganisms at a given temperature.

THERMODURIC [thur·mo·DYOO·rik]. Capable of surviving exposure to a high temperature.

THERMOLABILE [thur·mo·LAY·bile, thur·mo·LAY·bil]. Destroyed by heat at temperatures below 100°C (212°F).

THERMOPHILE [THUR·mo·file]. An organism that grows best at temperatures above 45°C.

THERMOSTABLE [thur·mo·STAY·bul]. Relatively resistant to heat; resistant to temperatures of 100°C (212°F).

THYLAKOIDS Flattened membranous sacs which contain the photosynthetic pigments of the cell. In cyanobacteria they occur within the cytoplasm; in photosynthetic eucaryotes they occur within the chloroplasts.

THYMINE [THIGH·meen]. One kind of pyrimidine, a component of DNA but not RNA.

THYMUS-DERIVED LYMPHOCYTES (T CELLS OR T LYMPHOCYTES). Lymphocytes that differentiate in the thymus gland and are mainly responsible for cell-mediated immunity. They possess characteristic surface antigens.

TINCTURE. An alcoholic solution of a medicinal substance.

TINEA [TIN·ee·uh]. Ringworm, which is caused by fungi.

TISSUE. A collection of cells forming a structure.

TISSUE CULTURE. A growth of tissue cells in a laboratory medium.

TISSUE PLASMINOGEN ACTIVATOR (TPA). A protease that catalyzes the conversion of blood plasminogen to plasmin, an enzyme that dissolves the fibrin of blood clots. The genetically engineered product is used for treating patients with heart disease.

TOXEMIA [tahk·SEE·mee·uh]. The presence of toxins in the blood.

TOXIGENICITY. The ability to produce a toxin.

TOXIN [TAHK·sin]. A poisonous substance, such as a bacterial toxin, elaborated by an organism.

TOXIN-ANTITOXIN. A mixture of toxin and antitoxin containing slightly more toxin than antitoxin. This was formerly used to produce an active immunity.

TOXOID [TAHK·soyd]. A toxin that has been treated to destroy its toxic properties without affecting its antigenic properties.

TRANSAMINATION. A biochemical reaction in which the amino group (—NH$_2$) on an amino acid is exchanged for the keto group (—C = O) of an α-keto acid to form a new amino acid and a new α-keto acid.

TRANSCRIPTION. The process in which a complementary single-stranded *m*RNA is synthesized from one of the DNA strands of a gene.

TRANSDUCTION. The transfer of genetic material from one bacterium to another through the agency of a virus.

TRANSFER RNA. A specific RNA for each amino acid that becomes esterified to the terminal adenosine. Each of the 60 or so *t*RNAs has a specific trinucleotide sequence that interacts with a complementary sequence in *m*RNA. Abbreviation: *t*RNA. Also called *soluble RNA* (*s*RNA).

TRANSFORMATION. (1) A type of gene transfer in which a recipient cell acquires a fragment of DNA that is present in free form in the surrounding

medium. (2) The change of a normal animal or plant cell into one having the properties of a tumor cell or a cancer cell, such as the loss of contact inhibition.

TRANSFORMED CELLS. Cells that have new inheritable properties due to the acquiring of a fragment of DNA from the surrounding medium.

TRANSLATION. The process in which genetic information in *m*RNA directs the order of assembly of the specific amino acids during protein synthesis by ribosomes.

TRANSMISSION ELECTRON MICROSCOPY (TEM). Technique whereby electrons penetrate a specimen and produce an image on a fluorescent screen.

TRANSOVARIAN PASSAGE. The transmission of a pathogen by arthropods through the eggs to offspring.

TRANSPEPTIDASE. An enzyme that breaks the linkage between the fourth and fifth amino acids, converting the pentapeptides to tetrapeptides, in bacterial cell-wall biosynthesis.

TRANSPOSONS. Small pieces of DNA containing genetic information that allows them to insert themselves into chromosomes at numerous locations, thereby causing mutations.

TRANSVERSE BINARY FISSION [BYE·nuh·ree]. An asexual reproductive process in which a single cell divides transversely into two cells.

TREMATODES. Flatworms called *flukes*.

TRIBE. A taxonomic group containing a number of related genera within a family.

TRICARBOXYLIC ACID CYCLE [trye·kar·bock·SIL·ik]. *See* **citric acid cycle.**

TRICHOME. A single row of distinct cells in which there is a large area of contact between the adjacent cells (in contrast to a chain of cells).

TRICKLING FILTER. A secondary treatment process in which sewage is trickled over a bed of rocks so that microorganisms can break down organic wastes.

*t*RNA. *See* **transfer RNA.**

TROPHIC STAGE [tro·fik]. The vegetative stage of free-living protozoa.

TROPHOZOITE [tro·fo·zo·ite]. The vegetative form of a protozoan.

TRYPSIN [TRIP·sin]. A proteolytic enzyme in pancreatic juice.

TSS TOXIN-1. Toxin associated with toxic shock syndrome; produced by certain strains of *Staphylococcus aureus*.

TUBERCLE [TYOO·bur·kul]. A nodule, the specific lesion of tuberculosis.

TUBERCULATE CONIDIA. Conidia of *Histoplasma capsulatum* that have projections.

TUBERCULIN [tyoo·BUR·kyoo·lin]. An extract of the tuberculosis bacillus capable of eliciting an inflammatory reaction in an animal that has been sensitized by the presence of living or dead tubercle bacilli.

TURBIDIMETRY. A method of estimating bacterial growth or populations by the measurement of the degree of opacity (or turbidity) of the suspension.

TYNDALLIZATION. A process of fractional sterilization with flowing steam.

TYPE-CULTURE COLLECTION. A depository of microorganisms and cells maintained for use as reference.

TYPE SPECIES. The species that is the permanent reference example of a genus.

TYPE STRAIN. The strain that is the permanent reference strain of a species; it is the strain to which all other strains must be compared in order to be included in the species.

ULTRACENTRIFUGE. A high-speed centrifuge used for the determination of the particle size of viruses and proteins.

ULTRAFILTRATION. A method for the removal of all but the very smallest particles, e.g., viruses, from a fluid medium.

ULTRASONIC WAVES. Sound waves of high intensity beyond the audible range, used for the destruction of microbes or the cleaning of materials.

ULTRAVIOLET RAYS. Electromagnetic radiations having a wavelength from about 3900 to about 2000 Å.

UNCOUPLING AGENTS. Chemicals that poison cells by carrying protons freely across membranes, thereby destroying the proton gradient needed for synthesis of ATP.

UNDULATING. Exhibiting a wavelike motion.

UNICELLULAR. Having a single cell.

UPWELLING. The rise of water from a deeper to a shallower depth in an ocean; the rise brings nutrients to the surface region.

UREA. A soluble nitrogenous compound, $H_2N—CO—NH_2$, found in the urine of humans and other mammals.

UREASE. An enzyme that catalyzes the hydrolysis of urea.

VACCINATION. Inoculation with a biologic preparation (a vaccine) to produce immunity.

VACCINE. A preparation of killed or attenuated microorganisms, or their components, or their products, that is used to induce active immunity against a disease.

VACUOLE [VAK·yoo·ole]. A clear space in the cytoplasm of a cell.

V AND W PROTEINS. A complex of two cell-wall proteins in *Yersinia pestis* that inhibits phagocytosis.

V FACTOR. Nicotinamide adenine dinucleotide; required for the growth of certain *Haemophilus* spp.

VARIANT. An organism showing some variation from the parent culture.

VASCULAR. Containing specialized vessels for the conduction of fluids: blood and lymph in animals, sap and water in plants.

VDRL TEST. Venereal Disease Research Laboratory test; a microscopic agglutination screening test for the detection of reagin (antibodies against cardiolipin) in the serum of syphilitic patients.

VECTOR. An agent, such as an insect, capable of mechanically or biologically transferring a pathogen from one organism to another.

VEGETATIVE STAGE. The stage of active growth, as opposed to the resting or spore stages.

VENEREAL. Sexually transmitted.

VIABLE [VYE·uh·bul]. Capable of living, growing, and developing; alive.

VIBRIO [VIB·ree·o]. A bacterium that is curved with a twist but has less than one complete turn or twist (in contrast to a helical bacterium). *Vibrio* is a genus of Gram-negative bacteria.

VIRAL HEMAGGLUTINATION. The ability of some viruses, such as those causing mumps, measles, and influenza, to agglutinate red blood cells from certain species of animals, notably chicken or guinea pig red blood cells, or human type O red blood cells.

VIRAL NEUTRALIZATION. Inhibition of viral agglutination by antibodies binding to the virus.

VIREMIA [vye·REE·mee·uh]. The presence of virus in the bloodstream.

VIRION [VYE·ree·on]. The complete mature virus particle.

VIROLOGY. The study of viruses.

VIROPEXIS. The engulfment of whole virions by cells in a phagocytic process.

VIRUCIDE [VYE·ru·side]. An agent that kills viruses.

VIRULENCE [VIR·yoo·lunce]. The degree of pathogenicity exhibited by a strain of microorganisms.

VIRUSES. Noncellular infectious agents that pass through filters that prevent the passage of bacteria; obligate intracellular parasites.

VOGES-PROSKAUER REACTION. A test for the presence of acetylmethylcarbinol to assist in distinguishing between species of the coliform group. Abbreviation: VP test.

VOLUTIN. *See* **granules, metachromatic**.

WASSERMANN TEST. A complement-fixation test for syphilis.

WASTEWATER. Used water supply of a community.

WATERBORNE INFECTION. Disease acquired through drinking water contaminated with pathogenic microorganisms.

WEIL-FELIX TEST. An agglutination test for typhus using *Proteus* spp. as antigens.

WESTERN BLOT. Detection of proteins immobilized on a filter by complementary reaction with specific antibody.

WET-MOUNT PREPARATION. Technique to examine living organisms by placing a drop of specimen on a glass slide and covering the drop with a cover slip.

WIDAL TEST. A slide agglutination test for typhoid or paratyphoid fever.

X FACTOR. Heme; required for the growth of certain *Haemophilus* spp.

YEAST. A kind of fungus that is unicellular and lacks typical mycelia.

YOLK SAC. The membrane covering the yolk of an egg.

ZONATION [zo·NAY·shun]. The distribution of organisms in zones; specifically, a stratification of certain kinds of algae at certain depths and locations in the ocean.

ZOOFLAGELLATE [zo·o·FLAJ·uh·lut, zo·o·FLAJ·uh·lait]. An animal-like form of flagellate. Compare **phytoflagellate**.

ZOOGLOEA [zo·o·GLEE·uh]. Masses composed of microorganisms which are embedded in a common matrix of slime.

ZOONOSIS [zo·ahn·uh·sis, zo·o·no·sis]. An animal disease transmissible to human beings.

ZOOPLANKTON [zo·o·plank·tun]. A collective term for the nonphotosynthetic organisms present in plankton. *Compare* **phytoplankton.**

ZOOSPORE [zo·o·spore]. A motile, flagellate spore.

ZYGOMYCETES. One of four groups of terrestial fungi. Crosswalls are absent in the hyphae of this group.

ZYGOSPORE [zye·go·spore]. A kind of sexual spore resulting from the fusion of two similar gametes in some fungi.

ZYGOTE [zye·gote]. An organism produced by the union of two gametes.

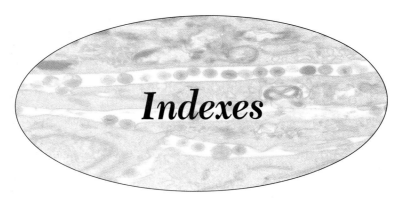

NAME INDEX

Page numbers in **boldface** indicate illustrations or tables.

ORGANISM INDEX

References are by generic or specific name. Higher category taxa are in Subject Index. Page numbers in **boldface** indicate illustrations or tables.

SUBJECT INDEX

Page numbers in **boldface** indicate illustrations or tables.